69144

A BOOK OF
THE SHORT STORY

SELECTED AND EDITED, WITH THE
HISTORY AND TECHNIQUE OF THE SHORT STORY,
NOTES, AND BIBLIOGRAPHIES

BY

E. A. CROSS, Ph.D.

HEAD OF THE DEPARTMENT OF LITERATURE AND
LANGUAGES, COLORADO STATE TEACHERS COLLEGE

88

‹‹‹›››

AMERICAN BOOK COMPANY

NEW YORK   CINCINNATI   CHICAGO

BOSTON   ATLANTA

Cross's A Book of the Short Story
E. P. 5

FOREWORD

A generation ago there were very few if any courses in colleges and universities which dealt with phases of contemporary literature. Courses in drama, poetry, fiction, or the literary essay had a way of stopping somewhere short of the nineteen-hundreds, as if literature were not good until it had aged. And when college teachers began to look with a tolerant eye upon what was written in the generation just before their time, or even upon the literature of their own generation, the short story was the last to be favored with the approval of the scholarly smile.

It was the good fortune of the present writer to be one of the pioneers in the effort to introduce high school and college students to contemporary literature. There is some justification for the once familiar admonition: "When a new book comes out, read an old one." But it needs to be questioned. Why is a literary form that has developed since 1850 less praiseworthy than one that developed just after 1350? Is a perfect short story as a piece of literary art on a lower level than a perfect sonnet?

It may be well to read an old book when a new one is published. But why not read both the time-honored classic *and* the modern piece? The point is no longer in need of argument. Time has settled the matter. There are today no fewer courses in which the classics are studied—but there are decidedly fuller opportunities to become acquainted with writers who are trying to express the thoughts and feelings of our own times by using literary forms that have been perfected in our own century or generation.

Among literary forms that have been most popular with the modern reading public, the short story stands out with particular emphasis. Its concrete handling of human problems and situations which have come within the experience or under the observation of the reader gives it a close and dramatic appeal. The consummate skill with which its best exponents are able, in brief compass, to flash a clear interpretation of character or to illuminate the tangle of human motives makes the short story seem a natural part of our hurried present day.

This compilation has for its main object the presentation of a body of short stories sufficiently extensive to illustrate what has been achieved up to date and sufficiently varied in character to appeal to all tastes. Naturally the emphasis is upon the work of American and British authors, although French, Irish, Scandinavian, Italian, and Russian writers all have representation. This is not a collection of the *best* short stories, although a larger number of those chosen would certainly be satisfactory candidates for the highest rank. It is, rather, a collection of representative short stories which the compiler's many years of teaching have shown to be adequate for a college course.

In the preparation of this book there has been no effort made to get together a manual for the beginner in the *writing* of short stories. A number of these already exist. But it is possible that the analysis of the structure of the short story from the reader's point of view may be helpful to the beginner in writing by clarifying his notions about the handling of plot, theme, suspense, and the other elements of technique. Hence the very brief and simple discussion of the facts of the history and technique of the short story in the eight brief chapters which make up Part One. Throughout this preliminary discussion, reference is constantly made to illustrative material in short stories, novels, and plays, so that the statements made may be tested at all points. The object of Part One is to help in making the reading of the stories included in Part Two more interesting by enabling the reader to have some inkling of the techniques of skilled writers.

Brief introductory notes, largely biographical, precede the various stories. Study suggestions are grouped at the back of the book. The selected bibliographies will make it possible for those who so desire to extend their reading and study of the short story far beyond the limits of the material included in this book.

Thanks are due to my colleague, Miss Josephine Hawes, a teacher of the short story in Colorado Teachers College for a number of years, who has assisted materially by suggesting stories to be included and in the compilation of the bibliographies at the end of the volume.

A considerable portion of Part One appeared in the author's *The Short Story* (copyright, 1914) and is here reprinted by arrangement with A. C. McClurg & Company, the original publishers. Other copyright acknowledgments are made in connection with various stories included in the body of the text.

E. A. C.

CONTENTS

FOREWORD   iii

Part One—History and Technique of the Short Story

Chapter I: THE HISTORY OF THE SHORT STORY   3

Chapter II: THE MATERIALS FROM WHICH STORIES ARE MADE   12

Chapter III: THE SHORT STORY IS AN IMPRESSION FROM LIFE   17

Chapter IV: PLOT   26

Chapter V: THE CHARACTERS   41

Chapter VI: OTHER MEANS USED IN DEVELOPING A THEME   47

Chapter VII: THE MANAGEMENT OF THE MATERIALS   55

Chapter VIII: A PLAN FOR THE STUDY OF A SHORT STORY   62

Part Two—Selected Short Stories

THE BIBLE: THE PRODIGAL SON   75

JAMES HOGG: THE MYSTERIOUS BRIDE   77

WASHINGTON IRVING: RIP VAN WINKLE   89

SIR WALTER SCOTT: WANDERING WILLIE'S TALE   102

ALEXANDER PUSHKIN: THE PISTOL SHOT   117

EDGAR ALLAN POE: LIGEIA   128

NATHANIEL HAWTHORNE: DR. HEIDEGGER'S EXPERIMENT   141

FRANCIS BRET HARTE: THE OUTCASTS OF POKER FLAT   149

CHARLES DICKENS: DR. MARIGOLD'S PRESCRIPTIONS   158

PROSPER MÉRIMÉE: TAKING THE REDOUBT   179

THOMAS BAILEY ALDRICH: MARJORIE DAW   184

HENRY CUYLER BUNNER: THE LOVE LETTERS OF SMITH   200

ALPHONSE DAUDET: THE LAST CLASS   209

HENRY JAMES: THE LESSON OF THE MASTER 213

FRANK RICHARD STOCKTON: THE LADY, OR THE TIGER? 263

THOMAS HARDY: THE THREE STRANGERS 269

ROBERT LOUIS STEVENSON: WILL O' THE MILL 287

RUDYARD KIPLING: THE MAN WHO WOULD BE KING 307

GUY DE MAUPASSANT: THE NECKLACE 335

LEO TOLSTOY: THREE ARSHINS OF LAND 343

LEO TOLSTOY: WHERE LOVE IS, THERE GOD IS ALSO 352

BJÖRNSTJERNE BJÖRNSON: THE FATHER 362

ANTON PAVLOVICH CHEKHOV: THE DARLING 365

MARY E. WILKINS FREEMAN: THE REVOLT OF "MOTHER" 375

CHAUNCEY THOMAS: THE SNOW STORY 388

CHARLOTTE PERKINS GILMAN: THE YELLOW WALLPAPER 400

JAMES LANE ALLEN: KING SOLOMON OF KENTUCKY 414

JOSEPH CONRAD: HEART OF DARKNESS 431

ARTHUR MORRISON: ON THE STAIRS 502

HAMLIN GARLAND: MARTHA'S FIREPLACE 506

SIR ARTHUR CONAN DOYLE: THE ADVENTURE OF THE
SPECKLED BAND 520

HERBERT GEORGE WELLS: THE DOOR IN THE WALL 541

LUIGI PIRANDELLO: THE RESERVED COFFIN 555

LEONID NIKOLAIEVICH ANDREYEV: THE SEVEN THAT
WERE HANGED 564

JAMES BRENDAN CONNOLLY: THE TRUTH OF THE OLIVER
CROMWELL 615

JACK LONDON: SAMUEL 639

RUTH SAWYER: THE PRINCESS AND THE VAGABONE 655

O. HENRY: A MUNICIPAL REPORT 665

ANATOLE FRANCE: THE PROCURATOR OF JUDEA 678

OWEN WISTER: THE DRAKE WHO HAD MEANS OF HIS OWN 690

SELMA LAGERLÖF: THE OUTLAWS 708

CONTENTS

Konrad Bercovici: THE BEAR TAMER'S DAUGHTER   722

Melville Davisson Post: AFTER HE WAS DEAD   736

Maxwell Struthers Burt: THE WATER HOLE   746

Irvin Shrewsbury Cobb: THE GREAT AUK   760

Armistead C. Gordon: THE SILENT INFARE   781

John Russell: JETSAM   789

Frank R. Adams: 3000 MILES AWAY   804

Seumas O'Kelly: THE WEAVER'S GRAVE   819

Margaret Prescott Montague: ENGLAND TO AMERICA   858

Wilbur Daniel Steele: FOR THEY KNOW NOT WHAT
     THEY DO   871

Stacy Aumonier: A SOURCE OF IRRITATION   886

Anzia Yezierska: THE FAT OF THE LAND   897

Katherine Mansfield: THE FLY   915

Helen Rose Hull: CLAY SHUTTERED DOORS   920

Henry Sydnor Harrison: MISS HINCH   936

Ruth Suckow: THE MAN OF THE FAMILY   952

William M. John: NEITHER JEW NOR GREEK   965

Walter D. Edmonds: WHO KILLED RUTHERFORD?   977

Ernest Hemingway: FIFTY GRAND   986

R. Hernekin Baptist: CIVILIZATION   1006

Katharine Brush: NIGHT CLUB   1017

Frank O'Connor: GUESTS OF THE NATION   1028

SELECTED BIBLIOGRAPHIES   1039

STUDY NOTES   1057

INDEX   1101

PART ONE

HISTORY AND TECHNIQUE OF THE SHORT STORY

CHAPTER I

THE HISTORY OF THE SHORT STORY

Two facts about the short story are very significant: it is probably
the oldest literary form, and it was the latest in point of time to receive
exact definition of its purpose and scope, and full unfolding of its
artistic and dramatic resources. The first fact means that the short
story is a vital and not an artificial form of literature, and fits itself
instinctively to certain impulses and interests of men; the second fact—
the fact that the short story had to wait for the insight and skill of men
of the genius of Poe, Hawthorne, Stevenson, Kipling, and Maupassant
—means that as a literary form the short story ranks with the highest
and most exacting forms of art.—*Hamilton W. Mabie.*

AMONG unlettered people of our own time the practice of telling
and retelling stories of their experiences, stories that they have
heard, or stories that they have imagined, is a most common form of
diversion. This custom of telling brief tales is perhaps as old as oral
language, for man seems to find in fiction, however crude, a means of
diversion and entertainment. Men dwelling in caves in the stone age,
men gathered around savage camp fires, men "sitting at the gates of
Damascus or Baghdad," whiled away the time and entertained those
within earshot with diverting tales—crude pieces of fiction; but the
evolution of the short story from these earliest pieces of oral fiction to
the artistic short story of the present day has been a long and slow
process, reaching its culmination in the tales and stories of Poe and Hawthorne less than a century ago—almost within the memory of men now
living—and coming to its perfection in those of Maupassant, Stevenson, and Kipling in the time of the generation just passing.

Dr. William J. Dawson in his *Makers of English Fiction* calls fiction
a kind of lie told in such a manner as to make it seem true. With some
such idea in mind Professor Charles F. Horne in *The Technique of the
Novel* shows that fiction is literally older than speech, for even the cat,
he says, practices a cunning fiction when she strolls away from the half-
dead mouse with a disinterested, somewhat bored look, only to turn and
spring lightly upon it again as it tries to drag itself away. But for a

3

study of the actual beginnings of prose fiction in speech we must rely upon the records of the earliest tales set down in writing.

The Prose Tale and the Short Story.—The men who told the tales around the savage camp fires or within the huts of barbarians, or "at the gates of Damascus or Baghdad," perhaps had no other aim than to entertain by rehearsing an actual occurrence. They had not even as much skill in arranging their stories, in omitting irrelevant matters, in coloring with imagination, as the loafer around the rusty stove in a village store exhibits today as he offers his worn stock of fiction to his companions for the tenth or sixtieth time. The ordinary tale in prose is very different from the artistic short story. Every one is familiar with the back-fence conversation, "cackleization," or total-recall, which cannot omit irrelevant details, but which must include every circumstance in time-sequence between the beginning and culmination of the delectable gossip. There is a vast difference between such narrations and the real short story.

The Tales of the Magicians.—The most ancient record of prose stories is an Egyptian collection of tales contained in the ancient papyri. These stories are called by English scholars the *Tales of the Magicians.* Some of the stories of this collection are certainly as old as 2700 B.C., and most scholars believe that the true date is approximately 4000 B.C. The sons of King Cheops (the great pyramid builder) are trying to entertain their father with some interesting stories. When one son has told the king some marvelous tale that he has heard, another steps forward and begins his story of "strange things." Perhaps the best known of these tales is a very brief one called *The Shipwrecked Sailor.* A translation of this may be found in Jessup and Canby's *The Book of the Short Story.* A sailor is shipwrecked upon a mysterious island, all his companions perishing. The island is ruled by a great serpent, and inhabited only by serpents. These treat the unfortunate sailor kindly, and send him home with rich gifts when the next ship passes that way.

Such in brief is the story. What it lacks of meeting the technical requirements of the short story in the modern sense will be apparent after reading the later chapters in this book on the technique of the short story.[1]

Another of these shorter narratives is the story of *The Doomed Prince.*

[1]Some sources for the Egyptian stories:
   W. M. Flinders Petrie, *Egyptian Tales*, 2 vols.
   C. D. Warner, *Library of the World's Best Literature*, Vol. XIII.
   The Universal Anthology, Vol. I.
   Clark and Lieber, *Great Short Stories of the World.*
   E. A. Cross, *World Literature.*

Unfortunately the papyrus that contains this story is mutilated. Just when the reader comes to the critical point in the story, he reaches the place where the papyrus is torn across and is thus prevented from ever knowing whether the prince escaped his doom or met the tragic end predicted for him.

The Egyptians had other stories longer and more elaborate than the two already mentioned. All of them are interesting to modern readers. Three may be mentioned here. They are: *The Two Brothers—Anpu and Bata*, *Setna and the Magic Book*, and *The Story of Sanehat*.

The Arabian Nights' Entertainments.—To try to make a list of the collections of oriental tales in the order of their age would be unprofitable, for exact dates are not known. The oldest reference to *The Thousand and One Nights* is 987 A.D. The stories are doubtless much older than that. Many devices have been employed by writers, ancient and modern, to give some degree of unity to a series of unrelated tales. The need of such devices is seen in the *Tales of the Magicians*, the *Canterbury Tales*, and the *Tales of a Wayside Inn*, to take an ancient, a Renaissance, and a modern instance. Perhaps, none of the devices has exceeded in cleverness that of the *Arabian Nights*. Schariar, Sultan of India, is accustomed to select a new wife for each new day, and to have her put to death the following morning. Scheherazade, daughter of the grand vizier, being selected one day, tells the sultan an interesting story at night and promises another for the following night. The sultan spares her life in order to hear the next story. This is kept up for a thousand and one nights (till the author of the volume has exhausted his stock of stories) and then the law requiring the sacrifice of the bride of a day is repealed, since it has been so long disregarded. Probably the best known of the stories from the *Arabian Nights' Entertainments* are *Aladdin and his Wonderful Lamp*, and *Ali Baba and the Forty Thieves*, but a dozen others are just as interesting and should be known by all students of the short story.

Old Testament Stories.—The Hebrews were a religious people. It is not at all strange, then, that when they told stories, they should have had in mind a purpose beyond mere entertainment. Most of their stories have a distinct lesson to teach. Jotham's parable of *The Trees Choosing a King* (Judges 9:7-15) is an ironical reminder of how the people have chosen the worst of the sons of Jerubbaal to be his successor and their king. The purpose of *The Book of Ruth* may have been any one of three or four: To show the lineage of David; to show that Jehovah of the Israelites might also be the God of a Moabite—a foreigner; to show how faithfulness and service are rewarded; or some similar theme. *The*

Book of Jonah is probably as pure a piece of fiction as Jesus' parable of *The Prodigal Son.* The Israelites had all along thought of Jehovah as a national deity. Some prophet with a wider vision than the mass of his countrymen wished to teach them that there are no village gods and national gods, but that Jehovah is God of the whole world—of the solid land, of the sea and the creatures of the deep, of even distant heathen Nineveh, as well as of Canaan. To impress this truth he told the story of a prophet who did everything he could to avoid that conclusion and to disregard God's command to preach in Nineveh. The story closes on a half-humorous note—Jonah sulking in the shade of the gourd vine because God had shown mercy to a people not of Israel. *The Prodigal Son* differs from this story in that it avoids actual names and places. It is presented as pure fiction to impress a definite theme: Just as an earthly father forgives a wayward son, so does the Heavenly Father forgive his own wayward ones when they return repentant from their wanderings. In *The Book of Jonah* the prophet veiled his fiction behind the fact that somewhere in the indistinct past there had been a lesser prophet named Jonah to whom he could ascribe these imaginary experiences. These books of the Old Testament were written at different times between 350 B.C. and 750 B.C.

Ancient Hindu Stories.—India is not without representation in old prose stories. The *Panchatantra* is a collection of old Hindu poems, fables, and prose fiction. Among the readable stories in prose is the fable of *The Raven, the Rat, and the Pigeons.* This is one of the Pilpay, or Bidpai fables in the *Panchatantra.* These fables are probably as old as the fables of Æsop. There are also short prose stories inserted as independent episodes in both of the great Indian epics, the *Ramayana* and the *Mahabharata. Lex Talionis* is a good example of such stories in the *Ramayana,* and *Love Stronger Than Death* is a fine story from the *Mahabharata.*

Greek and Roman Tales.—Although the Greeks were masters in other forms of art and literature, their contribution to prose fiction was so small and so little known as to have made little or no impression upon subsequent writers of tales. There are, however, two stories which should not be omitted from this account. Early in the second Christian century Lucius Apuleius, a Roman Platonic philosopher, born in Africa, wrote in Latin a book called *Metamorphoses, or The Golden Ass.* It is a loosely connected narrative with occasionally a detached episode standing out as a distinct tale. The story of *Cupid and Psyche* is such an episode, and one which has survived to the present time. In the fourth or fifth century A.D. a Greek named Longus wrote a simple story of a shepherd boy named Daphnis and his love for Chloe, a shepherd girl. The story as a work of art is of no great importance, but its plot has been the basis of stories in several languages down through the centuries.

Gesta Romanorum.—There are two remarkable circumstances about the collection of stories called *Gesta Romanorum* (Deeds of the Romans). The first is that this Latin book was probably written in England (about 1300); and the second, that only a few of the 181 tales in the common text have anything to do with the Romans. This book, to which we look with great respect as the inspiration of many a writer of tales and the source of many a plot still used in fiction, is a collection of about all the good stories known to the men of those times. Dr. W. J. Dawson, in his *Great English Short Story Writers*, gives a hint of the influence of these stories when he shows how the germ of one of Aristotle's stories was preserved in the eleventh tale of *Gesta Romanorum*. This tale called *Of the Poison of Sin* subsequently furnished the plot used by Hawthorne in *Rappaccini's Daughter*, by Holmes in *Elsie Venner*, and by Richard Garnett in *The Poison Maid*. It is possible that the modern Spanish dramatist Benavente is indirectly indebted to this ancient tale for the theme of his tragedy *La Malquerida* (The Passion Flower). Others of these plots may easily be traced in modern stories.

This book was not prepared for mere entertainment, however. Each of the tales is followed by a moral application. One may readily surmise that the medieval parish priest used these stories to illustrate his sermons, much as he did the lives of the saints.

The reader must remember that these stories were not invented by the compiler of the book. They were merely collected from all known sources, and some of them, at least, must be almost as old as the love of fiction itself.

Beast Fables and Picaresque Tales.—Two other forms of ancient fiction helped to mould the love for short tales in prose. These are, first, the Beast Fables, such as the Pilpay fables, Æsop's fables, the stories of Reynard the Fox, and Joel Chandler Harris's modern Uncle Remus stories. The other group is made up of the Rogue Stories (called picaresque from the Spanish *pícaro*, a rogue), such as the German *Tyll Eulenspiegel*, the Spanish *Little Lazarus of Tormes*, the English adventure stories of Sir John Mandeville, and those of that other cheerful and picturesque liar, Baron Munchausen. Each of these, and the fairy tale too, has contributed something, either of character, setting, or incident, to the technique of the modern short story.

Boccaccio's Decameron (1353).—There is an Italian collection of stories in prose which has exerted as great an influence upon the makers of fiction as the *Gesta Romanorum*. The *Decameron*, as this collection of one hundred tales was called from the fact that the telling was supposed to extend over a period of ten days, was the work of the story-teller and poet, Boccaccio (1313–1375). Like the *Gesta Romanorum* this is again just a collection of well-known tales held together by an enveloping device similar to those used later by Chaucer in the *Canterbury Tales*, and by Longfellow in the *Tales of a Wayside Inn*. One of the most famous of the stories of the *Decameron* is *The Story of Patient Griselda* used by Chaucer about 1386 as *The Clerk's Tale* in the *Canterbury Tales*. Chaucer says in his prologue to this tale that he learned it from "Fraunceys Petrark, the laureate poete," at Padua. Petrarch was a friend of Boccaccio, and was probably visited by Chaucer on one of his journeys to Italy.

The passion for collecting old tales and weaving them together after the fashion of the *Decameron* was widespread. Similar books were made by Gower (*Confessio Amantis*), by Lydgate (*Falls of Princes*), and by others in England in the early fifteenth century.

Sir Thomas Malory's Morte d'Arthur.—More important than any other of these medieval books, and the one that has exerted the largest influence on English literature, is one that has been used less by the writers of fiction than by poets—the *Morte d'Arthur* (about 1470) of Sir Thomas Malory. This book is the final form of the stories of King Arthur, and was the principal source of Tennyson's Arthurian cycle, the *Idylls of the King*.

Episodes in Longer Stories.—In these paragraphs the progress of short tales in prose has been sketched from the earliest known beginnings to comparatively modern times. Before we begin to consider the change from the ancient prose tale to the modern short story, however, some account must be taken of episodes which occasionally appeared as chapters in longer works of fiction. There are chapters in Cervantes' *Don Quixote*, in Bunyan's *Pilgrim's Progress*, and in other early works of fiction, which, taken from the book, make distinct units. The technique of the modern novel does not admit the digression of the detached episode, but after the advent of the real novel, while its form was still plastic, such detached episodes were admitted. *The Tale of the Old Man of the Hill* in Fielding's *Tom Jones* (1748), *Wandering Willie's Tale* in Scott's *Redgauntlet* (1824), and *The Princess' Tragedy* in Thackeray's *Barry Lyndon* illustrate the employment of this device. Had there been public taste and a vehicle for the publication of short stories, such as our modern magazines provide, it is probable that these novelists would have omitted such digressions from their larger stories and would have published them in the magazines as short stories, just as many of our novelists now use the chips from their workshops, the episodes in their larger pieces of fiction, as material for independent short stories.

The Influence of the Essayists.—Printing had come to be comparatively inexpensive, and readers quite numerous, by the beginning of the eighteenth century. There was, accordingly, a demand for cheap periodical publications by a body of readers large enough to warrant the experiment. The contents of such papers as the *Spectator* and the *Tatler* of Addison and Steele, and the *Guardian* of Johnson were news of the town and social comment, and commonly an essay, usually light in tone, concerning some topic which the author thought would be of general interest. Occasionally one of these essays was presented in the form of fiction—a brief tale. Sometimes these sketches were loosely joined together by an enveloping scheme something like that used in the series of essays by Addison called the *Sir Roger de Coverley Papers*. A good example of fiction in these periodical publications is Addison's story called *The Vision of Mirza* in the *Spectator* (1711).

No doubt such pieces as these inspired the writers of fiction of the early years of the nineteenth century and turned them toward the *tale*, refined and polished in style, but still lacking some of the essential qualities of plot, form, restraint, economy of material and the like of the modern short story. Prominent among these writers were the Scottish poet, James Hogg, "The Ettrick Shepherd," (1770–1835), and the American, Washington Irving (1783–1859). From the volume of *Tales and Sketches* of the former the story of *The Mysterious Bride* may be taken as a typical short story. Irving's tales, *The Legend of Sleepy Hollow* and *Rip Van Winkle*, are familiar to all.

Hawthorne and Poe.—As any form of art is growing toward perfection, those who practice it are usually unconscious of the technical processes which they employ. The genius, once in a long while, manages his materials in such a way as to produce the artistic result; but even the genius in the formative period of the art follows no law but the law of necessity, which he instinctively feels will produce the effect he desires. When such an artistic effect has been produced a few dozens of times, then men of analytic minds study the processes employed by the great artists and deduce the technical principles involved in the production of the artistic effect. Such a body of technical knowledge once having been established is the common property ever after of both the true artist and the mere craftsman. The greatest genius of all is the one who has the instinctive power to create, and then becomes conscious of the means which he has used. In dramatic literature Shakespeare was such a genius. He had the creative mind of the unconscious artist; then he became consciously aware of the means which were needed to produce a given effect—of the minute details of the technique of dramatic poetry and stagecraft—and so he is reckoned the greatest dramatic poet of the world.

The honor of producing the genius who first became conscious of the technique of the short story is perhaps due to America. In a measure Hawthorne (1804–1864) was conscious of the means he used. In a greater measure this consciousness of means was Poe's (1809–1849). Short stories were produced before the time of these men, but when a writer succeeded in producing such a story, it seemed by chance that he did so, for he did not follow up his success by writing other stories in which he employed the elements of artistic technique seized by chance in the successful short story.

If we reduce the technical requirements of the real story to the very lowest terms—say the necessity of producing a single narrative effect— we shall find a number of tales before Hawthorne and Poe which meet this single technical specification: Defoe's *The Apparition of Mrs. Veal* (1706), Addison's *The Vision of Mirza* (1711), Hogg's *The Mysterious Bride* (1820), Scott's *Wandering Willie's Tale* (1824), Austin's *Peter Rugg, the Missing Man* (1824), Irving's *Rip Van Winkle* (1819), and *The Legend of Sleepy Hollow* (1819). Each of these succeeds in producing a single narrative effect. But when we add to this singleness of impression other elements that we now consider essential, such as the greatest economy of means, the embodiment of a single idea or theme, a unity of tone, the use of a fitting background, truth in the portrayal of characters, etc., we find that most of them, perhaps all, fall short in one or more of these particular requirements.

Admitting that there were many delightful tales before the time of Poe and Hawthorne, even some true short stories, we must say again that it was these men who became conscious of the art of story writing and made use of their knowledge time after time.

The Modern Short Story.—Since Poe pointed out the way, there have been thousands of writers of short stories the world over, and hundreds of these—first, second, and maybe tenth-rate writers—have understood the art better than either Poe or Hawthorne. Among these hundreds there have been a few men and women of genius with great stories to tell and a thorough mastery of the mechanics of their art who have, as a consequence, surpassed those geniuses who had the materials without the conscious knowledge of technique.

The short story in recent years has become so effective a means of representing life that no one today needs to feel that the serious novel is the only form of fiction worthy of study and consideration. Compared with the more extensive novel, the short story is what the sonnet is to the longer lyric poem—an artistic vessel of a definite form into which an author may pour his plastic material and fix some great and worthy idea in a mold of beauty.

The technique once established, masters of the art of short story writing have sprung up in nearly every civilized country; but America and France have led, with England, Russia, and Germany closely following. In all these countries the writers have recognized the essentials of short story technique; but mechanical perfection has been approached most nearly in France and America. The present treatise does not assert that every piece of fiction worthy of the name of short story will conform to every technical detail of the typical short story, but it sets up certain standards to which the short story as a type of fiction usually conforms, making due allowances for individuality in authors and in pieces of work. To make clear what those technical elements of the short story are will be the business of the following chapters.

The Chronological Development of the Short Story.—Those who are interested in the development of the short story from its beginnings in English until the present time may find a scholarly and illuminating treatment of this phase of the subject in Dr. Henry Seidel Canby's *The Short Story in English*. This book is an exhaustive account, a "documented investigation," of the evolution of this phase of fiction in English.

A briefer treatment of the same subject may be seen in Canby's *A Study of the Short Story*, pp. 1–77. For a series of stories arranged chronologically to illustrate the historical development of the short story the reader is referred to the same volume, pp. 79–273, or to Brander Matthews' *The Short Story*, or to Jessup and Canby's *The Book of the Short Story*. It is not the purpose of the present volume to enlarge upon this phase of the subject. What follows will be a study of the form and meaning of the short story as it is written by the masters of today.

CHAPTER II

THE MATERIALS FROM WHICH STORIES ARE MADE

POLONIUS: *What do you read, my lord?*
HAMLET: *Words, words, words.*

IT IS true that stories are made of words, but it would be merely witty and a trifle insolent today, as it was in Hamlet's time, to say we read nothing but words. Words are only the vehicles for the conveyance of ideas from mind to mind. The actual materials at the command of the story writer are People, Incidents, and Settings.

People.—Instead of people one is tempted to say *characters*, for there are a number of good stories about animals and a few concerning inanimate objects. But after all, when we read such stories, they interest us because the characters exhibit human qualities or reflect some light on human nature. Edward Peple has a capital story, *A Night Out*, in which the principal actors and speakers are cats—a patrician blue-blooded Thomas, a disreputable alley Tom, and some of the latter's female friends of doubtful gentility. This story is true to cat character, but we are interested in it because the author has humorously hit off some human characteristics, which are too serious to be treated lightly in a piece of fiction dealing with people, and which would lose much in attractiveness if treated as a profound study in human psychology, such as it really is. Charles Johnstone's *Chrysal; or, The Adventures of a Guinea*, was interesting to readers a hundred and fifty years ago, not because it related the journeyings and experiences of a coin, but because it pictured the life of *people* in various social levels and in various places. After all, then, a story, to be interesting to human beings, must be a story about *people*.

Incidents.—A writer who wishes to go beyond mere portrait painting, one who wishes to get his people into some sort of action, must have them do something or have something happen to them. There have been seen in print many excellent "character sketches"—pictures of interesting or odd people in some characteristic pose or action, but in the greater number of good short stories the writer will select one, or two, or three characters and have them participate in one or more incidents. This means that the characters will be placed in situations where there is action. The characters may dominate the action, make the thing or things happen; or they may have things happen to them, and so be dominated by the action. Whatever happens in the story will be significant to the characters by way of causing them to do certain things or preventing them from doing what they had planned.

When the student comes to the study of the ideas that are put into stories and the making of story designs or plots, he will see that the incidents in a given story are so arranged as to develop the author's idea or story theme. Imagine, for example, that an author wishes to write a story to show that the course of an individual's life is often changed by mere chance. He may take a character and place him in three situations one after another in which the element of chance alone will make his success. Or the element of chance may be such as to thwart his progress and drive him to defeat and ruin. Out of a hundred possible incidents that the writer may invent for his story he is compelled by the idea or theme of the story to choose just those few that will act upon the character to make or break him.

Setting.—School dramatics are sometimes arranged to be presented without any stage properties or scenery beyond the usual schoolroom platform, desk, and chairs. But these little plays take on new life when the stage is set to present a picture of the place and time represented by the drama, and when the characters themselves appear in appropriate costumes and make-up. The setting, or background, of a story does for a piece of fiction just what painted scenery, stage properties, costumes, and make-up do for a play.

When we speak of *Setting*, we mean something more than a scene of action, a place where something happens to somebody. *Place* is essential and the most important, but *Time* also must be taken account of. And then there are both *Atmosphere* and *Tone* that call for attention. Suppose a story writer is planning a story that will picture a turning point in the life of a girl of eighteen. The writer has decided that she is to be a country girl. Out of the many possible country situations he chooses a ranch in Wyoming. Then he decides that the incidents will happen in the fall. He now has both place and time. But Wyoming ranches are of many kinds—some remote, lonely, and desolate, and some in spots that are romantic and beautiful. The writer must choose the kind of scene that will supply the atmosphere he needs for the kind of story he has planned to tell. And then one other thing. In sketching in the place, time, and atmosphere, he must write in such a way that the tone of the story is apparent from the beginning. If the story is to be tragic, romantic, hilarious, gloomy, cynical, or what not, this should be suggested early in the story as the preliminaries are being written. All of this may be called the *Setting*, the stage upon which the action is to take place. Or one may call it the *Background*, for it resembles the background of a picture in several respects. The *setting* or *background* of a story is made up of all the elements which the author combines to prevent the action from seeming to take place in some vague, blank locality. In other words, the setting gives to the characters and incidents "a local habitation and a name."

Stories of Character, Incident, or Setting.—The early attempts to classify stories in terms of their construction recognized a predominating element. A story was called "a story of setting" if the picture presented by the background was more attractive than either incidents or characters. It was considered "a story of character" if character portrayal or character development seemed uppermost in the author's mind. Or it was "a story of incident" if what happened was of greater interest than the people or the time and place.

Some writers have gone so far as to say that the predominating element should reveal its presence and importance in the opening paragraph of the story. A story opening with conversation would be a story of character. One beginning with a descriptive paragraph would be throughout a story of setting. And one whose first paragraph related a happening would be considered a story of incident.

There are a few writers of short stories who seem to have consciously striven to sound the keynote in the opening sentence or paragraph by emphasizing character, or setting, or incident. Poe once said that the end of the story must be in the writer's mind at the very beginning, and that the first paragraph, the first sentence, must be a part of the preparation for the culmination.

This statement was probably the foundation of the belief that a story of a certain kind had to begin with material of its own kind. Poe had in mind, perhaps, the ultimate solution of the story which was to be held in suspense till the end, but foreseen from the beginning and foreshadowed by the enveloping atmosphere from the very first word. While many of his stories exemplify the principle under discussion, it seems more likely that it should just have happened so, incidentally, in striking the dominant tone and creating the pervading atmosphere in the opening paragraphs. One does not often see in other short stories any evidence of any established conviction that stories of character must begin with some remark about a character or some speech; that stories of incident must start off with an incident; or stories of setting with description.

THE PREDOMINANT ELEMENT

Some one of the three elements is usually more prominent than the other two, although in most cases all three are present. As an exercise in technical skill, an author might write a story in which the *setting* itself would be made much of without any emphasis upon either character or incidents. One could conceive of an author's wish to make a larger body of readers than he could reach with a descriptive essay acquainted with a scene that he knew and was fond of. Let him make a story with vague figures passing through a series of slight incidents taking place in some enchanting corner of the world, and one would have a story of *setting*. These are not common. Poe's *The Domain of Arnheim* is one such, however, although not technically a short story.

It would be possible to write a story the action of which should take place in some vague, unidentified locality, with no description of the setting, and no hint as to the kind of stage upon which the drama was enacted. The characters in such a story might be indistinct—little more than figures endowed with the power of voluntary motion—but the story might present *incidents* so absorbing that the reader would take no notice of the blank background and the characterless figures. This would be a story of *incident*. In the modern short story such extreme exaltation of incident is not common, but in the tales of the *Arabian Nights* it is often seen. In fact, the incidents in ancient tales might have occurred almost anywhere to almost anyone. Those old stories are almost pure tales of incident. In such modern short stories as Poe's *The Pit and the Pendulum*, Mérimée's *The Taking of the Redoubt*, and Stockton's *The Lady, or the Tiger?* character and setting are subordinated to incident.

Or, again, *character* might be magnified to the practical exclusion of the other two elements, as it is in *The Prodigal Son;* but in most of our modern stories no one of the three elements excludes the other two. The commonest form of story is either a story portraying or developing a character, with incidents and setting adequately employed but subordinated to the main element of character, or a story in which the incidents are made more prominent than the characters or background.

A story could hardly be written in which character, incident, and background were kept equally prominent, nor is it desirable that one should be so written. The great story is one which shows development in a character which is significant and worth knowing, making this apparent by means of a series of incidents, interesting and attention-compelling in themselves, with all exhibited upon a stage of action, a background or setting, worthy of the people and the incidents. The study of any literary form should be an aid to the student in determining whether a piece is of merely temporary interest or of such a quality as to be of permanent value. In other words, the student who comes to understand what qualities are to be expected will be able to distinguish between the good and the bad, the indifferent and the poor. Let it be understood that a short story to be well worth while must embody a theme which is true, and which is important enough to repay the reader for the time spent in thinking it through, and that this theme must be artistically presented by the use of incidents and a setting commensurate with the idea, and the student will have at his command the first principles upon which to base a judgment of the stories which he reads.

◄◄◄◄◄◄◄◄◄◄◄◄◄◄◄◄◄◄◄◄◄◄◄◄◄◄◄◄◄◄◄◄◄◇►►►►►►►►►►►►►►►►►►►►►►►►►►►►►►►►►►

CHAPTER III

THE SHORT STORY IS AN IMPRESSION FROM LIFE

LIKE the novel, the short story is a piece of fiction producing a unified effect. Unlike the novel, its single effect is usually an *impression*, instead of a deliberate marshaling together of a large number of diverse elements into a unity. The novel is complex—many experiences, usually of a number of people, pieced together into unity. It is a broad cross section of life—broad enough to cut through many experiences of many people, but still showing them as a unified part of life. The short story is a cross section of life, too, but of a single life or at most of a thread of life where it crosses and becomes entangled with one or two other subordinated threads—a section through the knot. To illustrate this in a concrete way: George Eliot's *Silas Marner* shows how a man's soul may be saved alive through the influence of a child. The method of the novelist is to exhibit the man at a moment when his soul is "nearest the city of destruction," and then, incident by incident, to show the soul growing back into right relationships with mankind, and a renewed trust in God. This theme of *Silas Marner* in short story form is used in Bret Harte's *The Luck of Roaring Camp*. But the short story writer must be impressionistic. He must be swift, choosing one or two incidents near the culmination of the novelist's series, and, merely hinting at the other incidents of the series and the other people involved, he must produce a convincing *impression* of the truth of his theme.

It cannot be assumed, however, that the culminating chapters of a novel could be drawn off and used as a short story. The mechanical structure of the story is as distinct and complete as that of the novel, and while in some cases the culminating chapters of a novel might furnish the material for a short story, that material would have to be worked into the form of a short story before it could stand alone.

HOW THE IMPRESSION IS MADE

Assuming that a short story is an impression from life, the first topic that presents itself for elucidation is the technical means which may be employed to make that impression. Let us call the impression which the author wishes to make the *theme* of the story. All other devices, technical processes, materials, and methods of handling the materials may be called the *means* that are to be used in the process of making the theme clear to the reader, and of making it so impressive that it may be effective. In the main these means are enumerated below.

WHAT IS MEANT BY THE THEME

The theme of a piece of fiction is the central idea that the author wishes to set forth in his story. It is that phenomenon of nature or of human life which he wishes to make clear to his readers. The theme has been called the "meaning" of the piece of literature. When Edgar Allan Poe spoke of the "single narrative effect" toward which every part of the story leads, he probably had in mind the same thing that we now have when we speak of "the theme," "the essential meaning," "the underlying idea," "the thesis," "the central thought," etc.

THE MEANS USED IN DEVELOPING A THEME

Having determined what particular "impression from life" he is to present in his story, the author's next step is to take stock of the means at his command capable of being used in exhibiting this theme. The following list includes most of these. They are: *Plot, Characters, Setting, Emotion, Tone, Appearance of Truth, Suspense, Suggestion and Restraint,* and *Style.* The detailed treatment of these matters is taken up in later chapters.

It is a mistake to think that the theme of a story is the same as the moral which used to be attached to a fable, or that the theme can always be stated in the form of a moral or philosophical truth. In many cases it is doubtful whether the author ever consciously formulated the theme. But it is true that a story, if it is worth while at all, does embody some significant impression of life. This impression *may* admit of a positive statement in the form of a truth, such as "The good are rewarded, and the wicked punished," but it need not. Themes are so different in their nature that no clear idea of their variety can be obtained without grouping them, like with like.

While the theme of a story is an impression of life, it is not often that a story writer is content merely to build up a story around an impression, although that method has been used occasionally by writers of the highest rank. Ordinarily the author, having made some observation of life and having discovered what he regards as a truth, wishes to put that discovery before the world in a convincing piece of fiction. Melville Davisson Post has often heard the old saying, "Murder will out." He conceives the idea of illustrating that theme in a short story. He has a murder committed unseen by any human being, by a man who would be suspected by no one in the community where the act was committed. And then the author contrives to have the murdered man, after he was dead, convict the murderer. Thus he shows that "murder will out." Knowing the power which the human will exerts upon the physical being, Edgar Allan Poe imagines the possibility of a will strong enough to overcome death itself. This is the theme of *Ligeia*. Guy de Maupassant observes that effects in nature are sometimes out of all proportion to causes. Twice he embodies this idea in fiction—in *The Piece of String* and in *The Necklace*. Stated concretely, this theme is actually worded in the latter, "How little a thing is needed for us to be lost or to be saved!" Enough has been shown by these four examples chosen at random to indicate that themes are of various kinds. It is hardly possible under half a dozen headings to classify all the kinds of themes, for there are sure to be, now and then, stories that refuse to submit to the bonds of general classification. Nevertheless, under a few heads the typical themes may be catalogued.

In commenting upon *Will o' the Mill* Stevenson has definitely stated what his theme was. He had heard it said that actions might be forgiven but that God himself could not forgive the hanger-back. One's sins, and mistakes actually made, might be pardoned, but the man who remains inactive, refuses to hazard the plunge, could never be held guiltless. So, Stevenson said, he wrote *Will o' the Mill* to make out the best case he could for the hanger-back. Instead of supporting an old saying as Post does in *After He Was Dead*, Stevenson supports the opposite of the statement which gave him the basis for the story.

In determining what the theme of a story is, the beginner must guard against confusing the terms "theme" and "moral." He must not ask, What does this story teach? for many stories do not teach at all in the sense of presenting a moral lesson. But rather let him begin his statement of the theme by saying to himself, The author's purpose in writing this story was to show that . . . Now complete the sentence and you will have the *theme* or *author's purpose* stated. One might say that Joseph Conrad wrote *Heart of Darkness* to show that civilization is a very thin veneer and quickly wears off when the civilized man is surrounded on every side by savagery. To make that statement is to state the theme of the story. To try to make a moral of it would be to misrepresent Conrad's purpose altogether in writing the story. Here is an attempt to attach a *moral* to the story: "Avoid the company of savage men or you will become like them." But to say that that was Conrad's idea when he wrote the story would be to inject a meaning into it that the author never even thought of.

Sometimes the theme is a lesson, a "moral"; but more commonly it is not. Take, for example, Jack London's story of character, entitled *Samuel.* Here we have a true impression of life. Stated in terms of the author's primary purpose the theme is as follows: This story was written to delineate the character of a woman, with a liking for a name, without a touch of superstition, and with a will so indomitable as to make it impossible for her to compromise with her convictions, no matter how strongly prompted to do so by the calamities which befell her or how often her simple and superstitious neighbors suggested compromise or surrender to her. The story is an inquiry into the reasons for liking or disliking things. Its theme is Margaret Henan's haunting problem, "The why of like." Try to state the theme as a "moral," and you have something like this: If you tempt God with a foolish persistency, He will visit you with untold calamity. And this the author apparently does not believe. Assuredly he does not allow such a conviction to take possession of his principal character, Margaret Henan. To her the cause of calamity is just as much a mystery as it is to Job, for she, like Job, is unaware of any sin at all commensurate with her sorrows.

GROUPS OF THEMES

It is easy to make lists of story themes and group together those that are similar in kind. But the reader must understand that any such classification is artificial and is made only as a device to help students to a clear understanding of what the story writers are trying to do. For study purposes we may arrange a hundred stories into eight or ten groups on the basis of the similarity of the central thought or theme of the stories. That does not mean that there are exactly eight or ten possible kinds of ideas that can be put into stories. There may be sixteen or forty-five, all depending upon who makes up the lists of themes. One person may make his headings very general, and so have only a few. He may use such headings as Human Interest Stories, Adventure Stories, Stories of Emotions and Passions, Mystery Stories, and the like. Another may list all stories under the three heads: Character Studies, Stories of Incident, and Stories of Setting. Still another may use a totally different set of headings such as Adventure, Sea Stories, Love Stories, Detective Stories, Stories of Terror, Idyllic Stories, or a score of other headings just as good as any of the others that have been mentioned. Regard any such groupings only as a mechanical or logical device to help the reader to separate a number of stories into related groups for the purpose of study and to aid him in arriving at a clear understanding of the stories themselves.

In this chapter we are saying that many stories can be grouped under the seven headings that follow. This does not mean that there are no other kinds of stories. Nor does it mean that an author beginning to write a story says to himself, "I believe today I'll try my hand upon a story that will illustrate the lawlessness of nature." The classifications we are using are conventional and arbitrary. They are made after the stories are written, made to assist students in analyzing stories, not to guide a story writer in constructing a piece of fiction. It must be admitted that most story writers have never heard of these particular groupings, even though they may have in mind some kind of logical classification of themes.

1. The Exhibition of Some Natural Law, or Apparent Lawlessness of Nature.—A story might be made to illustrate even so prosaic a thing as the physical law that action and reaction are equal and in opposite directions. Likewise the philosophical law that like causes produce like effects might be embodied in a short story. These would be themes illustrating *natural laws;* but when Maupassant shows how picking up a piece of string ultimately caused the death of an old peasant, his theme is the irony of fate. He shows how the effect of an insignificant action is sometimes out of all proportion to the cause.

2. An Illustration of a Phase of Human Nature.—In *Dr. Jekyll and Mr. Hyde*, Robert Louis Stevenson shows that both good and evil are in the nature of man, and that the lower, meaner part subdues the nobler if occasionally allowed to run riot. A deep conviction of the newer psychology was anticipated in Robert Herrick's *The Master of the Inn.* In this story he says that if the half-forgotten troubles of the soul which lie below the level of consciousness can be brought to the surface and aired in oral confession, the physical ills, indirectly caused by the blot on the soul, will vanish and leave the body strong and responsive to the will.

One other illustration of this kind of theme is seen in James Lane Allen's *King Solomon of Kentucky.* No matter how low a man may sink, the story seems to declare, there is some spark of the heroic left in him, and this may be aroused if the stimulus be of the right kind, at the right time, and sufficiently strong. The same theme is seen in John Russell's *Jetsam.*

3. The Exhibition of Some Human Passion in a Striking, Unusual, or Tense Situation.—The passion most frequently exhibited in magazine fiction is love. But writers have used over and over all the elemental human passions, such as hate, fear, jealousy, indignation, superstition, devotion to duty, loyalty to friends or kinsmen, loyalty to clan or country, and the like.

H. C. Bunner's whimsical story, *The Love Letters of Smith*, is a love story the tone of which is humorous. Jealousy is the theme of James B. Connolly's *The Truth of the Oliver Cromwell*; indignation is exhibited in Mary E. Wilkins Freeman's *The Revolt of "Mother"*; superstition, in Arthur Morrison's *On the Stairs*.

The student should not expect to be able to relate every touch that the writer puts into his story to a single theme element, uncolored by others. For example, the *setting* of each of the stories mentioned in this group is so carefully treated that along with his main impression (his theme) the author, without doubt, was very much interested in the place and the people.

The student needs to be warned against the statement of themes in terms so general that they do not discriminate at all. It is easy to say that a story is "a love story," "a southern story," or "a sea story," without being specific about the truth of life which it contains. In most cases such designations apply to the *setting* and not to the *theme* at all.

4. The Reproduction of a Phase of Life in a Given Time, Place, or Occupation.—Authors do not ordinarily use place, time, and occupation as the themes of stories. These are usually nothing more than the setting, or background, for some theme of greater general interest. Once in a while, however, we see stories, which appear to be written with no other purpose than to make a picture of life, bringing forward what is usually the background and placing it in the focus of interest as the main theme. New England village life is exhibited in Mrs. Freeman's *A Village Lear*; life in old New Orleans and the South, in George W. Cable's *Posson Jone'*; newspaper life, in Richard Harding Davis's *A Derelict*; and Colorado mining life in Hamlin Garland's *The Spirit of Sweetwater*.

In all of these stories, place, time, and occupation are background and not theme. In other words, *A Derelict* belongs in group 2 with Allen's *King Solomon of Kentucky*. Garland's *The Spirit of Sweetwater* is a story of the regenerating power of love, and belongs to group 3. However, in *Père Raphael*, the sequel to *Posson Jone'*, Cable seems to have had in mind no other theme than the reproduction of a phase of life in a particular place at a particular time—the New Orleans of 1820. It properly belongs to group 4.

5. The Delineation of Character.—The characters pictured in stories whose main purpose is character portrayal are in most cases in some way unusual, striking, odd, or peculiar. Examples of short stories having character portrayal as the objective point—the theme—may be seen in Sir Arthur Quiller-Couch's *The Drawn Blind*, in Ruth McEnery

Stuart's *Napoleon Jackson*, and in Thomas Bailey Aldrich's *Quite So*. Since, however, the peculiarity in the character of Cordelia Pinsent in *The Drawn Blind* is her inability to believe her son capable of doing wrong (a characteristic of mothers generally), the story might be put into group 3. Quiller-Couch seems, however, to have been more interested in showing how Mrs. Pinsent's confidence in the integrity of her son was exhibited by this particular mother rather than in elucidating the general idea that mothers fail to see the shortcomings of their sons.

6. *The Development or Disintegration of Character Under the Stress of Some Emotion or Circumstance.*—This group will overlap both group 5 and group 3, but many examples may be cited in which the *main* purpose of the author was to show development or breaking down of character under emotional stress. Hawthorne's *The Great Stone Face* shows development under the influence of a high ideal; Maupassant's *A Coward* shows disintegration under the strain of physical fear. Because of the fact that the story is limited in length there is hardly room for much *growth* of character, for growth is not a mushroom process where human character is concerned. Only a few great short stories have adequately managed character development. Character *portrayal* is the business of the short story writer; realistic character *development*, that of the novelist. The short story writer may, however, create so convincing an impression of character growth or disintegration as to produce the illusion of the whole process in actual operation. This is one of the supreme tests of the literary genius, and is worth striving for. Björnson's *The Father* is a story of the development of character. Dickens's *Dr. Marigold's Prescriptions* is a story primarily interested in character portrayal.

7. *An Impression of Life.*—Hawthorne was in the habit of setting down in his notebooks vague impressions with the intention of making stories at some later time to embody the impressions. One of his notes reads, "The print of blood of a naked foot to be traced through the streets of a town." This impression is probably the germ of *Dr. Grimshawe's Secret*. Henry James confessed that the appearance of a peculiar or striking character often inspired him to invent a setting and incidents in which such a character might naturally act a significant part. Robert Louis Stevenson once told his cousin, Graham Balfour, that the impression of atmosphere led him to create the characters and incidents of *The Merry Men*, his purpose being to convey to others the feeling he himself had had when he saw the island that is the setting for that story. One could well believe that Stevenson had no other purpose in mind than to contrast the vagabond poet, Villon, with the comfortable but

colorless citizen, Seigneur de Brisetout, in *A Lodging for the Night*. This gives one an impression of life, and no more.

In such stories as these there is no universal truth to be taught, no moral to be impressed, no new theory or cause to be advanced, no strange corner of the world to be exploited. Evidently the author wishes merely to entertain with a good story; and to do this he simply embodies an impression.

This group will include a great many stories not easily classified under the other heads. It will be a sort of receptacle for the multitude of miscellaneous stories that refuse to consort with those typical stories which have class characteristics.

THE WRITER'S PRIMARY PURPOSE

The theme the author had most prominently in mind cannot always be determined at the first glance, though it usually comes to the surface after careful study. For this reason two people reading the same story may not agree as to its theme. *The Truth of the Oliver Cromwell* will illustrate how the theme of a story might, by different readers, be put into different groups. One reader, seeing no development or disintegration of character, might put the theme into the third group, "The exhibition of some human passion (jealousy) in a striking, unusual, or tense situation." Another might put it in group 6 on account of the disintegration of character under the influence of jealousy. Still another might see no more in it than an impression of life, as in group 7. It might be regarded as nothing more than the portrayal of the characters of New England fishermen (group 5). Or, lastly, some reader might place the theme in group 4, "The reproduction of a phase of life (New England fishing life) in a particular locality and occupation."

Doubtless all these elements are in the story. In most stories, besides the main theme, several other interests enter. To determine what the real theme is one has to put himself in the place of the author as he begins his story and ask himself, What is the single impression which the story is to make? If the story is well written, the "single impression" that the author desired will become apparent.

In *The Truth of the Oliver Cromwell* the author used New England fishing life (group 4) as background. The theme is much more definite than a classification in group 7 usually permits, and goes farther than group 3; that is, the story shows disintegration of character under the influence of jealousy, and that (group 6) is its theme. Character portrayal (group 5) is only a means of making the main impression, as are also the incidents and setting.

THE GREATEST THEMES

Great stories will be found in all the groups mentioned above, for greatness does not depend upon theme alone. The greatest themes, however, are those dealing with some universal phase of human life—with some matter supremely interesting to mankind in any country and in any period of time.

Love, Jealousy and Hate, Devotion to an Ideal, Courage, and Fear—all the elemental emotions—do not depend upon time or place; and so stories embodying such themes as these were popular a thousand years ago, if artistically presented; they are read with keen interest today; and will thrill their multitudes of readers a thousand years hence. Our manners change; our speech changes; we build differently; we come to think differently; our ethical and religious principles undergo a slow transformation—but there are elemental depths below these currents which, if they change at all, change like nature itself with the slow march of millenniums. *The Odyssey* has endured the wear of ages not simply because it is an absorbing adventure story illuminated by the fire of poetic imagination, but chiefly because its theme is one of the simple, elemental, great things at the bottom of human nature—the triumph of mind over circumstances. Given a sufficient motive—the faithful Penelope in peril at home, waiting the ten long years after the fall of Troy—Homer shows the adventurous and crafty Ulysses meeting and overcoming the obstacles set up by nature and man and the gods; and humanity in sympathy with the sorely tried adventurer follows him with breathless interest and rejoices with a species of savage joy in his triumphs. Such themes are simple, but they lie close to the foundation of human experience. Universality of interest lifts the epics above the nation which originated them and makes them world stories.

The writer of a short story who succeeds in embodying in his fiction one of these simple but fundamental interests of the human race has taken the first step toward the production of a story really great.

It is not important that a student should be able to read a given story and place it without doubt or hesitation in one of these seven groups. Three students reading such stories as Jack Doyle's *Boston Blackie's Mary* or Helen Hull's *Clay Shuttered Doors* might classify them in several different groups, or they might by chance all place them in the same group. The classification is unimportant. It is significant, however, that all three readers should understand the picture of life the artist has drawn in the story and be emotionally stirred by it.

CHAPTER IV

PLOT

The *plot* of a story is the plan which the author makes for the purpose of developing or exhibiting his theme or idea.

HAVING once determined what phase of life he wishes to picture for his readers, the writer's next step in story-making is to construct a framework upon which he can exhibit his picture of life. Robert Herrick desires to show that a hurt of the spirit rankles in the flesh, and that the flesh can be made whole only by thinking more of others than of self, working for others, and at last laying bare the wound of the soul in open recognition and oral confession. His next problem is to lay a plan for the exhibition of this theme. Briefly, the plan he constructs is this: A great surgeon suddenly fails because of the loss of nervous control. Trying all sorts of cures without any benefit, he comes finally to an old man who has discovered the secret of lifting the burden from the soul in order to restore the body. The surgeon at last tells his story to the man whom he has wronged long ago. He is absolved, and goes back to his work once more master of himself.

But a plot cannot be made merely by adding incident to incident, like laying dominoes down end to end in a long row. It must be put together more like constructing a house of building blocks. Each incident grows out of the one preceding. First there is a foundation, then a super-structure; then, having reached the desired height, the builder, with a more rapid movement, adds the culmination in roof and dome or spire.

The necessity of an organized structure in story-telling has been recognized by scholars for many hundreds of years. Aristotle set down the requirement of "a beginning, a middle, and an end," having in mind the same thing, perhaps, that a modern student has when he speaks of the Preliminary Situation, the Complication of the threads of the plot, and the Resolution of the complexity; i.e., the solution of the problem the writer has set up.

While this principle of plot construction has long been known, the practice of making a plot after this manner is recent. The older writers of tales tried to interest their readers merely by joining together a number of interesting incidents after the fashion of the row of dominoes. The short story writer of today starts with an idea or theme, chooses characters, a setting, etc., and then gives the readers the Preliminary Situation—the relation of the characters to each other and their surroundings. This accomplished, he begins the climb up his plot-ladder toward the Culmination of the story. In this climb the incidents of the story form the steps. The upward movement is not, then, along a smooth incline, but step by step, incident by incident, each depending upon the one preceding and making natural the one to come, until the author leads the reader to a height from whence he can see the way to a solution of the complexity created during the time of the movement upward. The solution of the complexity we call the *Culmination*. If we think of the making of a story in terms of another figure of speech, we might call this process the weaving together of the threads of the plot. Just before the culmination, the threads seem to be in an inextricable tangle—a knot, where all the threads of causation cross each other. Then comes the culmination. The knot is untied—or maybe cut—and the story rounds itself out into a natural conclusion.

PLOT CONSTRUCTION IN A DRAMA

Since both the novel and the short story are forms of prose fiction, one would expect their structure to be similar. The fact is, however, that the short story and the stage play are more nearly alike than the short story and the novel. If you go to the theater and give close attention to the mechanism of a play on the stage, you will observe that the dramatist has constructed his play in distinct sections or steps, and that each of these sections makes an act. Suppose, by way of illustration, that we use an old standard drama, Oscar Wilde's *Lady Windermere's Fan*, written in 1892 and seen frequently on the stage through the forty and more years since its first production. First, what is the idea in this play? Oscar Wilde has observed that it is a common belief that people are either good or bad, and that so far as character is concerned people are either black or white. His own observation is that there is often some good in even the worst of us and some evil in the best of us. He decides to write a play to show that truth about human nature. That, then, is the *theme* of the play he proposes to write. His next task is to construct a plot upon which he can show up or exhibit this idea or theme.

He says to himself, "Let's imagine a young wife who has been brought up in a very strict and puritanical home and has never met with temptation to do wrong or commit a sin. She thinks white is white and black is black, with no compromise, no light or dark gray shades in between the two. Now, let's put her through a series of experiences in which she will discover that there is weakness in herself and a tendency under the stress of temptation to drop down to a level of thinking and action that she could never have imagined of herself before. Also let's have her discover generosity, willingness to sacrifice self for someone else, and other good qualitites in a character whom she has always regarded as thoroughly bad. And when this uncompromising puritan is convinced that there is evil in the best of us and good in the worst of us, the observer looking on at the play will also be convinced."

This is a rough, general sketch of Oscar Wilde's plan, or plot, to write a play that will embody the theme already stated. Here is the plot worked out in specific detail:

First Act: Lady Windermere, a young wife with a child about a year old, is planning an informal dance to celebrate her twenty-first birthday. Afternoon callers (Lord Darlington and the Duchess of Berwick and her daughter) drop in, and in the gossipy talk over the tea they let Lady Windermere know that her husband has been giving much time to a questionable woman named Mrs. Erlynne, and that he is spending a great deal of money on her. Immediately after the callers go, young Lord Windermere comes in and requests his wife to send an invitation to Mrs. Erlynne for her dance that evening. This Lady Windermere indignantly refuses to do. Lord Windermere then writes the invitation himself and sends it. The wife thereupon declares that if "that woman" comes she will strike her across the face with her fan, a birthday gift that day from her husband. And with this threat the act closes.

What has been accomplished thus far? The chief characters have been introduced to the audience. They are Lady Windermere (Margaret), Lord Windermere (Arthur), Lord Darlington (a cynical young aristocrat who will later propose an elopement with Margaret), and the Duchess of Berwick, a gossip and necessary go-between. Mrs. Erlynne has been introduced thus far only by name and reputation. The theme of the drama has been stated. In the afternoon conversation Lord Darlington had maintained that people could not be classified into "good people" and "bad people." Lady Windermere insisted that all people were either good or bad, and that she would not tolerate the bad. When her husband first asked and then demanded an invitation for Mrs. Erlynne, whom his wife regarded as a "bad woman," and she refused to send it, we have an incident injected into the situation that makes action of some kind necessary and a tragic break possible. This is the Initial Incident, or dramatic starting point of the play. It is the incident that sets up an opposition demanding action and a solution. In the act, then, we have come to an understanding of the *Time*, the *Place*, the principal *Characters* and their relation to each other, the state of affairs as it existed before the play opened, the problem or *Theme* of the play, and the *Initial Incident* that has started a series of acts that must lead up to some kind of a solution of the problem. In this play the initial incident has come in at the very end of the act. It usually occurs somewhere after the middle of the first act—not necessarily at the very end.

Second Act: The ball at Lady Windermere's house the same evening. Numerous guests arrive. Mrs. Erlynne arrives but Lady Windermere in her nervous agitation drops her fan. During the evening Lord Windermere dances with Mrs. Erlynne and pays a good deal of attention to her. Lady Windermere, overcome with righteous indignation and jealousy, determines to leave her husband and child and elope with Lord Darlington. She writes a note for her husband and slips out. Mrs. Erlynne finds the note and reads it. The audience now learns that Mrs. Erlynne is Lady Windermere's mother trying to find her way back into society unknown to her daughter, but with the aid of her rich son-in-law. She determines to sacrifice her own chances to save her daughter from the mistake she herself had made twenty years before.

This is the first step upward toward the solution of the problem.

Third Act: This takes place in Lord Darlington's apartment about midnight. Mrs. Erlynne finds her daughter alone in Lord Darlington's living room, and persuades her for the sake of her husband and child to return home. Mrs. Erlynne does not make herself known as Margaret's mother. Just as they are about to leave, the men are heard on the stairs. Margaret slips behind the heavy drapes of a bay window near the door to wait for a chance to escape unseen. Mrs. Erlynne steps into the bedroom. In her haste Margaret had left her fan on the table. Lord Darlington, Lord Windermere, and four or five other men come in. Darlington does not know that Lady Windermere has followed his suggestion. The fan is discovered, and to prevent a quarrel about it Mrs. Erlynne steps out and calls attention to herself long enough to allow Margaret to escape. Then to save her daughter's reputation she admits that she has come to Darlington's rooms and has brought the fan.

This act is the dramatic and emotional culmination of the drama. The theme has been worked out. Margaret is convinced that there is the possibility of a great deal of evil in good women (represented by herself) and much good in bad women (represented by Mrs. Erlynne).

It has taken but two scenes to work out the theme. The play could end there on the high tension of the culminating scene, but the author decided to use another act to ease the action down to a reconciliation and understanding between husband and wife.

Fourth Act: The next morning back in Lady Windermere's house. Reconciliation of the two. Mrs. Erlynne calls to return the fan and to announce her determination to leave England. She is to marry Lord Augustus Lorton. She keeps her identity unknown to her daughter.

To make a novel of the story of Lady Windermere would have required four or five hundred pages, and the novel would have dealt with her whole life, with many incidents preceding this one dramatic situation, and many after it. The time covered would be perhaps as much as forty years. Here in a drama a single crucial day of only eighteen

---

A Typical Plot Diagram of a Drama

The following diagram will help to make clear the movement of the plot in *Lady Windermere's Fan:*

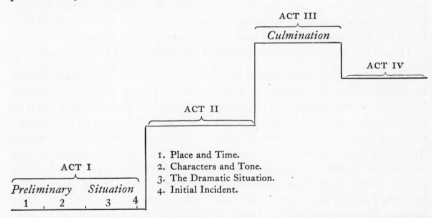

Act I. Presents the items of (1) place and time, (2) the characters and their relations to each other, including an insight into what had happened before the play opened, (3) the keynote or tone of the drama, whether comic, serious, or tragic, and (4) the initial incident.

Act II. After the initial incident, Act II complicates the situation to the point that a solution must be found.

Act III. The culmination of the drama brings about the solution made necessary by the events of Act II.

Act IV. Drops the action down to a serene and quiet ending on a happy note.

hours is used. This same situation would make an excellent short story. In other words the materials that go into a novel do not often lend themselves to the drama or short story; but usually the material that would make a good play could be put into a short story very effectively.

THE PLOT OF A TYPICAL SHORT STORY

In analyzing the plot of a short story, it is important to have in mind some concrete instance which can be used as an illustration. For that purpose, Maupassant's well-known and perfectly constructed story, *The Piece of String*, is given here complete. The paragraphs in italics have been inserted by the editor to indicate and explain the successive steps in the development of the plot.

THE PIECE OF STRING[1]

By Guy de Maupassant

[Henri René Albert Guy de Maupassant (1850–1893) was a French writer of short stories, plays, and novels. He was born in the country, educated in the best schools, and graduated from the College of Rouen. His literary training was the care of his godfather, Gustave Flaubert, the celebrated French novelist. Flaubert was noted for the pains he took to perfect the form of what he wrote. Through a long apprenticeship, publishing nothing till his thirtieth year, Maupassant learned the lesson so well that he perhaps surpassed his master. Practically all the writers and critics regard him as the great master of form in story structure. His themes are usually of absorbing interest, but the level of life he pictures is often low and seems repellent to many. He is, however, a convincing realist, notwithstanding his cynical view of life and the unpleasant situations he presents. His works most read in English are: The novel, *Pierre et Jean* (1888), and the stories, *The Tallow Ball* (1880), *The Horla* (1887), *The Conscript, A Coward, The Necklace*, and *The Piece of String*. The last two years of his life were clouded by depression, disease, and partial insanity. He died in a private asylum in Paris in his forty-third year.]

(PRELIMINARY SITUATION. *First, the author sketches in the background of his picture like a painter making a background on his canvas for the picture that is to fill the foreground and be the feature of principal interest. Then the principal character of the story, Master Hauchecorne, is brought in, and we are ready for the Initial Incident.*)

[1]Reprinted from *Little French Masterpieces*, with the permission of G. P. Putnam's Sons.

ON all the roads about Goderville the peasants and their wives were coming towards the town, for it was market day. The men walked at an easy gait, the whole body thrown forward with every movement of their long, crooked legs, misshapen by hard work, by the bearing down on the plough, which at the same time causes the left shoulder to rise and the figure to slant; by the mowing of the grain, which makes one hold his knees apart in order to obtain a firm footing; by all the slow and laborious tasks of the fields. Their starched blue blouses, glossy as if varnished, adorned at the neck and wrists with a bit of white stitchwork, puffed out about their bony chests like balloons on the point of taking flight, from which protruded a head, two arms, and two feet.

Some of them led a cow or a calf at the end of a rope. And their wives, walking behind the beast, lashed it with a branch still covered with leaves, to hasten its pace. They carried on their arms great baskets, from which heads of chickens or of ducks were thrust forth. And they walked with a shorter and quicker step than their men, their stiff, lean figures wrapped in scanty shawls pinned over their flat breasts, their heads enveloped in a white linen cloth close to the hair, with a cap over all.

Then a char-à-bancs passed, drawn by a jerky-paced nag, with two men seated side by side shaking like jelly, and a woman behind, who clung to the side of the vehicle to lessen the rough jolting.

On the square at Goderville there was a crowd, a medley of men and beasts. The horns of the cattle, the high hats, with a long, hairy nap, of the wealthy peasants, and the headdresses of the peasant women, appeared on the surface of the throng. And the sharp, shrill, high-pitched voices formed an incessant, uncivilized uproar, over which soared at times a roar of laughter from the powerful chest of a sturdy yokel, or the prolonged bellow of a cow fastened to the wall of a house.

There was an all-pervading smell of the stable, of milk, of the dung-hill, of hay, and of perspiration—that acrid, disgusting odor of man and beast peculiar to country people.

(THEME. *The theme of this story is that an insignificant act or incident may be enough to ruin a man's life; or to say it another way, sometimes little things have a bearing on life altogether out of proportion to their size. The Initial Incident will be one of those little, unimportant acts of a human being. In this case it is an old man picking up a bit of string out of the road.*)

Master Hauchecorne, of Bréauté, had just arrived at Goderville, and was walking towards the square, when he saw a bit of string on the ground. Master Hauchecorne, economical like every true Norman, thought that it was well to pick up everything that might be of use;

and he stooped painfully, for he suffered with rheumatism. He took the piece of slender cord from the ground, and was about to roll it up carefully, when he saw Master Malandain, the harness-maker, standing in his doorway and looking at him. They had formerly had trouble on the subject of a halter, and had remained at odds, being both inclined to bear malice. Master Hauchecorne felt a sort of shame at being seen thus by his enemy, fumbling in the mud for a bit of string. He hurriedly concealed his treasure in his blouse, then in his breeches pocket; then he pretended to look on the ground for something else, which he did not find; and finally he went on towards the market, his head thrust forward, bent double by his pains.

He lost himself at once in the slow-moving, shouting crowd, kept in a state of excitement by the interminable bargaining. The peasants felt of the cows, went away, returned, sorely perplexed, always afraid of being cheated, never daring to make up their minds, watching the vendor's eye, striving incessantly to detect the tricks of the man and the defect in the beast.

The women, having placed their great baskets at their feet, took out their fowls, which lay on the ground, their legs tied together, with frightened eyes and scarlet combs.

They listened to offers, adhered to their prices, short of speech and impassive of face; or else, suddenly deciding to accept the lower price offered, they would call out to the customer as he walked slowly away: "All right, Mast' Anthime. You can have it."

Then, little by little, the square became empty, and when the Angelus struck midday those who lived too far away to go home betook themselves to the various inns.

(*Scene 1. The first step toward the breaking of the old man's spirit is his arrest.*)

At Jourdain's the common room was full of customers, as the great yard was full of vehicles of every sort—carts, cabriolets, tilburys, unnamable carriages, shapeless, patched, with their shafts reaching heavenward like arms, or with their noses in the ground and their tails in the air.

The vast fireplace, full of clear flame, cast an intense heat against the backs of the row on the right of the table. Three spits were revolving, laden with chickens, pigeons, and legs of mutton; and a delectable odor of roast meat, and of gravy dripping from the browned skin, came forth from the hearth, stirred the guests to merriment, and made their mouths water.

All the aristocracy of the plough ate there, at Mast' Jourdain's, the innkeeper and horse trader—a shrewd rascal who had money.

The dishes passed and were soon emptied, like the jugs of yellow cider. Every one told of his affairs, his sales, and his purchases. They inquired about the crops. The weather was good for green stuffs, but a little wet for wheat.

Suddenly a drum rolled in the yard, in front of the house. In an instant everybody was on his feet, save a few indifferent ones; and they all ran to the door and windows, with their mouths still full and napkins in hand.

Having finished his long tattoo, the public crier shouted in a jerky voice, making his pauses in the wrong places:

"The people of Goderville, and all those present at the market are informed that between—nine and ten o'clock this morning on the Beuzeville—road, a black leather wallet was lost, containing five hundred—francs, and business papers. The finder is requested to carry it to—the mayor's office at once, or to Master Fortuné Houlbrèque of Manneville. A reward of twenty francs will be paid."

Then he went away. They heard once more in the distance the muffled roll of the drum and the indistinct voice of the crier.

Then they began to talk about the incident, reckoning Master Houl-brèque's chance of finding or not finding his wallet.

And the meal went on.

They were finishing their coffee when the corporal of gendarmes appeared in the doorway.

He inquired:

"Is Master Hauchecorne of Bréauté here?"

Master Hauchecorne, who was seated at the farther end of the table, answered:

"Here I am."

And the corporal added:

"Master Hauchecorne, will you be kind enough to go to the mayor's office with me? Monsieur the mayor would like to speak to you."

The peasant, surprised and disturbed, drank his *petit verre* at one swallow, rose, and even more bent than in the morning, for the first steps after each rest were particularly painful, he started off, repeating:

"Here I am, here I am."

And he followed the brigadier.

(*Scene 2. The second step is Hauchecorne's examination before the mayor, and his failure to convince the mayor of his innocence.*)

The mayor was waiting for him, seated in an arm-chair. He was the local notary, a stout, solemn-faced man, given to pompous speeches.

"Master Hauchecorne," he said, "you were seen this morning, on the Beuzeville road, to pick up the wallet lost by Master Houlbrèque of Manneville."

The rustic, dumfounded, stared at the mayor, already alarmed by this suspicion which had fallen upon him, although he failed to understand it.

"I, I—I picked up that wallet?"

"Yes, you."

"On my word of honor, I didn't even so much as see it."

"You were seen."

"They saw me, me? Who was it saw me?"

"Monsieur Malandain, the harness-maker."

Thereupon the old man remembered and understood; and flushing with anger, he cried:

"Ah! he saw me, did he, that sneak? He saw me pick up this string, look, m'sieu' mayor."

And, fumbling in the depths of his pocket, he produced the little piece of cord.

But the mayor was incredulous and shook his head.

"You won't make me believe, Master Hauchecorne, that Monsieur Malandain, who is a man deserving of credit, mistook this string for a wallet."

The peasant, in a rage, raised his hand, spit to one side to pledge his honor, and said:

"It's God's own truth, the sacred truth, all the same, m'sieu' mayor. I say it again, by my soul and my salvation."

"After picking it up," rejoined the mayor, "you hunted a long while in the mud, to see if some piece of money hadn't fallen out."

The good man was suffocated with wrath and fear.

"If any one can tell—if any one can tell lies like that, to ruin an honest man! If any one can say—"

To no purpose did he protest; he was not believed.

He was confronted with Monsieur Malandain, who repeated and maintained his declaration. They insulted each other for a whole hour. At his own request, Master Hauchecorne was searched. They found nothing on him. At last the mayor, being sorely perplexed, discharged him, but warned him that he proposed to inform the prosecuting attorney's office and to ask for orders.

(*Scene 3. The neighbors believe the old man guilty of theft.*)

The news had spread. On leaving the mayor's office, the old man was surrounded and questioned with serious or bantering curiosity, in which, however, there was no trace of indignation. And he began to tell the story of the string. They did not believe him. They laughed.

He went his way, stopping his acquaintances, repeating again and again his story and his protestations, showing his pockets turned inside out, to prove that he had nothing.

They said to him:

"Go on, you old rogue!"

And he lost his temper, lashing himself into a rage, feverish with excitement, desperate because he was not believed, at a loss what to do, and still telling his story.

Night came. He must needs go home. He started with three neighbors, to whom he pointed out the place where he had picked up the bit of string; and all the way he talked of his misadventure.

During the evening he made a circuit of the village of Bréauté, in order to tell everybody about it. He found none but incredulous listeners.

He was ill over it all night.

(*Scene 4. The old man believes his troubles are over when the purse is found and returned.*)

The next afternoon, about one o'clock, Marius Paumelle, a farm-hand employed by Master Breton, a farmer of Ymauville, restored the wallet and its contents to Master Houlbrèque of Manneville.

The man claimed that he had found it on the road; but, being unable to read, he had carried it home and given it to his employer.

The news soon became known in the neighborhood; Master Hauchecorne was informed of it. He started out again at once, and began to tell his story, now made complete by the dénouement. He was triumphant.

"What made me feel bad," he said, "wasn't so much the thing itself, you understand, but the lying. There's nothing hurts you so much as being blamed for lying."

All day long he talked of his adventure; he told it on the roads to people who passed; at the wine-shop to people who were drinking; and after church on the following Sunday. He even stopped strangers to tell them about it. His mind was at rest now, and yet something embarrassed him, although he could not say just what it was. People seemed to laugh while they listened to him. They did not seem convinced. He felt as if remarks were made behind his back.

(*Scene 5. The culmination or turning point. Failing to establish his innocence, Hauchecorne gradually goes to pieces.*)

On Tuesday of the next week, he went to market at Goderville, impelled solely by the longing to tell his story.

Malandain, standing in his doorway, began to laugh when he saw him coming. Why?

He accosted a farmer from Criquetot, who did not let him finish, but poked him in the pit of his stomach, and shouted in his face:

"Go on, you old fox!" Then he turned on his heel.

Master Hauchecorne was speechless, and more and more disturbed. Why did he call him "old fox"?

When he was seated at the table, in Jourdain's inn, he set about explaining the affair once more.

A horse-trader from Montivilliers called out to him:

"Nonsense, nonsense, you old dodger! I know all about your string!"

"But they've found the wallet!" faltered Hauchecorne.

"None of that, old boy; there's one who finds it, and there's one who carries it back. I don't know just how you did it, but I understand you."

The peasant was fairly stunned. He understood at last. He was accused of having sent the wallet back by a confederate, an accomplice.

He tried to protest. The whole table began to laugh.

He could not finish his dinner, but left the inn amid a chorus of jeers.

He returned home, shamefaced and indignant, suffocated by wrath, by confusion, and all the more cast down because, with his Norman cunning, he was quite capable of doing the thing with which he was charged, and even of boasting of it as a shrewd trick. He had a confused idea that his innocence was impossible to establish, his craftiness being so well known. And he was cut to the heart by the injustice of the suspicion.

(*Conclusion. In despair the old peasant slips down to his death.*)

Thereupon he began once more to tell of the adventure, making the story longer each day, adding each time new arguments, more forcible protestations, more solemn oaths, which he devised and prepared in his hours of solitude, his mind being wholly engrossed by the story of the string. The more complicated his defence and the more subtle his reasoning, the less he was believed.

"Those are a liar's reasons," people said behind his back.

He realized it; he gnawed his nails, and exhausted himself in vain efforts.

He grew perceptibly thinner.

Now the jokers asked him to tell the story of "The Piece of String" for their amusement, as a soldier who has seen service is asked to tell about his battles. His mind, attacked at its source, grew feebler.

Late in December he took to his bed.

In the first days of January he died, and in the delirium of the death agony, he protested his innocence, repeating:

"A little piece of string—a little piece of string—see, here it is, m'sieu' mayor."

PLOT DIAGRAMS

A stair-step diagram can easily be drawn to represent the rise of the action in this story. It will have the usual level line of the preliminary situation, in which necessary facts of time, place, characters and general background are being established before any rise of the story toward a culmination can take place. Then it will indicate the initial incident and the five little scenes that carry the story up to its culmination. After this it will show the short scene that lets the story down to its conclusion with the death of the old peasant.

Diagrams are of value only for the purpose of helping the reader or student to visualize the course of the action in a story. They have no value in themselves. Three students of this story might each draw a diagram of it, and all three diagrams be slightly different. Yet each one would represent the structure of the story as that particular student saw it.

A Stair-step Plot Diagram for "The Piece of String"

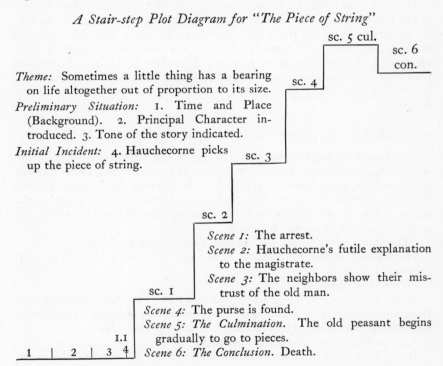

Theme: Sometimes a little thing has a bearing on life altogether out of proportion to its size.
Preliminary Situation: 1. Time and Place (Background). 2. Principal Character introduced. 3. Tone of the story indicated.
Initial Incident: 4. Hauchecorne picks up the piece of string.

Scene 1: The arrest.
Scene 2: Hauchecorne's futile explanation to the magistrate.
Scene 3: The neighbors show their mistrust of the old man.
Scene 4: The purse is found.
Scene 5: The Culmination. The old peasant begins gradually to go to pieces.
Scene 6: The Conclusion. Death.

Instead of the stair-step diagram some readers find one of an entirely different type suggestive of the action in certain kinds of stories. This is the rocket diagram, beginning with the slow movement on the level for the usual items of time, place, characters, and tone. Then follows the initial incident and immediately a sharp rise of the story like a rocket going up. At the culmination there is the flash of the rocket at its height and a turn before the stick comes down.

Rocket Plots

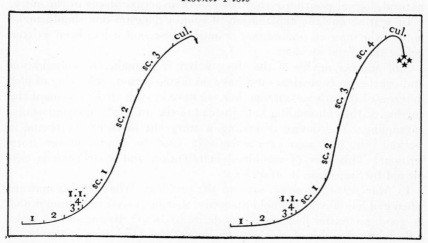

If the story ends at the culminating point with a snap and a crackle, as many of O. Henry's do, the diagram may show the rocket flashing into a burst of stars as at the right.

The diagrams thus far shown give pictures of stories in which the plot structure follows the logical order. First there is the background or setting of time and place, introduction of characters, and the establishment of the tone of the story. Then comes the initial incident, followed by the succession of scenes that carry the story upward by logical steps to its culmination.

Not all stories are planned in this perfectly logical order, but the diagram can be varied so as to exhibit almost any plot structure. Frequently the writer will begin with the initial incident and then go back and insert the preliminary situation. This gives the story a lively and interesting beginning, which the more leisurely story, opening with the preliminary situation, may not have; but it also has a fault. It must pause after its lively opening and ask the reader to wait for the necessary explanation of the conditions which precede the initial incident—unless the author can deftly suggest the preliminary situation as the plot mounts step by step. Such deft suggestion is high art and, consequently, is somewhat rare. In such a story the mounting of the staircase will probably be slower than in the other type. It will be noted that the facts in the preliminary situation are present, and that their logical place is before the initial incident, even though the story actually begins with the initial incident. In a diagram the incidents are placed in their natural, logical position rather than in their actual places in the story.

In writing out the explanation of such a diagram one should make note of the inferred preliminary situation, just as if it had been written before the initial incident.

Still another device of the story writer is to make the culmination and conclusion coincident, and have no falling action. Thinking of plot in terms of threads woven together, we have in such an arrangement the cutting of the culminating knot instead of the process of untying or disentangling. The device of ending a story the moment the theme is worked out, has been very effectively used by many master story writers. This sort of combined culmination and conclusion is employed by Stevenson in *Markheim*.

In *Markheim* Stevenson sets up the problem, What shall a man do when evil has laid such a hold upon him that he cannot turn from it and do good, no matter how strong his desire to do so? By means of a carefully planned series of incidents he shows how Markheim is convinced that his course is necessarily downward. Then instead of carefully working from this culmination, or crisis, in the man's career through a series of steps in a falling action, the story ends abruptly with Markheim's decision to cease acting altogether—to give up his life, and so conquer evil in the one possible way left for him.

THE PLOT IN A DETECTIVE STORY

The detective story furnishes another and a strange plot scheme. The story opens with a brief preliminary situation; then the knot is tied by someone setting a problem for the detective to solve. The remainder of the story is the solution of the problem set in the beginning—the untangling of the knotted threads.

In terms of the diagram used thus far in this book there is a preliminary situation, and an initial incident (setting up the problem); then the story is falling action down to the conclusion. This action consists of the steps in the solution of the mystery. There is no culmination, in the sense in which the term has already been employed.

SUMMARY

Plot in fiction has been somewhat fantastically called "The Road of a Soul," and in a sense this is a true statement of what plot is. But in a book of this kind it seems better to use the more mechanical definition, quite prosaic to be sure, which was placed at the head of this chapter: Plot is the plan, the framework, which the author uses for developing and exhibiting his theme.

◄◄◄◄◄◄◄◄◄◄◄◄◄◄◄◄◄◄◄◄◄◄◄◄◄◄◄◄◄◄◄►►►►►►►►►►►►►►►►►►►►►►►►►►►►

CHAPTER V

THE CHARACTERS

SINCE the short story has for its main purpose the exhibition of some phase of life, usually human life, it follows that characters must be selected and used in some plot in order to embody the theme. An essayist might in an abstract philosophical essay show that a certain thing is true about humanity, and do it without using characters; but the materials of the story-teller are people—concrete things, and not abstract observations. The story writer chooses a theme, makes a plan, and then selects his people. He may not proceed in this order but these three things he is obliged to do.

HOW MANY CHARACTERS

The story is short in the actual number of words used. The theme may be a great one—some profound life truth—but the author must embody even such a theme in three or four thousand words. The lower limit is about one thousand, and the upper, seven. Of course, there are a few stories that fall below a thousand words and some which go beyond seven thousand—even as high as ten thousand—but these are unusual. The writer of a short story wishes, of course, to make his theme stand out as clearly as possible and to make the truth of it convincing; yet he must do this in about three or four thousand words. To do so he must draw upon every resource at his command to produce intensity, and at the same time practice a rigid economy in the use of means. These necessities seem to oppose each other and to place the author in a dilemma, but in reality they work together. The author who succeeds in placing one or two characters in a single tense situation so as to produce conviction of the truth of his theme really gains in intensity of impression over the novelist who may use a wider range of characters and plot incidents.

In practice the story writers have found themselves most successful when they have employed one or two or three characters. *The Prodigal Son* has three characters, all necessary; Poe's *Ligeia* has only two real people; Stevenson's *Markheim* has but two, only one of these being significant.

41

WHAT KIND OF PEOPLE

In the first place, the characters must be real people—not abstract qualities in human form and name, nor mere types. They must seem like and act like the people one meets in the actual world. Most people are so constituted that in a given situation they will act just as one might expect them to act. Their actions should be consistent with their predominant traits of character. Still, human beings have personal characteristics and idiosyncrasies that must be taken into the account. They do not always act alike in like situations. The author who creates a character whose conduct can be accurately predicted by the reader from the beginning has not drawn a man or woman, but a type. To be real, characters must be both typical and individual—and *individual first*.

THE CHARACTERS MUST BE WORTH KNOWING

Either the character must be unusual, such a person as we do not commonly have the opportunity of meeting; or if he is such a one as we meet every day, we must in print meet him in some striking situation not frequent in everyday experience. If he is an ordinary person, and the plot incidents ordinary too, the story writer has just one possible excuse left for bringing his character into print. He can reveal the deep impressions which such experiences make on such people—impressions, intellectual or emotional, which lie too deep to appear to a casual observer at a chance meeting. The characters may be worthy of attention either because of innate significant qualities, or by reason of the ways in which they react to soul-trying situations, or both.

UNUSUAL PEOPLE

For most of us the points of contact with life are limited in number, and we are not conceited enough to consider "the rustic cackle of our bourg the murmur of the mighty world." We welcome the readings of life which the skilled observer and interpreter can bring to us from his part of the world of experience. There are portions of the world that we cannot visit and could not understand if we were there. There are levels of society too high and levels too low for some of us. There are some people whom we cannot meet face to face and know intimately, and others whom we would not meet if we could; but in our own rooms, being properly introduced by the story teller, we may consort with principalities and powers and not feel out of place, or with knights and ladies of low degree, or no degree, and profit by the meeting. The writers of stories make such meetings possible for us.

PEOPLE IN UNUSUAL SITUATIONS

As with the characters, so it is with situations. We are all earth-bound. We cannot go everywhere; we cannot see everything that we would be interested in if we could meet those situations as first-hand experiences. But as readers we can make servants of authors and ask them to see for us and show us many characters as they pass through experiences that we cannot have. Having a thousand of these trained observers at our command the world over, we can draw upon their knowledge of things and people and emotions beyond our range of experience. If they deal with the commonest situations of life, they have yet a means of instructing us, for they can give us interpretations of life that lie beneath the surface of things observed. They can present a condensation and simplification of actual life that is more illuminating than the casual experiences of life can possibly be to us.

UNUSUAL IMPRESSIONS OF CHARACTERS AND LIFE

Then, too, we must remember that every effect of experience with life does not show upon the countenance of the chance-met person. If you go out upon the street, you may meet a man or woman who has just passed through some tragic hour of intellectual or emotional experience, and yet you may not be aware of it from any look or action. They may show no outward sign of the stirred depths—at least no sign that you or I can read. Here the trained interpreter steps in and sees for us and makes us see. The writer of fiction also can, from his knowledge of life, set up a problem in imagination and ask himself what would happen if certain characters with certain characteristics should go through certain physical, mental, or emotional experiences; and to answer his question he may construct an imagined plot to show the result, thus making a piece of fiction, a story.

CONDENSATIONS OF EXPERIENCE

In actual life there are no sharp beginnings and no sudden endings such as we see in fiction. Seldom does a series of events happen in a continuous sequence so as to make a unified plot with the emphases in the right places and without irrelevant digressions. A man's acts and the things that happen to him depend, more or less, on what he has been already, and the kind of experiences he has passed through. Sharp and sudden beginnings do not occur in life as they must appear to occur in fiction. Significant experiences in life do not end suddenly, but continue to exert an influence after a given series has apparently terminated.

While events are occurring which might be wrought into the plot of a story, there are many other experiences of the character that have nothing to do with those of the story plot. The writer of a short story disregards all the experiences except those which pertain to the plot. He rearranges even those that he retains so as to present them in the order which will most emphatically impress his theme. He takes notice of only those characters who enact the scenes in his plot. This service to the reader may be fitly termed *simplification* of life, *elimination* of the irrelevant incidents and characters, and *condensation* of diffused experience. It is a simple thing to say that this is what the author does for us, but this is the great task in plot-making.

CHARACTER PORTRAYAL AND DEVELOPMENT

The brevity of the short story prevents much development of character. In people who are possessed of characters worthy of study, such changes as make or mar a character do not ordinarily occur within the lapse of time occupied by a short story. Exaltation or disintegration of character is a slow process, but it may have been going on unseen for a long time, like the preparation of a calendar clock to change the figures on the dial. The story writer may begin his narrative just before the change occurs, and in his fiction hurry the character through the series of experiences up to the tense moment when the change becomes apparent, and in this way show actual development of character by seizing upon what in biology the evolutionists call the "transmutation period." While this process is possible, it is not the most common manner of treating character in the short story. Development of character is managed with greater skill in the novel, for in a book the author has leisure and room to develop his characters naturally, using no hot-house forcing process. The *portrayal* of character is, more properly, the business of the story writer. This consists of showing what the character *is* in a given situation. It is, in fact, the process of painting a portrait that reveals the character as he really is at the time of the culmination of the story, and not an attempt to use the process of the moving picture machine to show the evolution of character.

THE TWO METHODS OF DELINEATING CHARACTER

There are two methods of delineating character, commonly designated by the terms *direct* and *indirect*. The direct method calls for simple description; the indirect allows the character to reveal himself in what he says and does. Of course, the direct method is the easier of the two, but by no means the more effective, unless used by a master artist.

When Arthur Morrison says in the second paragraph of his story, *On the Stairs*, "Three flights up, a gaunt woman with bare forearms stayed on her way to listen at a door," he is directly describing Mrs. Manders. But when he lets us become acquainted with her by means of what she says in such a speech as this, "Ah, well, we all of us comes to it some day, sooner or later, and it's often a 'appy release," he is effectively using the indirect method of character revelation. By the direct method we have learned something of her appearance, and now by the indirect we have come to know a little about her philosophy of life. Another resource of the indirect method is the opportunity which it possesses of interpreting the speeches of the characters by means of the remarks which the author combines with the speeches. Notice the effect of the following speech and remark from Mr. Morrison's story. "When I lost my pore 'usband," said the gaunt woman, *with a certain brightening*, "I give 'im a 'ansome funeral." The author here tells us how Mrs. Manders *looked* when she made that speech, and thus he gives us a better opportunity of knowing her than the mere speech in black and white could have given—the same, in fact, that we might have had if we could have seen her as she said the words.

It would be a mistake to assume that a writer chooses one of these methods to the exclusion of the other. One may feel a preference for one method or the other, but in practice, for the sake of variety, both would be freely intermingled. The writer who feels that he is particularly successful in hitting off a character in a few well-chosen descriptive sentences would naturally prefer to use the direct method. The indirect would appeal to one who is especially skillful in writing conversation. But neither could afford to use his own way exclusively.

The older method of writing a long and detailed description of a character before presenting the character in speech and action is seldom seen in modern stories. The practice now is to present the character in a descriptive sentence or two, and then show him in some characteristic action and speeches; and after a time, again to drop in a line or two of direct delineation, continuing this process until the reader comes to feel that he knows the character in the same way that he comes to know people in real life.

There is an interesting variation of the indirect method that should be touched upon before the subject is dismissed. Sometimes an author lets a character make his impression upon you by showing you how he has impressed other characters in the story. There are two ways of doing this. The first of these is to allow the characters to talk about some one who is absent, and so introduce the absent one to the reader.

The other device is to show the reader the *effect* the character has upon others. Both of these are shown in the following excerpts from Richard Harding Davis' *A Derelict*. A group of newspaper reporters are talking about Channing, the derelict:

One of the *World* men looked up and laughed.

"I wonder if he'll run across Channing out there," he said. The men at the table smiled, a kindly, indulgent smile. The name seemed to act upon their imagination as a shower upon the close air of a summer day.

"That's so," said Norris. "He wrote me last month from Port-au-Prince that he was moving on to Jamaica. He said that he was at that moment introducing the president to a new cocktail, and as he had no money to pay his passage to Kingston, he was trying to persuade him to send him on there as his Haitian Consul. He said in case he couldn't get appointed Consul he had an offer to go as cook on an oil tramp."

The men around the table laughed. It was the pleased, proud laugh that flutters the family dinner-table when the infant son and heir says something precocious and impudent.

. . . . . .

"I never saw a man who wouldn't help Charlie along or lend him a dollar." He glanced at the faces about him and then winked at the Boston man. "They all of them look guilty, don't they?" he said.

"Charlie Channing," murmured the baseball reporter, gently, as though he were pronouncing the name of a girl. He raised his glass. "Here's to Charlie Channing," he repeated. Norris set down his empty glass and showed it to the Boston man.

"That's his only enemy," he said. "Write! Heavens, how that man can write!"

CHAPTER VI

OTHER MEANS USED IN DEVELOPING A THEME

PLOT and character, the two most important of the author's means for the exhibition of his theme, have each required a chapter for their treatment. The remaining five in a first study of fiction, such as this is, may be included in a single chapter.

SETTING

In a story like *The Prodigal Son* there is no attempt to establish time and place, but Arthur Morrison's *On the Stairs* is a "tale of a mean street" in modern London. Its setting is as definite as the setting of a play in which painted scenery, costumes, supernumeraries, and manners, all help the words to say: "These incidents took place in a certain place at a definite time." The manner of *The Prodigal Son* implies an oriental setting—"somewhere east of Suez,"—but as for definite setting of time and place, there is none. Only recently, in fact, have writers of stories come to recognize the value of background. Millet in painting his *Angelus* might have shown upon a bare white canvas a man and woman standing in prayer, and might even thus have given us a picture with a large meaning; but what a richness of associated ideas comes to it when we see back of the two figures the stretch of brown field, the distant shadowy trees, the spire of the church, and the evening glow in the sky! Background for a story serves the same purpose as background in a picture, or the setting of a drama—painted scenery, costumes, properties, comment of secondary characters, movement of supernumeraries, etc. It suggests, maybe actually designates, time, place, tone, and atmosphere.

EMOTION

In the chapter on story themes the matter of the kinds of emotions, such as love, fear, jealousy, hope, joy, was given some consideration. A word needs to be added here about the use of emotion in the mechanical arrangement of the story. The story should be so arranged as to show an increase in the intensity of the emotion up to the point of the culmination of the plot. The highest point of emotional intensity should coincide with the topmost step of the plot-ladder—the point where the plot problem is solved, the major knot untied or cut (to employ the terms used by another). If these points do not coincide, if the emotion reaches its height before the plot culmination is reached, or afterward, the effect produced is disconcerting. Interest falls off if the emotional height is reached too early; and you feel the incongruity of an emotional culmination coming after the turn in the plot and during the part of the action that falls away toward the well-rounded conclusion.

TONE

We all recognize in the best stories a certain unity of tone. The story may be tragic, humorous, keenly witty, satirical, ironical, somber, joyous, foreboding, or serious; and in keeping with the keynote the author succeeds usually in making the setting or background of his story reflect the kind of atmosphere that would be consonant with the tone.

The tone of a story is usually indicated in the opening sentences. These strike, as one might say, the keynote of the whole composition. Notice the indications of gloom and the forebodings of impending disaster in the opening paragraphs of Poe's *The Fall of the House of Usher*. Now, the important thing in the matter of tone is unity. One would be shocked in reading such a story as this of Poe's if a ludicrous incident were inserted a third of the way from the beginning, and further on a descriptive paragraph picturing a beautiful summer evening, with soft moonlight and the scent of honeysuckle enveloping a romantic young pair in the park beside the decaying house of Usher.

Unity of tone does not, however, preclude variety, as one might suppose. Life is not sympathetic with the emotions of human beings unless by mere coincidence. A story in which the prevailing tone is that of apprehension of calamity might have some speeches which are hilariously humorous, if the speeches were made by some one unaware of the danger, or by a hysterical character, or by one who had become careless of consequences or who wished to dispel the apprehensiveness of others. The drunken porter scene in *Macbeth* and the speeches of Tom of Bedlam in the storm scene in *King Lear* are examples of diversity of tone in drama. These examples show that the contrast in tone felt so keenly by the audience or reader does not, in fact, break the unity, but deepens the feeling of tragedy induced by the whole piece.

It is, however, much more difficult to insert a note of seriousness or tragedy into a piece of literature the prevailing tone of which is light or humorous. The effect is usually one of incongruity, and is not convincing. An attempt at seriousness by some one of the characters in a story of light tone may be used effectively by contrast to augment the fun made by the others. The seriousness of Mrs. Hilary in Anthony Hope's *The House Opposite* is contrasted with the levity of Hilary and Mr. Carter. The unity of tone, that of humorous levity, is maintained as the total effect of the story. Read Thomas Bailey Aldrich's *Goliath* and try to determine what devices are employed to maintain the tone of mock seriousness in this story, which on the surface promises to be tragic.

Finally, the effect of tone should not be monotony but rather the production of unity by means of the harmonious employment of variety.

STYLE

Style is a quality in composition about which a great deal has been said in a general way, but it is incapable of simple technical analysis. In one sense—that in which it is conceived by Robert Louis Stevenson, the novelist, in his essay, *On Some Technical Elements of Style in Literature*, and by Clayton Hamilton, the critic, in his *Materials and Methods of Fiction*—the laws of style may be determined and exactly stated. For to Hamilton prose style means the manner of composition which produces the effects that distinguish literary prose from mere informational writing such as one expects in reading a treatise, say, on "Nature's Ways of Scattering Seeds." This is a real distinction, and to produce the artistic effects of literary prose a writer, instinctively or consciously, employs certain poetic combinations of speech sounds, certain orderings of words and phrases in his sentences, certain figures of speech (poetic in their associations), all of which produce a pleasurable stimulation of the æsthetic sense of the reader and satisfy the demands of art in harmony, proportion, and restraint. Hamilton would say, then, that a writer either has style or has no style.

But most readers and critics understand the term style to mean the *individual manner* of a writer. Accepting this statement, one might speak of a style as being good or tolerable or downright bad; as being poetic, straightforward, terse, nervous, bald, florid, or any one of a dozen other descriptive terms. One might compare the style of one author with another. The student of a short story might examine it for the peculiarities of composition which distinguish the compositions of its author from those of others. Peculiarities of sentence arrangement, of word order, and of phrase-making might be noticed. The fondness of the author for certain words, or certain similes and metaphors; his taste for poetic words—poetic on account of their associations or on account of their sound—onomatopeia, assonance, alliteration, parallel and balanced structure; these, or their lack, and many other individual characteristics, mark the composition of one author as different from another.

Differences in manner make it possible for a reader to recognize a certain author by his writing. Since these will occur to the student as he reads the stories, no special purpose could be effectively served by an attempt to catalogue them.

Rather than think of style as an author's individual manner of writing, it would seem better to reserve the word for a more specialized meaning in literature. We say of a woman's hat or coat that "it has style." We mean that there is something about that particular article of apparel that gives it distinction, that puts it in a class with the most artistic hats and coats that are being worn by people of good taste this season. *Style* in this sense means "endowed with artistic distinction." And so in literature the abstract word *style* implies the manner of expression that is distinguished by artistic qualities.

If one wishes merely to distinguish between the manner of two writers, neither of whom may have the artistic quality which we designate by the abstract word *style*, it would be more appropriate to use the term *manner* rather than *style*. Say, this story is written with all the marks of Brown's manner, and is not at all in the manner of Green.

To say what *style in literature* is would be to launch into an extended chapter to arrive at an understanding of a single word. Let us be content here to say that style is the sum of all those bits of literary skill that go to make up a piece of distinguished prose composition. It consists of bringing together the right vowel combinations and variations, getting the consonant sounds together so as to please the ear with harmonious sounds, and so as not to offend with inharmonious combinations. It means composition that has an unobtrusive, loose rhythm, that avoids combinations of words hard to pronounce together, that selects the exact word for a given meaning without drawing pedantically upon one's stock of technical and rare words, that does a hundred other things contributing to pleasing, exact, and just expression without undue effort or pedantic display. To write with style in this conception of it is to rise to the level of the artists in other forms of expression—poetry, painting, musical composition, sculpture, and the like. Style is the height of literary attainment—saying something worth saying, and saying it with artistic distinction.

THE APPEARANCE OF TRUTH

One of the commonest mistakes of the amateur story writer is to select his incidents from actual life, believing that he will thus produce a convincing piece of fiction. It is very often harder to make a strange thing that has actually happened seem really true than it is to imagine a series of events and breathe into them the breath of real life. Many a one has a few stories which he hesitates to tell except to friends who know him very well. These events, he knows, have actually happened; but he also knows them to be the kind of truths that are stranger than fiction. In a student's story which came to a teacher's desk recently for criticism there was a mystery to be solved. A young man in a hunting party had shot and killed a man with whom he had quarreled some time before. It looked like murder; but the young man protested that it was an accident, although he was unable to explain how it was possible for such a thing to happen. When the truth came out, it was learned that the young man was riding under a hickory tree when the shot was fired, and that a nut falling from the tree had hit the hair-trigger of his rifle and caused the fatality. In answer to the teacher's objection to this incident on the ground of improbability the student said: "I know of a case where this actually happened." Maybe so, but what a strain upon one's credulity! It can hardly be made to seem true. What we have here would be an accident not likely to happen to one man in a million riding under that hickory tree with a gun in his hand.

It is not, however, impossible to use actual incidents. James B. Connolly says of his own employment of facts: "Most of the stories I have written have been founded on facts. I start with a fact. Something happens in life, and sets a man thinking; and to account for it he builds up his own theory, supplying motives, action, and result, out of his own knowledge of life." Mr. Connolly begins with a fact and then builds upon it, as all writers of fiction do, supplying from imagination where the facts are insufficient for the illumination of the theme, leaving out what would obscure the appearance of truth, and arranging what is left in a sequence that will give the whole matter an air of truth not originally a part of the actual fact or facts. In a recent novel by a distinguished American novelist an incident occurred that was useful in disposing of two characters near the end of the book. A friendly critic asked the novelist how she happened to use that seemingly impossible and wholly unconvincing episode to account for the death of that man and woman. The novelist replied: "That was the only real incident in the whole story; but I should have known better than to use an actual incident that could not be made to seem real." In fiction the Actual is of much less importance than the Appearance of Truth—verisimilitude.

SOME DEFINITIONS AND DISTINCTIONS

Realism and Romance.—Each of these terms, Realism and Romance, has a meaning to most readers which conforms pretty closely to the generally accepted meaning; and yet the connotations of the words differ with individual readers. Writers were once distinguished as *Classic* or *Romantic*. Those who looked back to the age of the classics for themes, treatment, literary conventions, and rules of construction were called classic writers; and those who flouted the classic rules and traditions, and looked into the remote in time and place for their plots, and to no authority for their manner of treatment, were called romantic.

These terms have been discarded in their original applications, but *Romance* still has a shadow of its original meaning. It also means much more. It means freedom from restraint, warmth of treatment, breadth of imagination, and protest against the obvious and the actual. The motive of love is usually embodied in romantic fiction, but this does not exclude it from the realistic. Love will have a very different handling, however, in a realistic story from that which it gets in the romantic. This is not saying that all romantic fiction has all these qualities, or that realistic fiction has none of them, but that a piece in which these qualities predominate is designated as Romantic.

Realism in fiction has been defined negatively by Bliss Perry in the following terms: "Realistic fiction is that which does not shrink from the commonplace or from the unpleasant in its effort to depict things as they are, life as it is." To say the same thing the other way about: Realistic fiction seeks to present a picture of things as they are, and life as it is. In doing so the writer often has to include the commonplace and the unpleasant. The temperate realist is careful, however, to keep the unpleasant and the commonplace in fiction within the proportions which they have in real life.

Idealism.—Idealism in fiction is an attempt to see things as they should be. The writer may, in the main, follow either the romantic plan or the realistic. If, as a realist, he deals with the actual, he eliminates or disregards the imperfections. If he writes as a romantic, his imagination neglects those elements which would mar the perfect creation.

Symbolism.—In either romantic or realistic literature there may be a mystic or a hidden meaning below the obvious meaning. This is seen more often in poetry and the drama than in short stories. Spenser's *Faerie Queene* has a series of such meanings. Tennyson's *Idylls of the King* is a series of romantic pieces dominated by a symbolistic meaning. William Butler Yeats presents Ireland in her struggle for liberty in *Kathleen ni Houlihan*, as does also Lady Gregory in *The Rising of the Moon*. These plays are at once realistic, idealistic, and symbolic. The *Idylls of the King* are romantic, idealistic, and symbolic.

DISTINCTIONS IN TERMS

The opposing terms are Realism and Romance. Idealism and Symbolism may be associated with either, though as a matter of fact they more often go with Romance.

Realism and Romance are terms used to designate the *method* which an author adopts. Idealism is an end to be attained, and it may be attained by an author using either method. Symbolism is a *device*, and may be associated with either method of writing in connection with idealism or without it.

The way to learn to recognize these qualities in fiction is not through definitions, or enumerations of the qualities of each, but by reading widely until one gets a feeling for realism and for romance, and so becomes able to identify them by means of their total impression, as one recognizes an acquaintance, and not by means of conformity to a list of distinctive attributes or qualities.

THE SHORT STORY, THE NOVELETTE, AND THE NOVEL

Since the terms, *Short Story*, *Novelette*, and *Novel* are used to distinguish the forms of fiction which one meets in his reading, an effort should be made here to distinguish them, one from the other.

"The *Short Story* aims to produce a single narrative effect with the greatest economy of means that is consistent with the utmost emphasis."

Such is the distinction made by Clayton Hamilton.

The *Novelette* borrows from the technique of both the story and the novel. From the story it get the idea of a single plot without digression, but it does not employ the greatest economy of means to produce an effect. Like the novel it may use a larger number of incidents in its plot structure than the story, and each of these incidents may be more fully developed through conversation, narration, and description. In the main, however, a novelette is more like a story than a novel. It is, in fact, as it is sometimes called, a "long short."

The *Novel* may have a main plot and one or more sub-plots parallel with or in contrast to the main plot. One or more characters in each sub-plot may play a part or parts in the main plot and so tie the two, three, or four separate actions into a unified whole. In working out his design the novelist may use many incidents in depicting or developing his characters, or in working out his theme. He may use a more deliberate method in reporting the conversations, letting them work out in full. The story writer at best can give only significant "samples" of the talk. Many characters may be used in a novel; and to produce a given effect the writer may let one set of characters work through a scene, and then, for fear that the impression has not been made strong enough, he may have other groups go through similar processes with other sets of incidents. The story writer, practicing the utmost economy of his means, may make but a single trial at producing a given impression.

CHAPTER VII

THE MANAGEMENT OF THE MATERIALS

POINT OF VIEW

STUDENTS of fiction recognize four distinct points of view which the author may choose from. 1. The first person. He may choose to tell his story as if he were the chief character, or some character of secondary importance who looks on and reports what the more important characters do and say. 2. The limited third person. He may represent himself as an interested observer, looking on and giving an account of what an actual onlooker could see and know. 3. The omniscient third person. From this point of view the author may tell everything that happens everywhere, even what the characters are thinking, the motives back of the thoughts, and the philosophy of life which accounts for the motives. 4. Diaries or letters, or entries in a diary only occasionally and for the sake of variety. Success in this form is elusive. Perhaps the best-known story in the form of letters is Thomas Bailey Aldrich's *Marjorie Daw;* and the most skillful performance with a series of documents of various sorts is Brander Matthews and H. C. Bunner's *The Documents in the Case.*

Combinations of two or more of the four points of view are not unusual. In a narrative written in the first or third person, letters and papers are frequently introduced; and in the letter form, narrative from the point of view of the first or third person is nearly always resorted to in getting over some situation hard to make clear by means of the letters. *Marjorie Daw* is brought to a close by using narrative in the third person.

Each of these points of view has some distinctive advantage and some disadvantages. If the story is in the first person and the narrator is the chief character, it is not in very good taste for him to tell how he bore himself in some test of skill, or wit, or courage. The device adopted by most writers who wish to retain the vividness of first-hand narrative in an adventure story or story of triumph of intellect is to have the story told in the first person by an interested onlooker. Poe lets the husband of the heroine tell how by indomitable will Ligeia conquers death. Dr. Watson recounts the triumphs of Sherlock Holmes. David Balfour tells of the remarkable encounters and victories of Alan Breck.

55

The use of the omniscient third person is the easiest method of all, but it is likely to miss the vividness that accompanies the face-to-face narration of one who saw and heard. There is a danger, too, of knowing so much, as this god-like abstraction looks down on his creatures and their works, that the story becomes unconvincing, even absurd. Skillfully used, however, as this method is by most of our best story writers, it is very effective.

The narrative in the limited third person, recounting only what some unseen interested observer could have seen, heard, and known, requires the greatest skill, and when well done is perhaps the most effective of all. In the limited third person the observer may be entirely outside the story, as is the case with the omniscient third person; or the author may choose to see his characters through the eyes of some secondary character in the story, and report (in the third person) only what that character could know or infer from what he saw and heard. In such a case the author's judgment of his characters would have to be in accord with the probable judgment such a character would form under the given conditions.

TITLES

The purpose of a title is the same as that of a label on a package of merchandise offered for sale. It should be attractive, and should correctly characterize the contents of the story. To be attractive it should be short and definite, and worded so as to catch the attention through pleasing sound or some interesting turn of expression. In characterizing the contents the truth should be told as far as the title goes, but something should be left to imagination. *The Gate of the Hundred Sorrows* is a title rather longer than usual, but the wording is rhythmic, and the suggestion is of something dreamy and mysterious. A reader at all susceptible to suggestion could not pass such a label without investigating the contents of the package. Kipling's titles are usually of this compelling kind. Think of *The Man Who Would Be King*, *The Man Who Was*, *Without Benefit of Clergy*, *The Courting of Dinah Shadd*, *The Brushwood Boy*, and *They*. Contrast such titles as *A Branch Road*, *A Kentucky Cardinal*, *Goliath*, and *Fame's Little Day*, with titles like *An Experience on a Vacation*, *Margaret's Duty, or, How She Saved the Train*, *The Difficulties of Building a Railroad in Uganda*, and *Patty's Perilous Predicament*.

A whole chapter might be written on what to avoid and what effects to strive for in selecting a title for a story. For the student, however, the better practice is to examine many stories and try to discover what attracts, what repels, and what leaves one merely uninterested.

BEGINNINGS

Two distinct methods of making beginnings are employed. The writer is aware that there are facts which the reader must know before the story can actually be set into motion. If he begins with simple narrative, the story is likely to be slow in getting started. On the other hand the device of opening with a bit of attractive conversation can be successful only when the author succeeds in going forward. This is not easy, for the facts of time, place, characters, background, etc., must be presented, and they are not easily presented in dialogue. Often after the opening speeches the writer halts the story to explain the situation, and sometimes the halt leaves the characters in an awkward suspense. Both plans have been used with success. In *The Whirligig of Life* O. Henry uses the natural order of preliminary situation in narrative, giving time and place, introducing the three characters, and describing them; then follow the initial incident and the incidents which form the scenes of the story leading up to the culmination.

See how briefly these preliminary facts are put before the reader:

Justice of the Peace Benaja Widdup sat in the door of his office. [First character.] Halfway to the zenith the Cumberland range rose blue-gray in the afternoon haze. [Time and place.] A speckled hen swaggered down the main street of the "settlement," cackling foolishly. [Atmosphere and background.]

Up the road came a sound of creaking axles, and then a slow cloud of dust, and then a bull-cart bearing Ransie Bilbro and his wife. [The other two characters.] The cart stopped at the justice's door, and the two climbed down. [Action.] Ransie was a narrow six feet of sallow brown skin and yellow hair. The imperturbability of the mountains hung upon him like a suit of armor. [Two sentences describing the chief male character.] The woman was calicoed, angled, snuff-brushed, and weary with unknown desires. Through it all gleamed a faint protest of cheated youth unconscious of its loss. [Two sentences describing the third character.]

"We-all," said the woman, in a voice like the wind blowing through pine boughs, "wants a divo'ce." [Initial incident. The tone of the story has also become apparent.]

Mary E. Wilkins Freeman's *The Revolt of "Mother"* begins with dialogue and carries on the conversation so deftly that by the introduction of a few comments and explanatory remarks the whole preliminary situation is made clear without a pause in the progress of the story:

"Father!"
"What is it?"
"What are them men diggin' over there in the field for?"

There was a sudden dropping and enlarging of the lower part of the old man's face, as if some heavy weight had settled therein; he shut his mouth tight and went on harnessing the great bay mare. He hustled the collar on to her neck with a jerk.

"Father!"

The dialogue, narrative, description, and author's comments are thus skillfully woven together through two or three pages until the whole preliminary situation is made clear to the reader without delay or break in the continuity.

From an observation of Poe's on the purpose of fiction some recent writers have concluded that a hint of the nature of the story will always appear in the manner of the beginning—if the story is properly constructed. They say that a story of incident will begin with action; a story of character, with a bit of dialogue, revealing characteristics of the speakers; or a story of setting (background), with description.

While this is usually true of Poe's tales and stories, it is not characteristic of stories by writers of today. Occasionally a writer instinctively feels the propriety of beginning in accordance with this principle and realizes what his story gains by the directness of approach involved in such a method. But an examination of a large number of stories does not show any uniformity of practice in this particular.

However, it may be said that a story is strengthened, if in the very beginning its end is clearly in the author's view, and if he can make his purpose clear to the reader. Any device—the one mentioned above, or another—that makes clear to the reader the purpose and end of the story is a valuable one, provided that it does not eliminate the element of suspense so necessary to plots of nearly every kind.

CONVERSATION

Story writers seem more and more inclined to use the dramatic method of developing their plots. Some of the stories of Hawthorne and Poe are told almost entirely in narrative in the third person with very little conversation. Now and then a writer of current short stories will allow his characters to tell everything in direct discourse, using almost no comment of the author, no description, and no simple narration. The mass of readers doubtless are strongly attracted to a story that shows much conversation as one glances through the pages; but this method— an imitation of the method of the playwright—may be no more than a passing vogue, as dialect was, only a very few years ago. The impression is abroad that recent stories are as much as seventy-five per cent conversation. An examination of a hundred recent stories by representative autnors would probably show that not more than forty per cent of the words occur in the direct discourse. The other sixty per cent would be divided between author's comment on and explanation of the speeches, and narrative and descriptive paragraphs.

Recent stories show a decided increase in skill in handling the explanatory remarks which accompany the speeches. In their simplest form these guide words of the author are "he said," "said he," "she said," and "said she." Such remarks reveal nothing of character. The use of adverbs suggests the character, the temperament, the manners, and the mood of the speaker. The substitution of other words for *said* gives variety and may even take the place of description in drawing a character. The most recent development of this kind is the custom of omitting these remarks altogether wherever the speakers can be differentiated without them. This is the purely dramatic method, commendable if not made into a fad. It can be carried so far as to rob the story of much of the charm that the technique of fiction permits, but which that of drama does not have.

SUSPENSE

From the very beginning a story should be so planned that with a given set of characters in a given situation or series of incidents the outcome is inevitable. This does not imply, however, that the reader can accurately foresee from the initial incident what that outcome is to be. In fact, the element of suspense, of uncertainty of outcome, is one of the elements which contribute most to that increase of emotional tension induced by a good story as one approaches the culmination. The solution of the plot should come after some suspense and with a note of surprise, but should not be incredible. For, as one looks back over a well-constructed story, he should see that the culmination was not only natural, but also that it was carefully prepared for and held in suspense so as to produce a deeper impression through the suddenness of the well-prepared stroke.

SUGGESTION AND RESTRAINT

One of the very noticeable differences in the manner of the amateur and the professional writer of stories is in the management of suggestion and restraint. It is well understood that economy is a very important element in the technique of the short story. Now, the unskillful writer feels obliged to go into detail in every portion of his story. Given the task of writing *The Whirligig of Life*, he would have made it something like this:

"As the Justice of the Peace of a little mountain settlement in Eastern Tennessee sat in the doorway of the cabin that served him as an office, toward the middle of a summer afternoon in the year of 19—, he was surprised to see in the distance beyond a turn of the road a cloud of dust, indicating the approach of a wheeled vehicle. He hastily drew on his boots, for it was his custom to wear these articles of apparel (considered so necessary in localities nearer the centers of refinement) only during the few minutes in the week when he was engaged in the discharge of his official duties. In about five minutes he was able to discern the cause of the cloud of dust. An observer not a native of the place would have been surprised at the time required for the vehicle to round the turn in the narrow mountain road, little better than a path, but Benaja Widdup had lived there all his life, and his father and father's father before him. Instinctively he knew that the dust was being raised by an ox-cart, and so he was not surprised at all when he descried such a conveyance, drawn by the little red bull which he knew belonged to a young man who lived in a small clearing six or seven miles up the trail toward the wooded heights of the Cumberlands, which in the afternoon haze would have made a beautiful picture for one who had the artistic temperament. But Benaja Widdup had it not; neither did Ransie Bilbro nor his wife Ariela, the occupants of the cart, for life to them was a dull reality. They depended for their livelihood upon the few acres of yellow-bladed corn that clung precariously to the clay hillside, and the game that could still be trapped or shot in the mountains. The cart drew up beside the door. Ransie threw the single rope line around the upright stick that stood in the center of the dashboard of the cart and climbed down on one side of the cart while his wife climbed down on the other, the little red bull browsing on a bunch of already half-stripped hazel bushes which grew beside the road."

The purpose of this long paragraph is to create the atmosphere for the story, to suggest time and place, and to introduce the characters. To do this nearly four hundred words are employed, and yet the picture lacks sharpness of outline. All the details are included that O. Henry used in the original. He employed only a hundred words for that part of the story. Compelled by the technical demands of the short story, he restrained any impulse toward using fullness of detail, and produced all the effects that fullness would seem to assure, by the employment of suggestion; and, as a consequence, the total impression is more definite than that produced by the long paragraph.

Take as a second illustration the use of suggestion and restraint in the character descriptions in *The Whirligig of Life*. "Ransie was a narrow six feet of sallow brown skin and yellow hair. The imperturbability of the mountains hung upon him like a suit of armor. The woman was calicoed, angled, snuff-brushed, and weary with unknown desires. Through it all gleamed a faint protest of cheated youth, unconscious of its loss." Two characters done in fifty words. Imagine, if you can, how an amateur would have seized upon this opportunity to present full-length, detailed portraits of these two characters. The method of O. Henry is like that of the cartoonist who gives in two or three strokes of his pencil the significant lines of a figure, and allows the imagination to supply the rest.

Observe the description of the blind woman in Kipling's *They*, of Mrs. Bathurst in the story of that name, and of Carnehan in *The Man Who Would Be King*. It is surprising how full these descriptions seem, and how few words are actually found when you have summed them up. In these stories one may observe another device in the use of suggestion that has not yet been mentioned. This is the scattering of the descriptive phrases and sentences through the story, thus strengthening the illusion of a portrait in detail.

All successful writers practice a rigid restraint in the use of incidents, in the dialogue, in their comment upon the action, and in every other means they use, just as they do in the elements of technique which have been treated with considerable fullness in the foregoing paragraphs. The principal device that they use to avoid such a piling up of details as would dull the sharpness of outline in the total impression is skillful suggestion.

ENDINGS

Two common methods of bringing a story to a close are employed by the most successful short story writers. The one terminates the story abruptly with the culmination of the plot, at the highest point of emotional interest. This is the method of Stevenson in *Markheim* and of Poe in *Ligeia*. The other passes over the culmination and in a quieter mood drops down to a well-rounded conclusion. Maupassant's *The Piece of String* and O. Henry's *The Whirligig of Life* are so constructed. This falling action may be no more than a few lines and a single incident, or it may be as much as a third of the whole story. In *The Whirligig of Life* it is about one-sixth of the whole story. The culmination comes with the realization on the part of Ransie and Ariela that they really love each other and cannot live apart. The conclusion is the part of the story involving their re-marriage and setting out for their cabin in the mountains.

C H A P T E R   V I I I

A PLAN FOR THE STUDY OF A SHORT STORY

THE questions which follow are intended to suggest a series of topics so arranged as to give a complete review of the technique of a story. In applying the questions to a particular story, care should be taken to avoid an application so literal as to deaden the interest in the story itself. If a written review is attempted, these questions should be used as topics for paragraphs, not mere question-and-answer responses like a court cross-examination. The whole review when complete should be in the form of a paper such as one would be willing to present as a part of a program in a literary club.

ITEMS IN A STUDY PLAN

1. Write a brief synopsis of the story, using not more than three paragraphs—fewer if possible.

2. What observation does it make about life? That is, what is its central idea or theme? Is the theme true? Does the author believe it to be true, or is it only a possible fancy?

3. Outline the plot, showing (a) the preliminary situation, (b) the initial incident, (c) the incidents which form the scenes or steps of the story leading up to the culmination or solution of the problem the author has set for himself, (d) the culmination, (e) the steps after the culminating incident (if there are any), (f) the conclusion.

4. What is the tone of the story: tragic, serious, humorous, farcical, poetic, dreamy? Use one of these or any other word that characterizes the tone.

5. Is this primarily a story of character, incident, or setting?

6. Make a list of the characters.

    a. The principal characters.

    b. Those of secondary importance.

    c. Those used merely as background, if there are any such.

7. Which of the characters have distinct individuality? Are any merely personified types of some quality or passion, such as greed, jealousy, hate, etc.? Are there any merely impersonal figures?

8. In delineating characters does the author describe them (by direct

delineation), or does he make the characters reveal themselves in speech and action (indirect delineation)? If he uses both methods, which is predominant?

9. Are the characters true to life; are they better or worse than people in actual life; or are they caricatures (with actual characteristics exaggerated) of people such as one might know in actual life?

10. Is there any character, speech, or situation that does not seem true to life?

11. Does the emotional tension increase and the story move with increasing rapidity as the culmination is approached?

12. Is the setting interesting for its own sake, or is it used merely as a background for the characters and incidents?

13. What seems to have suggested the title?

14. Is the author's point of view:
   a. The first person?
   b. The limited third person?
   c. The omniscient third person?
   d. Letters or a diary?
   e. A combination of two or more of these?

15. Comment upon the author's skill in the use of conversation. Does he use a variety of "guide words," substitutes for "he said" and "said he?" Does he effectively use adverbs and descriptive phrases to indicate the manner in which a thing is said, and thus to give you a picture of the character speaking or help you to understand the mood or the personality of the character.

16. Comment upon the writer's use of adjectives and adverbs. Is it effective? Is it natural? Does he exaggerate and overemphasize by using adjectives and adverbs too strong for the situation, or by employing words not in common use?

17. What method of beginning is employed?

18. Does the author ever insert his own opinion into the story independent of the characters? Give examples.

19. About what per cent of the words occur in direct discourse? What per cent in simple narrative? What per cent in description?

20. Are there any unrelated episodes—incidents that do not aid in developing the plot?

21. How much time elapses in the working out of the plot? Account for the time scheme in detail.

22. Is the author's method that of the realist or that of the romanticist? In connection with your comment on his method make note of idealism, or symbolism, or both.

23. Make note of any effects of style which are pleasing. Any which are unpleasant. Any that are characteristic of or peculiar to the author.

24. The most effective short story is one that employs (1) characters highly worth knowing, and through these works out a great (2) theme upon a (3) stage (background or setting) suited to the (4) action and the people of the story. Does the story you are studying fall short in any of these four specifications? Make this last item your main criticism and estimate of the literary value of the story.

A SHORT STORY FOR STUDY

The value of any scheme for organizing the results of studying a short story will depend upon the clearness with which such a scheme takes care of all the essential points discussed in foregoing chapters. As an example for study, one of O. Henry's stories is given below to be read in the light of the scheme just outlined. It will be followed by a summary of the results that such a reading may reasonably be expected to show. The rows of asterisks used in the story indicate its natural divisions.

THE WHIRLIGIG OF LIFE [1]

By O. Henry

[William Sydney Porter (1862–1910), known by his pen name as O. Henry, was born at Greensboro, North Carolina, and died in New York. He began his literary work as a newspaper writer in Texas. The settings for his early stories are in the South and West, but in later years he drew his inspiration from the city about him. In the selection of themes, and in technical treatment, he resembles Maupassant, and has been called the "American Maupassant."]

JUSTICE of the Peace Benaja Widdup sat in the door of his office. Halfway to the zenith the Cumberland range rose blue-gray in the afternoon haze. A speckled hen swaggered down the main street of the "settlement," cackling foolishly.

Up the road came a sound of creaking axles, and then a slow cloud of dust, and then a bull-cart bearing Ransie Bilbro and his wife. The cart stopped at the justice's door, and the two climbed down. Ransie was a narrow six feet of sallow brown skin and yellow hair. The imperturbability of the mountains hung upon him like a suit of armor. The woman was calicoed, angled, snuff-brushed, and weary with un-

---

[1] Copyrighted 1910. Reprinted by special arrangement with Doubleday, Doran and Company, publishers.

known desires. Through it all gleamed a faint protest of cheated youth unconscious of its loss.

* * * *

The justice of the peace slipped his feet into his shoes, for the sake of dignity, and moved to let them enter.

"We-all," said the woman, in a voice like the wind blowing through pine boughs, "wants a divo'ce." She looked at Ransie to see if he noted any flaw or ambiguity or evasion or partiality or self-partisanship in her statement of their business.

"A divo'ce," repeated Ransie, with a solemn nod. "We-all can't git along together nohow. It's lonesome enough fur to live in the mount'ins when a man and a woman keers for one another. But when she's a-spittin' like a wildcat or a-sullenin' like a hoot-owl in the cabin, a man ain't got no call to live with her."

"When he's a no-'count varmint," said the woman, without any especial warmth, "a-traipsin' along of scalawags and moonshiners and a-layin' on his back pizen 'ith co'n whisky, and a-pesterin' folks with a pack o' hungry, triflin' houn's to feed!"

"When she keeps a-throwin' skillet lids," came Ransie's antiphony, "and slings b'ilin' water on the best coon-dog in the Cumberlands, and sets herself agin' cookin' a man's victuals, and keeps him awake o' nights accusin' him of a sight of doin's!"

"When he's al'ays a-fightin' the revenuers, and gits a hard name in the mount'ins fur a mean man, who's gwine to be able fur to sleep o' nights?"

The justice of the peace stirred deliberately to his duties. He placed his one chair and a wooden stool for his petitioners. He opened his book of statutes on the table and scanned the index. Presently he wiped his spectacles and shifted his inkstand.

"The law and the statutes," said he, "air silent on the subjeck of divo'ce as fur as the jurisdiction of this co't air concerned. But, accordin' to equity and the constitution and the golden rule, it's a bad barg'in that can't run both ways. If a justice of the peace can marry a couple, it's plain that he is bound to be able to divo'ce 'em. This here office will issue a decree of divo'ce and abide by the decision of the Supreme Co't to hold it good."

Ransie Bilbro drew a small tobacco-bag from his trousers pocket. Out of this he shook upon the table a five-dollar note. "Sold a b'arskin and two foxes fur that," he remarked. "It's all the money we got."

"The regular price of a divo'ce in this co't," said the justice, "air five dollars." He stuffed the bill into the pocket of his homespun vest with a deceptive air of indifference. With much bodily toil and mental travail he wrote the decree upon half a sheet of foolscap, and then copied it upon the other. Ransie Bilbro and his wife listened to his reading of the document that was to give them freedom:

"Know all men by these presents that Ransie Bilbro and his wife, Ariela Bilbro, this day personally appeared before me and promises that hereinafter they will neither love, honor, nor obey each other, neither for better nor worse, being of sound mind and body, and accept summons for divorce according to the peace and dignity of the State. Herein fail not, so help you God. Benaja Widdup, justice of the peace in and for the county of Piedmont, State of Tennessee."

The justice was about to hand one of the documents to Ransie. The voice of Ariela delayed the transfer. Both men looked at her. Their dull masculinity was confronted by something sudden and unexpected in the woman.

"Jedge, don't you give him that air paper yit. 'Tain't all settled, nohow. I got to have my rights first. I got to have my ali-money. 'Tain't no kind of a way to do fur a man to divo'ce his wife 'thout her havin' a cent fur to do with. I'm a-layin' off to be a-goin' up to brother Ed's up on Hogback Mount'in. I'm bound fur to hev a pa'r of shoes and some snuff and things besides. Ef Rance kin affo'd a divo'ce, let him pay me ali-money."

Ransie Bilbro was stricken to dumb perplexity. There had been no previous hint of alimony. Women were always bringing up startling and unlooked-for issues. Justice Benaja Widdup felt that the point demanded judicial decision. The authorities were also silent on the subject of alimony. But the woman's feet were bare. The trail of Hogback Mountain was steep and flinty.

"Ariela Bilbro," he asked, in official tones, "how much did you 'low would be good and sufficient ali-money in the case befo' the co't?"

"I 'lowed," she answered, "fur the shoes and all, to say five dollars. That ain't much for ali-money, but I reckon that'll git me up to brother Ed's."

"The amount," said the justice, "air not onreasonable. Ransie Bilbro, you air ordered by the co't to pay the plaintiff the sum of five dollars befo' the decree of divo'ce air issued."

"I hain't no mo' money," breathed Ransie, heavily. "I done paid you all I had."

"Otherwise," said the justice, looking severely over his spectacles, "you are in contempt of co't."

"I reckon if you gimme till tomorrow," pleaded the husband, "I mout be able to rake or scrape it up somewhars. I never looked for to be a-payin' no ali-money."

"The case air adjourned," said Benaja, "till tomorrow, when you-all will present yo'selves and obey the order of the co't. Followin' of which the decrees of divo'ce will be delivered." He sat down in the door and began to loosen a shoestring.

* * * *

"We mout as well go down to Uncle Ziah's," decided Ransie, "and spend the night." He climbed into the cart on one side, and Ariela climbed in on the other. Obeying the flap of his rope, the little red bull slowly came around on a tack, and the cart crawled away in the nimbus arising from its wheels.

Justice of the Peace Benaja Widdup smoked his elderstem pipe. Late in the afternoon he got his weekly newspaper, and read it until the twilight dimmed its lines. Then he lit the tallow candle on his table, and read until the moon arose, marking the time for supper. He lived in the double log cabin on the slope near the girdled poplar. Going home to supper he crossed a little branch darkened by a laurel thicket. The dark figure of a man stepped from the laurels and pointed a rifle at his breast. His hat was pulled down low, and something covered most of his face.

"I want yo' money," said the figure, "'thout any talk. I'm gettin' nervous, and my finger's wabblin' on this here trigger."

"I've only got f-f-five dollars," said the justice, producing it from his vest pocket.

"Roll it up," came the order, "and stick it in the end of this here gun-bar'l."

The bill was crisp and new. Even fingers that were clumsy and trembling found little difficulty in making a spill of it and inserting it (this with less ease) into the muzzle of the rifle.

"Now I reckon you kin be goin' along," said the robber.

The justice lingered not on his way.

* * * *

The next day came the little red bull, drawing the cart to the office door. Justice Benaja Widdup had his shoes on, for he was expecting a visit. In his presence Ransie Bilbro handed to his wife a five-dollar bill. The official's eye sharply viewed it. It seemed to curl up as though it had been rolled and inserted into the end of a gun-barrel. But the justice refrained from comment. It is true that other bills might be inclined to curl.

He handed each one a decree of divorce. Each stood awkwardly silent, slowly folding the guarantee of freedom. The woman cast a shy glance full of constraint at Ransie.

"I reckon you'll be goin' back up to the cabin," she said, "along 'ith the bull-cart. There's bread in the tin box settin' on the shelf. I put the bacon in the b'ilin'-pot to keep the houn's from gettin' it. Don't forget to wind the clock tonight."

"You air a-goin' to your brother Ed's?" asked Ransie, with fine unconcern.

"I was 'lowin' to get along up thar afore night. I ain't sayin' as they'll pester theyselves any to make me welcome, but I hain't nowhar else fur to go. It's a right smart ways, and I reckon I better be goin'. I'll be a-sayin' good-bye, Ranse—that is, if you keer fur to say so."

"I don't know as anybody's a houn' dog," said Ransie, in a martyr's voice, "fur to not want to say good-bye—'less you air so anxious to git away that you don't want me to say it."

Ariela was silent. She folded the five-dollar bill and her decree carefully, and placed them in the bosom of her dress. Benaja Widdup watched the money disappear with mournful eyes behind his spectacles.

And then with his next words he achieved rank (as his thoughts ran) with either the great crowd of the world's sympathizers or the little crowd of its great financiers.

"Be kind o' lonesome in the old cabin tonight, Ranse," he said.

Ransie Bilbro stared out at the Cumberlands, clear blue now in the sunlight. He did not look at Ariela.

"I 'low it might be lonesome," he said; "but when folks gits mad and wants a divo'ce, you can't make folks stay."

"There's others wanted a divo'ce," said Ariela, speaking to the wooden stool. "Besides, nobody don't want nobody to stay."

"Nobody never said they didn't."

"Nobody never said they did. I reckon I better start on now to brother Ed's."

"Nobody can't wind that old clock."

"Want me to go back along 'ith you in the cart and wind it fur you, Ranse?"

The mountaineer's countenance was proof against emotion. But he reached out a big hand and enclosed Ariela's thin brown one. Her soul peeped out once through her impassive face, hallowing it.

"Them houn's shan't pester you no more," said Ransie. "I reckon I been mean and low down. You wind that clock, Ariela."

"My heart hit's in that cabin, Ranse," she whispered, "along 'ith you. I ain't a-goin' to git mad no more. Le's be startin', Ranse, so's we kin git home by sundown."

Justice of the Peace Benaja Widdup interposed as they started for the door, forgetting his presence.

"In the name of the State of Tennessee," he said, "I forbid you-all to be a-defyin' of its laws and statutes.

"This co't is mo' than willin' and full of joy to see the clouds of discord and misunderstandin' rollin' away from two lovin' hearts, but it air the duty of the co't to p'eserve the morals and integrity of the state. The co't reminds you that you air no longer man and wife, but air divo'ced by regular decree, and as such air not entitled to the benefits and 'purtenances of the mattermonial estate."

Ariela caught Ransie's arm. Did those words mean that she must now lose him when they had just learned the lesson of life?

"But the co't air prepared," went on the justice, "fur to remove the disabilities set up by the decree of the divo'ce. The co't air on hand to perform the solemn ceremony of marri'ge, thus fixin' things up and enablin' the parties in the case to resume the honor'ble and elevatin' state of mattermony which they desires. The fee fur performin' said ceremony will be, in this case, to wit, five dollars."

Ariela caught the gleam of promise in his words. Swiftly her hand went to her bosom. Freely as an alighting dove the bill fluttered to the justice's table. Her sallow cheek colored as she stood hand in hand with Ransie and listened to the reuniting words.

Ransie helped her into the cart, and climbed in beside her. The little red bull turned once more, and they set out, hand-clasped, for the mountains.

Justice of the Peace Benaja Widdup sat in his door and took off his shoes. Once again he fingered the bill tucked down in his vest pocket. Once again the speckled hen swaggered down the main street of the "settlement," cackling foolishly.

SUMMARY OF STUDY

The student, instead of writing the study in outline as this one is, should write it out in full like an essay, term paper, or paper for a literary club.

1. *Synopsis.* Ransie and Ariela Bilbro apply to Benaja Widdup, a mountain justice of the peace, for a divorce. When they find that they can really be rid of each other, they are not so sure they want the divorce. Having paid all he had for the decree, Ransie has to wait till the following day before he can pay five dollars as alimony. That evening he robs the justice of the money he has just paid him and gives it to Ariela. The next morning the two return to the justice's office and decide to go home together. The justice reminds them that they are divorced, but remarries them for the oft-exchanged five-dollar bill.

2. *Theme.* Divorce would often be unnecessary if the married pair could be made to forget their little annoyances, and realize their real affection for each other.

The author treats the theme as if he believed it to be true; and the reader is convinced of its truth in this particular case, and perhaps pretty generally as well.

3. *Outline.*

    I. Preliminary Situation.

        1. Time—The present.

        2. Place—The Tennessee mountains.

        3. The characters introduced.

    II. Initial Incident—The application for a divorce.

III. Development of the plot.

Scene 1. The divorce granted and paid for and the demand for alimony.

Scene 2. The robbery of the justice of the peace.

Scene 3. The second appearance of the couple in the justice's court. The re-marriage.

Culmination. The decision of the couple to go home together.

Conclusion. Setting out for home.

Note: The incidents of the speckled hen at the beginning and at the end make a kind of whimsical pair of parenthesis marks to bind the whole story together.

4. *Tone.* Humorous with underlying seriousness.

5. This is a story of character.

6. a. Principal characters. Ransie and Ariela Bilbro.

b. Secondary character. Benaja Widdup.

7. All of the characters have distinct individuality.

8. Some very brief but effective direct delineation of character is used, but the indirect method predominates.

9. and 10. All the characters, incidents, speeches, and situations seem to be true to the kind of life involved in this story.

11. There is no marked increase in speed or in emotional tension as the culmination is approached; but these mountaineers are slow of action and speech, and such an increase of speed and emotional tension would not seem natural in this story.

12. The setting is mere background, but an interesting one.

13. The title was apparently suggested by the swift revolution of the affections and plans of these two people.

14. The point of view is that of the omniscient third person.

15. In the conversation O. Henry uses as guide-words *said, repeated, came Ransie's antiphony, remarked, asked, answered, breathed, pleaded, decided, came the order, whispered,* and *went on.* There are in the whole story thirty-eight speeches by the three characters. Seven of them are without any guide-words at all. The other thirty-one are introduced each by one of the twelve guide-words already enumerated. *Said* is used seventeen times. The other fourteen speeches are introduced by one or another of the remaining eleven words. This means that the writer usually uses *said* or no guide-word at all. Or if he uses any other word than *said* he uses it sparingly. But even with this economical use of such words his conversation seems natural and easy. Indeed it is very effective.

16. O. Henry is also skillful in the use of adverbs to indicate the

manner in which a speech was uttered and thus to reveal character, but he is sparing in the employment of such words and phrases. In the thirty-eight speeches in this story the adverb or phrase is used with only ten of them.

17. The logical beginning is used.

18. The author does not insert any comment of his own.

19. The direct discourse, conversation or dialogue, is almost exactly fifty per cent. Description, narrative, and author's comment in about equal proportions make up the other fifty.

20. There are no episodes in the story that are not directly and closely related to the development of the story. This means that there are no digressions.

21. The time scheme makes an allowance for about twenty hours— from the arrival of the cart, in the middle of one afternoon to the departure for the cabin the next morning.

22. The author's method in this story is realistic, untouched by the mood of either idealism or symbolism.

23. O. Henry's style is that of a master of words. He uses dialect and makes it the actual speech of his characters. His use of humor that does not offend by dropping to the level of ridicule in a serious situation is pleasing. The descriptions are brief and rapid, but very clear and effective.

24. The characters are from lowly life, but are worth knowing. The situation is one of intense general interest. The setting is interesting and the incidents compel our attention. Perhaps one would not care to call this one of the very great stories, but it is a story of considerable worth.

PART TWO

SELECTED SHORT STORIES

THE PRODIGAL SON

Luke 15:11–32

[*The Prodigal Son* is one of the parables of Jesus. It is, of course, deliberate fiction told to make a great truth plain. No title was given for it, but this story is always called *The Prodigal Son*, though *The Forgiving Father* would be more appropriate.]

A CERTAIN man had two sons: and the younger of them said to his father, "Father, give me the portion of goods that falleth to me." And he divided unto them his living.

And not many days after the younger son gathered all together, and took his journey into a far country, and there wasted his substance with riotous living.

And when he had spent all, there arose a mighty famine in that land; and he began to be in want. And he went and joined himself to a citizen of that country; and he sent him into his fields to feed swine.

And he would fain have filled his belly with the husks that the swine did eat: and no man gave unto him.

And when he came to himself, he said, "How many hired servants of my father's have bread enough and to spare, and I perish with hunger! I will arise and go to my father, and will say unto him, 'Father, I have sinned against heaven, and before thee, and am no more worthy to be called thy son: make me as one of thy hired servants.'"

And he arose, and came to his father.

But when he was yet a great way off, his father saw him, and had compassion, and ran, and fell on his neck, and kissed him.

And the son said unto him, "Father, I have sinned against heaven, and in thy sight, and am no more worthy to be called thy son."

But the father said to his servants, "Bring forth the best robe, and put it on him; and put a ring on his hand, and shoes on his feet:

"And bring hither the fatted calf, and kill it; and let us eat, and be merry: for this my son was dead, and is alive again; he was lost, and is found." And they began to be merry.

Now his elder son was in the field: and as he came and drew nigh to the house, he heard music and dancing. And he called one of the servants, and asked what these things meant.

And he said unto him, "Thy brother is come; and thy father hath killed the fatted calf, because he hath received him safe and sound."

And he was angry, and would not go in: therefore came his father out, and entreated him. And he answering said to his father, "Lo, these

75

many years do I serve thee, neither transgressed I at any time thy commandment; and yet thou never gavest me a kid, that I might make merry with my friends: but as soon as this thy son was come, which hath devoured thy living, . . . thou hast killed for him the fatted calf."

And he said unto him, "Son, thou art ever with me, and all that I have is thine.

"It was meet that we should make merry, and be glad: for this thy brother was dead, and is alive again; and was lost, and is found."

THE MYSTERIOUS BRIDE

By James Hogg

[James Hogg (1770–1835) was born at Ettrick, Selkirkshire, Scotland, a year before the birth of Sir Walter Scott. He is commonly known as the "Ettrick Shepherd," and is more famous for his verse than for his prose tales. The story following is from his *Winter Evening Tales*, published in 1820.]

A GREAT number of people nowadays are beginning broadly to insinuate that there are no such things as ghosts, or spiritual beings visible to mortal sight. Even Sir Walter Scott is turned renegade, and, with his stories made up of half-and-half, like Nathaniel Gow's toddy, is trying to throw cold water on the most certain, though most impalpable, phenomena of human nature. The bodies are daft. Heaven mend their wits! Before they had ventured to assert such things, I wish they had been where I have often been; or, in particular, where the Laird of Birkendelly was on St. Lawrence's Eve, in the year 1777, and sundry times subsequent to that.

Be it known, then, to every reader of this relation of facts that happened in my own remembrance that the road from Birkendelly to the great muckle village of Balmawhapple (commonly called the muckle town, in opposition to the little town that stood on the other side of the burn)—that road, I say, lay between two thornhedges, so well kept by the Laird's hedger, so close, and so high, that a rabbit could not have escaped from the highway into any of the adjoining fields. Along this road was the Laird riding on the Eve of St. Lawrence, in a careless, indifferent manner, with his hat to one side, and his cane dancing a hornpipe before him. He was, moreover, chanting a song to himself; and I have heard people tell what song it was, too. There was once a certain, or rather uncertain, bard, ycleped Robert Burns, who made a number of good songs; but this that the Laird sang was an amorous song of great antiquity, which, like all the said bard's best songs, was sung one hundred and fifty years before he was born. It began thus:

> I am the Laird of Windy-wa's,
> I cam nae here without a cause,
> An' I hae gotten forty fa's
>   In coming o'er the knowe, joe.
> The night it is baith wind and weet;
> The morn it will be snaw and sleet;

My shoon are frozen to my feet;
O, rise an' let me in, joe!
Let me in this ae night, . . .

This song was the Laird singing, while, at the same time, he was smudging and laughing at the catastrophe, when, ere ever aware, he beheld, a short way before him, an uncommonly elegant and beautiful girl walking in the same direction with him. "Aye," said the Laird to himself, "here is something very attractive indeed! Where the deuce can she have sprung from? She must have risen out of the earth, for I never saw her till this breath. Well, I declare I have not seen such a female figure—I wish I had such an assignation with her as the Laird of Windy-wa's had with his sweetheart."

As the Laird was half-thinking, half-speaking this to himself, the enchanting creature looked back at him with a motion of intelligence that she knew what he was half-saying, half-thinking, and then vanished over the summit of the rising ground before him, called the Birky Brow. "Aye, go your ways!" said the Laird; "I see by you, you'll not be very hard to overtake. You cannot get off the road, and I'll have a chat with you before you make the Deer's Den."

The Laird jogged on. He did not sing the Laird of Windy-wa's any more, for he felt a stifling about his heart; but he often repeated to himself, "She's a very fine woman!—a very fine woman indeed!—and to be walking here by herself! I cannot comprehend it."

When he reached the summit of the Birky Brow he did not see her, although he had a longer view of the road than before. He thought this very singular, and began to suspect that she wanted to escape him, although apparently rather lingering on him before. "I shall have another look at her, however," thought the Laird, and off he set at a flying trot. No. He came first to one turn, then another. There was nothing of the young lady to be seen. "Unless she take wings and fly away, I shall be up with her," quoth the Laird, and off he set at the full gallop.

In the middle of his career he met with Mr. McMurdie, of Aulton, who hailed him with, "Hilloa, Birkendelly! Where the deuce are you flying at that rate?"

"I was riding after a woman," said the Laird, with great simplicity, reining in his steed.

"Then I am sure no woman on earth can long escape you, unless she be in an air balloon."

"I don't know that. Is she far gone?"

"In which way do you mean?"

"In this."

"Aha-ha-ha! Hee-hee-hee!" nichered McMurdie, misconstruing the Laird's meaning.

"What do you laugh at, my dear sir? Do you know her, then?"

"Ho-ho-ho! Hee-hee-hee! How should I, or how can I, know her, Birkendelly, unless you inform me who she is?"

"Why, that is the very thing I want to know of you. I mean the young lady whom you met just now."

"You are raving, Birkendelly. I met no young lady, nor is there a single person on the road I have come by, while you know that for a mile and a half forward your way she could not get out of it."

"I know that," said the Laird, biting his lip and looking greatly puzzled; "but confound me if I understand this; for I was within speech of her just now on the top of the Birky Brow there, and, when I think of it, she could not have been even thus far as yet. She had on a pure white gauze frock, a small green bonnet and feathers, and a green veil, which, flung back over her left shoulder, hung below her waist, and was altogether such an engaging figure that no man could have passed her on the road without taking some note of her. Are you not making game of me? Did you not really meet with her?"

"On my word of truth and honor, I did not. Come, ride back with me, and we shall meet her still, depend on it. She has given you the go-by on the road. Let us go; I am only to call at the mill about some barley for the distillery, and will return with you to the big town."

Birkendelly returned with his friend. The sun was not yet set, yet McMurdie could not help observing that the Laird looked thoughtful and confused, and not a word could he speak about anything save this lovely apparition with the white frock and the green veil; and lo! when they reached the top of Birky Brow there was the maiden again before them, and exactly at the same spot where the Laird first saw her before, only walking in the contrary direction.

"Well, this is the most extraordinary thing that I ever knew!" exclaimed the Laird.

"What is it, sir?" said McMurdie.

"How that young lady could have eluded me," returned the Laird. "See, here she is still!"

"I beg your pardon, sir, I don't see her. Where is she?"

"There, on the other side of the angle; but you are short-sighted. See, there she is ascending the other eminence in her white frock and green veil, as I told you. What a lovely creature!"

"Well, well, we have her fairly before us now, and shall see what she is like at all events," said McMurdie.

Between the Birky Brow and this other slight eminence there is an obtuse angle of the road at the part where it is lowest, and, in passing this, the two friends necessarily lost sight of the object of their curiosity. They pushed on at a quick pace, cleared the low angle—the maiden was not there! They rode full speed to the top of the eminence from whence a long extent of road was visible before them—there was no human creature in view. McMurdie laughed aloud, but the Laird turned pale as death and bit his lip. His friend asked him good-humoredly why he was so much affected. He said, because he could not comprehend the meaning of this singular apparition or illusion, and it troubled him the more as he now remembered a dream of the same nature which he had had, and which terminated in a dreadful manner.

"Why, man, you are dreaming still," said McMurdie. "But, never mind; it is quite common for men of your complexion to dream of beautiful maidens with white frocks, and green veils, bonnets, feathers, and slender waists. It is a lovely image, the creation of your own sanguine imagination, and you may worship it without any blame. Were her shoes black or green? And her stockings—did you note them? The symmetry of the limbs, I am sure you did! Good-bye; I see you are not disposed to leave the spot. Perhaps she will appear to you again."

So saying, McMurdie rode on toward the mill, and Birkendelly, after musing for some time, turned his beast's head slowly round, and began to move toward the great muckle village.

The Laird's feelings were now in terrible commotion. He was taken beyond measure with the beauty and elegance of the figure he had seen, but he remembered, with a mixture of admiration and horror, that a dream of the same enchanting object had haunted his slumbers all the days of his life; yet, how singular that he should never have recollected the circumstance till now! But farther, with the dream there were connected some painful circumstances which, though terrible in their issue, he could not recollect so as to form them into any degree of arrangement.

As he was considering deeply of these things and riding slowly down the declivity, neither dancing his cane nor singing the Laird of Windy-wa's, he lifted up his eyes, and there was the girl on the same spot where he saw her first, walking deliberately up the Birky Brow. The sun was down, but it was the month of August and a fine evening, and the Laird, seized with an unconquerable desire to see and speak with that incomparable creature, could restrain himself no longer, but shouted out to her to stop till he came up. She beckoned acquiescence, and slackened her pace into a slow movement. The Laird turned the corner quickly, but when he had rounded it the maiden was still there, though on the summit of the brow. She turned round, and, with an ineffable smile and curtsy, saluted him, and again moved slowly on. She vanished gradually beyond the summit, and while the green feathers were still nodding in view, and so nigh that the Laird could have touched them with a fishing-rod, he reached the top of the brow himself. There was no living soul there, nor onward, as far as his view reached. He now trembled in every limb, and, without knowing what he did, rode straight on to the big town, not daring well to return and see what he had seen for three several times; and certain he would see it again when the shades of evening were deepening, he deemed it proper and prudent to decline the pursuit of such a phantom any farther.

He alighted at the Queen's Head, called for some brandy and water, quite forgot what was his errand to the great muckle town that afternoon, there being nothing visible to his mental sight but lovely images, with white gauze frocks and green veils. His friend McMurdie joined him; they drank deep, bantered, reasoned, got angry, reasoned themselves calm again, and still all would not do. The Laird was conscious that he had seen the beautiful apparition, and, moreover, that she was the very maiden, or the resemblance of her, who, in the irrevocable decrees of Providence, was destined to be his. It was in vain that McMurdie reasoned of impressions on the imagination, and

> Of fancy moulding in the mind,
> Light visions on the passing wind.

Vain also was a story that he told him of a relation of his own, who was greatly harassed by the apparition of an officer in a red uniform that haunted him day and night, and had very nigh put him quite distracted several times, till at length his physician found out the nature of this illusion so well that he knew, from the state of his pulse, to an hour when the ghost of the officer would appear, and by bleeding, low diet, and emollients contrived to keep the apparition away altogether.

The Laird admitted the singularity of this incident, but not that it was one in point; for the one, he said, was imaginary, the other real, and that no conclusions could convince him in opposition to the authority of his own senses. He accepted of an invitation to spend a few days with McMurdie and his family, but they all acknowledged afterward that the Laird was very much like one bewitched.

As soon as he reached home he went straight to the Birky Brow, certain of seeing once more the angelic phantom, but she was not there. He took each of his former positions again and again, but the desired vision would in no wise make its appearance. He tried every day and every hour of the day, all with the same effect, till he grew absolutely desperate, and had the audacity to kneel on the spot and entreat of Heaven to see her. Yes, he called on Heaven to see her once more, whatever she was, whether a being of earth, heaven, or hell.

He was now in such a state of excitement that he could not exist; he grew listless, impatient, and sickly, took to his bed, and sent for McMurdie and the doctor; and the issue of the consultation was that Birkendelly consented to leave the country for a season, on a visit to his only sister in Ireland, whither we must accompany him for a short space.

His sister was married to Captain Bryan, younger, of Scoresby, and they two lived in a cottage on the estate, and the Captain's parents and sisters at Scoresby Hall. Great was the stir and preparation when the gallant young Laird of Birkendelly arrived at the cottage, it never being doubted that he came to forward a second bond of connection with the family, which still contained seven dashing sisters, all unmarried, and all alike willing to change that solitary and helpless state for the envied one of matrimony—a state highly popular among the young women of Ireland. Some of the Misses Bryan had now reached the years of womanhood, several of them scarcely, but these small disqualifications made no difference in the estimation of the young ladies themselves; each and all of them brushed up for the competition with high hopes and unflinching resolutions. True, the elder ones tried to check the younger in their goodnatured, forthright Irish way; but they retorted, and persisted in their superior pretensions. Then there was such shopping in the county town! It was so boundless that the credit of the Hall was finally exhausted, and the old Squire was driven to remark that, "Och, and to be sure it was a dreadful and tirrabell concussion, to be put upon the equipment of seven daughters all at the same moment, as if the young gentleman could marry them all! Och, then, poor dear shoul, he would be after finding that one was sufficient, if not one too many. And therefore there was no occasion, none at all, at all, and that there was not, for any of them to rig out more than one."

It was hinted that the Laird had some reason for complaint at this time, but as the lady sided with her daughters, he had no chance. One of the items of his account was thirty-seven buckling-combs, then greatly in vogue. There were black combs, pale combs, yellow combs, and gilt ones, all to suit or set off various complexions; and if other articles bore any proportion at all to these, it had been better for the Laird and all his family that Birkendelly had never set foot in Ireland.

The plan was all concocted. There was to be a grand dinner at the Hall, at which the damsels were to appear in all their finery, a ball to follow, and note be taken which of the young ladies was their guest's choice, and measures taken accordingly. The dinner and the ball took place; and what a pity I may not describe that entertainment, the dresses, and the dancers, for they were all exquisite in their way, and *outre* beyond measure. But such details only serve to derange a winter evening's tale such as this.

Birkendelly having at this time but one model for his choice among womankind, all that ever he did while in the presence of ladies was to look out for some resemblance to her, the angel of his fancy; and it so happened that in one of old Bryan's daughters named Luna, or, more familiarly, Loony, he perceived, or thought he perceived, some imaginary similarity in form and air to the lovely apparition. This was the sole reason why he was incapable of taking his eyes off from her the whole of that night; and this incident settled the point, not only with the old people, but even the young ladies were forced, after every exertion on their own parts, to "yild t' p'int to their sister Loony, who certainly was not the mist genteelest nor mist handsomest of that guid-lucking fimily."

The next day Lady Luna was dispatched off to the cottage in grand style, there to live hand in glove with her supposed lover. There was no standing all this. There were the two paddocked together, like a ewe and a lamb, early and late; and though the Laird really appeared to have, and probably had, some delight in her company, it was only in contemplating that certain indefinable air of resemblance which she bore to the sole image impressed on his heart. He bought her a white gauze frock, a green bonnet and feather, with a veil, which she was obliged to wear thrown over her left shoulder, and every day after, six times a day, was she obliged to walk over a certain eminence at a certain distance before her lover. She was delighted to oblige him; but still, when he came up, he looked disappointed, and never said, "Luna, I love you; when are we to be married?" No, he never said any such thing, for all her looks and expressions of fondest love; for, alas! in all this dalliance he was only feeding a mysterious flame that preyed upon his vitals, and proved too severe for the powers either of reason or religion to extinguish. Still, time flew lighter and lighter by, his health was restored, the bloom of his cheek returned, and the frank and simple confidence of Luna had a certain charm with it that reconciled him to his sister's Irish economy. But a strange incident now happened to him which deranged all his immediate plans.

He was returning from angling one evening, a little before sunset, when he saw Lady Luna awaiting him on his way home. But instead of rushing up to meet him as usual, she turned, and walked up the rising ground before him.

"Poor sweet girl! how condescending she is," said he to himself, "and how like she is in reality to the angelic being whose form and features are so deeply impressed on my heart! I now see it is no fond or fancied resemblance. It is real! real! real! How I long to clasp her in my arms, and tell her how I love her; for, after all, that is the girl that is to be mine, and the former a vision to impress this the more on my heart."

He posted up the ascent to overtake her. When at the top she turned, smiled and curtsied. Good heavens! it was the identical lady of his fondest adoration herself, but lovelier, far lovelier, than ever. He expected every moment that she would vanish, as was her wont; but she did not— she awaited him, and received his embraces with open arms. She was a being of real flesh and blood, courteous, elegant, and affectionate. He kissed her hand, he kissed her glowing cheek, and blessed all the powers of love who had thus restored her to him again, after undergoing pangs of love such as man never suffered.

"But, dearest heart, here we are standing in the middle of the highway," said he; "suffer me to conduct you to my sister's house, where you shall have an apartment with a child of nature having some slight resemblance to yourself." She smiled, and said, "No, I will not sleep with Lady Luna tonight. Will you please to look round you, and see where you are." He did so, and behold they were standing on the Birky Brow, on the only spot where he had ever seen her. She smiled at his embarrassed look, and asked if he did not remember aught of his coming over from Ireland. He said he thought he did remember something of it, but love with him had long absorbed every other sense. He then asked her to his own house, which she declined, saying she could only meet him on that spot till after their marriage, which could not be before St. Lawrence's Eve come three years. "And now," said she, "we must part. My name is Jane Ogilvie, and you were betrothed to me before you were born. But I am come to release you this evening, if you have the slightest objection."

He declared he had none; and kneeling, swore the most solemn oath to be hers forever, and to meet her there on St. Lawrence's Eve next, and every St. Lawrence's Eve until that blessed day on which she had consented to make him happy by becoming his own forever. She then asked him affectionately to change rings with her, in pledge of their faith and troth, in which he joyfully acquiesced; for she could not have then asked any conditions which in the fullness of his heart's love, he would not have granted; and after one fond and affectionate kiss, and repeating all their engagements over again, they parted.

Birkendelly's heart was now melted within him, and all his senses overpowered by one overwhelming passion. On leaving his fair and kind one, he got bewildered, and could not find the road to his own house, believing sometimes that he was going there, and sometimes to his sister's, till at length he came, as he thought, upon the Liffey, at its junction with Loch Allan; and there, in attempting to call for a boat, he awoke from a profound sleep, and found himself lying in his bed within his sister's house, and the day sky just breaking.

If he was puzzled to account for some things in the course of his dream, he was much more puzzled to account for them now that he was wide awake. He was sensible that he had met his love, had embraced, kissed, and exchanged vows and rings with her, and, in token of the truth and reality of all these, her emerald ring was on his finger, and his own away; so there was no doubt that they had met—by what means it was beyond the power of man to calculate.

There was then living with Mrs. Bryan an old Scotswoman, commonly styled Lucky Black. She had nursed Birkendelly's mother, and been dry-nurse to himself and sister; and having more than a mother's attachment for the latter, when she was married, old Lucky left her country to spend the last of her days in the house of her beloved young lady. When the Laird entered the breakfast-parlor that morning she was sitting in her black velvet hood, as usual, reading *The Fourfold State of Man*, and, being paralytic and somewhat deaf, she seldom regarded those who went or came. But chancing to hear him say something about the ninth of August, she quitted reading, turned round her head to listen, and then asked, in a hoarse, tremulous voice: "What's that he's saying? What's the unlucky callant saying about the ninth of August? Aih? To be sure it is St. Lawrence's Eve, although the tenth be his day. It's ower true, ower true, ower true for him an' a' his kin, poor man! Aih? What was he saying then?"

The men smiled at her incoherent earnestness, but the lady, with true feminine condescension, informed her, in a loud voice, that Allan had an engagement in Scotland on St. Lawrence's Eve. She then started up, extended her shriveled hands, that shook like the aspen, and panted out: "Aih, aih? Lord preserve us! Whaten an engagement has he on St. Lawrence's Eve? Bind him! bind him! Shackle him wi' bands of steel, and of brass, and of iron! Oh, may He whose blessed will was pleased to leave him an orphan sae soon, preserve him from the fate which I tremble to think on!"

She then tottered round the table, as with supernatural energy, and seizing the Laird's right hand, she drew it close to her unstable eyes, and then perceiving the emerald ring chased in blood, she threw up her arms with a jerk, opened her skinny jaws with a fearful gape, and uttering a shriek that made all the house yell, and every one within it to tremble, she fell back lifeless and rigid on the floor. The gentlemen both fled, out of sheer terror; but a woman never deserts her friends in extremity. The lady called her maids about her, had her old nurse conveyed to bed, where every means were used to restore animation. But, alas, life was extinct! The vital spark had fled forever, which filled all their hearts with grief, disappointment, and horror, as some dreadful tale of mystery was now sealed up from their knowledge, which, in all likelihood, no other could reveal. But to say the truth, the Laird did not seem greatly disposed to probe it to the bottom.

Not all the arguments of Captain Bryan and his lady, nor the simple entreaties of Lady Luna, could induce Birkendelly to put off his engagement to meet his love on the Birky Brow on the evening of the ninth of August; but he promised soon to return, pretending that some business of the utmost importance called him away. Before he went, however, he asked his sister if ever she had heard of such a lady in Scotland as Jane Ogilvie. Mrs. Bryan repeated the name many times to herself, and said that the name undoubtedly was once familiar to her, although she thought not for good, but at that moment she did not recollect one single individual of the name. He then showed her the emerald ring that had been the death of Lucky Black; but the moment the lady looked at it, she made a grasp at it to take it off by force, which she had very nearly effected. "Oh, burn it! burn it!" cried she; "it is not a right ring! Burn it!"

"My dear sister, what fault is in the ring?" said he. "It is a very pretty ring, and one that I set great value by."

"Oh, for Heaven's sake, burn it, and renounce the giver!" cried she. "If you have any regard for your peace here or your soul's welfare hereafter, burn that ring! If you saw with your own eyes, you would easily perceive that that is not a ring befitting a Christian to wear."

This speech confounded Birkendelly a good deal. He retired by himself and examined the ring, and could see nothing in it unbecoming a Christian to wear. It was a chased gold ring, with a bright emerald, which last had a red foil, in some lights giving it a purple gleam, and inside was engraven *Elegit*, much defaced, but that his sister could not see; therefore he could not comprehend her vehement injunctions concerning it. But that it might no more give her offence, or any other, he sewed it within his vest, opposite his heart, judging that there was something in it which his eyes were withholden from discerning.

Thus he left Ireland with his mind in great confusion, groping his way, as it were, in a hole of mystery, yet with the passion that preyed on his heart and vitals more intense than ever. He seems to have had an impression all his life that some mysterious fate awaited him, which the correspondence of his dreams and day visions tended to confirm. And though he gave himself wholly up to the sway of one overpowering passion, it was not without some yearnings of soul, manifestations of terror, and so much earthly shame, that he never more mentioned his love, or his engagements, to any human being, not even to his friend McMurdie, whose company he forthwith shunned.

It is on this account that I am unable to relate what passed between the lovers thenceforward. It is certain they met at the Birky Brow that St. Lawrence's Eve, for they were seen in company together; but of the engagements, vows, or dalliance that passed between them I can say nothing; nor of all their future meetings, until the beginning of August, 1781, when the Laird began decidedly to make preparations for his approaching marriage; yet not as if he and his betrothed had been going to reside at Birkendelly, all his provisions rather bespeaking a meditated journey.

On the morning of the ninth he wrote to his sister, and then arraying himself in his new wedding suit, and putting the emerald ring on his finger, he appeared all impatience, until toward evening, when he sallied out on horseback to his appointment. It seems that his mysterious inamorata had met him, for he was seen riding through the big town before sunset, with a young lady behind him, dressed in white and green, and the villagers affirmed that they were riding at the rate of fifty miles an hour! They were seen to pass a cottage called Mosskilt, ten miles farther on, where there was no highway, at the same tremendous speed; and I could never hear that they were any more seen, until the following morning, when Birkendelly's fine bay horse was found lying dead at his own stable door; and shortly after his master was likewise discovered lying, a blackened corpse, on the Birky Brow at the very spot where the mysterious but lovely dame had always appeared to him. There was neither wound, bruise, nor dislocation in his whole frame; but his skin was of a livid color, and his features terribly distorted.

This woful catastrophe struck the neighborhood with great consternation, so that nothing else was talked of. Every ancient tradition and modern incident were raked together, compared, and combined; and certainly a most rare concatenation of misfortunes was elicited. It was authenticated that his father had died on the same spot that day twenty years, and his grandfather that day forty years, the former, as was supposed, by a fall from his horse when in liquor, and the latter, nobody knew how; and now this Allan was the last of his race, for Mrs. Bryan had no children.

It was, moreover, now remembered by many, and among the rest by the Rev. Joseph Taylor, that he had frequently observed a young lady, in white and green, sauntering about the spot on a St. Lawrence's Eve.

When Captain Bryan and his lady arrived to take possession of the premises, they instituted a strict inquiry into every circumstance; but nothing further than what was related to them by Mr. McMurdie could be learned of this Mysterious Bride, besides what the Laird's own letter bore. It ran thus:

Dearest Sister—I shall before this time tomorrow be the most happy, or most miserable, of mankind, having solemnly engaged myself this night to wed a young and beautiful lady, named Jane Ogilvie, to whom it seems I was betrothed before I was born. Our correspondence has been of a most private and mysterious nature; but my troth is pledged, and my resolution fixed. We set out on a far journey to the place of her abode on the nuptial eve, so that it will be long before I see you again. Yours till death,

ALLAN GEORGE SANDISON.

Birkendelly, *August 8, 1781.*

That very same year, an old woman, named Marion Haw, was returned upon that, her native parish, from Glasgow. She had led a migratory life with her son—who was what he called a bell-hanger, but in fact a tinker of the worst grade—for many years, and was at last returned to the muckle town in a state of great destitution. She gave the parishioners a history of the Mysterious Bride, so plausibly correct, but withal so romantic, that everybody said of it (as is often said of my narratives, with the same narrow-minded prejudice and injustice) that it was a made story. There were, however, some strong testimonies of its veracity.

She said that the first Allan Sandison, who married the great heiress of Birkendelly, was previously engaged to a beautiful young lady named Jane Ogilvie, to whom he gave anything but fair play; and, as she believed, either murdered her, or caused her to be murdered, in the midst of a thicket of birch and broom, at a spot which she mentioned; and she had good reason for believing so, as she had seen the red blood and the new grave, when she was a little girl, and ran home and mentioned it to her grandfather, who charged her as she valued her life never to mention that again, as it was only the nombles and hide of a deer which he himself had buried there. But when, twenty years subsequent to that, the wicked and unhappy Allan Sandison was found dead on that very spot, and lying across the green mound, then nearly level with the surface, which she had once seen a new grave, she then for the first time ever thought of a Divine Providence; and she added, "For my grandfather, Neddy Haw, he dee'd too; there's naebody kens how, nor ever shall."

As they were quite incapable of conceiving from Marion's description anything of the spot, Mr. McMurdie caused her to be taken out to the Birky Brow in a cart, accompanied by Mr. Taylor and some hundreds of the town's folks; but whenever she saw it, she said, "Aha, birkies! the haill kintra's altered now. There was nae road here than; it gaed straight ower the tap o' the hill. An' let me see—there's the thorn where the cushats biggit; an' there's the auld birk that I ance fell aff an' left my shoe sticking i' the cleft. I can tell ye, birkies, either the deer's grave or bonny Jane Ogilvie's is no twa yards aff the place where that Horse's hind-feet are standin'; sae ye may howk, an' see if there be ony remains."

The minister and McMurdie and all the people stared at one another, for they had purposely caused the horse to stand still on the very spot where both the father and son had been found dead. They digged, and deep, deep below the road they found part of the slender bones and skull of a young female, which they deposited decently in the churchyard. The family of the Sandisons is extinct, the Mysterious Bride appears no more on the Eve of St. Lawrence, and the wicked people of the great muckle village have got a lesson on divine justice written to them in lines of blood.

RIP VAN WINKLE

By *Washington Irving*

[Before the short story became a recognized literary form there were narratives concerned with adventure, unusual or mysterious experiences, mysteries, ghosts, and the like. One of the early American writers of this kind of tale was Washington Irving (1783–1859). He was born in New York, one of a family of eleven children of Deacon William Irving and his wife Sarah Sanders, the father Scotch and the mother a daughter of an English clergyman. The family was prosperous, and so able to give this precocious, undersized boy the advantages of travel and an informal education. At one time or another he was mildly interested in law, in newspaper work, and in politics, but his life interest was in literature. Among his longer literary works is a burlesque *History of New York* ascribed to an imaginary Dutch chronicler, Diedrich Knicker-bocker. This was published in 1809. Ten years later he published a group of essays and tales which he called *The Sketch Book*. This little volume outlives his more serious works. In it there appeared the story of *Rip Van Winkle*, supposed to have been found among the papers of Diedrich Knickerbocker. This and *The Legend of Sleepy Hollow* in the same volume are the two most famous works of Irving.

After an eventful life in New York, Scotland, England, and Spain Washington Irving spent the last thirteen years of his life, a famous and respected author, at the house called "Sunnyside" at Tarrytown, New York.]

WHOEVER has made a voyage up the Hudson must remember the Kaatskill mountains. They are a dismembered branch of the great Appalachian family, and are seen away to the west of the river, swelling up to a noble height, and lording it over the surrounding country. Every change of season, every change of weather, indeed, every hour of the day, produces some change in the magical hues and shapes of these mountains; and they are regarded by all the good wives, far and near, as perfect barometers. When the weather is fair and settled, they are clothed in blue and purple, and print their bold outlines on the clear evening sky; but sometimes, when the rest of the landscape is cloudless, they will gather a hood of gray vapors about their summits, which, in the last rays of the setting sun, will glow and light up like a crown of glory.

At the foot of these fairy mountains, the voyager may have descried the light smoke curling up from a village, whose shingle-roofs gleam among the trees, just where the blue tints of the upland melt away into the fresh green of the nearer landscape. It is a little village, of great antiquity, having been founded by some of the Dutch colonists in the early times of the province, just about the beginning of the government of the good Peter Stuyvesant (may he rest in peace!), and there were some of the houses of the original settlers standing within a few years, built of small yellow bricks brought from Holland, having latticed windows and gable fronts, surmounted with weather-cocks.

In that same village, and in one of these very houses (which, to tell the precise truth, was sadly time-worn and weather-beaten), there lived, many years since, while the country was yet a province of Great Britain, a simple, good-natured fellow, of the name of Rip Van Winkle. He was a descendant of the Van Winkles who figured so gallantly in the chivalrous days of Peter Stuyvesant, and accompanied him to the siege of Fort Christina. He inherited, however, but little of the martial character of his ancestors. I have observed that he was a simple, good-natured man; he was, moreover, a kind neighbor, and an obedient, hen-pecked husband. Indeed, to the latter circumstance might be owing that meekness of spirit which gained him such universal popularity; for those men are most apt to be obsequious and conciliating abroad who are under the discipline of shrews at home. Their tempers, doubtless, are rendered pliant and malleable in the fiery furnace of domestic tribulation; and a curtain-lecture is worth all the sermons in the world for teaching the virtues of patience and long-suffering. A termagant wife may, therefore, in some respects, be considered a tolerable blessing; and, if so, Rip Van Winkle was thrice blessed.

Certain it is, that he was a great favorite among all the good wives of the village, who, as usual with the amiable sex, took his part in all family squabbles; and never failed, whenever they talked those matters over in their evening gossipings, to lay all the blame on Dame Van Winkle. The children of the village, too, would shout with joy whenever he approached. He assisted at their sports, made their playthings, taught them to fly kites and shoot marbles, and told them long stories of ghosts, witches, and Indians. Whenever he went dodging about the village, he was surrounded by a troop of them, hanging on his skirts, clambering on his back, and playing a thousand tricks on him with impunity; and not a dog would bark at him throughout the neighborhood.

The great error in Rip's composition was an insuperable aversion to all kinds of profitable labor. It could not be from the want of assiduity or perseverance, for he would sit on a wet rock, with a rod as long and heavy as a Tartar's lance, and fish all day without a murmur, even though he should not be encouraged by a single nibble. He would carry a fowling-piece on his shoulder for hours together, trudging through woods and swamps, and up hill and down dale, to shoot a few squirrels or wild pigeons. He would never refuse to assist a neighbor even in the roughest toil, and was a foremost man at all country frolics for husking Indian corn, or building stone fences. The women of the village, too, used to employ him to run their errands, and to do such little odd jobs as their less obliging husbands would not do for them. In a word, Rip was ready to attend to anybody's business but his own; but as to doing family duty, and keeping his farm in order, he found it impossible.

In fact, he declared it was of no use to work on his farm; it was the most pestilent little piece of ground in the whole country; everything about it went wrong, and would go wrong, in spite of him. His fences were continually falling to pieces; his cow would either go astray, or get among the cabbages; weeds were sure to grow quicker in his fields than anywhere else; the rain always made a point of setting in just as he had some out-of-door work to do; so that though his patrimonial estate had dwindled away under his management, acre by acre, until there was little more left than a mere patch of Indian corn and potatoes, yet it was the worst conditioned farm in the neighborhood.

His children, too, were as ragged and wild as if they belonged to nobody. His son Rip, an urchin begotten in his own likeness, promised to inherit the habits, with the old clothes, of his father. He was generally seen trooping like a colt at his mother's heels, equipped in a pair of his father's cast-off galligaskins, which he had much ado to hold up with one hand, as a fine lady does her train in bad weather.

Rip Van Winkle, however, was one of those happy mortals, of foolish, well-oiled dispositions, who take the world easy, eat white bread or brown, whichever can be got with least thought or trouble, and would rather starve on a penny than work for a pound. If left to himself, he would have whistled life away in perfect contentment; but his wife kept continually dinning in his ears about his idleness, his carelessness and the ruin he was bringing on his family. Morning, noon and night, her tongue was incessantly going, and everything he said or did was sure to produce a torrent of household eloquence. Rip had but one way of replying to all lectures of the kind, and that, by frequent use, had grown into a habit. He shrugged his shoulders, shook his head, cast up his eyes, but said nothing. This, however, always provoked a fresh volley from his wife; so that he was fain to draw off his forces, and take to the outside of the house—the one side which, in truth, belongs to a hen-pecked husband.

Rip's sole domestic adherent was his dog Wolf, who was as much hen-pecked as his master; for Dame Van Winkle regarded them as companions in idleness, and even looked upon Wolf with an evil eye, as the cause of his master's going so often astray. True it is, in all points of spirit befitting an honorable dog, he was as courageous an animal as ever scoured the woods; but what courage can withstand the ever-during and all-besetting terrors of a woman's tongue? The moment

Wolf entered the house his crest fell, his tail drooped to the ground, or curled between his legs, he sneaked about with a gallows air, casting many a sidelong glance at Dame Van Winkle, and at the least flourish of a broomstick or ladle he would fly to the door with yelping precipitation.

Times grew worse and worse with Rip Van Winkle as years of matrimony rolled on: a tart temper never mellows with age, and a sharp tongue is the only edged tool that grows keener with constant use. For a long while he used to console himself, when driven from home, by frequenting a kind of perpetual club of the sages, philosophers, and other idle personages of the village, which held its sessions on a bench before a small inn, designated by a rubicund portrait of His Majesty, George the Third. Here they used to sit in the shade through a long, lazy summer's day, talking listlessly over village gossip, or telling endless sleepy stories about nothing. But it would have been worth any statesman's money to have heard the profound discussions that sometimes took place, when by chance an old newspaper fell into their hands from some passing traveler. How solemnly they would listen to the contents, as drawled out by Derrick Van Bummel, the schoolmaster, a dapper, learned little man, who was not to be daunted by the most gigantic word in the dictionary; and how sagely they would deliberate upon public events some months after they had taken place.

The opinions of this junta were completely controlled by Nicholas Vedder, a patriarch of the village, and landlord of the inn, at the door of which he took his seat from morning till night, just moving sufficiently to avoid the sun and keep in the shade of a large tree; so that the neighbors could tell the hour by his movements as accurately as by a sun-dial. It is true, he was rarely heard to speak, but smoked his pipe incessantly. His adherents, however (for every great man has his adherents), perfectly understood him, and knew how to gather his opinions. When anything that was read or related displeased him, he was observed to smoke his pipe vehemently, and to send forth short, frequent, and angry puffs; but when pleased, he would inhale the smoke slowly and tranquilly, and emit it in light and placid clouds; and sometimes, taking the pipe from his mouth, and letting the fragrant vapor curl about his nose, would gravely nod his head in token of perfect approbation.

From even this stronghold the unlucky Rip was at length routed by his termagant wife, who would suddenly break in upon the tranquillity of the assemblage, and call the members all to naught; nor was that august personage, Nicholas Vedder himself, sacred from the daring tongue of this terrible virago, who charged him outright with encouraging her husband in habits of idleness.

Poor Rip was at last reduced almost to despair; and his only alternative, to escape from the labor of the farm and clamor of his wife, was to take gun in hand and stroll away into the woods. Here he would some-

times seat himself at the foot of a tree, and share the contents of his
wallet with Wolf, with whom he sympathized as a fellow sufferer in
persecution. "Poor Wolf," he would say, "thy mistress leads thee a
dog's life of it; but never mind, my lad, whilst I live thou shalt never
want a friend to stand by thee!" Wolf would wag his tail, look wistfully
in his master's face; and if dogs can feel pity, I verily believe he reciprocated the sentiment with all his heart.

In a long ramble of the kind on a fine autumnal day, Rip had unconsciously scrambled to one of the highest parts of the Kaatskill mountains. He was after his favorite sport of squirrel shooting, and the still
solitudes had echoed and re-echoed with the reports of his gun. Panting
and fatigued, he threw himself, late in the afternoon, on a green knoll,
covered with mountain herbage, that crowned the brow of a precipice.
From an opening between the trees, he could overlook all the lower
country for many a mile of rich woodland. He saw at a distance the
lordly Hudson, far, far below him, moving on his silent but majestic
course, with the reflection of a purple cloud, or the sail of a lagging bark,
here and there sleeping on its glassy bottom, and at last losing itself in
the blue highlands.

On the other side he looked down into a deep mountain glen, wild,
lonely, and shagged, the bottom filled with fragments from the impending cliffs, and scarcely lighted by the reflected rays of the setting sun.
For some time Rip lay musing on this scene; evening was gradually
advancing; the mountains began to throw their long, blue shadows over
the valleys; he saw that it would be dark long before he could reach the
village, and he heaved a heavy sigh when he thought of encountering
the terrors of Dame Van Winkle.

As he was about to descend, he heard a voice from a distance, halloo-
ing, "Rip Van Winkle! Rip Van Winkle!" He looked round, but could
see nothing but a crow winging its solitary flight across the mountain.
He thought his fancy must have deceived him, and turned again to
descend, when he heard the same cry ring through the still evening air:
"Rip Van Winkle! Rip Van Winkle!"—at the same time Wolf bristled
up his back, and giving a low growl, skulked to his master's side, looking
fearfully down into the glen. Rip now felt a vague apprehension stealing
over him; he looked anxiously in the same direction, and perceived a
strange figure slowly toiling up the rocks, and bending under the weight
of something he carried on his back. He was surprised to see any human
being in this lonely and unfrequented place; but supposing it to be some
one of the neighborhood in need of his assistance, he hastened down to
yield it.

On nearer approach, he was still more surprised at the singularity of
the stranger's appearance. He was a short, square-built old fellow, with
thick bushy hair, and a grizzled beard. His dress was of the antique
Dutch fashion—a cloth jerkin strapped round the waist—several pair

of breeches, the outer one of ample volume, decorated with rows of buttons down the sides, and bunches at the knees. He bore on his shoulder a stout keg that seemed full of liquor, and made signs for Rip to approach and assist him with the load. Though rather shy and distrustful of this new acquaintance, Rip complied with his usual alacrity; and mutually relieving one another, they clambered up a narrow gully, apparently the dry bed of a mountain torrent. As they ascended, Rip every now and then heard long, rolling peals, like distant thunder, that seemed to issue out of a deep ravine, or rather cleft, between lofty rocks, toward which their rugged path conducted. He paused for an instant, but supposing it to be the muttering of one of those transient thunder showers which often take place in mountain heights, he proceeded. Passing through the ravine, they came to a hollow, like a small amphitheater, surrounded by perpendicular precipices, over the brinks of which impending trees shot their branches, so that you only caught glimpses of the azure sky and the bright evening cloud. During the whole time Rip and his companion had labored on in silence; for though the former marveled greatly what could be the object of carrying a keg of liquor up this wild mountain, yet there was something strange and incomprehensible about the unknown, that inspired awe and checked familiarity.

On entering the amphitheater, new objects of wonder presented themselves. On a level spot in the center was a company of odd-looking personages playing at ninepins. They were dressed in a quaint, outlandish fashion; some wore short doublets, others jerkins, with long knives in their belts, and most of them had enormous breeches of similar style with that of the guide's. Their visages, too, were peculiar: one had a large head, broad face, and small, piggish eyes; the face of another seemed to consist entirely of nose, and was surmounted by a white sugar-loaf hat, set off with a little red cock's tail. They all had beards of various shapes and colors. There was one who seemed to be the commander. He was a stout old gentleman, with a weather-beaten countenance; he wore a laced doublet, broad belt and hanger, high crowned hat and feather, red stockings, and high-heeled shoes, with roses in them. The whole group reminded Rip of the figures in an old Flemish painting, in the parlor of Dominie Van Shaick, the village parson, and which had been brought over from Holland at the time of the settlement.

What seemed particularly odd to Rip was, that, though these folks were evidently amusing themselves, yet they maintained the gravest faces, the most mysterious silence, and were, withal, the most melancholy party of pleasure he had ever witnessed. Nothing interrupted the stillness of the scene but the noise of the balls, which, whenever they were rolled, echoed along the mountains like rumbling peals of thunder.

As Rip and his companion approached them, they suddenly desisted from their play, and stared at him with such fixed, statue-like gaze, and such strange, uncouth, lackluster countenances, that his heart turned within him, and his knees smote together. His companion now emptied the contents of the keg into large flagons, and made signs to him to wait upon the company. He obeyed with fear and trembling; they quaffed the liquor in profound silence, and then returned to their game.

By degrees, Rip's awe and apprehension subsided. He even ventured, when no eye was fixed upon him, to taste the beverage, which he found had much of the flavor of excellent Hollands. He was naturally a thirsty soul, and was soon tempted to repeat the draught. One taste provoked another; and he reiterated his visits to the flagon so often that at length his senses were overpowered, his eyes swam in his head, his head gradually declined, and he fell into a deep sleep.

On waking, he found himself on the green knoll whence he had first seen the old man of the glen. He rubbed his eyes—it was a bright, sunny morning. The birds were hopping and twittering among the bushes, and the eagle was wheeling aloft, and breasting the pure mountain breeze. "Surely," thought Rip, "I have not slept here all night." He recalled the occurrences before he fell asleep. The strange man with a keg of liquor—the mountain ravine—the wild retreat among the rocks—the woe-begone party at ninepins—the flagon—"Oh! that flagon! that wicked flagon!" thought Rip—"what excuse shall I make to Dame Van Winkle?"

He looked round for his gun, but in place of the clean, well-oiled fowling-piece, he found an old firelock lying by him, the barrel incrusted with rust, the lock falling off, and the stock worm-eaten. He now suspected that the grave roisterers of the mountain had put a trick upon him, and, having dosed him with liquor, had robbed him of his gun. Wolf, too, had disappeared, but he might have strayed away after a squirrel or partridge. He whistled after him, and shouted his name, but all in vain; the echoes repeated his whistle and shout, but no dog was to be seen.

He determined to revisit the scene of the last evening's gambol, and if he met with any of the party, to demand his dog and gun. As he rose to walk he found himself stiff in the joints, and wanting in his usual activity "These mountain beds do not agree with me," thought Rip, "and if this frolic should lay me up with a fit of the rheumatism, I shall have a blessed time with Dame Van Winkle!" With some difficulty he got down into the glen; he found the gully up which he and his companion had ascended the preceding evening; but to his astonishment a mountain stream was now foaming down it, leaping from rock to rock, and filling the glen with babbling murmurs. He, however, made shift to scramble up its sides, working his toilsome way through thickets of birch, sassafras, and witch-hazel; and sometimes tripped up or entangled by the wild grapevines that twisted their coils or tendrils from tree to tree, and spread a kind of network in his path.

At length he reached to where the ravine had opened through the cliffs to the amphitheater; but no traces of such opening remained. The rocks presented a high, impenetrable wall, over which the torrent came tumbling in a sheet of feathery foam, and fell into a broad deep basin, black from the shadows of the surrounding forest. Here, then, poor Rip was brought to a stand. He again called and whistled after his dog; he was only answered by the cawing of a flock of idle crows, sporting high in air about a dry tree that overhung a sunny precipice; and who, secure in their elevation, seemed to look down and scoff at the poor man's perplexities. What was to be done? The morning was passing away, and Rip felt famished for want of his breakfast. He grieved to give up his dog and gun; he dreaded to meet his wife; but it would not do to starve among the mountains. He shook his head, shouldered the rusty firelock, and, with a heart full of trouble and anxiety, turned his steps homeward.

As he approached the village he met a number of people, but none whom he knew, which somewhat surprised him, for he had thought himself acquainted with every one in the country round. Their dress, too, was of a different fashion from that to which he was accustomed. They all stared at him with equal marks of surprise, and whenever they cast their eyes upon him, invariably stroked their chins. The constant recurrence of this gesture, induced Rip, involuntarily, to do the same, when, to his astonishment, he found his beard had grown a foot long!

He had now entered the skirts of the village. A troop of strange children ran at his heels, hooting after him, and pointing at his gray beard. The dogs, too, not one of which he recognized for an old acquaintance, barked at him as he passed. The very village was altered; it was larger and more populous. There were rows of houses which he had never seen before, and those which had been his familiar haunts had disappeared. Strange names were over the doors—strange faces at the windows—everything was strange. His mind now misgave him; he began to doubt whether both he and the world around him were not bewitched. Surely this was his native village, which he had left but the day before. There stood the Kaatskill Mountains—there ran the silver Hudson at a distance—there was every hill and dale precisely as it had always been. Rip was sorely perplexed. "That flagon last night," thought he, "has addled my poor head sadly!"

It was with some difficulty that he found the way to his own house, which he approached with silent awe, expecting every moment to hear the shrill voice of Dame Van Winkle. He found the house gone to decay—the roof fallen in, the windows shattered, and the doors off the hinges. A half-starved dog that looked like Wolf was skulking about it. Rip called him by name, but the cur snarled, showed his teeth, and passed on. This was an unkind cut indeed. "My very dog," sighed poor Rip, "has forgotten me!"

He entered the house, which, to tell the truth, Dame Van Winkle had always kept in neat order. It was empty, forlorn, and apparently abandoned. This desolateness overcame all his connubial fears—he called loudly for his wife and children—the lonely chambers rang for a moment with his voice, and then all again was silence.

He now hurried forth, and hastened to his old resort, the village inn—but it, too, was gone. A large, rickety wooden building stood in its place, with great gaping windows, some of them broken and mended with old hats and petticoats, and over the door was painted, "The Union Hotel, by Jonathan Doolittle." Instead of the great tree that used to shelter the quiet little Dutch inn of yore, there now was reared a tall naked pole, with something on the top that looked like a red night-cap, and from it was fluttering a flag, on which was a singular assemblage of stars and stripes;—all this was strange and incomprehensible. He recognized on the sign, however, the ruby face of King George, under which he had smoked so many a peaceful pipe; but even this was singularly metamorphosed. The red coat was changed for one of blue and buff, a sword was held in the hand instead of a scepter, the head was decorated with a cocked hat, and underneath was painted in large characters, GENERAL WASHINGTON.

There was, as usual, a crowd of folk about the door, but none that Rip recollected. The very character of the people seemed changed. There was a busy, bustling disputatious tone about it, instead of the accustomed phlegm and drowsy tranquillity. He looked in vain for the sage Nicholas Vedder, with his broad face, double chin, and fair long pipe, uttering clouds of tobacco smoke instead of idle speeches; or Van Bummel, the schoolmaster, doling forth the contents of an ancient newspaper. In place of these, a lean, bilious-looking fellow, with his pockets full of handbills, was haranguing vehemently about rights of citizens—elections—members of Congress—liberty—Bunker's Hill—heroes of '76—and other words, which were a perfect Babylonish jargon to the bewildered Van Winkle.

The appearance of Rip, with his long grizzled beard, his rusty fowling-piece, his uncouth dress, and an army of women and children at his heels, soon attracted the attention of the tavern politicians. They crowded round him, eying him from head to foot with great curiosity. The orator bustled up to him, and, drawing him partly aside, inquired "On which side he voted?" Rip stared in vacant stupidity. Another short but busy little fellow pulled him by the arm, and, rising on tiptoe, inquired in his ear, "Whether he was Federal or Democrat?" Rip was equally at a loss to comprehend the question; when a knowing, self-important old gentleman, in a sharp cocked hat, made his way through the crowd, putting them to the right and left with his elbows as he passed, and planting himself before Van Winkle, with one arm akimbo, the other resting on his cane, his keen eyes and sharp hat penetrating, as it were, into his very soul, demanded in an austere tone, "What brought him to the election with a gun on his shoulder, and a mob at his heels; and whether he meant to breed a riot in the village?"—"Alas! gentlemen," cried Rip, somewhat dismayed, "I am a poor, quiet man, a native of the place, and a loyal subject of the King, God bless him!"

Here a general shout burst from the by-standers—"A tory! a tory! a spy! a refugee! hustle him! away with him!" It was with great difficulty that the self-important man in the cocked hat restored order; and, having assumed a tenfold austerity of brow, demanded again of the unknown culprit, what he came there for, and whom he was seeking. The poor man humbly assured him that he meant no harm, but merely came there in search of some of his neighbors, who used to keep about the tavern.

"Well—who are they?—name them."

Rip bethought himself a moment, and inquired "Where's Nicholas Vedder?"

There was a silence for a little while, when an old man replied, in a thin, piping voice, "Nicholas Vedder! Why, he is dead and gone these eighteen years! There was a wooden tombstone in the churchyard that used to tell all about him, but that's rotten and gone too."

"Where's Brom Dutcher?"

"Oh, he went off to the army in the beginning of the war; some say he was killed at the storming of Stony Point—others say he was drowned in a squall at the foot of Antony's Nose. I don't know—he never came back again."

"Where's Van Bummel, the schoolmaster?"

"He went off to the wars, too; was a great militia general, and is now in congress."

Rip's heart died away at hearing of these sad changes in his home and friends, and finding himself thus alone in the world. Every answer puzzled him, too, by treating of such enormous lapses of time, and of matters which he could not understand: war—congress—Stony Point— he had no courage to ask after any more friends, but cried out in despair, "Does nobody here know Rip Van Winkle?"

"Oh, Rip Van Winkle!" exclaimed two or three, "oh, to be sure! that's Rip Van Winkle yonder, leaning against the tree."

Rip looked, and beheld a precise counterpart of himself, as he went up the mountain; apparently as lazy, and certainly as ragged. The poor fellow was now completely confounded. He doubted his own identity, and whether he was himself or another man. In the midst of his bewilderment, the man in the cocked hat demanded who he was, and what was his name.

"God knows," exclaimed he, at his wits' end; "I'm not myself—I'm somebody else—that's me yonder—no—that's somebody else got into my shoes—I was myself last night, but I fell asleep on the mountain, and they've changed my gun, and everything's changed, and I'm changed, and I can't tell what's my name, or who I am!"

The bystanders began now to look at each other, nod, wink significantly, and tap their fingers against their foreheads. There was a whisper, also, about securing the gun, and keeping the old fellow from doing mischief, at the very suggestion of which the self-important man in the cocked hat retired with some precipitation. At this critical moment a fresh, comely woman pressed through the throng to get a peep at the gray-bearded man. She had a chubby child in her arms, which, frightened at his looks, began to cry. "Hush, Rip," cried she, "hush, you little fool; the old man won't hurt you." The name of the child, the air of the mother, the tone of her voice, all awakened a train of recollections in his mind. "What is your name, my good woman?" asked he.

"Judith Gardenier."

"And your father's name?"

"Ah, poor man, Rip Van Winkle was his name, but it's twenty years since he went away from home with his gun, and never has been heard of since—his dog came home without him; but whether he shot himself, or was carried away by the Indians, nobody can tell. I was then but a little girl."

Rip had but one question more to ask; but he put it with a faltering voice:

"Where's your mother?"

Oh, she, too, had died but a short time since; she broke a blood vessel in a fit of passion at a New England peddler.

There was a drop of comfort, at least, in this intelligence. The honest man could contain himself no longer. He caught his daughter and her child in his arms. "I am your father!" cried he—"Young Rip Van Winkle once—old Rip Van Winkle now!—Does nobody know poor Rip Van Winkle?"

All stood amazed, until an old woman, tottering out from among the crowd, put her hand to her brow, and peering under it in his face for a moment, exclaimed, "Sure enough! It is Rip Van Winkle—it is himself! Welcome home again, old neighbor. Why, where have you been these twenty long years?"

Rip's story was soon told, for the whole twenty years had been to him but as one night. The neighbors stared when they heard it; some were seen to wink at each other, and put their tongues in their cheeks; and the self-important man in the cocked hat, who, when the alarm was over, had returned to the field, screwed down the corners of his mouth, and shook his head—upon which there was a general shaking of the head throughout the assemblage.

It was determined, however, to take the opinion of old Peter Vanderdonk, who was seen slowly advancing up the road. He was a descendant of the historian of that name, who wrote one of the earliest accounts of the province. Peter was the most ancient inhabitant of the village, and well versed in all the wonderful events and traditions of the neighborhood. He recollected Rip at once, and corroborated his story in the most satisfactory manner. He assured the company that it was a fact, handed down from his ancestor the historian, that the Kaatskill mountains had always been haunted by strange beings. That it was affirmed that the great Hendrick Hudson, the first discoverer of the river and country, kept a kind of vigil there every twenty years, with his crew of the Half-moon; being permitted in this way to revisit the scenes of his enterprise, and keep a guardian eye upon the river and the great city called by his name. That his father had once seen them in their old Dutch dresses playing at ninepins in a hollow of the mountain; and that he himself had heard, one summer afternoon, the sound of their balls, like distant peals of thunder.

To make a long story short, the company broke up and returned to the more important concerns of the election. Rip's daughter took him home to live with her; she had a snug, well-furnished house, and a stout, cheery farmer for a husband, whom Rip recollected for one of the urchins that used to climb upon his back. As to Rip's son and heir, who was the ditto of himself, seen leaning against the tree, he was employed to work on the farm; but evinced an hereditary disposition to attend to anything else but his business.

Rip now resumed his old walks and habits; he soon found many of his former cronies, though all rather the worse for the wear and tear of time; and preferred making friends among the rising generation, with whom he soon grew into great favor.

Having nothing to do at home, and being arrived at that happy age when a man can be idle with impunity, he took his place once more on the bench at the inn door, and was reverenced as one of the patriarchs of the village, and a chronicle of the old times "before the war." It was some time before he could get into the regular track of gossip, or could be made to comprehend the strange events that had taken place during his torpor. How that there had been a revolutionary war—that the country had thrown off the yoke of old England—and that, instead of being a subject of His Majesty, George III., he was now a free citizen of the United States. Rip, in fact, was no politician; the changes of states and empires made but little impression on him; but there was one species of despotism under which he had long groaned, and that was—petticoat government. Happily that was at an end; he had got his neck out of the yoke of matrimony, and could go in and out whenever he pleased, without dreading the tyranny of Dame Van Winkle. Whenever her name was mentioned, however, he shook his head, shrugged his shoulders, and cast up his eyes; which might pass either for an expression of resignation to his fate, or joy at his deliverance.

He used to tell his story to every stranger that arrived at Mr. Doolittle's hotel. He was observed, at first, to vary on some points every time he told it, which was, doubtless, owing to his having so recently awaked. It at last settled down precisely to the tale I have related, and not a man, woman, or child in the neighborhood but knew it by heart. Some always pretended to doubt the reality of it, and insisted that Rip had been out of his head, and that this was one point on which he always remained flighty. The old Dutch inhabitants, however, almost universally gave it full credit. Even to this day they never hear a thunder storm of a summer afternoon about the Kaatskill, but they say Hendrick Hudson and his crew are at their game of ninepins; and it is a common wish of all hen-pecked husbands in the neighborhood, when life hangs heavy on their hands, that they might have a quieting draught out of Rip Van Winkle's flagon.

WANDERING WILLIE'S TALE

By Sir Walter Scott

[Walter Scott (1771–1832) was the son of an Edinburgh lawyer. He, like his father, was educated for the law, in Edinburgh High School and Edinburgh University. Early in life he developed literary interests and ambitions. His legal education got him the important appointments as court clerk and sheriff of his county. In the field of poetry he collected ballads, wrote some of his own, and composed lyric poems and longer romantic narratives in verse. Among the latter are *The Lay of the Last Minstrel*, *The Lady of the Lake*, and *Marmion*. His greatest literary achievement was in the composition of the long series of *Waverley Novels*. Scott amassed a fortune from his writing, and built for himself the extensive Gothic manor house called "Abbotsford" on the bank of the Tweed near the English border. Then he lost his fortune through unwise investments, but succeeded before his death in keeping Abbotsford and paying all his debts.

Scott was old enough to have met Burns and to have distinctly remembered the great Scottish peasant poet. In his time there was no means of publishing short stories—no literary papers or monthly magazines. And since there was practically no demand for short stories, he wrote none. Now and then there was, however, a detached episode not a part of the main story, in one of his novels. The narrative related by Wandering Willie in the novel *Redgauntlet* is such a chapter. It is taken out of the volume and presented here separately as an example of short fiction before the time of Poe and Hawthorne. The story belongs to the same period as James Hogg's *The Mysterious Bride*, William Austin's *Peter Rugg, the Missing Man*, and Washington Irving's *Rip Van Winkle* and the *Legend of Sleepy Hollow*.

Wandering Willie's Tale is from Letter XI of Scott's *Redgauntlet: A Tale of the Eighteenth Century* (1824). The teller of the tale was a wandering fiddler, "Willie Steenson—Wandering Willie—the best fiddler that ever kittled thairm with horse-hair."]

YE maun have heard of Sir Robert Redgauntlet of the ilk, who lived in these parts before the dear years. The country will lang mind him; and our fathers used to draw breath thick if ever they heard him named. He was out wi' the Hielandmen in Montrose's time; and again he was in the hills wi' Glencairn in the saxteen hundred and fifty-twa; and sae when King Charles the Second came in, wha was in sic favor as the Laird of Redgauntlet? He was knighted at Lon'on court, wi' the king's ain sword; and being a red-hot prelatist, he came down here, rampauging like a lion, with commissions of lieutenancy (and of lunacy, for what I ken) to put down a' the Whigs and Covenanters in the country. Wild wark they made of it; for the Whigs were as dour as the Cavaliers were fierce, and it was which should first tire the other. Redgauntlet was aye for the strong hand; and his name is kenn'd as wide in the country as Claverhouse's or Tam Dalyell's. Glen, nor dargle, nor mountain, nor cave, could hide the puir hill-folk when Redgauntlet was out with bugle and bloodhound after them, as if they had been sae mony deer. And troth when they fand them, they didna make muckle mair ceremony than a Hielandman wi' a roebuck. It was just, "Will ye tak the test?" If not, "Make ready—present—fire!"—and there lay the recusant.

Far and wide was Sir Robert hated and feared. Men thought he had a direct compact with Satan; that he was proof against steel, and that bullets happed aff his buff-coat like hailstanes from a hearth; that he had a mear that would turn a hare on the side of Carrifra Gauns*—and muckle to the same purpose, of whilk mair anon. The best blessing they wared on him was, "Deil scowp wi' Redgauntlet!" He wasna a bad maister to his ain folk, though, and was weel aneugh liked by his tenants; and as for the lackies and troopers that rade out wi' him to the persecutions, as the Whigs ca'd those killing-times, they wad hae drunken themsells blind to his health at ony time.

Now you are to ken that my gudesire lived on Redgauntlet's grund; they ca' the place Primrose Knowe. We had lived on the grund, and under the Redgauntlets, since the riding-days, and lang before. It was a pleasant bit; and I think the air is callerer and fresher there than onywhere else in the country. It's a' deserted now; and I sat on the broken door-cheek three days since, and was glad I couldna see the plight the place was in; but that's a' wide o' the mark. There dwelt my gudesire, Steenie Steenson, a rambling, rattling chiel he had been in his young days and could play weel on the pipes; he was famous at "Hoopers and Girders"—a' Cumberland couldna touch him at "Jockie Lattin"—and he had the finest finger for the backlilt between Berwick and Carlisle. The like o' Steenie wasna the sort that they made Whigs o'. And so he became a Tory, as they ca' it, which we now ca' Jacobites, just out of a kind of needcessity, that he might belang to some side or other. He had nae ill-will to the Whig bodies, and liked little to see the blude rin, though, being obliged to follow Sir Robert in hunting and hoisting, watching and warding, he saw muckle mischief, and maybe did some, that he couldna avoid.

Now Steenie was a kind of favorite with his master, and kenn'd a' the folks about the castle, and was often sent for to play the pipes when they were at their merriment. Auld Dougal MacCallum, the butler, that had followed Sir Robert through gude and ill, thick and thin, pool and

*A precipitous side of a mountain in Moffatdale.—[Scott's note.]

stream, was specially fond of the pipes, and aye gae my gudesire his gude word wi' the laird; for Dougal could turn his master round his finger.

Weel, round came the Revolution, and it had like to have broken the hearts baith of Dougal and his master. But the change was not a'the-gither sae great as they feared, and other folk thought for. The Whigs made an unco crawing what they wad do with their auld enemies, and in special wi' Sir Robert Redgauntlet. But there were ower mony great folks dipped in the same doings to mak a spick and span new warld. So Parliament passed it a' ower easy; and Sir Robert, bating that he was held to hunting foxes instead of Covenanters, remained just the man he was.* His revel was as loud, and his hall as weel lighted, as ever it had been, though maybe he lacked the fines of the Nonconformists, that used to come to stock his larder and cellar; for it is certain he began to be keener about the rents than his tenants used to find him before, and they behoved to be prompt to the rent-day, or else the laird wasna pleased. And he was sic an awesome body, that naebody cared to anger him; for the oaths he swore, and the rage that he used to get into, and the looks that he put on, made men sometimes think him a devil incarnate.

Weel, my gudesire was nae manager—no that he was a very great misguider—but he hadna the saving gift, and he got twa terms' rent in arrear. He got the first brash at Whitsunday put ower wi' fair word and piping; but when Martinmas came, there was a summons from the grund-officer to come wi' the rent on a day preceese, or else Steenie behoved to flit. Sair wark he had to get the siller; but he was weel-freended, and at last he got the haill scraped thegither—a thousand merks; the maist of it was from a neighbor they ca'd Laurie Lapraik—a sly tod. Laurie had a walth o' gear—could hunt wi' the hound and rin wi' the hare—and be Whig or Tory, saunt or sinner, as the wind stood. He was a professor in this Revolution warld; but he liked an orra sough of this warld, and a tune on the pipes weel aneugh at a by-time; and abune a', he thought he had gude security for the siller he lent my gude-sire ower the stocking at Primrose Knowe.

Away trots my gudesire to Redgauntlet Castle wi' a heavy purse and a light heart, glad to be out of the laird's danger. Weel, the first thing he learned at the castle was, that Sir Robert had fretted himsell into a fit of the gout, because he did not appear before twelve o'clock. It wasna a'thegither for sake of the money, Dougal thought; but because he didna like to part wi' my gudesire aff the grund. Dougal was glad to see Steenie, and brought him into the great oak parlor, and there sat the

*The caution and moderation of King William III, and his principles of unlimited toleration, deprived the Cameronians of the opportunity they ardently desired, to retaliate the injuries which they had received during the reign of prelacy, and purify the land, as they called it, from the pollution of blood. They esteemed the Revolution, therefore, only a half measure, which neither comprehended the rebuilding the Kirk in its full splendor, nor the revenge of the death of the Saints on their persecutors.—[*Scott's note.*]

laird his leesome lane, excepting that he had beside him a great ill-favored jackanape, that was a special pet of his—a cankered beast it was, and mony an ill-natured trick it played; ill to please it was, and easily angered—ran about the haill castle, chattering and yowling, and pinching and biting folk, especially before ill weather, or disturbances in the state. Sir Robert ca'd it Major Weir, after the warlock that was burnt*; and few folk liked either the name or the conditions of the creature—they thought there was something in it by ordinar—and my gudesire was not just easy in mind when the door shut on him, and he saw himself in the room wi' naebody but the laird, Dougal MacCallum, and the major, a thing that hadna chanced to him before.

Sir Robert sat, or, I should say, lay, in a great armed chair, wi' his grand velvet gown, and his feet on a cradle; for he had baith gout and gravel, and his face looked as gash and ghastly as Satan's. Major Weir sat opposite to him, in a red laced coat, and the laird's wig on his head; and ay as Sir Robert girned wi' pain, the jackanape girned too, like a sheep's-head between a pair of tangs—an ill-faur'd, fearsome couple they were. The laird's buff-coat was hung on a pin behind him, and his broadsword and his pistols within reach; for he keepit up the auld fashion of having the weapons ready, and a horse saddled day and night, just as he used to do when he was able to loup on horseback, and away after ony of the hill-folk he could get speerings of. Some said it was for fear of the Whigs taking vengeance, but I judge it was just his auld custom—he wasna gien to fear onything. The rental-book, wi' its black cover and brass clasps, was lying beside him; and a book of sculduddry sangs was put betwixt the leaves, to keep it open at the place where it bore evidence against the goodman of Primrose Knowe, as behind the hand with his mails and duties. Sir Robert gave my gudesire a look as if he would have withered his heart in his bosom. Ye maun ken he had a way of bending his brows that men saw the visible mark of a horseshoe in his forehead, deep-dinted, as if it had been stamped there.

"Are ye come light-handed, ye son of a toom whistle?" said Sir Robert. "Zounds! if you are—"

My gudesire, with as gude a countenance as he could put on, made a leg, and placed the bag of money on the table wi' a dash, like a man that does something clever. The laird drew it to him hastily. "Is it all here, Steenie, man?"

"Your honor will find it right," said my gudesire.

"Here, Dougal," said the laird, "gie Steenie a tass of brandy downstairs, till I count the siller and write the receipt."

But they werena weel out of the room, when Sir Robert gied a yelloch that garr'd the castle rock. Back ran Dougal—in flew the livery-men—yell on yell gied the laird, ilk ane mair awfu' than the ither. My gude-

*A celebrated wizard, executed at Edinburgh for sorcery and other crimes.—[*Scott's note.*]

sire knew not whether to stand or flee, but he ventured back into the parlor, where a' was gaun hirdie-girdie—naebody to say "come in" or "gae out." Terribly the laird roared for cauld water to his feet, and wine to cool his throat; and "Hell, hell, hell, and its flames," was aye the word in his mouth. They brought him water, and when they plunged his swoln feet into the tub, he cried out it was burning; and folk say that it *did* bubble and sparkle like a seething cauldron. He flung the cup at Dougal's head, and said he had given him blood instead of burgundy; and, sure aneugh, the lass washed clotted blood aff the carpet the neist day. The jackanape they ca'd Major Weir, it jibbered and cried as if it was mocking its master. My gudesire's head was like to turn: he forgot baith siller and receipt, and downstairs he banged; but as he ran, the shrieks came faint and fainter; there was a deep-drawn shivering groan, and word gaed through the castle that the laird was dead.

Weel, away came my gudesire, wi' his finger in his mouth, and his best hope was that Dougal had seen the money-bag, and heard the laird speak of writing the receipt. The young laird, now Sir John, came from Edinburgh to see things put to rights. Sir John and his father never gree'd weel. Sir John had been bred an advocate, and afterwards sat in the last Scots Parliament and voted for the Union, having gotten, it was thought, a rug of the compensations; if his father could have come out of his grave he would have brained him for it on his awn hearthstane. Some thought it was easier counting with the auld rough knight than the fair-spoken young ane—but mair of that anon.

Dougal MacCallum, poor body, neither grat nor graned, but gaed about the house looking like a corpse, but directing, as was his duty, a' the order of the grand funeral. Now, Dougal looked aye waur and waur when night was coming, and was aye the last to gang to his bed, whilk was in a little round just opposite the chamber of dais, whilk his master occupied while he was living, and where he now lay in state, as they ca'd it, weel-a-day! The night before the funeral, Dougal could keep his awn counsel nae langer: he came doun with his proud spirit, and fairly asked auld Hutcheon to sit in his room with him for an hour. When they were in the round, Dougal took ae tass of brandy to himsell and gave another to Hutcheon, and wished him all health and lang life, and said that, for himsell, he wasna lang for this world; for that, every night since Sir Robert's death, his silver call had sounded from the state chamber, just as it used to do at nights in his lifetime, to call Dougal to help to turn him in his bed. Dougal said that, being alone with the dead on that floor of the tower (for naebody cared to wake Sir Robert Redgauntlet like another corpse), he had never daured to answer the call, but that now his conscience checked him for neglecting his duty; for, "though death breaks service," said MacCallum, "it shall never break my service to Sir Robert; and I will answer his next whistle, so be you will stand by me, Hutcheon."

Hutcheon had nae will to the wark, but he had stood by Dougal in battle and broil, and he wad not fail him at this pinch; so down the carles sat ower a stoup of brandy, and Hutcheon, who was something of a clerk, would have read a chapter of the Bible; but Dougal would hear naething but a blaud of Davie Lindsay, whilk was the waur preparation.

When midnight came, and the house was quiet as the grave, sure aneugh the silver whistle sounded as sharp and shrill as if Sir Robert was blowing it, and up got the twa auld serving-men and tottered into the room where the dead man lay. Hutcheon saw aneugh at the first glance; for there were torches in the room, which showed him the foul fiend in his ain shape, sitting on the laird's coffin! Ower he couped as if he had been dead. He could not tell how lang he lay in a trance at the door, but when he gathered himsell he cried on his neighbor, and getting nae answer, raised the house, when Dougal was found lying dead within twa steps of the bed where his master's coffin was placed. As for the whistle, it was gaen anes and aye; but mony a time was it heard at the top of the house on the bartizan, and amang the auld chimneys and turrets, where the howlets have their nests. Sir John hushed the matter up, and the funeral passed over without mair bogle-wark.

But when a' was ower, and the laird was beginning to settle his affairs, every tenant was called up for his arrears, and my gudesire for the full sum that stood against him in the rental-book. Weel, away he trots to the castle, to tell his story, and there he is introduced to Sir John, sitting in his father's chair, in deep mourning, with weepers and hanging cravat, and a small walking rapier by his side, instead of the auld broadsword that had a hundred weight of steel about it, what with blade, chape, and basket-hilt. I have heard their communing so often ower, that I almost think I was there mysell, though I couldna be born at the time. (In fact, Alan, my companion mimicked, with a good deal of humor, the flattering, conciliating tone of the tenant's address, and the hypocritical melancholy of the laird's reply. His grandfather, he said, had, while he spoke, his eye fixed on the rental-book, as if it were a mastiff-dog that he was afraid would spring up and bite him.)

"I wuss ye joy, sir, of the head seat, and the white loaf, and the braid lairdship. Your father was a kind man to friends and followers: muckle grace to you, Sir John, to fill his shoon—his boots, I suld say, for he seldom wore shoon, unless it were muils when he had the gout."

"Ay, Steenie," quoth the laird, sighing deeply, and putting his napkin to his een, "his was a sudden call, and he will be missed in the country; no time to set his house in order: weel prepared Godward, no doubt, which is the root of the matter, but left us behind a tangled hesp to wind, Steenie. Hem! hem! We maun go to business, Steenie; much to do, and little time to do it in."

Here he opened the fatal volume. I have heard of a thing they call Doomsday Book—I am clear it has been a rental of backganging tenants.

"Stephen," said Sir John, still in the same soft, sleekit tone of voice—"Stephen Stevenson, or Steenson, ye are down here for a year's rent behind the hand, due at last term."

Stephen. "Please your honor, Sir John, I paid it to your father."

Sir John. "Ye took a receipt, then, doubtless, Stephen; and can produce it?"

Stephen. "Indeed I hadna time, an it like your honor; for nae sooner had I set down the siller, and just as his honor, Sir Robert, that's gaen, drew it till him to count it, and write out the receipt, he was ta'en wi' the pains that removed him."

"That was unlucky," said Sir John, after a pause. "But ye maybe paid it in the presence of somebody. I want but a *talis qualis* evidence, Stephen. I would go ower strictly to work with no poor man."

Stephen. "Troth, Sir John, there was naebody in the room but Dougal MacCallum, the butler. But, as your honor kens, he has e'en followed his auld master."

"Very unlucky again, Stephen," said Sir John, without altering his voice a single note. "The man to whom ye paid the money is dead; and the man who witnessed the payment is dead too; and the siller, which should have been to the fore, is neither seen nor heard tell of in the repositories. How am I to believe a' this?"

Stephen. "I dinna ken, your honor; but there is a bit memorandum note of the very coins—for, God help me! I had to borrow out of twenty purses—and I am sure that ilka man there set down will take his grit oath for what purpose I borrowed the money."

Sir John. "I have little doubt ye *borrowed* the money, Steenie. It is the *payment* to my father that I want to have some proof of."

Stephen. "The siller maun be about the house, Sir John. And since your honor never got it, and his honor that was canna have ta'en it wi' him, maybe some of the family may have seen it."

Sir John. "We will examine the servants, Stephen; that is but reasonable."

But lackey and lass, and page and groom, all denied stoutly that they had ever seen such a bag of money as my gudesire described. What was waur, he had unluckily not mentioned to any living soul of them his purpose of paying his rent. Ae quean had noticed something under his arm, but she took it for the pipes.

Sir John Redgauntlet ordered the servants out of the room, and then said to my gudesire, "Now, Steenie, ye see ye have fair play; and, as I have little doubt ye ken better where to find the siller than ony other body, I beg, in fair terms, and for your own sake, that you will end this fasherie; for, Stephen, ye maun pay or flit."

"The Lord forgie your opinion," said Stephen, driven almost to his wit's end—"I am an honest man."

"So am I, Stephen," said his honor; "and so are all the folks in the house, I hope. But if there be a knave amongst us, it must be he that tells the story he cannot prove." He paused, and then added, mair sternly, "If I understand your trick, sir, you want to take advantage of some malicious reports concerning things in this family, and particularly respecting my father's sudden death, thereby to cheat me out of the money, and perhaps take away my character, by insinuating that I have received the rent I am demanding. Where do you suppose this money to be? I insist upon knowing."

My gudesire saw everything look sae muckle against him that he grew nearly desperate; however, he shifted from one foot to another, looked to every corner of the room, and made no answer.

"Speak out, sirrah," said the laird, assuming a look of his father's—a very particular ane, which he had when he was angry: it seemed as if the wrinkles of his frown made that selfsame fearful shape of a horse's shoe in the middle of his brow—"speak out, sir! I *will* know your thoughts. Do you suppose that I have this money?"

"Far be it frae me to say so," said Stephen.

"Do you charge any of my people with having taken it?"

"I wad be laith to charge them that may be innocent," said my gudesire; "and if there be any one that is guilty, I have nae proof."

"Somewhere the money must be, if there is a word of truth in your story," said Sir John; "I ask where you think it is—and demand a correct answer!"

"In hell, if you *will* have my thoughts of it," said my gudesire, driven to extremity "in hell! with your father, his jackanape, and his silver whistle."

Down the stairs he ran, for the parlor was nae place for him after such a word, and he heard the laird swearing blood and wounds behind him, as fast as ever did Sir Robert, and roaring for the bailie and the baron-officer.

Away rode my gudesire to his chief creditor, him they ca'd Laurie Lapraik, to try if he could make onything out of him; but when he tauld his story, he got but the warst word in his wame—thief, beggar, and dyvour were the saftest terms; and to the boot of these hard terms, Laurie brought up the auld story of his dipping his hand in the blood of God's saunts, just as if a tenant could have helped riding with the laird, and that a laird like Sir Robert Redgauntlet. My gudesire was by this time far beyond the bounds of patience, and while he and Laurie were at deil speed the liars, he was wanchancie aneugh to abuse Lapraik's doctrine as weel as the man, ond said things that garr'd folks' flesh grue that heard them; he wasna just himsell, and he had lived wi' a wild set in his day.

At last they parted, and my gudesire was to ride hame through the wood of Pitmurkie, that is a' fou of black firs, as they say. I ken the wood, but the firs may be black or white for what I can tell. At the entry of the wood there is a wild common, and on the edge of the common a little lonely change-house, that was keepit then by a hostler-wife—they suld hae ca'd her Tibbie Faw—and there puir Steenie cried for a mutchkin of brandy, for he had had no refreshment the haill day. Tibbie was earnest wi' him to take a bite o' meat, but he couldna think o't, nor would he take his foot out of the stirrup, and took off the brandy wholely at twa draughts, and named a toast at each—the first was, the memory of Sir Robert Redgauntlet, and might he never lie quiet in his grave till he had righted his poor bond-tenant; and the second was, a health to Man's Enemy, if he would but get him back the pock of siller, or tell him what came o't, for he saw the haill world was like to regard him as a thief and a cheat, and he took that waur than even the ruin of his house and hauld.

On he rode, little caring where. It was a dark night turned, and the trees made it yet darker, and he let the beast take its ain road through the wood; when, all of a sudden, from tired and wearied that it was before, the nag began to spring, and flee, and stend, that my gudesire could hardly keep the saddle; upon the whilk, a horseman ,suddenly riding up beside him, said, "That's a mettle beast of yours, freend; will you sell him?" So saying, he touched the horse's neck with his riding-wand, and it fell into its auld heigh-ho of a stumbling trot. "But his spunk's soon out of him, I think," continued the stranger, "and that is like mony a man's courage, that thinks he wad do great things till he come to the proof."

My gudesire scarce listened to this, but spurred his horse, with "Gude e'en to you, freend."

But it's like the stranger was ane that doesna lightly yield his point; for, ride as Steenie liked, he was aye beside him at the selfsame pace. At last my gudesire, Steenie Steenson, grew half angry, and, to say the truth, half feared.

"What is it that ye want with me, freend?" he said. "If ye be a robber, I have nae money; if ye be a leal man, wanting company, I have nae heart to mirth or speaking; and if ye want to ken the road, I scarce ken it mysell."

"If you will tell me your grief," said the stranger, "I am one that, though I have been sair misca'd in the world, am the only hand for helping my freends."

So my gudesire, to ease his ain heart, mair than from any hope of help, told him the story from beginning to end.

"It's a hard pinch," said the stranger; "but I think I can help you."

"If you could lend the money, sir, and take a lang day—I ken nae other help on earth," said my gudesire.

"But there may be some under the earth," said the stranger. "Come, I'll be frank wi' you; I could lend you the money on bond, but you would maybe scruple my terms. Now, I can tell you that your auld laird is disturbed in his grave by your curses, and the wailing of your family, and if ye daur venture to go to see him, he will give you the receipt."

My gudesire's hair stood on end at this proposal, but he thought his companion might be some humorsome chield that was trying to frighten him, and might end with lending him the money. Besides, he was bauld wi' brandy, and desperate wi' distress; and he said he had courage to go to the gate of hell, and a step farther, for that receipt.

The stranger laughed.

Weel, they rode on through the thickest of the wood, when, all of a sudden, the horse stopped at the door of a great house; and, but that he knew the place was ten miles off, my father would have thought he was at Redgauntlet Castle. They rode into the outer courtyard, through the muckle faulding yetts, and aneath the auld portcullis; and the whole front of the house was lighted, and there were pipes and fiddles, and as much dancing and deray within as used to be at Sir Robert's house at Pace and Yule, and such high seasons. They lap off, and my gudesire, as seemed to him, fastened his horse to the very ring he had tied him to that morning, when he gaed to wait on the young Sir John.

"God!" said my gudesire, "if Sir Robert's death be but a dream!"

He knocked at the ha' door just as he was wont, and his auld acquaintance, Dougal MacCallum—just after his wont, too,—came to open the door, and said, "Piper Steenie, are ye there, lad? Sir Robert has been crying for you."

My gudesire was like a man in a dream; he looked for the stranger, but he was gane for the time. At last he just tried to say, "Ha! Dougal Driveower, are ye living? I thought ye had been dead."

"Never fash yoursell wi' me," said Dougal, "but look to yoursell; and see ye tak naething frae onybody here, neither meat, drink, or siller, except just the receipt that is your ain."

So saying, he led the way through halls and trances that were weel kenn'd to my gudesire, and into the auld oak parlor; and there was as much singing of profane sangs, and birling of red wine, and speaking blasphemy and sculduddry, as had ever been in Redgauntlet Castle when it was at the blythest.

But, Lord take us in keeping! what a set of ghastly revellers they were that sat around that table! My gudesire kenn'd mony that had long before gane to their place, for often had he piped to the most part in the hall of Redgauntlet. There was the fierce Middleton, and the dissolute Rothes, and the crafty Lauderdale; and Dalyell, with his bald head and a beard to his girdle; and Earlshall, with Cameron's blude on his hand; and wild Bonshaw, that tied blessed Mr. Cargill's limbs till the blude sprung; and Dumbarton Douglas, the twice-turned traitor baith to country and king. There was the Bluidy Advocate MacKenyie, who, for his worldly wit and wisdom, had been to the rest as a god. And there was Claverhouse, as beautiful as when he lived, with his long, dark, curled locks streaming down over his laced buff-coat, and his left hand always on the right spule-blade, to hide the wound that the silver bullet had made. He sat apart from them all, and looked at them with a melancholy, haughty countenance; while the rest hallooed, and sang, and laughed, that the room rang. But their smiles were fearfully contorted from time to time; and their laughter passed into such wild sounds as made my gudesire's very nails grow blue, and chilled the marrow in his banes.

They that waited at the table were just the wicked servingmen and troopers that had done their work and cruel bidding on earth. There was the Lang Lad of the Nethertown, that helped to take Argyle; and the bishop's summoner, that they called the Deil's Rattle-bag; and the wicked guardsmen in their laced coats; and the savage Highland Amorites, that shed blood like water; and mony a proud serving-man, haughty of heart and bloody of hand, cringing to the rich, and making them wickeder than they would be; grinding the poor to powder, when the rich had broken them to fragments. And mony, mony mair were coming and ganging, a' as busy in their vocation as if they had been alive.

Sir Robert Redgauntlet, in the midst of a' this fearful riot, cried, wi' a voice like thunder, on Steenie Piper to come to the board-head where he was sitting, his legs stretched out before him, while the great broadsword rested against his chair, just as my gudesire had seen him the last time upon earth—the very cushion for the jackanape was close to him, but the creature itself was not there—it wasna its hour, it's likely; for he heard them say as he came forward, "Is not the major come yet?" And another answered, "The jackanape will be here betimes the morn." And when my gudesire came forward, Sir Robert, or his ghaist, or the deevil in his likeness, said, "Weel, piper, hae ye settled wi' my son for the year's rent?"

With much ado my father gat breath to say that Sir John would not settle without his honor's receipt.

"Ye shall hae that for a tune of the pipes, Steenie," said the appearance of Sir Robert. "Play us up, 'Weel hoddled, Luckie.'"

Now this was a tune my gudesire learned frae a warlock, that heard it when they were worshipping Satan at their meetings, and my gudesire had sometimes played it at the ranting suppers in Redgauntlet Castle, but never very willingly; and now he grew cauld at the very name of it, and said, for excuse, he hadna his pipes wi' him.

"MacCallum, ye limb of Beelzebub," said the fearfu' Sir Robert, "bring Steenie the pipes that I am keeping for him!"

MacCallum brought a pair of pipes might have served the piper of Donald of the Isles. But he gave my gudesire a nudge as he offered them; and looking secretly and closely, Steenie saw that the chanter was of steel, and heated to a white heat; so he had fair warning not to trust his fingers with it. So he excused himself again, and said he was faint and frightened, and had not wind aneugh to fill the bag.

"Then ye maun eat and drink, Steenie," said the figure; "for we do little else here; and it's ill speaking between a fou man and a fasting."

Now these were the very words that the bloody Earl of Douglas said to keep the king's messenger in hand, while he cut the head off MacLellan of Bombie, at the Threave Castle, and that put Steenie mair and mair on his guard. So he spoke up like a man, and said he came neither to eat, or drink, or make minstrelsy, but simply for his ain—to ken what was come o' the money he had paid, and to get a discharge for it; and he was so stout-hearted by this time that he charged Sir Robert for conscience' sake (he had no power to say the holy name), and as he hoped for peace and rest, to spread no snares for him, but just to give him his ain.

The appearance gnashed its teeth and laughed, but it took from a large pocket-book the receipt, and handed it to Steenie. "There is your receipt, ye pitiful cur; and for the money, my dog-whelp of a son may go look for it in the Cat's Cradle."

My gudesire uttered mony thanks, and was about to retire when Sir Robert roared aloud, "Stop though, thou sack-doudling son of a whore! I am not done with thee. Here we do nothing for nothing; and you must return on this very day twelvemonth to pay your master the homage that you owe me for my protection."

My father's tongue was loosed of a suddenty, and he said aloud, "I refer mysell to God's pleasure, and not to yours."

He had no sooner uttered the word than all was dark around him, and he sank on the earth with such a sudden shock, that he lost both breath and sense.

How lang Steenie lay there, he could not tell; but when he came to himsell, he was lying in the auld kirkyard of Redgauntlet parochine, just at the door of the family aisle, and the scutcheon of the auld knight, Sir Robert, hanging over his head. There was a deep morning fog on grass and gravestane around him, and his horse was feeding quietly beside the minister's twa cows. Steenie would have thought the whole was a dream, but he had the receipt in his hand, fairly written and signed by the auld laird; only the last letters of his name were a little disorderly, written like one seized with sudden pain.

Sorely troubled in his mind, he left that dreary place, rode through the mist to Redgauntlet Castle, and with much ado he got speech of the laird.

"Well, you dyvour bankrupt," was the first word, "have you brought me my rent?"

"No," answered my gudesire, "I have not; but I have brought your honor Sir Robert's receipt for it."

"How, sirrah? Sir Robert's receipt! You told me he had not given you one."

"Will your honor please to see if that bit line is right?"

Sir John looked at every line, and at every letter, with much attention, and at last at the date, which my gudesire had not observed—"From my appointed place,' he read, "this twenty-fifth of November."

"What! That is yesterday! Villain, thou must have gone to Hell for this!"

"I got it from your honor's father; whether he be in Heaven or Hell, I know not," said Steenie.

"I will delate you for a warlock to the Privy Council!" said Sir John. "I will send you to your master, the devil, with the help of a tar-barrel and a torch!"

"I intend to delate mysell to the Presbytery," said Steenie, "and tell them all I have seen last night, whilk are things fitter for them to judge of than a borrel man like me."

Sir John paused, composed himsell, and desired to hear the full history; and my gudesire told it him from point to point, as I have told it you—word for word, neither more nor less.

Sir John was silent again for a long time, and at last he said, very composedly, "Steenie, this story of yours concerns the honor of many a noble family besides mine; and if it be a leasing-making, to keep yourself out of my danger, the least you can expect is to have a red-hot iron driven through your tongue, and that will be as bad as scauding your fingers wi' a red-hot chanter. But yet it may be true, Steenie; and if the money cast up, I shall not know what to think of it. But where shall we find the Cat's Cradle? There are cats enough about the old house, but I think they kitten without the ceremony of bed or cradle."

"We were best ask Hutcheon," said my gudesire; "he kens a' the odd corners about as weel as—another serving-man that is now gane, and that I wad not like to name."

Aweel, Hutcheon, when he was asked, told them that a ruinous turret lang disused, next to the clock-house, only accessible by a ladder, for the opening was on the outside, and far above the battlements, was called of old the Cat's Cradle.

"There will I go immediately," said Sir John; and he took (with what purpose, Heaven kens) one of his father's pistols from the hall-table, where they had lain since the night he died, and hastened to the battlements.

It was a dangerous place to climb, for the ladder was auld and frail, and wanted ane or twa rounds. However, up got Sir John, and entered at the turret door, where his body stopped the only little light that was in the bit turret. Something flees at him wi' a vengeance, maist dang him back ower—bang! gaed the knight's pistol, and Hutcheon, that held the ladder, and my gudesire that stood beside him, hears a loud skelloch. A minute after, Sir John flings the body of the jackanape down to them, and cries that the siller is fund, and that they should come up and help him. And there was the bag of siller sure aneugh, and mony orra thing besides that had been missing for mony a day. And Sir John when he had riped the turret weel, led my gudesire into the dining-parlor, and took him by the hand, and spoke kindly to him, and said he was sorry he should have doubted his word, and that he would hereafter be a good master to him, to make amends.

"And now, Steenie," said Sir John, "although this vision of yours tends, on the whole, to my father's credit, as an honest man, that he should, even after his death, desire to see justice done to a poor man like you, yet you are sensible that ill dispositioned men might make bad constructions upon it, concerning his soul's health. So, I think, we had better lay the haill dirdum on the ill-deedie creature, Major Weir, and say naething about your dream in the wood of Pitmurkie. You had taken ower muckle brandy to be very certain about onything; and, Steenie, this receipt (his hand shook while he held it out), it's but a queer kind of document, and we will do best, I think, to put it quietly in the fire."

"Od, but for as queer as it is, it's a' the voucher I have for my rent," said my gudesire, who was afraid, it may be, of losing the benefit of Sir Robert's discharge.

"I will bear the contents to your credit in the rental-book, and give you a discharge under my own hand," said Sir John, "and that on the spot. And, Steenie, if you can hold your tongue about this matter, you shall sit, from this term downward, at an easier rent."

"Mony thanks to your honor," said Steenie, who saw easily in what corner the wind was; "doubtless I will be conformable to all your honor's commands; only I would willingly speak wi' some powerful minister on the subject, for I do not like the sort of soumons of appointment whilk your honor's father—"

"Do not call the phantom my father!" said Sir John, interrupting him.

"Weel, then, the thing that was so like him," said my gudesire; "he spoke of my coming back to see him this time twelve-month, and it's a weight on my conscience."

"Aweel, then," said Sir John, "if you be so much distressed in mind, you may speak to our minister of the parish; he is a douce man, regards the honor of our family, and the mair that he may look for some patronage from me."

Wi' that, my gudesire readily agreed that the receipt should be burnt, and the laird threw it into the chimney with his ain hand. Burn it would not for them, though; but away it flew up the lum, wi' a lang train of sparks at its tail, and a hissing noise like a squib.

My gudesire gaed down to the manse, and the minister, when he had heard the story, said it was his real opinion that, though my gudesire had gaen very far in tampering with dangerous matters, yet, as he had refused the devil's arles (for such was the offer of meat and drink), and had refused to do homage by piping at his bidding, he hoped, that if he held a circumspect walk hereafter, Satan could take little advantage by what was come and gane. And, indeed, my gudesire, of his ain accord, lang forswore baith the pipes and the brandy—it was not even till the year was out, and the fatal day past, that he would so much as take the fiddle, or drink usquebaugh or tippenny.

Sir John made up his story about the jackanape as he liked himsell; and some believe till this day there was no more in the matter than the filching nature of the brute. Indeed, ye'll no hinder some to threap that it was nane o' the Auld Enemy that Dougal and Hutcheon saw in the laird's room, but only that wanchancie creature, the major, capering on the coffin; and that, as to the blawing on the laird's whistle that was heard after he was dead, the filthy brute could do that as weel as the laird himself, if no better. But Heaven kens the truth, whilk first came out by the minister's wife, after Sir John and her ain gudeman were baith in the molds. And then, my gudesire, wha was failed in his limbs, but not in his judgment or memory—at least nothing to speak of—was obliged to tell the real narrative to his freends for the credit of his good name. He might else have been charged for a warlock.

The shades of evening were growing thicker around us as my conductor finished his long narrative with this moral—"Ye see, birkie, it is nae chancy thing to tak a stranger traveler for a guide, when ye are in an uncouth land."

"I should not have made that inference," said I. "Your grandfather's adventure was fortunate for himself, whom it saved from ruin and distress; and fortunate for his landlord also, whom it prevented from committing a gross act of injustice."

"Ay, but they had baith to sup the sauce o't sooner or later," said Wandering Willie. "What was fristed wasna forgiven. Sir John died before he was much over threescore; and it was just like of a moment's illness. And for my gudesire, though he departed in fullness of years, yet there was my father, a yauld man of forty-five, fell down betwixt the stilts of his pleugh, and raise never again, and left nae bairn but me, a puir sightless, fatherless, motherless creature, could neither work nor want. Things gaed weel aneugh at first; for Sir Redwald Redgauntlet, the only son of Sir John, and the oye of auld Sir Robert, and, wae's me! the last of the honorable house, took the farm aff our hands, and brought me into his household to have care of me. He liked music, and I had the best teachers baith England and Scotland could gie me. Mony a merry year was I wi' him; but wae's me! he gaed out with other pretty men in the Forty-five——I'll say nae mair about it. My head never settled weel since I lost him; and if I say another word about it, deil a bar will I have the heart to play the night. Look out, my gentle chap," he resumed in a different tone, "ye should see the lights at Brokenburn Glen by this time."

THE PISTOL SHOT

By *Alexander Pushkin*

[Alexander Pushkin (1799–1837) accomplished a great deal in a short life of only thirty-eight years. He is among the first of the modern Russian literary men. Early in life he was recognized as a poet. He is best known for three pieces of literary composition: a novel in verse called *Eugene Onegin*, from which the modern opera has been made; *The Queen of Spades*, the story later turned into an opera by Tschaikovsky; and a dramatic chronicle *Boris Godunov*, the basis of Mussorgsky's opera of that name. Stories and tales were considered as his less significant work, but even in these pieces one is aware of his realism, his wish to represent life as it is. Pushkin was unhappily married, and was killed in a duel over his wife.

The Pistol Shot was first published in 1830. The version that follows is after Prosper Mérimeé's translation into French.]

I

"We fired at each other."—Bariatynski.
"I vowed to kill him, according to the code of duelling, and I still have my shot to fire."—A Night on Guard.

WE were in camp in the village of ——. Everyone knows the life of an officer of the line: in the morning drill and horseback exercise; then comes dinner with the colonel of the regiment, or else at the Jewish restaurant; and at night drinks and cards. At ——, there were no entertainments of any kind, for no one had a marriageable daughter to bring out. We spent our time in each other's quarters, and at our evening gatherings there were uniforms only.

However, there was one man in our set who was not a soldier. He must have been about thirty-five and consequently we looked upon him as quite old. His experience had great weight with us, and besides his reserve, his grand air and sarcastic manner made a deep impression on us young men. There seemed to be something mysterious about his life. He looked like a Russian, though he bore a foreign name. In days gone by he had been in a regiment of Hussars where he was quite prominent at one time; but suddenly he had sent in his resignation, no one knew why, and had retired to this poor out-of-the-way village, where he fared very badly, while at the same time spending much money. He always wore a shabby overcoat and still he kept open house where every officer was made welcome. To tell the truth, his dinners generally consisted of two or three simple dishes prepared by his servant, an old discharged soldier, but the champagne always flowed. No one knew anything of his circumstances or his means, and no one dared ask him any questions on the subject. There were plenty of books in his house—mostly military—and a few novels. He lent them willingly and never asked for them again; on the other hand, he never returned those he borrowed. His one pastime was pistol shooting. The walls of his room were riddled with bullets, giving it the appearance of a honeycomb. A rich collection of pistols was the only luxury to be seen in the miserable house he occupied. The accuracy of his aim was remarkable, and if he had taken a bet that he could shoot the pompon on a helmet, not one of us would have hesitated to put the helmet on. Sometimes we talked of duelling, but Silvio (I will give him that name) never opened his lips on the subject. If someone asked him had he ever fought a duel, he answered shortly that he had, and that was all; he never entered into any particulars and it was evident that he disliked being asked such questions. We surmised that the death of one of his victims had left a blight on his life. Never for a minute would any of us have thought that he could have been guilty of faint-heartedness. There are some people whose very appearance precludes such an idea.

One day eight or ten of our officers were dining at Silvio's. We drank as much as usual, that is, excessively. When dinner was over, we begged of our host to take the bank in a game of faro. After refusing to do so, for he seldom played, he finally called for cards and laying fifty ducats on the table before him, he sat down and shuffled. We formed in a circle about him and the game began. When playing Silvio never uttered a word, neither objecting nor explaining. If a player made a mistake, he paid out exactly the amount due him or else credited it to himself. We were all familiar with his manner of playing and always let him have his own way. But on the day I speak of, there was with us an officer newly arrived who, through absent-mindedness, doubled his stakes on a certain card. Silvio took the chalk and marked down what was due him. The officer, convinced that there was a mistake, made some objections. Silvio, still mute, went on dealing as if he had not heard. The officer, out of patience by this time, took the brush and wiped off the figures. Silvio picked up the chalk and wrote them down again. At this, the officer, excited by the wine, by the play and the laughter of his comrades, and thinking he had been insulted, took up a brass candlestick and hurled it at Silvio, who by bending aside, averted the blow. Great was the uproar! Silvio rose, pale with rage, and with eyes blazing:

"My dear sir," he said, "you will please leave this room, and be thankful that this has happened in my house."

Not one of us doubted the outcome of this fray, and we all looked upon our new comrade as a dead man. The officer went out saying he was ready to meet the banker just as soon as it was convenient. The game proceeded a few minutes longer, but it was evident that the master of the house was not paying much attention to what was going on; we all left, one by one, and returned to our quarters discussing the while the vacancy in our ranks which was sure to take place.

Next morning, while at riding exercise, we all wondered if the poor lieutenant were dead or alive, when, to our surprise, he appeared among us. We plied him with questions and he answered that he had had no challenge from Silvio, which caused us all much surprise. We called on Silvio and found him in his yard, firing bullet after bullet at an ace nailed to the door. He received us in his usual manner, never mentioning the scene of the night before. Three days went by and the lieutenant was still alive. We kept saying to each other: "Will Silvio not fight?" amazed at such a thing. But Silvio did not fight. He simply gave a very lame explanation and that was all that was said.

This forbearance on his part did him much harm among us young men. A want of courage is never quite forgiven by youth, for to him fearlessness is the greatest quality one can possess and it excuses many faults. Still, after a while, all this was forgotten and by degrees Silvio regained his old ascendency over us.

I, alone, could never feel the same toward him. Being of a romantic turn of mind, I had loved this man, whose life was an enigma to us all, more than anyone else, and I had made him, in my thoughts, the hero of some mysterious drama. And he liked me, of this I felt sure, for when we were alone, dropping his sharp and sarcastic speeches, he would converse on all sorts of subjects, and unbend to me in a fascinating manner. Ever since that unlucky evening I speak of, the fact that he had been insulted and had not wiped out the offence in blood, worried me to such an extent that I never could feel at ease with him as in the days gone by. I even avoided looking at him, and Silvio was too clever and quick not to notice and guess at the reason. He seemed to me to feel it deeply. On two occasions, I thought I detected a wish on his part to explain matters, but I avoided him and he did not follow me. After that I never saw him except when others were present, and we never again resumed our intimate talks.

Those happy mortals, who live in cities where there is so much to see and do, can never imagine how important certain small happenings can become in an out-of-the-way village or town. One of these is the arrival of the mail. Tuesdays and Fridays, the offices of our regiment were besieged with men. One expected money, another a letter, and again others looked for newspapers. As a rule, everything was opened and read on the spot; news was given and the improvised post-office was full of animation. Silvio's letters were addressed in care of our regiment and he called for them with us. One day a letter was handed to him, the seal of which he broke hurriedly. While reading it his eyes flashed with suppressed excitement. None of the officers but myself noticed this, as they were all busy reading their own letters.

"Gentlemen," said Silvio, "business compels me to leave town immediately. I must go tonight. I hope none of you will refuse to dine with me for the last time. I will expect you," said he, turning to me pointedly. "I hope you will not disappoint me."

After saying which he went away in great haste, and we all retired to our own quarters, agreeing to meet at his house later.

I arrived at Silvio's at the hour he had named and found almost the whole regiment there. Everything he possessed was packed and the bare walls riddled with bullets stared back at us. We sat down to dinner and our host was in such a jovial mood that before long we were all in the greatest of spirits. Corks flew about; the froth rose in our glasses which we refilled as rapidly as they emptied. We all felt great affection for our host and wished him a pleasant journey with joy and prosperity at the end of it. It was very late when we got up from the table and while we were all picking out our caps in the hall, Silvio took me by the hand and detained me as I was about to leave.

"I must speak to you," he said in a low tone.

So I remained after the others went away and, seated facing each other, we smoked our pipes in silence for a while. Silvio seemed worried, and there was no trace of the feverish gaiety he had displayed in the earlier part of the evening. This dreadful pallor, the brilliancy of his eyes and the long puffs of smoke he blew from his mouth gave him the appearance of a fiend. After a few minutes he broke the silence.

"It may be," he said, "that we will never see each other again; before we part, I wish to explain certain things to you. You have noticed, perhaps, that I attach very little importance to the average man's opinion, but I like you and I feel I cannot leave without seeing you think better of me than you do."

He stopped to shake the ashes out of his pipe. I remained silent and avoided looking at him.

"It may have seemed strange to you," he continued, "that I did not ask any satisfaction from that drunkard, that young fool R——. You will admit that, having the choice of weapons, he was at my mercy and that there was not much chance of his killing me. I might call it generosity on my part, but I will not lie about it. If I could have given R—— a good lesson, without in any way risking my life, he would not have been rid of me so easily."

I looked at Silvio in the greatest surprise. Such an admission from him was astounding. He went on:

"As it is, unhappily, I have no right to risk my life. Six years ago, I received a blow and the man who struck me is still alive."

This excited my curiosity to an unusual degree.

"You did not meet him?" I asked. "Surely some extraordinary circumstance must have prevented your doing so?"

"I did meet him," answered Silvio, "and here you see the result of our encounter."

He rose and drew from a box near him a cap of red cloth with a gilt braid and tassel such as Frenchmen call *bonnet de police*. He put it on his head and I saw that a bullet had pierced it about an inch above the forehead.

"You know," said Silvio, "that I was in the Hussars of——, and you also know what kind of a disposition I have: I like to rule everyone. Well, in my youth, it was positively a passion with me. In my day, brawlers were in fashion and I was the foremost brawler of the regiment. To get drunk was then considered a thing to be proud of; I could outdrink the famous B——, celebrated in song by D. D——. Every day brought its duel, and every day saw me either the principal actor in one or else taking the part of a second. My comrades looked up to me, and our superior officers, who were constantly being transferred, considered me a plague of which they could not be rid.

"As for me, I kept on quietly (or rather riotously) in my glorious career, when one day there was transferred to our regiment a young fellow who was very wealthy and of good family. I will not name him to you, but never have I met a fellow with such unheard-of luck. Imagine having youth, a fine figure, no end of spirits, a daring which was utterly indifferent to danger, a great name, and unlimited means to do with as he liked, and you may have a faint idea of the impression he created among us. My power was gone in an instant. At first, dazzled by my reputation, he tried to make friends with me; but I received his advances very coldly, seeing which, he quietly dropped me without showing any annoyance whatever. I took such a dislike to him, when I saw his popularity in the regiment and his success with the ladies, that I was driven almost to despair. I tried to pick a quarrel with him, but to my sarcastic remarks he answered with caustic and unexpected wit that had the merit besides of being more cheerful than mine. He was always in jest, while I was in dead earnest. Finally one night, while at a ball in a Polish house, seeing how much the ladies admired him, especially our hostess with whom I had been very friendly, I whispered in his ear some insulting remark which I have long since forgotten. He turned around and struck me. We grasped our swords, some of the ladies fainted, and a few officers parted us. We went out immediately to fight it out right then and there.

"The three witnesses and myself reached the meeting-place, and I awaited the coming of my adversary with no ordinary impatience. The sun rose, and its intense heat was being felt more and more every minute when I finally saw him coming in the distance. He was on foot and in his shirt sleeves, carrying his uniform over his arm—he was attended by only one witness. I went forward to meet him, and I noticed that his cap, which he carried in his hand, was full of cherries. Our witnesses placed us twelve paces from each other. It was my privilege to shoot first, but what with passion and hatred blinding me I feared my aim would be poor, and to gain time to steady my hand, I offered to let him fire first. He refused to do so, and it was then agreed we would leave it to chance. Luck was, as usual, with this spoilt child of fortune. He fired and pierced my cap. It was now my turn, and I felt he was at my mercy. I looked at him with eagerness, hoping to find him at least a little uneasy. Not at all, for there he stood, within range of my pistol, coolly picking the ripest cherries out of his cap and blowing the pits in my direction where they fell at my feet.

"'What will I gain,' thought I, 'by taking his life, when he thinks so little of it?'

"A diabolical thought crossed my mind. I unloaded a pistol.

"'It seems,' I said, 'that you care very little whether you die or not at the present moment. You seem more anxious to breakfast instead. It will be as you please. I have no wish to disturb you.'

"'You will be kind enough to attend to your own business,' answered he, 'and to please fire, . . . but after all you may do as you like. You can always fire your shot when and where you like. I will always be at your call.'

"I went away with my witnesses to whom I said that I did not care to shoot just then, and the thing ended there.

"I sent in my resignation and retired to this out-of-the-way village. From that day to this, I have thought of nothing but revenge. And now, the time has come. . .!"

Silvio drew from his pocket the letter received that morning. Some-one, his lawyer it seemed, had written from Moscow that the *person in question* was soon to be married to a young and pretty girl.

"You can guess, I have no doubt," said Silvio, "who is *the person in question*. I am leaving for Moscow and we will see if he will look at death in the midst of bridal festivities with as much coolness as he did when facing it with a pound of cherries in his cap!"

After saying these words he rose and, throwing his cap viciously on the floor, he walked back and forth the length of the room like a caged tiger. I had listened to him without saying a word, stirred by very contradictory feelings.

A servant entered saying the carriage was at the door. Silvio grasped my hand, which he shook with all his might. He entered a small open carriage where were two boxes already, one containing his pistols and the other his luggage. We said good-bye once more, and he was driven away.

II

YEARS went by, when family matters compelled me to live in an obscure village in the district of ——. While looking after my interests, I often sighed for the enjoyable life I had led until then. The long solitary evenings of winter and spring were the hardest to bear. I could not become reconciled to their lonesomeness. Until the dinner hour I managed somehow to kill time by chatting with the starosty [Polish landowner], visiting my workmen and watching the new buildings being erected. But as soon as night came I was at a loss to know what to do. I knew by heart the few books I had found in the ancient bookcases and in the garret. All the stories known to my old housekeeper, Kirilovna, I had asked her to tell me over and over again, and the songs of the peasants saddened me. I drank everything at hand, soft drinks and others, until my head ached. I will even admit that at one time I thought I should become a drunkard from sheer desperation, the worst kind of drunkard, of which this district offered me a good many examples.

My nearest neighbors consisted of two or three of these confirmed inebriates, whose conversations were forever interspersed with sighs and hiccoughs, so that even complete solitude was to be preferred to their society. I finally got into the habit of dining as late as possible and retiring as early as I could afterward, and in that way I solved the problem of shortening the evenings and lengthening the days.

About four versts from my house was a beautiful property belonging to the Countess B———. It was occupied by her steward, the Countess herself never having lived in the place but a month at a time, and that in the first year of her marriage.

One day, in the second year of this lonely existence of mine, I heard that the Countess and her husband were to occupy their residence during the summer months. In the early part of June, they arrived with all their household.

The coming of a rich neighbor is always an event in the life of country people. The owners of property and their servants also speak of it two months before they arrive, and it is still a topic of interest three years after they have left. For my part, the fact that a young and pretty woman would live so near upset me very much. I was dying to see her, and the first Sunday after they were settled, I walked over after dinner to pay my respects to the lady and introduce myself as her nearest neighbor and her devoted slave.

A footman led me to the Count's library and left to announce me. This library was large and magnificently furnished. Against the walls were shelves filled with books, and on each one was a figure in bronze; above a marble mantelpiece stood a large mirror. The floor was covered with green cloth over which were thrown rich Persian rugs. Unused as I was in my hovel to any kind of luxury, it was so long since I had seen anything like this display of wealth that I actually felt timid and experienced inward tremblings while waiting for the Count, such as a country solicitor might feel when asking an audience of a minister. The door opened and a young man, about thirty-two years of age, entered. He greeted me in a most cordial and charming manner. I tried to appear at ease and was just going to make the usual commonplace remarks about being delighted at having such neighbors when he forestalled me by saying how welcome I was.

We sat down and his manner was so cordial that it soon dispelled my unusual timidity. I was just beginning to feel like my old self again when the Countess appeared in the doorway, and once more I grew desperately shy. She was a beauty. The Count introduced me and the more I tried to be natural and quite at ease, the more I looked awkward and embarrassed. My hosts, in order to give me time to recover from my bashfulness, chatted together, as if to show that they considered me an old acquaintance already and one to be treated as such, so that while walking about the library I looked at the books and pictures. As far as pictures are concerned, I am no connoisseur, but there was one there that attracted my attention. It represented a Swiss scene, and the beauty of the landscape did not attract me quite as much as did the fact that the canvas was pierced by two bullets evidently fired one on the other.

"That is a pretty good shot!" I cried, turning toward the Count.

"Yes," said he, "and rather a peculiar one. Are you a pistol shot?" he added.

"Why yes, a fairly good one," I answered, delighted to have a chance to speak of something with which I was familiar. "I think I could hit a card at thirty paces, with my own pistols of course."

"Really?" said the Countess, seemingly much interested. "And you, my dear," this to her husband, "could you hit a card at thirty paces?"

"I don't know about that," answered the Count, "I was a pretty good shot in my day, but it must be four years now since I used a pistol."

"In that case, sir," I continued, "I'll bet you anything that even at twenty paces you could not hit a card; because to excel at pistol-shooting one requires constant practice. I know this from experience. At home, I was considered one of the best shots in the regiment, but it happened once that I was a month without using a pistol, mine being at the gunsmith's. We were called to the shooting-gallery one day, and what do you think happened to me, sir? I missed a bottle standing twenty-five paces away, four times in succession. There was with us at the time a major of cavalry, a good fellow, who was forever joking: 'Faith, my friend,' he said to me, 'this is too much moderation. You have too great a respect for the bottle.' Believe me, sir, one must practise all the time. Otherwise, one gets rusty. The best marksman I ever knew practised every day, firing at least three shots before his dinner; he would no more have missed them than he would have omitted his cognac before dinner."

Both the Count and his wife seemed pleased to listen to me.

"And how did he shoot?" asked the Count.

"How? Let me tell you. He would see a fly on the wall. . . . You laugh? Madam——, I swear to you this is true. 'Eh! Kouska! a pistol!' Kouska would bring one loaded. Crack! there lay the fly flattened against the wall."

"What consummate skill!" cried the Count, "and what was this man's name?"

"Silvio, sir."

"Silvio!" cried the Count, starting to his feet. "You have known Silvio?"

"Have I known him? Well, rather. We were the greatest of friends; he was like one of us in the regiment. But it is five years now since I heard of him. And you also knew him?"

"Yes, I knew him well. Did he ever tell you a peculiar thing which happened to him once?"

"How he received a slap in the face, one evening, from a cad?"

"And did he tell you the name of this cad?"

"No, sir, he did not. Ah!" I cried, guessing at the truth. "Forgive me, sir, I did not know. Can it be you?"

"Yes, it was I," answered the Count, in an embarrassed manner, "and that picture with a hole in it is a souvenir of our last interview."

"For God's sake, my dear," said the Countess, "don't speak of it— the thought of it terrifies me to this day."

"No," said the Count. "I feel I ought to tell this gentleman. He knows how I offended his friend and it is only fair that he should learn how he revenged himself."

The Count drew an armchair for me to sit in, and I listened with the greatest interest to the following story:

"Five years ago we were married. We spent the first month of our honeymoon here in this house, and to it clings the memory of the happiest days of my life, coupled with one of the most painful experiences I have ever had.

"One evening, we had both gone out horseback riding. My wife's horse became very restless and she was so frightened that she begged me to lead him to the stables and she would walk back by herself. On reaching the house, I found a travelling coach at the door and was told that a man was waiting in the library. He had refused to give his name, saying he wished to see me on business. I came into this room and in the half light I saw a man with a beard standing before the mantel-piece, still in his dusty travelling clothes. I drew nearer to him, trying to place him in my memory.

"'You do not remember me, Count?' said he, in a voice that shook.

"'Silvio!' I cried.

"And to be candid with you, I felt as if my hair were standing on end.

"'Exactly,' he continued, 'and it is my turn to shoot. I have come to fire. Are you ready?'"

"I saw a pistol sticking out of his left pocket. I measured twelve paces and stood there in that corner, begging him to be quick about it, as my wife would return in a few moments. He said he wanted a light first, and I rang for candles.

"I closed the door after giving orders not to admit anyone, and once more I told him to proceed. He raised his pistol and took aim. . . . I was counting the seconds. . . . I was thinking of her. . . . All this lasted a full minute and suddenly Silvio lowered his weapon.

"'I am very sorry,' he said, 'but my pistol is not loaded with cherry pits . . . and bullets are hard. . . . After all, come to think of it, this does not look much like a duel. It is more like a murder. I am not in the habit of firing on an unarmed man. Let us begin all over again. Let us draw lots to see who will shoot first.'

"My head was in a whirl, and it turns out that I refused at first. Finally, we loaded our pistols and we put two papers in the very cap I had once perforated with a bullet. I took one of the papers and as luck would have it, I drew number one.

"'You are devilish lucky, Count!' said he, with a smile I will never forget.

"I cannot to this day understand it, but he finally compelled me to fire, . . . and my bullet hit that picture there."

The Count pointed to the landscape with the hole in it. His face was crimson. There was the Countess as white as a sheet, and as for me I barely suppressed a cry.

"I fired at him," continued the Count, "and thank God, I missed him.

"Then Silvio—at that moment he was positively hideous—stood back and took aim. Just then, the door opened. My wife came in and seeing us facing each other, threw herself in my arms. Her presence gave me back my courage.

"'My dear,' I said, 'do you not see that we are only jesting? How frightened you are! Go now, get a glass of water and come back to us. I will then introduce my old friend and comrade to you.'

"But my wife knew better than to believe my words.

"'Tell me, is what my husband says true?' she asked of the terrible Silvio. 'Is it true that this is only a jest?'

"'He is always jesting, Madam,' replied Silvio. 'Once upon a time he gave me a slap, in jest; again, in jest, he pierced my cap with a bullet, and a few minutes ago, still jesting, he just missed me. Now it is my turn to laugh a little.'

"Saying which, he took aim once more, with my wife looking on. She fell on her knees at his feet.

"'Get up, Masha!' I cried enraged. 'Are you not ashamed of yourself! And you, sir, do you wish to drive this poor woman crazy? Will you please fire, yes or no?'

"'I will not,' answered Silvio, 'I am satisfied. I saw you falter. You were pale with fright, and that is all I hoped to see. I compelled you to fire on me and I know you will never forget me. I leave you to your conscience.'

"He walked toward the door and turning round, he glanced at the picture with the bullet hole and without aiming at all, he fired, and doubled my shot. Then he went out. My wife fainted—none of the servants dared stop him, and the doors opened before him in great haste. On the porch he called for his carriage, and he was already some distance when I recovered from my bewilderment."

The Count stopped.

It was thus I heard the end of a story, the beginning of which interested me much. I have never seen Silvio. It was said that at the time of the insurrection of Alexander Ypsilanti, he was at the head of a regiment of rebels and that he was killed when their army was routed at Skouliani.

LIGEIA

By Edgar Allan Poe

[Edgar Allan Poe (1809–1849) was the son of an actor and an actress, both of whom died when he was a child. He was adopted by John Allan, a business man of wealth, of Richmond, Virginia. Mr. Allan had Poe educated in private schools in Richmond and in England. As a young man he was a student in the University of Virginia and the Military Academy at West Point, but left both before graduating. His life was a series of unfortunate episodes due largely to lack of stability of character. He began to write very early, publishing *Tamerlane and Other Poems* in 1827; but he did not reach the height of his fame until he wrote *The Raven* (1845). Both before and after this he wrote both prose and verse. His prose was either critical essays or fantastic tales.

Ligeia was first published in the *American Museum* at Baltimore(1838) and was later included in the famous collection, *Tales of the Grotesque and Arabesque* (Philadelphia, 1840).]

And the will therein lieth, which dieth not. Who knoweth the mysteries of the will, with its vigor? For God is but a great will pervading all things by nature of its intentness. Man doth not yield himself to the angels, nor unto death utterly, save only through the weakness of his feeble will.—JOSEPH GLANVILL.

I CANNOT, for my soul, remember how, when, or even precisely where, I first became acquainted with the lady Ligeia. Long years have since elapsed, and my memory is feeble through much suffering. Or, perhaps, I cannot *now* bring these points to mind, because in truth the character of my beloved, her rare learning, her singular yet placid cast of beauty, and the thrilling and enthralling eloquence of her low musical language, made their way into my heart by paces so steadily and stealthily progressive that they have been unnoticed and unknown. Yet I believe that I met her first and most frequently in some large, old, decaying city near the Rhine. Of her family I have surely heard her speak. That it is of a remotely ancient date cannot be doubted. Ligeia! Ligeia! Buried in studies of a nature more than all else adapted to deaden impressions of the outward world, it is by that sweet word alone—by Ligeia—that I bring before mine eyes in fancy the image of her who is no more. And now, while I write, a recollection flashes upon me that I have *never known* the paternal name of her who was my friend and my betrothed, and who became the partner of my studies, and finally the wife of my bosom. Was it a playful charge on the part of my Ligeia? or was it a test of my strength of affection, that I should institute no inquiries upon this point? or was it rather a caprice of my own—a wildly romantic offering on the shrine of the most passionate devotion? I but indistinctly recall the fact itself—what wonder that I have utterly forgotten the circumstances which originated or attended it? And, indeed, if ever that spirit which is entitled *Romance*—if ever she, the wan and the misty-winged Ashtophet of idolatrous Egypt, presided, as they tell, over marriages ill-omened, then most surely she presided over mine.

There is one dear topic, however, on which my memory fails me not. It is the *person* of Ligeia. In stature she was tall, somewhat slender, and, in her latter days, even emaciated. I would in vain attempt to portray the majesty, the quiet ease, of her demeanor, or the incomprehensible lightness and elasticity of her footfall. She came and departed as a shadow. I was never made aware of her entrance into my closed study, save by the dear music of her low sweet voice, as she placed her marble hand upon my shoulder. In beauty of face no maiden ever equaled her. It was the radiance of an opium-dream—an airy and spirit-lifting vision more wildly divine than the fantasies which hovered about the slumbering souls of the daughters of Delos. Yet her features were not of that regular mold which we have been falsely taught to worship in the classical labors of the heathen. "There is no exquisite beauty," says Bacon, Lord Verulam, speaking truly of all the forms and genera of beauty, "without some *strangeness* in the proportion." Yet, although I saw that the features of Ligeia were not of a classic regularity—although I perceived that her loveliness was indeed "exquisite," and felt that there was much of "strangeness" pervading it, yet I have tried in vain to detect the irregularity and to trace home my own perception of "the strange." I examined the contour of the lofty and pale forehead: it was faultless—how cold indeed that word when applied to a majesty so divine!—the skin rivaling the purest ivory, the commanding extent and repose, the gentle prominence of the regions above the temples; and then the raven-black, the glossy, the luxuriant and naturally-curling tresses, setting forth the full force of the Homeric epithet, "hyacinthine!" I looked at the delicate outlines of the nose—and nowhere but in the graceful medallions of the Hebrews had I beheld a similar perfection. There were the same luxurious smoothness of surface, the same scarcely perceptible tendency to the aquiline, the same harmoniously curved nostrils speaking the free spirit. I regarded the sweet mouth. Here was indeed the triumph of all things heavenly—the magnificent turn of the short upper lip—the soft, voluptuous slumber of the under—the dimples which sported, and the color which spoke—the teeth glancing back, with a brilliancy almost startling, every ray of the holy light which fell upon them in her serene and placid, yet most exultingly radiant of all smiles. I scrutinized the formation of the chin: and here, too, I found the gentleness of breadth, the softness and the majesty, the fulness and spirituality, of the Greek—the contour which the god Apollo revealed but in a dream to Cleomenes, the son of the Athenian. And then I peered into the large eyes of Ligeia.

For eyes we have no models in the remotely antique. It might have been, too, that in these eyes of my beloved lay the secret to which Lord Verulam alludes. They were, I must believe, far larger than the ordinary eyes of our own race. They were even fuller than the fullest of the gazelle eyes of the tribe of the valley of Nourjahad. Yet it was only at intervals—in moments of intense excitement—that this peculiarity became more than slightly noticeable in Ligeia. And at such moments was her beauty—in my heated fancy thus it appeared perhaps—the beauty of beings either above or apart from the earth, the beauty of the fabulous Houri of the Turk. The hue of the orbs was the most brilliant of black, and, far over them, hung jetty lashes of great length. The brows, slightly irregular in outline, had the same tint. The "strangeness," however, which I found in the eyes, was of a nature distinct from the formation, or the color, or the brilliancy of the features, and must, after all, be referred to the *expression.* Ah, word of no meaning! behind whose vast latitude of mere sound we intrench our ignorance of so much of the spiritual. The expression of the eyes of Ligeia! How for long hours have I pondered upon it! How have I, through the whole of a midsummer night, struggled to fathom it! What was it—that something more profound than the well of Democritus—which lay far within the pupils of my beloved? What *was* it? I was possessed with a passion to discover. Those eyes! those large, those shining, those divine orbs! they became to me twin stars of Leda, and I to them devoutest of astrologers.

There is no point, among the many incomprehensible anomalies of the science of mind, more thrillingly exciting than the fact—never, I believe, noticed in the schools—that in our endeavors to recall to memory something long forgotten, we often find ourselves *upon the very verge* of remembrance, without being able, in the end, to remember. And thus how frequently, in my intense scrutiny of Ligeia's eyes, have I felt approaching the full knowledge of their expression—felt it approaching, yet not quite be mine, and so at length entirely depart! And (strange, oh, strangest mystery of all!) I found, in the commonest objects of the universe, a circle of analogies to that expression. I mean to say that, subsequently to the period when Ligeia's beauty passed into my spirit, there dwelling as in a shrine, I derived, from many existences in the material world, a sentiment such as I felt always around, within me, by her large and luminous orbs. Yet not the more could I define that sentiment, or analyze, or even steadily view it. I recognized it, let me repeat, sometimes in the survey of a rapidly-growing vine—in the contemplation of a moth, a butterfly, a chrysalis, a stream of running water. I have felt it in the ocean; in the falling of a meteor. I have felt it in the glances of unusually aged people. And there are one or two stars in heaven (one especially, a star of the sixth magnitude, double and changeable, to be found near the large star in Lyra), in a telescopic scrutiny of which I have been made aware of the feeling. I have been filled with it by certain sounds from stringed instruments, and not unfrequently by passages from books. Among innumerable other instances, I well remember something in a volume of Joseph Glanvill, which (perhaps merely from its quaintness—who shall say?) never failed to inspire me with the sentiment: "And the will therein lieth, which dieth not. Who knoweth the mysteries of the will, with its vigor? For God is but a great will pervading all things by nature of its intentness. Man doth not yield himself to the angels, nor unto death utterly, save only through the weakness of his feeble will."

Length of years and subsequent reflection have enabled me to trace, indeed, some remote connection between this passage in the English moralist and a portion of the character of Ligeia. An *intensity* in thought, action, or speech, was possibly, in her, a result, or at least an index, of that gigantic volition which, during our long intercourse, failed to give other and more immediate evidence of its existence. Of all the women whom I have ever known, she, the outwardly calm, the ever-placid Ligeia, was the most violently a prey to the tumultuous vultures of stern passion. And of such passion I could form no estimate, save by the miraculous expansion of those eyes which at once so delighted and appalled me—by the almost magical melody, modulation, distinctness, and placidity of her very low voice—and by the fierce energy (rendered doubly effective by contrast with her manner of utterance) of the wild words which she habitually uttered.

I have spoken of the learning of Ligeia: it was immense—such as I have never known in woman. In the classical tongues was she deeply proficient; and as far as my own acquaintance extended in regard to the modern dialects of Europe, I have never known her at fault. Indeed upon any theme of the most admired, because simply the most abstruse, of the boasted erudition of the academy, have I *ever* found Ligeia at fault? How singularly, how thrillingly, this one point in the nature of my wife has forced itself, at this late period only, upon my attention! I said her knowledge was such as I have never known in woman—but where breathes the man who has traversed, and successfully, *all* the wide areas of moral, physical, and mathematical science? I saw not then what I now clearly perceive, that the acquisitions of Ligeia were gigantic, were astounding; yet I was sufficiently aware of her infinite supremacy to resign myself, with a child-like confidence, to her guidance through the chaotic world of metaphysical investigation at which I was most busily occupied during the earlier years of our marriage. With how vast a triumph, with how vivid a delight, with how much of all that is ethereal in hope, did I *feel*, as she bent over me in studies but little sought—but less known, that delicious vista by slow degrees expanding before me, down whose long, gorgeous, and all untrodden path, I might at length pass onward to the goal of a wisdom too divinely precious not to be forbidden!

How poignant, then, must have been the grief with which, after some years, I beheld my well-grounded expectations take wings to themselves and fly away! Without Ligeia I was but as a child groping benighted. Her presence, her readings alone, rendered vividly luminous the many mysteries of the transcendentalism in which we were immersed. Wanting the radiant luster of her eyes, letters, lambent and golden, grew duller than Saturnian lead. And now those eyes shone less and less frequently upon the pages over which I pored. Ligeia grew ill. The wild eyes blazed with a too—too glorious effulgence; the pale fingers became of the transparent waxen hue of the grave; and the blue veins upon the lofty forehead swelled and sank impetuously with the tides of the most gentle emotion. I saw that she must die—and I struggled desperately in spirit with the grim Azrael. And the struggles of the passionate wife were, to my astonishment, even more energetic than my own. There had been much in her stern nature to impress me with the belief that, to her, death would have come without its terrors; but not so. Words are impotent to convey any just idea of the fierceness of resistance with which she wrestled with the Shadow. I groaned in anguish at the pitiable spectacle. I would have soothed—I would have reasoned; but, in the intensity of her wild desire for life—for life—*but* for life—solace and reason were alike the uttermost of folly. Yet not until the last instance, amid the most convulsive writhings of her fierce spirit, was shaken the external placidity of her demeanor. Her voice grew more gentle—grew more low—yet I would not wish to dwell upon the wild meaning of the quietly uttered words. My brain reeled as I hearkened, entranced, to a melody more than mortal—to assumptions and aspirations which mortality had never before known.

That she loved me I should not have doubted; and I might have been easily aware that, in a bosom such as hers, love would have reigned no ordinary passion. But in death only was I fully impressed with the strength of her affection. For long hours, detaining my hand, would she pour out before me the overflowing of a heart whose more than passionate devotion amounted to idolatry. How had I deserved to be so blessed by such confessions? how had I deserved to be so cursed with the removal of my beloved in the hour of her making them? But upon this subject I cannot bear to dilate. Let me say only, that in Ligeia's more than womanly abandonment to a love, alas! all unmerited, all unworthily bestowed, I at length recognized the principle of her longing, with so wildly earnest a desire, for the life which was now fleeing so rapidly away. It is this wild longing, it is this eager vehemence of desire for life—*but* for life—that I have no power to portray, no utterance capable of expressing.

At high noon of the night in which she departed, beckoning me peremptorily to her side, she bade me repeat certain verses composed by herself not many days before. I obeyed her. They were these:

> Lo! 't is a gala night
>   Within the lonesome latter years.
> An angel throng, bewinged, bedight
>   In veils, and drowned in tears,
> Sit in a theater to see
>   A play of hopes and fears,
> While the orchestra breathes fitfully
>   The music of the spheres.
>
> Mimes, in the form of God on high,
>   Mutter and mumble low,
> And hither and thither fly;
>   Mere puppets they, who come and go
> At bidding of vast formless things
>   That shift the scenery to and fro,
> Flapping from out their condor wings
>   Invisible Woe.
>
> That motley drama—oh, be sure
>   It shall not be forgot!
> With its Phantom chased for evermore,
>   By a crowd that seize it not,
> Through a circle that ever returneth in
>   To the self-same spot;
> And much of Madness, and more of Sin,
>   And Horror the soul of the plot.
>
> But see, amid the mimic rout
>   A crawling shape intrude:
> A blood-red thing that writhes from out
>   The scenic solitude!
> It writhes—it writhes! with mortal pangs
>   The mimes become its food,
> And seraphs sob at vermin fangs
>   In human gore imbued.
>
> Out—out are the lights—out all!
>   And over each quivering form

The curtain, a funeral pall,
Comes down with the rush of a storm,
While the angels, all pallid and wan,
Uprising, unveiling, affirm
That the play is the tragedy, "Man,"
And its hero, the Conqueror Worm.

"O God!" half shrieked Ligeia, leaping to her feet and extending her arms aloft with a spasmodic movement, as I made an end of these lines—"O God! O Divine Father! shall these things be undeviatingly so? shall this conqueror be not once conquered? Are we not part and parcel in Thee? Who—who knoweth the mysteries of the will with its vigor? 'Man doth not yield him to the angels, *nor unto death utterly*, save only through the weakness of his feeble will.'"

And now, as if exhausted with emotion, she suffered her white arms to fall, and returned solemnly to her bed of death. And as she breathed her last sighs, there came mingled with them a low murmur from her lips. I bent to them my ear, and distinguished, again, the concluding words of the passage in Glanvill: "*Man doth not yield himself to the angels, nor unto death utterly, save only through the weakness of his feeble will.*"

She died: and I, crushed into the very dust with sorrow, could no longer endure the lonely desolation of my dwelling in the dim and decaying city by the Rhine. I had no lack of what the world calls wealth. Ligeia had brought me far more, very far more, than ordinarily falls to the lot of mortals. After a few months, therefore, of weary and aimless wandering, I purchased, and put in some repair, an abbey, which I shall not name, in one of the wildest and least frequented portions of fair England. The gloomy and dreary grandeur of the building, the almost savage aspect of the domain, the many melancholy and time-honored memories connected with both, had much in unison with the feelings of utter abandonment which had driven me into that remote and unsocial region of the country. Yet although the external abbey, with its verdant decay hanging about it, suffered but little alteration, I gave way with a child-like perversity, and perchance with a faint hope of alleviating my sorrows, to a display of more than regal magnificence within. For such follies, even in childhood, I had imbibed a taste, and now they came back to me as if in the dotage of grief. Alas, I feel how much even of incipient madness might have been discovered in the gorgeous and fantastic draperies, in the solemn carvings of Egypt, in the wild cornices and furniture, in the Bedlam patterns of the carpets of tufted gold! I had become a bounden slave in the trammels of opium, and my labors and my orders had taken a coloring from my dreams. But these absurdities I must not pause to detail. Let me speak only of that one chamber ever accursed, whither, in a moment of mental alienation, I led from the altar as my bride—as the successor of the unforgotten Ligeia—the fair-haired and blue-eyed Lady Rowena Trevanion, of Tremaine.

There is no individual portion of the architecture and decoration of that bridal chamber which is not now visibly before me. Where were the souls of the haughty family of the bride, when, through thirst of gold, they permitted to pass the threshold of an apartment *so* bedecked, a maiden and a daughter so beloved? I have said that I minutely remember the details of the chamber—yet I am sadly forgetful on topics of deep moment; and here there was no system, no keeping, in the fantastic display, to take hold upon the memory. The room lay in a high turret of the castellated abbey, was pentagonal in shape, and of capacious size. Occupying the whole southern face of the pentagon was the sole window—an immense sheet of unbroken glass from Venice—a single pane, and tinted of a leaden hue, so that the rays of either the sun or moon, passing through it, fell with a ghastly luster on the objects within. Over the upper portion of this huge window extended the trellis-work of an aged vine, which clambered up the massy walls of the turret. The ceiling, of gloomy-looking oak, was excessively lofty, vaulted, and elaborately fretted with the wildest and most grotesque specimens of a semi-Gothic, semi-Druidical device. From out the most central recess of this melancholy vaulting depended, by a single chain of gold with long links, a huge censer of the same metal, Saracenic in pattern, and with many perforations so contrived that there writhed in and out of them, as if endued with a serpent vitality, a continual succession of party-colored fires.

Some few ottomans and golden candelabra, of Eastern figure, were in various stations about; and there was the couch, too—the bridal couch—of an Indian model, and low, and sculptured of solid ebony, with a pall-like canopy above. In each of the angles of the chamber stood on end a gigantic sarcophagus of black granite, from the tombs of the kings over against Luxor, with their aged lids full of immemorial sculpture. But in the draping of the apartment lay, alas! the chief fantasy of all. The lofty walls, gigantic in height, even unproportionably so, were hung from summit to foot, in vast folds, with a heavy and massive-looking tapestry—tapestry of a material which was found alike as a carpet on the floor, as a covering for the ottomans and the ebony bed, as a canopy for the bed, and as the gorgeous volutes of the curtains which partially shaded the window. The material was the richest cloth of gold. It was spotted all over, at irregular intervals, with arabesque figures, about a foot in diameter, and wrought upon the cloth in patterns of the most jetty black. But these figures partook of the true character of the arabesque only when regarded from a single point of view. By a contrivance now common, and indeed traceable to a very remote period of antiquity, they were made changeable in aspect. To one entering the room, they bore the appearance of simple monstrosities; but upon a farther advance, this appearance gradually departed; and, step by step, as the visitor moved his station in the chamber, he saw himself surrounded by an endless succession of the ghastly forms which belong to the superstition of the Norman, or arise in the guilty slumbers of the monk. The phantasmagoric effect was vastly heightened by the artificial introduction of a strong continual current of wind behind the draperies, giving a hideous and uneasy animation to the whole.

In halls such as these, in a bridal chamber such as this, I passed, with the Lady of Tremaine, the unhallowed hours of the first month of our marriage—passed them with but little disquietude. That my wife dreaded the fierce moodiness of my temper—that she shunned me, and loved me but little—I could not help perceiving; but it gave me rather pleasure than otherwise. I loathed her with a hatred belonging more to demon than to man. My memory flew back (oh, with what intensity of regret!) to Ligeia, the beloved, the august, the beautiful, the entombed. I reveled in recollections of her purity, of her wisdom, of her lofty, her ethereal nature, of her passionate, her idolatrous love. Now, then, did my spirit fully and freely burn with more than all the fires of her own. In the excitement of my opium dreams (for I was habitually fettered in the shackles of the drug), I would call aloud upon her name, during the silence of the night, or among the sheltered recesses of the glens by day, as if, through the wild eagerness, the solemn passion, the consuming ardor of my longing for the departed, I could restore her to the pathway she had abandoned—ah, *could* it be forever?—upon the earth.

About the commencement of the second month of the marriage, the Lady Rowena was attacked with sudden illness, from which her recovery was slow. The fever which consumed her, rendered her nights uneasy; and in her perturbed state of half-slumber, she spoke of sounds, and of motions, in and about the chamber of the turret, which I concluded had no origin save in the distemper of her fancy, or perhaps in the phantasmagoric influences of the chamber itself. She became at length convalescent—finally, well. Yet but a brief period elapsed, ere a second more violent disorder again threw her upon a bed of suffering; and from this attack her frame, at all times feeble, never altogether recovered. Her illnesses were, after this epoch, of alarming character, and of more alarming recurrence, defying alike the knowledge and the great exertions of her physicians. With the increase of the chronic disease, which had thus apparently taken too sure hold upon her constitution to be eradicated by human means, I could not fail to observe a similar increase in the nervous irritation of her temperament, and in her excitability by trivial causes of fear. She spoke again, and now more frequently and pertinaciously, of the sounds—of the slight sounds

—and of the unusual motions among the tapestries, to which she had formerly alluded.

One night, near the closing in of September, she pressed this distressing subject with more than usual emphasis upon my attention. She had just awakened from an unquiet slumber, and I had been watching, with feelings half of anxiety, half of vague terror, the workings of her emaciated countenance. I sat by the side of her ebony bed, upon one of the ottomans of India. She partly arose, and spoke, in an earnest low whisper, of sounds which she *then* heard, but which I could not hear —of motions which she *then* saw, but which I could not perceive. The wind was rushing hurriedly behind the tapestries, and I wished to show her (what, let me confess it, I could not *all* believe) that those almost inarticulate breathings, and those very gentle variations of the figures upon the wall, were but the natural effects of that customary rushing of the wind. But a deadly pallor, overspreading her face, had proved to me that my exertions to reassure her would be fruitless. She appeared to be fainting, and no attendants were within call. I remembered where was deposited a decanter of light wine which had been ordered by her physicians, and hastened across the chamber to procure it. But, as I stepped beneath the light of the censer, two circumstances of a startling nature attracted my attention. I had felt that some palpable although invisible object had passed lightly by my person; and I saw that there lay upon the golden carpet, in the very middle of the rich luster thrown from the censer, a shadow—a faint, indefinite shadow of angelic aspect—such as might be fancied for the shadow of a shade. But I was wild with the excitement of an immoderate dose of opium, and heeded these things but little, nor spoke of them to Rowena. Having found the wine, I recrossed the chamber, and poured out a gobletful, which I held to the lips of the fainting lady. She had now partially recovered, however, and took the vessel herself, while I sank upon an ottoman near me, with my eyes fastened upon her person. It was then that I became distinctly aware of a gentle footfall upon the carpet, and near the couch; and in a second thereafter, as Rowena was in the act of raising the wine to her lips, I saw, or may have dreamed that I saw, fall within the goblet, as if from some invisible spring in the atmosphere of the room, three or four large drops of a brilliant and ruby-colored fluid. If this I saw—not so Rowena. She swallowed the wine unhesitatingly and I forbore to speak to her of a circumstance which must after all, I considered, have been but the suggestion of a vivid imagination, rendered morbidly active by the terror of the lady, by the opium, and by the hour.

Yet I cannot conceal it from my own perception that, immediately subsequent to the fall of the ruby-drops, a rapid change for the worse took place in the disorder of my wife; so that, on the third subsequent night, the hands of her menials prepared her for the tomb, and on the fourth, I sat alone, with her shrouded body, in that fantastic chamber which had received her as my bride. Wild visions, opium-engendered, flitted shadow-like before me. I gazed with unquiet eye upon the sarcophagi in the angles of the room, upon the varying figures of the drapery, and upon the writhing of the party-colored fires in the censer overhead. My eyes then fell, as I called to mind the circumstances of a former night, to the spot beneath the glare of the censer where I had seen the faint traces of the shadow. It was there, however, no longer; and breathing with greater freedom, I turned my glances to the pallid and rigid figure upon the bed. Then rushed upon me a thousand memories of Ligeia—and then came back upon my heart, with the turbulent violence of a flood, the whole of that unutterable woe with which I had regarded *her* thus enshrouded. The night waned; and still, with a bosom full of bitter thoughts of the one only and supremely beloved, I remained gazing upon the body of Rowena.

It might have been midnight, or perhaps earlier, or later, for I had taken no note of time, when a sob, low, gentle, but very distinct, startled me from my revery. I *felt* that it came from the bed of ebony—the bed of death. I listened in an agony of superstitious terror—but there was no repetition of the sound. I strained my vision to detect any motion in the corpse—but there was not the slightest perceptible. Yet I could not have been deceived. I *had* heard the noise, however faint, and my soul was awakened within me. I resolutely and perseveringly kept my attention riveted upon the body. Many minutes elapsed before any circumstance occurred tending to throw light upon the mystery. At length it became evident that a slight, a very feeble, and barely noticeable tinge of color had flushed up within the cheeks, and along the sunken small veins of the eyelids. Through a species of unutterable horror and awe, for which the language of mortality has no sufficiently energetic expression, I felt my heart cease to beat, my limbs grow rigid where I sat. Yet a sense of duty finally operated to restore my self-possession. I could no longer doubt that we had been precipitate in our preparations—that Rowena still lived. It was necessary that some immediate exertion be made; yet the turret was altogether apart from the portion of the abbey tenanted by the servants—there were none within call—I had no means of summoning them to my aid without leaving the room for many minutes—and this I could not venture to do. I therefore struggled alone in my endeavors to call back the spirit still hovering. In a short period it was certain, however, that a relapse had taken place; the color disappeared from both eyelid and cheek, leaving a wanness even more than that of marble; the lips became doubly shriveled and pinched up in the ghastly expression of death; a repulsive clamminess and coldness overspread rapidly the surface of the body; and all the usual rigorous stiffness immediately supervened. I fell back with a shudder upon the couch from which I had been so startlingly aroused, and again gave myself up to passionate waking visions of Ligeia.

An hour thus elapsed, when (could it be possible?) I was a second time aware of some vague sound issuing from the region of the bed. I listened—in extremity of horror. The sound came again—it was a sigh. Rushing to the corpse, I saw—distinctly saw—a tremor upon the lips. In a minute afterwards they relaxed, disclosing a bright line of the pearly teeth. Amazement now struggled in my bosom with the profound awe which had hitherto reigned there alone. I felt that my vision grew dim, that my reason wandered; and it was only by a violent effort that I at length succeeded in nerving myself to the task which duty thus once more had pointed out. There was now a partial glow upon the forehead and upon the cheek and throat; a perceptible warmth pervaded the whole frame; there was even a slight pulsation at the heart. The lady *lived*; and with redoubled ardor I betook myself to the task of restoration. I chafed and bathed the temples and the hands, and used every exertion which experience, and no little medical reading, could suggest. But in vain. Suddenly, the color fled, the pulsation ceased, the lips resumed the expression of the dead, and, in an instant afterward, the whole body took upon itself the icy chilliness, the livid hue, the intense rigidity, the sunken outline, and all the loathsome peculiarities of that which has been, for many days, a tenant of the tomb.

And again I sunk into visions of Ligeia—and again (what marvel that I shudder while I write?), *again* there reached my ears a low sob from the region of the ebony bed. But why shall I minutely detail the unspeakable horrors of that night? Why shall I pause to relate how, time after time, until near the period of the gray dawn, this hideous drama of revivification was repeated; how each terrific relapse was only into a sterner and apparently more irredeemable death; how each agony wore the aspect of a struggle with some invisible foe; and how each struggle was succeeded by I know not what of wild change in the personal appearance of the corpse? Let me hurry to a conclusion.

The greater part of the fearful night had worn away, and she who had been dead, once again stirred—and now more vigorously than hitherto, although arousing from a dissolution more appalling in its utter helplessness than any. I had long ceased to struggle or to move, and remained sitting rigidly upon the ottoman, a helpless prey to a whirl of violent emotions, of which extreme awe was perhaps the least terrible, the least consuming. The corpse, I repeat, stirred, and now more vigorously than before. The hues of life flushed up with unwonted energy into the countenance—the limbs relaxed—and, save that the eyelids were yet pressed heavily together, and that the bandages and draperies of the grave still imparted their charnel character to the figure, I might have dreamed that Rowena had indeed shaken off, utterly, the fetters of Death. But if this idea was not, even then, altogether adopted, I could at least doubt no longer, when, arising from the bed, tottering, with feeble steps, with closed eyes, and with the manner of one bewildered in a dream, the thing that was enshrouded advanced bodily and palpably into the middle of the apartment.

I trembled not—I stirred not—for a crowd of unutterable fancies connected with the air, the stature, the demeanor of the figure, rushing hurriedly through my brain, had paralyzed—had chilled me into stone. I stirred not—but gazed upon the apparition. There was a mad disorder in my thoughts—a tumult unappeasable. Could it, indeed, be the *living* Rowena who confronted me? Could it indeed be Rowena *at all*—the fair-haired, the blue-eyed Lady Rowena Trevanion of Tremaine? Why, *why* should I doubt it? The bandage lay heavily about the mouth—but then might it not be the mouth of the breathing Lady of Tremaine? And the cheeks—there were the roses as in her noon of life—yes, these might indeed be the fair cheeks of the living Lady of Tremaine. And the chin, with its dimples, as in health, might it not be hers? but *had she then grown taller since her malady?* What inexpressible madness seized me with that thought? One bound, and I had reached her feet! Shrinking from my touch, she let fall from her head the ghastly cerements which had confined it, and there streamed forth, into the rushing atmosphere of the chamber, huge masses of long and disheveled hair; *it was blacker than the wings of the midnight!* And now slowly opened *the eyes* of the figure which stood before me. "Here then, at least," I shrieked aloud, "can I never—can I never be mistaken—these are the full, and the black, and the wild eyes—of my lost love—of the Lady—of the LADY LIGEIA."

DR. HEIDEGGER'S EXPERIMENT

By Nathaniel Hawthorne

[Nathaniel Hawthorne (1804–1864) is one of the best known of American prose writers. Although occasionally before his time a writer like William Austin or James Hogg or Washington Irving met most of the technical requirements of the short story, it was Poe and Hawthorne who became conscious of the artistic elements of that form of fiction, and practiced the art systematically. Hawthorne was born at Salem, Massachusetts, and educated at Bowdoin College, graduating in 1825. From 1838 to 1840 he was employed in the Boston Custom House. In 1841 he joined the famous Brook Farm Association. From 1846 to 1849 he was again in the government civil service, being surveyor of the port of Salem. He served later, from 1853 to 1856, as consul to Liverpool, returning to the United States in 1860 after a residence in England and visits to Italy and other continental countries.

His chief works and the dates of publication are as follows: *Twice Told Tales* (1837 and 1842), *Mosses from an Old Manse* (1846), *The Scarlet Letter* (1850), *The House of the Seven Gables* (1851), *The Snow Image and Other Twice Told Tales* (1852), and *The Marble Faun* (1860). He died at Plymouth, New Hampshire.

Dr. Heidegger's Experiment was first published in *Twice Told Tales* (1837). It is here reprinted from the *Complete Works of Nathaniel Hawthorne* by permission of Houghton Mifflin Company, publishers.]

THAT very singular man, old Doctor Heidegger, once invited four venerable friends to meet him in his study. There were three white-bearded gentlemen, Mr. Medbourne, Colonel Killigrew, and Mr. Gascoigne, and a withered gentlewoman whose name was the Widow Wycherly. They were all melancholy old creatures, who had been unfortunate in life, and whose greatest misfortune it was that they were not long ago in their graves. Mr. Medbourne, in the vigor of his age, had been a prosperous merchant, but had lost his all by a frantic speculation, and was little better than a mendicant. Colonel Killigrew had wasted his best years, and his health and substance, in the pursuit of sinful pleasures, which had given birth to a brood of pains, such as the gout and divers other torments of soul and body. Mr. Gascoigne was a ruined politician, a man of evil fame, or at least had been so, till time had buried him from the knowledge of the present generation, and made him obscure instead of infamous. As for the Widow Wycherly, tradition tells us that she was a great beauty in her day; but, for a long while past, she had lived in deep seclusion, on account of certain scandalous stories which had prejudiced the gentry of the town against her. It is a circumstance worth mentioning that each of these three old gentlemen, Mr. Medbourne, Colonel Killigrew, and Mr. Gascoigne, were early lovers of the Widow Wycherly, and had once been on the point of cutting each other's throats for her sake. And, before proceeding further, I will merely hint that Doctor Heidegger and all his four guests were sometimes thought to be a little beside themselves; as is not unfrequently the case with old people, when worried either by present troubles or woful recollections.

"My dear friends," said Doctor Heidegger, motioning them to be seated, "I am desirous of your assistance in one of those little experiments with which I amuse myself here in my study."

If all stories were true, Doctor Heidegger's study must have been a very curious place. It was a dim, old-fashioned chamber, festooned with cobwebs and besprinkled with antique dust. Around the walls stood several oaken bookcases, the lower shelves of which were filled with rows of gigantic folios and black-letter quartos, and the upper with little parchment-covered duodecimos. Over the central bookcase was a bronze bust of Hippocrates, with which, according to some authorities, Doctor Heidegger was accustomed to hold consultations in all difficult cases of his practice. In the obscurest corner of the room stood a tall and narrow oaken closet, with its door ajar, within which doubtfully appeared a skeleton. Between two of the bookcases hung a looking-glass, presenting its high and dusty plate within a tarnished gilt frame. Among many wonderful stories related of this mirror, it was fabled that the spirits of all the doctor's deceased patients dwelt within its verge, and would stare him in the face whenever he looked thitherward. The opposite side of the chamber was ornamented with the full-length portrait of a young lady, arrayed in the faded magnificence of silk, satin, and brocade, and with a visage as faded as her dress. Above half a century ago Doctor Heidegger had been on the point of marriage with this young lady; but, being affected with some slight disorder, she had swallowed one of her lover's prescriptions, and died on the bridal evening. The greatest curiosity of the study remains to be mentioned; it was a ponderous folio volume, bound in black leather, with massive silver clasps. There were no letters on the back, and nobody could tell the title of the book. But it was well known to be a book of magic; and once, when a chambermaid had lifted it, merely to brush away the dust, the skeleton had rattled in its closet, the picture of the young lady had stepped one foot upon the floor, and several ghastly faces had peeped forth from the mirror, while the brazen head of Hippocrates had frowned, and said, "Forbear!"

Such was Doctor Heidegger's study. On the summer afternoon of our tale a small round table, as black as ebony, stood in the center of the room, sustaining a cut-glass vase of beautiful form and workmanship. The sunshine came through the window, between the heavy festoons of two faded damask curtains, and fell directly across this vase; so that a mild splendor was reflected from it on the ashen visages of the five old people who sat around. Four champagne glasses were also on the table.

"My dear old friends," repeated Doctor Heidegger, "may I reckon on your aid in performing an exceedingly curious experiment?"

Now Doctor Heidegger was a very strange old gentleman, whose eccentricity had become the nucleus for a thousand fantastic stories. Some of these fables, to my shame be it spoken, might possibly be traced back to mine own veracious self; and if any passages of the present tale should startle the reader's faith, I must be content to bear the stigma of a fiction-monger.

When the doctor's guests heard him talk of his proposed experiment, they anticipated nothing more wonderful than the murder of a mouse in an air-pump or the examination of a cobweb by the microscope, or some similar nonsense, with which he was constantly in the habit of pestering his intimates. But without waiting for a reply, Doctor Heidegger hobbled across the chamber, and returned with the same ponderous folio, bound in black leather, which common report affirmed to be a book of magic. Undoing the silver clasps, he opened the volume, and took from among its black-letter pages a rose, or what was once a rose, though now the green leaves and crimson petals had assumed one brownish hue, and the ancient flower seemed ready to crumble to dust in the doctor's hands.

"This rose," said Doctor Heidegger, with a sigh, "this same withered and crumbling flower, blossomed five and fifty years ago. It was given me by Sylvia Ward, whose portrait hangs yonder, and I meant to wear it in my bosom at our wedding. Five and fifty years it has been treasured between the leaves of this old volume. Now, would you deem it possible that this rose of half a century could ever bloom again?"

"Nonsense!" said the Widow Wycherly, with a peevish toss of her head. "You might as well ask whether an old woman's wrinkled face could ever bloom again."

"See!" answered Doctor Heidegger.

He uncovered the vase, and threw the faded rose into the water which it contained. At first, it lay lightly on the surface of the fluid, appearing to imbibe none of its moisture. Soon, however, a singular change began to be visible. The crushed and dried petals stirred, and assumed a deepening tinge of crimson, as if the flower were reviving from a death-like slumber; the slender stalk and twigs of foliage became green; and there was the rose of half a century, looking as fresh as when Sylvia Ward had first given it to her lover. It was scarcely full blown; for some of its delicate red leaves curled modestly around its moist bosom, within which two or three dewdrops were sparkling.

"That is certainly a very pretty deception," said the doctor's friends; carelessly, however, for they had witnessed greater miracles at a conjurer's show; "pray, how was it effected?"

"Did you never hear of the Fountain of Youth?" asked Doctor Heidegger, "which Ponce de Leon, the Spanish adventurer, went in search of, two or three centuries ago?"

"But did Ponce de Leon ever find it?" said the Widow Wycherly.

"No," answered Doctor Heidegger, "for he never sought it in the right place. The famous Fountain of Youth, if I am rightly informed, is situated in the southern part of the Floridian peninsula, not far from Lake Macaco. Its source is overshadowed by several gigantic magnolias, which, though numberless centuries old, have been kept as fresh as violets, by the virtues of this wonderful water. An acquaintance of mine, knowing my curiosity in such matters, has sent me what you see in the vase."

"Ahem!" said Colonel Killigrew, who believed not a word of the doctor's story; "and what may be the effect of this fluid on the human frame?"

"You shall judge for yourself, my dear Colonel," replied Doctor Heidegger; "and all of you, my respected friends, are welcome to so much of this admirable fluid as may restore to you the bloom of youth. For my own part, having had much trouble in growing old, I am in no hurry to grow young again. With your permission, therefore, I will merely watch the progress of the experiment."

While he spoke, Doctor Heidegger had been filling the four champagne glasses with the water of the Fountain of Youth. It was apparently impregnated with an effervescent gas, for little bubbles were continually ascending from the depths of the glasses, and bursting in silvery spray at the surface. As the liquor diffused a pleasant perfume, the old people doubted not that it possessed cordial and comfortable properties; and though utter sceptics as to its rejuvenescent power, they were inclined to swallow it at once. But Doctor Heidegger besought them to stay a moment.

"Before you drink, my respectable old friends," said he, "it would be well that, with the experience of a lifetime to direct you, you should draw up a few general rules for your guidance, in passing a second time through the perils of youth. Think what a sin and shame it would be if, with your peculiar advantages, you should not become patterns of virtue and wisdom to all the young people of the age!"

The doctor's four venerable friends made him no answer, except by a feeble and tremulous laugh; so very ridiculous was the idea that, knowing how closely repentance treads behind the steps of error, they should ever go astray again.

"Drink, then," said the doctor, bowing: "I rejoice that I have so well selected the subjects of my experiment."

With palsied hands they raised the glasses to their lips. The liquor, if it really possessed such virtues as Doctor Heidegger imputed to it, could not have been bestowed on four human beings who needed it more wofully. They looked as if they had never known what youth or pleasure was, but had been the offspring of nature's dotage, and always the gray, decrepit, sapless, miserable creatures, who now sat stooping round the doctor's table, without life enough in their souls or bodies to be animated even by the prospect of growing young again. They drank off the water, and replaced their glasses on the table.

Assuredly there was an almost immediate improvement in the aspect of the party, not unlike what might have been produced by a glass of generous wine, together with a sudden glow of cheerful sunshine, brightening over all their visages at once. There was a healthful suffusion on their cheeks, instead of the ashen hue that had made them look so corpselike. They gazed at one another, and fancied that some magic power had really begun to smooth away the deep and sad inscriptions which Father Time had been so long engraving on their brow. The Widow Wycherly adjusted her cap, for she felt almost like a woman again.

"Give us more of this wondrous water!" cried they, eagerly. "We are younger—but we are still too old! Quick—give us more!"

"Patience! patience!" quoth Doctor Heidegger, who sat watching the experiment with philosophic coolness. "You have been a long time growing old. Surely you might be content to grow young in half an hour! But the water is at your service."

Again he filled their glasses with the liquor of youth, enough of which still remained in the vase to turn half the old people in the city to the age of their own grandchildren. While the bubbles were yet sparkling on the brim, the doctor's four guests snatched their glasses from the table, and swallowed the contents at a single gulp. Was it delusion? Even while the draught was passing down their throats, it seemed to have wrought a change on their whole systems. Their eyes grew clear and bright; a dark shade deepened among their silvery locks; they sat round the table, three gentlemen of middle age, and a woman hardly beyond her buxom prime.

"My dear widow, you are charming!" cried Colonel Killigrew, whose eyes had been fixed upon her face, while the shadows of age were flitting from it like darkness from the crimson daybreak.

The fair widow knew of old that Colonel Killigrew's compliments were not always measured by sober truth; so she started up and ran to the mirror, still dreading that the ugly visage of an old woman would meet her gaze. Meanwhile the three gentlemen behaved in such a manner as proved that the water of the Fountain of Youth possessed some intoxicating qualities, unless, indeed, their exhilaration of spirits were merely a lightsome dizziness, caused by the sudden removal of the weight of years. Mr. Gascoigne's mind seemed to run on political topics, but whether relating to the past, present, or future could not easily be determined, since the same ideas and phrases have been in vogue these fifty years. Now he rattled forth full-throated sentences about patriotism, national glory, and the people's rights; now he muttered some perilous stuff or other, in a sly and doubtful whisper, so cautiously that even his own conscience could scarcely catch the secret; and now, again, he spoke in measured accents and a deeply deferential tone, as if a royal ear were listening to his well-turned periods. Colonel Killigrew all this time had been trolling forth a jolly bottle song, and ringing his glass in symphony with the chorus, while his eyes wandered toward the buxom figure of the Widow Wycherly. On the other side of the table Mr. Medbourne was involved in a calculation of dollars and cents, with which was strangely intermingled a project for supplying the East Indies with ice, by harnessing a team of whales to the polar icebergs.

As for the Widow Wycherly, she stood before the mirror, courtesying and simpering to her own image, and greeting it as the friend whom she loved better than all the world beside. She thrust her face close to the glass to see whether some long-remembered wrinkle or crow's-foot had indeed vanished. She examined whether the snow had so entirely melted from her hair that the venerable cap could be safely thrown aside. At last, turning briskly away, she came with a sort of dancing step to the table.

"My dear old doctor," cried she, "pray favor me with another glass!"

"Certainly, my dear madam, certainly!" replied the complaisant doctor. "See! I have already filled the glasses."

There, in fact, stood the four glasses, brimful of this wonderful water, the delicate spray of which, as it effervesced from the surface, resembled the tremulous glitter of diamonds. It was now so nearly sunset that the chamber had grown duskier than ever; but a mild and moonlike splendor gleamed from within the vase, and rested alike on the four guests, and on the doctor's venerable figure. He sat in a high-backed, elaborately carved oaken chair, with a gray dignity of aspect that might have well befitted that very Father Time, whose power had never been disputed, save by this fortunate company. Even while quaffing the third draught of the Fountain of Youth, they were almost awed by the expression of his mysterious visage.

But the next moment the exhilarating gush of young life shot through their veins. They were now in the happy prime of youth. Age, with its miserable train of cares, and sorrows, and diseases, was remembered only as the trouble of a dream, from which they had joyously awoke. The fresh gloss of the soul, so early lost, and without which the world's successive scenes had been but a gallery of faded pictures, again threw its enchantment over all their prospects. They felt like new-created beings in a new-created universe.

"We are young! We are young!" they cried, exultingly.

Youth, like the extremity of age, had effaced the strongly marked characteristics of middle life, and mutually assimilated them all. They were a group of merry youngsters, almost maddened with the exuberant frolicsomeness of their years. The most singular effect of their gayety was an impulse to mock the infirmity and decrepitude of which they had so lately been the victims. They laughed loudly at their old-fashioned attire—the wide-skirted coats and flapped waistcoats of the young men, and the ancient cap and gown of the blooming girl. One limped across the floor like a gouty grandfather; one set a pair of spectacles astride of his nose, and pretended to pore over the black-letter pages of the book of magic; a third seated himself in an armchair, and strove to imitate the venerable dignity of Doctor Heidegger. Then all shouted mirthfully, and leaped about the room. The Widow Wycherly —if so fresh a damsel could be called a widow—tripped up to the doctor's chair with a mischievous merriment in her rosy face.

"Doctor, you dear old soul," cried she, "get up and dance with me!" And then the four young people laughed louder than ever, to think what a queer figure the poor old doctor would cut.

"Pray excuse me," answered the doctor, quietly. "I am old and rheumatic, and my dancing days were over long ago. But either of these gay young gentlemen will be glad of so pretty a partner."

"Dance with me, Clara!" cried Colonel Killigrew.

"No, no, I will be her partner!" shouted Mr. Gascoigne.

"She promised me her hand fifty years ago!" exclaimed Mr. Medbourne.

They all gathered round her. One caught both her hands in his passionate grasp—another threw his arm about her waist—the third buried his hand among the curls that clustered beneath the widow's cap. Blushing, panting, struggling, chiding, laughing, her warm breath fanning each of their faces by turns, she strove to disengage herself, yet still remained in their triple embrace. Never was there a livelier picture of youthful rivalship, with bewitching beauty for the prize. Yet, by a strange deception, owing to the duskiness of the chamber and the antique dresses which they still wore, the tall mirror is said to have reflected the figures of the three old, gray, withered grandsires, ridiculously contending for the skinny ugliness of a shrivelled grandam.

But they were young: their burning passions proved them so. Inflamed to madness by the coquetry of the girl-widow, who neither granted nor quite withheld her favors, the three rivals began to interchange threatening glances. Still keeping hold of the fair prize, they grappled fiercely at one another's throats. As they struggled to and fro, the table was overturned, and the vase dashed into a thousand fragments. The precious Water of Youth flowed in a bright stream across the floor, moistening the wings of a butterfly, which, grown old in the decline of summer, had alighted there to die. The insect fluttered lightly through the chamber, and settled on the snowy head of Doctor Heidegger.

"Come, come, gentlemen!—come, Madame Wycherly!" exclaimed the doctor, "I really must protest against this riot."

They stood still and shivered; for it seemed as if gray Time were calling them back from their sunny youth, far down into the chill and darksome vale of years. They looked at old Doctor Heidegger, who sat in his carved arm-chair, holding the rose of half a century which he had rescued from among the fragments of the shattered vase. At the motion of his hand the rioters resumed their seats, the more readily because their violent exertions had wearied them, youthful though they were.

"My poor Sylvia's rose!" ejaculated Doctor Heidegger, holding it in the light of the sunset clouds; "it appears to be fading again."

And so it was. Even while the party were looking at it the flower continued to shrivel up, till it became as dry and fragile as when the doctor had first thrown it into the vase. He shook off the few drops of moisture which clung to its petals.

"I love it as well thus as in its dewy freshness," observed he, pressing the withered rose to his withered lips. While he spoke, the butterfly fluttered down from the doctor's snowy head, and fell upon the floor.

His guests shivered again. A strange chillness, whether of the body or spirit they could not tell, was creeping gradually over them all. They gazed at one another, and fancied that each fleeting moment snatched away a charm, and left a deepening furrow where none had been before. Was it an illusion? Had the changes of a lifetime been crowded into so brief a space, and were they now four aged people, sitting with their old friend, Doctor Heidegger?

"Are we grown old again so soon?" cried they, dolefully.

In truth, they had. The Water of Youth possessed merely a virtue more transient than that of wine. The delirium which it created had effervesced away. Yes, they were old again! With a shuddering impulse, that showed her a woman still, the widow clasped her skinny hands over her face, and wished that the coffin lid were over it, since it could be no longer beautiful.

"Yes, friends, ye are old again," said Doctor Heidegger; "and lo! the Water of Youth is all lavished on the ground. Well, I bemoan it not; for if the fountain gushed at my very doorstep, I would not stoop to bathe my lips in it—no, though its delirium were for years instead of moments. Such is the lesson ye have taught me!"

But the doctor's four friends had taught no such lesson to themselves. They resolved forthwith to make a pilgrimage to Florida, and quaff at morning, noon, and night, from the Fountain of Youth.

THE OUTCASTS OF POKER FLAT

By Bret Harte

[Francis Bret Harte (1836–1902) was born at Albany, New York, but was taken to California at the age of 15. The gold rush of '49 was past the frantic stage, but the boy saw a good deal of that romantic period. He was occupied with newspaper work in San Francisco in his early manhood. His most famous stories were those contributed to the *Overland Monthly*, of which he was the first editor. These are *The Luck of Roaring Camp* (1868), *Tennessee's Partner* (1869), and *The Outcasts of Poker Flat* (1869). Bret Harte was also famous for his humorous and pathetic narrative poems. From 1878 to 1880 Harte was American consul at Crefeld, Germany; and from 1880 to 1885 he was consul at Glasgow. He made his home in England for the remainder of his life.

The Outcasts of Poker Flat was first published in the *Overland Monthly*, January, 1869. It was included in Harte's first important book, *The Luck of Roaring Camp and Other Sketches* (Boston, 1870).]

AS Mr. John Oakhurst, gambler, stepped into the main street of Poker Flat on the morning of the 23d of November, 1850, he was conscious of a change in its moral atmosphere since the preceding night. Two or three men, conversing earnestly together, ceased as he approached, and exchanged significant glances. There was a Sabbath lull in the air, which, in a settlement unused to Sabbath influences, looked ominous.

Mr. Oakhurst's calm, handsome face betrayed small concern in these indications. Whether he was conscious of any predisposing cause was another question. "I reckon they're after somebody," he reflected; "likely it's me." He returned to his pocket the handkerchief with which he had been whipping away the red dust of Poker Flat from his neat boots, and quietly discharged his mind of any further conjecture.

In point of fact, Poker Flat was "after somebody." It had lately suffered the loss of several thousand dollars, two valuable horses, and a prominent citizen. It was experiencing a spasm of virtuous reaction, quite as lawless and ungovernable as any of the acts that had provoked it. A secret committee had determined to rid the town of all improper persons. This was done permanently in regard of two men who were then hanging from the boughs of a sycamore in the gulch, and temporarily in the banishment of certain other objectionable characters. I regret to say that some of these were ladies. It is but due to the sex, however, to state that their impropriety was professional, and it was only in such easily established standards of evil that Poker Flat ventured to sit in judgment.

Mr. Oakhurst was right in supposing that he was included in this category. A few of the committee had urged hanging him as a possible example and a sure method of reimbursing themselves from his pockets of the sums he had won from them. "It's agin justice," said Jim Wheeler, "to let this yer young man from Roaring Camp—an entire stranger—carry away our money." But a crude sentiment of equity residing in the breasts of those who had been fortunate enough to win from Mr. Oakhurst overruled this narrower local prejudice.

Mr. Oakhurst received his sentence with philosophic calmness, none the less coolly that he was aware of the hesitation of his judges. He was too much of a gambler not to accept fate. With him life was at best an uncertain game, and he recognized the usual percentage in favor of the dealer.

A body of armed men accompanied the deported wickedness of Poker Flat to the outskirts of the settlement. Besides Mr. Oakhurst, who was known to be a coolly desperate man, and for whose intimidation the armed escort was intended, the expatriated party consisted of a young woman familiarly known as "The Duchess;" another who had won the title of "Mother Shipton;" and "Uncle Billy," a suspected sluice-robber and confirmed drunkard. The cavalcade provoked no comments from the spectators, nor was any word uttered by the escort. Only when the gulch which marked the uttermost limit of Poker Flat was reached, the leader spoke briefly and to the point. The exiles were forbidden to return at the peril of their lives.

As the escort disappeared, their pent-up feelings found vent in a few hysterical tears from the Duchess, some bad language from Mother Shipton, and a Parthian volley of expletives from Uncle Billy. The philosophic Oakhurst alone remained silent. He listened calmly to Mother Shipton's desire to cut somebody's heart out, to the repeated statements of the Duchess that she would die in the road, and to the alarming oaths that seemed to be bumped out of Uncle Billy as he rode forward. With the easy good humor characteristic of his class, he insisted upon exchanging his own riding-horse, "Five-Spot," for the sorry mule which the Duchess rode. But even this act did not draw the party into any closer sympathy. The young woman readjusted her somewhat draggled plumes with a feeble, faded coquetry; Mother Shipton eyed the possessor of "Five-Spot" with malevolence, and Uncle Billy included the whole party in one sweeping anathema.

The road to Sandy Bar—a camp that, not having as yet experienced the regenerating influences of Poker Flat, consequently seemed to offer some invitation to the emigrants—lay over a steep mountain range. It was distant a day's severe travel. In that advanced season the party soon passed out of the moist, temperate regions of the foothills into the dry, cold, bracing air of the Sierras. The trail was narrow and difficult. At noon the Duchess, rolling out of her saddle upon the ground, declared her intention of going no farther, and the party halted.

The spot was singularly wild and impressive. A wooded amphitheater, surrounded on three sides by precipitous cliffs of naked granite, sloped gently toward the crest of another precipice that overlooked the valley. It was, undoubtedly, the most suitable spot for a camp, had camping been advisable. But Mr. Oakhurst knew that scarcely half the journey to Sandy Bar was accomplished, and the party were not equipped or provisioned for delay. This fact he pointed out to his companions curtly, with a philosophic commentary on the folly of "throwing up their hand before the game was played out." But they were furnished with liquor, which in this emergency stood them in place of food, fuel, rest, and pre-science. In spite of his remonstrances, it was not long before they were more or less under its influence. Uncle Billy passed rapidly from a belli-cose state into one of stupor, the Duchess became maudlin, and Mother Shipton snored. Mr. Oakhurst alone remained erect, leaning against a rock, calmly surveying them.

Mr. Oakhurst did not drink. It interfered with a profession which required coolness, impassiveness, and presence of mind, and, in his own language, he "couldn't afford it." As he gazed at his recumbent fellow exiles, the loneliness begotten of his pariah trade, his habits of life, his very vices, for the first time seriously oppressed him. He bestirred him-self in dusting his black clothes, washing his hands and face, and other acts characteristic of his studiously neat habits, and for a moment forgot his annoyance. The thought of deserting his weaker and more pitiable companions never perhaps occurred to him. Yet he could not help feel-ing the want of that excitement which, singularly enough, was most con-ducive to that calm equanimity for which he was notorious. He looked at the gloomy walls that rose a thousand feet sheer above the circling pines around him, at the sky ominously clouded, at the valley below, already deepening into shadow; and doing so, suddenly he heard his own name called.

A horseman slowly ascended the trail. In the fresh, open face of the newcomer Mr. Oakhurst recognized Tom Simson, otherwise known as "The Innocent," of Sandy Bar. He had met him some months before over a "little game," and had, with perfect equanimity, won the entire fortune—amounting to some forty dollars—of that guileless youth. After the game was finished, Mr. Oakhurst drew the youthful speculator be-hind the door and thus addressed him: "Tommy, you're a good little man, but you can't gamble worth a cent. Don't try it over again." He then handed him his money back, pushed him gently from the room, and so made a devoted slave of Tom Simson.

There was a remembrance of this in his boyish and enthusiastic greeting of Mr. Oakhurst. He had started, he said, to go to Poker Flat to seek his fortune. "Alone?" No, not exactly alone; in fact (a giggle), he had run away with Piney Woods. Didn't Mr. Oakhurst remember Piney? She that used to wait on the table at the Temperance House? They had been engaged a long time, but old Jake Woods had objected, and so they had run away, and were going to Poker Flat to be married, and here they were. And they were tired out, and how lucky it was they had found a place to camp, and company. All this the Innocent delivered rapidly, while Piney, a stout comely damsel of fifteen, emerged from behind the pine-tree, where she had been blushing unseen, and rode to the side of her lover.

Mr. Oakhurst seldom troubled himself with sentiment, still less with propriety; but he had a vague idea that the situation was not fortunate. He retained, however, his presence of mind sufficiently to kick Uncle Billy, who was about to say something, and Uncle Billy was sober enough to recognize in Mr. Oakhurst's kick a superior power that would not bear trifling. He then endeavored to dissuade Tom Simson from delaying further, but in vain. He even pointed out the fact that there was no provision, nor means of making a camp. But, unluckily, the Innocent met this objection by assuring the party that he was provided with an extra mule loaded with provisions, and by the discovery of a rude attempt at a log house near the trail. "Piney can stay with Mrs. Oakhurst," said the Innocent, pointing to the Duchess, "and I can shift for myself."

Nothing but Mr. Oakhurst's admonishing foot saved Uncle Billy from bursting into a roar of laughter. As it was, he felt compelled to retire up the cañon until he could recover his gravity. There he confided the joke to the tall pine-trees, with many slaps of his leg, contortions of his face, and the usual profanity. But when he returned to the party, he found them seated by a fire—for the air had grown strangely chill and the sky overcast—in apparently amicable conversation. Piney was actually talking in an impulsive girlish fashion to the Duchess, who was listening with an interest and animation she had not shown for many days. The Innocent was holding forth, apparently with equal effect, to Mr. Oakhurst and Mother Shipton, who was actually relaxing into amiability. "Is this yer a d—d picnic?" said Uncle Billy, with inward scorn, as he surveyed the sylvan group, the glancing firelight, and the tethered animals in the foreground. Suddenly an idea mingled with the alcoholic fumes that disturbed his brain. It was apparently of a jocular nature, for he felt impelled to slap his leg again and cram his fist into his mouth.

As the shadows crept slowly up the mountain, a slight breeze rocked the tops of the pine-trees and moaned through their long and gloomy aisles. The ruined cabin, patched and covered with pine boughs, was set apart for the ladies. As the lovers parted, they unaffectedly exchanged a kiss, so honest and sincere that it might have been heard above the swaying pines. The frail Duchess and the malevolent Mother Shipton were probably too stunned to remark upon this last evidence of simplicity, and so turned without a word to the hut. The fire was replenished, the men lay down before the door, and in a few minutes were asleep.

Mr. Oakhurst was a light sleeper. Toward morning he awoke benumbed and cold. As he stirred the dying fire, the wind, which was now blowing strongly, brought to his cheek that which caused the blood to leave it,—snow!

He started to his feet with the intention of awakening the sleepers, for there was no time to lose. But turning to where Uncle Billy had been lying, he found him gone. A suspicion leaped to his brain, and a curse to his lips. He ran to the spot where the mules had been tethered—they were no longer there. The tracks were already rapidly disappearing in the snow.

The momentary excitement brought Mr. Oakhurst back to the fire with his usual calm. He did not waken the sleepers. The Innocent slumbered peacefully, with a smile on his good-humored, freckled face; the virgin Piney slept beside her frailer sisters as sweetly as though attended by celestial guardians; and Mr. Oakhurst, drawing his blanket over his shoulders, stroked his mustaches and waited for the dawn. It came slowly in a whirling mist of snowflakes that dazzled and confused the eye. What could be seen of the landscape appeared magically changed. He looked over the valley, and summed up the present and future in two words, "Snowed in!"

A careful inventory of the provisions, which, fortunately for the party, had been stored within the hut, and so escaped the felonious fingers of Uncle Billy, disclosed the fact that with care and prudence they might last ten days longer. "That is," said Mr. Oakhurst *sotto voce* to the Innocent, "if you're willing to board us. If you ain't—and perhaps you'd better not—you can wait till Uncle Billy gets back with provisions." For some occult reason, Mr. Oakhurst could not bring himself to disclose Uncle Billy's rascality, and so offered the hypothesis that he had wandered from the camp and had accidentally stampeded the animals. He dropped a warning to the Duchess and Mother Shipton, who of course knew the facts of their associate's defection. "They'll find out the truth about us *all* when they find out anything," he added significantly, "and there's no good frightening them now."

Tom Simson not only put all his worldly store at the disposal of Mr. Oakhurst, but seemed to enjoy the prospect of their enforced seclusion. "We'll have a good camp for a week, and then the snow'll melt, and we'll all go back together." The cheerful gayety of the young man and Mr. Oakhurst's calm infected the others. The Innocent, with the aid of pine boughs, extemporized a thatch for the roofless cabin, and the Duchess directed Piney in the rearrangement of the interior with a taste and tact that opened the blue eyes of that provincial maiden to their fullest extent. "I reckon now you're used to fine things at Poker Flat," said Piney. The Duchess turned away sharply to conceal something that reddened her cheeks through their professional tint, and Mother Shipton requested Piney not to "chatter." But when Mr. Oakhurst returned from a weary search for the trail, he heard the sound of happy laughter echoed from the rocks. He stopped in some alarm, and his thoughts first naturally reverted to the whiskey, which he had prudently cached. "And yet it don't somehow sound like whiskey," said the gambler. It was not until he caught sight of the blazing fire through the still blinding storm, and the group around it, that he settled to the conviction that it was "square fun."

Whether Mr. Oakhurst had cached his cards with the whiskey as something debarred the free access of the community, I cannot say. It was certain that, in Mother Shipton's words, he "didn't say 'cards' once" during that evening. Happily the time was beguiled by an accordion, produced somewhat ostentatiously by Tom Simson from his pack. Notwithstanding some difficulties attending the manipulation of this instrument, Piney Woods managed to pluck several reluctant melodies from its keys, to an accompaniment by the Innocent on a pair of bone castanets. But the crowning festivity of the evening was reached in a rude camp-meeting hymn, which the lovers, joining hands, sang with great earnestness and vociferation. I fear that a certain defiant tone and Covenanter's swing to its chorus, rather than any devotional quality, caused it speedily to infect the others, who at last joined in the refrain:—

> "I'm proud to live in the service of the Lord,
> And I'm bound to die in His army."

The pines rocked, the storm eddied and whirled above the miserable group, and the flames of their altar leaped heavenward, as if in token of the vow.

At midnight the storm abated, the rolling clouds parted, and the stars glittered keenly above the sleeping camp. Mr. Oakhurst, whose professional habits had enabled him to live on the smallest possible amount of sleep, in dividing the watch with Tom Simson somehow managed to take upon himself the greater part of that duty. He excused himself to the Innocent by saying that he had "often been a week without sleep." "Doing what?" asked Tom. "Poker!" replied Oakhurst sententiously. "When a man gets a streak of luck,—nigger-luck,—he don't get tired. The luck gives in first. Luck," continued the gambler reflectively, "is a mighty queer thing. All you know about it for certain is that it's bound to change. And it's finding out when it's going to change that makes you. We've had a streak of bad luck since we left Poker Flat,—you come along, and slap you get into it, too. If you can hold your cards right along you're all right. For," added the gambler with cheerful irrelevance—

> "'I'm proud to live in the service of the Lord,
> And I'm bound to die in His army.'"

The third day came, and the sun, looking through the white-curtained valley, saw the outcasts divide their slowly decreasing store of provisions for the morning meal. It was one of the peculiarities of that mountain climate that its rays diffused a kindly warmth over the wintry landscape, as if in regretful commiseration of the past. But it revealed drift on drift of snow piled high around the hut,—a hopeless, uncharted, trackless sea of white lying below the rocky shores to which the castaways still clung. Through the marvelously clear air the smoke of the pastoral village of Poker Flat rose miles away. Mother Shipton saw it, and from a remote pinnacle of her rocky fastness hurled in that direction a final malediction. It was her last vituperative attempt, and perhaps for that reason was invested with a certain degree of sublimity. It did her good, she privately informed the Duchess. "Just you go out there and cuss, and see." She then set herself to the task of amusing "the child," as she and the Duchess were pleased to call Piney. Piney was no chicken, but it was a soothing and original theory of the pair thus to account for the fact that she didn't swear and wasn't improper.

When night crept up again through the gorges, the reedy notes of the accordion rose and fell in fitful spasms and long-drawn gasps by the flickering campfire. But music failed to fill entirely the aching void left by insufficient food, and a new diversion was proposed by Piney,—story-telling. Neither Mr. Oakhurst nor his female companions caring to relate their personal experiences, this plan would have failed too, but for the Innocent. Some months before he had chanced upon a stray copy of Mr. Pope's ingenious translation of the Iliad. He now proposed to narrate the principal incidents of that poem—having thoroughly mastered the argument and fairly forgotten the words—in the current vernacular of Sandy Bar. And so for the rest of that night the Homeric demigods again walked the earth. Trojan bully and wily Greek wrestled in the winds, and the great pines in the cañon seemed to bow to the wrath of the son of Peleus. Mr. Oakhurst listened with quiet satisfaction. Most especially was he interested in the fate of "Ash-heels," as the Innocent persisted in denominating the "swift-footed Achilles."

So, with small food and much of Homer and the accordion, a week passed over the heads of the outcasts. The sun again forsook them, and again from leaden skies the snowflakes were sifted over the land. Day by day closer around them drew the snowy circle, until at last they looked from their prison over drifted walls of dazzling white, that towered twenty feet above their heads. It became more and more difficult to replenish their fires, even from the fallen trees beside them, now half

hidden in the drifts. And yet no one complained. The lovers turned
from the dreary prospect and looked into each other's eyes, and were
happy. Mr. Oakhurst settled himself coolly to the losing game before
him. The Duchess, more cheerful than she had been, assumed the care
of Piney. Only Mother Shipton—once the strongest of the party—
seemed to sicken and fade. At midnight on the tenth day she called
Oakhurst to her side. "I'm going," she said, in a voice of querulous
weakness, "but don't say anything about it. Don't waken the kids.
Take the bundle from under my head, and open it." Mr. Oakhurst did
so. It contained Mother Shipton's rations for the last week, untouched.
"Give 'em to the child," she said, pointing to the sleeping Piney. "You've
starved yourself," said the gambler. "That's what they call it," said the
woman querulously, as she lay down again, and, turning her face to the
wall, passed quietly away.

The accordion and the bones were put aside that day, and Homer was
forgotten. When the body of Mother Shipton had been committed to
the snow, Mr. Oakhurst took the Innocent aside, and showed him a pair
of snowshoes, which he had fashioned from the old pack-saddle. "There's
one chance in a hundred to save her yet," he said, pointing to Piney;
"but it's there," he added, pointing toward Poker Flat. "If you can
reach there in two days she's safe." "And you?" asked Tom Simson.
"I'll stay here," was the curt reply.

The lovers parted with a long embrace. "You are not going, too?"
said the Duchess, as she saw Mr. Oakhurst apparently waiting to accompany him. "As far as the cañon," he replied. He turned suddenly and
kissed the Duchess, leaving her pallid face aflame, and her trembling
limbs rigid with amazement.

Night came, but not Mr. Oakhurst. It brought the storm again and
the whirling snow. Then the Duchess, feeding the fire, found that some
one had quietly piled beside the hut enough fuel to last a few days longer.
The tears rose to her eyes, but she hid them from Piney.

The women slept but little. In the morning, looking into each other's
faces, they read their fate. Neither spoke, but Piney, accepting the
position of the stronger, drew near and placed her arm around the
Duchess's waist. They kept this attitude for the rest of the day. That
night the storm reached its greatest fury, and, rending asunder the protecting vines, invaded the very hut.

Toward morning they found themselves unable to feed the fire, which
gradually died away. As the embers slowly blackened, the Duchess crept
closer to Piney, and broke the silence of many hours: "Piney, can you
pray?" "No, dear," said Piney simply. The Duchess, without knowing
exactly why, felt relieved, and, putting her head upon Piney's shoulder,
spoke no more. And so reclining, the younger and purer pillowing the
head of her soiled sister upon her virgin breast, they fell asleep.

The wind lulled as if it feared to waken them. Feathery drifts of snow, shaken from the long pine boughs, flew like white winged birds, and settled about them as they slept. The moon through the rifted clouds looked down upon what had been the camp. But all human stain, all trace of earthly travail, was hidden beneath the spotless mantle mercifully flung from above.

They slept all that day and the next, nor did they waken when voices and footsteps broke the silence of the camp. And when pitying fingers brushed the snow from their wan faces, you could scarcely have told from the equal peace that dwelt upon them which was she that had sinned. Even the law of Poker Flat recognized this, and turned away, leaving them still locked in each other's arms.

But at the head of the gulch, on one of the largest pine-trees, they found the deuce of clubs pinned to the bark with a bowie-knife. It bore the following, written in pencil in a firm hand:—

†

BENEATH THIS TREE
LIES THE BODY
OF
JOHN OAKHURST
WHO STRUCK A STREAK OF BAD LUCK
ON THE 23D OF NOVEMBER 1850,
AND
HANDED IN HIS CHECKS
ON THE 7TH DECEMBER, 1850.

⸸

And pulseless and cold, with a Derringer by his side and a bullet in his heart, though still calm as in life, beneath the snow lay he who was at once the strongest and yet the weakest of the outcasts of Poker Flat.

DOCTOR MARIGOLD'S PRESCRIPTIONS

By Charles Dickens

[Charles Dickens (1812–1870) was a writer of novels. He was at his best in the "three-decker novel," the novel published in three volumes. Only occasionally did he turn from the writing of long novels to the production of other forms of literature. The short story was not his best means of expression. He did not use economy of characters, incident, or words. *A Christmas Carol* and *The Cricket on the Hearth* are typical of his shorter narratives. *Doctor Marigold* is a closer approach to true short story form, but even here there is no acceptance of the limits that a writer like De Maupassant set for himself. Dickens was born near Portsmouth, passed through a difficult youth in London, became famous early and spent the latter years of his life in affluence in his house called Gadshill on the road from London to Canterbury.

Dr. Marigold's Prescriptions was written for the Christmas Number of *All the Year Round* for 1865. Dickens read it with great success in New York the following year.]

I. TO BE TAKEN IMMEDIATELY

I AM a Cheap Jack, and my own father's name was Willum Marigold. It was in his lifetime supposed by some that his name was William, but my own father always consistently said, No, it was Willum. On which point I content myself with looking at the argument this way: If a man is not allowed to know his own name in a free country, how much is he allowed to know in a land of slavery? As to looking at the argument through the medium of the Register, Willum Marigold come into the world before Registers come up much—and went out of it, too. They wouldn't have been greatly in his line, neither, if they had chanced to come up before him.

I was born on the Queen's highway, but it was the King's at that time. A doctor was fetched to my own mother by my own father, when it took place on a common; and in consequence of his being a very kind gentleman, and accepting no fee but a tea-tray, I was named Doctor, out of gratitude and compliment to him. There you have me. Doctor Marigold.

I am at present a middle-aged man of a broadish build, in cords, leggings, and a sleeved waistcoat, the strings of which is always gone behind. Repair them how you will, they go like fiddle-strings. You have been to the theater, and you have seen one of the wiolin-players screw up his wiolin, after listening to it as if it had been whispering the secret

158

to him that it feared it was out of order, and then you have heard it snap. That's as exactly similar to my waistcoat as a waistcoat and a wiolin can be like one another.

I am partial to a white hat, and I like a shawl round my neck wore loose and easy. Sitting down is my favorite posture. If I have a taste in point of personal jewelry, it is mother-of-pearl buttons. There you have me again, as large as life.

The doctor having accepted a tea-tray, you'll guess that my father was a Cheap Jack before me. You are right. He was. It was a pretty tray. It represented a large lady going along a serpentining uphill gravel-walk, to attend a little church. Two swans had likewise come astray with the same intentions. When I call her a large lady, I don't mean in point of breadth, for there she fell below my views, but she more than made it up in height; her height and slimness was—in short THE height of both.

I often saw that tray, after I was the innocently smiling cause (or more likely screeching one) of the Doctor's standing it upon a table against the wall in his consulting-room. Whenever my own father and mother were in that part of the country, I used to put my head (I have heard my own mother say it was flaxen curls at that time, though you wouldn't know an old hearth-broom from it now till you come to the handle and found it wasn't me) in at the doctor's door, and the doctor was always glad to see me, and said, "Aha, my brother practitioner! Come in, little M. D. How are your inclinations as to sixpence?"

You can't go on forever, you'll find, nor yet could my father nor yet my mother. If you don't go off as a whole when you are about due, you're liable to go off in part, and two to one your head's the part. Gradually my father went off his, and my mother went off hers. It was in a harmless way, but it put out the family where I boarded them. The old couple, though retired, got to be wholly and solely devoted to the Cheap Jack business, and were always selling the family off. Whenever the cloth was laid for dinner, my father began rattling the plates and dishes, as we do in our line when we put up crockery for a bid, only he had lost the trick of it, and mostly let 'em drop and broke 'em. As the old lady had been used to sit in the cart, and hand the articles out one by one to the old gentleman on the footboard to sell, just in the same way she handed him every item of the family's property, and they disposed of it in their own imaginations from morning to night. At last the old gentleman, lying bedridden in the same room with the old lady, cries out in the old patter, fluent, after having been silent for two days and nights: "Now here, my jolly companions every one—which the Nightingale club in a village was held, At the sign of the Cabbage and Shears, Where the singers no doubt would have greatly excelled, But for want of taste, voices, and ears—now, here, my jolly companions, every one, is a working model of a used-up old Cheap Jack, without a tooth in his head, and with a pain in every bone; so like life that it would be just as good if it wasn't better, just as bad if it wasn't worse, and just as new if it wasn't worn out. Bid for the working-model of the old Cheap Jack, who has drunk more gunpowder-tea with the ladies in his time than would blow the lid off a washer-woman's copper, and carry it as many thousands of miles higher than the moon as naught nix naught, divided by the national debt, carry nothing to the poor-rates, three under and two over. Now, my hearts of oak and men of straw, what do you say for the lot? Two shillings, a shilling, tenpence, eightpence, sixpence, fourpence. Twopence? Who said twopence? The gentleman in the scarecrow's hat? I am ashamed of the gentleman in the scarecrow's hat. I really am ashamed of him for his want of public spirit. Now I'll tell you what I'll do with you. Come! I'll throw you in a working model of an old woman that was married to the old Cheap Jack so long ago that upon my word and honor it took place in Noah's Ark, before the Unicorn could get in to forbid the banns by blowing a tune upon his horn. There now! Come! What do you say for both? I'll tell you what I'll do with you. I don't bear you malice for being so backward. Here! If you make me a bid that'll only reflect a little credit on your town, I'll throw you in a warming-pan for nothing, and lend you a toasting-fork for life. Now come; what do you say after that splendid offer? Say two pound, say thirty shillings, say a pound, say ten shillings, say five, say two and six? You don't say even two and six? You say two and three? No. You sha'n't have the lot for two and three. I'd sooner give it you, if you was good-looking enough. Here! Missis! Chuck the old man and woman into the cart, put the horse to, and drive 'em away and bury 'em!" Such were the last words of Willum Marigold, my own father, and they were carried out, by him and by his wife, my own mother, on one and the same day, as I ought to know, having followed as mourner.

My father had been a lovely one in his time at the Cheap Jack work, as his dying observations went to prove. But I top him. I don't say it because it's myself, but because it has been universally acknowledged by all that has had the means of comparison. I have worked at it. I have measured myself against other public speakers—Members of Parliament, Platforms, Pulpits, Counsel learned in the law—and where I have found 'em good, I have took a bit of imagination from 'em and where I have found 'em bad, I have let 'em alone. Now I'll tell you what. I mean to go down into my grave declaring that of all the callings ill-used in Great Britain, the Cheap Jack calling is the worst used. Why ain't we a profession? Why ain't we endowed with privileges? Why are we forced to take out a hawker's license, when no such thing is expected of the political hawkers? Where's the difference betwixt us? Except that we are Cheap Jacks and they are Dear Jacks, *I* don't see any difference but what's in our favor.

For look here! Say it's election time. I am on the footboard of my cart in the market place on a Saturday night. I put up a general miscellaneous lot. I say: "Now here, my free and independent woters, I'm a-going to give you such a chance as you never had in all your born days, nor yet the days preceding. Now I'll show you what I am a-going to do with you. Here's a pair of razors that'll shave you closer than the Board of Guardians; here's a flat-iron worth its weight in gold; here's a frying-pan artificially flavored with essence of beefsteaks to that degree that you've only got for the rest of your lives to fry bread and dripping in it and there you are replete with animal food; here's a genuine chronometer watch in such a solid silver case that you may knock at the door with it when you come home late from a social meeting, and rouse your wife and family, and save up your knocker for the postman; and here's half a dozen dinner-plates that you may play the cymbals with to charm the baby when it's fractious. Stop! I'll throw you in another article, and I'll give you that, and it's a rolling-pin; and ·if the baby can only get it well into its mouth when its teeth is coming and rub the gums once with it, they'll come through double, in a fit of laughter equal to being tickled. Stop again! I'll throw you in another article, because I don't like the looks of you, for you haven't the appearance of buyers unless I lose by you, and because I'd rather lose than not take money tonight, and that's a looking-glass in which you may see how ugly you look when you don't bid! What do you say now? Come! Do you say a pound? Not you, for you haven't got it. Do you say ten shillings? Not you, for you owe more to the tallyman. Well then, I'll tell you what I'll do with you. I'll heap 'em all on the footboard of the cart—there they are! razors, flat-iron, frying-pan, chronometer watch, dinner-plates, rolling-pin, and looking-glass—take 'em all away for four shillings, and I'll give you sixpence for your trouble!" This is me, the Cheap Jack. But on the Monday morning, in the same market place, comes the Dear Jack on the hustings—*his* cart—and what does *he* say? "Now my free and independent woters, I am a-going to give you such a chance" (he begins just like me) "as you never had in all your born days, and that's the chance of sending Myself to parliament. Now I'll tell you what I am a-going to do for you. Here's the interests of this magnificent town promoted above all the rest of the civilized and uncivilized earth. Here's your railways carried, and your neighbors' railways jockeyed. Here's all your sons in the Post-Office. Here's Britannia smiling on you. Here's the eyes of Europe on you. Here's uniwersal prosperity for you, repletion of animal food, golden cornfields, gladsome homesteads, and rounds of applause from your own hearts, all in one lot, and that's myself. Will you take me as I stand? You won't? Well, then I'll tell you what I'll do with you. Come now! I'll throw you in anything you ask for. There! Church-rates, abolition of church-rates, more malt tax, no malt tax, uniwersal education to the highest mark, or uniwersal ignorance to the lowest, total abolition of flogging in the army or a dozen for every private once a month all round. Wrongs of Men or Rights of Women—only say which it shall be, take 'em or leave 'em, and I'm of your opinion altogether, and the lot's your own on your own terms. There! You won't take it yet! Well, then I'll tell you what I'll do with you. Come! You *are* such free and independent woters, and I *am* so proud of you,—you *are* such a noble and enlightened constituency,—and I *am* so ambitious of the honor and dignity of being your member, which is by far the highest level to which the wings of the human mind can soar,—that I'll tell you what I'll do with you. I'll throw you in all the public houses in your magnificent town for nothing. Will that content you? It won't? You won't take the lot yet? Well, then, before I put the horse in and drive away, and make the offer to the next most magnificent town that can be discovered, I'll tell you what I'll do. Take the lot, and I'll drop two thousand pound in the streets of your magnificent town for them to pick up that can. Not enough? Now look here. This is the very · furthest that I'm a-going to. I'll make it two thousand five hundred. And still you won't? Here, missis! Put the horse—no, stop half a moment, I shouldn't like to turn my back upon you neither for a trifle. I'll make it two thousand seven hundred and fifty pound. There! Take the lot on your own terms, and I'll count out two thousand seven hundred and fifty pound on the footboard of the cart, to be dropped in the streets of your magnificent town for them to pick up that can. What do you say? Come now! You won't do better, and you may do worse. You take it! Hooray! Sold again and got the seat!"

These Dear Jacks soap the people shameful, but we Cheap Jacks don't. We tell 'em the truth about themselves to their faces, and scorn to court 'em. As to wenturesomeness in the way of puffing up the lots, the Dear Jacks beat us hollow. It is considered in the Cheap Jack calling, that better patter can be made out of a gun than any article we put up from the cart, except a pair of spectacles. I often hold forth about a gun for a quarter of an hour, and feel as if I need never leave off. But when I tell 'em what the gun can do, and what the gun has brought down, I never go half so far as the Dear Jacks do when they make speeches in praise of their guns,—their great guns that set 'em on to do it. Besides, I'm in business for myself; I ain't sent down into the market place to order, as they are. Besides, again, my guns don't know what I say in their laudation, and their guns do, and the whole concern of 'em have reason to be sick and ashamed all round. These are some of my arguments for declaring that the Cheap Jack calling is treated ill in Great Britain, and for turning warm when I think of the other Jacks in question setting themselves up to pretend to look down upon it.

I courted my wife from the footboard of the cart. I did indeed. She was a Suffolk young woman, and it was in Ipswich market place right opposite the corn-chandler's shop. I had noticed her up at a window last Saturday that was, appreciating highly. I had took to her, and I had said to myself, "If not already disposed of, I'll have that lot." Next Saturday that come, I pitched the cart on the same pitch, and I was in very high feather indeed, keeping 'em laughing the whole of the time, and getting off the goods briskly. At last I took out of my waist-coat-pocket a small lot wrapped in soft paper, and I put it this way (looking up at the window where she was). "Now here, my blooming English maidens, is an article, the last article of the present evening's sale, which I offer to only you, the lovely Suffolk Dumplings biling over with beauty, and I won't take a bid of a thousand pounds for from any man alive. Now what is it? Why, I'll tell you what it is. It's made of fine gold, and it's not broke, though there's a hole in the middle of it, and it's stronger than any fetter that ever was forged, though it's smaller than any finger in my set of ten. Why ten? Because, when my parents made over my property to me, I tell you true, there was twelve sheets, twelve towels, twelve table-cloths, twelve knives, twelve forks, twelve table-spoons, and twelve teaspoons, but my set of fingers was two short of a dozen, and could never since be matched. Now what else is it? Come, I'll tell you. It's a hoop of solid gold, wrapped in a silver curl-paper that I myself took off the shining locks of the ever beautiful old lady in Threadneedle Street, London City; I wouldn't tell you so if I hadn't the paper to show, or you mightn't believe it even of me. Now what else is it? It's a man-trap and a handcuff, the parish stocks and a leglock, all in gold and all in one. Now what else is it? It's a wedding-ring. Now I'll tell you what I'm a-going to do with it. I'm not a-going to offer this lot for money; but I mean to give it to the next of you beauties that laughs, and I'll pay her a visit tomorrow morning at exactly half after nine o'clock as the chimes go, and I'll take her out for a walk to put up the banns." *She* laughed, and got the ring handed up to her. When I called in the morning, she says, "O dear! It's never you, and you never mean it?" "It's ever me," says I, "and I am ever yours, and I ever mean it." So we got married, after being put up three times,—which, by the bye, is quite in the Cheap Jack way again, and shows once more how the Cheap Jack customs pervade society.

She wasn't a bad wife, but she had a temper. If she could have parted with that one article at a sacrifice, I wouldn't have swopped her away in exchange for any other woman in England. Not that I ever did swop her away, for we lived together till she died, and that was thirteen year. Now, my lords and ladies and gentlefolks all, I'll let you into a secret, though you won't believe it. Thirteen year of temper in a Palace would try the worst of you, but thirteen year of temper in a Cart would try the best of you. You are kept so very close to it in a cart, you see. There's thousands of couples among you getting on like sweet ile upon a whetstone in houses five and six pairs of stairs high, that would go to the Divorce Court in a cart. Whether the jolting makes it worse, I don't undertake to decide; but in a cart it does come home to you, and stick to you. Wiolence in a cart is so wiolent, and aggrawation in a cart is *so* aggrawating.

We might have had such a pleasant life! A roomy cart, with the large goods hung outside, and the bed slung underneath it when on the road, an iron pot and a kettle, a fireplace for the cold weather, a chimney for the smoke, a hanging shelf and a cupboard, a dog, and a horse. What more do you want? You draw off upon a bit of turf in a green lane or by the roadside, you hobble your old horse and turn him grazing, you light your fire upon the ashes of the last visitors, you cook your stew, and you wouldn't call the Emperor of France your father. But have a temper in the cart, flinging language and the hardest goods in stock at you, and where are you then? Put a name to your feelings.

My dog knew as well when she was on the turn as I did. Before she broke out, he would give a howl, and bolt. How he knew it, was a mystery to me; but the sure and certain knowledge of it would wake him up out of his soundest sleep, and he would give a howl, and bolt. At such times I wished I was him.

The worst of it was, we had a daughter born to us, and I love children with all my heart. When she was in her furies, she beat the child. This got to be so shocking, as the child got to be four or five year old, that I have many a time gone on with my whip over my shoulder, at the old horse's head, sobbing and crying worse than ever little Sophy did. For how could I prevent it? Such a thing is not to be tried with such a temper—in a cart—without coming to a fight. It's in the natural size and formation of a cart to bring it to a fight. And then the poor child got worse terrified than before, as well as worse hurt generally, and her mother made complaints to the next people we lighted on, and the word went round, "Here's a wretch of a Cheap Jack been a-beating his wife."

Little Sophy was such a brave child! She grew to be quite devoted to her poor father, though he could do so little to help her. She had a wonderful quantity of shining dark hair, all curling natural about her. It is quite astonishing to me now, that I didn't go tearing mad when I used to see her run from her mother before the cart, and her mother catch her by this hair, and pull her down by it, and beat her.

Such a brave child I said she was! Ah! with reason.

"Don't you mind next time, father dear," she would whisper to me, with her little face still flushed, and her bright eyes still wet; "if I don't cry out, you may know I am not much hurt. And even if I do cry out, it will only be to get mother to let go and leave off." What I have seen the little spirit bear—for me—without crying out!

Yet in other respects her mother took great care of her. Her clothes were always clean and neat, and her mother was never tired of working at 'em. Such is the inconsistency in things. Our being down in the marsh country in unhealthy weather, I consider the cause of Sophy's taking bad low fever; but however she took it, once she got it she turned away from her mother forevermore, and nothing would persuade her to be touched by her mother's hand. She would shiver and say, "No, no, no," when it was offered at, and would hide her face on my shoulder, and hold me tighter round the neck.

The Cheap Jack business had been worse than ever I had known it, what with one thing and what with another (and not least what with railroads, which will cut it all to pieces, I expect, at last), and I was run dry of money. For which reason, one night at that period of little Sophy's being so bad, either we must have come to a deadlock for victuals and drink, or I must have pitched the cart as I did.

I couldn't get the dear child to lie down or leave go of me, and indeed I hadn't the heart to try, so I stepped out on the footboard with her holding round my neck. They all set up a laugh when they see us, and one chuckle-headed Joskin (that I hated for it) made the bidding, "Tuppence for her!"

"Now, you country boobies," says I, feeling as if my heart was a heavy weight at the end of a broken sash-line, "I give you notice that I am a-going to charm the money out of your pockets, and to give you so much more than your money's worth that you'll only persuade yourselves to draw your Saturday night's wages ever again arterwards by the hopes of meeting me to lay 'em out with, which you never will, and why not? Because I've made my fortune by selling my goods on a large scale for seventy-five per cent. less than I give for 'em, and I am consequently to be elevated to the House of Peers next week, by the title of the Duke of Cheap and Markis Jackaloorul. Now let's know what you want tonight, and you shall have it. But first of all, shall I tell you why I have got this little girl round my neck? You don't want to know? Then you shall. She belongs to the Fairies. She's a fortune-teller. She can tell me all about you in a whisper, and can put me up to whether you're a-going to buy a lot or leave it. Now do you want a saw? No, she says you don't, because you're too clumsy to use one. Else here's a saw which would be a lifelong blessing to a handy man, at four shillings, at three-and-six, at three, at two-and-six, at two, at eighteen-pence. But none of you shall have it at any price, on account of your well-known awkwardness, which would make it manslaughter. The same objection applies to this set of three planes which I won't let you have neither, so don't bid for 'em. Now I am a-going to ask her what you do want." (Then I whispered, "Your head burns so that I am afraid it hurts you bad, my pet," and she answered, without opening her heavy eyes, "Just a little, father.") "Oh! This little fortune-teller says it's a memorandum-book you want. Then why didn't you mention it? Here it is. Look at it. Two hundred superfine hot-pressed wire-wove pages—if you don't believe me, count 'em—ready ruled for your expenses, an everlastingly pointed pencil to put 'em down with, a double-bladed penknife to scratch 'em out with, a book of printed tables to calculate your income with, and a camp-stool to sit down upon while you give your mind to it! Stop! And an umbrella to keep the moon off when you give your mind to it on a pitch-dark night. Now I won't ask you how much for the lot, but how little? How little you are thinking of? Don't be ashamed to mention it, because my fortune-teller knows already." (Then making believe to whisper, I kissed her, and she kissed me.) "Why, she says, you're thinking of as little as three and threepence! I couldn't have believed it, even of you, unless she told me. Three and threepence! And a set of printed tables in the lot that'll calculate your income up to forty thousand a year! With an income of forty thousand a year, you grudge three and sixpence. Well then, I'll tell you my opinion. I so despise the threepence that I'd sooner take three shillings. There. For three shillings, three shillings, three shillings! Gone. Hand 'em over to the lucky man."

As there had been no bid at all, everybody looked about and grinned at everybody, while I touched little Sophy's face, and asked her if she felt faint or giddy. "Not very, father. It will soon be over." Then turning from the pretty, patient eyes, which were opened now, and seeing nothing but grins across my lighted greasepot, I went on again in my Cheap Jack style. "Where's the butcher?" (my sorrowful eye had just caught sight of a fat young butcher on the outside of the crowd.) "She says the good luck is the butcher's. Where is he?" Everybody handed on the blushing butcher to the front, and there was a roar, and the butcher felt obliged to put his hand in his pocket, and take the lot. The party so picked out, in general, does feel obliged to take the lot,—good four times out of six. Then we had another lot, the counterpart of that one, and sold it sixpence cheaper, which is always wery much enjoyed. Then we had the spectacles. It ain't a special profitable lot, but I put 'em on, and I see what the Chancellor of the Exchequer is going to take off the taxes, and I see what the sweetheart of the young woman in the shawl is doing at home, and I see what the Bishops has got for dinner, and a deal more that seldom fails to fetch 'em up in their spirits; and the better their spirits the better their bids. Then we had the ladies' lot,—the teapot, tea-caddy, glass sugar-basin, half a dozen spoons, and a caudle-cup,—and all the time I was making similar excuses to give a look or two and say a word or two to my poor child. It was while the second ladies' lot was holding 'em enchained that I felt her lift herself a little on my shoulder to look across the dark street. "What troubles you, darling?" "Nothing troubles me, father. I am not at all troubled. But don't I see a pretty churchyard over there?" "Yes, my dear." "Kiss me twice, dear father, and lay me down to rest upon that churchyard grass so soft and green." I staggered back into the cart with her head dropped on my shoulder, and I says to her mother, "Quick. Shut the door! Don't let those laughing people see!" "What's the matter?" she cries. "O woman, woman," I tells her, "you'll never catch my little little Sophy by her hair again, for she has flown away from you!"

Maybe those were harder words than I meant 'em; but from that time forth my wife took to brooding, and would sit in the cart or walk beside it hours at a stretch, with her arms crossed and her eyes looking on the ground. When her furies took her (which was rather seldomer than before) they took her in a new way, and she banged herself about to that extent that I was forced to hold her. She got none the better for a little drink now and then, and through some years I used to wonder, as I plodded along at the old horse's head, whether there was many carts upon the road that held so much dreariness as mine, for all my being looked up to as the King of the Cheap Jacks. So sad our lives went on till one summer evening, when, as we were coming into Exeter out of the farther West of England, we saw a woman beating a child in a cruel manner, who screamed, "Don't beat me! O mother, mother, mother!" Then my wife stopped her ears, and ran away like a wild thing, and next day she was found in the river.

Me and my dog were all the company left in the cart now; and the dog learned to give a short bark when they wouldn't bid, and to give another and a nod of his head when I asked him, "Who said half a crown? Are you the gentleman sir, that offered half a crown?" He attained to an immense height of popularity, and I shall always believe taught himself entirely out of his own head to growl at any person in the crowd that bid as low as sixpence. But he got to be well on in years, and one night when I was conwulsing York with the spectacles, he took a conwulsion on his own account upon the very footboard by me, and it finished him.

Being naturally of a tender turn, I had dreadful lonely feelings on me arter this. I conquered 'em at selling times, having a reputation to keep (not to mention keeping myself), but they got me down in private, and rolled upon me. That's often the way with us public characters. See us on the footboard, and you'd give pretty well anything you possess to be us. See us off the footboard, and you'd add a trifle to be off your bargain. It was under those circumstances that I come acquainted with a giant. I might have been too high to fall into conversation with him, had it not been for my lonely feelings. For the general rule is, going round the country, to draw the line at dressing up. When a man can't trust his getting a living to his undisguised abilities, you consider him below your sort. And this giant when on view figured as a Roman.

He was a languid young man, which I attribute to the distance betwixt his extremities. He had a little head and less in it, he had weak eyes and weak knees, and altogether you couldn't look at him without feeling that there was greatly too much of him both for his joints and his mind. But he was an amiable though timid young man (his mother let him out, and spent the money), and we come acquainted when he was walking to ease the horse betwixt two fairs. He was called Rinaldo di Velasco, his name being Pickleson.

This giant, otherwise Pickleson, mentioned to me under the seal of confidence that, beyond his being a burden to himself his life was made a burden to him by the cruelty of his master towards a step-daughter who was deaf and dumb. Her mother was dead, and she had no living soul to take her part, and was used most hard. She traveled with his master's caravan only because there was nowhere to leave her, and this giant, otherwise Pickleson, did go so far as to believe that his master often tried to lose her. He was such a very languid young man, that I don't know how long it didn't take him to get this story out, but it passed through his defective circulation to his top extremity in course of time.

When I heard this account from the giant, otherwise Pickleson, and likewise that the poor girl had beautiful long dark hair, and was often pulled down by it and beaten, I couldn't see the giant through what stood in my eyes. Having wiped 'em, I gave him a sixpence (for he was kept as short as he was long), and he laid it out in two threepenn'orths of gin-and-water which so brisked him up, that he sang the Favorite Comic of Shivery Shakey, ain't it cold?—a popular effect which his master had tried every other means to get out of him as a Roman wholly in vain.

His master's name was Mim, a wery hoarse man, and I knew him to speak to. I went to that Fair as a mere civilian, leaving the cart outside the town, and I looked about the back of the Vans while the performing was going on, and at last, sitting dozing against a muddy cart-wheel, I come upon the poor girl who was deaf and dumb. At the first look I might almost have judged that she had escaped from the Wild Beast Show; but at the second I thought better of her, and thought that if she was more cared for and more kindly used she would be like my child. She was just the same age that my own daughter would have been, if her pretty head had not fell down upon my shoulder that unfortunate night.

To cut it short, I spoke confidential to Mim while he was beating the gong outside betwixt two lots of Pickleson's publics, and I put it to him, "She lies heavy on your own hands; what'll you take for her?" Mim was a most ferocious swearer. Suppressing that part of his reply which was much the longest part, his reply was "A pair of braces." "Now I'll tell you," says I, "what I'm going to do with you. I'm going to fetch you half a dozen pair of the primest braces in the cart, and then to take her away with me." Says Mim (again ferocious), "I'll believe it when I've got the goods, and no sooner." I made all the haste I could, lest he should think twice of it and the bargain was completed, which Pickle-son he was hereby so relieved in his mind that he come out at his little back door, longways like a serpent, and give us Shivery Shakey in a whisper among the wheels at parting.

It was happy days for both of us when Sophy and me began to travel in the cart. I at once gave her the name of Sophy, to put her ever towards me in the attitude of my own daughter. We soon made out to begin to understand one another, through the goodness of the Heavens, when she knowed that I meant true and kind by her. In a very little time she was wonderful fond of me. You have no idea what it is to have anybody wonderful fond of you, unless you have been got down and rolled upon by the lonely feelings that I have mentioned as having once got the better of me.

You'd have laughed—or the rewerse—it's according to your disposi-tion—if you could have seen me trying to teach Sophy. At first I was helped—you'd never guess by what—milestones. I got some large al-phabets in a box, all the letters separate on bits of bone, and say we was going to WINDSOR, I give her those letters in that order, and then at every milestone I showed her those same letters in that same order again, and pointed towards the abode of royalty. Another time I give her CART, and then chalked the same upon the cart. Another time I give her DOCTOR MARIGOLD, and hung a corresponding inscrip-tion outside my waistcoat. People that met us might stare a bit and laugh, but what did *I* care, if she caught the idea? She caught it after long patience and trouble, and then we did begin to get on swimmingly, I believe you! At first she was a little given to consider me the cart, and the cart the abode of royalty, but that soon wore off.

We had our signs, too, and they was hundreds in number. Sometimes she would sit looking at me and considering hard how to communicate with me about something fresh,—how to ask me what she wanted ex-plained,—and then she was (or I thought she was; what does it signify?) so like my child with those years added to her, that I half believed it was herself, trying to tell me where she had been to up in the skies, and what she had seen since that unhappy night when she flied away. She had a pretty face, and now that there was no one to drag at her bright dark hair, and it was all in order, there was a something touching in her looks that made the cart most peaceful and most quiet, though not at all melancholy. [N. B. In the Cheap Jack patter, we generally sound it lemonjolly, and it gets a laugh.]

The way she learnt to understand any look of mine was truly surpris-ing. When I sold of a night, she would sit in the cart unseen by them outside, and would give a eager look into my eyes when I looked in, and would hand me straight the precise article or articles I wanted. And then she would clap her hands, and laugh for joy. And as for me, seeing her so bright, and remembering what she was when I first lighted on her;

starved and beaten and ragged, leaning asleep against the muddy cart-wheel, it give me such heart that I gained a greater heighth of reputation than ever, and I put Pickleson down (by the name of Mim's Traveling Giant, otherwise Pickleson) for a fypunnote in my will.

This happiness went on in the cart till she was sixteen year old. By which time I began to feel not satisfied that I had done my whole duty by her, and to consider that she ought to have better teaching than I could give her. It drew a many tears on both sides when I commenced explaining my views to her; but what's right is right, and you can't neither by tears nor laughter do away with its character.

So I took her hand in mine, and I went with her one day to the Deaf and Dumb Establishment in London, and when the gentleman come to speak to us, I says to him: "Now I'll tell you what I'll do with you, sir. I am nothing but a Cheap Jack, but of late years I have laid by for a rainy day notwithstanding. This is my only daughter (adopted), and you can't produce a deafer nor a dumber. Teach her the most that can be taught her in the shortest separation that can be named,—state the figure for it,—and I am game to put the money down. I won't bate you a single farthing, sir, but I'll put down the money here and now, and I'll thankfully throw you in a pound to take it. There!" The gentle-man smiled, and then, "Well, well," says he, "I must first know what she has learned already. How do you communicate with her?" Then I showed him, and she wrote in printed writing many names of things and so forth; and we held some sprightly conversation, Sophy and me, about a little story in a book which the gentleman showed her, and which she was able to read. "This is most extraordinary," says the gentleman; "is it possible that you have been her only teacher?" "I have been her only teacher, sir," I says, "besides herself." "Then," says the gentleman, and more acceptable words was never spoke to me, "you're a clever fellow, and a good fellow." This he makes known to Sophy, who kisses his hands, claps her own, and laughs and cries upon it.

We saw the gentleman four times in all, and when he took down my name and asked how in the world it ever chanced to be Doctor, it come out that he was own nephew by the sister's side, if you'll believe me, to the very doctor that I was called after. This made our footing still easier, and he says to me:—

"Now, Marigold, tell me what more do you want your adopted daughter to know?"

"I want her, sir, to be cut off from the world as little as can be, con-sidering her deprivations, and therefore to be able to read whatever is wrote with perfect ease and pleasure."

"My good fellow," urges the gentleman, opening his eyes wide, "why, *I* can't do that myself!"

I took his joke, and give him a laugh (knowing by experience how flat you fall without it), and I mended my words accordingly.

"What do you mean to do with her afterwards?" asks the gentleman, with a sort of a doubtful eye. "To take her about the country?"

"In the cart, sir, but only in the cart. She will live a private life, you understand, in the cart. I should never think of bringing her infirmities before the public. I wouldn't make a show for any money."

The gentleman nodded and seemed to approve.

"Well," says he, "can you part with her for two years?"

"To do her that good,—yes, sir."

"There's another question," says the gentleman, looking towards her—"can she part with you for two years?"

I don't know that it was a harder matter of itself (for the other was hard enough to me), but it was harder to get over. However, she was pacified to it at last, and the separation betwixt us was settled. How it cut up both of us when it took place, and when I left her at the door in the dark of an evening, I don't tell. But I know this: remembering that night, I shall never pass that same establishment without a heart-ache and a swelling in the throat; and I couldn't put you up the best of lots in sight of it with my usual spirit,—no, not even the gun, nor the pair of spectacles,—for five hundred pound reward from the Secretary of State for the Home Department, and throw in the honor of putting my legs under his mahogany afterwards.

Still, the loneliness that followed in the cart was not the old loneliness, because there was a term put to it, however long to look forward to; and because I could think, when I was anyways down, that she belonged to me and I belonged to her. Always planning for her coming back, I bought in a few months' time another cart, and what do you think I planned to do with it? I'll tell you. I planned to fit it up with shelves and books for her reading, and to have a seat in it where I could sit and see her read, and think that I had been her first teacher. Not hurrying over the job, I had the fittings knocked together in contriving ways under my own inspection, and here was her bed in a berth with curtains, and there was her reading-table, and here was her writing-desk, and elsewhere was her books in rows upon rows, picters and no picters, bindings and no bindings, gilt-edged and plain, just as I could pick 'em up for her in lots up and down the country, North and South and West and East, Winds liked best and winds liked least, Here and there and gone astray, Over the hills and far away. And when I had got together pretty well as many books as the cart would neatly hold, a new scheme come into my head, which, as it turned out, kept my time and attention a good deal employed, and helped me over the two years' stile.

Without being of an awaricious temper, I like to be the owner of things. I shouldn't wish, for instance, to go partners with yourself in the Cheap Jack cart. It's not that I mistrust you, but that I'd rather know it was mine. Similarly, very likely you'd rather know it was yours.

Well! A kind of a jealousy began to creep into my mind when I reflected that all those books would have been read by other people long before they was read by her. It seemed to take away from her being the owner of 'em like. In this way, the question got into my head: Couldn't I have a book new-made express for her, which she should be the first to read?

It pleased me, that thought did; and as I never was a man to let a thought sleep (you must wake up all the whole family of thoughts you've got and burn their nightcaps, or you won't do in the Cheap Jack line), I set to work at it. Considering that I was in the habit of changing so much about the country, and that I should have to find out a literary character here to make a deal with, and another literary character there to make a deal with, as opportunities presented, I hit on the plan that this same book should be a general miscellaneous lot,—like the razors, flat-iron, chronometer watch, dinner-plates, rolling-pin, and looking-glass,—and shouldn't be offered as a single individual article, like the spectacles or the gun. When I had come to that conclusion, I come to another, which shall likewise be yours.

Often had I regretted that she never had heard me on the footboard, and that she never could hear me. It ain't that *I* am vain, but that *you* don't like to put your own light under a bushel. What's the worth of your reputation, if you can't convey the reason for it to the person you most wish to value it? Now I'll put it to you. Is it worth sixpence, fippence, fourpence, threepence, twopence, a penny, a half-penny, a farthing? No, it ain't. Not worth a farthing. Very well, then. My conclusion was that I would begin her book with some account of myself. So that, through reading a specimen or two of me on the footboard, she might form an idea of my merits there. I was aware that I couldn't do myself justice. A man can't write his eye (at least *I* don't know how to), nor yet can a man write his voice, nor the rate of his talk, nor the quickness of his action, nor his general spicy way. But he can write his turns of speech, when he is a public speaker,— and indeed I have heard that he very often does, before he speaks 'em.

Well! Having formed that resolution, then come the question of a name. How did I hammer that hot iron into shape? This way. The most difficult explanation I had ever had with her was, how I come to be called Doctor, and yet was no Doctor. After all, I felt that I had failed of getting it correctly into her mind, with my utmost pains. But trusting to her improvement in the two years, I thought that I might trust to her understanding it when she should come to read it as put down by my own hand. Then I thought I would |try a joke with her and watch how it took, by which of itself I might fully judge of her understanding it. We had first discovered the mistake we had dropped into, through her having asked me to prescribe for her when she had supposed me to be a Doctor in a medical point of view; so thinks I,

"Now, if I give this book the name of my Prescriptions, and if she catches the idea that my only Prescriptions are for her amusement and interest,—to make her laugh in a pleasant way, or to make her cry in a pleasant way—it will be a delightful proof to both of us that we have got over our difficulty." It fell out to absolute perfection. For when she saw the book, as I had it got up,—the printed and pressed book,— lying on her desk in her cart, and saw the title "Doctor Marigold's Prescriptions," she looked at me for a moment with astonishment, then fluttered the leaves, then broke out a-laughing in the charmingest way, then felt her pulse and shook her head, then turned the pages pretending to read them most attentive, then kissed the book to me, and put it to her bosom with both her hands. I never was better pleased in all my life!

But let me not anticipate. (I take that expression out of a lot of romances I bought for her. I never opened a single one of 'em—and I have opened many—but I found the romancer saying "let me not antici- pate." Which being so, I wonder why he did anticipate, or who asked him to it.) Let me not, I say, anticipate. This same book took up all my spare time. It was no play to get the other articles together in the general miscellaneous lot, but when it come to my own article! There! I couldn't have believed the blotting, nor yet the buckling to at it, nor the patience over it. Which again is like the footboard. The public have no idea.

At last it was done, and the two years' time was gone after all the other time before it, and where it's all gone to, who knows? The new cart was finished,—yellow outside, relieved with wermilion and brass fittings, —the old horse was put in it, a new 'un and a boy being laid on for the Cheap Jack cart,—and I cleaned myself up to go and fetch her. Bright cold weather it was, cart-chimneys smoking, carts pitched private on a piece of waste ground over at Wandsworth where you may see 'em from the Sou'western Railway when not upon the road. (Look out of the right-hand window going down.)

"Marigold," says the gentleman, giving his hand heartily, "I am very glad to see you."

"Yet I have my doubts, sir," says I, "if you can be half as glad to see me as I am to see you."

"The time has appeared so long,—has it, Marigold?"

"I won't say that, sir, considering its real length; but—"

"What a start, my good fellow!"

Ah! I should think it was! Grown such a woman, so pretty, so intelli- gent, so expressive! I knew then that she must be really like my child, or I could never have known her, standing quiet by the door.

"You are affected," says the gentleman, in a kindly manner.

"I feel, sir," says I, "that I am but a rough chap in a sleeved waist- coat."

"I feel," says the gentleman, "that it was you who raised her from misery and degradation, and brought her into communication with her kind. But why do we converse alone together, when we can converse so well with her? Address her in your own way."

"I am such a rough chap in a sleeved waistcoat, sir," says I, "and she is such a graceful woman, and she stands so quiet at the door!"

"Try if she moves at the old sign," says the gentleman.

They had got it up together o' purpose to please me! For when I give her the old sign, she rushed to my feet, and dropped upon her knees, holding up her hands to me with pouring tears of love and joy; and when I took her hands and lifted her, she clasped me round the neck, and lay there; and I don't know what a fool I didn't make of myself, until we all three settled down into talking without sound, as if there was a something soft and pleasant spread over the whole world for us.

II. TO BE TAKEN FOR LIFE

So every item of my plan was crowned with success. Our reunited life was more than all that we had looked forward to. Content and joy went with us as the wheels of the two carts went round, and the same stopped with us when the two carts stopped. I was as pleased and as proud as a Pug-Dog with his muzzle black-leaded for a evening party, and his tail extra curled by machinery.

But I had left something out of my calculations. Now, what had I left out? To help you to a guess, I'll say, a figure. Come. Make a guess, and guess right. Naught? No. Nine? No. Eight? No. Seven? No. Six? No. Five? No. Four? No. Three? No. Two? No. One? No. Now, I'll tell you what I'll do with you. I'll say it's another sort of figure altogether. There. Why then, says you, it's a mortal figure. No, nor yet a mortal figure. By such means you get yourself penned into a corner, and you can't help guessing a *im*-mortal figure. That's about it. Why didn't you say so sooner?

Yes. It was a immortal figure that I had altogether left out of my calculations. Neither man's nor woman's, but a child's. Girl's, or boy's? Boy's. "'I', says the sparrow, 'with my bow and arrow.'" Now you have got it.

We were down at Lancaster, and I had done two nights more than fair average business (though I cannot in honor recommend them as a quick audience) in the open square there, near the end of the street where Mr. Sly's King's Arms and Royal Hotel stands. Mim's traveling giant, otherwise Pickleson, happened at the self-same time to be a trying it on in the town. The genteel lay was adopted with him. No hint of a van. Green baize alcove leading up to Pickleson in a Auction Room. Printed poster, "Free list suspended, with the exception of that proud boast of an enlightened country, a free press. Schools admitted by private arrangement. Nothing to raise a blush in the cheek of youth or shock the most fastidious." Mim swearing most horrible and terrific, in a pink calico pay-place, at the slackness of the public. Serious hand-bill in the shops, importing that it was almost impossible to come to a right understanding of the history of David without seeing Pickleson.

I went to the Auction Room in question, and I found it entirely empty of everything but echoes and mouldiness, with the single exception of Pickleson on a piece of red drugget. This suited my purpose, as I wanted a private and confidential word with him, which was: "Pickle-son. Owing much happiness to you, I put you in my will for a fypun-note; but, to save trouble, here's fourpunten down, which may equally suit your views, and let us so conclude the transaction." Pickleson, who up to that remark had had the dejected appearance of a long Roman rushlight that couldn't anyhow get lighted, brightened up at his top extremity, and made his acknowledgments in a way which (for him) was parliamentary eloquence. He likewise did add, that, having ceased to draw as a Roman, Mim had made proposals for his going in as a con-werted Indian Giant worked upon by The Dairyman's Daughter. This, Pickleson, having no acquaintance with the tract named after that young woman, and not being willing to couple gag with his serious views, had declined to do, thereby leading to words and the total stoppage of the unfortunate young man's beer. All of which, during the whole of the interview, was confirmed by the ferocious growling of Mim down below in the pay-place, which shook the giant like a leaf.

But what was to the present point in the remarks of the traveling giant, otherwise Pickleson, was this: "Doctor Marigold"—I give his words without a hope of conveying their feebleness—"who is the strange young man that hangs about your carts?"—"The strange young *man?*" —I gives him back, thinking that he meant her, and his languid circula-tion had dropped a syllable. "Doctor," he returns, with a pathos calculated to draw a tear from even a manly eye, "I am weak, but not so weak yet as that I don't know my words. I repeat them, Doctor. The strange young man." It then appeared that Pickleson, being forced to stretch his legs (not that they wanted it) only at times when he couldn't be seen for nothing, to wit in the dead of the night and towards daybreak, had twice seen hanging about my carts, in that same town of Lancaster where I had been only two nights, this same unknown young man.

It put me rather out of sorts. What it meant as to particulars I no more foreboded then than you forebode now, but it put me rather out of sorts. Howsoever, I made light of it to Pickleson, and I took leave of Pickleson, advising him to spend his legacy in getting up his stamina, and to continue to stand by his religion. Towards morning I kept a lookout for the strange young man, and—what was more—I saw the strange young man. He was well dressed and well looking. He loitered very nigh my carts, watching them like as if he was taking care of them, and soon after daybreak turned and went away. I sent a hail after him, but he never started or looked round, or took the smallest notice.

We left Lancaster within an hour or two, on our way towards Carlisle. Next morning, at daybreak, I looked out again for the strange young man. I did not see him. But next morning I looked out again, and there he was once more. I sent another hail after him, but as before he gave not the slightest sign of being anyways disturbed. This put a thought into my head. Acting on it, I watched him in different manners and at different times not necessary to enter into, till I found that this strange young man was deaf and dumb.

The discovery turned me over, because I knew that a part of that establishment where she had been was allotted to young men (some of them well off), and I thought to myself, "If she favors him, where am I? and where is all that I have worked and planned for?" Hoping —I must confess to the selfishness—that she might *not* favor him, I set myself to find out. At last I was by accident present at a meeting between them in the open air, looking on leaning behind a fir-tree without their knowing of it. It was a moving meeting for all the three parties concerned. I knew every syllable that passed between them as well as they did. I listened with my eyes, which had come to be as quick and true with deaf and dumb conversation as my ears with the talk of people that can speak. He was a-going out to China as clerk in a merchant's house, which his father had been before him. He was in circumstances to keep a wife, and he wanted her to marry him, and go along with him. She persisted, no. He asked if she didn't love him. Yes, she loved him dearly, dearly; but she could never disappoint her beloved, good, noble, generous, and I-don't-know-what all father (meaning me, the Cheap Jack in the sleeved waistcoat), and she would stay with him, Heaven bless him! though it was to break her heart. Then she cried most bitterly, and that made up my mind.

While my mind had been in an unsettled state about her favoring this young man, I had felt that unreasonable towards Pickleson, that it was well for him he had got his legacy down. For I often thought, "If it hadn't been for this same weak-minded giant, I might never have come to trouble my head and wex my soul about the young man." But, once that I knew she loved him—once that I had seen her weep for him—it was a different thing. I made it right in my mind with Pickleson on the spot, and I shook myself together to do what was right by all.

She had left the young man by that time (for it took a few minutes to get me thoroughly well shook together), and the young man was leaning against another of the fir-trees—of which there was a cluster—with his face upon his arm. I touched him on the back. Looking up and seeing me, he says, in our deaf and dumb talk, "Do not be angry."

"I am not angry, good boy, I am your friend. Come with me."

I left him at the foot of the steps of the Library Cart, and I went up alone. She was drying her eyes.

"You have been crying, my dear."

"Yes, father."

"Why?"

"A headache."

"Not a heartache?"

"I said a headache, father."

"Doctor Marigold must prescribe for that headache."

She took up the book of my Prescriptions, and held it up with a forced smile, but seeing me keep still and look earnest she softly laid it down again, and her eyes were very attentive.

"The Prescription is not there, Sophy."

"Where is it?"

"Here, my dear."

I brought her young husband in, and I put her hand in his, and my only further words to both of them were these: "Doctor Marigold's last prescription. To be taken for life." After which I bolted.

When the wedding come off, I mounted a coat (blue, and bright buttons), for the first and last time in all my days, and I give Sophy away with my own hand. There were only us three and the gentleman who had had charge of her for those two years. I give the wedding dinner of four in the Library Cart. Pigeon pie, a leg of pickled pork, a pair of fowls, and suitable garden stuff. The best of drinks. I give them a speech, and the gentleman give us a speech, and all our jokes told, and the whole went off like a sky-rocket. In the course of the entertainment I explained to Sophy that I should keep the Library Cart as my living-cart when not upon the road, and that I should keep all her books for her just as they stood, till she come back to claim them. So she went to China with her young husband, and it was a parting sorrowful and heavy, and I got the boy I had another service; and so as of old, when my child and wife were gone, I went plodding along alone, with my whip over my shoulder, at the old horse's head.

Sophy wrote me many letters, and I wrote her many letters. About the end of the first year she sent me one in an unsteady hand: "Dearest father, not a week ago I had a darling little daughter, but I am so well that they let me write these words to you. Dearest and best father, I hope my child may not be deaf and dumb, but I do not yet know." When I wrote back, I hinted the question; but as Sophy never answered that question, I felt it to be a sad one, and I never repeated it. For a long time our letters were regular, but then they got irregular, through Sophy's husband being moved to another station, and through my being always on the move. But we were in one another's thoughts, I was equally sure, letters or no letters.

Five years, odd months, had gone since Sophy went away. I was still the King of the Cheap Jacks, and at a greater height of popularity than ever. I had had a first-rate autumn of it, and on the twenty-third of December, one thousand eight hundred and sixty-four, I found myself at Uxbridge, Middlesex, clean sold out. So I jogged up to London with the old horse, light and easy, to have my Christmas eve and Christmas day alone by the fire in the Library Cart, and then to buy a regular new stock of goods all round, to sell 'em again and get the money.

I am a neat hand at cookery, and I'll tell you what I knocked up for my Christmas-eve dinner in the Library Cart. I knocked up a beef-steak pudding for one, with two kidneys, a dozen oysters, and a couple of mushrooms thrown in. It's a pudding to put a man in good humor with everything except the two bottom buttons of his waistcoat. Having relished that pudding and cleared away, I turned the lamp low, and sat down by the light of the fire, watching it as it shone upon the backs of Sophy's books.

Sophy's books so brought up Sophy's self that I saw her touching face quite plainly, before I dropped off dozing by the fire. This may be a reason why Sophy, with her deaf and dumb child in her arms, seemed to stand silent by me all through my nap. I was on the road, off the road, in all sorts of places, North and South and West and East, Winds liked best and winds liked least, Here and there and gone astray, Over the hills and far away, and still she stood silent by me, with her silent child in her arms. Even when I woke with a start, she seemed to vanish, as if she had stood by me in that very place only a single instant before.

I had started at a real sound and the sound was on the steps of the cart. It was the light, hurried tread of a child, coming clambering up. That tread of a child had once been so familiar to me that for half a moment I believed I was a going to see a little ghost.

But the touch of a real child was laid upon the outer handle of the door, and the handle turned, and the door opened a little way, and a real child peeped in. A bright little comely girl with large dark eyes.

Looking full at me, the tiny creature took off her mite of a straw hat, and a quantity of dark curls fell all about her face. Then she opened her lips, and said in a pretty voice:

"Grandfather!"

"Ah, my God!" I cries out. "She can speak!"

"Yes, dear grandfather. And I am to ask you whether there was ever any one that I remind you of?"

In a moment Sophy was round my neck, as well as the child, and her husband was a-wringing my hand with his face hid, and we all had to shake ourselves together before we could get over it. And when we did begin to get over it, and I saw the pretty child a-talking, pleased and quick and eager and busy, to her mother, in the signs that I had first taught her mother, the happy and yet pitying tears fell rolling down my face.

TAKING THE REDOUBT

By Prosper Mérimée

[Prosper Mérimée (1803–1870), the French novelist, critic, historian, and statesman, was born at Paris and died at Cannes. As a statesman he rose to the rank of senator in 1853. As a historian he has a number of volumes to his credit. His novel *Columba* (1830) is pretty generally considered his best piece of fiction.

This translation of *Taking the Redoubt* (written in 1829) is reprinted from *Little French Masterpieces*, by permission of G. P. Putnam's Sons, publishers.]

A MILITARY friend of mine, who died of a fever in Greece a few years ago, told me one day about the first action in which he took part. His story made such an impression on me that I wrote it down from memory as soon as I had time. Here it is:

I joined the regiment on the fourth of September, in the evening. I found the colonel in camp. He received me rather roughly; but when he read General B——'s recommendation, his manner changed, and he said a few courteous words to me.

I was presented by him to my captain, who had just returned from a reconnaissance. This captain, with whom I hardly had time to become acquainted, was a tall, dark man, with a harsh, repellent face. He had been a private and had won his epaulets and his cross on the battlefield. His voice, which was hoarse and weak, contrasted strangely with his almost gigantic stature. I was told that he owed that peculiar voice to a bullet which had passed through his lungs at the battle of Jena.

When he learned that I was fresh from the school at Fontainebleau, he made a wry face and said:

"My lieutenant died yesterday."

I understood that he meant to imply: "You ought to take his place, and you are not capable of it."

A sharp retort came to my lips, but I restrained myself.

The moon rose behind the redoubt of Cheverino, about two gunshots from our bivouac. It was large and red, as it usually is when it rises. But on that evening it seemed to me of extraordinary size. For an instant the redoubt stood sharply out in black against the brilliant disk of the moon. It resembled the crater of a volcano at the instant of an eruption.

An old soldier, beside whom I happened to be, remarked upon the color of the moon.

"It is very red," said he; "that's a sign that it will cost us dear to take that famous redoubt!"

I have always been superstitious, and that prophecy, at that particular moment especially, affected me. I lay down, but I could not sleep. I rose and walked about for some time, watching the tremendously long line of camp-fires that covered the heights above the village of Cheverino.

When I thought that the fresh, sharp night air had cooled my blood sufficiently, I returned to the fire; I wrapped myself carefully in my cloak and closed my eyes, hoping not to open them before dawn. But sleep refused to come. Insensibly my thoughts took a gloomy turn. I said to myself that I had not a friend among the hundred thousand men who covered that plain. If I were wounded, I should be taken to a hospital and treated roughly by ignorant surgeons. All that I had heard of surgical operations came to my mind. My heart beat violently, and I instinctively arranged my handkerchief, and the wallet that I had in my breast pocket, as a sort of cuirass. I was worn out with fatigue, I nodded every moment, and every moment some sinister thought returned with renewed force and roused me with a start.

But weariness carried the day, and when they beat the reveille, I was sound asleep. We were drawn up in battle array, the roll was called, then we stacked arms, and everything indicated that we were to have a quiet day.

About three o'clock an aide-de-camp appeared, bringing an order. We were ordered under arms again; our skirmishers spread out over the plain; we followed them slowly, and after about twenty minutes, we saw all the advanced posts of the Russians fall back and return inside the redoubt.

A battery of artillery came into position at our right, another at our left, but both well in advance of us. They began a very hot fire at the enemy, who replied vigorously, and the redoubt of Cheverino soon disappeared beneath dense clouds of smoke.

Our regiment was almost protected from the Russian fire by a rise in the ground. Their balls, which, indeed, were rarely aimed at us, for they preferred to fire at our gunners, passed over our heads, or, at the worst, spattered us with dirt and small stones.

As soon as we received the order to advance, my captain looked at me with a close scrutiny which compelled me to run my hand over my budding moustache twice or thrice, as unconcernedly as I could. Indeed, I was not frightened, and the only fear I had was that he should believe that I was frightened. Those harmless cannonballs helped to maintain me in my heroically calm frame of mind. My self-esteem told me that I was really in danger, as I was at last under the fire of a battery. I was overjoyed to be so entirely at my ease, and I thought of the pleasure I should take in telling of the capture of the redoubt of Cheverino in Madame de B——'s salon on the Rue de Provence.

The colonel passed our company; he spoke to me:

"Well, you are going to see some sharp work for your début."

I smiled with an altogether martial air as I brushed my coat sleeve, on which a shot that struck the ground thirty yards away had spattered a little dust.

It seems that the Russians observed the ill success of their cannon-balls; for they replaced them with shells, which could more easily be made to reach us in the hollow where we were posted. A large piece of one took off my shako and killed a man near me.

"I congratulate you," said my captain, as I picked up my shako; "you're safe now for today."

I was acquainted with the military superstition which believes that the axiom, *Non bis in idem*, has the same application on a field of battle as in a court of justice. I proudly replaced my shako on my head.

"That is making a fellow salute rather unceremoniously," I said as gaily as I could. That wretched joke was considered first-rate, in view of the circumstances.

"I congratulate you," continued the captain; "you will get nothing worse, and you will command a company this evening; for I feel that the oven is being heated for me. Every time that I have been wounded the officer nearest me has been hit by a spent ball; and," he added in a low tone and almost as if he were ashamed, "their names always began with a P."

I feigned incredulity; many men would have done the same; many men, too, would have been, as I was, profoundly impressed by these prophetic words. Conscript as I was, I realized that I could not confide my sensations to any one, and that I must always appear cool and fearless.

After about half an hour the Russian fire sensibly diminished; thereupon we left our sheltered position to march upon the redoubt.

Our regiment consisted of three battalions. The second was ordered to turn the redoubt on the side of the entrance; the other two were to make the assault. I was in the third battalion.

As we came out from behind the species of ridge which had protected us, we were received by several volleys of musketry, which did little damage in our ranks. The whistling of the bullets surprised me; I kept turning my head, and thus induced divers jests on the part of my comrades, who were more familiar with that sound.

"Take it all in all," I said to myself, "a battle isn't such a terrible thing."

Non bis in idem, never twice in the same place.

We advanced at the double-quick, preceded by skirmishers; suddenly the Russians gave three hurrahs, three distinct hurrahs, then remained silent and ceased firing.

"I don't like this silence," said my captain; "it bodes us no good."

I considered that our men were a little too noisy, and I could not forbear making a mental comparison between their tumultuous shouting and the enemy's impressive silence.

We speedily reached the foot of the redoubt; the palisades had been shattered and the earth torn up by our balls. The soldiers rushed at these newly made ruins with shouts of "Vive l'Empereur!" louder than one would have expected to hear from men who had already shouted so much.

I raised my eyes, and I shall never forget the spectacle that I saw. The greater part of the smoke had risen, and hung like a canopy about twenty feet above the redoubt. Through a bluish haze one could see the Russian grenadiers behind their half-destroyed parapet, with arms raised, motionless as statues. It seems to me that I can see now each soldier, with his left eye fastened upon us, the right hidden by the levelled musket. In an embrasure, a few yards away, a man stood beside a cannon, holding a fusee.

I shuddered, and I thought that my last hour had come.

"The dance is going to begin," cried my captain. "Bonsoir!"

Those were the last words I heard him utter.

The drums rolled inside the redoubt. I saw all the muskets drop. I closed my eyes, and I heard a most appalling crash, followed by shrieks and groans. I opened my eyes, surprised to find myself still among the living. The redoubt was filled with smoke once more. I was surrounded by dead and wounded. My captain lay at my feet; his head had been shattered by a cannonball, and I was covered with his brains and his blood. Of all my company only six men and myself were left on our feet.

This carnage was succeeded by a moment of stupefaction. The colonel, placing his hat on the point of his sword, was the first to scale the parapet, shouting: "Vive l'Empereur!" He was followed instantly by all the survivors. I have a very dim remembrance of what followed. We entered the redoubt; how, I have no idea. We fought hand to hand, amid smoke so dense that we could not see one another. I believe that I struck, for my sabre was all bloody. At last I heard shouts of "Victory!" and as the smoke grew less dense, I saw blood and corpses completely covering the surface of the redoubt. The guns especially were buried beneath piles of bodies. About two hundred men, in the French uniform, were standing about in groups, with no pretence of order, some loading their muskets, others wiping their bayonets. Eleven hundred Russian prisoners were with them.

The colonel, covered with blood, was lying on a shattered caisson near the ravine. A number of soldiers were bustling about him. I approached.

"Where is the senior captain?" he asked a sergeant.

The sergeant shrugged his shoulders most expressively.

"And the senior lieutenant?"

TAKING THE REDOUBT 183

"Monsieur here, who arrived last night," said the sergeant, in a perfectly matter-of-fact tone.

The colonel smiled bitterly.

"Well, monsieur," he said, "you command in chief, order the entrance to the redoubt to be strengthened with these wagons, for the enemy is in force; but General C—— will see that you are supported."

"Colonel," I said, "are you severely wounded?"

"Finished, my boy, but the redoubt is taken!"

MARJORIE DAW

By Thomas Bailey Aldrich

[Thomas Bailey Aldrich (1836–1907) was a native of Portsmouth, New Hampshire. There the scenes were enacted that make up the delightful *Story of a Bad Boy*. Aldrich succeeded William Dean Howells as editor of the *Atlantic Monthly* in 1881, and continued in that high literary office till 1890.

There are only a few good short stories in the form of a series of letters. *Marjorie Daw* is one of the best of them. It was first published in the *Atlantic Monthly* (April, 1873) and later included in the collected volume, *Marjorie Daw, and Other People* (1873). It is here reprinted by permission of Houghton Mifflin Company, publishers.]

I.—DR. DILLON TO EDWARD DELANEY, ESQ., AT THE PINES, NEAR RYE, N. H.

August 8

MY Dear Sir: I am happy to assure you that your anxiety is without reason. Flemming will be confined to the sofa for three or four weeks, and will have to be careful at first how he uses his leg. A fracture of this kind is always a tedious affair. Fortunately, the bone was very skillfully set by the surgeon who chanced to be in the drugstore where Flemming was brought after his fall, and I apprehend no permanent inconvenience from the accident. *Flemming is doing perfectly well physically;* but I must confess that the irritable and morbid state of mind into which he has fallen causes me a great deal of uneasiness. He is the last man in the world who ought to break his leg. You know how impetuous our friend is ordinarily, what a soul of restlessness and energy, never content unless he is rushing at some object, like a sportive bull at a red shawl; but amiable withal. He is no longer amiable. His temper has become something frightful. Miss Fanny Flemming came up from Newport, where the family are staying for the summer, to nurse him; but he packed her off the next morning in tears. He has a complete set of Balzac's works, twenty-seven volumes, piled up near his sofa, to throw at Watkins whenever that exemplary serving-man appears with his meals. Yesterday I very innocently brought Flemming a small basket of lemons. You know it was a strip of lemon-peel on the curbstone that caused our friend's mischance. Well, he no sooner set his eyes upon these lemons than he fell into such a rage as I cannot adequately describe. This is only one of his moods, and the least distressing. At other times he sits with bowed head regarding his

184

splintered limb, silent, sullen, despairing. When this fit is on him—and it sometimes lasts all day—nothing can distract his melancholy. He refuses to eat, does not even read the newspapers; books, except as projectiles for Watkins, have no charms for him. His state is truly pitiable.

Now, if he were a poor man, with a family depending on his daily labor, this irritability and despondency would be natural enough. But in a young fellow of twenty-four, with plenty of money and seemingly not a care in the world, the thing is monstrous. If he continues to give way to his vagaries in this manner, he will end by bringing on an inflammation of the fibula. It was the fibula he broke. I am at my wits' end to know what to prescribe for him. I have anæsthetics and lotions, to make people sleep and to soothe pain; but I've no medicine that will make a man have a little common-sense. That is beyond my skill, but maybe it is not beyond yours. You are Flemming's intimate friend, his *fidus Achates*. Write to him, write to him frequently, distract his mind, cheer him up, and prevent him from becoming a confirmed case of melancholia. Perhaps he has some important plans disarranged by his present confinement. If he has, you will know, and will know how to advise him judiciously. I trust your father finds the change beneficial? I am, my dear sir, with great respect, etc.

II.—EDWARD DELANEY TO JOHN FLEMMING, WEST 38TH STREET, NEW YORK

August 9

My dear Jack: I had a line from Dillon this morning, and was rejoiced to learn that your hurt is not so bad as reported. Like a certain personage, you are not so black and blue as you are painted. Dillon will put you on your pins again in two or three weeks, if you will only have patience and follow his counsels. Did you get my note of last Wednesday? I was greatly troubled when I heard of the accident.

I can imagine how tranquil and saintly you are with your leg in a trough! It is deuced awkward, to be sure, just as we had promised ourselves a glorious month together at the seaside; but we must make the best of it. It is unfortunate, too, that my father's health renders it impossible for me to leave him. I think he has much improved; the sea air is his native element; but he still needs my arm to lean upon in his walks, and requires some one more careful than a servant to look after him. I cannot come to you, dear Jack, but I have hours of unemployed time on hand, and I will write you a whole post-office full of letters if that will divert you. Heaven knows, I haven't anything to write about. It isn't as if we were living at one of the beach houses; then I could do you some character studies, and fill your imagination with groups of sea-goddesses, with their (or somebody else's) raven and blond manes hanging down their shoulders. You should have Aphrodite in morning wrapper, in evening costume, and in her prettiest bathing suit. But we are far from all that here. We have rooms in a farm-house, on a cross-road, two miles from the hotels, and lead the quietest of lives.

I wish I were a novelist. This old house, with its sanded floors and high wainscots, and its narrow windows looking out upon a cluster of pines that turn themselves into æolian-harps every time the wind blows, would be the place in which to write a summer romance. It should be a story with the odors of the forest and the breath of the sea in it. It should be a novel like one of that Russian fellow's—what's his name?— Tourguénieff, Turguenef, Turgenif, Toorguniff, Turgénjew—nobody knows how to spell him. Yet I wonder if even a Liza or an Alexandra Paulovna could stir the heart of a man who has constant twinges in his leg. I wonder if one of our own Yankee girls of the best type, haughty and *spirituelle*, would be of any comfort to you in your present deplorable condition. If I thought so, I would hasten down to the Surf House and catch one for you; or, better still, I would find you one over the way.

Picture to yourself a large white house just across the road, nearly opposite our cottage. It is not a house, but a mansion, built, perhaps, in the colonial period, with rambling extensions, and gambrel roof, and a wide piazza on three sides—a self-possessed, high-bred piece of architecture, with its nose in the air. It stands back from the road, and has an obsequious retinue of fringed elms and oaks and weeping willows. Sometimes in the morning, and oftener in the afternoon, when the sun has withdrawn from that part of the mansion, a young woman appears on the piazza with some mysterious Penelope web of embroidery in her hand, or a book. There is a hammock over there—of pineapple fibre, it looks from here. A hammock is very becoming when one is eighteen, and has golden hair, and dark eyes, and an emerald-colored illusion dress looped up after the fashion of a Dresden china shepherdess, and is *chaussée* like a belle of the time of Louis Quatorze. All this splendor goes into that hammock, and sways there like a pond-lily in the golden afternoon. The window of my bedroom looks down on that piazza— and so do I.

But enough of this nonsense, which ill becomes a sedate young attorney taking his vacation with an invalid father. Drop me a line, dear Jack, and tell me how you really are. State your case. Write me a long, quiet letter. If you are violent or abusive, I'll take the law to you.

III.—JOHN FLEMMING TO EDWARD DELANEY

August 11

Your letter, dear Ned, was a godsend. Fancy what a fix I am in—I, who never had a day's sickness since I was born. My left leg weighs three tons. It is embalmed in spices and smothered in layers of fine linen, like a mummy. I can't move. I haven't moved for five thousand years. I'm of the time of Pharaoh.

I lie from morning till night on a lounge, staring into the hot street. Everybody is out of town enjoying himself. The brownstone-front houses across the street resemble a row of particularly ugly coffins set up on end. A green mould is settling on the names of the deceased, carved on the silver door-plates. Sardonic spiders have sewed up the key-holes. All is silence and dust and desolation. I interrupt this a moment, to take a shy at Watkins with the second volume of *César Birotteau.* Missed him! I think I could bring him down with a copy of Sainte-Beuve or the *Dictionnaire Universel,* if I had it. These small Balzac books somehow don't quite fit my hand; but I shall fetch him yet. I've an idea Watkins is tapping the old gentleman's Chateau Yquem. Duplicate key of the wine-cellar. Hibernian swarries in the front basement. Young Cheops up stairs, snug in his cerements. Watkins glides into my chamber, with that colorless, hypocritical face of his drawn out long like an accordion; but I know he grins all the way down stairs, and is glad I have broken my leg. Was not my evil star in the very zenith when I ran up to town to attend that dinner at Delmonico's? I didn't come up altogether for that. It was partly to buy Frank Livingstone's roan mare, Margot. And now I shall not be able to sit in the saddle these two months. I'll send the mare down to you at The Pines—is that the name of the place?

Old Dillon fancies that I have something on my mind. He drives me wild with lemons. Lemons for a mind diseased! Nonsense. I am only as restless as the devil under this confinement—a thing I'm not used to. Take a man who has never had so much as a headache or a toothache in his life, strap one of his legs in a section of water-spout, keep him in a room in the city for weeks, with the hot weather turned on, and then expect him to smile and purr and be happy! It is preposterous. I can't be cheerful or calm.

Your letter is the first consoling thing I have had since my disaster, ten days ago. It really cheered me up for half an hour. Send me a screed, Ned, as often as you can, if you love me. Anything will do. Write me more about that little girl in the hammock. That was very pretty, all that about the Dresden china shepherdess and the pond-lily; the imagery a little mixed, perhaps, but very pretty. I didn't suppose you had so much sentimental furniture in your upper story. It shows how one may be familiar for years with the reception-room of his neighbor, and never suspect what is directly under his mansard. I supposed your loft stuffed with dry legal parchments, mortgages and affidavits; you take down a package of manuscript, and lo! there are lyrics and sonnets and canzonettas. You really have a graphic descriptive touch, Edward Delaney, and I suspect you of anonymous love-tales in the magazines.

I shall be a bear until I hear from you again. Tell me all about your pretty *inconnue* across the road. What is her name? Who is she? Who's her father? Where's her mother? Who's her lover? You cannot imagine how this will occupy me. The more trifling, the better. My imprisonment has weakened me intellectually to such a degree that I find your epistolary gifts quite considerable. I am passing into my second childhood. In a week or two I shall take to India-rubber rings and prongs of coral. A silver cup, with an appropriate inscription, would be a delicate attention on your part. In the mean time, write!

IV.—EDWARD DELANEY TO JOHN FLEMMING

August 12

The sick pasha shall be amused. *Bismillah!* he wills it so. If the story teller becomes prolix and tedious—the bow-string and the sack, and two Nubians to drop him into the Piscataqua! But, truly, Jack, I have a hard task. There is literally nothing here—except the little girl over the way. She is swinging in the hammock at this moment. It is to me compensation for many of the ills of life to see her now and then put out a small kid boot, which fits like a glove, and set herself going. Who is she, and what is her name? Her name is Daw. Only daughter of Mr. Richard W. Daw, ex-colonel and banker. Mother dead. One brother at Harvard, elder brother killed at the battle of Fair Oaks, nine years ago. Old, rich family, the Daws. This is the homestead, where father and daughter pass eight months of the twelve; the rest of the year in Baltimore and Washington. The New England winter too many for the old gentleman. The daughter is called Marjorie—Marjorie Daw. Sounds odd at first, doesn't it? But after you say it over to yourself half a dozen times, you like it. There's a pleasing quaintness to it, something prim and violet-like. Must be a nice sort of girl to be called Marjorie Daw.

I had mine host of The Pines in the witness-box last night, and drew the foregoing testimony from him. He has charge of Mr. Daw's vegetable-garden, and has known the family these thirty years. Of course I shall make the acquaintance of my neighbors before many days. It will be next to impossible for me not to meet Mr. Daw or Miss Daw in some of my walks. The young lady has a favorite path to the sea-beach. I shall intercept her some morning, and touch my hat to her. Then the princess will bend her fair head to me with courteous surprise not unmixed with haughtiness. Will snub me, in fact. All this for thy sake, O Pasha of the Snapt Axle-tree! . . . How oddly things fall out! Ten minutes ago I was called down to the parlor—you know the kind of parlors in farmhouses on the coast, a sort of amphibious parlor, with sea-shells on the mantel-piece and spruce branches in the chimney-place—where I found my father and Mr. Daw doing the antique polite to each other. He had come to pay his respects to his new neighbors. Mr. Daw is a tall, slim gentleman of about fifty-five, with a florid face and snow-white mustache and side-whiskers. Looks like Mr. Dombey, or as Mr. Dombey would have looked if he had served a few years in the British Army. Mr. Daw was a colonel in the late war, commanding the regiment in which his son was a lieutenant. Plucky old boy, back-bone of New Hampshire granite. Before taking his leave, the colonel delivered himself of an invitation as if he were issuing a general order. Miss Daw has a few friends coming, at 4 P. M., to play croquet on the lawn (parade-ground) and have tea (cold rations) on the piazza. Will we honor them with our company? (or be sent to the guard-house). My father declines on the plea of ill-health. My father's son bows with as much suavity as he knows, and accepts.

In my next I shall have something to tell you. I shall have seen the little beauty face to face. I have a presentiment, Jack, that this Daw is a *rara avis!* Keep up your spirits, my boy, until I write you another letter —and send me along word how's your leg.

V.—EDWARD DELANEY TO JOHN FLEMMING

August 13

The party, my dear Jack, was as dreary as possible. A lieutenant of the navy, the rector of the Episcopal church at Stillwater, and a society swell from Nahant. The lieutenant looked as if he had swallowed a couple of his buttons, and found the bullion rather indigestible; the rector was a pensive youth, of the daffydowndilly sort; and the swell from Nahant was a very weak tidal wave indeed. The women were much better, as they always are; the two Miss Kingsburys of Phila-delphia, staying at the Sea-shell House, two bright and engaging girls. But Marjorie Daw!

The company broke up soon after tea, and I remained to smoke a cigar with the colonel on the piazza. It was like seeing a picture to see Miss Marjorie hovering around the old soldier, and doing a hundred gracious little things for him. She brought the cigars and lighted the tapers with her own delicate fingers, in the most enchanting fashion. As we sat there, she came and went in the summer twilight, and seemed, with her white dress and pale gold hair, like some lovely phantom that had sprung into existence out of the smoke-wreaths. If she had melted into air, like the statue of Galatea in the play, I should have been more sorry than surprised.

It was easy to perceive that the old colonel worshiped her, and she him. I think the relation between an elderly father and a daughter just blooming into womanhood the most beautiful possible. There is in it a subtle sentiment that cannot exist in the case of mother and daughter, or that of son and mother. But this is getting into deep water.

I sat with the Daws until half past ten, and saw the moon rise on the sea. The ocean, that had stretched motionless and black against the horizon, was changed by magic into a broken field of glittering ice, interspersed with marvelous silvery fjords. In the far distance the Isles of Shoals loomed up like a group of huge bergs drifting down on us. The Polar Regions in a June thaw! It was exceedingly fine. What did we talk about? We talked about the weather—and *you!* The weather has been disagreeable for several days past—and so have you. I glided from one topic to the other very naturally. I told my friends of your accident; how it has frustrated all our summer plans, and what our plans were. I played quite a spirited solo on the fibula. Then I described you; or, rather, I didn't. I spoke of your amiability, of your patience under this severe affliction; of your touching gratitude when Dillon brings you little presents of fruit; of your tenderness to your sister Fanny, whom you would not allow to stay in town to nurse you, and how you heroically sent her back to Newport, preferring to remain alone with Mary, the cook, and your man Watkins, to whom, by the way, you were devotedly attached. If you had been there, Jack, you wouldn't have known yourself. I should have excelled as a criminal lawyer, if I had not turned my attention to a different branch of jurisprudence.

Miss Marjorie asked all manner of leading questions concerning you. It did not occur to me then, but it struck me forcibly afterwards, that she evinced a singular interest in the conversation. When I got back to my room, I recalled how eagerly she leaned forward, with her full, snowy throat in strong moonlight, listening to what I said. Positively, I think I made her like you!

Miss Daw is a girl whom you would like immensely, I can tell you that. A beauty without affectation, a high and tender nature—if one can read the soul in the face. And the old colonel is a noble character, too.

I am glad the Daws are such pleasant people. The Pines is an isolated spot, and my resources are few. I fear I should have found life here somewhat monotonous before long, with no other society than that of my excellent sire. It is true, I might have made a target of the defenceless invalid; but I haven't a taste for artillery, *moi.*

VI.—JOHN FLEMMING TO EDWARD DELANEY

August 17

For a man who hasn't a taste for artillery, it occurs to me, my friend you are keeping up a pretty lively fire on my inner works. But go on. Cynicism is a small brass field-piece that eventually bursts and kills the artilleryman.

You may abuse me as much as you like, and I'll not complain; for I don't know what I should do without your letters. They are curing me. I haven't hurled anything at Watkins since last Sunday, partly because

I have grown more amiable under your teaching, and partly because Watkins captured my ammunition one night, and carried it off to the library. He is rapidly losing the habit he had acquired of dodging whenever I rub my ear, or make any slight motion with my right arm. He is still suggestive of the wine-cellar, however. You may break, you may shatter Watkins, if you will, but the scent of the Roederer will hang round him still.

Ned, that Miss Daw must be a charming person. I should certainly like her. I like her already. When you spoke in your first letter of seeing a young girl swinging in a hammock under your chamber window, I was somehow strangely drawn to her. I cannot account for it in the least. What you have subsequently written of Miss Daw has strengthened the impression. You seem to be describing a woman I have known in some previous state of existence, or dreamed of in this. Upon my word, if you were to send me her photograph, I believe I should recognize her at a glance. Her manner, that listening attitude, her traits of character, as you indicate them, the light hair and the dark eyes—they are all familiar things to me. Asked a lot of questions, did she? Curious about me? That is strange.

You would laugh in your sleeve, you wretched old cynic, if you knew how I lie awake nights, with my gas turned down to a star, thinking of The Pines and the house across the road. How cool it must be down there! I long for the salt smell in the air. I picture the colonel smoking his cheroot on the piazza. I send you and Miss Daw off on afternoon rambles along the beach. Sometimes I let you stroll with her under the elms in the moonlight, for you are great friends by this time, I take it, and see each other every day. I know your ways and your manners! Then I fall into a truculent mood, and would like to destroy somebody. Have you noticed anything in the shape of a lover hanging around the colonial Lares and Penates? Does that lieutenant of the horse-marines or that young Stillwater parson visit the house much? Not that I am pining for news of them, but any gossip of the kind would be in order. I wonder, Ned, you don't fall in love with Miss Daw. I am ripe to do it myself. Speaking of photographs, couldn't you manage to slip one of her *cartes-de-visite* from her album—she must have an album, you know—and send it to me? I will return it before it could be missed. That's a good fellow! Did the mare arrive safe and sound? It will be a capital animal this autumn for Central Park.

O—my leg? I forgot about my leg. It's better.

VII.—EDWARD DELANEY TO JOHN FLEMMING

August 20

You are correct in your surmises. I am on the most friendly terms with our neighbors. The colonel and my father smoke their afternoon cigar together in our sitting-room or on the piazza opposite, and I pass an hour or two of the day or the evening with the daughter. I am more and more struck by the beauty, modesty, and intelligence of Miss Daw. You ask me why I do not fall in love with her. I will be frank, Jack; I have thought of that. She is young, rich, accomplished, uniting in herself more attractions, mental and personal, than I can recall in any girl of my acquaintance; but she lacks the something that would be necessary to inspire in me that kind of interest. Possessing this unknown quantity, a woman neither beautiful nor wealthy nor very young could bring me to her feet. But not Miss Daw. If we were shipwrecked together on an uninhabited island—let me suggest a tropical island, for it costs no more to be picturesque—I would build her a bamboo hut, I would fetch her bread-fruit and cocoanuts, I would fry yams for her, I would lure the ingenuous turtle and make her nourishing soups, but I wouldn't make love to her—not under eighteen months. I would like to have her for a sister, that I might shield her and counsel her, and spend half my income on thread-laces and camel's-hair shawls. (We are off the island now.) If such were not my feeling, there would still be an obstacle to my loving Miss Daw. A greater misfortune could scarcely befall me than to love her. Flemming, I am about to make a revelation that will astonish you. I may be all wrong in my premises and consequently in my conclusions; but you shall judge.

That night when I returned to my room after the croquet party at the Daws', and was thinking over the trivial events of the evening, I was suddenly impressed by the air of eager attention with which Miss Daw had followed my account of your accident. I think I mentioned this to you. Well, the next morning, as I went to mail my letter, I overtook Miss Daw on the road to Rye, where the post-office is, and accompanied her thither and back, an hour's walk. The conversation again turned on you, and again I remarked that inexplicable look of interest which had lighted up her face the previous evening. Since then, I have seen Miss Daw perhaps ten times, perhaps oftener, and on each occasion I found that when I was not speaking of you, or your sister, or some person or place associated with you, I was not holding her attention. She would be absent-minded, her eyes would wander away from me to the sea, or to some distant object in the landscape; her fingers would play with the leaves of a book in a way that convinced me she was not listening. At these moments if I abruptly changed the theme—I did it several times as an experiment—and dropped some remark about my friend Flemming, then the sombre blue eyes would come back to me instantly.

Now, is not this the oddest thing in the world? No, not the oddest. The effect which you tell me was produced on you by my casual mention of an unknown girl swinging in a hammock is certainly as strange. You can conjecture how that passage in your letter of Friday startled me.

Is it possible, then, that two people who have never met, and who are hundreds of miles apart, can exert a magnetic influence on each other? I have read of such psychological phenomena, but never credited them. I leave the solution of the problem to you. As for myself, all other things being favorable, it would be impossible for me to fall in love with a woman who listens to me only when I am talking of my friend!

I am not aware that any one is paying marked attention to my fair neighbor. The lieutenant of the navy—he is stationed at Rivermouth —sometimes drops in of an evening, and sometimes the rector from Stillwater; the lieutenant the oftener. He was there last night. I would not be surprised if he had an eye to the heiress; but he is not formidable. Mistress Daw carries a neat little spear of irony, and the honest lieutenant seems to have a particular facility for impaling himself on the point of it. He is not dangerous, I should say; though I have known a woman to satirize a man for years, and marry him after all. Decidedly, the lowly rector is not dangerous; yet, again, who has not seen Cloth of Frieze victorious in the lists where Cloth of Gold went down?

As to the photograph. There is an exquisite ivorytype of Marjorie, in passe-partout, on the drawing-room mantel-piece. It would be missed at once, if taken. I would do anything reasonable for you, Jack; but I've no burning desire to be hauled up before the local justice of the peace, on a charge of petty larceny.

P. S.—Enclosed is a spray of mignonette, which I advise you to treat tenderly. Yes, we talked of you again last night, as usual. It is becoming a little dreary for me.

VIII.—EDWARD DELANEY TO JOHN FLEMMING

August 22

Your letter in reply to my last has occupied my thoughts all the morning. I do not know what to think. Do you mean to say that you are seriously half in love with a woman whom you have never seen,—with a shadow, a chimera? for what else can Miss Daw be to you? I do not understand it at all. I understand neither you nor her. You are a couple of ethereal beings moving in finer air than I can breathe with my commonplace lungs. Such delicacy of sentiment is something I admire without comprehending. I am bewildered. I am of the earth earthy, and I find myself in the incongruous position of having to do with mere souls, with natures so finely tempered that I run some risk of shattering them in my awkwardness. I am as Caliban among the spirits!

Reflecting on your letter, I am not sure it is wise in me to continue this correspondence. But no, Jack; I do wrong to doubt the good sense that forms the basis of your character. You are deeply interested in Miss Daw; you feel that she is a person whom you may perhaps greatly admire when you know her: at the same time you bear in mind that the chances are ten to five that, when you do come to know her, she will fall far short of your ideal, and you will not care for her in the least. Look at it in this sensible light, and I will hold back nothing from you.

Yesterday afternoon my father and myself rode over to Rivermouth with the Daws. A heavy rain in the morning had cooled the atmosphere and laid the dust. To Rivermouth is a drive of eight miles, along a winding road lined all the way with wild barberry-bushes. I never saw anything more brilliant than these bushes, the green of the foliage and the pink of the coral berries intensified by the rain. The colonel drove, with my father in front, Miss Daw and I on the back seat. I resolved that for the first five miles your name should not pass my lips. I was amused by the artful attempts she made, at the start, to break through my reticence. Then a silence fell upon her; and then she became suddenly gay. That keenness which I enjoyed so much when it was exercised on the lieutenant was not so satisfactory directed against myself. Miss Daw has great sweetness of disposition, but she can be disagreeable. She is like the young lady in the rhyme, with the curl on her forehead.

> "When she is good,
> She is very, very good,
> And when she is bad, she is horrid!"

I kept to my resolution, however; but on the return home I relented, and talked of your mare! Miss Daw is going to try a side-saddle on Margot some morning. The animal is a trifle too light for my weight. By the by, I nearly forgot to say Miss Daw sat for a picture yesterday to a Rivermouth artist. If the negative turns out well, I am to have a copy. So our ends will be accomplished without crime. I wish, though, I could send you the ivorytype in the drawing-room; it is cleverly colored, and would give you an idea of her hair and eyes, which of course the other will not.

No, Jack, the spray of mignonette did not come from me. A man of twenty-eight doesn't enclose flowers in his letters—to another man. But don't attach too much significance to the circumstances. She gives sprays of mignonette to the rector, sprays to the lieutenant. She has even given a rose from her bosom to your slave. It is her jocund nature to scatter flowers, like Spring.

If my letters sometimes read disjointedly, you must understand that I never finish one at a sitting, but write at intervals, when the mood is on me. The mood is not on me now.

IX.—EDWARD DELANEY TO JOHN FLEMMING

August 23

I have just returned from the strangest interview with Marjorie. She has all but confessed to me her interest in you. But with what modesty and dignity! Her words elude my pen as I attempt to put them on paper; and, indeed, it was not so much what she said as her manner; and that I cannot reproduce. Perhaps, it was of a piece with the strangeness of this whole business, that she should tacitly acknowledge to a third party the love she feels for a man she has never beheld! But I have lost, through your aid, the faculty of being surprised. I accept things as people do in dreams. Now that I am again in my room, it all appears like an illusion,—the black masses of Rembrandtish shadow under the trees, the fire-flies whirling in Pyrrhic dances among the shrubbery, the sea over there, Marjorie sitting on the hammock! It is past midnight, and I am too sleepy to write more.

Thursday Morning.

My father has suddenly taken it into his head to spend a few days at the Shoals. In the mean while you will not hear from me. I see Marjorie walking in the garden with the colonel. I wish I could speak to her alone, but shall probably not have an opportunity before we leave.

X.—EDWARD DELANEY TO JOHN FLEMMING

August 28

You were passing into your second childhood, were you? Your intellect was so reduced that my epistolary gifts seemed quite considerable to you, did they? I rise superior to the sarcasm in your favor of the 11th instant, when I notice that five days' silence on my part is sufficient to throw you into the depths of despondency.

We returned only this morning from Appledore, that enchanted island, —at four dollars per day. I find on my desk three letters from you! Evidently there is no lingering doubt in *your* mind as to the pleasure I derive from your correspondence. These letters are undated, but in what I take to be the latest are two passages that require my consideration. You will pardon my candor, dear Flemming, but the conviction forces itself upon me that as your leg grows stronger your head becomes weaker. You ask my advice on a certain point. I will give it. In my opinion you could do nothing more unwise than to address a note to Miss Daw, thanking her for the flower. It would, I am sure, offend her delicacy beyond pardon. She knows you only through me; you are to her an abstraction, a figure in a dream,—a dream from which the faintest shock would awaken her. Of course, if you enclose a note to me and insist on its delivery, I shall deliver it; but I advise you not to do so.

You say you are able, with the aid of a cane, to walk about your chamber, and that you purpose to come to The Pines the instant Dillon thinks you strong enough to stand the journey. Again I advise you not to. Do you not see that, every hour you remain away, Marjorie's glamor deepens, and your influence over her increases? You will ruin everything by precipitancy. Wait until you are entirely recovered; in any case, do not come without giving me warning. I fear the effect of your abrupt advent here—under the circumstances.

Miss Daw was evidently glad to see us back again, and gave me both hands in the frankest way. She stopped at the door a moment, this afternoon, in the carriage; she had been over to Rivermouth for her pictures. Unluckily, the photographer had spilt some acid on the plate, and she was obliged to give him another sitting. I have an intuition that something is troubling Marjorie. She had an abstracted air not usual with her. However, it may be only my fancy. . . . I end this, leaving several things unsaid, to accompany my father on one of those long walks which are now his chief medicine,—and mine!

XI.—EDWARD DELANEY TO JOHN FLEMMING

August 29

I write in great haste to tell you what has taken place here since my letter of last night. I am in the utmost perplexity. Only one thing is plain,—*you* must not dream of coming to The Pines. Marjorie has told her father everything! I saw her for a few minutes, an hour ago, in the garden; and, as near as I could gather from her confused statement, the facts are these: Lieutenant Bradly—that's the naval officer stationed at Rivermouth—has been paying court to Miss Daw for some time past, but not so much to her liking as to that of the colonel, who it seems is an old friend of the young gentleman's father. Yesterday (I knew she was in some trouble when she drove up to our gate) the colonel spoke to Marjorie of Bradly,—urged his suit, I infer. Marjorie expressed her dislike for the lieutenant with characteristic frankness, and finally confessed to her father—well, I really do not know what she confessed. It must have been the vaguest of confessions, and must have sufficiently puzzled the colonel. At any rate, it exasperated him. I suppose I am implicated in the matter, and that the colonel feels bitterly towards me. I do not see why: I have carried no messages between you and Miss Daw; I have behaved with the greatest discretion. I can find no flaw anywhere in my proceeding. I do not see that anybody has done anything—except the colonel himself.

It is probable, nevertheless, that the friendly relations between the two houses will be broken off. "A plague o' both your houses," say you. I will keep you informed, as well as I can, of what occurs over the way. We shall remain here until the second week in September. Stay where you are, or, at all events, do not dream of joining me. . . . Colonel Daw is sitting on the piazza looking rather wicked. I have not seen Marjorie since I parted with her in the garden.

XII.—EDWARD DELANEY TO THOMAS DILLON, M.D.,
MADISON SQUARE, NEW YORK

August 30

My dear Doctor: If you have any influence over Flemming, I beg of you to exert it to prevent his coming to this place at present. There are circumstances, which I will explain to you before long, that make it of the first importance that he should not come into this neighborhood. His appearance here, I speak advisedly, would be disastrous to him. In urging him to remain in New York, or to go to some inland resort, you will be doing him and me a real service. Of course you will not mention my name in this connection. You know me well enough, my dear doctor, to be assured that, in begging your secret coöperation, I have reasons that will meet your entire approval when they are made plain to you. We shall return to town on the 15th of next month, and my first duty will be to present myself at your hospitable door and satisfy your curiosity, if I have excited it. My father, I am glad to state, has so greatly improved that he can no longer be regarded as an invalid. With great esteem, I am, etc., etc.

XIII.—EDWARD DELANEY TO JOHN FLEMMING

August 31

Your letter, announcing your mad determination to come here, has just reached me. I beseech you to reflect a moment. The step would be fatal to your interests and hers. You would furnish just cause for irritation to R. W. D.; and, though he loves Marjorie tenderly, he is capable of going to any lengths if opposed. You would not like, I am convinced, to be the means of causing him to treat *her* with severity. That would be the result of your presence at The Pines at this juncture. I am annoyed to be obliged to point out these things to you. We are on very delicate ground, Jack; the situation is critical, and the slightest mistake in a move would cost us the game. If you consider it worth the winning, be patient. Trust a little to my sagacity. Wait and see what happens. Moreover, I understand from Dillon that you are in no condition to take so long a journey. He thinks the air of the coast would be the worst thing possible for you; that you ought to go inland, if anywhere. Be advised by me. Be advised by Dillon.

XIV.—TELEGRAMS

September 1

I.—TO EDWARD DELANEY

Letter received. Dillon be hanged. I think I ought to be on the ground.   J. F.

2.—TO JOHN FLEMMING

Stay where you are. You would only complicate matters. Do not move until you hear from me.   E. D.

3.—TO EDWARD DELANEY

My being at The Pines could be kept secret. I must see her. J. F.

4.—TO JOHN FLEMMING

Do not think of it. It would be useless. R. W. D. has locked M. in her room. You would not be able to effect an interview.   E. D.

5.—TO EDWARD DELANEY

Locked her in her room. Good God. That settles the question. I shall leave by the twelve-fifteen express.   J. F.

XV.—THE ARRIVAL

On the second of September, 187–, as the down express due at 3.40 left the station at Hampton, a young man, leaning on the shoulder of a servant, whom he addressed as Watkins, stepped from the platform into a hack, and requested to be driven to "The Pines." On arriving at the gate of a modest farm-house, a few miles from the station, the young man descended with difficulty from the carriage, and, casting a hasty glance across the road, seemed much impressed by some peculiarity in the landscape. Again leaning on the shoulder of the person Watkins, he walked to the door of the farm-house and inquired for Mr. Edward Delaney. He was informed by the aged man who answered his knock, that Mr. Edward Delaney had gone to Boston the day before, but that Mr. Jonas Delaney was within. This information did not appear satisfactory to the stranger who inquired if Mr. Edward Delaney had left any message for Mr. John Flemming. There *was* a letter for Mr. Flemming, if he were that person. After a brief absence the aged man reappeared with a Letter.

XVI.—EDWARD DELANEY TO JOHN FLEMMING

September 1

I am horror-stricken at what I have done! When I began this correspondence I had no other purpose than to relieve the tedium of your sick chamber. Dillon told me to cheer you up. I tried to. I thought you entered into the spirit of the thing. I had no idea, until within a few days, that you were taking matters *au sérieux*.

What can I say? I am in sackcloth and ashes. I am a pariah, a dog of an outcast. I tried to make a little romance to interest you, something soothing and idyllic, and, by Jove! I have done it only too well! My father doesn't know a word of this, so don't jar the old gentleman any more than you can help. I fly from the wrath to come—when you arrive! For O, dear Jack, there isn't any colonial mansion on the other side of the road, there isn't any piazza, there isn't any hammock,—there isn't any Marjorie Daw!!

THE LOVE LETTERS OF SMITH

By H. C. Bunner

[Another of the cleverly managed stories in which the letter plays an important part is Henry Cuyler Bunner's *The Love Letters of Smith*. Mr. Bunner (1855–1896) was born in Oswego, New York. He was editor of the well known American humorous magazine called *Puck*, a rival of the British *Punch* and later humorous magazines. As a writer he produced praiseworthy work in the forms of novel, short story, and verse. He is perhaps best remembered for the short stories collected under the title, *Short Sixes* (1890, 1894).

The Love Letters of Smith first appeared in *Puck* (July 23, 1890) and was later included in the first series of *Short Sixes*. It is reprinted here by permission of Charles Scribner's Sons, publishers.]

WHEN the little seamstress had climbed to her room in the story over the top story of the great brick tenement house in which she lived, she was quite tired out. If you do not understand what a story over a top story is, you must remember that there are no limits to human greed, and hardly any to the height of tenement houses. When the man who owned that seven-story tenement found that he could rent another floor, he found no difficulty in persuading the guardians of our building laws to let him clap another story on the roof, like a cabin on the deck of a ship; and in the southeasterly of the four apartments on this floor the little seamstress lived. You could just see the top of her window from the street—the huge cornice that had capped the original front, and that served as her window-sill now, quite hid all the lower part of the story on top of the top story.

The little seamstress was scarcely thirty years old, but she was such an old-fashioned little body in so many of her looks and ways that I had almost spelled her sempstress, after the fashion of our grandmothers. She had been a comely body, too; and would have been still, if she had not been thin and pale and anxious-eyed.

She was tired out tonight because she had been working hard all day for a lady who lived far up in the "New Wards" beyond Harlem River, and after the long journey home, she had to climb seven flights of tenement-house stairs. She was too tired both in body and in mind to cook the two little chops she had brought home. She would save them for breakfast, she thought. So she made herself a cup of tea on the miniature stove, and ate a slice of dry bread with it. It was too much trouble to make toast.

But after dinner she watered her flowers. She was never too tired for that; and the six pots of geraniums that caught the south sun on the top of the cornice did their best to repay her. Then she sat down in her rocking-chair by the window and looked out. Her eyrie was high above all the other buildings, and she could look across some low roofs opposite, and see the further end of Tompkins Square, with its sparse Spring green showing faintly through the dusk. The eternal roar of the city floated up to her and vaguely troubled her. She was a country girl, and although she had lived for ten years in New York, she had never grown used to that ceaseless murmur. Tonight she felt the languor of the new season as well as the heaviness of the physical exhaustion. She was almost too tired to go to bed.

She thought of the hard day done and the hard day to be begun after the night spent on the hard little bed. She thought of the peaceful days in the country, when she taught school in the Massachusetts village where she was born. She thought of a hundred small slights that she had to bear from people better fed than bred. She thought of the sweet green fields that she rarely saw nowadays. She thought of the long journey forth and back that must begin and end her morrow's work, and she wondered if her employer would think to offer to pay her fare. Then she pulled herself together. She must think of more agreeable things, or she could not sleep. And as the only agreeable things she had to think about were her flowers, she looked at the garden on top of the cornice.

A peculiar gritting noise made her look down, and she saw a cylindrical object that glittered in the twilight, advancing in an irregular and uncertain manner toward her flower-pots. Looking closer, she saw that it was a pewter beer-mug, which somebody in the next apartment was pushing with a two-foot rule. On top of the beer-mug was a piece of paper, and on this paper was written, in a sprawling, half-formed hand:

> porter
> pleas excuse the libberty And
> drink it

The seamstress started up in terror, and shut the window. She remembered that there was a man in the next apartment. She had seen him on the stairs, on Sundays. He seemed a grave, decent person; but— he must be drunk. She sat down on her bed, all a-tremble. Then she reasoned with herself. The man was drunk, that was all. He probably would not annoy her further. And if he did, she had only to retreat to Mrs. Mulvaney's apartment in the rear, and Mr. Mulvaney, who was a highly respectable man and worked in a boiler-shop, would protect her. So, being a poor woman who had already had occasion to excuse—and refuse—two or three "libberties" of like sort, she made up her mind to go to bed like a reasonable seamstress, and she did. She was rewarded, for when her light was out, she could see in the moonlight that the two-foot rule appeared again, with one joint bent back, hitched itself into the mug-handle, and withdrew the mug.

The next day was a hard one for the little seamstress, and she hardly thought of the affair of the night before until the same hour had come around again, and she sat once more by her window. Then she smiled at the remembrance. "Poor fellow," she said in her charitable heart, "I've no doubt he's *awfully* ashamed of it now. Perhaps he was never tipsy before. Perhaps he didn't know there was a lone woman in here to be frightened."

Just then she heard a gritting sound. She looked down. The pewter pot was in front of her, and the two-foot rule was slowly retiring. On the pot was a piece of paper, and on the paper was:

> porter
> good for the helth
> it makes meet

This time the little seamstress shut her window with a bang of indignation. The color rose to her pale cheeks. She thought that she would go down to see the janitor at once. Then she remembered the seven flights of stairs; and she resolved to see the janitor in the morning. Then she went to bed and saw the mug drawn back just as it had been drawn back the night before.

The morning came, but, somehow, the seamstress did not care to complain to the janitor. She hated to make trouble—and the janitor might think—and—and—well, if the wretch did it again she would speak to him herself, and that would settle it.

And so, on the next night, which was a Thursday, the little seamstress sat down by her window, resolved to settle the matter. And she had not sat there long, rocking in the creaking little rocking-chair which she had brought with her from her old home, when the pewter pot hove in sight, with a piece of paper on the top.

This time the legend read:

> Perhaps you are afrade i will
> adress you
> i am not that kind

The seamstress did not quite know whether to laugh or to cry. But she felt that the time had come for speech. She leaned out of her window and addressed the twilight heaven.

"Mr.—Mr.—sir—I—will you *please* put your head out of the window so that I can speak to you?"

The silence of the other room was undisturbed. The seamstress drew back, blushing. But before she could nerve herself for another attack a piece of paper appeared on the end of the two-foot rule

> when i Say a thing i
> mene it
> i have Sed i would not
> Adress you and i
> Will not

What was the little seamstress to do? She stood by the window and thought hard about it. Should she complain to the janitor? But the creature was perfectly respectful. No doubt he meant to be kind. He certainly was kind, to waste these pots of porter on her. She remembered the last time—and the first—that she had drunk porter. It was at home, when she was a young girl, after she had had the diphtheria. She remembered how good it was, and how it had given her back her strength. And without one thought of what she was doing, she lifted the pot of porter and took one little reminiscent sip—two little reminiscent sips—and became aware of her utter fall and defeat. She blushed now as she had never blushed before, put the pot down, closed the window, and fled to her bed like a deer to the woods.

And when the porter arrived the next night, bearing the simple appeal:

> Dont be afrade of it
> drink it all

the little seamstress arose and grasped the pot firmly by the handle, and poured its contents over the earth around her largest geranium. She poured the contents out to the last drop, and then she dropped the pot, and ran back and sat on her bed and cried, with her face hid in her hands.

"Now," she said to herself, "you've done it! And you're just as nasty and hard-hearted and suspicious and mean as—as pusley!"

And she wept to think of her hardness of heart. "He will never give me a chance to say I am sorry," she thought. And, really she might have spoken kindly to the poor man, and told him that she was much obliged to him, but that he really mustn't ask her to drink porter with him.

"But it's all over and done now," she said to herself as she sat at her window on Saturday night. And then she looked at the cornice, and saw the faithful little pewter pot traveling slowly toward her.

She was conquered. This act of Christian forbearance was too much for her kindly spirit. She read the inscription on the paper:

> porter is good for Flours
> but better for Fokes

and she lifted the pot to her lips, which were not half so red as her cheeks, and took a good, hearty, grateful draught.

She sipped in thoughtful silence after this first plunge, and presently she was surprised to find the bottom of the pot in full view.

On the table at her side a few pearl buttons were screwed up in a bit of white paper. She untwisted the paper and smoothed it out, and wrote in a tremulous hand—she *could* write a very neat hand—

Thanks.

This she laid on the top of the pot, and in a moment the bent two-foot rule appeared and drew the mail-carriage home. Then she sat still, enjoying the warm glow of the porter, which seemed to have permeated her entire being with a heat that was not at all like the unpleasant and oppressive heat of the atmosphere, an atmosphere heavy with the Spring damp. A gritting on the tin aroused her. A piece of paper lay under her eyes.

fine groing weather

Smith

it said.

Now it is unlikely that in the whole round and range of conversational commonplaces there was one other greeting that could have induced the seamstress to continue the exchange of communications. But this simple and homely phrase touched her country heart. What did *"groing weather"* matter to the toilers in this waste of brick and mortar? This stranger must be like herself, a country-bred soul, longing for the new green and the upturned brown mold of the country fields. She took up the paper, and wrote under the first message:

Fine

But that seemed curt; *for* she added: *"for"* what? She did not know. At last in desperation she put down *potatoes*. The piece of paper was withdrawn and came back with an addition:

Too mist for potatos.

And when the little seamstress had read this, and grasped the fact that *m-i-s-t* represented the writer's pronunciation of "moist," she laughed softly to herself. A man whose mind, at such a time, was seriously bent upon potatoes, was not a man to be feared. She found a half-sheet of note-paper, and wrote:

I lived in a small village before I came to New York, but I am afraid I do not know much about farming. Are you a farmer?

The answer came:

have ben most Every thing

farmed a Spel in Maine

Smith

As she read this, the seamstress heard a church clock strike nine. "Bless me, is it so late?" she cried, and she hurriedly penciled *Good Night*, thrust the paper out, and closed the window. But a few minutes later, passing by, she saw yet another bit of paper on the cornice, fluttering in the evening breeze. It said only *good nite*, and after a moment's hesitation, the little seamstress took it in and gave it shelter.

After this, they were the best of friends. Every evening the pot appeared, and while the seamstress drank from it at her window, Mr. Smith drank from its twin at his; and notes were exchanged as rapidly as Mr. Smith's early education permitted. They told each other their histories, and Mr. Smith's was one of travel and variety, which he seemed to consider quite a matter of course. He had followed the sea, he had farmed, he had been a logger and a hunter in the Maine woods. Now he was foreman of an East River lumber yard, and he was prospering. In a year or two he would have enough laid by to go home to Bucksport and buy a share in a ship-building business. All this dribbled out in the course of a jerky but variegated correspondence, in which autobiographic details were mixed with reflections, moral and philosophical. A few samples will give an idea of Mr. Smith's style:

> i was one trip to van demens
> land

To which the seamstress replied:

> It must have been very interesting.

But Mr. Smith disposed of this subject very briefly:

> it wornt

Further he vouchsafed:

> i seen a chinese cook in
> hong kong could cook flapjacks
> like your Mother

> a mishnery that sells Rum
> is the menest of Gods crechers

> a bulfite is not what it is
> cract up to Be

> the dagos are wussen the
> brutes

> i am 6 1¾
> but my Father was 6 foot 4

The seamstress had taught school one Winter, and she could not refrain from making an attempt to reform Mr. Smith's orthography.

One evening, in answer to this communication:

> i killd a Bare in Maine 600
> lbs waight

she wrote:

> Isn't it generally spelled Bear?

but she gave up the attempt when he responded:

> a bare is a mene animle any
> way you spel him

The Spring wore on, and the Summer came, and still the evening drink and the evening correspondence brightened the close of each day for the little seamstress. And the draught of porter put her to sleep each night, giving her a calmer rest than she had ever known during her stay in the noisy city; and it began, moreover, to make a little *"meet"* for her. And then the thought that she was going to have an hour of pleasant companionship somehow gave her courage to cook and eat her little dinner, however tired she was. The seamstress's cheeks began to blossom with the June roses.

And all this time Mr. Smith kept his vow of silence unbroken, though the seamstress sometimes tempted him with little ejaculations and exclamations to which he might have responded. He was silent and invisible. Only the smoke of his pipe, and the clink of his mug as he set it down on the cornice, told her that a living, material Smith was her correspondent. They never met on the stairs, for their hours of coming and going did not coincide. Once or twice they passed each other in the street—but Mr. Smith looked straight ahead of him, about a foot over her head. The little seamstress thought he was a very fine-looking man, with his six feet one and three-quarters and his thick brown beard. Most people would have called him plain.

Once she spoke to him. She was coming home one summer evening, and a gang of corner-loafers stopped her and demanded money to buy beer, as is their custom. Before she had time to be frightened, Mr. Smith appeared—whence, she knew not—scattered the gang like chaff, and, collaring two of the human hyenas, kicked them with deliberate, ponderous, alternate kicks, until they writhed in ineffable agony. When he let them crawl away, she turned to him and thanked him warmly, looking very pretty now, with the color in her cheeks. But Mr. Smith answered no word. He stared over her head, grew red in the face, fidgeted nervously, but held his peace until his eyes fell on a rotund Teuton, passing by.

"Say, Dutchy!" he roared. The German stood aghast.

"I ain't got nothing to write with!" thundered Mr. Smith, looking him in the eye. And then the man of his word passed on his way.

And so the summer went on, and the two correspondents chatted silently from window to window, hid from sight of all the world below by the friendly cornice. And they looked out over the roof, and saw the green of Tompkins Square grow darker and dustier as the months went on.

Mr. Smith was given to Sunday trips into the suburbs, and he never came back without a bunch of daisies or black-eyed Susans or, later, asters or golden-rod for the little seamstress. Sometimes, with a sagacity rare in his sex, he brought her a whole plant, with fresh loam for potting.

He gave her also a reel in a bottle, which, he wrote, he had *"maid"* himself, and some coral, and a dried flying-fish, that was somewhat fearful to look upon, with its sword-like fins and its hollow eyes. At first, she could not go to sleep with that flying-fish hanging on the wall.

But he surprised the little seamstress very much one cool September evening, when he shoved this letter along the cornice:

> Respected and Honored Madam:
> Having long and vainly sought an opportunity to convey to you the expression of my sentiments, I now avail myself of the privilege of epistolary communication to acquaint you with the fact that the Emotions which you have raised in my breast, are those which should point to Connubial Love and Affection rather than to simple Friendship. In short, Madam, I have the Honor to approach you with a Proposal, the acceptance of which will fill me with ecstatic Gratitude, and enable me to extend to you those Protecting Cares, which the Matrimonial Bond makes at once the Duty and the Privilege of him, who would, at no distant date, lead to the Hymeneal Altar one whose charms and virtues should suffice to kindle its Flames, without extraneous Aid
>
> Remaining Dear Madam,
> Your Humble Servant and
> Ardent Adorer, Smith.

The little seamstress gazed at his letter a long time. Perhaps she was wondering in what Ready Letter-Writer of the last century Mr. Smith had found his form. Perhaps she was amazed at the results of his first attempt at punctuation. Perhaps she was thinking of something else, for there were tears in her eyes and a smile on her small mouth.

But it must have been a long time, and Mr. Smith must have grown nervous, for presently another communication came along the line where the top of the cornice was worn smooth. It read:

>If not understood will you mary me?

The little seamstress seized a piece of paper and wrote:

>If I say Yes, will you speak to me?

Then she rose and passed it out to him, leaning out of the window, and their faces met.

THE LAST CLASS

By *Alphonse Daudet*

[Alphonse Daudet (1840–1897), French novelist and short story writer, son of a manufacturer, was born at Nimes. After a short and unsuccessful experience as a teacher, he went to Paris and devoted himself to literary work. While he achieved considerable fame by some of his longer productions—such as the Tartarin trilogy and *Sapho*—he has always been best known to the reading public by his impressionistic short stories, particularly those in *Letters from My Mill* (1869) and *Monday Tales* (1873). The presence in his work of a strong vein of sentiment, coupled with great sympathy for the poor, has caused many critics to compare his work favorably with that of Dickens.

The Last Class (La Dernière Classe) is one of the stories in *Monday Tales*. The translation is that of George Burnham Ives, and is reprinted here by permission of the publishers, Little, Brown and Company, Boston.]

I WAS very late for school that morning, and I was terribly afraid of being scolded, especially as Monsieur Hamel had told us that he should examine us on participles, and I did not know the first thing about them. For a moment I thought of staying away from school and wandering about the fields. It was such a warm, lovely day. I could hear the blackbirds whistling on the edge of the wood, and in the Rippert field, behind the sawmill, the Prussians going through their drill. All that was much more tempting to me than the rules concerning participles; but I had the strength to resist, and I ran as fast as I could to school.

As I passed the mayor's office, I saw that there were people gathered about the little board on which notices were posted. For two years all our bad news had come from that board—battles lost, conscriptions, orders from headquarters; and I thought without stopping:

"What can it be now?"

Then, as I ran across the square, Wachter the blacksmith, who stood there with his apprentice, reading the placard, called out to me:

"Don't hurry so, my boy; you'll get to your school soon enough!"

I thought that he was making fun of me, and I ran into Monsieur Hamel's little yard all out of breath.

Usually, at the beginning of school, there was a great uproar which could be heard in the street, desks opening and closing, lessons repeated aloud in unison, with our ears stuffed in order to learn quicker, and the teacher's stout ruler beating on the desk:

"A little more quiet!"

I counted on all this noise to get to my bench unnoticed; but as it happened, that day everything was quiet, like a Sunday morning. Through the open window I saw my comrades already in their places, and Monsieur Hamel walking back and forth with the terrible iron ruler under his arm. I had to open the door and enter, in the midst of that perfect silence. You can imagine whether I blushed and whether I was afraid!

But no! Monsieur Hamel looked at me with no sign of anger and said very gently:

"Go at once to your seat, my little Frantz; we were going to begin without you."

I stepped over the bench and sat down at once at my desk. Not until then, when I had partly recovered from my fright, did I notice that our teacher had on his handsome blue coat, his plaited ruff, and the black silk embroidered breeches, which he wore only on days of inspection or of distribution of prizes. Moreover, there was something extraordinary, something solemn about the whole class. But what surprised me most was to see at the back of the room, on the benches which were usually empty, some people from the village sitting, as silent as we were; old Hauser with his three-cornered hat, the ex-mayor, the ex-postman, and others besides. They all seemed depressed; and Hauser had brought an old spelling-book with gnawed edges, which he held wide-open on his knee, with his great spectacles askew.

While I was wondering at all this, Monsieur Hamel had mounted his platform, and in the same gentle and serious voice with which he had welcomed me, he said to us:

"My children, this is the last time that I shall teach you. Orders have come from Berlin to teach nothing but German in the schools of Alsace and Lorraine. The new teacher arrives tomorrow. This is the last class in French, so I beg you to be very attentive."

Those few words overwhelmed me. Ah! the villains! that was what they had posted at the mayor's office.

My last class in French!

And I barely knew how to write! So I should never learn! I must stop short where I was! How angry I was with myself because of the time I had wasted, the lessons I had missed, running about after nests or sliding on the Saar! My books, which only a moment before I thought so tiresome, so heavy to carry—my grammar, my sacred history—seemed to me now like old friends, from whom I should be terribly grieved to part. And it was the same about Monsieur Hamel. The thought that he was going away, that I should never see him again, made me forget the punishments, the blows with the ruler.

Poor man! It was in honor of that last lesson that he had put on his fine Sunday clothes; and I understood now why those old fellows from the village were sitting at the end of the room. It seemed to mean that they regretted not having come oftener to the school. It was also a very good way of thanking our teacher for his forty years of faithful service, and of paying their respects to the fatherland which was vanishing.

I was at that point in my reflections when I heard my name called. It was my turn to recite. What would I not have given to be able to say from beginning to end that famous rule about participles, in a loud, distinct voice, without a slip! But I got mixed up at the first words, and I stood there swaying against my bench, with a full heart, afraid to raise my head. I heard Monsieur Hamel speaking to me:

"I will not scold you, my little Frantz; you must be punished enough; that is the way it goes; every day we say to ourselves: 'Pshaw! I have time enough. I will learn tomorrow.' And then you see what happens. Ah! it has been the great misfortune of our Alsace always to postpone its lessons until tomorrow. Now those people are entitled to say to us: 'What! you claim to be French, and you can neither speak nor write your language!' In all this, my poor Frantz, you are not the guiltiest one. We all have our fair share of reproaches to address to ourselves.

"Your parents have not been careful enough to see that you were educated. They preferred to send you to work in the fields or in the factories, in order to have a few more sous. And have I nothing to reproach myself for? Have I not often made you water my garden instead of studying? And when I wanted to go fishing for trout, have I ever hesitated to dismiss you?"

Then, passing from one thing to another, Monsieur Hamel began to talk to us about the French language, saying that it was the most beautiful language in the world, the most clear, the most substantial; that we must always retain it among ourselves, and never forget it, because when a people falls into servitude, "so long as it clings to its language, it is as if it held the key to its prison." Then he took the grammar and read us our lesson. I was amazed to see how readily I understood. Everything that he said seemed so easy to me, so easy. I believed, too, that I had never listened so closely, and that he, for his part, had never been so patient with his explanations. One would have said that, before going away, the poor man desired to give us all his knowledge, to force it all into our heads at a single blow.

When the lesson was at an end we passed to writing. For that day Monsieur Hamel had prepared some entirely new examples, on which was written in a fine, round hand: "France, Alsace, France, Alsace." They were like little flags, waving all about the class, hanging from the rods of our desks. You should have seen how hard we all worked and how silent it was! Nothing could be heard save the grinding of the pens over the paper. At one time some cockchafers flew in; but no one paid any attention to them, not even the little fellows, who were struggling with their straight lines, with a will and conscientious application, as if even the lines were French. On the roof of the schoolhouse pigeons cooed in low tones, and I said to myself as I listened to them: "I wonder if they are going to compel them to sing in German too!"

From time to time, when I raised my eyes from my paper, I saw Monsieur Hamel sitting motionless in his chair and staring at the objects about him as if he wished to carry away in his glance the whole of his little schoolhouse. Think of it! For forty years he had been there in the same place, with his yard in front of him and his class just as it was! But the benches and desks were polished and rubbed by use; the walnuts in the yard had grown, and the hop-vine which he himself had planted now festooned the windows even to the roof. What a heart-rending thing it must have been for that poor man to leave all those things, and to hear his sister walking back and forth in the room overhead, packing their trunks! For they were to go away the next day—to leave the province forever.

However, he had the courage to keep the class to the end. After the writing, we had the lesson in history; then the little ones sang all together the ba, be, bi, bo, bu. Yonder, at the back of the room, old Hauser had put on his spectacles, and, holding his spelling-book in both hands, he spelled out the letters with them. I could see that he too was applying himself. His voice shook with emotion, and it was so funny to hear him, that we all longed to laugh and to cry. Ah! I shall remember that last class.

Suddenly the church clock struck twelve, then the Angelus rang. At the same moment the bugles of the Prussians returning from drill blared under our windows. Monsieur Hamel rose, pale as death, from his chair. Never had he seemed to me so tall.

"My friends," he said, "my friends, I . . . I . . . . . ."

But something suffocated him. He could not finish the sentence.

Thereupon he turned to the blackboard, took a piece of chalk, and, bearing on with all his might, he wrote in the largest letters he could:

"Vive la France!"

Then he stood there, with his head resting against the wall, and without speaking, he motioned to us with his hand:

"That is all; go."

THE LESSON OF THE MASTER

By Henry James

[Henry James (1843–1916) was born in New York, the son of Henry James, philosopher and theologian, and a brother of the distinguished American psychologist and philosopher, William James, of Harvard. His early years were spent in New York City, but he lived mostly in Geneva from his twelfth to seventeenth year. A part of his education was acquired in Harvard. There he became acquainted with the American literary leaders, Charles Eliot Norton and William Dean Howells, and began his contributions to the *Atlantic Monthly*. Returning to Europe, he came to know the leading writers in England and France. His first volume of stories was called *A Passionate Pilgrim* (1875). This was followed by many novels and stories through a long and distinguished career. All his stories are profound studies of character. Many find him difficult to read because of his philosophic attitude, but he is a skillful story teller and a master of English style.

Among his novels are the following: *The American, The Europeans, Daisy Miller, Washington Square, The Portrait of a Lady, The Bostonians, What Maisie Knew, The Awkward Age, The Wings of the Dove, The Ambassadors,* and *The Golden Bowl.*

Most of Henry James's short stories run to greater length than is customary in the nineteen-thirties. Several of the best are novelettes. A few of his well-known shorter stories are: *A Passionate Pilgrim, The Lesson of the Master, The Turn of the Screw, A Light Man,* and *Julia Bride.*

The Lesson of the Master is reprinted from *The Lesson of the Master and Other Stories* (1892) by permission of The Macmillan Company, publishers.]

I

HE had been told the ladies were at church, but this was corrected by what he saw from the top of the steps—they descended from a great height in two arms, with a circular sweep of the most charming effect—at the threshold of the door which, from the long bright gallery, overlooked the immense lawn. Three gentlemen, on the grass, at a distance, sat under the great trees, while the fourth figure showed a crimson dress that told as a "bit of color" amid the fresh rich green. The servant had so far accompanied Paul Overt as to introduce him to this view, after asking him if he wished first to go to his room. The young man declined that privilege, conscious of no disrepair from so short and easy a journey and always liking to take at once a general perceptive possession of a new scene. He stood there a little with his eyes on the group and on the admirable picture, the wide grounds of an old country-house near London—that only made it better—on a splendid Sunday in June. "But that lady, who's *she?*" he said to the servant before the man left him.

"I think she's Mrs. St. George, sir."

"Mrs. St. George the wife of the distinguished—" Then Paul Overt checked himself, doubting if a footman would know.

"Yes, sir—probably, sir," said his guide, who appeared to wish to intimate that a person staying at Summersoft would naturally be, if only by alliance, distinguished. His tone, however, made poor Overt himself feel for the moment scantly so.

"And the gentlemen?" Overt went on.

"Well, sir, one of them's General Fancourt."

"Ah yes, I know; thank you." General Fancourt was distinguished, there was no doubt of that, for something he had done, or perhaps even hadn't done—the young man couldn't remember which—some years before in India. The servant went away, leaving the glass doors open into the gallery, and Paul Overt remained at the head of the wide double staircase, saying to himself that the place was sweet and promised a pleasant visit, while he leaned on the balustrade of fine old ironwork which, like all the other details, was of the same period as the house. It all went together and spoke in one voice—a rich English voice of the early part of the eighteenth century. It might have been church-time on a summer's day in the reign of Queen Anne: the stillness was too perfect to be modern, the nearness counted so as distance, and there was something so fresh and sound in the originality of the large smooth house, the expanse of beautiful brickwork that showed for pink rather than red and that had been kept clear of messy creepers by the law under which a woman with a rare complexion disdains a veil. When Paul Overt became aware that the people under the trees had noticed him, he turned back through the open doors into the great gallery which was the pride of the place. It marched across from end to end and seemed—with its bright colors, its high panelled windows, its faded flowered chintzes, its quickly-recognised portraits and pictures, the blue-and-white china of its cabinets, and the attenuated festoons and rosettes of its ceiling—a cheerful upholstered avenue into the other century.

Our friend was slightly nervous; that went with his character as a student of fine prose, went with the artist's general disposition to vibrate; and there was a particular thrill in the idea that Henry St. George might be a member of the party. For the young aspirant he had remained a high literary figure, in spite of the lower range of production to which he had fallen after his three first great successes, the comparative absence of quality in his later work. There had been moments when Paul Overt almost shed tears for this; but now that he was near him—he had never met him—he was conscious only of the fine original source and of his own immense debt. After he had taken a turn or two up and down the gallery he came out again and descended the steps. He was but slenderly supplied with a certain social boldness—it was really a weakness in him —so that, conscious of a want of acquaintance with the four persons in the distance, he gave way to motions recommended by their not committing him to a positive approach. There was a fine English awkwardness in this—he felt that too as he sauntered vaguely and obliquely across the lawn, taking an independent line. Fortunately there was an equally fine English directness in the way one of the gentlemen presently rose and made as if to "stalk" him, though with an air of conciliation and reassurance. To this demonstration Paul Overt instantly responded, even if the gentleman were not his host. He was tall, straight and elderly, and had, like the great house itself, a pink smiling face, and into the bargain a white moustache. Our young man met him halfway while he laughed and said: "Er—Lady Watermouth told us you were coming; she asked me just to look after you." Paul Overt thanked him, liking him on the spot, and turned round with him to walk toward the others. "They've all gone to church—all except us," the stranger continued as they went; "we're just sitting here—it's so jolly." Overt pronounced it jolly indeed: it was such a lovely place. He mentioned that he was having the charming impression for the first time.

"Ah, you've not been here before?" said his companion. "It's a nice little place—not much to *do*, you know." Overt wondered what he wanted to "do"—he felt that he himself was doing so much. By the time they came to where the others sat he had recognised his initiator for a military man and—such was the turn of Overt's imagination—had found him thus still more sympathetic. He would naturally have a need for action, for deeds at variance with the pacific pastoral scene. He was evidently so good-natured, however, that he accepted the inglorious hour for what it was worth. Paul Overt shared it with him and with his companions for the next twenty minutes; the latter looked at him and he looked at them without knowing much who they were, while the talk went on without much telling him even what it meant. It seemed indeed to mean nothing in particular; it wandered, with casual pointless pauses and short terrestrial flights, amid names of persons and places— names which, for our friend, had no great power of evocation. It was all sociable and slow, as was right and natural of a warm Sunday morning.

His first attention was given to the question, privately considered, of whether one of the two younger men would be Henry St. George. He knew many of his distinguished contemporaries by their photographs, but had never, as happened, seen a portrait of the great misguided novelist. One of the gentlemen was unimaginable—he was too young;

and the other scarcely looked clever enough, with such mild, undiscriminating eyes. If those eyes were St. George's, the problem presented by the ill-matched parts of his genius would be still more difficult of solution. Besides, the deportment of their proprietor was not, as regards the lady in the red dress, such as could be natural, toward the wife of his bosom, even to a writer accused by several critics of sacrificing too much to manner. Lastly Paul Overt had a vague sense that if the gentleman with the expressionless eyes bore the name that had set his heart beating faster (he also had contradictory conventional whiskers—the young admirer of the celebrity had never in a mental vision seen *his* face in so vulgar a frame), he would have given him a sign of recognition or of friendliness, would have heard of him a little, would know something about "Ginistrella," would have an impression of how that fresh fiction had caught the eye of real criticism. Paul Overt had a dread of being grossly proud, but even morbid modesty might view the authorship of "Ginistrella" as constituting a degree of identity. His soldierly friend became clear enough: he was "Fancourt," but was also "the General"; and he mentioned to the new visitor in the course of a few moments that he had but lately returned from twenty years' service abroad.

"And now you remain in England?" the young man asked.

"Oh, yes; I've bought a small house in London."

"And I hope you like it," said Overt, looking at Mrs. St. George.

"Well, a little house in Manchester Square—there's a limit to the enthusiasm *that* inspires."

"Oh I meant being at home again—being back in Piccadilly."

"My daughter likes Piccadilly—that's the main thing. She's very fond of art and music and literature and all that kind of thing. She missed it in India and she finds it in London, or she hopes she'll find it. Mr. St. George has promised to help her—he has been awfully kind to her. She has gone to church—she's fond of that too—but they'll all be back in a quarter of an hour. You must let me introduce you to her—she'll be so glad to know you. I dare say she has read every blest word you've written."

"I shall be delighted—I haven't written so very many," Overt pleaded, feeling, and without resentment, that the General at least was vagueness itself about that. But he wondered a little why, expressing this friendly disposition, it didn't occur to the doubtless eminent soldier to pronounce the word that would put him in relation with Mrs. St. George. If it was a question of introductions Miss Fancourt—apparently as yet unmarried —was far away, while the wife of his illustrious confrère was almost between them. This lady struck Paul Overt as altogether pretty, with a surprising juvenility and a high smartness of aspect, something that—he could scarcely have said why—served for mystification. St. George certainly had every right to a charming wife, but he himself would never have imagined the important little woman in the aggressively Parisian dress the partner for life, the *alter ego*, of a man of letters. That partner in general, he knew, that second self, was far from presenting herself in a single type; observation had taught him that she was not inveterately, not necessarily plain. But he had never before seen her look so much as if her prosperity had deeper foundations than an ink-spotted study-table littered with proof-sheets. Mrs. St. George might have been the wife of a gentleman who "kept" books rather than wrote them, who carried on great affairs in the City and made better bargains than those that poets mostly make with publishers. With this she hinted at a success more personal—a success peculiarly stamping the age in which society, the world of conversation, is a great drawing-room with the City for its antechamber. Overt numbered her years at first as some thirty, and then ended by believing that she might approach her fiftieth. But she somehow in this case juggled away the excess and the difference—you only saw them in a rare glimpse, like the rabbit in the conjuror's sleeve. She was extraordinarily white, and her every element and item was pretty; her eyes, her ears, her hair, her voice, her hands, her feet—to which her relaxed attitude in her wicker chair gave a great publicity— and the numerous ribbons and trinkets with which she was bedecked. She looked as if she had put on her best clothes to go to church and then had decided they were too good for that and had stayed at home. She told a story of some length about the shabby way Lady Jane had treated the Duchess, as well as an anecdote in relation to a purchase she had made in Paris—on her way back from Cannes; made for Lady Egbert, who had never refunded the money. Paul Overt suspected her of a tendency to figure great people as larger than life, until he noticed the manner in which she handled Lady Egbert, which was so sharply mutinous that it reassured him. He felt he should have understood her better if he might have met her eye; but she scarcely so much as glanced at him. "Ah, here they come—all the good ones!" she said at last; and Paul Overt admired at his distance the return of the churchgoers— several persons, in couples and threes, advancing in a flicker of sun and shade at the end of a large green vista formed by the level grass and the overarching boughs.

"If you mean to imply that *we're* bad, I protest," said one of the gentlemen—"after making one's self agreeable all the morning!"

"Ah, if they've found you agreeable—!" Mrs. St. George gaily cried. "But if we're good, the others are better."

"They must be angels then," said the amused General.

"Your husband was an angel, the way he went off at your bidding," the gentleman who had first spoken declared to Mrs. St. George.

"At my bidding?"

"Didn't you make him go to church?"

"I never made him do anything in my life but once—when I made him burn up a bad book. That's all!" At her "That's all!" our young friend

broke into an irrepressible laugh; it lasted only a second, but it drew her
eyes to him. His own met them, though not long enough to help him to
understand her; unless it were a step toward this that he saw on the
instant how the burnt book—the way she alluded to it!—would have
been one of her husband's finest things.

"A bad book?" her interlocutor repeated.

"I didn't like it. He went to church because your daughter went," she
continued to General Fancourt. "I think it my duty to call your attention to his extraordinary demonstrations to your daughter."

"Well, if you don't mind them, I don't!" the General laughed.

"*Il s'attache à ses pas.* But I don't wonder—she's so charming."

"I hope she won't make him burn any books!" Paul Overt ventured to
exclaim.

"If she'd make him write a few, it would be more to the purpose," said
Mrs. St. George. "He has been of a laziness of late—!"

Our young man stared—he was so struck with the lady's phraseology.
Her "Write a few" seemed to him almost as good as her "That's all."
Didn't she, as the wife of a rare artist, know what it was to produce *one*
perfect work of art? How in the world did she think they were turned
off? His private conviction was that, admirably as Henry St. George
wrote, he had written for the last ten years, and especially for the last
five, only too much, and there was an instant during which he felt inwardly solicited to make this public. But before he had spoken a diversion was effected by the return of the absentees. They strolled up
dispersedly—there were eight or ten of them—and the circle under the
trees rearranged itself as they took their place in it. They made it much
larger, so that Paul Overt could feel—he was always feeling that sort of
thing, as he said to himself—that if the company had already been
interesting to watch, the interest would now become intense. He shook
hands with his hostess, who welcomed him without many words, in the
manner of a woman able to trust him to understand and conscious that
so pleasant an occasion would in every way speak for itself. She offered
him no particular facility for sitting by her; when they had all subsided
again, he found himself still next General Fancourt, with an unknown
lady on his other flank.

"That's my daughter—that one opposite," the General said to him
without loss of time. Overt saw a tall girl, with magnificent red hair, in a
dress of a pretty grey-green tint and of a limp silken texture, a garment
that clearly shirked every modern effect. It had therefore somehow the
stamp of the latest thing, so that our beholder quickly took her for nothing if not contemporaneous.

"She's very handsome—very handsome," he repeated while he considered her. There was something noble in her head, and she appeared
fresh and strong.

Her good father surveyed her with complacency, remarking soon:

"She looks too hot—that's her walk. But she'll be all right presently. Then I'll make her come over and speak to you."

"I should be sorry to give you that trouble. If you were to take me over *there*—!" the young man murmured.

"My dear sir, do you suppose I put myself out that way? I don't mean for you, but for Marian," the General added.

"*I* would put myself out for her soon enough," Overt replied; after which he went on: "Will you be so good as to tell me which of those gentlemen is Henry St. George?"

"The fellow talking to my girl. By Jove, he *is* making up to her—they're going off for another walk."

"Ah, is that he—really?" Our friend felt a certain surprise, for the personage before him seemed to trouble a vision which had been vague only while not confronted with the reality. As soon as the reality dawned the mental image, retiring with a sigh, became substantial enough to suffer a slight wrong. Overt, who had spent a considerable part of his short life in foreign lands, made now, but not for the first time, the reflection that whereas in those countries he had almost always recognised the artist and the man of letters by his personal "type," the mould of his face, the character of his head, the expression of his figure and even the indications of his dress, so in England this identification was as little as possible a matter of course, thanks to the greater conformity, the habit of sinking the profession instead of advertising it, the general diffusion of the air of the gentleman—the gentleman committed to no particular set of ideas. More than once, on returning to his own country, he had said to himself about people met in society: "One sees them in this place and that, and one even talks with them; but to find out what they *do* one would really have to be a detective." In respect to several individuals whose work he was the opposite of "drawn to"—perhaps he was wrong—he found himself adding, "No wonder they conceal it—when it's so bad!" He noted that oftener than in France and in Germany his artist looked like a gentleman—that is, like an English one—while, certainly outside a few exceptions, his gentleman didn't look like an artist. St. George was not one of the exceptions; that circumstance he definitely apprehended before the great man had turned his back to walk off with Miss Fancourt. He certainly looked better behind than any foreign man of letters—showed for beautifully correct in his tall black hat and his superior frock coat. Somehow, all the same, these very garments—he wouldn't have minded them so much on a week-day—were disconcerting to Paul Overt, who forgot for the moment that the head of the profession was not a bit better dressed than himself. He had caught a glimpse of a regular face, a fresh color, a brown moustache and a pair of eyes surely never visited by a fine frenzy, and he promised himself to study these denotements on the first occasion. His superficial sense was that their owner might have passed for a lucky stockbroker—a gentleman driving eastward every morning from a sanitary suburb in a smart dog-cart. That carried out the impression already derived from his wife. Paul's glance, after a moment, travelled back to this lady, and he saw how her own had followed her husband as he moved off with Miss Fancourt. Overt permitted himself to wonder a little if she were jealous when another woman took him away. Then he made out that Mrs. St. George wasn't glaring at the indifferent maiden. Her eyes rested but on her husband, and with unmistakable serenity. That was the way she wanted him to be—she liked his conventional uniform. Overt longed to hear more about the book she had induced him to destroy.

II

As they all came out from luncheon General Fancourt took hold of him with an "I say, I want you to know my girl!" as if the idea had just occurred to him and he hadn't spoken of it before. With the other hand he possessed himself all paternally of the young lady. "You know all about him. I've seen you with his books. She reads everything—everything!" he went on to Paul. The girl smiled at him and then laughed at her father. The General turned away and his daughter spoke—"Isn't papa delightful?"

"He is indeed, Miss Fancourt."

"As if I read you because I read 'everything'!"

"Oh, I don't mean for saying that," said Paul Overt. "I liked him from the moment he began to be kind to me. Then he promised me this privilege."

"It isn't for you he means it—it's for me. If you flatter yourself that he thinks of anything in life but me, you'll find you're mistaken. He introduces every one. He thinks me insatiable."

"You speak just like him," laughed our youth.

"Ah, but sometimes I want to"—and the girl colored. "I don't read everything—I read very little. But I *have* read you."

"Suppose we go into the gallery," said Paul Overt. She pleased him greatly, not so much because of this last remark—though that of course was not too disconcerting—as because, seated opposite to him at luncheon, she had given him for half an hour the impression of her beautiful face. Something else had come with it—a sense of generosity, of an enthusiasm which, unlike many enthusiasms, was not all manner. That was not spoiled for him by his seeing that the repast had placed her again in familiar contact with Henry St. George. Sitting next her this celebrity was also opposite our young man, who had been able to note that he multiplied the attentions lately brought by his wife to the General's notice. Paul Overt had gathered as well that this lady was not in the least discomposed by these fond excesses and that she gave every sign of an unclouded spirit. She had Lord Masham on one side of her and on the other the accomplished Mr. Mulliner, editor of the new high-class lively evening paper which was expected to meet a want felt in circles increasingly conscious that Conservatism must be made amusing, and unconvinced when assured by those of another political color that it was already amusing enough. At the end of an hour spent in her company Paul Overt thought her still prettier than at the first radiation, and if her profane allusions to her husband's work had not still rung in his ears he should have liked her—so far as it could be a question of that in connection with a woman to whom he had not yet spoken and to whom probably he should never speak if it were left to her. Pretty women were a clear need to this genius, and for the hour it was Miss Fancourt who supplied the want. If Overt had promised himself a closer view the occasion was now of the best, and it brought consequences felt by the young man as important. He saw more in St. George's face, which he liked the better for its not having told its whole story in the first three minutes. That story came out as one read, in short instalments—it was excusable that one's analogies should be somewhat professional—and the text was a style considerably involved, a language not easy to translate at sight. There were shades of meaning in it and a vague perspective of history which receded as you advanced. Two facts Paul had particularly heeded. The first of these was that he liked the measured mask much better at inscrutable rest than in social agitation; its almost convulsive smile above all displeased him (as much as any impression from that source could), whereas the quiet face had a charm that grew in proportion as stillness settled again. The change to the expression of gaiety excited, he made out, very much the private protest of a person sitting gratefully in the twilight when the lamp is brought in too soon. His second reflection was that, though generally averse to the flagrant use of ingratiating arts by a man of age "making up" to a pretty girl, he was not in this case too painfully affected: which seemed to prove either that St. George had a light hand or the air of being younger than he was, or else that Miss Fancourt's own manner somehow made everything right.

Overt walked with her into the gallery, and they strolled to the end of it, looking at the pictures, the cabinets, the charming vista, which harmonised with the prospect of the summer afternoon, resembling it by a long brightness, with great divans and old chairs that figured hours of rest. Such a place as that had the added merit of giving those who came into it plenty to talk about. Miss Fancourt sat down with her new acquaintance on a flowered sofa, the cushions of which, very numerous, were tight ancient cubes of many sizes, and presently said: "I'm so glad to have a chance to thank you."

"To thank me—?" He had to wonder.

"I liked your book so much. I think it splendid."

She sat there smiling at him, and he never asked himself which book she meant; for after all he had written three or four. That seemed a vulgar detail, and he wasn't even gratified by the idea of the pleasure she told him—her handsome bright face told him—he had given her. The feeling she appealed to, or at any rate the feeling she excited, was something larger, something that had little to do with any quickened pulsation of his own vanity. It was responsive admiration of the life she embodied, the young purity and richness of which appeared to imply that real success was to resemble *that*, to live, to bloom, to present the perfection of a fine type, not to have hammered out headachy fancies with a bent back at an ink-stained table. While her grey eyes rested on him— there was a widish space between these, and the division of her rich-colored hair, so thick that it ventured to be smooth, made a free arch above them—he was almost ashamed of that exercise of the pen which it was her present inclination to commend. He was conscious he should have liked better to please her in some other way. The lines of her face were those of a woman grown, but the child lingered on in her complexion and in the sweetness of her mouth. Above all she was natural—that was indubitable now; more natural than he had supposed at first, perhaps on account of her æsthetic toggery, which was conventionally unconventional, suggesting what he might have called a tortuous spontaneity. He had feared that sort of thing in other cases, and his fears had been justified; for, though he was an artist to the essence, the modern reactionary nymph, with the brambles of the woodland caught in her folds and a look as if the satyrs had toyed with her hair, made him shrink not as a man of starch and patent leather, but as a man potentially himself a poet or even a faun. The girl was really more candid than her costume, and the best proof of it was her supposing her liberal character suited by any uniform. This was a fallacy, since if she was draped as a pessimist he was sure she liked the taste of life. He thanked her for her appreciation—aware at the same time that he didn't appear to thank her enough and that she might think him ungracious. He was afraid she would ask him to explain something he had written, and he always winced at that—perhaps too timidly—for to his own ear the explanation of a work of art sounded fatuous. But he liked her so much as to feel a confidence that in the long run he should be able to show her he wasn't rudely evasive. Moreover she surely wasn't quick to take offence, wasn't irritable; she could be trusted to wait. So when he said to her, "Ah, don't talk of anything I've done, don't talk of it *here;* there's another man in the house who's the actuality!"—when he uttered this short sincere protest it was with the sense that she would see in the words neither mock humility nor the impatience of a successful man bored with praise.

"You mean Mr. St. George—isn't he delightful?"

Paul Overt met her eyes, which had a cool morning-light that would have half-broken his heart if he hadn't been so young. "Alas, I don't know him. I only admire him at a distance."

"Oh, you *must* know him—he wants so to talk to you," returned Miss

Fancourt, who evidently had the habit of saying the things that, by her quick calculation, would give people pleasure. Paul saw how she would always calculate on everything's being simple between others.

"I shouldn't have supposed he knew anything about me," he professed.

"He does, then—everything. And if he didn't I should be able to tell him."

"To tell him everything?" our friend smiled.

"You talk just like the people in your book," she answered.

"Then they must all talk alike."

She thought a moment, not a bit disconcerted. "Well, it must be so difficult. Mr. St. George tells me it *is*—terribly. I've tried too—and I find it so. I've tried to write a novel."

"Mr. St. George oughtn't to discourage you," Paul went so far as to say.

"You do much more—when you wear that expression."

"Well, after all, why try to be an artist?" the young man pursued. "It's so poor—so poor!"

"I don't know what you mean," said Miss Fancourt, who looked grave.

"I mean as compared with being a person of action—as living your works."

"But what's art but an intense life—if it be real?" she asked. "I think it's the only one—everything else is so clumsy!" Her companion laughed, and she brought out with her charming serenity what next struck her. "It's so interesting to meet so many celebrated people."

"So I should think—but surely it isn't new to you."

"Why, I've never seen any one—any one: living always in Asia."

The way she talked of Asia somehow enchanted him. "But doesn't that continent swarm with great figures? Haven't you administered provinces in India and had captive rajahs and tributary princes chained to your car?"

It was as if she didn't care even *should* he amuse himself at her cost. "I was with my father, after I left school to go out there. It was delightful being with him—we're alone together in the world, he and I—but there was none of the society I like best. One never heard of a picture—never of a book, except bad ones."

"Never of a picture? Why, wasn't all life a picture?"

She looked over the delightful place where they sat. "Nothing to compare to this. I adore England!" she cried.

It fairly stirred in him the sacred chord. "Ah, of course I don't deny that we must do something with her, poor old dear, yet!"

"She hasn't been touched, really," said the girl.

"Did Mr. St. George say that?"

There was a small and, as he felt, harmless spark of irony in his question; which, however, she answered very simply, not noticing the insinuation. "Yes, he says England hasn't been touched—not consider-ing all there is," she went on eagerly. "He's so interesting about our country. To listen to him makes one want so to do something."

"It would make *me* want to," said Paul Overt, feeling strongly, on the instant, the suggestion of what she said and that of the emotion with which she said it, and well aware of what an incentive, on St. George's lips, such a speech might be.

"Oh, you—as if you hadn't! I should like so to hear you talk to-gether," she added ardently.

"That's very genial of you; but he'd have it all his own way. I'm prostrate before him."

She had an air of earnestness. "Do you think, then, he's so perfect?"

"Far from it. Some of his later books seem to me of a queerness—!"

"Yes, yes—he knows that."

Paul Overt stared. "That they seem to me of a queerness—?"

"Well, yes, or at any rate that they're not what they should be. He told me he didn't esteem them. He has told me such wonderful things—he's so interesting."

There was a certain shock for Paul Overt in the knowledge that the fine genius they were talking of had been reduced to so explicit a con-fession and had made it, in his misery, to the first comer; for though Miss Fancourt was charming, what was she after all but an immature girl encountered at a country-house? Yet precisely this was part of the sentiment he himself had just expressed: he would make way com-pletely for the poor peccable great man not because he didn't read him clear, but altogether because he did. His consideration was half com-posed of tenderness for superficialities which he was sure their perpe-trator judged privately, judged more ferociously than any one, and which represented some tragic intellectual secret. He would have his reasons for his psychology *à fleur de peau*, and these reasons could only be cruel ones, such as would make him dearer to those who already were fond of him. "You excite my envy. I have my reserves, I discriminate—but I love him," Paul said in a moment. "And seeing him for the first time this way is a great event for me."

"How momentous—how magnificent!" cried the girl. "How delicious to bring you together!"

"*Your* doing it—that makes it perfect," our friend returned.

"He's as eager as you," she went on. "But it's so odd you shouldn't have met."

"It's not really so odd as it strikes you. I've been out of England so much—made repeated absences all these last years."

She took this in with interest. "And yet you write of it as well as if you were always here."

"It's just the being away perhaps. At any rate the best bits, I sus-pect, are those that were done in dreary places abroad."

"And why were they dreary?"

"Because they were health-resorts—where my poor mother was dying."

"Your poor mother?"—she was all sweet wonder.

"We went from place to place to help her to get better. But she never did. To the deadly Riviera (I hate it!), to the high Alps, to Algiers, and far away—a hideous journey—to Colorado."

"And she isn't better?" Miss Fancourt went on.

"She died a year ago."

"Really?—like mine! Only that's years since. Some day you must tell me about your mother," she added.

He could at first, on this, only gaze at her. "What right things you say! If you say them to St. George, I don't wonder he's in bondage."

It pulled her up for a moment. "I don't know what you mean. He doesn't make speeches and professions at all—he isn't ridiculous."

"I'm afraid you consider then that I am."

"No, I don't"—she spoke it rather shortly. And then she added: "He understands—understands everything."

The young man was on the point of saying jocosely: "And I don't— is that it?" But these words, in time, changed themselves to others slightly less trivial. "Do you suppose he understands his wife?"

Miss Fancourt made no direct answer, but after a moment's hesitation put it: "Isn't she charming?"

"Not in the least!"

"Here he comes. Now you must know him," she went on. A small group of visitors had gathered at the other end of the gallery and had been there overtaken by Henry St. George, who strolled in from a neighboring room. He stood near them a moment, not falling into the talk but taking up an old miniature from a table and vaguely regarding it. At the end of a minute he became aware of Miss Fancourt and her companion in the distance; whereupon, laying down his miniature, he approached them with the same procrastinating air, his hands in his pockets and his eyes turned, right and left, to the pictures. The gallery was so long that this transit took some little time, especially as there was a moment when he stopped to admire the fine Gainsborough. "He says Mrs. St. George has been the making of him," the girl continued in a voice slightly lowered.

"Ah, he's often obscure!" Paul laughed.

"Obscure?" she repeated as if she heard it for the first time. Her eyes rested on her other friend, and it wasn't lost upon Paul that they appeared to send out great shafts of softness. "He's going to speak to us!" she fondly breathed. There was a sort of rapture in her voice, and our friend was startled. "Bless my soul, does she care for him like *that*?— is she in love with him?" he mentally enquired. "Didn't I tell you he was eager?" she had meanwhile asked of him.

"It's eagerness dissimulated," the young man returned as the subject of their observation lingered before his Gainsborough. "He edges toward us shyly. Does he mean that she saved him by burning that book?"

"That book? what book did she burn?" The girl quickly turned her face to him.

"Hasn't he told you, then?"

"Not a word."

"Then he doesn't tell you everything!" Paul had guessed that she pretty much supposed he did. The great man had now resumed his course and come nearer; in spite of which his more qualified admirer risked a profane observation. "St. George and the Dragon is what the anecdote suggests!"

His companion, however, didn't hear it; she smiled at the dragon's adversary. "He *is* eager—he is!" she insisted.

"Eager for you—yes."

But meanwhile she had called out: "I'm sure you want to know Mr. Overt. You'll be great friends, and it will always be delightful to me to remember I was here when you first met and that I had something to do with it."

There was a freshness of intention in the words that carried them off; nevertheless our young man was sorry for Henry St. George, as he was sorry at any time for any person publicly invited to be responsive and delightful. He would have been so touched to believe that a man he deeply admired should care a straw for him that he wouldn't play with such a presumption if it were possibly vain. In a single glance of the eye of the pardonable master he read—having the sort of divination that belonged to his talent—that his personage had ever a store of friendly patience, which was part of his rich outfit, but was versed in no printed page of a rising scribbler. There was even a relief, a simplification, in that: liking him so much already for what he had done, how could one have liked him any more for a perception which must at the best have been vague? Paul Overt got up, trying to show his compassion, but at the same instant he found himself encompassed by St. George's happy personal art—a manner of which it was the essence to conjure away false positions. It all took place in a moment. Paul was conscious that he knew him now, conscious of his handshake and of the very quality of his hand; of his face, seen nearer and consequently seen better, of a general fraternising assurance, and in particular of the circumstance that St. George didn't dislike him (as yet at least) for being imposed by a charming but too gushing girl, attractive enough without such danglers. No irritation at any rate was reflected in the voice with which he questioned Miss Fancourt as to some project of a walk— a general walk of the company round the park. He had soon said something to Paul about a talk—"We must have a tremendous lot of talk; there are so many things, aren't there?"—but our friend could see this idea wouldn't in the present case take very immediate effect. All the same he was extremely happy, even after the matter of the walk had been settled—the three presently passed back to the other part of the gallery, where it was discussed with several members of the party; even when, after they had all gone out together, he found himself for half an hour conjoined with Mrs. St. George. Her husband had taken the advance with Miss Fancourt, and this pair were quite out of sight. It was the prettiest of rambles for a summer afternoon—a grassy circuit, of immense extent, skirting the limit of the park within. The park was completely surrounded by its old mottled but perfect red wall, which, all the way on their left, constituted in itself an object of interest. Mrs. St. George mentioned to him the surprising number of acres thus enclosed, together with numerous other facts relating to the property and the family, and the family's other properties: she couldn't too strongly urge on him the importance of seeing their other houses. She ran over the names of these and rang the changes on them with the facility of practice, making them appear an almost endless list. She had received Paul Overt very amiably on his breaking ground with her by the mention of his joy in having just made her husband's acquaintance, and struck him as so alert and so accommodating a little woman that he was rather ashamed of his *mot* about her to Miss Fancourt; though he reflected that a hundred other people, on a hundred occasions, would have been sure to make it. He got on with Mrs. St. George, in short, better than he expected; but this didn't prevent her suddenly becoming aware that she was faint with fatigue and must take her way back to the house by the shortest cut. She professed that she hadn't the strength of a kitten and was a miserable wreck; a character he had been too preoccupied to discern in her while he wondered in what sense she could be held to have been the making of her husband. He had arrived at a glimmering of the answer when she announced that she must leave him, though this perception was of course provisional. While he was in the very act of placing himself at her disposal for the return, the situation underwent a change; Lord Masham had suddenly turned up, coming back to them, overtaking them, emerging from the shrubbery—Overt could scarcely have said how he appeared—and Mrs. St. George had protested that she wanted to be left alone and not to break up the party. A moment later she was walking off with Lord Masham. Our friend fell back and joined Lady Watermouth, to whom he presently mentioned that Mrs. St. George had been obliged to renounce the attempt to go further.

"She oughtn't to have come out at all," her ladyship rather grumpily remarked.

"Is she so very much of an invalid?"

"Very bad indeed." And his hostess added with still greater austerity:

"She oughtn't really to come to one!" He wondered what was implied by this, and presently gathered that it was not a reflection on the lady's conduct or her moral nature: it only represented that her strength was not equal to her aspirations.

III

The smoking-room at Summersoft was on the scale of the rest of the place—high, light, commodious and decorated with such refined old carvings and mouldings that it seemed rather a bower for ladies who should sit at work at fading crewels than a parliament of gentlemen smoking strong cigars. The gentlemen mustered there in considerable force on the Sunday evening, collecting mainly at one end, in front of one of the cool, fair fireplaces of white marble, the entablature of which was adorned with a delicate little Italian "subject." There was another in the wall that faced it, and, thanks to the mild summer night, a fire in neither; but a nucleus for aggregation was furnished on one side by table in the chimney-corner laden with bottles, decanters and tall tumblers. Paul Overt was a faithless smoker; he would puff a cigarette for reasons with which tobacco had nothing to do. This was particularly the case on the occasion of which I speak; his motive was the vision of a little direct talk with Henry St. George. The "tremendous" communion of which the great man had held out hopes to him earlier in the day had not yet come off, and this saddened him considerably, for the party was to go its several ways immediately after breakfast on the morrow. He had, however, the disappointment of finding that apparently the author of "Shadowmere" was not disposed to prolong his vigil. He wasn't among the gentlemen assembled when Paul entered, nor was he one of those who turned up, in bright habiliments, during the next ten minutes. The young man waited a little, wondering if he had only gone to put on something extraordinary; this would account for his delay as well as contribute further to Overt's impression of his tendency to do the approved superficial thing. But he didn't arrive—he must have been putting on something more extraordinary than was probable. Our hero gave him up, feeling a little injured, a little wounded, at this loss of twenty coveted words. He wasn't angry, but he puffed his cigarette sighingly, with the sense of something rare possibly missed. He wandered away with his regret and moved slowly round the room, looking at the old prints on the walls. In this attitude he presently felt a hand on his shoulder and a friendly voice in his ear: "This is good. I hoped I should find you. I came down on purpose." St. George was there without a change of dress and with a fine face—his graver one—to which our young man all in a flutter responded. He explained that it was only for the Master—the idea of a little talk—that he had sat up, and that, not finding him, he had been on the point of going to bed.

"Well, you know, I don't smoke—my wife doesn't let me," said St. George, looking for a place to sit down. "It's very good for me—very good for me. Let us take that sofa."

"Do you mean smoking's good for you?"

"No, no—her not letting me. It's a great thing to have a wife who's so sure of all the things one can do without. One might never find them out one's self. She doesn't allow me to touch a cigarette." They took possession of a sofa at a distance from the group of smokers, and St. George went on: "Have you got one yourself?"

"Do you mean a cigarette?"

"Dear no—a wife!"

"No; and yet I'd give up my cigarette for one."

"You'd give up a good deal more than that," St. George returned. "However, you'd get a great deal in return. There's a something to be said for wives," he added, folding his arms and crossing his outstretched legs. He declined tobacco altogether and sat there without returning fire. His companion stopped smoking, touched by his courtesy; and after all they were out of the fumes, their sofa was in a far-away corner. It would have been a mistake, St. George went on, a great mistake for them to have separated without a little chat: "For I know all about you," he said, "I know you're very remarkable. You've written a very distinguished book."

"And how do you know it?" Paul asked.

"Why, my dear fellow, it's in the air, it's in the papers, it's everywhere." St. George spoke with the immediate familiarity of a confrère— a tone that seemed to his neighbor the very rustle of the laurel. "You're on all men's lips and, what's better, on all women's. And I've just been reading your book."

"Just? You hadn't read it this afternoon," said Overt.

"How do you know that?"

"I think you should know how I know it," the young man laughed.

"I suppose Miss Fancourt told you."

"No indeed—she led me rather to suppose you had."

"Yes—that's much more what she'd do. Doesn't she shed a rosy glow over life? But you didn't believe her?" asked St. George.

"No, not when you came to us there."

"Did I pretend? did I pretend badly?" But without waiting for an answer to this St. George went on: "You ought always to believe such a girl as that—always, always. Some women are meant to be taken with allowances and reserves; but you must take *her* just as she is."

"I like her very much," said Paul Overt.

Something in his tone appeared to excite on his companion's part a momentary sense of the absurd; perhaps it was the air of deliberation attending this judgment. St. George broke into a laugh to reply. "It's the best thing you can do with her. She's a rare young lady! In point of fact, however, I confess I hadn't read you this afternoon."

"Then you see how right I was in this particular case not to believe Miss Fancourt."

"How right? how can I agree to that when I lost credit by it?"

"Do you wish to pass exactly for what she represents you? Certainly you needn't be afraid," Paul said.

"Ah, my dear young man, don't talk about passing—for the likes of me! I'm passing away—nothing else than that. She has a better use for her young imagination (isn't it fine?) than in 'representing' in any way such a weary, wasted, used-up animal!" The Master spoke with a sudden sadness that produced a protest on Paul's part; but before the protest could be uttered he went on, reverting to the latter's striking novel: "I had no idea you were so good—one hears of so many things. But you're surprisingly good."

"I'm going to be surprisingly better," Overt made bold to reply.

"I see that, and it's what fetches me. I don't see so much else—as one looks about—that's going to be surprisingly better. They're going to be consistently worse—most of the things. It's so much easier to be worse—heaven knows I've found it so. I'm not in a great glow, you know, about what's breaking out all over the place. But you *must* be better, you really must keep it up. I haven't of course. It's very difficult—that's the devil of the whole thing, keeping it up. But I see you'll be able to. It will be a great disgrace if you don't."

"It's very interesting to hear you speak of yourself; but I don't know what you mean by your allusions to your having fallen off," Paul Overt observed with pardonable hypocrisy. He liked his companion so much now that the fact of any decline of talent or of care had ceased for the moment to be vivid to him.

"Don't say that—don't say that," St. George returned gravely, his head resting on the top of the sofa-back and his eyes on the ceiling. "You know perfectly what I mean. I haven't read twenty pages of your book without seeing that you can't help it."

"You make me very miserable," Paul ecstatically breathed.

"I'm glad of that, for it may serve as a kind of warning. Shocking enough it must be, especially to a young fresh mind, full of faith—the spectacle of a man meant for better things sunk at my age in such dishonor." St. George, in the same contemplative attitude, spoke softly but deliberately, and without perceptible emotion. His tone indeed suggested an impersonal lucidity that was practically cruel—cruel to himself—and made his young friend lay an argumentative hand on his arm. But he went on while his eyes seemed to follow the graces of the eighteenth-century ceiling: "Look at me well, take my lesson to heart—for it *is* a lesson. Let that good come of it at least that you shudder with your pitiful impression, and that this may help to keep you straight in the future. Don't become in your old age what I have in mine—the depressing, the deplorable illustration of the worship of false gods!"

"What do you mean by your old age?" the young man asked.

"It has made me old. But I like your youth."

Paul answered nothing—they sat for a minute in silence. They heard the others going on about the governmental majority. Then "What do you mean by false gods?" he enquired.

His companion had no difficulty whatever in saying, "The idols of the market; money and luxury and 'the world'; placing one's children and dressing one's wife; everything that drives one to the short and easy way. Ah, the vile things they make one do!"

"But surely one's right to want to place one's children."

"One has no business to have any children," St. George placidly declared. "I mean of course if one wants to do anything good."

"But aren't they an inspiration—an incentive?"

"An incentive to damnation, artistically speaking."

"You touch on very deep things—things I should like to discuss with you," Paul said. "I should like you to tell me volumes about yourself. This is a great feast for *me!*"

"Of course it is, cruel youth. But to show you I'm still not incapable, degraded as I am, of an act of faith, I'll tie my vanity to the stake for you and burn it to ashes. You must come and see me—you must come and see us," the Master quickly substituted. "Mrs. St. George is charming; I don't know whether you've had any opportunity to talk with her. She'll be delighted to see you; she likes great celebrities, whether incipient or predominant. You must come and dine—my wife will write to you. Where are you to be found?"

"This is my little address"—and Overt drew out his pocketbook and extracted a visiting-card. On second thoughts, however, he kept it back, remarking that he wouldn't trouble his friend to take charge of it but would come and see him straightway in London and leave it at his door if he should fail to obtain entrance.

"Ah, you'll probably fail; my wife's always out—or when she isn't out is knocked up from having *been* out. You must come and dine—though that won't do much good either, for my wife insists on big dinners." St. George turned it over further, but then went on: "You must come down and see us in the country, that's the best way; we've plenty of room and it isn't bad."

"You've a house in the country?" Paul asked enviously.

"Ah, not like this! But we have a sort of place we go to—an hour from Euston. That's one of the reasons."

"One of the reasons?"

"Why my books are so bad."

"You must tell me all the others!" Paul longingly laughed.

His friend made no direct rejoinder to this, but spoke again abruptly. "Why have I never seen you before?"

The tone of the question was singularly flattering to our hero, who felt it to imply the great man's now perceiving he had for years missed something. "Partly, I suppose, because there has been no particular reason why you should see me. I haven't lived in the world—in your world. I've spent many years out of England, in different places abroad."

"Well, please don't do it any more. You must do England—there's such a lot of it."

"Do you mean I must write about it?"—and Paul struck the note of the listening candor of a child.

"Of course you must. And tremendously well, do you mind? That takes off a little of my esteem for this thing of yours—that it goes on abroad. Hang 'abroad'! Stay at home and do things here—do subjects we can measure."

"I'll do whatever you tell me," Overt said, deeply attentive. "But pardon me if I say I don't understand how you've been reading my book," he added. "I've had you before me all the afternoon, first in that long walk, then at tea on the lawn, till we went to dress for dinner, and all the evening at dinner and in this place."

St. George turned his face about with a smile. "I gave it but a quarter of an hour."

"A quarter of an hour's immense, but I don't understand where you put it in. In the drawing-room after dinner you weren't reading—you were talking to Miss Fancourt."

"It comes to the same thing, because we talked about 'Ginistrella.' She described it to me—she lent me her copy."

"Lent it to you?"

"She travels with it."

"It's incredible," Paul blushed.

"It's glorious for you, but it also turned out very well for me. When the ladies went off to bed, she kindly offered to send the book down to me. Her maid brought it to me in the hall, and I went to my room with it. I hadn't thought of coming here, I do that so little. But I don't sleep early, I always have to read an hour or two. I sat down to your novel on the spot, without undressing, without taking off anything but my coat. I think that's a sign my curiosity had been strongly roused about it. I read a quarter of an hour, as I tell you, and even in a quarter of an hour I was greatly struck."

"Ah, the beginning isn't very good—it's—the whole thing!" said Overt, who had listened to this recital with extreme interest. "And you laid down the book and came after me?" he asked.

"That's the way it moved me. I said to myself, 'I see it's off his own bat, and he's there, by the way, and the day's over, and I haven't said twenty words to him.' It occurred to me that you'd probably be in the smoking-room and that it wouldn't be too late to repair my omission. I wanted to do something civil to you, so I put on my coat and came down. I shall read your book again when I go up."

Our friend faced round in his place—he was touched as he had scarce ever been by the picture of such a demonstration in his favor. "You're really the kindest of men. *Cela s'est passé comme ça?*—and I've been sitting here with you all this time and never apprehended it and never thanked you!"

"Thank Miss Fancourt—it was she who wound me up. She has made me feel as if I had read your novel."

"She's an angel from heaven!" Paul declared.

"She is indeed. I've never seen any one like her. Her interest in literature's touching—something quite peculiar to herself; she takes it all so seriously. She feels the arts and she wants to feel them more. To those who practise them it's almost humiliating—her curiosity, her sympathy, her good faith. How can anything be as fine as she supposes it?"

"She's a rare organisation," the younger man sighed.

"The richest I've ever seen—an artistic intelligence really of the first order. And lodged in such a form!" St. George exclaimed.

"One would like to represent such a girl as that," Paul continued.

"Ah, there it is—there's nothing like life!" said his companion. "When you're finished, squeezed dry and used up and you think the sack's empty, you're still appealed to, you still get touches and thrills, the idea springs up—out of the lap of the actual—and shows you there's always something to be done. But I shan't do it—she's not for me!"

"How do you mean, not for you?"

"Oh, it's all over—she's for you, if you like."

"Ah, much less!" said Paul. "She's not for a dingy little man of letters; she's for the world, the bright rich world of bribes and rewards. And the world will take hold of her—it will carry her away."

"It will try—but it's just a case in which there may be a fight. It would be worth fighting, for a man who had it in him, with youth and talent on his side."

These words rang not a little in Paul Overt's consciousness—they held him briefly silent. "It's a wonder she has remained as she is; giving herself away so—with so much to give away."

"Remaining, you mean, so ingenuous—so natural? Oh, she doesn't care a straw—she gives away because she overflows. She has her own feelings, her own standards; she doesn't keep remembering that she must be proud. And then she hasn't been here long enough to be spoiled; she has picked up a fashion or two, but only the amusing ones. She's a provincial—a provincial of genius," St. George went on; "her very blunders are charming, her mistakes are interesting. She has come back from Asia with all sorts of excited curiosities and unappeased appetites. She's first-rate herself and she expends herself on the second-rate. She's life herself and she takes a rare interest in imitations. She mixes all things up, but there are none in regard to which she hasn't perceptions. She sees things in a perspective—as if from the top of the Himalayas— and she enlarges everything she touches. Above all she exaggerates— to herself, I mean. She exaggerates you and me!"

There was nothing in that description to allay the agitation caused in our younger friend by such a sketch of a fine subject. It seemed to him to show the art of St. George's admired hand, and he lost himself in gazing at the vision—this hovered there before him—of a woman's figure which should be part of the glory of a novel. But at the end of a moment the thing had turned into smoke, and out of the smoke—the last puff of a big cigar—proceeded the voice of General Fancourt, who had left the others and come and planted himself before the gentlemen on the sofa. "I suppose that when you fellows get talking you sit up half the night."

"Half the night?—*jamais de la vie!* I follow a hygiene"—and St. George rose to his feet.

"I see—you're hothouse plants," laughed the General. "That's the way you produce your flowers."

"I produce mine between ten and one every morning—I bloom with a regularity!" St. George went on.

"And with a splendor!" added the polite General, while Paul noted how little the author of "Shadowmere" minded, as he phrased it to himself, when addressed as a celebrated story-teller. The young man had an idea *he* should never get used to that; it would always make him uncomfortable—from the suspicion that people would think they had to—and he would want to prevent it. Evidently his great colleague had toughened and hardened—had made himself a surface. The group of men had finished their cigars and taken up their bedroom candlesticks; but before they all passed out Lord Watermouth invited the pair of guests who had been so absorbed together to "have" something. It happened that they both declined; upon which General Fancourt said: "Is that the hygiene? You don't water the flowers?"

"Oh, I should drown them!" St. George replied; but, leaving the room still at his young friend's side, he added whimsically, for the latter's benefit, in a lower tone: "My wife doesn't let me."

"Well, I'm glad I'm not one of you fellows!" the General richly concluded.

The nearness of Summersoft to London had this consequence, chilling to a person who had had a vision of sociability in a railway-carriage, that most of the company, after breakfast, drove back to town, entering their own vehicles, which had come out to fetch them, while their servants returned by train with their luggage. Three or four young men, among whom was Paul Overt, also availed themselves of the common convenience; but they stood in the portico of the house and saw the others roll away. Miss Fancourt got into a victoria with her father after she had shaken hands with our hero and said, smiling in the frankest way in the world, "I *must* see you more. Mrs. St. George is so nice; she has promised to ask us both to dinner together." This lady and her husband took their places in a perfectly-appointed brougham—she required a closed carriage—and as our young man waved his hat to them in response to their nods and flourishes he reflected that, taken together, they were an honorable image of success, of the material rewards and the social credit of literature. Such things were not the full measure, but he nevertheless felt a little proud for literature.

IV

Before a week had elapsed he met Miss Fancourt in Bond Street, at a private view of the works of a young artist in "black-and-white" who had been so good as to invite him to the stuffy scene. The drawings were admirable, but the crowd in the one little room was so dense that he felt himself up to his neck in a sack of wool. A fringe of people at the outer edge endeavored by curving forward their backs and presenting, below them, a still more convex surface of resistance to the pressure of the mass, to preserve an interval between their noses and the glazed mounts of the pictures; while the central body, in the comparative gloom projected by a wide horizontal screen hung under the skylight and allowing only a margin for the day, remained upright, dense and vague, lost in the contemplation of its own ingredients. This contemplation sat especially in the sad eyes of certain female heads, surmounted with hats of strange convolution and plumage, which rose on long necks above the others. One of the heads, Paul perceived, was much the most beautiful of the collection, and his next discovery was that it belonged to Miss Fancourt. Its beauty was enhanced by the glad smile she sent him across surrounding obstructions, a smile that drew him to her as fast as he could make his way. He had seen for himself at Summersoft that the last thing her nature contained was an affectation of indifference; yet even with this circumspection he took a fresh satisfaction in her not having pretended to await his arrival with composure. She smiled as radiantly as if she wished to make him hurry, and as soon as he came within earshot she broke out in her voice of joy: "He's here—he's here; he's coming back in a moment!"

"Ah, your father?" Paul returned as she offered him her hand.

"Oh, dear no, this isn't in my poor father's line. I mean Mr. St. George. He has just left me to speak to some one—he's coming back. It's he who brought me—wasn't it charming?"

"Ah, that gives him a pull over me—I couldn't have 'brought' you, could I?"

"If you had been so kind as to propose it—why not you as well as he?" the girl returned with a face that, expressing no cheap coquetry, simply affirmed a happy fact.

"Why, he's a *père de famille*. They've privileges," Paul explained. And then quickly: "Will you go to see places with *me?*" he asked.

"Anything you like," she smiled. "I know what you mean, that girls have to have a lot of people—!" Then she broke off: "I don't know; I'm free. I've always been like that—I can go about with any one. I'm so glad to meet you," she added with a sweet distinctness that made those near her turn round.

"Let me at least repay that speech by taking you out of this squash," her friend said. "Surely people aren't happy here!"

"No, they're awfully *mornes*, aren't they? But I'm very happy indeed and I promised Mr. St. George to remain on this spot till he comes back. He's going to take me away. They send him invitations for things of this sort—more than he wants. It was so kind of him to think of me."

"They also send me invitations of this kind—more than *I* want. And if thinking of *you* will do it—!" Paul went on.

"Oh, I delight in them—everything that's life, everything that's London!"

"They don't have private views in Asia, I suppose," he laughed. "But what a pity that for this year, even in this gorged city, they're pretty well over."

"Well, next year will do, for I hope you believe we're going to be friends always. Here he comes!" Miss Fancourt continued before Paul had time to respond.

He made out St. George in the gaps of the crowd, and this perhaps led to his hurrying a little to say: "I hope that doesn't mean I'm to wait till next year to see you."

"No, no—aren't we to meet at dinner on the twenty-fifth?" she panted with an eagerness as happy as his own.

"That's almost next year. Is there no means of seeing you before?"

She stared with all her brightness. "Do you mean you'd *come?*"

"Like a shot, if you'll be so good as to ask me!"

"On Sunday then—this next Sunday?"

"What have I done that you should doubt it?" the young man asked with delight.

Miss Fancourt turned instantly to St. George, who had now joined them, and announced triumphantly: "He's coming on Sunday—this next Sunday!"

"Ah, my day—my day too!" said the famous novelist, laughing, to their companion.

"Yes, but not yours only. You shall meet in Manchester Square; you shall talk—you shall be wonderful!"

"We don't meet often enough," St. George allowed, shaking hands with his disciple. "Too many things—ah, too many things! But we must make it up in the country in September. You won't forget you've promised me that?"

"Why, he's coming on the twenty-fifth—you'll see him then," said the girl.

"On the twenty-fifth?" St. George asked vaguely.

"We dine with you; I hope you haven't forgotten. He's dining out that day," she added gaily to Paul.

"Oh, bless me, yes—that's charming! And you're coming? My wife didn't tell me," St. George said to him. "Too many things—too many things!" he repeated.

"Too many people—too many people!" Paul exclaimed, giving ground before the penetration of an elbow.

"You oughtn't to say that. They all read you."

"Me? I should like to see them! Only two or three at most," the young man returned.

"Did you ever hear anything like that? He knows, haughtily, how good he is!" St. George declared, laughing, to Miss Fancourt. "They read *me*, but that doesn't make me like them any better. Come away from them, come away!" And he led the way out of the exhibition.

"He's going to take me to the Park," Miss Fancourt observed to Overt with elation as they passed along the corridor that led to the street.

"Ah, does he go there?" Paul asked, taking the fact for a somewhat unexpected illustration of St. George's *mœurs*.

"It's a beautiful day—there'll be a great crowd. We're going to look at the people, to look at types," the girl went on. "We shall sit under the trees; we shall walk by the Row."

"I go once a year—on business," said St. George, who had overheard Paul's question.

"Or with a country cousin, didn't you tell me? I'm the country cousin!" she continued over her shoulder to Paul as their friend drew her toward a hansom to which he had signalled. The young man watched them get in; he returned, as he stood there, the friendly wave of the hand with which, ensconced in the vehicle beside her, St. George took leave of him. He even lingered to see the vehicle start away and lose itself in the confusion of Bond Street. He followed it with his eyes; it put to him embarrassing things. "She's not for *me*!" the great novelist had said emphatically at Summersoft; but his manner of conducting himself toward her appeared not quite in harmony with such a conviction. How could he have behaved differently if she *had* been for him? An indefinite envy rose in Paul Overt's heart as he took his way on foot alone; a feeling addressed alike, strangely enough, to each of the occupants of the hansom. How much he should like to rattle about London with such a girl! How much he should like to go and look at "types" with St. George!

The next Sunday at four o'clock he called in Manchester Square, where his secret wish was gratified by his finding Miss Fancourt alone. She was in a large bright friendly occupied room, which was painted red all over, draped with the quaint, cheap, florid stuffs that are represented as coming from southern and eastern countries, where they are fabled to serve as the counterpanes of the peasantry, and bedecked with pottery of vivid hues, ranged on casual shelves, and with many watercolour drawings from the hand (as the visitor learned) of the young lady herself, commemorating with a brave breadth the sunsets, the mountains, the temples and palaces of India. He sat an hour—more than an hour, two hours—and all the while no one came in. His hostess was so good as to remark, with her liberal humanity, that it was delightful they weren't interrupted: it was so rare in London, especially at that season, that people got a good talk. But luckily now, of a fine Sunday, half the world went out of town, and that made it better for those who didn't go, when these others were in sympathy. It was the defect of London—one of two or three, the very short list of those she recognised in the teeming world-city she adored—that there were too few good chances for talk: you never had time to carry anything far.

"Too many things, too many things!" Paul said, quoting St. George's exclamation of a few days before.

"Ah yes, for him there are too many—his life's too complicated."

"Have you seen it *near?* That's what I should like to do; it might explain some mysteries," her visitor went on. She asked him what mysteries he meant, and he said: "Oh, peculiarities of his work, inequalities, superficialities. For one who looks at it from the artistic point of view it contains a bottomless ambiguity."

She became at this, on the spot, all intensity. "Ah, do describe that more—it's so interesting. There are no such suggestive questions. I'm so fond of them. He thinks he's a failure—fancy!" she beautifully wailed.

"That depends on what his ideal may have been. With his gifts it ought to have been high. But till one knows what he really proposed to himself—! Do *you* know by chance?" the young man broke off.

"Oh, he doesn't talk to me about himself. I can't make him. It's too provoking."

Paul was on the point of asking what, then, he did talk about, but discretion checked it and he said instead: "Do you think he's unhappy at home?"

She seemed to wonder. "At home?"

"I mean in his relations with his wife. He has a mystifying little way of alluding to her."

"Not to me," said Marian Fancourt with her clear eyes. "That wouldn't be right, would it?" she asked gravely.

"Not particularly; so I'm glad he doesn't mention her to you. To praise her might bore you, and he has no business to do anything else. Yet he knows you better than me."

"Ah, but he respects *you!*" the girl cried as with envy.

Her visitor stared a moment, then broke into a laugh. "Doesn't he respect you?"

"Of course, but not in the same way. He respects what you've done —he told me so the other day."

Paul drank it in, but retained his faculties. "When you went to look at types?"

"Yes—we found so many: he has such an observation of them! He talked a great deal about your book. He says it's really important."

"Important! Ah, the grand creature!"—and the author of the work in question groaned for joy.

"He was wonderfully amusing, he was inexpressibly droll, while we walked about. He sees everything; he has so many comparisons and images, and they're always exactly right. *C'est d'un trouvé,* as they say!"

"Yes, with his gifts, such things as he ought to have done!" Paul sighed.

"And don't you think he *has* done them?"

Ah, it was just the point. "A part of them, and of course even that part's immense. But he might have been one of the greatest. However, let us not make this an hour of qualifications. Even as they stand," our friend earnestly concluded, "his writings are a mine of gold."

To this proposition she ardently responded, and for half an hour the pair talked over the Master's principal productions. She knew them well—she knew them even better than her visitor, who was struck with her critical intelligence and with something large and bold in the movement in her mind. She said things that startled him and that evidently had come to her directly; they weren't picked-up phrases—she placed them too well. St. George had been right about her being first-rate, about her not being afraid to gush, not remembering that she must be proud. Suddenly something came back to her, and she said: "I recollect that he did speak of Mrs. St. George to me once. He said, apropos of something or other, that she didn't care for perfection."

"That's a great crime in an artist's wife," Paul returned.

"Yes, poor thing!" and the girl sighed with a suggestion of many reflections, some of them mitigating. But she presently added: "Ah, perfection, perfection—how one ought to go in for it! I wish *I* could."

"Every one can in his way," her companion opined.

"In *his* way, yes—but not in hers. Women are so hampered—so condemned! Yet it's a kind of dishonor if you don't, when you want to *do* something, isn't it?" Miss Fancourt pursued, dropping one train in her quickness to take up another, an accident that was common with her. So these two young persons sat discussing high themes in their eclectic drawing-room, in their London "season"—discussing, with extreme seriousness, the high theme of perfection. It must be said in extenuation of this eccentricity that they were interested in the business. Their tone had truth and their emotion beauty; they weren't posturing for each other or for some one else.

The subject was so wide that they found themselves reducing it; the perfection to which for the moment they agreed to confine their speculations was that of the valid, the exemplary work of art. Our young woman's imagination, it appeared, had wandered far in that direction, and her guest had the rare delight of feeling in their conversation a full interchange. This episode will have lived for years in his memory and even in his wonder; it had the quality that fortune distils in a single drop at a time—the quality that lubricates many ensuing frictions. He still, whenever he likes, has a vision of the room, the bright, red, sociable talkative room with the curtains that, by a stroke of successful audacity, had the note of vivid blue. He remembers where certain things stood, the particular book open on the table and the almost intense odor of the flowers placed, at the left, somewhere behind him. These facts were the fringe, as it were, of a fine special agitation which had its birth in those two hours and of which perhaps the main sign was in its leading him inwardly and repeatedly to breathe "I had no idea there was any one like this—I had no idea there was any one like this!" Her freedom amazed him and charmed him—it seemed so to simplify the practical question. She was on the footing of an independent personage—a motherless girl who had passed out of her teens and had a position and responsibilities, who wasn't held down to the limitations of a little miss. She came and went with no dragged duenna, she received people alone, and, though she was totally without hardness, the question of protection or patronage had no relevancy in regard to her. She gave such an impression of the clear and the noble combined with the easy and the natural that in spite of her eminent modern situation she suggested no sort of sisterhood with the "fast" girl. Modern she was indeed, and made Paul Overt, who loved old color, the golden glaze of time, think with some alarm of the muddled palette of the future. He couldn't get used to her interest in the arts he cared for; it seemed too good to be real —it was so unlikely an adventure to tumble into such a well of sympathy. One might stray into the desert easily—that was on the cards and that was the law of life; but it was too rare an accident to stumble on a crystal well. Yet if her aspirations seemed at one moment too extravagant to be real, they struck him at the next as too intelligent to be false. They were both high and lame, and, whims for whims, he preferred them to any he had met in a like relation. It was probable enough she would leave them behind—exchange them for politics or "smartness" or mere prolific maternity, as was the custom of scribbling, daubing, educated flattered girls in an age of luxury and a society of leisure. He noted that the water-colors on the walls of the room she sat in had mainly the quality of being naïves, and reflected that naïveté in art is like a zero in a number: its importance depends on the figure it is united with. Meanwhile, however, he had fallen in love with her. Before he went away, at any rate, he said to her: "I thought St. George was coming to see you today, but he doesn't turn up."

For a moment he supposed she was going to cry, "*Comment donc?* Did you come here only to meet him?" But the next he became aware of how little such a speech would have fallen in with any note of flirtation he had as yet perceived in her. She only replied: "Ah yes, but I don't think he'll come. He recommended me not to expect him." Then she gaily but all gently added: "He said it wasn't fair to you. But I think I could manage two."

"So could I," Paul Overt returned, stretching the point a little to meet her. In reality his appreciation of the occasion was so completely an appreciation of the woman before him that another figure in the scene, even so esteemed a one as St. George, might for the hour have appealed to him vainly. He left the house wondering what the great man had meant by its not being fair to him; and, still more than that, whether he had actually stayed away from the force of that idea. As he took his course through the Sunday solitude of Manchester Square, swinging his stick and with a good deal of emotion fermenting in his soul, it appeared to him he was living in a world strangely magnanimous. Miss Fancourt had told him it was possible she should be away, and that her father should be, on the following Sunday, but that she had the hope of a visit from him in the other event. She promised to let him know should their absence fail, and then he might act accordingly. After he had passed into one of the streets that open from the Square he stopped, without definite intentions, looking sceptically for a cab. In a moment he saw a hansom roll through the place from the other side and come a part of the way toward him. He was on the point of hailing the driver when he noticed a "fare" within; then he waited, seeing the man prepare to deposit his passenger by pulling up at one of the houses. The house was apparently the one he himself had just quitted; at least he drew that inference as he recognised Henry St. George in the person who stepped out of the hansom. Paul turned off as quickly as if he had been caught in the act of spying. He gave up his cab—he preferred to walk; he would go nowhere else. He was glad St. George hadn't renounced his visit altogether—that would have been too absurd. Yes, the world was magnanimous, and even he himself felt so as, on looking at his watch, he noted but six o'clock, so that he could mentally congratulate his successor on having an hour still to sit in Miss Fancourt's drawing-room. He himself might use that hour for another visit, but by the time he reached the Marble Arch the idea of such a course had become incongruous to him. He passed beneath that architectural effort and walked into the Park till he had got upon the spreading grass. Here he continued to walk; he took his way across the elastic turf and came out by the Serpentine. He watched with a friendly eye the diversions of the London people, he bent a glance almost encouraging on the young ladies paddling their sweethearts about the lake and the guardsmen tickling tenderly with their bearskins the artificial flowers in the Sunday hats of their partners. He prolonged his meditative walk; he went into Kensington Gardens, he sat upon the penny chairs, he looked at the little sailboats launched upon the round pond and was glad he had no engagement to dine. He repaired for this purpose, very late, to his club, where he found himself unable to order a repast and told the waiter to bring whatever there was. He didn't even observe what he was served with, and he spent the evening in the library of the establishment, pretending to read an article in an American magazine. He failed to discover what it was about; it appeared in a dim way to be about Marian Fancourt.

Quite late in the week she wrote to him that she was not to go into the country—it had only just been settled. Her father, she added, would never settle anything, but put it all on her. She felt her responsibility—she had to—and since she was forced, this was the way she had decided. She mentioned no reasons, which gave our friend all the clearer field for bold conjecture about them. In Manchester Square on this second Sunday he esteemed his fortune less good, for she had three or four other visitors. But there were three or four compensations; perhaps the greatest of which was that, learning how her father had after all, at the last hour, gone out of town alone, the bold conjecture I just now spoke of found itself becoming a shade more bold. And then her presence was her presence, and the personal red room was there and was full of it, whatever phantoms passed and vanished, emitting incomprehensible sounds. Lastly, he had the resource of staying till every one had come and gone and of believing this grateful to her, though she gave no particular sign. When they were alone together, he came to his point. "But St. George did come—last Sunday. I saw him as I looked back."

"Yes, but it was the last time."

"The last time?"

"He said he would never come again."

Paul Overt stared. "Does he mean he wishes to cease to see you?"

"I don't know what he means," the girl bravely smiled. "He won't at any rate see me here."

"And pray why not?"

"I haven't the least idea," said Marian Fancourt, whose visitor found her more perversely sublime than ever yet as she professed this clear helplessness.

V

"Oh I say, I want you to stop a little," Henry St. George said to him at eleven o'clock the night he dined with the head of the profession. The company—none of it indeed *of* the profession—had been numerous and was taking its leave; our young man, after bidding good-night to his hostess, had put out his hand in farewell to the master of the house. Besides drawing from the latter the protest I have cited, this movement provoked a further priceless word about their chance now to have a talk, their going into his room, his having still everything to say. Paul Overt was all delight at this kindness; nevertheless he mentioned in weak jocose qualification the bare fact that he had promised to go to another place which was at a considerable distance.

"Well, then, you'll break your promise, that's all. You quite awful humbug!" St. George added in a tone that confirmed our young man's ease.

"Certainly I'll break it—but it was a real promise."

"Do you mean to Miss Fancourt? You're following her?" his friend asked.

He answered by a question. "Oh, is *she* going?"

"Base imposter!" his ironic host went on. "I've treated you hand-somely on the article of that young lady: I won't make another con-cession. Wait three minutes—I'll be with you." He gave himself to his departing guests, accompanied the long-trained ladies to the door. It was a hot night, the windows were open, the sound of the quick carriages and of the linkmen's call came into the house. The affair had rather glittered; a sense of festal things was in the heavy air: not only the influence of that particular entertainment, but the suggestion of the wide hurry of pleasure which in London on summer nights fills so many of the happier quarters of the complicated town. Gradually Mrs. St. George's drawing-room emptied itself; Paul was left alone with his hostess, to whom he explained the motive of his waiting. "Ah yes, some intellectual, some *professional*, talk," she leered; "at this season doesn't one miss it? Poor dear Henry, I'm so glad!" The young man looked out of the win-dow a moment, at the called hansoms that lurched up, at the smooth broughams that rolled away. When he turned round, Mrs. St. George had disappeared; her husband's voice rose to him from below—he was laughing and talking, in the portico, with some lady who awaited her carriage. Paul had solitary possession, for some minutes, of the warm deserted rooms where the covered tinted lamplight was soft, the seats had been pushed about, and the odor of flowers lingered. They were large, they were pretty, they contained objects of value; everything in the picture told of a "good house." At the end of five minutes a servant came in with a request from the Master that he would join him downstairs; upon which, descending, he followed his conductor through a long passage to an apartment thrown out, in the rear of the habitation, for the special requirements, as he guessed, of a busy man of letters.

St. George was in his shirt-sleeves in the middle of a large, high room —a room without windows, but with a wide skylight at the top, that of a place of exhibition. It was furnished as a library, and the serried bookshelves rose to the ceiling, a surface of incomparable tone produced by dimly-gilt "backs" interrupted here and there by the suspension of old prints and drawings. At the end furthest from the door of admission was a tall desk, of great extent, at which the person using it could write only in the erect posture of a clerk in a counting-house; and stretched from the entrance to this structure was a wide, plain band of crimson cloth, as straight as a garden-path and almost as long, where, in his mind's eye, Paul at once beheld the Master pace to and fro during vexed hours—hours, that is, of admirable composition. The servant gave him a coat, an old jacket with a hang of experience, from a cupboard in the wall, retiring afterwards with the garment he had taken off. Paul Overt welcomed the coat; it was a coat for talk, it promised confidences— having visibly received so many—and had tragic literary elbows. "Ah, we're practical—we're practical!" St. George said as he saw his visitor look the place over. "Isn't it a good big cage for going round and round? My wife invented it, and she locks me up here every morning."

Our young man breathed—by way of tribute—with a certain oppression. "You don't miss a window—a place to look out?"

"I did at first awfully; but her calculation was just. It saves time, it has saved me many months in these ten years. Here I stand, under the eye of day—in London of course, very often, it's rather a bleared old eye—walled in to my trade. I can't get away—so the room's a fine lesson in concentration. I've learnt the lesson, I think; look at that big bundle of proofs and acknowledge it." He pointed to a fat roll of papers, on one of the tables, which had not been undone.

"Are you bringing out another—?" Paul asked in a tone the fond deficiencies of which he didn't recognise till his companion burst out laughing, and indeed scarce even then.

"You humbug, you humbug!"—St. George appeared to enjoy caressing him, as it were, with that opprobrium. "Don't I know what you think of them?" he asked, standing there with his hands in his pockets and with a new kind of smile. It was as if he were going to let his young votary see him all now.

"Upon my word in that case you know more than I do!" the latter ventured to respond, revealing a part of the torment of being able neither clearly to esteem nor distinctly to renounce him.

"My dear fellow," said the more and more interesting Master, "don't imagine I talk about my books specifically; they're not a decent subject —*il ne manquerait plus que ça!* I'm not so bad as you may apprehend. About myself, yes, a little, if you like; though it wasn't for that I brought you down here. I want to ask you something—very much indeed; I value this chance. Therefore sit down. We're practical, but there *is* a sofa, you see—for she does humor my poor bones so far. Like all really great administrators and disciplinarians she knows when wisely to relax." Paul sank into the corner of a deep leathern couch, but his friend remained standing and explanatory. "If you don't mind, in this room, this is my habit. From the door to the desk and from the desk to the door. That shakes up my imagination gently; and don't you see what a good thing it is that there's no window for her to fly out of? The eternal standing as I write (I stop at that bureau and put it down, when anything comes, and so we go on) was rather wearisome at first, but we adopted it with an eye to the long run: you're in better order—if your legs don't break down!—and you can keep it up for more years. Oh we're practical—we're practical!" St. George repeated, going to the table and taking up all mechanically the bundle of proofs. But, pulling off the wrapper, he had a change of attention that appealed afresh to our hero. He lost himself a moment, examining the sheets of his new book, while the younger man's eyes wandered over the room again.

"Lord, what good things I should do if I had such a charming place as this to do them in!" Paul reflected. The outer World, the world of accident and ugliness, was so successfully excluded, and within the rich protecting square, beneath the patronising sky, the dream-figures, the summoned company, could hold their particular revel. It was a fond prevision of Overt's rather than an observation on actual data, for which occasions had been too few, that the Master thus more closely viewed would have the quality, the charming gift, of flashing out, all surprisingly, in personal intercourse and at moments of suspended or perhaps even of diminished expectation. A happy relation with him would be a thing proceeding by jumps, not by traceable stages.

"Do you read them—really?" he asked, laying down the proofs on Paul's enquiring of him how soon the work would be published. And when the young man answered, "Oh yes, always," he was moved to mirth again by something he caught in his manner of saying that. "You go to see your grandmother on her birthday—and very proper it is, especially as she won't last for ever. She has lost every faculty and every sense; she neither sees, nor hears, nor speaks; but all customary pieties and kindly habits are respectable. Only you're strong if you *do* read 'em! *I* couldn't, my dear fellow. You *are* strong, I know; and that's just a part of what I wanted to say to you. You're very strong indeed. I've been going into your other things—they've interested me immensely. Some one ought to have told me about them before—some one I could believe. But whom can one believe? You're wonderfully on the right road—it's awfully decent work. Now do you mean to keep it up?—that's what I want to ask you."

"Do I mean to do others?" Paul asked, looking up from his sofa at his erect inquisitor and feeling partly like a happy little boy when the schoolmaster is gay, and partly like some pilgrim of old who might have consulted a world-famous oracle. St. George's own performance had been infirm, but as an adviser he would be infallible.

"Others—others? Ah, the number won't matter; one other would do, if it were really a further step—a throb of the same effort. What I mean is, have you it in your heart to go in for some sort of decent perfection?"

"Ah decency, ah perfection—!" the young man sincerely sighed. "I talked of them the other Sunday with Miss Fancourt."

It produced on the Master's part a laugh of odd acrimony. "Yes, they'll 'talk' of them as much as you like! But they'll do little to help one to them. There's no obligation of course; only you strike me as capable," he went on. "You must have thought it all over. I can't believe you're without a plan. That's the sensation you give me, and it's so rare that it really stirs one up—it makes you remarkable. If you haven't a plan, if you *don't* mean to keep it up, surely you're within your rights; it's nobody's business, no one can force you, and not more than two or three people will notice you don't go straight. The others— *all* the rest, every blest soul in England, will think you do—will think you *are* keeping it up: upon my honor they will! I shall be one of the two or three who know better. Now the question is whether you can do it for two or three. Is that the stuff you're made of?"

It locked his guest a minute as in closed throbbing arms. "I could do it for one, if you were the one."

"Don't say that; I don't deserve it; it scorches me," he protested with eyes suddenly grave and glowing. "The 'one' is of course one's self, one's conscience, one's idea, the singleness of one's aim. I think of that pure spirit as a man thinks of a woman he has in some detested hour of his youth loved and forsaken. She haunts him with reproachful eyes, she lives for ever before him. As an artist, you know, I've married for money." Paul stared and even blushed a little, confounded by this avowal; whereupon his host, observing the expression of his face, dropped a quick laugh and pursued: "You don't follow my figure. I'm not speaking of my dear wife, who had a small fortune—which, however, was not my bribe. I fell in love with her, as many other people have done. I refer to the mercenary muse whom I led to the altar of literature. Don't, my boy, put your nose into *that* yoke. The awful jade will lead you a life!"

Our hero watched him, wondering and deeply touched. "Haven't you been happy?"

"Happy? It's a kind of hell."

"There are things I should like to ask you," Paul said after a pause.

"Ask me anything in all the world. I'd turn myself inside out to save you."

"To 'save' me?" he quavered.

"To make you stick to it—to make you see it through. As I said to you the other night at Summersoft, let my example be vivid to you."

"Why, your books are not so bad as that," said Paul, fairly laughing and feeling that if ever a fellow had breathed the air of art—!

"So bad as what?"

"Your talent's so great that it's in everything you do, in what's less good as well as in what's best. You've some forty volumes to show for it—forty volumes of wonderful life, of rare observation, of magnificent ability."

"I'm very clever, of course I know that"—but it was a thing, in fine, this author made nothing of. "Lord, what rot they'd all be if I hadn't been! I'm a successful charlatan," he went on—"I've been able to pass off my system. But do you know what it is? It's *carton-pierre*."

"*Carton-pierre?*" Paul was struck, and gaped.

"Lincrusta-Walton!"

"Ah, don't say such things—you make me bleed!" the younger man protested. "I see you in a beautiful, fortunate home, living in comfort and honor."

"Do you call it honor?"—his host took him up with an intonation that often comes back to him. "That's what I want *you* to go in for. I mean the real thing. This is brummagem."

"Brummagem?" Paul ejaculated while his eyes wandered, by a movement natural at the moment, over the luxurious room.

"Ah, they make it so well today—it's wonderfully deceptive!"

Our friend thrilled with the interest and perhaps even more with the pity of it. Yet he wasn't afraid to seem to patronise when he could still so far envy. "Is it deceptive that I find you living with every appearance of domestic felicity—blest with a devoted, accomplished wife, with children whose acquaintance I haven't yet had the pleasure of making, but who *must* be delightful young people, from what I know of their parents?"

St. George smiled as for the candor of his question. "It's all excellent, my dear fellow—heaven forbid I should deny it. I've made a great deal of money; my wife has known how to take care of it, to use it without wasting it, to put a good bit of it by, to make it fructify. I've got a loaf on the shelf; I've got everything in fact but the great thing."

"The great thing?" Paul kept echoing.

"The sense of having done the best—the sense which is the real life of the artist and the absence of which is his death, of having drawn from his intellectual instrument the finest music that nature had hidden in it, of having played it as it should be played. He either does that or he doesn't—and if he doesn't, he isn't worth speaking of. Therefore, precisely, those who really know *don't* speak of him. He may still hear a great chatter, but what he hears most is the incorruptible silence of Fame. I've squared her, you may say, for my little hour—but what's my little hour? Don't imagine for a moment," the Master pursued, "that I'm such a cad as to have brought you down here to abuse or to complain of my wife to you. She's a woman of distinguished qualities, to whom my obligations are immense; so that, if you please, we'll say nothing about her. My boys—my children are all boys—are straight and strong, thank God, and have no poverty of growth about them, no penury of needs. I receive periodically the most satisfactory attestation from Harrow, from Oxford, from Sandhurst—oh we've done the best for them!—of their eminence as living, thriving, consuming organisms."

"It must be delightful to feel that the son of one's loins is at Sandhurst," Paul remarked enthusiastically.

"It is—it's charming. Oh, I'm a patriot!"

The young man then could but have the greater tribute of questions to pay. "Then what did you mean—the other night at Summersoft—by saying that children are a curse?"

"My dear youth, on what basis are we talking?" and St. George dropped upon the sofa at a short distance from him. Sitting a little sideways, he leaned back against the opposite arm with his hands raised and interlocked behind his head. "On the supposition that a certain perfection's possible and even desirable—isn't it so? Well, all I say is that one's children interfere with perfection. One's wife interferes. Marriage interferes."

"You think, then, the artist shouldn't marry?"

"He does so at his peril—he does so at his cost."

"Not even when his wife's in sympathy with his work?"

"She never is—she can't be! Women haven't a conception of such things."

"Surely they on occasion work themselves," Paul objected.

"Yes, very badly indeed. Oh, of course, often, they think they understand, they think they sympathize. Then it is they're most dangerous. Their idea is that you shall do a great lot and get a great lot of money. Their great nobleness and virtue, their exemplary conscientiousness as British females, is in keeping you up to that. My wife makes all my bargains with my publishers for me, and has done so for twenty years. She does it consummately well—that's why I'm really pretty well off. Aren't you the father of their innocent babes, and will you withhold from them their natural sustenance? You asked me the other night if they're not an immense incentive. Of course they are—there's no doubt of that!"

Paul turned it over: it took, from eyes he had never felt open so wide, so much looking at. "For myself I've an idea I need incentives."

"Ah well then, *n'en parlons plus!*" his companion handsomely smiled.

"*You* are an incentive, I maintain," the young man went on. "You don't affect me in the way you'd apparently like to. Your great success is what I see—the pomp of Ennismore Gardens!"

"Success?"—St. George's eyes had a cold, fine light. "Do you call it success to be spoken of as you'd speak of me if you were sitting here with another artist—a young man intelligent and sincere like yourself? Do you call it success to make you blush—as you *would* blush!—if some foreign critic (some fellow, of course I mean, who should know what he was talking about and should have shown you he did, as foreign critics like to show it) were to say to you: 'He's the one, in this country, whom they consider the most perfect, isn't he?' Is it success to be the occasion of a young Englishman's having to stammer as you would have to stammer at such a moment for old England? No, no; success is to have made people wriggle to another tune. Do try it!"

Paul continued all gravely to glow. "Try what?"

"Try to do some really good work."

"Oh, I want to, heaven knows!"

"Well, you can't do it without sacrifices—don't believe that for a moment," the Master said. "I've made none. I've had everything. In other words I've missed everything."

"You've had the full, rich, masculine, human, general life, with all the responsibilities and duties and burdens and sorrows and joys—all the domestic and social initiations and complications. They must be immensely suggestive, immensely amusing," Paul anxiously submitted.

"Amusing?"

"For a strong man—yes."

"They've given me subjects without number, if that's what you mean; but they've taken away at the same time the power to use them. I've touched a thousand things, but which one of them have I turned into gold? The artist has to do only with that—he knows nothing of any baser metal. I've led the life of the world, with my wife and my progeny; the clumsy, conventional, expensive, materialised, vulgarised, brutalised life of London. We've got everything handsome, even a carriage—we're perfect Philistines and prosperous, hospitable, eminent people. But, my dear fellow, don't try to stultify yourself and pretend you don't know what we *haven't* got. It's bigger than all the rest. Between artists—come!" the Master wound up. "You know as well as you sit there that you'd put a pistol-ball into your brain if you had written my books!"

It struck his listener that the tremendous talk promised by him at Summersoft had indeed come off, and with a promptitude, a fulness, with which the latter's young imagination had scarcely reckoned. His impression fairly shook him, and he throbbed with the excitement of such deep soundings and such strange confidences. He throbbed indeed with the conflict of his feelings—bewilderment and recognition and alarm, enjoyment and protest and assent, all commingled with tenderness (and a kind of shame in the participation) for the sores and bruises exhibited by so fine a creature, and with a sense of the tragic secret nursed under his trappings. The idea of *his*, Paul Overt's, becoming the occasion of such an act of humility, made him flush and pant, at the same time that his consciousness was in certain directions too much alive not to swallow—and not intensely to taste—every offered spoonful of the revelation. It had been his odd fortune to blow upon the deep waters, to make them surge and break in waves of strange eloquence. But how couldn't he give out a passionate contradiction of his host's last extravagance, how couldn't he enumerate to him the parts of his work he loved, the splendid things he had found in it, beyond the compass of any other writer of the day? St. George listened a while, courteously; then he said, laying his hand on his visitor's: "That's all very well; and if your idea's to do nothing better, there's no reason you shouldn't have as many good things as I—as many human and material appendages, as many sons or daughters, a wife with as many gowns, a house with as many servants, a stable with as many horses, a heart with as many aches." The Master got up when he had spoken thus—he stood a moment—near the sofa looking down on his agitated pupil. "Are you possessed of any property?" it occurred to him to ask.

"None to speak of."

"Oh, well, then there's no reason why you shouldn't make a goodish income—it you set about it the right way. Study *me* for that—study me well. You may really have horses."

Paul sat there some minutes without speaking. He looked straight before him—he turned over many things. His friend had wandered away, taking up a parcel of letters from the table where the roll of proofs had lain. "What was the book Mrs. St. George made you burn—the one she didn't like?" our young man brought out.

"The book she made me burn—how did you know that?" The Master looked up from his letters quite without the facial convulsion the pupil had feared.

"I heard her speak of it at Summersoft."

"Ah yes—she's proud of it. I don't know—it was rather good."

"What was it about?"

"Let me see." And he seemed to make an effort to remember. "Oh yes—it was about myself." Paul gave an irrepressible groan for the disappearance of such a production, and the elder man went on: "Oh but *you* should write it—*you* should do me." And he pulled up—from the restless motion that had come upon him; his fine smile a generous glare. "There's a subject, my boy: no end of stuff in it!"

Again Paul was silent, but it was all tormenting. "Are there no women who really understand—who can take part in a sacrifice?"

"How can they take part? They themselves are the sacrifice. They're the idol and the altar and the flame."

"Isn't there even *one* who sees further?" Paul continued.

For a moment St. George made no answer; after which, having torn up his letters, he came back to the point all ironic. "Of course I know the one you mean. But not even Miss Fancourt."

"I thought you admired her so much."

"It's impossible to admire her more. Are you in love with her?" St. George asked.

"Yes," Paul Overt presently said.

"Well, then, give it up."

Paul stared. "Give up my 'love'?"

"Bless me, no. Your idea." And then as our hero but still gazed: "The one you talked with her about. The idea of a decent perfection."

"She'd help it—she'd help it!" the young man cried.

"For about a year—the first year, yes. After that she'd be as a millstone round its neck."

Paul frankly wondered. "Why she has a passion for the real thing, for good work—for everything you and I care for most."

"'You and I' is charming, my dear fellow!" his friend laughed. "She has it indeed, but she'd have a still greater passion for her children—and very proper too. She'd insist on everything's being made comfortable, advantageous, propitious for them. That isn't the artist's business."

"The artist—the artist! Isn't he a man all the same?"

St. George had a grand grimace. "I mostly think not. You know as well as I what he has to do: the concentration, the finish, the independence he must strive for from the moment he begins to wish his work really decent. Ah, my young friend, his relation to women, and especially to the one he's most intimately concerned with, is at the mercy of the damning fact that whereas he can in the nature of things have but one standard, they have about fifty. That's what makes them so superior," St. George amusingly added. "Fancy an artist with a change of standards as you'd have a change of shirts or of dinner-plates. To *do* it—to do it and make it divine—is the only thing he has to think about. 'Is it done or not?' is his only question. Not 'Is it done as well as a proper solicitude for my dear little family will allow?' He has nothing to do with the relative—he has only to do with the absolute; and a dear little family may represent a dozen relatives."

"Then you don't allow him the common passions and affections of men?" Paul asked.

"Hasn't he a passion, an affection, which includes all the rest? Besides, let him have all the passions he likes—if he only keeps his independence. He must be able to be poor."

Paul slowly got up. "Why then did you advise me to make up to her?"

St. George laid a hand on his shoulder. "Because she'd make a splendid wife! And I hadn't read you then."

The young man had a strained smile. "I wish you had left me alone!"

"I didn't know that that wasn't good enough for you," his host returned.

"What a false position, what a condemnation of the artist, that he's a mere disfranchised monk and can produce his effect only by giving up personal happiness. What an arraignment of art!" Paul went on with a trembling voice.

"Ah, you don't imagine by chance that I'm defending art? 'Arraignment'—I should think so! Happy the societies in which it hasn't made its appearance, for from the moment it comes they have a consuming ache, they have an incurable corruption, in their breast. Most assuredly is the artist in a false position! But I thought we were taking him for granted. Pardon me," St. George continued: " 'Ginistrella' made me!"

Paul stood looking at the floor—one o'clock struck, in the stillness, from a neighboring church-tower. "Do you think she'd ever look at me?" he put to his friend at last.

"Miss Fancourt—as a suitor? Why shouldn't I think it? That's why I've tried to favor you—I've had a little chance or two of bettering your opportunity."

"Forgive my asking you, but do you mean by keeping away yourself?" Paul said with a blush.

"I'm an old idiot—my place isn't there," St. George stated gravely.

"I'm nothing yet, I've no fortune; and there must be so many others," his companion pursued.

The Master took this considerably in, but made little of it. "You're a gentleman and a man of genius. I think you might do something."

"But if I must give that up—the genius?"

"Lots of people, you know, think I've kept mine," St. George wonderfully grinned.

"You've a genius for mystification!" Paul declared, but grasping his hand gratefully in attenuation of this judgment.

"Poor dear boy, I do worry you! But try, try, all the same. I think your chances are good and you'll win a great prize."

Paul held fast the other's hand a minute; he looked into the strange deep face. "No, I *am* an artist—I can't help it!"

"Ah show it then!" St. George pleadingly broke out. "Let me see before I die the thing I most want, the thing I yearn for: a life in which the passion—ours—is really intense. If you can be rare, don't fail of it! Think what it is—how it counts—how it lives!"

They had moved to the door and he had closed both his hands over his companion's. Here they paused again and our hero breathed deep. "I want to live!"

"In what sense?"

"In the greatest."

"Well then, stick to it—see it through."

"With your sympathy—your help?"

"Count on that—you'll be a great figure to me. Count on my highest appreciation, my devotion. You'll give me satisfaction—if that has any weight with you!" After which, as Paul appeared still to waver, his host added: "Do you remember what you said to me at Summersoft?"

"Something infatuated, no doubt!"

"'I'll do anything in the world you tell me.' You said that."

"And you hold me to it?"

"Ah, what am I?" the Master expressively sighed.

"Lord, what things I shall have to do!" Paul almost moaned as he departed.

VI

"It goes on too much abroad—hang abroad!" These or something like them had been the Master's remarkable words in relation to the action of "Ginistrella"; and yet, though they had made a sharp impression on the author of that work, like almost all spoken words from the same source, he a week after the conversation I have noted left England for a long absence and full of brave intentions. It is not a perversion of the truth to pronounce that encounter the direct cause of his departure. If the oral utterance of the eminent writer had the privilege of moving him deeply, it was especially on his turning it over at leisure, hours and days later, that it appeared to yield him its full meaning and exhibit its extreme importance. He spent the summer in Switzerland and, having in September begun a new task, determined not to cross the Alps till he should have made a good start. To this end he returned to a quiet corner he knew well, on the edge of the Lake of Geneva and within sight of the towers of Chillon: a region and a view for which he had an affection that sprang from old associations and was capable of mysterious revivals and refreshments. Here he lingered late, till the snow was on the nearer hills, almost down to the limit to which he could climb when his stint, on the shortening afternoons, was performed. The autumn was fine, the lake was blue, and his book took form and direction. These felicities, for the time, embroidered his life, which he suffered to cover him with its mantle. At the end of six weeks he felt he had learnt St. George's lesson by heart, had tested and proved its doctrine. Nevertheless he did a very inconsistent thing: before crossing the Alps he wrote to Marian Fancourt. He was aware of the perversity of this act, and it was only as a luxury, an amusement, the reward of a strenuous autumn, that he justified it. She had asked of him no such favor when, shortly before he left London, three days after their dinner in Ennismore Gardens, he went to take leave of her.

It was true she had had no ground—he hadn't named his intention of absence. He had kept his counsel for want of due assurance: it was that particular visit that was, the next thing, to settle the matter. He had paid the visit to see how much he really cared for her, and quick departure, without so much as an explicit farewell, was the sequel to this enquiry, the answer to which had created within him a deep yearning. When he wrote her from Clarens he noted that he owed her an explanation (more than three months after!) for not having told her what he was doing.

She replied now briefly but promptly, and gave him a striking piece of news; that of the death, a week before, of Mrs. St. George. This exemplary woman had succumbed, in the country, to a violent attack of inflammation of the lungs—he would remember that for a long time she had been delicate. Miss Fancourt added that she believed her husband overwhelmed by the blow; he would miss her too terribly— she had been everything in life to him. Paul Overt, on this, immediately wrote to St. George. He would from the day of their parting have been glad to remain in communication with him, but had hitherto lacked the right excuse for troubling so busy a man. Their long nocturnal talk came back to him in every detail, but this was no bar to an expression of proper sympathy with the head of the profession, for hadn't that very talk made it clear that the late accomplished lady was the influence that ruled his life? What catastrophe could be more cruel than the extinction of such an influence? This was to be exactly the tone taken by St. George in answering his young friend upwards of a month later. He made no allusion of course to their important discussion. He spoke of his wife as frankly and generously as if he had quite forgotten that occasion, and the feeling of deep bereavement was visible in his words. "She took everything off my hands—off my mind. She carried on our life with the greatest art, the rarest devotion, and I was free, as few men can have been, to drive my pen, to shut myself up with my trade. This was a rare service—the highest she could have rendered me. Would I could have acknowledged it more fitly!"

A certain bewilderment, for our hero, disengaged itself from these remarks: they struck him as a contradiction, a retractation, strange on the part of a man who hadn't the excuse of witlessness. He had certainly not expected his correspondent to rejoice in the death of his wife, and it was perfectly in order that the rupture of a tie of more than twenty years should have left him sore. But if she had been so clear a blessing, what in the name of consistency had the dear man meant by turning *him* upside down that night—by dosing him to that degree, at the most sensitive hour of his life, with the doctrine of renunciation? If Mrs. St. George was an irreparable loss, then her husband's inspired advice had been a bad joke and renunciation was a mistake. Overt was on the point of rushing back to London to show that, for his part, he was perfectly willing to consider it so, and he went so far as to take the manuscript of the first chapters of his new book out of his table-drawer and insert it into a pocket of his portmanteau. This led to his catching a glimpse of certain pages he hadn't looked at for months, and that accident, in turn, to his being struck with the high promise they revealed—a rare result of such retrospections, which it was his habit to avoid as much as possible: they usually brought home to him that the glow of composition might be a purely subjective and misleading emotion. On this occasion a certain belief in himself disengaged itself whimsically from the serried erasures of his first draft, making him think it best after all to pursue his present trial to the end. If he could write so well under the rigor of privation, it might be a mistake to change the conditions before that spell had spent itself. He would go back to London of course, but he would go back only when he should have finished his book. This was the vow he privately made, restoring his manuscript to the table-drawer. It may be added that it took him a long time to finish his book, for the subject was as difficult as it was fine, and he was literally embarrassed by the fulness of his notes. Something within him warned him he must make it supremely good—otherwise he should lack, as regards his private behavior, a handsome excuse. He had a horror of this deficiency and found himself as firm as need be on the question of the lamp and the file. He crossed the Alps at last and spent the winter, the spring, the ensuing summer, in Italy, where still, at the end of a twelvemonth, his task was unachieved. "Stick to it—see it through": this general injunction of St. George's was good also for the particular case. He applied it to the utmost, with the result that when in its slow order the summer had come round again he felt he had given all that was in him. This time he put his papers into his portmanteau, with the address of his publisher attached, and took his way northward.

He had been absent from London for two years; two years which, seeming to count as more, had made such a difference in his own life—through the production of a novel far stronger, he believed, than "Ginistrella"—that he turned out into Piccadilly, the morning after his arrival, with a vague expectation of changes, of finding great things had happened. But there were few transformations in Piccadilly—only three or four big red houses where there had been low black ones—and the brightness of the end of June peeped through the rusty railings of the Green Park and glittered in the varnish of the rolling carriages as he had seen it in other, more cursory Junes. It was a greeting he appreciated; it seemed friendly and pointed, added to the exhilaration of his finished book, of his having his own country and the huge, oppressive, amusing city that suggested everything, that contained everything, under his hand again. "Stay at home and do things here—do subjects we can measure," St. George had said; and now it struck him he should ask nothing better than to stay at home for ever. Late in the afternoon he took his way to Manchester Square, looking out for a number he hadn't forgotten. Miss Fancourt, however, was not at home, so that he turned rather dejectedly from the door. His movement brought him face to face with a gentleman just approaching it and recognised on another glance as Miss Fancourt's father. Paul saluted this personage, and the General returned the greeting with his customary good manner —a manner so good, however, that you could never tell whether it meant he placed you. The disappointed caller felt the impulse to address him; then, hesitating, became both aware of having no particular remark to make, and convinced that though the old soldier remembered him he remembered him wrong. He therefore went his way without computing the irresistible effect his own evident recognition would have on the General, who never neglected a chance to gossip. Our young man's face was expressive, and observation seldom let it pass. He hadn't taken ten steps before he heard himself called after with a friendly semi-articulate "Er—I beg your pardon!" He turned round, and the General, smiling at him from the porch, said: "Won't you come in? I won't leave you the advantage of me!" Paul declined to come in, and then felt regret, for Miss Fancourt, so late in the afternoon, might return at any moment. But her father gave him no second chance; he appeared mainly to wish not to have struck him as ungracious. A further look at the visitor had recalled something, enough at least to enable him to say: "You've come back, you've come back?" Paul was on the point of replying that he had come back the night before, but he suppressed, the next instant, this strong light on the immediacy of his visit and, giving merely a general assent, alluded to the young lady he deplored not having found. He had come late in the hope she would be in. "I'll tell her—I'll tell her," said the old man; and then he added quickly, gallantly: "You'll be giving us something new? It's a long time, isn't it?" Now he remembered him right.

"Rather long. I'm very slow," Paul explained. "I met you at Summersoft a long time ago."

"Oh, yes—with Henry St. George. I remember very well. Before his poor wife—" General Fancourt paused a moment, smiling a little less. "I dare say you know."

"About Mrs. St. George's death? Certainly—I heard at the time."

"Oh, no, I mean—I mean he's to be married."

"Ah, I've not heard that!" But just as Paul was about to add "To whom?" the General crossed his intention.

"When did you come back? I know you've been away—by my daughter. She was very sorry. You ought to give her something new."

"I came back last night," said our young man, to whom something had occurred which made his speech for the moment a little thick.

"Ah, most kind of you to come so soon. Couldn't you turn up at dinner?"

"At dinner?" Paul just mechanically repeated, not liking to ask whom St. George was going to marry, but thinking only of that.

"There are several people, I believe. Certainly St. George. Or after-wards if you like better. I believe my daughter expects—" He appeared to notice something in the visitor's raised face (on his steps he stood higher) which led him to interrupt himself, and the interruption gave him a momentary sense of awkwardness, from which he sought a quick issue. "Perhaps, then, you haven't heard she's to be married."

Paul gaped again. "To be married?"

"To Mr. St. George—it has just been settled. Odd marriage, isn't it?" Our listener uttered no opinion on this point: he only continued to stare. "But I dare say it will do—she's so awfully literary!" said the General.

Paul had turned very red. "Oh, it's a surprise—very interesting, very charming! I'm afraid I can't dine—so many thanks!"

"Well, you must come to the wedding!" cried the General. "Oh, I remember that day at Summersoft. He's a great man, you know."

"Charming—charming!" Paul stammered for retreat. He shook hands with the General and got off. His face was red and he had the sense of its growing more and more crimson. All the evening at home— he went straight to his rooms and remained there dinnerless—his cheek burned at intervals as if it had been smitten. He didn't understand what had happened to him, what trick had been played him, what treachery practised. "None, none," he said to himself. "I've nothing to do with it. I'm out of it—it's none of my business." But that bewildered murmur was followed again and again by the incongruous ejaculation: "Was it a plan—was it a plan?" Sometimes he cried to himself, breathless, "Have I been duped, sold, swindled?" If at all, he was an absurd, an abject victim. It was as if he hadn't lost her till now. He had renounced her, yes; but that was another affair—that was a closed but not a locked door. Now he seemed to see the door quite slammed in his face. Did he expect her to wait—was she to give him his time like that: two years at a stretch? He didn't know what he had expected—he only knew what he hadn't. It wasn't this—it wasn't this. Mystification, bitterness, and wrath rose and boiled in him when he thought of the deference, the devotion, the credulity with which he had listened to St. George. The evening wore on and the light was long; but even when it had darkened he remained without a lamp. He had flung himself on the sofa, where he lay through the hours with his eyes either closed or gazing at the gloom, in the attitude of a man teaching himself to bear something, to bear having been made a fool of. He had made it too easy—that idea passed over him like a hot wave. Suddenly, as he heard eleven o'clock strike, he jumped up, remembering what General Fancourt had said about his coming after dinner. He'd go—he'd see her at least; perhaps he should see what it meant. He felt as if some of the elements of a hard sum had been given him and the others were wanting: he couldn't do his sum till he had got all his figures.

He dressed and drove quickly, so that by half-past eleven he was at Manchester Square. There were a good many carriages at the door— a party was going on; a circumstance which at the last gave him a slight relief, for now he would rather see her in a crowd. People passed him on the staircase; they were going away, going "on" with the hunted herd- like movement of London society at night. But sundry groups remained in the drawing-room, and it was some minutes, as she didn't hear him announced, before he discovered and spoke to her. In this short interval he had seen St. George talking to a lady before the fireplace; but he at once looked away, feeling unready for an encounter, and therefore couldn't be sure the author of "Shadowmere" noticed him. At all events he didn't come over; though Miss Fancourt did as soon as she saw him—she almost rushed at him, smiling, rustling, radiant, beautiful. He had forgotten what her head, what her face offered to the sight; she was in white, there were gold figures on her dress, and her hair was a casque of gold. He saw in a single moment that she was happy, happy with an aggressive splendor. But she wouldn't speak to him of that, she would speak only of himself.

"I'm so delighted; my father told me. How kind of you to come!" She struck him as so fresh and brave, while his eyes moved over her, that he said to himself irresistibly: "Why to *him*, why not to youth, to strength, to ambition, to a future? Why, in her rich young force, to failure, to abdication, to superannuation?" In his thought at that sharp moment he blasphemed even against all that had been left of his faith in the peccable master. "I'm so sorry I missed you," she went on. "My father told me. How charming of you to have come so soon!"

"Does that surprise you?" Paul Overt asked.

"The first day? No, from you—nothing that's nice." She was inter- rupted by a lady who bade her good-night, and he seemed to read that it cost her nothing to speak to him in that tone; it was her old liberal lavish way, with a certain added amplitude that time had brought; and if this manner began to operate on the spot, at such a juncture in her history, perhaps in the other days too it had meant just as little or as much—a mere mechanical charity, with the difference now that she was satisfied, ready to give but in want of nothing. Oh, she was satisfied— and why shouldn't she be? Why shouldn't she have been surprised at his coming the first day—for all the good she had ever got from him? As the lady continued to hold her attention, Paul turned from her with a strange irritation in his complicated artistic soul and a sort of disin- terested disappointment. She was so happy that it was almost stupid— a disproof of the extraordinary intelligence he had formerly found in her. Didn't she know how bad St. George could be, hadn't she recog- nised the awful thinness—? If she didn't, she was nothing, and if she did, why such an insolence of serenity? This question expired as our young man's eyes settled at last on the genius who had advised him in a great crisis. St. George was still before the chimney-piece, but now he was alone—fixed, waiting, as if he meant to stop after every one—and he met the clouded gaze of the young friend so troubled as to the degree of his right (the right his resentment would have enjoyed) to regard himself as a victim. Somehow the ravage of the question was checked by the Master's radiance. It was as fine in its way as Marian Fancourt's, it denoted the happy human being; but also it represented to Paul Overt that the author of "Shadowmere" had now definitely ceased to count—ceased to count as a writer. As he smiled a welcome across the place, he was almost *banal*, was almost smug. Paul fancied that for a moment he hesitated to make a movement, as if, for all the world, he *had* his bad conscience; then they had already met in the middle of the room and had shaken hands—expressively, cordially on St. George's part. With which they had passed back together to where the elder man had been standing, while St. George said: "I hope you're never going away again. I've been dining here; the General told me." He was handsome, he was young, he looked as if he had still a great fund of life. He bent the friendliest, most unconfessing eyes on his disciple of a couple of years before; asked him about everything, his health, his plans, his late occupations, the new book. "When will it be out—soon, soon, I hope? Splendid, eh? That's right; you're a comfort, you're a luxury! I've read you all over again these last six months." Paul waited to see if he'd tell him what the General had told him in the afternoon and what Miss Fancourt, verbally at least, of course hadn't. But as it didn't come out he at last put the question, "Is it true, the great news I hear—that you're to be married?"

"Ah, you *have* heard it, then?"

"Didn't the General tell you?" Paul asked.

The Master's face was wonderful. "Tell me what?"

"That he mentioned it to me this afternoon?"

"My dear fellow, I don't remember. We've been in the midst of people. I'm sorry, in that case, that I lose the pleasure, myself, of announcing to you a fact that touches me so nearly. It *is* a fact, strange as it may appear. It has only just become one. Isn't it ridiculous?" St. George made this speech without confusion, but on the other hand, so far as our friend could judge, without latent impudence. It struck his interlocutor that, to talk so comfortably and coolly, he must simply have forgotten what had passed between them. His next words, however, showed he hadn't, and they produced, as an appeal to Paul's own memory, an effect which would have been ludicrous if it hadn't been cruel. "Do you recall the talk we had at my house that night, into which Miss Fancourt's name entered? I've often thought of it since."

"Yes; no wonder you said what you did"—Paul was careful to meet his eyes.

"In the light of the present occasion? Ah but there was no light then. How could I have foreseen this hour?"

"Didn't you think it probable?"

"Upon my honor, no," said, Henry St. George. "Certainly I owe you that assurance. Think how my situation has changed."

"I see—I see," our young man murmured.

His companion went on as if, now that the subject had been broached, he was, as a person of imagination and tact, quite ready to give every satisfaction—being both by his genius and his method so able to enter into everything another might feel. "But it's not only that; for honestly, at my age, I never dreamed—a widower with big boys and with so little else! It has turned out differently from anything one could have dreamed, and I'm fortunate beyond all measure. She has been so free, and yet she consents. Better than any one else perhaps—for I remember how you liked her before you went away, and how she liked you—you can intelligently congratulate me."

"She has been so free!" Those words made a great impression on Paul Overt, and he almost writhed under that irony in them as to which it so little mattered whether it was designed or casual. Of course she had been free, and appreciably perhaps by his own act; for wasn't the Master's allusion to her having liked him a part of the irony too? "I thought that by your theory you disapproved of a writer's marrying."

"Surely—surely. But you don't call me a writer?"

"You ought to be ashamed," said Paul.

"Ashamed of marrying again?"

"I won't say that—but ashamed of your reasons."

The elder man beautifully smiled. "You must let me judge of them, my good friend."

"Yes; why not? For you judged wonderfully of mine."

The tone of these words appeared suddenly, for St. George, to suggest the unsuspected. He stared as if divining a bitterness. "Don't you think I've been straight?"

"You might have told me at the time perhaps."

"My dear fellow, when I say I couldn't pierce futurity—!"

"I mean afterwards."

The Master wondered. "After my wife's death?"

"When this idea came to you."

"Ah, never, never! I wanted to save you, rare and precious as you are."

Poor Overt looked hard at him. "Are you marrying Miss Fancourt to save me?"

"Not absolutely, but it adds to the pleasure. I shall be the making of you," St. George smiled. "I was greatly struck, after our talk, with the brave devoted way you quitted the country, and still more perhaps with your force of character in remaining abroad. You're very strong—you're wonderfully strong."

Paul tried to sound his shining eyes; the strange thing was that he seemed sincere—not a mocking fiend. He turned away, and as he did so heard the Master say something about his giving them all the proof, being the joy of his old age. He faced him again, taking another look. "Do you mean to say you've stopped writing?"

"My dear fellow, of course I have. It's too late. Didn't I tell you?"

"I can't believe it!"

"Of course you can't—with your own talent! No, no; for the rest of my life I shall only read *you*."

"Does she know that—Miss Fancourt?"

"She will—she will." Did he mean this, our young man wondered, as a covert intimation that the assistance he should derive from that young lady's fortune, moderate as it was, would make the difference of putting it in his power to cease to work ungratefully an exhausted vein? Somehow, standing there in the ripeness of his successful manhood, he didn't suggest that any of his veins were exhausted. "Don't you remember the moral I offered myself to you that night as pointing?" St. George continued. "Consider at any rate the warning I am at present."

This was too much—he *was* the mocking fiend. Paul turned from him with a mere nod for good-night and the sense in a sore heart that he might come back to him and his easy grace, his fine way of arranging things, some time in the far future, but couldn't fraternise with him now. It was necessary to his soreness to believe for the hour in the intensity of his grievance—all the more cruel for its not being a legal one. It was doubtless in the attitude of hugging this wrong that he descended the stairs without taking leave of Miss Fancourt, who hadn't been in view at the moment he quitted the room. He was glad to get out into the honest, dusky, unsophisticating night, to move fast, to take his way home on foot. He walked a long time, going astray, paying no attention. He was thinking of too many other things. His steps recovered their direction, however, and at the end of an hour he found himself before his door in the small, inexpensive, empty street. He lingered, questioning himself still before going in, with nothing around and above him but moonless blackness, a bad lamp or two and a few far-away dim stars. To these last faint features he raised his eyes; he had been saying to himself that he should have been "sold" indeed, diabolically sold, if now, on his new foundation, at the end of a year, St. George were to put forth something of his prime quality—something of the type of "Shadowmere" and finer than his finest. Greatly as he admired his talent Paul literally hoped such an incident wouldn't occur; it seemed to him just then that he shouldn't be able to bear it. His late adviser's words were still in his ears—"You're very strong, wonderfully strong."

Was he really? Certainly he would have to be, and it might a little serve for revenge. *Is* he? the reader may ask in turn, if his interest has followed the perplexed young man so far. The best answer to that perhaps is that he's doing his best, but that it's too soon to say. When the new book came out in the autumn, Mr. and Mrs. St. George found it really magnificent. The former still has published nothing, but Paul doesn't even yet feel safe. I may say for him, however, that if this event were to occur, he would really be the very first to appreciate it: which is perhaps a proof that the Master was essentially right and that Nature had dedicated him to intellectual, not to personal passion.

THE LADY, OR THE TIGER?

By Frank R. Stockton

[Francis Richard Stockton (1834–1902) was born in Philadelphia and spent his life as a writer and editor. He was at one time or another on the editorial staffs of *Hearth and Home*, *St. Nicholas*, and the *Century Magazine*. His best work is in short story form, although he wrote the novels, *Rudder Grange* (1879), and *The Casting Away of Mrs. Lecks and Mrs. Aleshine* (1886). *The Lady, or the Tiger?* is not only his most famous story, but one of the most famous stories in American literature.

The question Mr. Stockton asks in *The Lady, or the Tiger?* is not What would that princess do? but What would *a* woman do? He leaves the princess a vague generalization of the feminine. If he had wanted the reader to know what her choice was, he could easily have made it apparent by drawing her character sharply and clearly. To his tantalizing question there is no answer. One woman would have sacrificed her own love to save her beloved. Another would have sent him to the tiger rather than into the arms of her rival.

The Lady, or the Tiger? was first published in the *Century Magazine* (November, 1882), and later included in *The Lady, or the Tiger? and Other Stories* (1884). It is here reprinted by permission of Charles Scribner's Sons, publishers.]

IN the very olden time there lived a semi-barbaric king, whose ideas, though somewhat polished and sharpened by the progressiveness of distant Latin neighbors, were still large, florid, and untrammeled, as became the half of him which was barbaric. He was a man of exuberant fancy, and, withal, of an authority so irresistible that, at his will, he turned his varied fancies into facts. He was greatly given to self-communing; and, when he and himself agreed upon anything, the thing was done. When every member of his domestic and political systems moved smoothly in its appointed course, his nature was bland and genial; but whenever there was a little hitch, and some of his orbs got out of their orbits, he was blander and more genial still, for nothing pleased him so much as to make the crooked straight, and crush down uneven places.

Among the borrowed notions by which his barbarism had become semified was that of the public arena, in which, by exhibitions of manly and beastly valor, the minds of his subjects were refined and cultured.

But even here the exuberant and barbaric fancy asserted itself. The arena of the king was built, not to give the people an opportunity of hearing the rhapsodies of dying gladiators, nor to enable them to view the inevitable conclusion of a conflict between religious opinions and hungry jaws, but for purposes far better adapted to widen and develop the mental energies of the people. This vast amphitheater, with its encircling galleries, its mysterious vaults, and its unseen passages, was an agent of poetic justice, in which crime was punished, or virtue rewarded, by the decrees of an impartial and incorruptible chance.

When a subject was accused of a crime of sufficient importance to interest the king, public notice was given that on an appointed day the fate of the accused person would be decided in the king's arena—a structure which well deserved its name; for, although its form and plan were borrowed from afar, its purpose emanated solely from the brain of this man, who, every barleycorn a king, knew no tradition to which he owed more allegiance than pleased his fancy, and who ingrafted on every adopted form of human thought and action the rich growth of his barbaric idealism.

When all the people had assembled in the galleries, and the king, surrounded by his court, sat high up on his throne of royal state on one side of the arena, he gave a signal, a door beneath him opened, and the accused subject stepped out into the amphitheater. Directly opposite him, on the other side of the enclosed space, were two doors, exactly alike and side by side. It was the duty and the privilege of the person on trial to walk directly to these doors and open one of them. He could open either door he pleased: he was subject to no guidance or influence but that of the aforementioned impartial and incorruptible chance. If he opened the one, there came out of it a hungry tiger, the fiercest and most cruel that could be procured, which immediately sprang upon him, and tore him to pieces, as a punishment for his guilt. The moment that the case of the criminal was thus decided, doleful iron bells were clanged, great wails went up from the hired mourners posted on the outer rim of the arena, and the vast audience, with bowed heads and downcast hearts, wended slowly their homeward way, mourning greatly that one so young and fair, or so old and respected, should have merited so dire a fate.

But, if the accused person opened the other door, there came from it a lady, the most suitable to his years and station that his majesty could select among his fair subjects; and to this lady he was immediately married, as a reward of his innocence. It mattered not that he might already possess a wife and family, or that his affections might be engaged upon an object of his own selection: the king allowed no such subordinate arrangements to interfere with his great scheme of retribution and reward. The exercises, as in the other instance, took place immediately, and in the arena. Another door opened beneath the king, and a priest, followed by a band of choristers, and dancing maidens blowing joyous airs on golden horns and treading an epithalamic measure, advanced to where the pair stood, side by side; and the wedding was promptly and cheerily solemnized. Then the gay brass bells rang forth their merry peals, the people shouted glad hurrahs, and the innocent man, preceded by children strewing flowers on his path, led his bride to his home.

This was the king's semi-barbaric method of administering justice. Its perfect fairness is obvious. The criminal could not know out of which door would come the lady: he opened either he pleased, without having the slightest idea whether, in the next instant, he was to be devoured or married. On some occasions the tiger came out of one door, and on some out of the other. The decisions of this tribunal were not only fair, they were positively determinate: the accused person was instantly punished if he found himself guilty; and, if innocent, he was rewarded on the spot, whether he liked it or not. There was no escape from the judgments of the king's arena.

The institution was a very popular one. When the people gathered together on one of the great trial days they never knew whether they were to witness a bloody slaughter or a hilarious wedding. This element of uncertainty lent an interest to the occasion which it could not otherwise have attained. Thus the masses were entertained and pleased, and the thinking part of the community could bring no charge of unfairness against this plan; for did not the accused person have the whole matter in his own hands?

This semi-barbaric king had a daughter as blooming as his most florid fancies, and with a soul as fervent and imperious as his own. As is usual in such cases, she was the apple of his eye, and was loved by him above all humanity. Among his courtiers was a young man of that fineness of blood and lowness of station common to the conventional heroes of romance who love royal maidens. This royal maiden was well satisfied with her lover, for he was handsome and brave to a degree unsurpassed in all this kingdom; and she loved him with an ardor that had enough of barbarism in it to make it exceedingly warm and strong. This love affair moved on happily for many months, until one day the king happened to discover its existence. He did not hesitate nor waver in regard to his duty in the premises. The youth was immediately cast into prison, and a day was appointed for his trial in the king's arena. This, of course, was an especially important occasion; and his majesty, as well as all the people, was greatly interested in the workings and development of this trial. Never before had such a case occurred; never before had a subject dared to love the daughter of a king. In after-years such things became commonplace enough; but then they were, in no slight degree, novel and startling.

The tiger-cages of the kingdom were searched for the most savage and relentless beasts, from which the fiercest monster might be selected for the arena; and the ranks of maiden youth and beauty throughout the land were carefully surveyed by competent judges, in order that the young man might have a fitting bride in case fate did not determine for him a different destiny. Of course, everybody knew that the deed with which the accused was charged had been done. He had loved the princess, and neither he, she, nor any one else thought of denying the fact; but the king would not think of allowing any fact of this kind to interfere with the workings of the tribunal, in which he took such great delight and satisfaction. No matter how the affair turned out, the youth would be disposed of; and the king would take an æsthetic pleasure in watching the course of events, which would determine whether or not the young man had done wrong in allowing himself to love the princess.

The appointed day arrived. From far and near the people gathered, and thronged the great galleries of the arena; and crowds, unable to gain admittance, massed themselves against its outside walls. The king and his court were in their places, opposite the twin doors—those fateful portals, so terrible in their similarity.

All was ready. The signal was given. A door beneath the royal party opened, and the lover of the princess walked into the arena. Tall, beautiful, fair, his appearance was greeted with a low hum of admiration and anxiety. Half the audience had not known so grand a youth had lived among them. No wonder the princess loved him! What a terrible thing for him to be there!

As the youth advanced into the arena, he turned, as the custom was, to bow to the king: but he did not think at all of that royal personage; his eyes were fixed upon the princess, who sat to the right of her father. Had it not been for the moiety of barbarism in her nature, it is probable that lady would not have been there; but her intense and fervid soul would not allow her to be absent on an occasion in which she was so terribly interested. From the moment that the decree had gone forth, that her lover should decide his fate in the king's arena, she had thought of nothing, night or day, but this great event and the various subjects connected with it. Possessed of more power, influence, and force of character than any one who had ever before been interested in such a case, she had done what no other person had done—she had possessed herself of the secret of the doors. She knew in which of the two rooms, that lay behind those doors, stood the cage of the tiger, with its open front, and in which waited the lady. Through these thick doors, heavily curtained with skins on the inside, it was impossible that any noise or suggestion should come from within to the person who should approach to raise the latch of one of them; but gold, and the power of a woman's will, had brought the secret to the princess.

And not only did she know in which room stood the lady ready to emerge, all blushing and radiant, should her door be opened, but she knew who the lady was. It was one of the fairest and loveliest of the damsels of the court who had been selected as the reward of the accused youth, should he be proved innocent of the crime of aspiring to one so far above him; and the princess hated her. Often had she seen, or imagined that she had seen, this fair creature throwing glances of admiration upon the person of her lover, and sometimes she thought these glances were perceived and even returned. Now and then she had seen them talking together; it was but for a moment or two, but much can be said in a brief space; it may have been on most unimportant topics, but how could she know that? The girl was lovely, but she had dared to raise her eyes to the loved one of the princess; and, with all the intensity of the savage blood transmitted to her through long lines of wholly barbaric ancestors, she hated the woman who blushed and trembled behind that silent door.

When her lover turned and looked at her, and his eye met hers as she sat there paler and whiter than any one in the vast ocean of anxious faces about her, he saw, by that power of quick perception which is given to those whose souls are one, that she knew behind which door crouched the tiger, and behind which stood the lady. He had expected her to know it. He understood her nature, and his soul was assured that she would never rest until she had made plain to herself this thing, hidden to all other lookers-on, even to the king. The only hope for the youth in which there was any element of certainty was based upon the success of the princess in discovering this mystery; and the moment he looked upon her, he saw she had succeeded, as in his soul he knew she would succeed.

Then it was that his quick and anxious glance asked the question: "Which?" It was as plain to her as if he shouted it from where he stood. There was not an instant to be lost. The question was asked in a flash; it must be answered in another.

Her right arm lay on the cushioned parapet before her. She raised her hand, and made a slight, quick movement toward the right. No one but her lover saw her. Every eye but his was fixed on the man in the arena.

He turned, and with a firm and rapid step he walked across the empty space. Every heart stopped beating, every breath was held, every eye was fixed immovably upon that man. Without the slightest hesitation, he went to the door on the right, and opened it.

Now, the point of the story is this: Did the tiger come out of that door, or did the lady?

The more we reflect upon this question, the harder it is to answer. It involves a study of the human heart which leads us through devious mazes of passion, out of which it is difficult to find our way. Think of it, fair reader, not as if the decision of the question depended upon yourself, but upon that hot-blooded, semi-barbaric princess, her soul at a white heat beneath the combined fires of despair and jealousy. She had lost him, but who should have him?

How often, in her waking hours and in her dreams, had she started in wild horror, and covered her face with her hands as she thought of her lover opening the door on the other side of which waited the cruel fangs of the tiger!

But how much oftener had she seen him at the other door! How in her grievous reveries had she gnashed her teeth, and torn her hair, when she saw his start of rapturous delight as he opened the door of the lady! How her soul had burned in agony when she had seen him rush to meet that woman, with her flushing cheek and sparkling eye of triumph; when she had seen him lead her forth, his whole frame kindled with the joy of recovered life; when she had heard the glad shouts from the multitude, and the wild ringing of the happy bells; when she had seen the priest, with his joyous followers, advance to the couple, and make them man and wife before her very eyes; and when she had seen them walk away together upon their path of flowers, followed by the tremendous shouts of the hilarious multitude, in which her one despairing shriek was lost and drowned!

Would it not be better for him to die at once, and go to wait for her in the blessed regions of semi-barbaric futurity?

And yet, that awful tiger, those shrieks, that blood!

Her decision had been indicated in an instant, but it had been made after days and nights of anguished deliberation. She had known she would be asked, she had decided what she would answer, and, without the slightest hesitation, she had moved her hand to the right.

The question of her decision is one not to be lightly considered, and it is not for me to presume to set myself up as the one person able to answer it. And so I leave it with all of you: Which came out of the opened door—the lady, or the tiger?

THE THREE STRANGERS

By Thomas Hardy

[Thomas Hardy (1840–1928) was the last of the great English novelists of the Victorian period. The most popular of his novels, *Tess of the D'Urbervilles*, was published in 1891, and *Jude, the Obscure*, his last, five years later. We associate Dickens and Thackeray with the 1860's and 1870's and Meredith and Hardy with the 'seventies and 'eighties. Hardy's name is a part of the twentieth century, but his novels were done in the final quarter of the nineteenth. In his old age, he turned once more to lyric poetry, the literary interest of his young manhood.

Dorsetshire in southern England was Hardy's home throughout his long life. He was born in the village of Upper Bockhampton. His father was a stone mason and builder. Thomas had only a limited formal education in the local schools, but studied architecture under competent men and spent his early manhood in the restoration of some of the fine old churches. After his success as a novelist was assured, he built the house called Max Gate a mile or two from Dorchester, the "Casterbridge" of his novels, and lived there until his death at the age of eighty-seven.

Hardy was never the popular novelist like Dickens. He dealt seriously with the ironies of life and love and the indifference of fate, with man's struggle against a hostile or unfriendly universe. His stories of love are powerful and gripping, but never sweet and sentimental. Even so, he has a keen sense of humor which shows itself in his rustic characters. Many regard his *The Return of the Native* (1878) as his greatest book.

Hardy's best short stories are included in the two collections, *Wessex Tales* (1888) and *Life's Little Ironies* (1894). *The Three Strangers* first appeared in *Longman's Magazine* (March, 1883), and was later included in *Wessex Tales*.]

AMONG the few features of agricultural England which retain an appearance but little modified by the lapse of centuries, may be reckoned the high, grassy, and furzy downs, coombs, or ewe-leases, as they are indifferently called, that fill a large area of certain counties in the south and southwest. If any mark of human occupation is met with hereon, it usually takes the form of the solitary cottage of some shepherd.

Fifty years ago such a lonely cottage stood on such a down, and may possibly be standing there now. In spite of its loneliness, however, the spot, by actual measurement, was not more than five miles from a county-town. Yet that affected it little. Five miles of irregular upland,

269

during the long inimical seasons, with their sleets, snows, rains, and mists, afford withdrawing space enough to isolate a Timon or a Nebuchadnezzar; much less, in fair weather, to please that less repellent tribe, the poets, philosophers, artists, and others who "conceive and meditate of pleasant things."

Some old earthen camp or barrow, some clump of trees, at least some starved fragment of ancient hedge is usually taken advantage of in the erection of these forlorn dwellings. But, in the present case, such a kind of shelter had been disregarded. Higher Crowstairs, as the house was called, stood quite detached and undefended. The only reason for its precise situation seemed to be the crossing of two footpaths at right angles hard by, which may have crossed there and thus for a good five hundred years. Hence the house was exposed to the elements on all sides. But, though the wind up here blew unmistakably when it did blow, and the rain hit hard whenever it fell, the various weathers of the winter season were not quite so formidable on the coomb as they were imagined to be by dwellers on low ground. The raw rimes were not so pernicious as in the hollows, and the frosts were scarcely so severe. When the shepherd and his family who tenanted the house were pitied for their sufferings from the exposure, they said that upon the whole they were less inconvenienced by "wuzzes and flames" (hoarses and phlegms) than when they had lived by the stream of a snug neighboring valley.

The night of March 28, 182—, was precisely one of the nights that were wont to call forth these expressions of commiseration. The level rainstorm smote walls, slopes, and hedges like the clothyard shafts of Senlac and Crecy. Such sheep and outdoor animals as had no shelter stood with their buttocks to the winds; while the tails of little birds trying to roost on some scraggy thorn were blown inside-out like umbrellas. The gable-end of the cottage was stained with wet, and the eavesdroppings flapped against the wall. Yet never was commiseration for the shepherd more misplaced. For that cheerful rustic was entertaining a large party in glorification of the christening of his second girl.

The guests had arrived before the rain began to fall, and they were all now assembled in the chief or living room of the dwelling. A glance into the apartment at eight o'clock on this eventful evening would have resulted in the opinion that it was as cosy and comfortable a nook as could be wished for in boisterous weather. The calling of its inhabitant was proclaimed by a number of highly-polished sheep-crooks without stems that were hung ornamentally over the fireplace, the curl of each shining crook varying from the antiquated type engraved in the patriarchal pictures of old family Bibles to the most approved fashion of the last local sheep-fair. The room was lighted by half-a-dozen candles, having wicks only a trifle smaller than the grease which enveloped them, in candlesticks that were never used but at high-days, holy-days, and family feasts. The lights were scattered about the room, two of them standing on the chimney-piece. This position of candles was in itself significant. Candles on the chimney-piece always meant a party.

On the hearth, in front of a back-brand to give substance, blazed a fire of thorns, that crackled "like the laughter of the fool."

Nineteen persons were gathered here. Of these, five women, wearing gowns of various bright hues, sat in chairs along the wall; girls shy and not shy filled the window-bench; four men, including Charley Jake the hedge-carpenter, Elijah New the parish-clerk, and John Pitcher, a neighboring dairyman, the shepherd's father-in-law, lolled in the settle; a young man and maid, who were blushing over tentative *pourparlers* on a life-companionship, sat beneath the corner-cupboard; and an elderly engaged man of fifty or upward moved restlessly about from spots where his betrothed was not to the spot where she was. Enjoyment was pretty general, and so much the more prevailed in being unhampered by conventional restrictions. Absolute confidence in each other's good opinion begat perfect ease, while the finishing stroke of manner, amounting to a truly princely serenity, was lent to the majority by the absence of any expression or trait denoting that they wished to get on in the world, enlarge their minds, or do any eclipsing thing whatever—which nowadays so generally nips the bloom and *bonhomie* of all except the two extremes of the social scale.

Shepherd Fennel had married well, his wife being a dairyman's daughter from a vale at a distance, who brought fifty guineas in her pocket—and kept them there, till they should be required for ministering to the needs of a coming family. This frugal woman had been somewhat exercised as to the character that should be given to the gathering. A sit-still party had its advantages; but an undisturbed position of ease in chairs and settles was apt to lead on the men to such an unconscionable deal of toping that they would sometimes fairly drink the house dry. A dancing-party was the alternative; but this, while avoiding the foregoing objection on the score of good drink, had a counterbalancing disadvantage in the matter of good victuals, the ravenous appetites engendered by the exercise causing immense havoc in the buttery. Shepherdess Fennel fell back upon the intermediate plan of mingling short dances with short periods of talk and singing, so as to hinder any ungovernable rage in either. But this scheme was entirely confined to her own gentle mind: the shepherd himself was in the mood to exhibit the most reckless phases of hospitality.

The fiddler was a boy of those parts, about twelve years of age, who had a wonderful dexterity in jigs and reels, though his fingers were so small and short as to necessitate a constant shifting for the high notes, from which he scrambled back to the first position with sounds not of unmixed purity of tone. At seven the shrill tweedle-dee of this youngster had begun, accompanied by a booming ground-bass from Elijah New, the parish-clerk, who had thoughtfully brought with him his favorite musical instrument, the serpent. Dancing was instantaneous, Mrs. Fennel privately enjoining the players on no account to let the dance exceed the length of a quarter of an hour.

But Elijah and the boy, in the excitement of their position, quite forgot the injunction. Moreover, Oliver Giles, a man of seventeen, one of the dancers, who was enamored of his partner, a fair girl of thirty-three rolling years, had recklessly handed a new crown-piece to the musicians, as a bribe to keep going as long as they had muscle and wind. Mrs. Fennel, seeing the steam begin to generate on the countenances of her guests, crossed over and touched the fiddler's elbow and put her hand on the serpent's mouth. But they took no notice, and fearing she might lose her character of genial hostess if she were to interfere too markedly, she retired and sat down helpless. And so the dance whizzed on with cumulative fury, the performers moving in their planet-like courses, direct and retrograde, from apogee to perigee, till the hand of the well-kicked clock at the bottom of the room had traveled over the circumference of an hour.

While these cheerful events were in course of enactment within Fennel's pastoral dwelling, an incident having considerable bearing on the party had occurred in the gloomy night without. Mrs. Fennel's concern about the growing fierceness of the dance corresponded in point of time with the ascent of a human figure to the solitary hill of Higher Crowstairs from the direction of the distant town. This personage strode on, through the rain without a pause, following the little-worn path which, further on in its course, skirted the shepherd's cottage.

It was nearly the time of full moon, and on this account, though the sky was lined with a uniform sheet of dripping cloud, ordinary objects out of doors were readily visible. The sad wan light revealed the lonely pedestrian to be a man of supple frame; his gait suggested that he had somewhat passed the period of perfect and instinctive agility, though not so far as to be otherwise than rapid of motion when occasion required. At a rough guess, he might have been about forty years of age. He appeared tall, but a recruiting sergeant, or other person accustomed to the judging of men's heights by the eye, would have discerned that this was chiefly owing to his gauntness, and that he was not more than five-feet-eight or nine.

Notwithstanding the regularity of his tread, there was caution in it, as in that of one who mentally feels his way; and despite the fact that it was not a black coat nor a dark garment of any sort that he wore, there was something about him which suggested that he naturally belonged to the black-coated tribes of men. His clothes were of fustian, and his boots hobnailed, yet in his progress he showed not the mud-accustomed bearing of hobnailed and fustianed peasantry.

By the time that he had arrived abreast of the shepherd's premises the rain came down, or rather came along, with yet more determined violence. The outskirts of the little settlement partially broke the force of wind and rain, and this induced him to stand still. The most salient of the shepherd's domestic erections was an empty sty at the forward corner of his hedgeless garden, for in these latitudes the principle of masking the homelier features of your establishment by a conventional frontage was unknown. The traveler's eye was attracted to this small building by the pallid shine of the wet slates that covered it. He turned aside, and, finding it empty, stood under the pent-roof for shelter.

While he stood, the boom of the serpent within the adjacent house, and the lesser strains of the fiddler, reached the spot as an accompaniment to the surging hiss of the flying rain on the sod, its louder beating on the cabbage-leaves of the garden, on the eight or ten beehives just discernible by the path, and its dripping from the eaves into a row of buckets and pans that had been placed under the walls of the cottage. For at Higher Crowstairs, as at all such elevated domiciles, the grand difficulty of housekeeping was an insufficiency of water; and a casual rainfall was utilized by turning out, as catchers, every utensil that the house contained. Some queer stories might be told of the contrivances for economy in suds and dish-waters that are absolutely necessitated in upland habitations during the droughts of summer. But at this season there were no such exigencies; a mere acceptance of what the skies bestowed was sufficient for an abundant store.

At last the notes of the serpent ceased and the house was silent. This cessation of activity aroused the solitary pedestrian from the reverie into which he had lapsed, and, emerging from the shed, with an apparently new intention, he walked up the path to the house-door. Arrived here, his first act was to kneel down on a large stone beside the row of vessels, and to drink a copious draught from one of them. Having quenched his thirst he rose and lifted his hand to knock, but paused with his eye upon the panel. Since the dark surface of the wood revealed absolutely nothing, it was evident that he must be mentally looking through the door, as if he wished to measure thereby all the possibilities that a house of this sort might include, and how they might bear upon the question of his entry.

In his indecision he turned and surveyed the scene around. Not a soul was anywhere visible. The garden-path stretched downward from his feet, gleaming like the track of a snail; the roof of the little well (mostly dry), the well-cover, the top rail of the garden-gate, were varnished with the same dull liquid glaze; while, far away in the vale, a faint whiteness of more than usual extent showed that the rivers were high in the meads. Beyond all this winked a few bleared lamplights through the beating drops—lights that denoted the situation of the county-town from which he had appeared to come. The absence of all notes of life in that direction seemed to clinch his intentions, and he knocked at the door.

Within, a desultory chat had taken the place of movement and musical sound. The hedge-carpenter was suggesting a song to the company, which nobody just then was inclined to undertake, so that the knock afforded a not unwelcome diversion.

"Walk in!" said the shepherd promptly.

The latch clicked upward, and out of the night our pedestrian appeared upon the door-mat. The shepherd arose, snuffed two of the nearest candles, and turned to look at him.

Their light disclosed that the stranger was dark in complexion and not unprepossessing as to feature. His hat, which for a moment he did not remove, hung low over his eyes, without concealing that they were large, open, and determined, moving with a flash rather than a glance round the room. He seemed pleased with his survey, and, baring his shaggy head, said, in a rich deep voice, "The rain is so heavy, friends, that I ask leave to come in and rest awhile."

"To be sure, stranger," said the shepherd. "And faith, you've been lucky in choosing your time, for we are having a bit of a fling for a glad cause—though, to be sure, a man could hardly wish that glad cause to happen more than once a year."

"Nor less," spoke up a woman. "For 'tis best to get your family over and done with, as soon as you can, so as to be all the earlier out of the fag o't."

"And what may be this glad cause?" asked the stranger.

"A birth and christening," said the shepherd.

The stranger hoped his host might not be made unhappy either by too many or too few of such episodes, and being invited by a gesture to a pull at the mug, he readily acquiesced. His manner, which, before entering, had been so dubious, was now altogether that of a careless and candid man.

"Late to be traipsing athwart this coomb—hey?" said the engaged man of fifty.

"Late it is, master, as you say.—I'll take a seat in the chimney-corner, if you have nothing to urge against it, ma'am; for I am a little moist on the side that was next the rain."

Mrs. Shepherd Fennel assented, and made room for the self-invited comer, who, having got completely inside the chimney-corner, stretched out his legs and his arms with the expansiveness of a person quite at home.

"Yes, I am rather cracked in the vamp," he said freely, seeing that the eyes of the shepherd's wife fell upon his boots, "and I am not well fitted either. I have had some rough times lately, and have been forced to pick up what I can get in the way of wearing, but I must find a suit better fit for working-days when I reach home."

"One of hereabouts?" she inquired.

"Not quite that—further up the country."

"I thought so. And so be I; and by your tongue you come from my neighborhood."

"But you would hardly have heard of me," he said quickly. "My time would be long before yours, ma'am, you see."

This testimony to the youthfulness of his hostess had the effect of stopping her cross-examination.

"There is only one thing more wanted to make me happy," continued the newcomer. "And that is a little baccy, which I am sorry to say I am out of."

"I'll fill your pipe," said the shepherd.

"I must ask you to lend me a pipe likewise."

"A smoker, and no pipe about 'ee?"

"I have dropped it somewhere on the road."

The shepherd filled and handed him a new clay pipe, saying, as he did so, "Hand me your baccy box—I'll fill that too, now I am about it."

The man went through the movement of searching his pockets.

"Lost that too?" said his entertainer, with some surprise.

"I am afraid so," said the man with some confusion. "Give it to me in a screw of paper." Lighting his pipe at the candle with a suction that drew the whole flame into the bowl, he resettled himself in the corner and bent his looks upon the faint steam from his damp legs, as if he wished to say no more.

Meanwhile the general body of guests had been taking little notice of this visitor by reason of an absorbing discussion in which they were engaged with the band about a tune for the next dance. The matter being settled, they were about to stand up when an interruption came in the shape of another knock at the door.

At sound of the same the man in the chimney-corner took up the poker and began stirring the brands as if doing it thoroughly were the one aim of his existence; and a second time the shepherd said, "Walk in!" In a moment another man stood upon the straw-woven door-mat. He too was a stranger.

This individual was one of a type radically different from the first. There was more of the commonplace in his manner, and a certain jovial cosmopolitanism sat upon his features. He was several years older than the first arrival, his hair being slightly frosted, his eyebrows bristly, and his whiskers cut back from his cheeks. His face was rather full and flabby, and yet it was not altogether a face without power. A few grog-blossoms marked the neighborhood of his nose. He flung back his long drab greatcoat, revealing that beneath it he wore a suit of cinder-gray shade throughout, large heavy seals, of some metal or other that would take a polish, dangling from his fob as his only personal ornament. Shaking the water-drops from his low-crowned glazed hat, he said, "I must ask for a few minutes' shelter, comrades, or I shall be wetted to my skin before I get to Casterbridge."

"Make yourself at home, master," said the shepherd, perhaps a trifle less heartily than on the first occasion. Not that Fennel had the least tinge of niggardliness in his composition; but the room was far from large, spare chairs were not numerous, and damp companions were not altogether desirable at close quarters for the women and girls in their bright-colored gowns.

However, the second comer, after taking off his greatcoat, and hanging his hat on a nail in one of the ceiling-beams as if he had been specially invited to put it there, advanced and sat down at the table. This had been pushed so closely into the chimney-corner to give all available room to the dancers, that its inner edge grazed the elbow of the man who had ensconced himself by the fire; and thus the two strangers were brought into close companionship. They nodded to each other by way of breaking the ice of unacquaintance, and the first stranger handed his neighbor the family mug—a huge vessel of brown ware, having its upper edge worn away like a threshold by the rub of whole generations of thirsty lips that had gone the way of all flesh, and bearing the following inscription burnt upon its rotund side in yellow letters:—

THERE IS NO FUN

UNTIL I CUM

The other man, nothing loth, raised the mug to his lips, and drank on, and on, and on—till a curious blueness overspread the countenance of the shepherd's wife, who had regarded with no little surprise the first stranger's free offer to the second of what did not belong to him to dispense.

"I knew it!" said the toper to the shepherd with much satisfaction. "When I walked up your garden before coming in, and saw the hives all of a row, I said to myself, 'Where there's bees there's honey, and where there's honey there's mead.' But mead of such a truly comfortable sort as this I really didn't expect to meet in my older days." He took yet another pull at the mug, till it assumed an ominous elevation.

"Glad you enjoy it!" said the shepherd warmly.

"It is goodish mead," assented Mrs. Fennel, with an absence of enthusiasm which seemed to say that it was possible to buy praise for one's cellar at too heavy a price. "It is trouble enough to make—and really I hardly think we shall make any more. For honey sells well, and we ourselves can make shift with a drop o' small mead and metheglin for common use from the comb-washings."

"O, but you'll never have the heart!" reproachfully cried the stranger in cinder-gray, after taking up the mug a third time and setting it down empty. "I love mead, when 'tis old like this, as I love to go to church o' Sundays, or to relieve the needy any day of the week."

"Ha, ha, ha!" said the man in the chimney-corner, who, in spite of the taciturnity induced by the pipe of tobacco, could not or would not refrain from this slight testimony to his comrade's humor.

Now the old mead of those days, brewed of the purest first-year or maiden honey, four pounds to the gallon—with its due complement of white of eggs, cinnamon, ginger, cloves, mace, rosemary, yeast, and processes of working, bottling, and cellaring—tasted remarkably strong; but it did not taste so strong as it actually was. Hence, presently the stranger in cinder-gray at the table, moved by its creeping influence, unbuttoned his waistcoat, threw himself back in his chair, spread his legs, and made his presence felt in various ways.

"Well, well, as I say," he resumed, "I am going to Casterbridge, and to Casterbridge I must go. I should have been almost there by this time; but the rain drove me into your dwelling, and I'm not sorry for it."

"You don't live in Casterbridge?" said the shepherd.

"Not as yet; though I shortly mean to move there."

"Going to set up in trade, perhaps?"

"No, no," said the shepherd's wife. "It is easy to see that the gentleman is rich, and don't want to work at anything."

The cinder-gray stranger paused, as if to consider whether he would accept that definition of himself. He presently rejected it by answering, "Rich is not quite the word for me, dame. I do work, and I must work. And even if I only get to Casterbridge by midnight I must begin work there at eight tomorrow morning. Yes, het or wet, blow or snow, famine or sword, my day's work tomorrow must be done."

"Poor man! Then, in spite o' seeming, you be worse off than we?" replied the shepherd's wife.

"'Tis the nature of my trade, men and maidens. 'Tis the nature of my trade more than my poverty. . . . But really and truly I must up and off, or I shan't get a lodging in the town." However, the speaker did not move, and directly added, "There's time for one more draught of friendship before I go; and I'd perform it at once if the mug were not dry."

"Here's a mug o' small," said Mrs. Fennel. "Small, we call it, though to be sure 'tis only the first wash o' the combs."

"No," said the stranger disdainfully, "I won't spoil your first kindness by partaking o' your second."

"Certainly not," broke in Fennel. "We don't increase and multiply every day, and I'll fill the mug again." He went away to the dark place under the stairs where the barrel stood. The shepherdess followed him.

"Why should you do this?" she said reproachfully, as soon as they were alone. "He's emptied it once, though it held enough for ten people; and now he's not contented wi' the small, but must needs call for more o' the strong! And a stranger unbeknown to any of us. For my part, I don't like the look o' the man at all."

"But he's in the house, my honey; and 'tis a wet night, and a christening. Daze it, what's a cup of mead more or less? There'll be plenty more next bee-burning."

"Very well—this time, then," she answered, looking wistfully at the barrel. "But what is the man's calling, and where is he one of, that he should come in and join us like this?"

"I don't know. I'll ask him again."

The catastrophe of having the mug drained dry at one pull by the stranger in cinder-gray was effectually guarded against this time by Mrs. Fennel. She poured out his allowance in a small cup, keeping the large one at a discreet distance from him. When he had tossed off his portion the shepherd renewed his inquiry about the stranger's occupation.

The latter did not immediately reply, and the man in the chimney-corner, with sudden demonstrativeness, said, "Anybody may know my trade—I'm a wheelwright."

"A very good trade for these parts," said the shepherd.

"And anybody may know mine—if they've the sense to find it out," said the stranger in cinder-gray.

"You may generally tell what a man is by his claws," observed the hedge-carpenter, looking at his own hands. "My fingers be as full of thorns as an old pincushion is of pins."

The hands of the man in the chimney-corner instinctively sought the shade, and he gazed into the fire as he resumed his pipe. The man at the table took up the hedge-carpenter's remark, and added smartly, "True; but the oddity of my trade is that, instead of setting a mark upon me, it sets a mark upon my customers."

No observation being offered by anybody in elucidation of this enigma, the shepherd's wife once more called for a song. The same obstacles presented themselves as at the former time—one had no voice, another had forgotten the first verse. The stranger at the table, whose soul had now risen to a good working temperature, relieved the difficulty by exclaiming that, to start the company, he would sing himself. Thrusting one thumb into the arm-hole of his waistcoat, he waved the other hand in the air, and, with an extemporizing gaze at the shining sheep-crooks above the mantelpiece, began:—

> "O my trade it is the rarest one,
> Simple shepherds all—
> My trade is a sight to see;
> For my customers I tie, and take them up on high,
> And waft 'em to a far countree!"

The room was silent when he had finished the verse—with one exception, that of the man in the chimney-corner, who, at the singer's word, "Chorus!" joined him in a deep bass voice of musical relish—

> "And waft 'em to a far countree!"

Oliver Giles, John Pitcher the dairyman, the parish-clerk, the engaged man of fifty, the row of young women against the wall, seemed lost in thought not of the gayest kind. The shepherd looked meditatively on the ground, the shepherdess gazed keenly at the singer, and with some suspicion; she was doubting whether this stranger were merely singing an old song from recollection, or was composing one there and then for the occasion. All were as perplexed at the obscure revelation as the guests at Belshazzar's Feast, except the man in the chimney-corner, who quietly said, "Second verse, stranger," and smoked on.

The singer thoroughly moistened himself from his lips inwards, and went on with the next stanza as requested:—

> "My tools are but common ones,
> Simple shepherds all—
> My tools are no sight to see:
> A little hempen string, and a post whereon to swing,
> Are implements enough for me!"

Shepherd Fennel glanced round. There was no longer any doubt that the stranger was answering his question rhythmically. The guests one and all started back with suppressed exclamations. The young woman engaged to the man of fifty fainted half-way, and would have proceeded, but finding him wanting in alacrity for catching her she sat down trembling.

"O, he's the——!" whispered the people in the background, mentioning the name of an ominous public officer. "He's come to do it! 'Tis to be at Casterbridge jail tomorrow—the man for sheep-stealing—the poor clock-maker we heard of, who used to live away at Shottsford and had no work to do—Timothy Summers, whose family were a-starving, and so he went out of Shottsford by the high-road, and took a sheep in open daylight, defying the farmer and the farmer's wife and the farmer's lad, and every man jack among 'em. He" (and they nodded towards the stranger of the deadly trade) "is come from up the country to do it because there's not enough to do in his own county-town, and he's got the place here now our own county man's dead; he's going to live in the same cottage under the prison wall."

The stranger in cinder-gray took no notice of this whispered string of observations, but again wetted his lips. Seeing that his friend in the chimney-corner was the only one who reciprocated his joviality in any way, he held out his cup towards that appreciative comrade, who also held out his own. They clinked together, the eyes of the rest of the room hanging upon the singer's actions. He parted his lips for the third verse; but at that moment another knock was audible upon the door. This time the knock was faint and hesitating.

The company seemed scared; the shepherd looked with consternation towards the entrance, and it was with some effort that he resisted his alarmed wife's deprecatory glance, and uttered for the third time the welcoming words, "Walk in!"

The door was gently opened, and another man stood upon the mat.

He, like those who had preceded him, was a stranger. This time it was a short, small personage, of fair complexion, and dressed in a decent suit of dark clothes.

"Can you tell me the way to——?" he began: when, gazing round the room to observe the nature of the company amongst whom he had fallen, his eyes lighted on the stranger in cinder-gray. It was just at the instant when the latter, who had thrown his mind into his song with such a will that he scarcely heeded the interruption, silenced all whispers and inquiries by bursting into his third verse:

"Tomorrow is my working day,
                            Simple shepherds all—
Tomorrow is a working day for me:
For the farmer's sheep is slain, and the lad who did
    it ta'en,
And on his soul may God ha' merc-y!"

The stranger in the chimney-corner, waving cups with the singer so heartily that his mead splashed over on the hearth, repeated in his bass voice as before:

"And on his soul may God ha' merc-y!"

All this time the third stranger had been standing in the doorway. Finding now that he did not come forward or go on speaking, the guests particularly regarded him. They noticed to their surprise that he stood before them the picture of abject terror—his knees trembling, his hand shaking so violently that the door-latch by which he supported himself rattled audibly: his white lips were parted, and his eyes fixed on the merry officer of justice in the middle of the room. A moment more and he had turned, closed the door, and fled.

"What a man can it be?" said the shepherd.

The rest, between the awfulness of their late discovery and the odd conduct of this third visitor, looked as if they knew not what to think, and said nothing. Instinctively they withdrew further and further from the grim gentleman in their midst, whom some of them seemed to take for the Prince of Darkness himself, till they formed a remote circle, an empty space of floor being left between them and him——

". . . circulus, cujus centrum diabolus."

The room was so silent—though there were more than twenty people in it—that nothing could be heard but the patter of the rain against the window-shutters, accompanied by the occasional hiss of a stray drop that fell down the chimney into the fire, and the steady puffing of the man in the corner, who had now resumed his pipe of long clay.

The stillness was unexpectedly broken. The distant sound of a gun reverberated through the air—apparently from the direction of the county-town.

"Be jiggered!" cried the stranger who had sung the song, jumping up.

"What does that mean?" asked several.

"A prisoner escaped from the jail—that's what it means."

All listened. The sound was repeated, and none of them spoke, but the man in the chimney-corner, who said quietly, "I've often been told that in this county they fire a gun at such times; but I never heard it till now."

"I wonder if it is *my* man?" murmured the personage in cinder-gray.

"Surely it is!" said the shepherd involuntarily. "And surely we've zeed him! That little man who looked in at the door by now, and quivered like a leaf when he zeed ye and heard your song!"

"His teeth chattered, and the breath went out of his body," said the dairyman.

"And his heart seemed to sink within him like a stone," said Oliver Giles.

"And he bolted as if he'd been shot at," said the hedge-carpenter.

"True—his teeth chattered, and his heart seemed to sink; and he bolted as if he'd been shot at," slowly summed up the man in the chimney-corner.

"I didn't notice it," remarked the hangman.

"We were all a-wondering what made him run off in such a fright," faltered one of the women against the wall, "and now 'tis explained!"

The firing of the alarm-gun went on at intervals, low and sullenly, and their suspicions became a certainty. The sinister gentleman in cinder-gray roused himself. "Is there a constable here?" he asked, in thick tones. "If so, let him step forward."

The engaged man of fifty stepped quavering out from the wall, his betrothed beginning to sob on the back of the chair.

"You are a sworn constable?"

"I be, sir."

"Then pursue the criminal at once, with assistance, and bring him back here. He can't have gone far."

"I will, sir, I will—when I've got my staff. I'll go home and get it, and come sharp here, and start in a body."

"Staff!—never mind your staff; the man'll be gone!"

"But I can't do nothing without my staff—can I, William, and John, and Charles Jake? No; for there's the king's royal crown a-painted on en in yaller and gold, and the lion and the unicorn, so as when I raise en up and hit my prisoner, 'tis made a lawful blow thereby. I wouldn't 'tempt to take up a man without my staff—no, not I. If I hadn't the law to gie me courage, why, instead o' my taking up him he might take up me!"

"Now, I'm a king's man myself, and can give you authority enough for this," said the formidable officer in gray. "Now then, all of ye, be ready. Have ye any lanterns?"

"Yes—have ye any lanterns?—I demand it!" said the constable.

"And the rest of you able-bodied——"

"Able-bodied men—yes—the rest of ye!" said the constable.

"Have you some good stout staves and pitchforks——"

"Staves and pitchforks—in the name o' the law! And take 'em in yer hands and go in quest, and do as we in authority tell ye!"

Thus aroused, the men prepared to give chase. The evidence was, indeed, though circumstantial, so convincing, that but little argument was needed to show the shepherd's guests that after what they had seen, it would look very much like connivance if they did not instantly pursue the unhappy third stranger, who could not as yet have gone more than a few hundred yards over such uneven country.

A shepherd is always well provided with lanterns; and lighting these hastily, and with hurdle-staves in their hands, they poured out of the door, taking a direction along the crest of the hill, away from the town, the rain having fortunately a little abated.

Disturbed by the noise, or possibly by unpleasant dreams of her baptism, the child who had been christened began to cry heart-brokenly in the room overhead. These notes of grief came down through the chinks of the floor to the ears of the women below, who jumped up one by one, and seemed glad of the excuse to ascend and comfort the baby, for the incidents of the last half-hour greatly oppressed them. Thus in the space of two or three minutes the room on the ground-floor was deserted quite.

But it was not for long. Hardly had the sound of footsteps died away when a man returned round the corner of the house from the direction the pursuers had taken. Peeping in at the door, and seeing nobody there, he entered leisurely. It was the stranger of the chimney-corner, who had gone out with the rest. The motive of his return was shown by his helping himself to a cut piece of skimmer-cake that lay on a ledge beside where he had sat, and which he had apparently forgotten to take with him. He also poured out half a cup more mead from the quantity that remained, ravenously eating and drinking these as he stood. He had not finished when another figure came in just as quietly—his friend in cinder-gray.

"O—you here?" said the latter, smiling. "I thought you had gone to help in the capture." And this speaker also revealed the object of his return by looking solicitously round for the fascinating mug of old mead.

"And I thought you had gone," said the other, continuing his skimmer-cake with some effort.

"Well, on second thoughts, I felt there were enough without me," said the first confidentially, "and such a night as it is, too. Besides, 'tis the business o' the Government to take care of its criminals—not mine."

"True; so it is. And I felt as you did, that there were enough without me."

"I don't want to break my limbs running over the humps and hollows of this wild country."

"Nor I neither, between you and me."

"These shepherd-people are used to it—simple-minded souls, you know, stirred up to anything in a moment. They'll have him ready for me before the morning, and no trouble to me at all."

"They'll have him, and we shall have saved ourselves all labor in the matter."

"True, true. Well, my way is to Casterbridge; and 'tis as much as my legs will do to take me that far. Going the same way?"

"No, I am sorry to say! I have to get home over there" (he nodded indefinitely to the right), "and I feel as you do, that it is quite enough for my legs to do before bedtime."

The other had by this time finished the mead in the mug, after which, shaking hands heartily at the door, and wishing each other well, they went their several ways.

In the meantime the company of pursuers had reached the end of the hog's-back elevation which dominated this part of the down. They had decided on no particular plan of action; and, finding that the man of the baleful trade was no longer in their company, they seemed quite unable to form any such plan now. They descended in all directions down the hill, and straightway several of the party fell into the snare set by Nature for all misguided midnight ramblers over this part of the cretaceous formation. The "lanchets," or flint slopes, which belted the escarpment at intervals of a dozen yards, took the less cautious ones unawares, and losing their footing on the rubbly steep they slid sharply downwards, the lanterns rolling from their hands to the bottom, and there lying on their sides till the horn was scorched through.

When they had again gathered themselves together, the shepherd, as the man who knew the country best, took the lead, and guided them round these treacherous inclines. The lanterns, which seemed rather to dazzle their eyes and warn the fugitive than to assist them in the exploration, were extinguished, due silence was observed; and in this more rational order they plunged into the vale. It was a grassy, briery, moist defile, affording some shelter to any person who had sought it; but the party perambulated it in vain, and ascended on the other side. Here they wandered apart, and after an interval closed together again to report progress. At the second time of closing in they found themselves near a lonely ash, the single tree on this part of the coomb, probably sown there by a passing bird some fifty years before. And here, standing a little to one side of the trunk, as motionless as the trunk itself, appeared the man they were in quest of, his outline being well defined against the sky beyond. The band noiselessly drew up and faced him.

"Your money or your life!" said the constable sternly to the still figure.

"No, no," whispered John Pitcher. "'Tisn't our side ought to say that. That's the doctrine of vagabonds like him, and we be on the side of the law."

"Well, well," replied the constable impatiently; "I must say something, mustn't I? and if you had all the weight o' this undertaking upon your mind, perhaps you'd say the wrong thing too!—Prisoner at the bar, surrender, in the name of the Father—the Crown, I mane!"

The man under the tree seemed now to notice them for the first time, and, giving them no opportunity whatever for exhibiting their courage, he strolled slowly towards them. He was, indeed, the little man, the third stranger; but his trepidation had in a great measure gone.

"Well, travelers," he said, "did I hear ye speak to me?"

"You did: you've got to come and be our prisoner at once!" said the constable. "We arrest 'ee on the charge of not biding in Casterbridge jail in a decent proper manner to be hung tomorrow morning. Neighbors, do your duty, and seize the culpet!"

On hearing the charge, the man seemed enlightened, and, saying not another word, resigned himself with preternatural civility to the search-party, who, with their staves in their hands, surrounded him on all sides, and marched him back towards the shepherd's cottage.

It was eleven o'clock by the time they arrived. The light shining from the open door, a sound of men's voices within, proclaimed to them as they approached the house that some new events had arisen in their absence. On entering they discovered the shepherd's living to be invaded by two officers from Casterbridge jail, and a well-known magistrate who lived at the nearest country-seat, intelligence of the escape having become generally circulated.

"Gentlemen," said the constable, "I have brought back your man— not without risk and danger; but every one must do his duty! He is inside this circle of able-bodied persons, who have lent me useful aid, considering their ignorance of Crown work. Men, bring forward your prisoner!" And the third stranger was led to the light.

"Who is this?" said one of the officials.

"The man," said the constable.

"Certainly not," said the turnkey; and the first corroborated his statement.

"But how can it be otherwise?" asked the constable. "Or why was he so terrified at sight o' the singing instrument of the law who sat there?" Here he related the strange behavior of the third stranger on entering the house during the hangman's song.

"Can't understand it," said the officer coolly. "All I know is that it is not the condemned man. He's quite a different character from this one; a gauntish fellow, with dark hair and eyes, rather good-looking and with a musical bass voice that if you heard it once you'd never mistake as long as you lived."

"Why, souls—'twas the man in the chimney-corner!"

"Hey—what?" said the magistrate, coming forward after inquiring particulars from the shepherd in the background. "Haven't you got the man after all?"

"Well, sir," said the constable, "he's the man we were in search of, that's true; and yet he's not the man we were in search of. For the man we were in search of was not the man we wanted, sir, if you understand my every-day way; for 'twas the man in the chimney-corner!"

"A pretty kettle of fish altogether!" said the magistrate. "You had better start for the other man at once."

The prisoner now spoke for the first time. The mention of the man in the chimney-corner seemed to have moved him as nothing else could do. "Sir," he said, stepping forward to the magistrate, "take no more trouble about me. The time is come when I may as well speak. I have done nothing; my crime is that the condemned man is my brother. Early this afternoon I left home at Shottsford to tramp it all the way to Caster-bridge jail to bid him farewell, I was benighted, and called here to rest and ask the way. When I opened the door I saw before me the very man, my brother, that I thought to see in the condemned cell at Caster-bridge. He was in this chimney-corner; and jammed close to him, so that he could not have got out if he had tried, was the executioner who'd come to take his life, singing a song about it and not knowing that it was his victim who was close by, joining in to save appearances. My brother looked a glance of agony at me, and I knew he meant, 'Don't reveal what you see; my life depends on it.' I was so terror-struck that I could hardly stand, and, not knowing what I did, I turned and hurried away."

The narrator's manner and tone had the stamp of truth, and his story made a great impression on all around. "And do you know where your brother is at the present time?" asked the magistrate.

"I do not. I have never seen him since I closed this door."

"I can testify to that, for we've been between ye ever since," said the constable.

"Where does he think to fly to?—what is his occupation?"

"He's a watch-and-clock-maker, sir."

"'A said 'a was a wheelwright—a wicked rogue," said the constable.

"The wheels of clocks and watches he meant, no doubt," said Shepherd Fennel. "I thought his hands were palish for's trade."

"Well, it appears to me that nothing can be gained by retaining this poor man in custody," said the magistrate; "your business lies with the other, unquestionably."

And so the little man was released off-hand; but he looked nothing the less sad on that account, it being beyond the power of the magistrate or constable to raze out the written troubles in his brain, for they concerned another whom he regarded with more solicitude than himself. When this was done, and the man had gone his way, the night was found to be so far advanced that it was deemed useless to renew the search before the next morning.

Next day, accordingly, the quest for the clever sheep-stealer became general and keen, to all appearance at least. But the intended punishment was cruelly disproportioned to the transgression, and the sympathy of a great many country-folk in that district was strongly on the side of the fugitive. Moreover, his marvelous coolness and daring in hob-and-nobbing with the hangman, under the unprecedented circumstances of the shepherd's party, won their admiration. So that it may be questioned if all those who ostensibly made themselves so busy in exploring woods and fields and lanes were quite so thorough when it came to the private examination of their own lofts and outhouses. Stories were afloat of a mysterious figure being occasionally seen in some old overgrown trackway or other remote from turnpike roads; but when a search was instituted in any of these suspected quarters nobody was found. Thus the days and weeks passed without tidings.

In brief, the bass-voiced man of the chimney-corner was never recaptured. Some said that he went across the sea, others that he did not, but buried himself in the depths of a populous city. At any rate, the gentleman in cinder-gray never did his morning's work at Casterbridge, nor met anywhere at all, for business purposes, the genial comrade with whom he had passed an hour of relaxation in the lonely house on the coomb.

The grass has long been green on the graves of Shepherd Fennel and his frugal wife; the guests who made up the christening party have mainly followed their entertainers to the tomb; the baby in whose honor they all had met is a matron in the sere and yellow leaf. But the arrival of the three strangers at the shepherd's that night, and the details connected therewith, is a story as well known as ever in the country about Higher Crowstairs.

WILL O' THE MILL

By Robert Louis Stevenson

[Robert Louis Balfour Stevenson (1850–1894) was one of the masters of English prose of recent times. He was born in Edinburgh, Scotland, the son of Thomas Stevenson, a noted civil engineer. He was educated for the law in Edinburgh University, but intended from the beginning to be a literary man. In his travels in search of health, he finally made his way to Samoa in the South Seas in 1889, where he spent the remaining years of his life.

Stevenson's literary work consists of novels, stories, lyric poems, essays, travels, and letters. His famous *A Child's Garden of Verses* was published in 1885. His chief novels and longer stories are *Treasure Island* (1883), *Prince Otto* (1885), *Dr. Jekyll and Mr. Hyde* (1886), *Kidnapped* (1886), *The Merry Men* (1886), *The Black Arrow* (1888), *The Master of Ballantrae* (1889), *The Wrecker* (1891–92), *David Balfour* (1893), *The Ebb Tide* (1894), *St. Ives* (unfinished, but completed by A. T. Quiller-Couch), and *Weir of Hermiston* (unfinished).

Will o' the Mill, first published in 1878, was later included in the collection, *New Arabian Nights* (1882). It is here reprinted from the Biographical Edition of the *Complete Works of Robert Louis Stevenson*, by permission of Charles Scribner's Sons, publishers.]

I

THE PLAIN AND THE STARS

THE Mill where Will lived with his adopted parents stood in a falling valley between pinewoods and great mountains. Above, hill after hill soared upwards until they soared out of the depth of the hardiest timber, and stood naked against the sky. Some way up, a long gray village lay like a seam or a rag of vapor on a wooded hillside; and when the wind was favorable, the sound of the church bells would drop down, thin and silvery, to Will. Below, the valley grew ever steeper and steeper, and at the same time widened out on either hand; and from an eminence beside the mill it was possible to see its whole length and away beyond it over a wide plain, where the river turned and shone, and moved on from city to city on its voyage towards the sea. It chanced that over this valley there lay a pass into a neighboring kingdom; so that, quiet and rural as it was, the road that ran along beside the river was a high thoroughfare between two splendid and powerful societies. All through the summer, traveling-carriages came crawling up, or went plunging briskly downwards past the mill; and as it happened that the other side was very much easier of ascent, the path was not much frequented, except by people going in one direction; and of all the carriages that Will saw go by, five-sixths were plunging briskly downwards and only one-sixth crawling up. Much more was this the case with foot-passengers. All the light-footed tourists, all the peddlers laden with strange wares, were tending downward like the river that accompanied their path. Nor was this all; for when Will was yet a child a disastrous war arose over a great part of the world. The newspapers were full of defeats and victories, the earth rang with cavalry hoofs, and often for days together and for miles around the coil of battle terrified good people from their labors in the field. Of all this, nothing was heard for a long time in the valley; but at last one of the commanders pushed an army over the pass by forced marches, and for three days horse and foot, cannon and tumbril, drum and standard, kept pouring downward past the mill. All day the child stood and watched them on their passage—the rhythmical stride, the pale, unshaven faces tanned about the eyes, the discolored regimentals and the tattered flags, filled him with a sense of weariness, pity, and wonder; and all night long, after he was in bed, he could hear the cannon pounding and the feet trampling, and the great armament sweeping onward and downward past the mill. No one in the valley ever heard the fate of the expedition, for they lay out of the way of gossip in those troublous times; but Will saw one thing plainly, that not a man returned. Whither had they all gone? Whither went all the tourists and peddlers with strange wares? whither all the brisk barouches with servant in the dicky? whither the water of the stream, ever coursing downward and ever renewed from above? Even the wind blew oftener down the valley, and carried the dead leaves along with it in the fall. It seemed like a great conspiracy of things animate and inanimate; they all went downward, fleetly and gaily downward, and only he, it seemed, remained behind, like a stock upon the wayside. It sometimes made him glad when he noticed how the fishes kept their heads up stream. They, at least, stood faithfully by him, while all else were posting downward to the unknown world.

One evening he asked the miller where the river went.

"It goes down the valley," answered he, "and turns a power of mills —six score mills, they say, from here to Unterdeck—and is none the wearier after all. And then it goes out into the lowlands, and waters the great corn country, and runs through a sight of fine cities (so they say) where kings live all alone in great palaces, with a sentry walking up and down before the door. And it goes under bridges with stone men upon them, looking down and smiling so curious at the water, and living folks leaning their elbows on the wall and looking over, too. And then it goes on and on, and down through marshes and sands, until at last it falls into the sea, where the ships are that bring parrots and tobacco from the Indies. Ay, it has a long trot before it as it goes singing over our weir, bless its heart!"

"And what is the sea?" asked Will.

"The sea!" cried the miller. "Lord help us all, it is the greatest thing God made! That is where all the water in the world runs down into a great salt lake. There it lies, as flat as my hand and as innocent-like as a child; but they do say when the wind blows it gets up into water-mountains bigger than any of ours, and swallows down great ships bigger than our mill, and makes such a roaring that you can hear it miles away upon the land. There are great fish in it five times bigger than a bull, and one old serpent as long as our river and as old as all the world, with whiskers like a man, and a crown of silver on her head."

Will thought he had never heard anything like this, and he kept on asking question after question about the world that lay away down the river, with all its perils and marvels, until the old miller became quite interested himself, and at last took him by the hand and led him to the hilltop that overlooks the valley and the plain. The sun was near setting, and hung low down in a cloudless sky. Everything was defined and glorified in golden light. Will had never seen so great an expanse of country in his life; he stood and gazed with all his eyes. He could see the cities, and the woods and fields, and the bright curves of the river, and far away to where the rim of the plain trenched along the shining heavens. An over-mastering emotion seized upon the boy, soul and body; his heart beat so thickly that he could not breathe; the scene swam before his eyes; the sun seemed to wheel round and round, and throw off, as it turned, strange shapes which disappeared with the rapidity of thought, and were succeeded by others. Will covered his face with his hands, and burst into a violent fit of tears; and the poor miller, sadly disappointed and perplexed, saw nothing better for it than to take him up in his arms and carry him home in silence.

From that day forward Will was full of new hopes and longings. Something kept tugging at his heartstrings; the running water carried his desires along with it as he dreamed over its fleeting surface; the wind, as it ran over innumerable tree-tops, hailed him with encouraging words; branches beckoned downward; the open road, as it shouldered round the angles and went turning and vanishing fast and faster down the valley, tortured him with its solicitations. He spent long whiles on the eminence, looking down the rivershed and abroad on the flat low-lands, and watched the clouds that traveled forth upon the sluggish wind and trailed their purple shadows on the plain; or he would linger by the wayside, and follow the carriages with his eyes as they rattled downward by the river. It did not matter what it was; everything that went that way, were it cloud or carriage, bird or brown water in the stream, he felt his heart flow out after it in an ecstasy of longing.

We are told by men of science that all the ventures of mariners on the sea, all that counter-marching of tribes and races that confounds old history with its dust and rumor, sprang from nothing more abstruse than the laws of supply and demand, and a certain natural instinct for cheap rations. To anyone thinking deeply, this will seem a dull and pitiful explanation. The tribes that came swarming out of the North and East, if they were indeed pressed onward from behind by others, were drawn at the same time by the magnetic influence of the South and West. The fame of other lands had reached them; the name of the eternal city rang in their ears; they were not colonists, but pilgrims; they traveled towards wine and gold and sunshine, but their hearts were set on something higher. That divine unrest, that old stinging trouble of humanity that makes all high achievements and all miserable failure, the same that spread wings with Icarus, the same that sent Columbus into the desolate Atlantic, inspired and supported these barbarians on their perilous march. There is one legend which profoundly represents their spirit, of how a flying party of these wanderers encountered a very old man shod with iron. The old man asked them whither they were going; and they answered with one voice: "To the Eternal City!" He looked upon them gravely. "I have sought it," he said, "over the most part of the world. Three such pairs as I now carry on my feet have I worn out upon this pilgrimage, and now the fourth is growing slender underneath my steps. And all this while I have not found the city." And he turned and went his own way alone, leaving them astonished.

And yet this would scarcely parallel the intensity of Will's feeling for the plain. If he could only go far enough out there, he felt as if his eyesight would be purged and clarified, as if his hearing would grow more delicate, and his very breath would come and go with luxury. He was transplanted and withering where he was; he lay in a strange country and was sick for home. Bit by bit, he pieced together broken notions of the world below: of the river, ever moving and growing until it sailed forth into the majestic ocean; of the cities, full of brisk and beautiful people, playing fountains, bands of music and marble palaces, and lighted up at night from end to end with artificial stars of gold; of the great churches, wise universities, brave armies, and untold money lying stored in vaults; of the high-flying vice that moved in the sunshine, and the stealth and swiftness of midnight murder. I have said he was sick as if for home: the figure halts. He was like someone lying in twilit, formless pre-existence, and stretching out his hands lovingly towards many-colored, many-sounding life. It was no wonder he was unhappy, he would go and tell the fish: they were made for their life, wished for no more than worms and running water, and a hole below a falling bank; but he was differently designed, full of desires and aspirations, itching at the fingers, lusting with the eyes, whom the whole variegated world could not satisfy with aspects. The true life, the true bright sunshine, lay far out upon the plain. And O! to see this sunlight once before he died! to move with a jocund spirit in a golden land! to hear the trained singers and sweet church bells, and see the holiday gardens! "And O fish!" he would cry, "if you would only turn your noses down stream, you could swim so easily into the fabled waters and see the vast ships passing over your heads like clouds, and hear the great water-hills making music over you all day long!" But the fish kept looking patiently in their own direction, until Will hardly knew whether to laugh or cry.

Hitherto the traffic on the road had passed by Will, like something seen in a picture; he had perhaps exchanged salutations with a tourist, or caught sight of an old gentleman in a traveling cap at a carriage window; but for the most part it had been a mere symbol, which he contemplated from apart and with something of a superstitious feeling. A time came at last when this was to be changed. The miller, who was a greedy man in his way, and never forewent an opportunity of honest profit, turned the mill-house into a little wayside inn, and, several pieces of good fortune falling in opportunely, built stables and got the position of postmaster on the road. It now became Will's duty to wait upon people, as they sat to break their fasts in the little arbor at the top of the mill garden; and you may be sure that he kept his ears open, and learned many new things about the outside world as he brought the omelette or the wine. Nay, he would often get into conversation with single guests, and by adroit questions and polite attention, not only gratify his own curiosity, but win the goodwill of the travelers. Many complimented the old couple on their serving-boy; and a professor was eager to take him away with him, and have him properly educated in the plain. The miller and his wife were mightily astonished and even more pleased. They thought it a very good thing that they should have opened their inn. "You see," the old man would remark, "he has a kind of talent for a publican; he never would have made anything else!" And so life wagged on in the valley, with high satisfaction to all concerned but Will. Every carriage that left the inn door seemed to take a part of him away with it; and when people jestingly offered him a lift, he could with difficulty command his emotion. Night after night he would dream that he was awakened by flustered servants, and that a splendid equipage waited at the door to carry him down into the plain; night after night; until the dream, which had seemed all jollity to him at first, began to take on a color of gravity, and the nocturnal summons and waiting equipage occupied a place in his mind as something to be both feared and hoped for.

One day, when Will was about sixteen, a fat young man arrived at sunset to pass the night. He was a contented-looking fellow, with a jolly eye, and carried a knapsack. While dinner was preparing, he sat in the arbor to read a book; but as soon as he had begun to observe Will, the book was laid aside; he was plainly one of those who prefer living people to people made of ink and paper. Will, on his part, although he had not been much interested in the stranger at first sight, soon began to take a great deal of pleasure in his talk, which was full of good nature and good sense, and at last conceived a great respect for his character and wisdom.

They sat far into the night; and about two in the morning Will opened his heart to the young man, and told him how he longed to leave the valley and what bright hopes he had connected with the cities of the plain. The young man whistled, and then broke into a smile.

"My young friend," he remarked, "you are a very curious little fellow, to be sure, and wish a great many things which you will never get. Why, you would feel quite ashamed if you knew how the little fellows in these fairy cities of yours are all after the same sort of nonsense, and keep breaking their hearts to get up into the mountains. And let me tell you, those who go down into the plains are a very short while there before they wish themselves heartily back again. The air is not so light, nor so pure; nor is the sun any brighter. As for the beautiful men and women, you would see many of them in rags and many of them deformed with horrible disorders; and a city is so hard a place for people who are poor and sensitive that many choose to die by their own hand."

"You must think me very simple," answered Will. "Although I have never been out of this valley, believe me, I have used my eyes. I know how one thing lives on another; for instance, how the fish hangs in the eddy to catch his fellows; and the shepherd, who makes so pretty a picture carrying home the lamb, is only carrying it home for dinner. I do not expect to find all things right in your cities. That is not what troubles me; it might have been that once upon a time; but although I live here always, I have asked many questions and learned a great deal in these last years, and certainly enough to cure me of my old fancies. But you would not have me die like a dog and not see all that is to be seen, and do all that a man can do, let it be good or evil? you would not have me spend all my days between this road here and the river, and not so much as make a motion to be up and live my life?—I would rather die out of hand," he cried, "than linger on as I am doing."

"Thousands of people," said the young man, "live and die like you, and are none the less happy."

"Ah!" said Will, "if there are thousands who would like, why should not one of them have my place?"

It was quite dark; there was a hanging lamp in the arbor which lit up the table and the faces of the speakers; and along the arch, the leaves upon the trellis stood out illuminated against the night sky, a pattern of transparent green upon a dusky purple. The fat young man rose, and, taking Will by the arm, led him out under the open heavens.

"Did you ever look at the stars?" he asked, pointing upwards.

"Often and often," answered Will.

"And do you know what they are?"

"I have fancied many things."

"They are worlds like ours," said the young man. "Some of them less; many of them a million times greater; and some of the least sparkles that you see are not only worlds, but whole clusters of worlds turning about each other in the midst of space. We do not know what there may be in any of them; perhaps the answer to all our difficulties or the cure of all our sufferings: and yet we can never reach them; not all the skill of the craftiest of men can fit out a ship for the nearest of these our neighbors, nor would the life of the most aged suffice for such a journey. When a great battle has been lost or a dear friend is dead, when we are hipped or in high spirits, there they are unweariedly shining overhead. We may stand down here a whole army of us together, and shout until we break our hearts, and not a whisper reaches them. We may climb the highest mountain, and we are no nearer them. All we can do is to stand down here in the garden and take off our hats; the starshine lights upon our heads, and where mine is a little bald, I dare say you can see it glisten in the darkness. The mountain and the mouse. That is like to be all we shall ever have to do with Arcturus or Aldebaran. Can you apply a parable?" he added, laying his hand upon Will's shoulder. "It is not the same thing as a reason, but usually vastly more convincing."

Will hung his head a little, and then raised it once more to heaven. The stars seemed to expand and emit a sharper brilliancy; and as he kept turning his eyes higher and higher, they seemed to increase in multitude under his gaze.

"I see," he said, turning to the young man. "We are in a rat-trap."

"Something of that size. Did you ever see a squirrel turning in a cage? and another squirrel sitting philosophically over his nuts? I needn't ask you which of them looked more of a fool."

II

THE PARSON'S MARJORY

After some years the old people died, both in one winter, very carefully tended by their adopted son, and very quietly mourned when they were gone. People who had heard of his roving fancies supposed he would hasten to sell the property, and go down the river to push his fortunes. But there was never any sign of such an intention on the part of Will. On the contrary, he had the inn set on a better footing, and hired a couple of servants to assist him in carrying it on; and there he settled down, a kind, talkative, inscrutable young man, six feet three in his stockings, with an iron constitution and a friendly voice. He soon began to take rank in the district as a bit of an oddity: it was not much to be wondered at from the first, for he was always full of notions, and kept calling the plainest common-sense in question; but what most raised the report upon him was the odd circumstance of his courtship with the parson's Marjory.

The parson's Marjory was a lass about nineteen, when Will would be about thirty; well enough looking, and much better educated than any other girl in that part of the country, as became her parentage. She held her head very high, and had already refused several offers of marriage with a grand air, which had got her hard names among the neighbors. For all that she was a good girl, and one that would have made any man well contented.

Will had never seen much of her; for although the church and parsonage were only two miles from his own door, he was never known to go there but on Sundays. It chanced, however, that the parsonage fell into disrepair, and had to be dismantled; and the parson and his daughter took lodgings for a month or so, on very much reduced terms, at Will's inn. Now, what with the inn, and the mill, and the old miller's savings, our friend was a man of substance; and besides that, he had a name for good temper and shrewdness, which make a capital portion in marriage; and so it was currently gossiped, among their well-wishers, that the parson and his daughter had not chosen their temporary lodging with their eyes shut. Will was about the last man in the world to be cajoled or frightened into marriage. You had only to look into his eyes, limpid and still like pools of water, and yet with a sort of clear light that seemed to come from within, and you would understand at once that here was one who knew his own mind, and would stand to it immovably. Marjory herself was no weakling by her looks, with strong, steady eyes and a resolute and quiet bearing. It might be a question whether she was not Will's match in steadfastness, after all, or which of them would rule the roast in marriage. But Marjory had never given it a thought, and accompanied her father with the most unshaken innocence and unconcern.

The season was still so early that Will's customers were few and far between; but the lilacs were already flowering, and the weather was so mild that the party took dinner under the trellis, with the noise of the river in their ears and the woods ringing about them with the songs of birds. Will soon began to take a particular pleasure in these dinners. The parson was rather a dull companion, with a habit of dozing at table; but nothing rude or cruel ever fell from his lips. And as for the parson's daughter, she suited her surroundings with the best grace imaginable; and whatever she said seemed so pat and pretty that Will conceived a great idea of her talents.

He could see her face, as she leaned forward, against a background of rising pinewoods; her eyes shone peaceably; the light lay around her hair like a kerchief; something that was hardly a smile rippled her pale cheeks, and Will could not contain himself from gazing on her in an agreeable dismay. She looked, even in her quietest moments, so complete in herself, and so quick with life down to her finger tips and the very skirts of her dress, that the remainder of created things became no more than a blot by comparison; and if Will glanced away from her to her surroundings, the trees looked inanimate and senseless, the clouds hung in heaven like dead things, and even the mountain tops were disenchanted. The whole valley could not compare in looks with this one girl.

Will was always observant in the society of his fellow creatures: but his observation became almost painfully eager in the case of Marjory. He listened to all she uttered, and read her eyes, at the same time, for the unspoken commentary. Many kind, simple, and sincere speeches found an echo in his heart. He became conscious of a soul beautifully poised upon itself, nothing doubting, nothing desiring, clothed in peace. It was not possible to separate her thoughts from her appearance. The turn of her wrist, the still sound of her voice, the light in her eyes, the lines of her body, fell in tune with her grave and gentle words, like the accompaniment that sustains and harmonizes the voice of the singer. Her influence was one thing, not to be divided or discussed, only to be felt with gratitude and joy. To Will, her presence recalled something of his childhood, and the thought of her took its place in his mind beside that of dawn, of running water, and of the earliest violets and lilacs. It is the property of things seen for the first time, or for the first time after long, like the flowers in spring, to reawaken in us the sharp edge of sense and that impression of mystic strangeness which otherwise passes out of life with the coming of years; but the sight of a loved face is what renews a man's character from the fountain upwards.

One day after dinner Will took a stroll among the firs; a grave beatitude possessed him from top to toe, and he kept smiling to himself and the landscape as he went. The river ran between the stepping-stones with a pretty wimple; a bird sang loudly in the wood; the hilltops looked immeasurably high, and as he glanced at them from time to time, seemed to contemplate his movements with a beneficent but awful curiosity. His way took him to the eminence which overlooked the plain; and there he sat down upon a stone, and fell into deep and pleasant thought. The plain lay abroad with its cities and silver river; everything was asleep, except a great eddy of birds which kept rising and falling and going round and round in the blue air. He repeated Marjory's name aloud, and the sound of it gratified his ear. He shut his eyes, and her image sprang up before him, quietly luminous and attended with good thoughts. The river might run forever; the birds fly higher and higher till they touched the stars. He saw it was empty bustle after all; for here, without stirring a foot, waiting patiently in his own narrow valley, he also had attained the better sunlight.

The next day Will made a sort of declaration across the dinner-table, while the parson was filling his pipe.

"Miss Marjory," he said, "I never knew anyone I liked so well as you. I am mostly a cold, unkindly sort of man; not from want of heart, but out of strangeness in my way of thinking; and people seem far away from me. 'Tis as if there were a circle round me, which kept every one out but you; I can hear the others talking and laughing; but you come quite close. Maybe, this is disagreeable to you?" he asked.

Marjory made no answer.

"Speak up, girl," said the parson.

"Nay, now," returned Will, "I wouldn't press her, parson. I feel tongue-tied myself, who am not used to it; and she's a woman, and little more than a child, when all is said. But for my part, as far as I can understand what people mean by it, I fancy I must be what they call in love. I do not wish to be held as committing myself; for I may be wrong; but that is how I believe things are with me. And if Miss Marjory should feel any otherwise on her part, mayhap she would be so kind as shake her head."

Marjory was silent, and gave no sign that she had heard.

"How is that, parson?" asked Will.

"The girl must speak," replied the parson, laying down his pipe. "Here's our neighbor who says he loves you, Madge. Do you love him, ay or no?"

"I think I do," said Marjory, faintly.

"Well then, that's all that could be wished!" cried Will, heartily. And he took her hand across the table, and held it a moment in both of his with great satisfaction.

"You must marry," observed the parson, replacing his pipe in his mouth.

"Is that the right thing to do, think you?" demanded Will.

"It is indispensable," said the parson.

"Very well," replied the wooer.

Two or three days passed away with great delight to Will, although a bystander might scarce have found it out. He continued to take his meals opposite Marjory, and to talk with her and gaze upon her in her father's presence; but he made no attempt to see her alone, nor in any other way changed his conduct towards her from what it had been since the beginning. Perhaps the girl was a little disappointed, and perhaps not unjustly; and yet if it had been enough to be always in the thought of another person, and so pervade and alter his whole life, she might have been thoroughly contented. For she was never out of Will's mind for an instant. He lay over the stream, and watched the dust of the eddy, and the poised fish, and straining weeds; he wandered out alone into the purple even, with all the blackbirds piping round him in the wood; he rose early in the morning, and saw the sky turn from gray to gold, and the light leap upon the hill-tops; and all the while he kept wondering if he had never seen such things before, or how it was that they should look so different now. The sound of his own mill-wheel, or of the wind among the trees, confounded and charmed his heart. The most enchanting thoughts presented themselves unbidden in his mind.

He was so happy that he could not sleep at night, and so restless that he could hardly sit still out of her company. And yet it seemed as if he avoided her rather than sought her out.

One day, as he was coming home from a ramble, Will found Marjory in the garden picking flowers, and as he came up with her, slackened his pace and continued walking by her side.

"You like flowers?" he said.

"Indeed I love them dearly," she replied. "Do you?"

"Why, no," said he, "not so much. They are a very small affair, when all is done. I can fancy people caring for them greatly, but not doing as you are just now."

"How?" she asked, pausing and looking up at him.

"Plucking them" said he. "They are a deal better off where they are, and look a deal prettier, if you go to that."

"I wish to have them for my own," she answered, "to carry them near my heart, and keep them in my room. They tempt me when they grow here; they seem to say, 'Come and do something with us;' but once I have cut them and put them by, the charm is laid, and I can look at them with quite an easy heart."

"You wish to possess them," replied Will, "in order to think no more about them. It's a bit like killing the goose with the golden eggs. It's a bit like what I wished to do when I was a boy. Because I had a fancy for looking out over the plain, I wished to go down there—where I couldn't look out over it any longer. Was not that fine reasoning? Dear, dear, if they only thought of it, all the world would do like me; and you would let your flowers alone, just as I stay up here in the mountains."

Suddenly he broke off sharp. "By the Lord!" he cried. And when she asked him what was wrong, he turned the question off, and walked away into the house with rather a humorous expression of face.

He was silent at table; and after the night had fallen and the stars had come out overhead, he walked up and down for hours in the court-yard and garden with an uneven pace. There was still a light in the window of Marjory's room: one little oblong patch of orange in a world of dark blue hills and silver starlight. Will's mind ran a great deal on the window; but his thoughts were not very lover-like. "There she is in her room," he thought, "and there are the stars overhead—a blessing upon both!" Both were good influences in his life; both soothed and braced him in his profound contentment with the world. And what more should he desire with either? The fat young man and his councils were so present to his mind, that he threw back his head, and, putting his hands before his mouth, shouted aloud to the populous heavens.

Whether from the position of his head or the sudden strain of the exertion, he seemed to see a momentary shock among the stars, and a diffusion of frosty light pass from one to another along the sky. At the same instant, a corner of the blind was lifted and lowered again at once. He laughed a loud ho-ho! "One and another!" thought Will. "The stars tremble and the blind goes up. Why, before Heaven, what a great magician I must be! Now if I were only a fool, should not I be in a pretty way?" And he went off to bed, chuckling to himself: "If I were only a fool!"

The next morning, pretty early, he saw her once more in the garden, and sought her out.

"I have been thinking about getting married," he began abruptly; "and after having turned it all over, I have made up my mind it's not worth while."

She turned upon him for a single moment; but his radiant, kindly appearance would, under the circumstances, have disconcerted an angel, and she looked down again upon the ground in silence. He could not see her tremble.

"I hope you don't mind," he went on, a little taken aback. "You ought not. I have turned it all over, and upon my soul there's nothing in it. We should never be one whit nearer than we are just now, and, if I am a wise man, nothing like so happy."

"It is unnecessary to go round about with me," she said. "I very well remember that you refused to commit yourself; and now that I see you were mistaken, and in reality have never cared for me, I can only feel sad that I have been so far misled."

"I ask your pardon," said Will stoutly; "you do not understand my meaning. As to whether I have ever loved you or not, I must leave that to others. But for one thing, my feeling is not changed; and for another, you may make it your boast that you have made my whole life and character something different from what they were. I mean what I say; no less. I do not think getting married is worth while. I would rather you went on living with your father, so that I could walk over and see you once, or maybe twice a week, as people go to church, and then we should both be all the happier between whiles. That's my notion. But I'll marry you if you will," he added.

"Do you know that you are insulting me?" she broke out.

"Not I, Marjory," said he; "if there is anything in a clear conscience, not I. I offer all my heart's best affection; you can take it or want it, though I suspect it's beyond either your power or mine to change what has once been done, and set me fancy-free. I'll marry you if you like; but I tell you again and again, it's not worth while, and we had best stay friends. Though I am a quiet man I have noticed a heap of things in my life. Trust in me, and take things as I propose; or, if you don't like that, say the word, and I'll marry you out of hand."

There was a considerable pause, and Will, who began to feel uneasy, began to grow angry in consequence.

"It seems you are too proud to say your mind," he said. "Believe me, that's a pity. A clean shrift makes simple living. Can a man be more downright or honorable to a woman than I have been? I have said my say, and given you your choice. Do you want me to marry you? or will you take my friendship, as I think best? or have you had enough of me for good? Speak out for the dear God's sake! You know your father told you a girl should speak her mind in these affairs."

She seemed to recover herself at that, turned without a word, walked rapidly through the garden, and disappeared into the house, leaving Will in some confusion as to the result. He walked up and down the garden, whistling softly to himself. Sometimes he stopped and contemplated the sky and hill-tops; sometimes he went down to the tail of the weir and sat there, looking foolishly in the water. All this dubiety and perturbation was so foreign to his nature and the life which he had resolutely chosen for himself, that he began to regret Marjory's arrival. "After all," he thought, "I was as happy as a man need be. I could come down here and watch my fishes all day long if I wanted: I was as settled and contented as my old mill."

Marjory came down to dinner, looking very trim and quiet; and no sooner were all three at table than she made her father a speech, with her eyes fixed upon her plate, but showing no other sign of embarrassment or distress.

"Father," she began, "Mr. Will and I have been talking things over. We see that we have each made a mistake about our feelings, and he has agreed, at my request, to give up all idea of marriage, and be no more than my very good friend, as in the past. You see, there is no shadow of a quarrel, and indeed I hope we shall see a great deal of him in the future, for his visits will always be welcome in our house. Of course, father, you will know best, but perhaps we should do better to leave Mr. Will's house for the present. I believe, after what has passed, we should hardly be agreeable inmates for some days."

Will, who had commanded himself with difficulty from the first, broke out upon this into an inarticulate noise, and raised one hand with an appearance of real dismay, as if he were about to interfere and contradict. But she checked him at once, looking up at him with a swift glance and an angry flush upon her cheek.

"You will perhaps have the good grace," she said, "to let me explain these matters for myself."

Will was put entirely out of countenance by her expression and the ring of her voice. He held his peace, concluding that there were some things about this girl beyond his comprehension, in which he was exactly right.

The poor parson was quite crestfallen. He tried to prove that this was no more than a true lovers' tiff, which would pass off before night;

and when he was dislodged from that position, he went on to argue that where there was no quarrel there could be no call for a separation; for the good man liked both his entertainment and his host. It was curious to see how the girl managed them, saying little all the time, and that very quietly, and yet twisting them round her finger and insensibly leading them wherever she would by feminine tact and generalship. It scarcely seemed to have been her doing—it seemed as if things had merely so fallen out—that she and her father took their departure that same afternoon in a farm cart, and went farther down the valley, to wait, until their own house was ready for them, in another hamlet. But Will had been observing closely, and was well aware of her dexterity and resolution. When he found himself alone he had a great many curious matters to turn over in his mind. He was very sad and solitary, to begin with. All the interest had gone out of his life, and he might look up at the stars as long as he pleased, he somehow failed to find support or consolation. And then he was in such a turmoil of spirit about Marjory. He had been puzzled and irritated at her behavior, and yet he could not keep himself from admiring it. He thought he recognized a fine, perverse angel in that still soul which he had never hitherto suspected; and though he saw it was an influence that would fit but ill with his own life of artificial calm, he could not keep himself from ardently desiring to possess it. Like a man who has lived among shadows and now meets the sun, he was both pained and delighted.

As the days went forward he passed from one extreme to another; now pluming himself on the strength of his determination, now despising his timid and silly caution. The former was, perhaps, the true thought of his heart, and represented the regular tenor of the man's reflections; but the latter burst forth from time to time with an unruly violence, and then he would forget all consideration, and go up and down his house or garden or walk among the firwoods like one who is beside himself with remorse. To equable, steady-minded Will this state of matters was intolerable; and he determined, at whatever cost, to bring it to an end. So, one warm summer afternoon he put on his best clothes, took a thorn switch in his hand, and set out down the valley by the river. As soon as he had taken his determination, he had regained at a bound his customary peace of heart, and he enjoyed the bright weather and the variety of the scene without any admixture of alarm or unpleasant eagerness. It was nearly the same to him how the matter turned out. If she accepted him, he would have to marry her this time, which perhaps was all for the best. If she refused him, he would have done his utmost, and might follow his own way in the future with an untroubled conscience. He hoped, on the whole, she would refuse him; and then, again, as he saw the brown roof which sheltered her, peeping through some willows at an angle of the stream, he was half inclined to reverse the wish, and more than half ashamed of himself for this infirmity of purpose.

Marjory seemed glad to see him, and gave him her hand without affectation or delay.

"I have been thinking about this marriage," he began.

"So have I," she answered. "And I respect you more and more for a very wise man. You understood me better than I understood myself; and I am now quite certain that things are all for the best as they are."

"At the same time—" ventured Will.

"You must be tired," she interrupted. "Take a seat and let me fetch you a glass of wine. The afternoon is so warm; and I wish you not to be displeased with your visit. You must come quite often; once a week, if you can spare the time; I am always so glad to see my friends."

"Oh, very well," thought Will to himself. "It appears I was right after all." And he paid a very agreeable visit, walked home again in capital spirits, and gave himself no further concern about the matter.

For nearly three years Will and Marjory continued on these terms, seeing each other once or twice a week without any word of love between them; and for all that time I believe Will was nearly as happy as a man can be. He rather stinted himself the pleasure of seeing her; and he would often walk half-way over to the parsonage, and then back again, as if to whet his appetite. Indeed there was one corner of the road, whence he could see the church-spire wedged into a crevice of the valley between sloping firwoods, with a triangular snatch of plain by way of background, which he greatly affected as a place to sit and moralize in before returning homewards; and the peasants got so much into the habit of finding him there in the twilight that they gave it the name of "Will o' the Mill's Corner."

At the end of the three years Marjory played him a sad trick by suddenly marrying somebody else. Will kept his countenance bravely, and merely remarked that, for as little as he knew of women, he had acted very prudently in not marrying her himself three years before. She plainly knew very little of her own mind, and, in spite of a deceptive manner, was as fickle and flighty as the rest of them. He had to congratulate himself on an escape, he said, and would take a higher opinion of his own wisdom in consequence. But at heart, he was reasonably displeased, moped a good deal for a month or two, and fell away in flesh, to the astonishment of the serving-lads.

It was perhaps a year after this marriage that Will was awakened late one night by the sound of a horse galloping on the road, followed by precipitate knocking at the inn door. He opened his window and saw a farm servant, mounted and holding a led horse by the bridle, who told him to make what haste he could and go along with him; for Marjory was dying, and had sent urgently to fetch him to her bedside. Will was no horseman, and made so little speed upon the way that the poor young wife was very near her end before he arrived. But they had some minutes' talk in private, and he was present and wept very bitterly while she breathed her last.

III

DEATH

Year after year went away into nothing, with great explosions and outcries in the cities on the plain; red revolt springing up and being suppressed in blood, battle swaying hither and thither, patient astronomers in observatory towers picking out and christening new stars, plays being performed in lighted theaters, people being carried into hospitals on stretchers, and all the usual turmoil and agitation of men's lives in crowded centers. Up in Will's valley only the winds and seasons made an epoch; the fish hung in the swift stream, the birds circled overhead, the pine-tops rustled underneath the stars, the tall hills stood over all; and Will went to and fro minding his wayside inn, until the snow began to thicken on his head. His heart was young and vigorous; and if his pulses kept a sober time, they still beat strong and steady in his wrists. He carried a ruddy stain on either cheek, like a ripe apple; he stooped a little, but his step was still firm; and his sinewy hands were reached out to all men with a friendly pressure. His face was covered with those wrinkles which are got in open air, and which, rightly looked at, are no more than a sort of permanent sunburning; such wrinkles heighten the stupidity of stupid faces; but to a person like Will, with his clear eyes and smiling mouth, only give another charm by testifying to a simple and easy life. His talk was full of wise sayings. He had a taste for other people; and other people had a taste for him. When the valley was full of tourists in the season, there were merry nights in Will's arbor; and his views, which seemed whimsical to his neighbors, were often enough admired by learned people out of towns and colleges. Indeed, he had a very noble old age, and grew daily better known; so that his fame was heard of in the cities of the plain; and young men who had been summer travelers spoke together in cafes of Will o' the Mill and his rough philosophy. Many and many an invitation, you may be sure, he had; but nothing could tempt him from his upland valley. He would shake his head and smile over his tobacco pipe with a deal of meaning. "You come too late," he would answer. "I am a dead man now: I have lived and died already. Fifty years ago you would have brought my heart into my mouth; and now you do not even tempt me. But that is the object of long living, that man should cease to care about life." And again: "There is only one difference between a long life and a good dinner; that, in the dinner, the sweets come last." Or once more: "When I was a boy, I was a bit puzzled, and hardly knew whether it was myself or the world that was curious and worth looking into. Now, I know it is myself, and stick to that."

He never showed any symptom of frailty, but kept stalwart and firm to the last; but they say he grew less talkative towards the end, and would listen to other people by the hour in an amused and sympathetic silence. Only, when he did speak, it was more to the point and more charged with old experience. He drank a bottle of wine gladly; above all, at sunset on the hilltop or quite late at night under the stars in the arbor. The sight of something attractive and unattainable seasoned his enjoyment, he would say; and he professed he had lived long enough to admire a candle all the more when he could compare it with a planet.

One night, in his seventy-second year, he awoke in bed in such uneasiness of body and mind that he arose and dressed himself and went out to meditate in the arbor. It was pitch dark, without a star; the river was swollen, and the wet woods and meadows loaded the air with perfume. It had thundered during the day, and it promised more thunder for the morrow. A murky, stifling night for a man of seventy-two! Whether it was the weather or the wakefulness, or some little touch of fever in his old limbs, Will's mind was besieged by tumultuous and crying memories. His boyhood, the night with the fat young man, the death of his adopted parents, the summer days with Marjory, and many of those small circumstances, which seem nothing to another, and are yet the very gist of a man's own life to himself—things seen, words heard, looks misconstrued—arose from their forgotten corners and usurped his attention. The dead themselves were with him, not merely taking part in this thin show of memory that defiled before his brain, but revisiting his bodily senses as they do in profound and vivid dreams. The fat young man leaned his elbows on the table opposite; Marjory came and went with an apronful of flowers between the garden and the arbor; he could hear the old parson knocking out his pipe or blowing his resonant nose. The tide of his consciousness ebbed and flowed: he was sometimes half asleep and drowned in his recollections of the past; and sometimes he was broad awake, wondering at himself. But about the middle of the night he was startled by the voice of the dead miller calling to him out of the house as he used to do on the arrival of custom. The hallucination was so perfect that Will sprang from his seat and stood listening for the summons to be repeated; and as he listened he became conscious of another noise besides the brawling of the river and the ringing in his feverish ears. It was like the stir of horses and the creaking of harness, as though a carriage with an impatient team had been brought up upon the road before the courtyard gate. At such an hour, upon this rough and dangerous pass, the supposition was no better than absurd; and Will dismissed it from his mind, and resumed his seat upon the arbor chair; and sleep closed over him again like running water. He was once again awakened by the dead miller's call, thinner and more spectral than before; and once again he heard the noise of an equipage upon the road. And so thrice and four times, the same dream, or the same fancy, presented itself to his senses; until at length, smiling to himself as when one humors a nervous child, he proceeded towards the gate to set his uncertainty at rest.

From the arbor to the gate was no great distance, and yet it took Will some time; it seemed as if the dead thickened around him in the court, and crossed his path at every step. For, first, he was suddenly surprised by an overpowering sweetness of heliotropes; it was as if his garden had been planted with this flower from end to end, and the hot, damp night had drawn forth all their perfumes in a breath. Now the heliotrope had been Marjory's favorite flower, and since her death not one of them had ever been planted in Will's ground.

"I must be going crazy," he thought. "Poor Marjory and her heliotropes!"

And with that he raised his eyes towards the window that had once been hers. If he had been bewildered before, he was now almost terrified; for there was a light in the room; the window was an orange oblong as of yore; and the corner of the blind was lifted and let fall as on the night when he stood and shouted to the stars in his perplexity. The illusion only endured an instant; but it left him somewhat unmanned, rubbing his eyes and staring at the outline of the house and the black night behind it. While he thus stood, and it seemed as if he must have stood there quite a long time, there came a renewal of the noises on the road: and he turned in time to meet a stranger, who was advancing to meet him across the court. There was something like the outline of a great carriage discernible on the road behind the stranger, and, above that, a few black pine-tops, like so many plumes.

"Master Will?" asked the newcomer, in brief military fashion.

"That same, sir," answered Will. "Can I do anything to serve you?"

"I have heard you much spoken of, Master Will," returned the other; "much spoken of, and well. And though I have both hands full of business, I wish to drink a bottle of wine with you in your arbor. Before I go, I shall introduce myself."

Will led the way to the trellis, and got a lamp lighted and a bottle uncorked. He was not altogether unused to such complimentary interviews, and hoped little enough from this one, being schooled by many disappointments. A sort of cloud had settled on his wits and prevented him from remembering the strangeness of the hour. He moved like a person in his sleep; and it seemed as if the lamp caught fire and the bottle came uncorked with the facility of thought. Still, he had some curiosity about the appearance of his visitor, and tried in vain to turn the light into his face; either he handled the lamp clumsily, or there was a dimness over his eyes; but he could make out little more than a shadow at the table with him. He stared and stared at this shadow, as he wiped out the glasses, and began to feel cold and strange about the heart.

The silence weighed upon him, for he could hear nothing now, not even the river, but the drumming of his own arteries in his ears.

"Here's to you," said the stranger, roughly.

"Here is my service, sir," replied Will, sipping his wine, which somehow tasted oddly.

"I understand you are a very positive fellow," pursued the stranger. Will made answer with a smile of some satisfaction and a little nod.

"So am I," continued the other; "and it is the delight of my heart to tramp on people's corns. I will have nobody positive but myself: not one. I have crossed the whims, in my time, of kings and generals and great artists. And what would you say," he went on, "if I had come up here on purpose to cross yours?"

Will had it on his tongue to make a sharp rejoinder; but the politeness of an old innkeeper prevailed; and he held his peace and made answer with a civil gesture of the hand.

"I have," said the stranger. "And if I did not hold you in a particular esteem, I should make no words about the matter. It appears you pride yourself on staying where you are. You mean to stick by your inn. Now I mean you shall come for a turn with me in my barouche; and before this bottle's empty, so you shall."

"That would be an odd thing, to be sure," replied Will, with a chuckle. "Why, sir, I have grown here like an old oak-tree; the Devil himself could hardly root me up: and for all I perceive you are a very entertaining old gentleman, I would wager you another bottle you lose your pains with me."

The dimness of Will's eyesight had been increasing all this while; but he was somehow conscious of a sharp and chilling scrutiny which irritated and yet overmastered him.

"You need not think," he broke out suddenly, in an explosive, febrile manner that startled and alarmed himself, "that I am a stay-at-home because I fear anything under God. God knows I am tired enough of it all; and when the time comes for a longer journey than ever you dream of, I reckon I shall find myself prepared."

The stranger emptied his glass and pushed it away from him. He looked down for a little, and then, leaning over the table, tapped Will three times upon the forearm with a single finger. "The time has come!" he said solemnly.

An ugly thrill spread from the spot he touched. The tones of his voice were dull and startling, and echoed strangely in Will's heart.

"I beg your pardon," he said, with some discomposure. "What do you mean?"

"Look at me, and you will find your eyesight swim. Raise your hand; it is dead-heavy. This is your last bottle of wine, Master Will, and your last night upon the earth."

"You are a doctor?" quavered Will.

"The best that ever was," replied the other; "for I cure both mind and body with the same prescription. I take away all pain and I forgive all sins; and where my patients have gone wrong in life, I smooth out all complications and set them free again upon their feet."

"I have no need of you," said Will.

"A time comes for all men, Master Will," replied the doctor, "when the helm is taken out of their hands. For you, because you were prudent and quiet, it has been long of coming, and you have had long to discipline yourself for its reception. You have seen what is to be seen about your mill; you have sat close all your days like a hare in its form; but now that is at an end; and," added the doctor, getting on his feet, "you must arise and come with me."

"You are a strange physician," said Will, looking steadfastly upon his guest.

"I am a natural law," he replied, "and people call me Death."

"Why did you not tell me so at first?" cried Will. "I have been waiting for you these many years. Give me your hand, and welcome."

"Lean upon my arm," said the stranger, "for already your strength abates. Lean on me as heavily as you need; for though I am old, I am very strong. It is but three steps to my carriage, and there all your trouble ends. Why, Will," he added, "I have been yearning for you as if you were my own son; and of all the men that ever I came for in my long days, I have come for you most gladly. I am caustic, and sometimes offend people at first sight; but I am a good friend at heart to such as you."

"Since Marjory was taken," returned Will, "I declare before God you were the only friend I had to look for."

So the pair went arm-in-arm across the courtyard.

One of the servants awoke about this time and heard the noise of horses pawing before he dropped asleep again; all down the valley that night there was a rushing as of a smooth and steady wind descending towards the plain; and when the world rose next morning, sure enough Will o' the Mill had gone at last upon his travels.

THE MAN WHO WOULD BE KING

By Rudyard Kipling

[Rudyard Kipling was born in 1865 in Bombay, India. He was educated in England (Westward Ho, Devonshire), but returned to India at seventeen and went into newspaper work. He left India in 1890, lived for a short period in Vermont, and finally returned to England and established a permanent home in Sussex, not far from the site of the Battle of Hastings. While Mr. Kipling has done distinguished work in the form of the novel, notably in *The Light That Failed*, and *Kim*, his permanent fame will probably rest upon his poetry and short stories. Among his collections of short stories are *Plain Tales from the Hills* (1887), *The Day's Work* (1898), and *Rewards and Fairies* (1910). *The Man Who Would Be King* is one of the best of Kipling's early stories. It was written in India when the author was about twenty-two, and included in *The Phantom 'Rickshaw and Other Stories* (1888).]

"Brother to a prince and fellow to a beggar if he be found worthy."

THE law, as quoted, lays down a fair conduct of life, and one not easy to follow. I have been fellow to a beggar again and again under circumstances which prevented either of us finding out whether the other was worthy. I have still to be brother to a prince, though I once came near to kinship with what might have been a veritable king and was promised the reversion of a kingdom—army, law-courts, revenue and policy all complete. But today I greatly fear that my king is dead, and if I want a crown I must go and hunt it for myself.

The beginning of everything was in a railway train upon the road to Mhow from Ajmir. There had been a Deficit in the Budget, which necessitated traveling not second-class, which is only half as dear as first-class, but by intermediate, which is very awful indeed. There are no cushions in the intermediate class, and the population are either intermediate, which is Eurasian, or native, which for a long night journey is nasty, or loafer, which is amusing though intoxicated. Intermediates do not patronize refreshment-rooms. They carry their food in bundles and pots, and buy sweets from the native sweetmeat sellers, and drink the roadside water. That is why in the hot weather intermediates are taken out of the carriages dead, and in all weathers are most properly looked down upon.

My particular intermediate happened to be empty till I reached Nasirabad, when a huge gentleman in shirt-sleeves entered and, following the custom of intermediates, passed the time of day. He was a wanderer and a vagabond like myself, but with an educated taste for whisky. He told tales of things he had seen and done, of out-of-the-way corners of the Empire into which he had penetrated, and of adventures in which he risked his life for a few days' food. "If India was filled with men like you and me, not knowing more than the crows where they'd get their next day's rations, it isn't seventy millions of revenue the land would be paying—it's seven hundred millions," said he; and as I looked at his mouth and chin I was disposed to agree with him. We talked politics—the politics of loaferdom that sees things from the underside where the lath and plaster is not smoothed off—and we talked postal arrangements because my friend wanted to send a telegram back from the next station to Ajmir, which is the turning-off place from the Bombay to the Mhow line as you travel westward. My friend had no money beyond eight annas which he wanted for dinner, and I had no money at all, owing to the hitch in the Budget before mentioned. Further, I was going into a wilderness where, though I should resume touch with the Treasury, there were no telegraph offices. I was, therefore, unable to help him in any way.

"We might threaten a station-master to make him send a wire on tick," said my friend, "but that'd mean inquiries for you and for me, and I've got my hands full these days. Did you say you were traveling back along this line within any days?"

"Within ten," I said.

"Can't you make it eight?" said he. "Mine is rather urgent business."

"I can send your telegram within ten days if that will serve you," I said.

"I couldn't trust the wire to fetch him now I think of it. It's this way. He leaves Delhi on the 23d for Bombay. That means he'll be running through Ajmir about the night of the 23d."

"But I'm going into the Indian Desert," I explained.

"Well *and* good," said he. "You'll be changing at Marwar Junction to get into Jodhpore territory—you must do that—and he'll be coming through Marwar Junction in the early morning of the 24th by the Bombay Mail. Can you be at Marwar Junction on that time? 'Twon't be inconveniencing you, because I know that there's precious few pickings to be got out of those Central India States—even though you pretend to be correspondent of the *Backwoodsman*."

"Have you ever tried that trick?" I asked.

"Again and again, but the Residents find you out, and then you get escorted to the Border before you've time to get your knife into them. But about my friend here. I *must* give him word o' mouth to tell him what's come to me or else he won't know where to go. I would take it more than kind of you if you was to come out of Central India in time to catch him at Marwar Junction, and say to him: 'He has gone south for the week.' He'll know what that means. He's a big man with a red beard, and a great swell he is. You'll find him sleeping like a gentleman with all his luggage round him in a second-class compartment. But don't you be afraid. Slip down the window and say: 'He has gone south for the week,' and he'll tumble. It's only cutting your time of stay in those parts by two days. I ask you as a stranger—going to the west," he said with emphasis.

"Where have *you* come from," said I.

"From the East," said he, "and I am hoping that you will give him the message on the square—for the sake of my mother as well as your own."

Englishmen are not usually softened by appeals to the memory of their mothers, but for certain reasons, which will be fully apparent, I saw fit to agree.

"It's more than a little matter," said he, "and that's why I ask you to do it—and now I know that I can depend on you doing it. A second-class carriage at Marwar Junction, and a red-haired man asleep in it. You'll be sure to remember. I get out at the next station, and I must hold on there till he comes or sends me what I want."

"I'll give the message if I catch him," I said, "and for the sake of your mother as well as mine I'll give a word of advice. Don't try to run the Central India States just now as the correspondent of the *Backwoodsman*. There's a real one knocking about here, and it might lead to trouble."

"Thank you," said he simply, "and when will the swine be gone? I can't starve because he's ruining my work. I wanted to get hold of the Degumber Rajah down here about his father's widow, and give him a jump."

"What did he do to his father's widow, then?"

"Filled her up with red pepper and slippered her to death as she hung from a beam. I found that out myself and I'm the only man that would dare going into the state to get hush-money for it. They'll try to poison me, same as they did in Chortumna when I went on the loot there. But you'll give the man at Marwar Junction my message?"

He got out at a little roadside station, and I reflected. I had heard, more than once, of men personating correspondents of newspapers and bleeding small native states with threats of exposure, but I had never met any of the caste before. They lead a hard life, and generally die with great suddenness. The native states have a wholesome horror of English newspapers, which may throw light on their peculiar methods of government, and do their best to choke correspondents with champagne, or drive them out of their mind with four-in-hand barouches. They do not understand that nobody cares a straw for the internal administration of native states so long as oppression and crime are kept within decent limits, and the ruler is not drugged, drunk or diseased from one end of the year to the other. Native states were created by

Providence in order to supply picturesque scenery, tigers and tall writing. They are the dark places of the earth, full of unimaginable cruelty, touching the Railway and the Telegraph on one side, and on the other the days of Harun-al-Raschid. When I left the train I did business with divers kings, and in eight days passed through many changes of life. Sometimes I wore dress clothes and consorted with princes and politicals, drinking from crystal and eating from silver. Sometimes I lay out upon the ground and devoured what I could get from a plate made of a flapjack, and drank the running water, and slept under the same rug as my servant. It was all in the day's work.

Then I headed for the Great Indian Desert upon the proper date, as I had promised, and the night mail set me down at Marwar Junction, where a funny little happy-go-lucky, native-managed railway runs to Jodhpore. The Bombay Mail from Delhi makes a short halt at Marwar. She arrived as I got in, and I had just time to hurry to her platform and go down the carriages. There was only one second-class on the train. I slipped the window and looked down upon a flaming red beard, half-covered by a railway rug. That was my man, fast asleep, and I dug him gently in the ribs. He woke with a grunt and I saw his face in the light of the lamps. It was a great and shining face.

"Tickets again?" said he.

"No," said I. "I am to tell you that he is gone south for the week. He is gone south for the week!"

The train had begun to move out. The red man rubbed his eyes. "He has gone south for the week," he repeated. "Now that's just like his impidence. Did he say that I was to give you anything? 'Cause I won't."

"He didn't," I said and dropped away, and watched the red lights die out in the dark. It was horribly cold because the wind was blowing off the sands. I climbed into my own train—not an intermediate carriage this time—and went to sleep.

If the man with the beard had given me a rupee I should have kept it as a memento of a rather curious affair. But the consciousness of having done my duty was my only reward.

Later on I reflected that two gentlemen like my friends could not do any good if they foregathered and personated correspondents of newspapers, and might, if they "stuck up" one of the little rat-trap states of Central India or Southern Rajputana, get themselves into serious difficulties. I therefore took some trouble to describe them as accurately as I could remember to people who would be interested in deporting them: and succeeded, so I was later informed, in having them headed back from the Degumber borders.

Then I became respectable, and returned to an office where there were no kings and no incidents except the daily manufacture of a newspaper. A newspaper office seems to attract every conceivable sort of person to the prejudice of discipline. Zenana-mission ladies arrive, and beg that the editor will instantly abandon all his duties to describe a Christian prize-giving in a back slum of a perfectly inaccessible village; colonels who have been overpassed for commands sit down and sketch the outline of a series of ten, twelve or twenty-four leading articles on Seniority versus Selection; missionaries wish to know why they have not been permitted to escape from their regular vehicles of abuse and swear at a brother missionary under special patronage of the editorial we; stranded theatrical companies troop up to explain that they cannot pay for their advertisements, but on their return from New Zealand or Tahiti will do so with interest; inventors of patent punkah-pulling machines, carriage couplings and unbreakable swords and axletrees call with specifications in their pockets and hours at their disposal; tea companies enter and elaborate their prospectuses with the office pens; secretaries of ball committees clamor to have the glories of their last dance more fully expounded; strange ladies rustle in and say: "I want a hundred lady's cards printed *at once*, please," which is manifestly part of an editor's duty; and every dissolute ruffian that ever tramped the Grand Trunk Road makes it his business to ask for employment as a proof-reader. And, all the time, the telephone bell is ringing madly, and kings are being killed on the Continent, and empires are saying "You're another," and Mister Gladstone is calling down brimstone upon the British Dominions, and the little black copy boys are whining "*kaa-pi chay-ha-yeh*" (copy wanted) like tired bees, and most of the paper is as blank as Modred's shield.

But that is the amusing part of the year. There are other six months wherein none ever come to call, and the thermometer walks inch by inch up to the top of the glass, and the office is darkened to just above reading light, and the press machines are red-hot to touch, and nobody writes anything but accounts of amusements in the hill-stations, or obituary notices. Then the telephone becomes a tinkling terror, because it tells you of the sudden deaths of men and women that you knew intimately, and the prickly heat covers you as with a garment, and you sit down and write: "A slight increase of sickness is reported from the Khuda Janta Khan District. The outbreak is purely sporadic in its nature, and thanks to the energetic efforts of the district authorities, is now almost at an end. It is, however, with deep regret we record the death, etc."

Then the sickness really breaks out, and the less recording and reporting the better for the peace of the subscribers. But the empires and kings continue to divert themselves as selfishly as before, and the foreman thinks that a daily paper really ought to come out once in twenty-four hours, and all the people at the hill-stations in the middle of their amusements say: "Good gracious! Why can't the paper be sparkling? I'm sure there's plenty going on up here."

That is the dark half of the moon, and as the advertisements say, "must be experienced to be appreciated."

It was in that season, and a remarkably evil season that the paper began running the last issue of the week on Saturday night, which is to say Sunday morning, after the custom of a London paper. This was a great convenience, for immediately after the paper was put to bed the dawn would lower the thermometer from 96° to almost 84° for half an hour, and in that chill—you have no idea how cold is 84° on the grass until you begin to pray for it—a very tired man could set off to sleep ere the heat roused him.

One Saturday night it was my pleasant duty to put the paper to bed alone. A king or courtier or a courtesan or a community was going to die or get a new constitution, or do something that was important on the other side of the world, and the paper was to be held open till the latest possible minute in order to catch the telegram. It was a pitchy black night, as stifling as a June night can be, and the *loo*, the red-hot wind from the westward, was booming among the tinder-dry trees and pretending that the rain was on its heels. Now and again a spot of almost boiling water would fall on the dust with the flop of a frog, but all our weary world knew that was only pretense. It was a shade cooler in the press-room than the office, so I sat there while the type clicked and clicked, and the night-jars hooted at the windows, and the all but naked compositors wiped the sweat from their foreheads and called for water. The thing that was keeping us back, whatever it was, would not come off, though the *loo* dropped and the last type was set, and the whole round earth stood still in the choking heat, with its finger on its lip, to await the event. I drowsed, and wondered whether the telegraph was a blessing, and whether this dying man or struggling people was aware of the inconvenience the delay was causing. There was no special reason beyond the heat and worry to make tension, but as the clock hands crept up to three o'clock and the machines spun their flywheels two and three times to see that all was in order, before I said the word that would set them off, I could have shrieked aloud.

Then the roar and rattle of the wheels shivered the quiet into little bits. I rose to go away, but two men in white clothes stood in front of me. The first one said: "It's him!" The second said: "So it is!" And they both laughed almost as loudly as the machinery roared, and mopped their foreheads. "We see there was a light burning across the road and we were sleeping in that ditch there for coolness, and I said to my friend here: 'The office is open. Let's come along and speak to him as turned us back from the Degumber State,'" said the smaller of the two. He was the man I had met in the Mhow train, and his fellow was the red-bearded man of Marwar Junction. There was no mistaking the eyebrows of the one or the beard of the other.

I was not pleased, because I wished to go to sleep, not to squabble with loafers. "What do you want?" I asked.

"Half an hour's talk with you cool and comfortable, in the office," said the red-bearded man. "We'd *like* some drink—the contrack doesn't begin yet, Peachey, so you needn't look—but what we really want is advice. We don't want money. We ask you as a favor, because you did us a bad turn about Degumber."

I led from the press-room to the stifling office with the maps on the walls, and the red-haired man rubbed his hands. "That's something like," said he. "This was the proper shop to come to. Now, sir, let me introduce to you Brother Peachey Carnehan, that's him, and Brother Daniel Dravot, that is *me*, and the less said about our professions the better, for we have been most things in our time. Soldier, sailor, compositor, photographer, proofreader, street preacher, and correspondents of the *Backwoodsman*, when we thought the paper wanted one. Carnehan is sober, and so am I. Look at us first and see that's sure. It will save you cutting into my talk. We'll take one of your cigars apiece, and you shall see us light it."

I watched the test. The men were absolutely sober, so I gave them each a tepid peg.

"Well *and* good," said Carnehan of the eyebrows, wiping the froth from his mustache. "Let me talk now, Dan. We have been all over India, mostly on foot. We have been boiler-fitters, engine-drivers, petty contractors, and all that, and we have decided that India isn't big enough for such as us."

They certainly were too big for the office. Dravot's beard seemed to fill half the room and Carnehan's shoulders the other half, as they sat on the big table. Carnehan continued: "The country isn't half worked out because they that governs it won't let you touch it. They spend all their blessed time in governing it, and you can't lift a spade, nor chip a rock, nor look for oil, nor anything like that without all the Government saying: 'Leave it alone and let us govern.' Therefore, such as it is, we will let it alone, and go away to some other place where a man isn't crowded and can come to his own. We are not little men, and there is nothing that we are afraid of except drink, and we have signed a contrack on that. *Therefore* we are going away to be kings."

"Kings in our own right," muttered Dravot.

"Yes, of course," I said. "You've been tramping in the sun, and it's a very warm night, and hadn't you better sleep over the notion? Come tomorrow."

"Neither drunk nor sunstruck," said Dravot. "We have slept over the notion half a year, and require to see books and atlases, and we have decided that there is only one place now in the world that two strong men can Sar-a-*whack*. They call it Kafiristan. By my reckoning it's the top-hand corner of Afghanistan, not more than three hundred miles from Peshawar. They have two-and-thirty heathen idols there, and we'll be the thirty-third. It's a mountainous country, and the women of those parts are very beautiful."

"But that is provided against in the contrack," said Carnehan. "Neither women nor liquor, Daniel."

"And that's all we know, except that no one has gone there and they fight, and in any place where they fight a man who knows how to drill men can always be a king. We shall go to those parts and say to any king we find: 'D'you want to vanquish your foes?' and we will show him how to drill men; for that we know better than anything else. Then we will subvert that king and seize his throne and establish a dy-nasty."

"You'll be cut to pieces before you're fifty miles across the border," I said. "You have to travel through Afghanistan to get to that country. It's one mass of mountains and peaks and glaciers, and no Englishman has been through it. The people are utter brutes, and even if you reached them you couldn't do anything."

"That's more like," said Carnehan. "If you could think us a little more mad we would be more pleased. We have come to you to know about this country, to read a book about it, and to be shown maps. We want you to tell us that we are fools and to show us your books."

He turned to the bookcases.

"Are you at all in earnest?" I said.

"A little," said Dravot sweetly. "As big a map as you have got, even if it's all blank where Kafiristan is, and any books you've got. We can read, though we aren't very educated."

I uncased the big thirty-two-miles-to-the-inch map of India, and two smaller Frontier maps, hauled down volume Inf-Kan of the *Encyclopædia Britannica*, and the men consulted them.

"See here!" said Dravot, his thumb on the map. "Up to Jagdallak, Peachey and me know the road. We was there with Roberts's Army. We'll have to turn off to the right at Jagdallak through Laghmann territory. Then we get among the hills—fourteen thousand feet—fifteen thousand—it will be cold work there, but it don't look very far on the map."

I handed him Wood on the *Sources of the Oxus*. Carnehan was deep in the *Encyclopædia*.

"They're a mixed lot," said Dravot reflectively; "and it won't help us to know the names of their tribes. The more tribes the more they'll fight, and the better for us. From Jagdallak to Ashang. H'mm!"

"But all the information about the country is as sketchy and inaccurate as can be," I protested. "No one knows anything about it really. Here's the file of the *United Services' Institute*. Read what Bellew says."

"Blow Bellew!" said Carnehan. "Dan, they're an all-fired lot of heathens, but this book here says they think they're related to us English."

I smoked while the men pored over Raverty, Wood, the maps and the *Encyclopædia*.

"There is no use your waiting," said Dravot politely. "It's about four o'clock now. We'll go before six o'clock if you want to sleep, and we won't steal any of the papers. Don't you sit up. We're two harmless lunatics, and if you come tomorrow evening down to the Serai we'll say good-by to you."

"You *are* two fools," I answered. "You'll be turned back at the frontier or cut up the minute you set foot in Afghanistan. Do you want any money or a recommendation down-country? I can help you to the chance of work next week."

"Next week we shall be hard at work ourselves, thank you," said Dravot. "It isn't so easy being a king as it looks. When we've got our kingdom in going order we'll let you know, and you can come up and help us to govern it."

"Would two lunatics make a contrack like that?" said Carnehan, with subdued pride, showing me a greasy half-sheet of note-paper on which was written the following. I copied it, then and there, as a curiosity:

This Contract between me and you persuing witnesseth in the name of God—Amen and so forth.

(One)   That me and you will settle this matter together: *i.e.*, to be Kings of Kafiristan.

(Two)   That you and me will not, while this matter is being settled, look at any liquor, nor any woman black, white or brown, so as to get mixed up with one or the other harmful.

(Three)   That we conduct ourselves with dignity and discretion, and if one of us gets into trouble the other will stay by him.

Signed by you and me this day.

Peachey Taliaferro Carnehan.

Daniel Dravot.

Both Gentlemen at Large.

"There was no need for the last article," said Carnehan, blushing modestly; "but it looks regular. Now you know the sort of men that loafers are—we *are* loafers, Dan, until we get out of India—and *do* you think that we would sign a contrack like that unless we was in earnest? We have kept away from the two things that make life worth having."

"You won't enjoy your lives much longer if you are going to try this idiotic adventure. Don't set the office on fire," I said, "and go away before nine o'clock."

I left them still poring over the maps and making notes on the back of the "contrack." "Be sure to come down to the Serai tomorrow," were their parting words.

The Kumharsen Serai is the great four-square sink of humanity where the strings of camels and horses from the North load and unload. All the nationalities of Central Asia may be found there, and most of the folk of India proper. Balkh and Bokhara there meet Bengal and Bombay, and try to draw eye-teeth. You can buy ponies, turquoises, Persian pussy-cats, saddle-bags, fat-tailed sheep and musk in the Kumharsen Serai, and get many strange things for nothing. In the afternoon I went down there to see whether my friends intended to keep their word or were lying about drunk.

A priest attired in fragments of ribbons and rags stalked up to me, gravely twisting a child's paper whirligig. Behind him was his servant bending under the load of a crate of mud toys. The two were loading up two camels, and the inhabitants of the Serai watched them with shrieks of laughter.

"The priest is mad," said a horse-dealer to me. "He is going up to Kabul to sell toys to the Amir. He will either be raised to honor or have his head cut off. He came in here this morning and has been behaving madly ever since."

"The witless are under the protection of God," stammered a flat-cheeked Usbeg in broken Hindi. "They foretell future events."

"Would they could have foretold that my caravan would have been cut up by the Shinwaris almost within shadow of the Pass!" grunted the Eusufzai agent of a Rajputana trading-house whose goods had been feloniously diverted into the hands of other robbers just across the border, and whose misfortunes were the laughing-stock of the bazaar. "Ohé, priest, whence come you and whither do you go?"

"From Roum have I come," shouted the priest, waving his whirligig; "from Roum, blown by the breath of a hundred devils across the sea! O thieves, robbers, liars, the blessing of Pir Khan on pigs, dogs and perjurers! Who will take the Protected of God to the north to sell charms that are never still to the Amir? The camels shall not gall, the sons shall not fall sick, and the wives shall remain faithful while they are away, of the men who give me place in their caravan. Who will assist me to slipper the King of the Roos with a golden slipper with a silver heel? The protection of Pir Khan be upon his labors!" He spread out the skirts of his gabardine and pirouetted between the lines of tethered horses.

"There starts a caravan from Peshawar to Kabul in twenty days, *Huzrut*," said the Eusufzai trader. "My camels go therewith. Do thou also go and bring us good-luck."

"I will go even now!" shouted the priest. "I will depart upon my winged camels, and be at Peshawar in a day! Ho! Hazar Mir Khan," he yelled to his servant, "drive out the camels, but let me first mount my own."

He leaped on the back of his beast as it knelt, and, turning round to me, cried: "Come thou also, Sahib, a little along the road, and I will sell thee a charm—an amulet that shall make thee King of Kafiristan."

Then the light broke upon me, and I followed the two camels out of the Serai till we reached open road and the priest halted.

"What d'you think o' that?" said he in English. "Carnehan can't talk their patter, so I've made him my servant. He makes a handsome servant. 'Tisn't for nothing that I've been knocking about the country for fourteen years. Didn't I do that talk neat? We'll hitch on to a caravan at Peshawar till we get to Jagdallak, and then we'll see if we can get donkeys for our camels, and strike into Kafiristan. Whirligigs for the Amir, O Lor'! Put your hand under the camelbags and tell me what you feel."

I felt the butt of a Martini, and another and another.

"Twenty of 'em," said Dravot placidly. "Twenty of 'em, and ammunition to correspond, under the whirligigs and the mud dolls."

"Heaven help you if you are caught with those things!" I said. "A Martini is worth her weight in silver among the Pathans."

"Fifteen hundred rupees of capital—every rupee we could beg, borrow, or steal—are invested on these two camels," said Dravot. "We won't get caught. We're going through the Khaiber with a regular caravan. Who'd touch a poor mad priest?"

"Have you got everything you want?" I asked, overcome with astonishment.

"Not yet, but we shall soon. Give us a memento of your kindness, *Brother.* You did me a service yesterday, and that time in Marwar. Half my kingdom shall you have, as the saying is." I slipped a small charm compass from my watch-chain and handed it up to the priest.

"Good-by," said Dravot, giving me his hand cautiously. "It's the last time we'll shake hands with an Englishman these many days. Shake hands with him, Carnehan," he cried, as the second camel passed me.

Carnehan leaned down and shook hands. Then the camels passed away along the dusty road, and I was left alone to wonder. My eye could detect no failure in the disguises. The scene in the Serai attested that they were complete to the native mind. There was just the chance, therefore, that Carnehan and Dravot would be able to wander through Afghanistan without detection. But, beyond, they would find death, certain and awful death.

Ten days later a native friend of mine, giving me the news of the day from Peshawar, wound up his letter with: "There has been much laughter here on account of a certain mad priest who is going in his estimation to sell petty gauds and insignificant trinkets which he ascribes as great charms to H. H. the Amir of Bokhara. He passed through Peshawar and associated himself to the Second Summer caravan that goes to Kabul. The merchants are pleased because through super-stition they imagine that such mad fellows bring good fortune."

The two, then, were beyond the border. I would have prayed for them, but that night a real king died in Europe, and demanded an obituary notice.

The wheel of the world swings through the same phases again and again. Summer passed and winter thereafter, and came and passed again. The daily paper continued and I with it, and upon the third summer there fell a hot night, a night-issue, and a strained waiting for something to be telegraphed from the other side of the world, exactly as had happened before. A few great men had died in the past two years, the machines worked with more clatter and some of the trees in the office garden were a few feet taller. But that was all the difference.

I passed over to the press-room, and went through just such a scene as I have already described. The nervous tension was stronger than it had been two years before and I felt the heat more acutely. At three o'clock I cried "Print off," and turned to go, when there crept to my chair what was left of a man. He was bent into a circle, his head was sunk between his shoulders, and he moved his feet one over the other like a bear. I could hardly see whether he walked or crawled—this rag-wrapped, whining cripple who addressed me by name, crying that he was come back. "Can you give me a drink?" he whimpered. "For the Lord's sake, give me a drink!"

I went back to the office, the man following with groans of pain, and I turned up the lamp.

"Don't you know me?" he gasped, dropping into a chair, and he turned his drawn face, surmounted by a shock of gray hair, to the light.

I looked at him intently. Once before had I seen eyebrows that met over the nose in an inch-broad black band, but for the life of me I could not tell where.

"I don't know you," I said, handing him the whisky. "What can I do for you?"

He took a gulp of the spirit raw, and shivered in spite of the suffocating heat.

"I've come back," he repeated; "and I was the King of Kafiristan—me and Dravot—crowned kings we was! In this office we settled it—you setting there and giving us the books. I am Peachey—Peachey Taliaferro Carnehan, and you've been setting here ever since—O Lord!"

I was more than a little astonished and expressed my feelings accordingly.

"It's true," said Carnehan, with a dry cackle, nursing his feet, which were wrapped in rags. "True as gospel, kings we were, with crowns upon our heads—me and Dravot—poor Dan—oh, poor, poor Dan, that would never take advice, not though I begged of him!"

"Take the whisky," I said, "and take your own time. Tell me all you can recollect of everything from beginning to end. You got across the border on your camels, Dravot dressed as a mad priest, and you his servant. Do you remember that?"

"I ain't mad—yet, but I shall be that way soon. Of course I remember. Keep looking at me, or maybe my words will go all to pieces. Keep looking at me in my eyes and don't say anything."

I leaned forward and looked into his face as steadily as I could. He dropped one hand upon the table and I grasped it by the wrist. It was twisted like a bird's claw, and upon the back was a ragged, red, diamond-shaped scar.

"No, don't look there. Look at *me*," said Carnehan. "That comes afterwards, but for the Lord's sake don't distrack me. We left with that caravan, me and Dravot playing all sorts of antics to amuse the people we were with. Dravot used to make us laugh in the evening when all the people was cooking their dinners—cooking their dinners, and . . . what did they do then? They lit little fires with sparks that went into Dravot's beard, and we all laughed—fit to die. Little red fires they was, going into Dravot's big red beard—so funny." His eyes left mine and he smiled foolishly.

"You went as far as Jagdallak with that caravan," I said at a venture, "after you had lit those fires. To Jagdallak, where you turned off to try to get into Kafiristan."

"No, we didn't neither. What are you talking about? We turned off before Jagdallak, because we heard the roads was good. But they wasn't good enough for our two camels—mine and Dravot's. When we left the caravan Dravot took off all his clothes and mine too, and said we would be heathen, because the Kafirs didn't allow Mohammedans to talk to them. So we dressed betwixt and between, and such a sight as Daniel Dravot I never saw yet nor expect to see again. He burned half his beard, and slung a sheepskin over his shoulder, and shaved his head into patterns. He shaved mine, too, and made me wear outrageous things to look like a heathen. That was in a most mountainous country, and our camels couldn't go along any more because of the mountains. They were tall and black, and coming home I saw them fight like wild goats—there are lots of goats in Kafiristan. And these mountains, they never keep still, no more than the goats. Always fighting they are, and don't let you sleep at night."

"Take some more whisky," I said very slowly. "What did you and Daniel Dravot do when the camels could go no farther because of the rough roads that led into Kafiristan?"

"What did which do? There was a party called Peachey Taliaferro Carnehan that was with Dravot. Shall I tell you about him? He died out there in the cold. Slap from the bridge fell old Peachey, turning and twisting in the air like a penny whirligig that you can sell to the

Amir.—No; they was two for three ha'pence, those whirligigs, or I am much mistaken and woeful sore. And then these camels were no use, and Peachey said to Dravot: 'For the Lord's sake, let's get out of this before our heads are chopped off,' and with that they killed the camels all among the mountains, not having anything in particular to eat, but first they took off the boxes with the guns and the ammunition, till two men came along driving four mules. Dravot up and dances in front of them, singing: 'Sell me four mules.' Says the first man: 'If you are rich enough to buy you are rich enough to rob'; but before ever he could put his hand to his knife Dravot breaks his neck over his knee, and the other party runs away. So Carnehan loaded the mules with the rifles that was taken off the camels, and together we starts forward into those bitter cold mountainous parts, and never a road broader than the back of your hand."

He paused for a moment, while I asked him if he could remember the nature of the country through which he had journeyed.

"I am telling you as straight as I can, but my head isn't as good as it might be. They drove nails through it to make me hear better how Dravot died. The country was mountainous and the mules were most contrary, and the inhabitants was dispersed and solitary. They went up and up, and down and down, and that other party, Carnehan, was imploring of Dravot not to sing and whistle so loud, for fear of bringing down the tremenjus avalanches. But Dravot says that if a king couldn't sing it wasn't worth being king, and whacked the mules over the rump, and never took no heed for ten cold days. We came to a big level valley all among the mountains, and the mules were near dead, so we killed them, not having anything in special for them or us to eat. We sat upon the boxes, and played odd and even with the cartridges that was jolted out.

"Then ten men with bows and arrows ran down that valley chasing twenty men with bows and arrows, and the row was tremenjus. They was fair men—fairer than you or me—with yellow hair and remarkable well built. Says Dravot, unpacking the guns: 'This is the beginning of the business. We'll fight for the ten men,' and with that he fires two rifles at the twenty men, and drops one of them at two hundred yards from the rock where we was sitting. The other men began to run, but Carnehan and Dravot sits on the boxes picking them off at all ranges, up and down the valley. Then we goes up to the ten men that had run across the snow, too, and they fires a footy little arrow at us. Dravot he shoots above their heads and they all falls down flat. Then he walks over them and kicks them, and then he lifts them up and shakes hands all around to make them friendly like. He calls them and gives them the boxes to carry, and waves his hand for all the world as though he was king already. They take the boxes and him across the valley and up the hill into a pine wood on the top, where there was half a dozen big stone idols. Dravot he goes to the biggest—a fellow they call Imbra—and lays a rifle and a cartridge at his feet, rubbing his nose respectful with his own nose, patting him on the head, and saluting in front of it. He turns round to the men and nods his head, and says 'That's all right. I'm in the know, too, and all these old jim-jams are my friends.' Then he opens his mouth and points down it, and when the first man brings him food, he says—'No'; and when the second man brings him food, he says—'No'; but when one of the old priests and the boss of the village brings him food, he says—'Yes,' very haughty, and eats it slow. That was how we came to our first village, without any trouble, just as though we had tumbled from the skies. But we tumbled from one of those damned rope-bridges, you see, and you couldn't expect a man to laugh much after that."

"Take some whisky and go on," I said. "That was the first village you came into. How did you get to be king?"

"I wasn't king," said Carnehan. "Dravot he was the king, and a handsome man he looked with the gold crown on his head and all. Him and the other party stayed in that village, and every morning Dravot sat by the side of old Imbra, and the people came and worshiped. That was Dravot's order. Then a lot of men came into the valley, and Carnehan and Dravot picks them off with the rifles before they knew where they was, and runs down into the valley and up again the other side, and finds another village, same as the first one, and the people all falls down flat on their faces, and Dravot says, 'Now what is the trouble between you two villages?' and the people points to a woman, as fair as you or me, that was carried off, and Dravot takes her back to the first village and counts up the dead—eight there was. For each dead man Dravot pours a little milk on the ground and waves his arms like a whirligig and 'That's all right,' says he. Then he and Carnehan takes the big boss of each village by the arm and walks them down into the valley, and shows them how to scratch a line with a spear right down the valley, and gives each a sod of turf from both sides o' the line. Then all the people comes down and shouts like the devil and all, and Dravot says, 'Go and dig the land, and be fruitful and multiply,' which they did, though they didn't understand. Then we asks the names of things in their lingo—bread and water and fire and idols and such, and Dravot leads the priest of each village up to the idol, and says he must sit there and judge the people, and if anything goes wrong he is to be shot.

"Next week they was all turning up the land in the valley as quiet as bees and much prettier, and the priests heard all the complaints and told Dravot in dumb show what it was about. 'That's just the beginning,' says Dravot. 'They think we're gods.' He and Carnehan picks out twenty good men and shows them how to click off a rifle and form fours, and advance in line, and they was very pleased to do so, and clever to see the hang of it. Then he takes out his pipe and his baccy-pouch and leaves one at one village and one at the other, and off we two goes to see what was to be done in the next valley. That was all rock, and there was a little village there, and Carnehan says,—'Send 'em to the old valley to plant,' and takes 'em there and gives 'em some land that wasn't took before. They were a poor lot, and we blooded 'em with a kid before letting 'em into the new kingdom. That was to impress the people, and then they settled down quiet, and Carnehan went back to Dravot, who had got into another valley all snow and ice and most mountainous. There was no people there and the army got afraid, so Dravot shoots one of them, and goes on till he finds some people in a village, and the army explains that unless the people wants to be killed they had better not shoot their little matchlocks; for they had match-locks. We makes friends with the priest and I stays there alone with two of the army, teaching the men how to drill, and a thundering big chief comes across the snow with kettle-drums and horns twanging, because he heard there was a new god kicking about. Carnehan sights for the brown of the men half a mile across the snow and wings one of them. Then he sends a message to the chief that, unless he wished to be killed, he must come and shake hands with me and leave his arms behind. The chief comes alone first, and Carnehan shakes hands with him and whirls his arms about same as Dravot used, and very much surprised that chief was, and strokes my eyebrows. Then Carnehan goes alone to the chief and asks him in dumb show if he had an enemy he hated. 'I have,' said the chief. So Carnehan weeds out the pick of his men, and sets the two of the army to show them drill and at the end of two weeks the men can maneuver about as well as volunteers. So he marches with the chief to a great big plain on the top of a mountain, and the chief's men rushes into a village and takes it; we three Martinis firing into the brown of the enemy. So we took that village too, and I gives the chief a rag from my coat, and says, 'Occupy till I come,' which was Scriptural. By way of a reminder, when me and the army was eighteen hundred yards away, I drops a bullet near him standing on the snow, and all the people falls flat on their faces. Then I sends a letter to Dravot, wherever he be by land or by sea."

At the risk of throwing the creature out of train I interrupted, "How could you write a letter up yonder?"

"The letter? Oh! The letter! Keep looking at me between the eyes, please. It was a string-talk letter, that we'd learned the way of it from a blind beggar in the Punjab."

I remembered that there had once come to the office a blind man with a knotted twig and a piece of string which he wound round the twig according to some cipher of his own. He could, after the lapse of days or hours, repeat the sentence which he had reeled up. He had reduced the alphabet to eleven primitive sounds; and tried to teach me his method, but failed.

"I sent that letter to Dravot," said Carnehan; "and told him to come back because this kingdom was growing too big for me to handle, and then I struck for the first valley, to see how the priests were working. They called the village we took along with the chief, Bashkai, and the first village we took Er-Heb. The priests at Er-Heb was doing all right, but they had a lot of pending cases about land to show me, and some men from another village had been firing arrows at night. I went out and looked for that village and fired four rounds at it from a thousand yards. That used all the cartridges I cared to spend, and I waited for Dravot, who had been away two or three months, and I kept my people quiet.

"One morning I heard the devil's own noise of drums and horns, and Dan Dravot marches down the hill with his army and a tail of hundreds of men, and, which was the most amazing—a great gold crown on his head. 'My Gord, Carnehan,' says Daniel, 'this is a tremenjus business, and we've got the whole country as far as it's worth having. I am the son of Alexander by Queen Semiramis, and you're my younger brother and a god too! It's the biggest thing we've ever seen. I've been marching and fighting for six weeks with the army, and every footy little village for fifty miles has come in rejoiceful; and more than that, I've got the key of the whole show, as you'll see, and I've got a crown for you! I told 'em to make two of 'em at a place called Shu, where the gold lies in the rock like suet in mutton. Gold I've seen, and turquoise I've kicked out of the cliffs, and there's garnets in the sands of the river, and here's a chunk of amber that a man brought me. Call up all the priests and, here, take your crown.'

"One of the men opens a black hair bag and I slips the crown on. It was too small and too heavy, but I wore it for the glory. Hammered gold it was—five-pound weight, like a hoop of a barrel.

"'Peachey,' says Dravot, 'we don't want to fight no more. The craft's the trick, so help me!' and he brings forward that same chief that I left at Bashkai—Billy Fish we called him afterwards, because he was so like Billy Fish that drove the big tank-engine at Mach on the Bolan in the old days. 'Shake hands with him,' says Dravot, and I shook hands and nearly dropped, for Billy Fish gave me the grip. I said nothing, but tried him with the fellowcraft grip. He answers all right, and I tried the master's grip, but that was a slip. 'A fellowcraft he is!' I says to Dan. 'Does he know the word?' 'He does,' says Dan, 'and all the priests know. It's a miracle! The chiefs and the priests can work a fellowcraft lodge in a way that's very like ours, and they've cut the marks on the rocks, but they don't know the third degree, and they've come to find out. It's Gord's truth. I've known these long years that the Afghans knew up to the fellowcraft degree, but this is a miracle. A god and a grand-master of the craft am I, and a lodge in the third degree I will open, and we'll raise the head priests and the chiefs of the villages.'

"'It's against all the law,' I says, 'holding a lodge without warrant from any one; and we never held office in any lodge.'

"'It's a master-stroke of policy,' says Dravot. 'It means running the country as easy as a four-wheeled bogy on a down grade. We can't stop to inquire now, or they'll turn against us. I've forty chiefs at my heel, and passed and raised according to their merits they shall be. Billet these men on the villages, and see that we run up a lodge of some kind. The temple of Imbra will do for the lodge room. The women must make aprons as you show them. I'll hold a levee of chiefs tonight and lodge tomorrow.'

"I was fair run off my legs, but I wasn't such a fool as not to see what a pull this craft business gave us. I showed the priests' families how to make aprons of the degrees, but for Dravot's apron the blue border and marks was made of turquoise lumps on white hide, not cloth. We took a great square stone in the temple for the master's chair, and little stones for the officers' chairs, and painted the black pavement with white squares, and did what we could to make things regular.

"At the levee which was held that night on the hillside with big bon-fires, Dravot gives out that him and me were gods and sons of Alexander, and past grand-masters in the craft, and was come to make Kafiristan a country where every man should eat in peace and drink in quiet, and specially obey us. Then the chiefs come round to shake hands, and they was so hairy and white and fair it was just shaking hands with old friends. We gave them names according as they were like men we had known in India—Billy Fish, Holly Dilworth, Pikky Kergan that was bazaar-master when I was at Mhow, and so on and so on.

"*The* most amazing miracle was at lodge next night. One of the old priests was watching us continuous, and I felt uneasy, for I knew we'd have to fudge the ritual, and I didn't know what the men knew. The old priest was a stranger come in from beyond the village of Bashkai. The minute Dravot puts on the master's apron that the girls had made for him, the priest fetches a whoop and a howl, and tries to overturn the stone that Dravot was sitting on. 'It's all up now,' I says. 'That comes of meddling with the craft without warrant!' Dravot never winked an eye, not when ten priests took and tilted over the grand-master's chair—which was to say the stone of Imbra. The priest begins rubbing the bottom of it to clear away the black dirt, and presently he shows all the other priests the master's mark, same as was on Dravot's apron, cut into the stone. Not even the priests of the temple of Imbra knew it was there. The old chap falls flat on his face at Dravot's feet and kisses 'em. 'Luck again,' says Dravot, across the lodge to me, 'they say it's the missing mark that no one could understand the why of. We're more than safe now.' Then he bangs the butt of his gun for a gavel and says: 'By virtue of the authority vested in me by my own right hand and the help of Peachey, I declare myself Grand-Master of all Freemasonry in Kafiristan in this the mother lodge o' the country, and King of Kafiristan equally with Peachey!' At that he puts on his crown and I puts on mine—I was doing senior warden—and we opens the lodge in most ample form. It was an amazing miracle! The priests moved in lodge through the first two degrees almost without telling, as if the memory was coming back to them. After that Peachey and Dravot raised such as was worthy—high priests and chiefs of far-off villages. Billy Fish was the first, and I can tell you we scared the soul out of him. It was not in any way according to ritual, but it served our turn. We didn't raise more than ten of the biggest men because we didn't want to make the degree common. And they was clamoring to be raised.

"'In another six months,' says Dravot, 'we'll hold another communication and see how you are working.' Then he asks them about their villages, and learns that they was fighting one against the other and were fair sick and tired of it. And when they wasn't doing that they was fighting with the Mohammedans. 'You can fight those when they come into our country,' says Dravot. 'Tell off every tenth man of your tribes for a frontier guard, and send two hundred at a time to this valley to be drilled. Nobody is going to be shot or speared any more so long as he does well, and I know that you won't cheat me because you're white people—sons of Alexander—and not like common, black Mohammedans. You are *my* people, and by God,' says he, running off into English at the end—'I'll make a damned fine nation of you, or I'll die in the making!'

"I can't tell all we did for the next six months, because Dravot did a lot I couldn't see the hang of, and he learned their lingo in a way I never could. My work was to help the people plow, and now and again go out with some of the army and see what the other villages were doing, and make 'em throw rope bridges across the ravines which cut up the country horrid. Dravot was very kind to me, but when he walked up and down in the pine wood pulling that bloody red beard of his with both fists I knew he was thinking plans I could not advise him about and I just waited for orders.

"But Dravot never showed me disrespect before the people. They were afraid of me and the army, but they loved Dan. He was the best of friends with the priests and the chiefs; but any one could come across the hills with a complaint and Dravot would hear him out fair and call four priests together and say what was to be done. He used to call in Billy Fish from Bashkai and Pikky Kargan from Shu, and an old chief we called Kefuzelum—it was like enough to his real name—and held councils with 'em when there was any fighting to be done in small villages. That was his Council of War, and the four priests of Bashkai, Shu, Khawak and Madora was his Privy Council. Between the lot of 'em they sent me, with forty men and twenty rifles, and sixty men carrying turquoises, into the Ghorband country to buy those hand-made Martini rifles that come out of the Amir's workshops at Kabul, from one of the Amir's Herati regiments that would have sold the very teeth out of their mouths for turquoises.

"I stayed in Ghorband a month, and gave the Governor there the pick of my baskets for hush-money, and bribed the colonel of the regiment some more, and between the two and the tribes people, we got more than a hundred hand-made Martinis, a hundred good Kohat Jezails that'll throw to six hundred yards, and forty man-loads of very bad ammunition for the rifles. I came back with what I had, and distributed 'em among the men that the chiefs sent in to me to drill. Dravot was too busy to attend to those things, but the old army that we first made helped me, and we turned out five hundred men that could drill, and two hundred that knew how to hold arms pretty straight. Even those cork-screwed, hand-made guns was a miracle to them. Dravot talked big about powder-shops and factories, walking up and down in the pine wood when the winter was coming on.

"'I won't make a nation,' says he. 'I'll make an empire! These men aren't niggers; they're English! Look at their eyes—look at their mouths. Look at the way they stand up. They sit on chairs in their own houses. They're the Lost Tribes, or something like it, and they've grown to be English. I'll take a census in the spring if the priests don't get frightened. There must be fair two million of 'em in these hills. The villages are full o' little children. Two million people—two hundred and fifty thousand fighting men—and all English! They only want the rifles and a little drilling. Two hundred and fifty thousand men, ready to cut in on Russia's right flank when she tries for India! Peachey, man,' he says, chewing his beard in great hunks, 'we shall be emperors—emperors of the earth. Rajah Brooke will be a suckling to us. I'll treat with the Viceroy on equal terms. I'll ask him to send me twelve picked English—twelve that I know of—to help us govern a bit. There's Mackray, Sergeant-pensioner at Segowli—many's the good dinner he's given me, and his wife a pair of trousers. There's Donkin, the Warder of Tounghoo Jail; there's hundreds that I could lay my hands on if I was in India. The Viceroy shall do it for me. I'll send a man through in the spring for those men, and I'll write for a dispensation from the grand lodge for what I've done as grand master. That—and all the Sniders that'll be thrown out when the native troops in India take up the Martini. They'll be worn smooth, but they'll do for fighting in these hills. Twelve English, a hundred thousand Sniders run through the Amir's country in driblets—I'd be content with twenty thousand in one year—and we'd be an empire. When everything was shipshape, I'd hand over the crown—this crown I'm wearing now—to Queen Victoria on my knees, and she'd say: "Rise up, Sir Daniel Dravot." Oh, it's big! It's big, I tell you! But there's so much to be done in every place—Bashkai, Khawak, Shu, and everywhere else.'

"'What is it?' I says. 'There are no more men coming in to be drilled this autumn. Look at those fat, black clouds. They're bringing the snow.'

"'It isn't that,' says Daniel, putting his hand very hard on my shoulder; 'and I don't wish to say anything that's against you, for no other living man would have followed me and made me what I am as you have done. You're a first-class commander-in-chief, and the people know you; but—it's a big country, and somehow you can't help me, Peachey, in the way I want to be helped.'

"'Go to your blasted priests, then!' I said, and I was sorry when I made that remark, but it did hurt me sore to find Daniel talking so superior when I'd drilled all the men, and done all he told me.

"'Don't let's quarrel, Peachey,' says Daniel without cursing. 'You're a king too, and the half of this kingdom is yours; but can't you see, Peachey, we want cleverer men than us now—three or four of 'em, that we can scatter about for our deputies. It's a huge great state, and I can't always tell the right thing to do, and I haven't time for all I want to do, and here's the winter coming on and all.' He put half his beard into his mouth, and it was as red as the gold of his crown.

"'I'm sorry, Daniel,' says I. 'I've done all I could. I've drilled the men and shown the people how to stack their oats better; and I've brought in those tinware rifles from Ghorband—but I know what you're driving at. I take it kings always feel oppressed that way.'

"'There's another thing, too,' says Dravot, walking up and down. 'The winter's coming and these people won't be giving much trouble, and if they do we can't move about. I want a wife.'

"'For Gord's sake leave the women alone!' I says. 'We've both got all the work we can, though I *am* a fool. Remember the contrack and keep clear o' women.'

"'The contrack only lasted till such time as we was kings; and kings we have been these months past,' says Dravot, weighing his crown in his hand. 'You go get a wife too, Peachey, a nice, strappin', plump girl that'll keep you warm in the winter. They're prettier than English girls, and we can take the pick of 'em. Boil 'em once or twice in hot water, and they'll come as fair as chicken and ham.'

"'Don't tempt me!' I says. 'I will not have any dealings with a woman, not till we are a dam' side more settled than we are now. I've been doing the work o' two men and you've been doing the work o' three. Let's lie off a bit, and see if we can get some better tobacco from Afghan country and run in some good liquor; but no women.'

"'Who's talking o' *women?*' says Dravot. 'I said *wife*—a queen to breed a king's son for the king. A queen out of the strongest tribe, that'll make them your blood-brothers, and that'll lie by your side and tell you all the people thinks about you and their own affairs. That's what I want.'

"'Do you remember that Bengali woman I kept at Mogul Serai when I was a plate layer?' says I. 'A fat lot o' good she was to me. She taught me the lingo and one or two other things; but what happened? She ran away with the station master's servant and half my month's pay. Then she turned up at Dadur Junction in tow of a half-caste, and had the impidence to say I was her husband—all among the drivers in the running-shed!'

"'We've done with that,' says Dravot. 'These women are whiter than you or me, and a queen I will have for the winter months.'

"'For the last time o' asking, Dan, do *not*,' I says. 'It'll only bring us harm. The Bible says that kings ain't to waste their strength on women, 'specially when they've got a new raw kingdom to work over.'

"'For the last time of answering I will,' says Dravot, and he went away through the pine-trees looking like a big red devil. The long sun hit his crown and beard on one side, and the two blazed like hot coals.

"But getting a wife was not as easy as Dan thought. He put it before the Council, and there was no answer till Billy Fish said he'd better ask the girls. Dravot damned them all round. 'What's wrong with me?' he shouts, standing by the idol Imbra. 'Am I a dog or am I not enough of a man for your wenches? Haven't I put the shadow of my hand over this country? Who stopped the last Afghan raid?' It was me really, but Dravot was too angry to remember. 'Who bought your guns? Who repaired the bridges? Who's the grand master of the sign cut in the stone?' and he thumped his hand on the block that he used to sit on in lodge, and at council, which opened like lodge always. Billy Fish said nothing and no more did the others. 'Keep your hair on, Dan,' said I, 'and ask the girls. That's how it's done at home, and these people are quite English.'

"'The marriage of the king is a matter of state,' says Dan, in a white-hot rage, for he could feel, I hope, that he was going against his better mind. He walked out of the council room, and the others sat still, looking at the ground.

"'Billy Fish,' says I to the Chief of the Bashkai, 'what's the difficulty here? A straight answer to a true friend.' 'You know,' says Billy Fish. 'How should a man tell you, who knows everything? How can daughters of men marry gods or devils? It's not proper.'

"I remembered something like that in the Bible; but if, after seeing us as long as they had, they still believed we were gods, it wasn't for me to undeceive them.

"'A god can do anything,' says I. 'If the king is fond of a girl he'll not let her die.' 'She'll have to,' said Billy Fish. 'There are all sorts of gods and devils in these mountains, and now and again a girl marries one of them and isn't seen any more. Besides, you two know the mark cut in the stone. Only the gods know that. We thought you were men till you showed the sign of the master.'

"I wished then that we had explained about the loss of the genuine secrets of a Master Mason at the first go-off; but I said nothing. All that night there was a blowing of horns in a little dark temple half-way down the hill and I heard a girl crying fit to die. One of the priests told us that she was being prepared to marry the king.

"'I'll have no nonsense of that kind,' says Dan. 'I don't want to interfere with your customs, but I'll take my own wife.' 'The girl's a little bit afraid,' says the priest. 'She thinks she's going to die, and they are a-heartening her up down in the temple.'

"'Hearten her very tender, then,' says Dravot, 'or I'll hearten you with the butt of a gun so that you'll never want to be heartened again.' He licked his lips, did Dan, and stayed up walking about more than half the night, thinking of the wife that he was going to get in the morning. I wasn't any means comfortable, for I knew that dealings with a woman in foreign parts, though you was crowned king twenty times over, could not but be risky. I got up very early in the morning while Dravot was asleep, and I saw the priests talking together in whispers, and the chiefs talking together, too, and they looked at me out of the corners of their eyes.

"'What is up, Fish?' I says to the Bashkai man, who was wrapped up in his furs and looking splendid to behold.

"'I can't rightly say,' says he; 'but if you can induce the king to drop all this nonsense about marriage you'll be doing him and me and yourself a great service.'

"'That I do believe,' says I. 'But sure, you know, Billy, as well as me, having fought against and for us, that the king and me are nothing more than two of the finest men that God Almighty ever made. Nothing more, I do assure you.'

"'That may be,' says Billy Fish, 'and yet I should be sorry if it was.' He sinks his head upon his great fur coat for a minute and thinks. 'King,' says he, 'be you man or god or devil, I'll stick by you today. I have twenty of my men with me, and they will follow me. We'll go to Bashkai until the storm blows over.'

"A little snow had fallen in the night, and everything was white except the greasy fat clouds that blew down and down from the north. Dravot came out with his crown on his head, swinging his arms and stamping his feet, and looking more pleased than Punch.

"'For the last time drop it, Dan,' says I in a whisper. 'Billy Fish here says that there will be a row.'

"'A row among my people!' says Dravot. 'Not much. Peachey, you're a fool not to get a wife too. Where's the girl?' says he with a voice as loud as the braying of a jackass. 'Call up all the chiefs and priests, and let the emperor see if his wife suits him.'

"There was no need to call any one. They were all there leaning on their guns and spears round the clearing in the center of the pine wood.

A deputation of priests went down to the little temple to bring up the girl, and the horns blew fit to wake the dead. Billy Fish saunters round and gets as close to Daniel as he could, and behind him stood his twenty men with matchlocks. Not a man of them under six feet. I was next to Dravot, and behind me was twenty men of the regular army. Up comes the girl, and a strapping wench she was, covered with silver and turquoises, but white as death, and looking back every minute at the priests.

"'She'll do,' said Dan, looking her over. 'What's to be afraid of, lass? Come and kiss me.' He puts his arm round her. She shuts her eyes, gives a bit of a squeak, and down goes her face in the side of Dan's flaming red beard.

"'The slut's bitten me!' says he, clapping his hand to his neck; and sure enough his hand was red with blood. Billy Fish and two of his matchlock-men catches hold of Dan by the shoulders and drags him into the Bashkai lot, while the priests howl in their lingo, 'Neither god nor devil but a man!' I was all taken aback, for a priest cut at me in front, and the army began firing into the Bashkai men.

"'God A'mighty!' says Dan. 'What is the meaning o' this?'

"'Come back! Come away!' says Billy Fish. 'Ruin and mutiny is the matter. We'll break for Bashkai if we can.'

"I tried to give some sort of orders to my men—the men o' the regular army—but it was no use, so I fired into the brown of 'em with an English Martini and drilled three beggars in a line. The valley was full of shouting, howling creatures, and every soul was shrieking, 'Not a god nor a devil but only a man!' The Bashkai troops stuck to Billy Fish all they were worth, but their matchlocks wasn't half as good as the Kabul breech-loaders, and four of them dropped. Dan was bellowing like a bull, for he was very wrathy; and Billy Fish had a hard job to prevent him running out at the crowd.

"'We can't stand,' said Billy Fish. 'Make a run for it down the valley! The whole place is against us.' The matchlock-men ran, and we went down the valley in spite of Dravot's protestations. He was swearing horribly and crying out that he was a king. The priests rolled great stones on us, and the regular army fired hard, and there wasn't more than six men, not counting Dan, Billy Fish and me, that came down to the bottom of the valley alive.

"Then they stopped firing and the horns in the temple blew again. 'Come away—for Gord's sake come away!' says Billy Fish. 'They'll send runners out to all the villages before ever we get to Bashkai. I can protect you there,' but I can't do anything now.'

"My own notion is that Dan began to go mad in his head from that hour. He stared up and down like a stuck pig. Then he was all for walking back alone and killing the priests with his bare hands, which he could have done. 'An emperor am I,' says Daniel, 'and next year I shall be a knight of the queen.'

"'All right, Dan,' says I; 'but come along now while there's time.'

"'It's your fault,' says he, 'for not looking after your army better. There was mutiny in the midst, and you didn't know—you damned engine-driving, plate-laying, missionaries'-pass hunting hound!' He sat upon a rock and called me every foul name he could lay tongue to. I was too heartsick to care, though it was all his foolishness that brought the smash.

"'I'm sorry, Dan,' says I, 'but there's no accounting for natives. This business is our Fifty-Seven. Maybe we'll make something out of it yet, when we've got back to Bashkai.'

"'Let's get to Bashkai, then,' says Dan, 'and by God, when I come back here again I'll sweep the valley so there isn't a bug in a blanket left!'

"We walked all that day, and all that night Dan was stumping up and down on the snow, chewing his beard and muttering to himself.

"'There's no hope o' getting clear,' says Billy Fish. 'The priests will have sent runners to the villages to say that you are only men. Why didn't you stick on as gods till things was more settled? I'm a dead man,' says Billy Fish, and he throws himself down on the snow and begins to pray to his gods.

"Next morning we was in a cruel bad country—all up and down, no level ground at all, and no food either. The six Bashkai men looked at Billy Fish hungry-wise as if they wanted to ask something, but they said never a word. At noon we came to the top of a flat mountain all covered with snow, and when we climbed up into it, behold, there was an army in position waiting in the middle!

"'The runners have been very quick,' says Billy Fish, with a little bit of a laugh. 'They are waiting for us.'

"Three or four men began to fire from the enemy's side, and a chance shot took Daniel in the calf of the leg. That brought him to his senses. He looks across the snow at the army, and sees the rifles that we had brought into the country.

"'We're done for,' says he. 'They are Englishmen, these people— and it's my blasted nonsense that has brought you to this. Get back, Billy Fish, and take your men away; you've done what you could, and now cut for it. Carnehan,' says he, 'shake hands with me and go along with Billy. Maybe they won't kill you. I'll go and meet 'em alone. It's me that did it. Me, the king!'

"'Go!' says I. 'Go to Hell, Dan. I'm with you here. Billy Fish, you clear out and we two will meet those folk.'

"'I'm a chief,' says Billy Fish quite quiet. 'I stay with you. My men can go.'

"The Bashkai fellows didn't wait for a second word but ran off, and Dan and me and Billy Fish walked across to where the drums were drumming and the horns were horning. It was cold—awful cold. I've

got that cold in the back of my head now. There's a lump of it there."
The punkah-coolies had gone to sleep. Two kerosene lamps were blazing in the office, and the perspiration poured down my face and splashed on the blotter as I leaned forward. Carnehan was shivering, and I feared that his mind might go. I wiped my face, took a fresh grip of the piteously mangled hands and said, "What happened after that?"
The momentary shift of my eyes had broken the clear current.
"What was you pleased to say?" whined Carnehan. "They took them without any sound. Not a little whisper all along the snow, not though the king knocked down the first man that set hand on him—not though old Peachey fired his last cartridge into the brown of 'em. Not a single solitary sound did those swines make. They just closed up tight, and I tell you their furs stunk. There was a man called Billy Fish, a good friend of us all, and they cut his throat, Sir, then and there, like a pig; and the king kicks up the bloody snow and says:—'We've had a dashed fine run for our money. What's coming next?' But Peachey, Peachey Taliaferro, I tell you, Sir, in confidence as betwixt two friends, he lost his head, Sir. No, he didn't either. The king lost his head, so he did, all along o' one of those cunning rope-bridges. Kindly let me have the paper-cutter, Sir. It tilted this way. They marched him a mile across that snow to a rope-bridge over a ravine with a river at the bottom. You may have seen such. They prodded him behind like an ox. 'Damn your eyes!' says the king. 'D'you suppose I can't die like a gentleman?' He turns to Peachey—Peachey that was crying like a child. 'I've brought you to this, Peachey,' says he. 'Brought you out of your happy life to be killed in Kafiristan, where you was late commander-in-chief of the emperor's forces. Say you forgive me, Peachey.' 'I do,' says Peachey. 'Fully and freely do I forgive you, Dan.' 'Shake hands, Peachey,' says he. 'I'm going now.' Out he goes, looking neither right nor left, and when he was plumb in the middle of those dizzy dancing ropes, 'Cut, you beggars,' he shouts; and they cut, and old Dan fell, turning round and round and round, twenty thousand miles, for he took half an hour to fall till he struck the water, and I could see his body caught on a rock with the gold crown close beside.
"But do you know what they did to Peachey between two pine-trees? They crucified him, Sir, as Peachey's hands will show. They used wooden pegs for his hands and his feet; and he didn't die. He hung there and screamed; and they took him down next day and said it was a miracle that he wasn't dead. They took him down—poor old Peachey that hadn't done them any harm—that hadn't done them any . . ."
He rocked to and fro and wept bitterly, wiping his eyes with the back of his scarred hands and moaning like a child for some ten minutes.
"They was cruel enough to feed him up in the temple, because they said he was more of a god than old Daniel that was a man. Then they turned him out on the snow, and told him to go home; and Peachey

came home in about a year, begging along the roads quite safe; for Daniel Dravot he walked before and said: 'Come along, Peachey. It's a big thing we're doing.' The mountains they danced at night, and the mountains they tried to fall on Peachey's head, but Dan he held up his hand and Peachey came along bent double. He never let go of Dan's hand, and he never let go of Dan's head. They gave it to him as a present in the temple, to remind him not to come again, and though the crown was pure gold, and Peachey was starving, never would Peachey sell the same. You knew Dravot, Sir! You knew Right Worshipful Brother Dravot! Look at him now!"

He fumbled in the mass of rags round his bent waist; brought out a black horsehair bag embroidered with silver thread; and shook therefrom onto my table—the dried, withered head of Daniel Dravot! The morning sun that had long been paling the lamps struck the red beard and blind, sunken eyes; struck, too, a heavy circlet of gold studded with raw turquoises, that Carnehan placed tenderly on the battered temples.

"You behold now," said Carnehan, "the Emperor in his habit as he lived—the King of Kafiristan with his crown upon his head. Poor old Daniel that was a monarch once!"

I shuddered, for, in spite of defacements manifold, I recognized the head of the man of Marwar Junction. Carnehan rose to go. I attempted to stop him. He was not fit to walk abroad. "Let me take away the whisky and give me a little money," he gasped. "I was a king once. I'll go to the deputy commissioner and ask to set in the poor-house till I get my health. No, thank you, I can't wait till you get a carriage for me. I've urgent private affairs—in the south—at Marwar."

He shambled out of the office and departed in the direction of the deputy commissioner's house. That day at noon I had occasion to go down the blinding hot Mall, and I saw a crooked man crawling along the white dust of the roadside, his hat in his hand, quavering dolorously after the fashion of street-singers at home. There was not a soul in sight, and he was out of all possible earshot of the houses. And he sang through his nose, turning his head from right to left:

> "The Son of Man goes forth to war,
>   A golden crown to gain:
> His blood-red banner streams afar—
>   Who follows in his train?"

I waited to hear no more, but put the poor wretch into my carriage and drove him off to the nearest missionary for eventual transfer to the asylum. He repeated the hymn twice while he was with me, whom he did not in the least recognize, and I left him singing it to the missionary.

Two days later I inquired after his welfare of the superintendent of the asylum.

"He was admitted suffering from sunstroke. He died early yesterday morning," said the superintendent. "Is it true that he was half an hour bareheaded in the sun at midday?"

"Yes," said I; "but do you happen to know if he had anything upon him by any chance when he died?"

"Not to my knowledge," said the superintendent.

And there the matter rests.

THE NECKLACE

By Guy de Maupassant

[The life of Guy de Maupassant (1850–1893) was brief and somber. Even so the credit of making the short story form what it came to be in the first quarter of the twentieth century is partly due to this brilliant Frenchman. From his boyhood he intended to become a writer and was most carefully taught the art of writing by his godfather, Gustave Flaubert, the distinguished realistic novelist. The greater part of Maupassant's writing is in the form of compact, realistic short stories made after a pattern. Two novels attest his ability in the realm of longer pieces of fiction. These are *Une Vie* (1883) and *Pierre et Jean* (1888).

Maupassant's *The Piece of String* is reprinted on pp. 31–37. The version of *The Necklace* which follows is reprinted from *Little French Masterpieces*, by permission of G. P. Putnam's Sons, publishers.]

SHE was one of those pretty and charming girls who are sometimes, as if by a mistake of destiny, born in a family of clerks. She had no dowry, no expectations, no means of being known, understood, loved, wedded, by any rich and distinguished man, and so she let herself be married to a petty clerk at the Ministry of Public Instruction.

She dressed plainly because she could not dress well, but she was as unhappy as though she had really fallen from her proper station; since with women there is neither caste nor rank; and beauty, grace, and charm act instead of family and birth. Natural fineness, instinct for what is elegant, suppleness of wit, are the sole hierarchy, and make from women of the people the equals of the very greatest ladies.

She suffered ceaselessly, feeling herself born for all the delicacies and all the luxuries. She suffered from the poverty of her dwelling, from the wretched look of the walls, from the worn-out chairs, from the ugliness of the curtains. All those things of which another woman of her rank would never even have been conscious, tortured her and made her angry. The sight of the little Breton peasant who did her humble housework aroused in her regrets which were despairing and distracted dreams. She thought of the silent antechambers hung with Oriental tapestry, lit by tall bronze candelabra, and of the two great footmen in knee-breeches who sleep in the big arm-chairs, made drowsy by the heavy warmth of the furnace. She thought of the long salons fitted up with ancient silk, of the delicate furniture carrying priceless curiosities, and of the coquettish perfumed boudoirs made for talks at five o'clock with

335

intimate friends, with men famous and sought after, whom all women envy, and whose attention they all desire.

When she sat down to dinner before the round table covered with a tablecloth three days old, opposite her husband, who uncovered the soup-tureen and declared with an enchanted air, "Ah, the delicious stew! I don't know anything better than that," she thought of dainty dinners, of shining silverware, of tapestry which peopled the walls with ancient personages and with strange birds flying in the midst of a fairy forest; and she thought of delicious dishes served on marvelous plates, and of the whispered gallantries which you listen to with a sphinx-like smile, while you are eating the pink flesh of a trout or the wings of a quail.

She had no dresses, no jewels, nothing. And she loved nothing but that; she felt made for that. She would so have liked to please, to be envied, to be charming, to be sought after.

She had a friend, a former schoolmate at the convent, who was rich and whom she did not like to go and see any more, because she suffered so much when she came back.

But, one evening, her husband returned home with a triumphant air, and holding a large envelope in his hand.

"There," said he, "there is something for you."

She tore the paper sharply, and drew out a printed card which bore these words:

The Minister of Public Instruction and Mme. Georges Ramponneau request the honor of M. and Mme. Loisel's company at the palace of the Ministry on Monday evening, January 18th.

Instead of being delighted, as her husband hoped, she threw the invitation on the table with disdain, murmuring:

"What do you want me to do with that?"

"But, my dear, I thought you would be glad. You never go out, and this is such a fine opportunity. I had awful trouble to get it. Every one wants to go; it is very select, and they are not giving many invitations to clerks. The whole official world will be there."

She looked at him with an irritated eye, and she said, impatiently:

"And what do you want me to put on my back?"

He had not thought of that; he stammered:

"Why, the dress you go to the theater in. It looks very well to me."

He stopped, distracted, seeing that his wife was crying. Two great tears descended slowly from the corners of her eyes towards the corners of her mouth. He stuttered:

"What's the matter? What's the matter?"

But by a violent effort she had conquered her grief, and she replied, with a calm voice, while she wiped her wet cheeks:

"Nothing. Only I have no dress, and therefore I can't go to this ball. Give your card to some colleague whose wife is better equipped than I."

He was in despair. He resumed:

"Come, let us see, Mathilde. How much would it cost, a suitable dress which you could use on other occasions, something very simple?"

She reflected several seconds, making her calculations and wondering also what sum she could ask without drawing on herself an immediate refusal and a frightened exclamation from the economical clerk.

Finally she replied, hesitatingly:

"I don't know exactly, but I think I could manage it with four hundred francs."

He had grown a little pale, because he was laying aside just that amount to buy a gun and treat himself to a little shooting next summer on the plain of Nanterre, with several friends who went to shoot larks down there, of a Sunday.

But he said:

"All right. I will give you four hundred francs. And try to have a pretty dress."

The day of the ball drew near, and Mme. Loisel seemed sad, uneasy, anxious. Her dress was ready, however. Her husband said to her one evening:

"What is the matter? Come, you've been so queer these last three days."

And she answered:

"It annoys me not to have a single jewel, not a single stone, nothing to put on. I shall look like distress. I should almost rather not go at all."

He resumed:

"You might wear natural flowers. It's very stylish at this time of the year. For ten francs you can get two or three magnificent roses."

She was not convinced.

"No; there's nothing more humiliating than to look poor among other women who are rich."

But her husband cried:

"How stupid you are! Go look up your friend Mme. Forestier, and ask her to lend you some jewels. You're quite thick enough with her to do that."

She uttered a cry of joy.

"It's true. I never thought of it."

The next day she went to her friend and told of her distress.

Mme. Forestier went to a wardrobe with a glass door, took out a large jewel-box, brought it back, opened it, and said to Mme. Loisel:

"Choose, my dear."

She saw first of all some bracelets, then a pearl necklace, then a Venetian cross, gold and precious stones of admirable workmanship. She tried on the ornaments before the glass, hesitated, could not make up her mind to part with them, to give them back. She kept asking:
"Haven't you any more?"
"Why, yes. Look. I don't know what you like."
All of a sudden she discovered, in a black satin box, a superb necklace of diamonds; and her heart began to beat with an immoderate desire. Her hands trembled as she took it. She fastened it around her throat, outside her high-necked dress, and remained lost in ecstasy at the sight of herself.
Then she asked, hesitating, filled with anguish:
"Can you lend me that, only that?"
"Why, yes, certainly."
She sprang upon the neck of her friend, kissed her passionately, then fled with her treasure.

The day of the ball arrived. Mme. Loisel made a great success. She was prettier than them all, elegant, gracious, smiling, and crazy with joy. All the men looked at her, asked her name, endeavored to be introduced. All the attachés of the Cabinet wanted to waltz with her. She was remarked by the Minister himself.
She danced with intoxication, with passion, made drunk by pleasure, forgetting all in the triumph of her beauty, in the glory of her success, in a sort of cloud of happiness composed of all this homage, of all this admiration, of all these awakened desires, and of that sense of complete victory which is so sweet to a woman's heart.
She went away about four o'clock in the morning. Her husband had been sleeping since midnight, in a little deserted anteroom, with three other gentlemen whose wives were having a very good time.
He threw over her shoulders the wraps which he had brought, modest wraps of common life, whose poverty contrasted with the elegance of the ball dress. She felt this, and wanted to escape so as not to be remarked by the other women who were enveloping themselves in costly furs.
Loisel held her back.
"Wait a bit. You will catch cold outside. I will go and call a cab."
But she did not listen to him, and rapidly descended the stairs. When they were in the street, they did not find a carriage; and they began to look for one, shouting after the cabmen whom they saw passing by at a distance.
They went down towards the Seine, in despair, shivering with cold. At last they found on the quay one of those ancient noctambulant coupés which, exactly as if they were ashamed to show their misery during the day, are never seen 'round Paris until after nightfall.
It took them to their door in the Rue des Martyrs, and once more,

sadly, they climbed up homeward. All was ended for her. And as to him, he reflected that he must be at the Ministry at ten o'clock.

She removed the wraps, which covered her shoulders, before the glass, so as once more to see herself in all her glory. But suddenly she uttered a cry. She had no longer the necklace around her neck!

Her husband, already half undressed, demanded:

"What is the matter with you?"

She turned madly towards him.

"I have—I have—I've lost Mme. Forestier's necklace."

He stood up, distracted.

"What! How? Impossible!"

And they looked in the folds of her dress, in the folds of her cloak, in her pockets, everywhere. They did not find it.

He asked:

"You're sure you had it on when you left the ball?"

"Yes, I felt it in the vestibule of the palace."

"But if you had lost it in the street we should have heard it fall. It must be in the cab."

"Yes. Probably. Did you take his number?"

"No. And you, didn't you notice it?"

"No."

They looked, thunderstruck, at one another. At last Loisel put on his clothes.

"I shall go back on foot," said he, "over the whole route which we have taken, to see if I can't find it."

And he went out. She sat waiting on a chair in her ball dress, without strength to go to bed, overwhelmed, without fire, without a thought.

Her husband came back about seven o'clock. He had found nothing.

He went to Police Headquarters, to the newspaper offices, to offer a reward; he went to the cab companies—everywhere, in fact, whither he was urged by the least suspicion of hope.

She waited all day, in the same condition of mad fear before this terrible calamity.

Loisel returned at night with a hollow, pale face; he had discovered nothing.

"You must write to your friend," said he, "that you have broken the clasp of her necklace, and that you are having it mended. That will give us time to turn around."

She wrote at his dictation.

At the end of a week they had lost all hope.

And Loisel, who had aged five years, declared:

"We must consider how to replace that ornament."

The next day they took the box which had contained it, and they went to the jeweler whose name was found within. He consulted his books.

"It was not I, Madame, who sold that necklace; I must simply have furnished the case."

Then they went from jeweler to jeweler, searching for a necklace like the other, consulting their memories, sick, both of them, with chagrin and with anguish.

They found, in a shop at the Palais Royal, a string of diamonds which seemed to them exactly like the one they looked for. It was worth forty thousand francs. They could have it for thirty-six.

So they begged the jeweler not to sell it for three days yet. And they made a bargain that he should buy it back for thirty-four thousand francs, in case they found the other one before the end of February.

Loisel possessed eighteen thousand francs which his father had left him. He would borrow the rest.

He did borrow, asking a thousand francs of one, five hundred francs of another, five louis here, three louis there. He gave notes, took up ruinous obligations, dealt with usurers, and all the race of lenders. He compromised all the rest of his life, risked his signature without even knowing if he could meet it; and, frightened by the pains yet to come, by the black misery which was about to fall upon him, by the prospect of all the physical privations and of all the moral tortures which he was to suffer, he went to get the new necklace, putting down upon the merchant's counter thirty-six thousand francs.

When Mme. Loisel took back the necklace, Mme. Forestier said to her, with a chilly manner:

"You should have returned it sooner. I might have needed it."

She did not open the case, as her friend had so much feared. If she had detected the substitution, what would she have thought, what would she have said? Would she not have taken Mme. Loisel for a thief?

Mme. Loisel now knew the horrible existence of the needy. She took her part, moreover, all on a sudden, with heroism. That dreadful debt must be paid. She would pay it. They dismissed their servant; they changed their lodgings; they rented a garret under the roof.

She came to know what heavy housework meant, and the odious cares of the kitchen. She washed the dishes, using her rosy nails on the greasy pots and pans. She washed the dirty linen, the shirts, and the dish cloths, which she dried upon a rope; she carried the slops down to the street every morning, and carried up the water, stopping for breath at every landing. And, dressed like a woman of the people, she went to the fruiterer, the grocer, the butcher, her basket on her arm, bargaining, insulted, defending her miserable money sou by sou.

Each month they had to meet some notes, renew others, obtain more time.

Her husband worked in the evening making a fair copy of some trades-man's accounts, and late at night he often copied manuscript for five sous a page.

And this life lasted ten years.

At the end of ten years they had paid everything, everything, with the rates of usury, and the accumulations of the compound in-terest.

Mme. Loisel looked old now. She had become the woman of impover-ished households—strong and hard and rough. With frowsy hair, skirts askew, and red hands, she talked loud while washing the floor with great swishes of water. But sometimes, when her husband was at the office, she sat down near the window, and she thought of that gay evening of long ago, of that ball where she had been so beautiful and so fêted.

What would have happened if she had not lost that necklace? Who knows? who knows? How life is strange and changeful! How little a thing is needed for us to be lost or to be saved!

But one Sunday, having gone to take a walk in the Champs Élysées to refresh herself from the labors of the week, she suddenly perceived a woman who was leading a child. It was Mme. Forestier, still young, still beautiful, still charming.

Mme. Loisel felt moved. Was she going to speak to her? Yes, cer-tainly. And now that she had paid, she was going to tell her all about it. Why not?

She went up.

"Good-day, Jeanne."

The other, astonished to be familiarly addressed by this plain good-wife, did not recognize her at all, and stammered:

"But—Madame!—I do not know—You must have mistaken."

"No. I am Mathilde Loisel."

Her friend uttered a cry.

"Oh, my poor Mathilde! How you are changed!"

"Yes, I have had days hard enough since I have seen you, days wretched enough—and that because of you!"

"Of me! How so?"

"Do you remember that diamond necklace which you lent me to wear at the ministerial ball?"

"Yes. Well?"

"Well, I lost it."

"What do you mean? You brought it back."

"I brought you back another just like it. And for this we have been ten years paying. You can understand that it was not easy for us, us who had nothing. At last it is ended, and I am very glad."

Mme. Forestier had stopped.

"You say that you bought a necklace of diamonds to replace mine?"

"Yes. You never noticed it, then! They were very like."

And she smiled with a joy which was proud and naïve at once.

Mme. Forestier, deeply moved, took her two hands.

"Oh, my poor Mathilde! Why, my necklace was paste. It was worth at most five hundred francs!"

THREE ARSHINS OF LAND

By Leo N. Tolstoy

[Count Leo (Lyof) Nikolayevich Tolstoy (1828–1910) was one of the great men of the nineteenth century. He is well known the world over as social reformer, religious mystic, and novelist. He was born in the province of Tula, Russia, educated at the University of Kazan and served as a young soldier in the Caucasus and in the Crimean Wars. After the liberation of the Russian serfs he retired to his estates in Southern Russia and there lived among the peasants as a friend and helper. In his old age he wrote little stories dealing with peasant problems and had them printed and distributed without copyright and at a very small cost. The story *Three Arshins of Land, or How Much Land Does a Man Need?* is one of these stories. *Where Love Is, There God Is Also* is another.

Among his best known novels may be mentioned *War and Peace* (1864–66), a novel of Russian life from 1805 to 1815; *Anna Karenina* (1875–77), *The Death of Ivan Ilyitch* (1884); *The Kreutzer Sonata* (1889); and *Resurrection* (1900).

The translation of *Three Arshins of Land* was made by Archibald J. Wolfe and is reprinted here by permission of the translator.]

PAKHOM'S neighbor was a lady who owned a little estate. She had one hundred and twenty dessyatins.[1] For a long time she had never harmed the peasants in any way, living in peace with them. But lately she had installed a retired soldier as superintendent, and he worried the peasants with fines. No matter how careful Pakhom was, a horse would invade his neighbor's oat-field, or his cow would stray into her garden or the calves into the pasture. There was a fine for everything.

Pakhom paid, growled, beat his family, and in the course of the summer laid up much sin upon his soul because of the superintendent. He found relief only by keeping his cattle in the yard. He begrudged the fodder, but he was thus spared much anxiety.

In the winter the rumor spread that his neighbor meant to dispose of her land and that the superintendent thought of buying it. When the peasants heard this they were greatly troubled.

If the superintendent becomes the master, they judged, there will be no end to the fines.

They importuned the lady to sell the land to the community and not

[1] A dessyatin is about 2.7 acres.

343

to the superintendent. As they promised to pay her more than the latter, she agreed. The peasants held a meeting, then met again, but came to no understanding. The Devil sowed dissensions. Finally they decided that each should buy land according to his means, and the owner consented again.

When Pakhom heard that a neighboring peasant had bought twenty dessyatins of the land, with time extension to pay one-half of the purchase price, he became envious. "They'll sell the whole land, and I'll go empty-handed." He consulted with his wife. "The peasants are buying land. We must get ten dessyatins," he said. They considered how to arrange the matter.

They had saved a hundred rubles. They sold a foal, one-half of their beehives, hired the son out as a laborer, and thus succeeded in scraping one-half of the money together.

Pakhom looked over a tract of land of fifteen dessyatins, with a grove, and negotiated with his neighbor. He contracted for the fifteen dessyatins and paid his earnest money. Then they drove to the city and made out the deed. He paid one-half of the money and agreed to pay the rest in two years. Pakhom now had land.

He borrowed money from his brother-in-law, bought seed and sowed the purchased land. Everything came up beautifully. Inside of a year he was able to pay off his debts to the neighbor and to his brother-in-law. Pakhom was now a landowner in his own right. He cultivated his own ground, and cut his own pasturage. He was] overjoyed. The grass had another look; different kinds of flowers seemed to bloom on it. Once upon a time this land had looked to him the same as any other, but now it was a specially blessed piece of God's earth.

Pakhom was enjoying life. Everything would be well now if the peasants only left his fields alone, if they did not let their cattle graze on his meadows. He admonished them in a friendly fashion. But they did not desist from driving their cows on his land, and at night the strangers' horses invaded his grain. Pakhom chased them and for a time did not lay it up against the peasants. Finally, however, he lost patience and made a complaint to the court. He knew very well, tho, that necessity forced the peasants to do this, not love of wrongdoing. Still, he thought, he would have to teach them a lesson, or they would graze his land bare. A good lesson might be useful.

With the help of the court he taught them more than one lesson; more than one peasant was fined. And so it happened that the peasants were in no amiable mood towards him and were eager to play tricks on him. He was soon at loggerheads with all his neighbors. His land had grown, but the confines of the community seemed all too narrow now.

One day, as he was seated at home, a traveling peasant asked for a lodging. Pakhom kept him over night, gave him plenty of meat and drink, inquired where he came from and talked of this and that. The peasant related that he was on the way from the lower Volga region, where he had been working. Many peasants had settled there. They were received into the community and ten dessyatins were allotted to each. Beautiful land! It made the heart feel glad to see it full of sheaves. A peasant had come there naked and poor, with empty hands, and now he had fifty dessyatins under wheat. Last year he sold his one crop of wheat for five thousand rubles.

Pakhom listened with delight. He thought: why plague oneself in this crowded section, if one can live fine elsewhere? I will sell my land and property and from the proceeds I will buy land on the lower Volga and start a farm. Here in this crowded corner there is nothing but quarreling. I will go and look things over for myself.

When summer came he started on his journey. He went by boat to Samara on the Volga, then four hundred versts[1] on foot. When he arrived at his journey's end he found things even as they had been reported to him. Ten dessyatins were allotted to each person, and the mujiks were glad to receive the stranger into the community. If a man brought money with him he was welcome and could buy as much land as he pleased. Three rubles a dessyatin was the price for the best land.

When Pakhom had investigated everything, he returned home, sold his land at a profit, sold his homestead and cattle, took leave from his community, and, when the spring came around, he journeyed with his family to the new lands.

When he reached his destination with his family, Pakhom settled in a large village and registered in the community. Having treated the elders, he received his papers in good order. He had been taken into the community, and, in addition to the pasturage, land for five souls— fifty dessyatins in all—were allotted to him. He built a homestead and bought cattle. His allotment was twice as large as his former holdings. And what fertile land! He had enough of everything and could keep as many head of cattle as he wished.

In the beginning, while he was building and equipping his homestead, he was well satisfied. But after he had lived there a while he began to feel that the new lands were too narrow. The first year Pakhom sowed wheat on his allotted land. It came up bountifully, and this created a desire to have more land at his disposal. He drove over to the merchant and leased some land for a year. The seed yielded a plentiful harvest. Unfortunately the fields were quite far from the village and the gathered grain had to be carted for a distance of fifteen versts. He saw peasant traders in the neighborhood owning dairies and amassing wealth. How much better were it, thought Pakhom, to buy land instead of leasing it, and to start dairying. That would give me a well-rounded property, all in one hand.

Then he came across a peasant who owned five hundred dessyatins of

[1] A verst is approximately seven-tenths of a mile.

land, but found himself ruined and was eager to dispose of his property at a low figure. They closed a deal. Pakhom was to pay fifteen hundred rubles, one-half down, one-half later.

About this time a traveling merchant stopped at Pakhom's farm to feed his horses. They drank tea and spoke of this and that. The merchant told him that he was on his way home from the land of the Bashkirs. He had bought land there, about five thousand dessyatins, and had paid one thousand rubles for it. Pakhom made inquiries. The merchant willingly gave information.

"Only one thing is needful," he explained, "and that is to do some favor to their Chief. I distributed raiment and rugs among them, which cost me a hundred rubles, and I divided a chest of tea between them, and whoever wanted it had his fill of vodka. I got the dessyatin land for twenty copeks. Here is the deed. The land along the river and even on the steppes is wheat-growing land."

Pakhom made further inquiries.

"You couldn't walk the land through in a year," reported the merchant. "All this is Bashkir-land. The men are as simple as sheep; one could buy from them almost for nothing."

And Pakhom thought: "Why should I buy for my thousand rubles five hundred dessyatins of land and hang a debt around my neck, while for the same amount I can acquire immeasurable property."

Pakhom inquired the way to the land of the Bashkirs. As soon as he had seen the merchant off, he made ready for the journey. He left the land and the homestead in his wife's charge and took only one of his farmhands along. In a neighboring city they bought a chest of tea, other presents, and some vodka, as the merchant had instructed them.

They rode and rode. They covered five hundred versts and on the seventh day they came into the land of the Bashkirs and found everything just as the merchant had described. On the riverside and in the steppes the Bashkirs live in kibitkas. They do not plow. They eat no bread. Cows and horses graze on the steppes. Foals are tied behind the tents, and mares are taken to them twice daily. They make kumyss out of mare's milk, and the women shake the kumyss to make cheese. The men drink kumyss and tea, eat mutton, and play the flute all day long. They are all fat and merry, and idle the whole summer through. Ignorant folk, they cannot speak Russian, but they were very friendly.

When they caught sight of Pakhom, the Bashkirs left their tents and surrounded him. An interpreter was at hand, whom Pakhom informed that he had come to buy land. The Bashkirs showed their joy and led Pakhom into their good tent. They bade him sit down on a fine rug, propped him up with downy cushions and treated him to tea and kumyss. They also slaughtered a sheep and offered him meat. Pakhom fetched from his tarantass the chest of tea and other presents and distributed them among the Bashkirs. The Bashkirs were overjoyed.

They talked and talked among themselves and finally they ordered the interpreter to speak.

"They want me to tell you," said the interpreter, "that they have taken a liking to you. It is our custom to favor the guest in all possible ways and to return gifts for gifts. You have given us presents, now tell us what do you like of what we have so that we may give you presents also."

"Most of all I like land," replied Pakhom. "We're crowded where I am at home and everything is already under the plow. But you have good land and plenty of it. In all my born days I have never seen land like yours."

The Bashkirs were now talking again, and all at once it looked as tho they were quarreling. Pakhom asked why they were quarreling. The interpreter replied:

"Some of them think that the Chief should be consulted, and that no agreement ought to be made without him; but the others say it can be done without the Chief just as well."

While the Bashkirs were yet arguing, a man with a hat of fox fur entered the tent. Everybody stopped talking and they all rose. "This is the Chief."

Pakhom immediately produced the best sleeping robe and five pounds of tea. The Chief accepted the presents and sat down in the place of honor. The Bashkirs spoke to him. He listened, smiled and addressed Pakhom in Russian.

"Well," he said, "that can be done. Help yourself, wherever it suits you. There is plenty of land."

"How can I do this, tho," thought Pakhom. "Some official confirmation is necessary. Otherwise they say today, help yourself, but afterwards they may take it away again." And he said:

"Thank you for these good words. You have plenty of land, and I need but little. Only I must know what land belongs to me. It must be measured and I need some sort of a confirmation. For God's will rules over life and death. You are good people and you give me the land; but it may happen that your children will take it away again."

The Chief laughed. "Surely this can be done," he agreed. "A confirmation so strong that it cannot be made stronger."

Pakhom replied: "I heard that a merchant had been here among you. You sold him land and gave him a deed. I should like to have it the same way."

The Chief immediately understood. "This too can be done," he exclaimed. "We have a writer. We will drive to the city and have the seals put on."

"We have but one price: one thousand rubles a day."

Pakhom failed to comprehend what sort of measure a day would be. "How many dessyatins will that make?"

"That we cannot figure out. For one day we sell you as much land as you can walk around in one day. The price of one day is one thousand rubles."

Pakhom looked surprised. "One can walk around a lot of land in one day," he said.

The Chief smiled. "Everything will be yours, but on one condition. If in the course of the day you do not return to the place you start from, your money is lost."

"But how can it be noted how far I have gone?"

"We will stay right at the starting point. Our lads will ride behind you. Where you command they will drive in a stake. Then we shall mark furrows from stake to stake. Choose your circle to suit yourself, only before sunset be back at the spot where you started from. All the land that you walk around shall be yours."

Pakhom assented. It was decided to start early in the morning. They conversed for a while, drank kumyss and tea and ate more mutton. When the night set in Pakhom retired to sleep and the Bashkirs dispersed. In the morning they were to meet again in order to journey to the starting point.

Pakhom could not fall asleep. He had his mind on the land. What manner of things he thought of introducing there! "A whole principality I have before me! I can easily make fifty versts in one day. The days are long now. Fifty versts encompass ten thousand dessyatins. I will have to knuckle down to no one. I'll plow as much as may suit me; the rest I'll use for a pasturage."

The whole night through he was unable to close his eyes; only towards morning he dozed restlessly. Hardly had he begun to doze when he saw a vision. He was lying in his kibitka and heard laughter outside. To see who it was that laughed he stepped out of the kibitka and found the chief of the Bashkirs. He was holding his hands to his sides and fairly shaking with laughter. Pakhom approached him in his dream to find out why he was laughing, but now, instead of the Bashkir, he saw the merchant who had come to his farm and told him of this land. Just as he wanted to ask him how long he had been there, he saw that it was no longer the merchant but that mujik who had called on him at his old homestead and told him of the lower Volga region. And now again it was no longer the mujik but the Devil himself, with horns and hoofs, and he laughed and stared at one spot. What is he looking upon? wondered Pakhom; why is he laughing? In his dream he saw a man lying outstretched, barefoot, clad only in a shirt and pair of trousers, with his face turned upward, white as a sheet. As he looked again to see what manner of man it was, he saw clearly that it was he himself.

He awoke with the horror of it. What dreadful things one sees in a dream! He looked about. It was commencing to dawn. The people must be roused. It was time to journey to the starting place.

Pakhom arose, waked his servant, who had been sleeping in the tarantass, harnessed the horses and went to wake the Bashkirs.

"It is time," he said, "to travel to the steppe."

The Bashkirs got up, assembled, and the chief came among them. Again they drank tea and wanted to treat Pakhom, but he urged them to be off.

"If we go, let it be done at once," he remarked. "It is high time."

The Bashkirs made ready, some of them on horseback, others in tarantasses. Pakhom, accompanied by his servant, drove in his own cart. They came to the steppe as the morning sun was beginning to crimson the sky, and driving over to a little hillock they gathered together. The chief came towards Pakhom and pointed with his hand to the steppes.

"All this land that you see," he said, "as far as your eye can reach, is ours. Choose to suit yourself."

Pakhom's eyes shone. In the distance he saw grass land, smooth as the palm of his hand, black as poppy seeds. In the deeper places the grass was growing shoulder high.

The chief took his fur cap and placed it in the middle of the hill. "This is the landmark. Here place your gold. Your servant will stay here. Go from this point hence and come back again. All the land which you encompass walking is yours."

Pakhom took out the money and laid it on the cap. He took off his coat, keeping the vest on, took a bag of bread, tied a flat water bottle to his belt, pulled up his top boots and made ready to go. He hesitated for a while which direction to take. The view was everywhere enchanting. Finally he said to himself: "I'll go towards the rising of the sun." He faced the East and stretched himself waiting for the sun to appear above the horizon. There was no time to lose. It is better walking in the cool of the morning. The riders took up their positions behind him. As soon as the sun was visible, he set off, followed by the men on horseback.

He walked neither briskly nor slowly. He had walked about a verst without stopping when he ordered a stake to be driven in. Once again in motion, he hastened his steps and soon ordered another stake to be put in. He looked back; the hill was still to be seen with the people on it. Looking up at the sun he figured that he had walked about five versts. It had grown warm, so he doffed his vest. Five versts further the heat began to trouble him. Another glance at the sun showed him it was time for breakfast. "I have already covered a good stretch," he thought. "Of course, there are four of these to be covered today; still it is too early to turn yet; but I'll take my boots off." He sat down, took off his boots and went on. The walking was now easier. "I can go five versts more," he thought, "and then turn to the left." The further he went, the more beautiful the land grew. He walked straight ahead. As he looked again, the hill was hardly to be seen, and the people on it looked like ants.

"Now it's time to turn back," he thought. "How hot I am! I feel like having a drink." He took his bottle with water and drank while walking. Then he made them drive in another stake and turned to the left. He walked and walked; the grass was high, the sun beat down with evergrowing fierceness. Weariness now set in. A glance at the sun showed him that it was midday. "I must rest," he thought. He stopped and ate a little bread. "If I sit down to eat, I'll fall asleep." He stood for a while, caught his breath and walked on. For a time it was easy. The food had refreshed him and given him new strength. But it was too oppressively hot, and sleep threatened to overcome him. He felt exhausted. "Well," he thought, "an hour of pain for an age of joy."

In this second direction he walked nearly ten versts. He meant then to turn to the left, but lo! the section was so fine—a luxuriant dale. Pity to give it up! What a wonderful place for flax! And again he walked straight on, appropriated the dale and marked the place with a stake. Now only he made his second turning. Casting his glance at the starting point he could hardly discern any people on the hill. "Must be about fifteen versts away. I have made the two sides too long and I must shorten the third. Though the property will turn out irregular in this way, what else can be done? I must turn in and walk straight toward the hill. I must hasten and guard against useless turns. I have plenty of land now." And he turned and walked straight toward the hill.

Pakhom's feet ached. He had worked them almost to a standstill. His knees were giving way. He felt like taking a rest, but he dared not. He had no time; he must be back before sunset. The sun does not wait. He ran on as though someone were driving him.

"Did I not make a mistake? Did I not try to grab too much? If I only get back in time! It is so far off, and I am all played out. If only all my trouble and labor be not in vain! I must exert myself to the utmost."

He shivered and ran onward in a trot. His feet were bleeding now. Still he ran. He cast off his vest, the boots, the bottle, the cap. "I was too greedy! I have ruined all! I can't get back by sunset!"

It was getting worse all the time. Fear shortened his breath. He ran on. The shirt and trousers were sticking to his body, his mouth was all dried out, his bosom was heaving like the bellows in a forge, his heart was beating like a hammer, the knees felt as though they were another's and gave under him.

He hardly thought of the land now; he merely thought what to do so as not to die from exertion. Yes, he feared to die, but he could not stop. "I have run so much that if I stop now they will call me a fool."

The Bashkirs, he could hear clearly, were screaming and calling. Their noise added fuel to his burning heart. With the last effort of his strength he ran. The sun was close to the horizon, but the hill was quite near now. The Bashkirs were beckoning, calling. He saw the fur cap, saw his money in it, saw the chief squatting on the ground with his hands at his stomach. He remembered his dream. "Earth there is a-plenty," he thought, "but will God let me live thereon? Ah, I have destroyed myself." And still he kept on running.

He looked at the sun. It was large and crimson, touching the earth and beginning to sink. He reached the foot of the hill. The sun had gone down. A cry of woe escaped from his lips. He thought all was lost. But he remembered that the sun must yet be visible from a higher spot. He rushed up the hill. There was the cap. He stumbled and fell, but reached the cap with his hands. "Good lad!" exclaimed the chief. "You have gained much land."

As Pakhom's servant rushed to his side and tried to lift him, blood was flowing from his mouth. He was dead.

The servant lamented.

The chief was still squatting on the ground, and now he began laughing loudly and holding his sides. Then he rose to his feet, threw a spade to the servant and said, "Here, dig!"

The Bashkirs all clambered to their feet and drove away. The servant remained alone with the corpse.

He dug a grave for Pakhom, the measure of his body from head to foot—three arshins[1] and no more. There he buried Pakhom.

[1]An arshin is about two feet.

WHERE LOVE IS, THERE GOD IS ALSO

By Leo N. Tolstoy

[The version of this story by an unknown translator appeared in *The Outlook* and is reprinted by permission.]

IN a certain city dwelt Martin Avdyeeich, the cobbler. He lived in a cellar, a wretched little hole with a single window. The window looked up towards the street, and through it Martin could just see the passers-by. It is true that he could see little more than their boots, but Martin Avdyeeich could read a man's character by his boots; so he needed no more. Martin Avdyeeich had lived long in that one place, and had many acquaintances. Few indeed were the boots in that neighborhood which had not passed through his hands at some time or other. On some he would fasten new soles, to others he would give side-pieces, others again he would stitch all round, and even give them new uppers if need be. And often he saw his own handiwork through the window. There was always lots of work for him, for Avdyeeich's hand was cunning and his leather good; nor did he overcharge, and always kept his word. He always engaged to do a job by a fixed time if he could; but if he could not, he said so at once, and deceived no man. So every one knew Avdyeeich, and he had no lack of work. Avdyeeich had always been a pretty good man, but as he grew old he began to think more about his soul, and draw nearer to his God. While Martin was still a journeyman his wife had died; but his wife had left him a little boy—three years old. Their other children had not lived. All the eldest had died early. Martin wished at first to send his little child into the country to his sister, but afterwards he thought better of it. "My Kapitoshka," thought he, "will feel miserable in a strange household. He shall stay here with me." And so Avdyeeich left his master, and took to living in lodgings alone with his little son. But God did not give Avdyeeich happiness in his children. No sooner had the little one begun to grow up and be a help and a joy to his father's heart, than a sickness fell upon Kapitoshka; the little one took to his bed, lay there in a raging fever for a week, and then died. Martin buried his son in despair—so desperate was he that he began to murmur against God. Such disgust of life overcame him that he more than once begged God that he might die; and he reproached God for taking not him, an old man, but his darling, his only son, instead. And after that Avdyeeich left off going to church.

And, lo! one day there came to Avdyeeich from the Troitsa Monastery an aged peasant-pilgrim—it was already the eighth year óf his pilgrimage. Avdyeeich fell a-talking with him, and began to complain of

352

his great sorrow. "As for living any longer, thou man of God," said he, "I desire it not. Would only that I might die! That is my sole prayer to God. I am now a man who has no hope."

And the old man said to him: "Thy speech, Martin, is not good. How shall we judge the doings of God? God's judgments are not our thoughts. God willed that thy son shouldst die, but that thou shouldst live. Therefore 'twas the best thing both for him and for thee. It is because thou wouldst fain have lived for thy own delight that thou dost now despair."

"But what then *is* a man to live for?" asked Avdyeeich.

And the old man answered: "For God, Martin! He gave thee life, and for Him therefore must thou live. When thou dost begin to live for Him, thou wilt grieve about nothing more, and all things will come easy to thee."

Martin was silent for a moment, and then he said: "And how must one live for God?"

"Christ hath shown us the way. Thou knowest thy letters. Buy the Gospels and read; there thou wilt find out how to live for God. There everything is explained."

These words made the heart of Avdyeeich burn within him, and he went the same day and bought for himself a New Testament printed in very large type, and began to read.

Avdyeeich set out with the determination to read it only on holidays; but as he read, it did his heart so much good that he took to reading it every day. And the second time he read until all the kerosene in the lamp had burnt itself out, and for all that he could not tear himself away from the book. And so it was every evening. And the more he read, the more clearly he understood what God wanted of him, and how it behooved him to live for God; and his heart grew lighter and lighter continually. Formerly, whenever he lay down to sleep he would only sigh and groan, and think of nothing but Kapitoshka, but now he would only say to himself: "Glory to Thee! Glory to Thee, O Lord! Thy will be done!"

Henceforth the whole life of Avdyeeich was changed. Formerly, whenever he had a holiday, he would go to the tavern to drink tea, nor would he say "no" to a drop of brandy now and again. He would tipple with his comrades, and though not actually drunk, would, for all that, leave the inn a bit merry, babbling nonsense and talking loudly and censoriously. He had done with all that now. His life became quiet and joyful. With the morning light he sat down to his work, worked out his time, then took down his lamp from the hook, placed it on the table, took down his book from the shelf, bent over it, and sat him down to read. And the more he read the more he understood, and his heart grew brighter and happier.

It happened once that Martin was up reading till very late. He was reading St. Luke's Gospel. He was reading the sixth chapter, and as he read he came to the words: "And to him that smiteth thee on the one cheek, offer also the other." This passage he read several times, and presently he came to that place where the Lord says: "And why call ye me Lord, Lord, and do not the things which I say? Whosoever cometh to Me, and heareth My sayings, and doeth them, I will show you whom he is like. He is like a man which built an house, and dug deep, and laid the foundations on a rock. And when the flood arose, the storm beat vehemently upon that house, and could not shake it, for it was founded upon a rock. But he that heareth and doeth not, is like a man that without a foundation built an house upon the sand, against which the storm did beat vehemently, and immediately it fell, and the ruin of that house was great."

Avdyeeich read these words through and through, and his heart was glad. He took off his glasses, laid them on the book, rested his elbow on the table, and fell a-thinking. And he began to measure his own life by these words. And he thought to himself, "Is my house built on the rock or on the sand? How good to be as on a rock! How easy it all seems to thee sitting alone here! It seems as if thou wert doing God's will to the full, and so thou takest no heed and fallest away again. And yet thou wouldst go on striving, for so it is good for thee. O Lord, help me!" Thus thought he, and would have laid him down, but it was a grief to tear himself away from the book. And so he began reading the seventh chapter. He read all about the Centurion, he read all about the Widow's Son, he read all about the answer to the disciples of St. John; and so he came to that place where the rich Pharisee invited our Lord to be his guest. And he read all about how the woman who was a sinner anointed His feet and washed them with her tears, and how He justified her. And so he came at last to the forty-fourth verse, and there he read these words, "And He turned to the woman and said to Simon, Seest thou this woman? I entered into thine house, thou gavest Me no water for My feet; but she has washed My feet with tears and wiped them with the hairs of her head. Thou gavest Me no kiss, but this woman, since the time I came in, hath not ceased to kiss My feet. Mine head with oil thou didst not anoint." And again Avdyeeich took off his glasses, and laid them on the book, and fell a-thinking.

"So it is quite plain that I, too, have something of the Pharisee about me. Am I not always thinking of myself? Am I not always thinking of drinking tea, and keeping myself as warm and cosy as possible, without thinking at all about the guest? Simon thought about himself, but did not give the slightest thought to his guest. But who was his guest? The Lord Himself. And suppose He were to come to me, should I treat Him as the Pharisee did?"

And Avdyeeich leaned both his elbows on the table and, without perceiving it, fell a-dozing.

"Martin!"—it was as the voice of someone close to his ear. Martin started up from his nap. "Who's there?"

He turned round, he gazed at the door, but there was no one. Again he dozed off. Suddenly he heard quite plainly,

"Martin, Martin, I say! Look tomorrow into the street. I am coming."

Martin awoke, rose from his chair, and began to rub his eyes. And he did not know himself whether he had heard these words asleep or awake. He turned down the lamp and laid him down to rest.

At dawn next day Avdyeeich arose, prayed to God, lit his stove, got ready his gruel and cabbage soup, filled his samovar, put on his apron, and sat him down by his window to work. There Avdyeeich sits and works, and thinks of nothing but the things of yesternight. His thoughts were divided. He thought at one time that he must have gone off dozing, and then again he thought he really must have heard that voice. It might have been so, thought he.

Martin sits at the window and looks as much at his window as at his work, and whenever a strange pair of boots passes by, he bends forward and looks out of the window, so as to see the face as well as the feet of the passers-by. The house porter passed by in new felt boots, the water-carrier passed by, and after that there passed close to the window an old soldier, one of Nicholas's veterans, in tattered old boots, with a shovel in his hands. Avdyeeich knew him by his boots. The old fellow was called Stepanuich, and lived with the neighboring shopkeeper, who harbored him of his charity. His duty was to help the porter. Stepanuich stopped before Avdyeeich's window to sweep away the snow. Avdyeeich cast a glance at him, and then went on working as before.

"I'm not growing sager as I grow older," thought Avdyeeich, with some self-contempt. "I make up my mind that Christ is coming to me, and, lo! 'tis only Stepanuich clearing away the snow. Thou simpleton, thou! thou art wool-gathering!" Then Avdyeeich made ten more stitches, and then he stretched his head once more towards the window. He looked through the window again, and there he saw that Stepanuich had placed the shovel against the wall, and was warming himself and taking breath a bit.

"The old man is very much broken," thought Avdyeeich to himself. "It is quite plain that he has scarcely strength enough to scrape away the snow. Suppose I make him drink a little tea! the samovar, too, is just on the boil." Avdyeeich put down his awl, got up, placed the samovar on the table, put some tea in it, and tapped on the window with his fingers. Stepanuich turned round and came to the window. Avdyeeich beckoned to him, and then went and opened the door.

"Come in and warm yourself a bit," cried he. "You're a bit chilled, eh?"

"Christ requite you! Yes, and all my bones ache, too," said Stepanuich. Stepanuich came in, shook off the snow, and began to wipe his feet so as not to soil the floor, but he tottered sadly.

"Don't trouble about wiping your feet. I'll rub it off myself. It's all in the day's work. Come in and sit down," said Avdyeeich. "Here, take a cup of tea."

And Avdyeeich filled two cups, and gave one to his guest, and he poured his own tea out into the saucer and began to blow it.

Stepanuich drank his cup, turned it upside down, put a gnawed crust on the top of it, and said, "Thank you." But it was quite plain that he wanted to be asked to have some more.

"Have a drop more. Do!" said Avdyeeich, and poured out fresh cups for his guest and himself, and as Avdyeeich drank his cup, he could not help glancing at the window from time to time.

"Dost thou expect anyone?" asked his guest.

"Do I expect anyone? Well, honestly, I hardly know. I am expecting, and I am not expecting, and there's a word which has burnt itself right into my heart. Whether it was a vision or no, I know not. Look now, my brother! I was reading yesterday about our little Father Christ, how He suffered, how He came on earth. Hast thou heard of Him, eh?"

"I have heard, I have heard," replied Stepanuich, "but we poor ignorant ones know not our letters."

"Anyhow, I was reading about this very thing—how He came down upon earth. I was reading how He went to the Pharisee, and how the Pharisee did not receive Him at all. Thus I thought, and so, about yesternight, little brother mine, I read that very thing, and bethought me how the Honorable did not receive our little Father Christ honorably. But suppose, I thought, if He came to one like me—would I receive Him? Simon at any rate did not receive Him at all. Thus I thought, and so thinking, fell asleep. I fell asleep, I say, little brother mine, and I heard my name called. I started up. A voice was whispering at my very ear. 'Look out tomorrow!' it said, 'I am coming.' And so it befell twice. Now look! wouldst thou believe it? the idea stuck to me—I scold myself for my folly, and yet I look for Him, our little Father Christ!"

Stepanuich shook his head and said nothing, but he drank his cup dry and put it aside. Then Avdyeeich took up the cup and filled it again.

"Drink some more. 'Twill do thee good. Now it seems to me that when our little Father went about on earth, He despised no one, but sought unto the simple folk most of all. He was always among the simple folk. Those disciples of His, too, he chose most of them from amongst our brother-laborers, sinners like unto us. He that exalteth himself, He says, shall be abased, and he that abaseth himself shall be exalted. Ye, says He, call me Lord, and I, says He, wash your feet. He who would be the first among you, He says, let him become the servant of all. And therefore it is that He says, Blessed are the lowly, the peacemakers, the humble, and the longsuffering."

Stepanuich forgot his tea. He was an old man, soft-hearted, and tearful. He sat and listened, and the tears rolled down his cheeks.

"Come, drink a little more," said Avdyeeich. But Stepanuich crossed himself, expressed his thanks, pushed away his cup, and got up.

"I thank thee, Martin Avdyeeich," said he. "I have fared well at thy hands, and thou hast refreshed me both in body and soul."

"Thou wilt show me a kindness by coming again. I am very glad to have a guest," said Avdyeeich. Stepanuich departed, and Martin poured out the last drop of tea, drank it, washed up, and again sat down by the window to work—he had some back-stitching to do. He stitched and stitched, and now and then cast glances at the window—he was looking for Christ, and could think of nothing but Him and His works. And the divers sayings of Christ were in his head all the time.

Two soldiers passed by, one in regimental boots, the other in boots of his own making; after that, the owner of the next house passed by in nicely brushed goloshes. A baker with a basket also passed by. All these passed by in turn, and then there came alongside the window a woman in worsted stockings and rustic shoes, and as she was passing by she stopped short in front of the partition wall. Avdyeeich looked up at her from his window, and he saw that the woman was a stranger and poorly clad, and that she had a little child with her. She was leaning up against the wall with her back to the wind, and tried to wrap the child up, but she had nothing to wrap it up with. The woman wore summer clothes, and thin enough they were. And from out of his corner Avdyeeich heard the child crying and the woman trying to comfort it, but she could not. Then Avdyeeich got up, went out of the door and on to the steps, and cried, "My good woman! my good woman!"

The woman heard him and turned round.

"Why dost thou stand out in the cold there with the child? Come inside! In the warm room thou wilt be better able to tend him. This way!"

The woman was amazed. What she saw was an old fellow in an apron and with glasses on his nose, calling to her. She came towards him.

They went down the steps together—they went into the room. The old man led the woman to the bed. "There," said he, "sit down, gossip, nearer to the stove, and warm and feed thy little one. . . ."

He went to the table, got some bread and a dish, opened the oven door, put some cabbage soup into the dish, took out a pot of gruel, but it was not quite ready, so he put some cabbage soup only into the dish, and placed it on the table. Then he fetched bread, took down the cloth from the hook, and spread it on the table.

"Sit down and have something to eat, gossip," said he, "and I will sit down a little with the youngster. I have had children of my own, and know how to manage them."

The woman crossed herself, sat down at the table, and began to eat, and Avdyeeich sat down on the bed with the child. Avdyeeich smacked his lips at him again and again, but his lack of teeth made it a clumsy joke at best. And all the time the child never left off shrieking. Then Avdyeeich hit upon the idea of shaking his finger at him, so he snapped his fingers up and down, backwards and forwards, right in front of the child's mouth, because his finger was black and sticky with cobbler's wax. And the child stared at the finger and was silent, and presently it began to laugh. And Avdyeeich was delighted. But the woman went on eating, and told him who she was and whence she came.

"I am a soldier's wife," she said: "my eight months' husband they drove right away from me, and nothing has been heard of him since. I took a cook's place till I became a mother. They could not keep me and the child. It is now three months since I have been drifting about without any fixed resting-place. I have eaten away my all. I wanted to be a wet-nurse, but people wouldn't have me: 'Thou art too thin,' they said. I have just been to the merchant's wife where our grandmother lives, and there they promised to take me in. I thought it was all right, but she told me to come again in a week. But she lives a long way off. I am chilled to death, and he is quite tired out. But, God be praised! our landlady has compassion on us, and gives us shelter for Christ's sake. But for that I don't know how we could live through it all."

Avdyeeich sighed, and said, "And have you no warm clothes?"

"Ah, kind friend! this is indeed warm-clothes time, but yesterday I pawned away my last shawl for two *grivenki*."

The woman went to the bed and took up the child, but Avdyeeich stood up, went to the wall cupboard, rummaged about a bit, and then brought back with him an old jacket.

"Look!" said he, "'Tis a shabby thing, 'tis true, but it will do to wrap up in."

The woman looked at the old jacket, then she gazed at the old man, and, taking the jacket, fell a-weeping. Avdyeeich also turned away, crept under the bed, drew out a trunk, and seemed to be very busy about it, whereupon he again sat down opposite the woman.

Then the woman said: "Christ requite thee, dear little father! It is plain that it was He who sent me by thy window. When I first came out it was warm, and now it has turned very cold. And He it was, little father, who made thee look out of the window and have compassion on wretched me."

Avdyeeich smiled slightly, and said: "Yes, He must have done it, for I looked not out of the window in vain, dear gossip!"

And Avdyeeich told his dream to the soldier's wife also, and how he had heard a voice promising that the Lord should come to him that day.

"All things are possible," said the woman. Then she rose up, put on the jacket, wrapped it round her little one, and then began to curtsy and thank Avdyeeich once more.

"Take this for Christ's sake," said Avdyeeich, giving her a two-*grivenka* piece, "and redeem your shawl." The woman crossed herself, Avdyeeich crossed himself, and then he led the woman to the door.

The woman went away. Avdyeeich ate up the remainder of the cabbage soup, washed up, and again sat down to work. He worked on and on, but he did not forget the window, and whenever the window was darkened, he immediately looked up to see who was passing. Acquaintances passed, strangers passed, but there was no one in particular.

But now Avdyeeich sees how, right in front of his window, an old woman, a huckster, has taken her stand. She carries a basket of apples. Not many now remained; she had evidently sold them nearly all. Across her shoulder she carried a sack full of shavings. She must have picked them up near some new building, and was taking them home with her. It was plain that the sack was straining her shoulder. She wanted to shift it on to the other shoulder, so she rested the sack on the pavement, placed the apple-basket on a small post, and set about shaking down the shavings in the sack. Now while she was shaking down the sack, an urchin in a ragged cap suddenly turned up, goodness knows from whence, grabbed at one of the apples in the basket, and would have made off with it, but the wary old woman turned quickly round and gripped the youth by the sleeve. The lad fought and tried to tear himself loose, but the old woman seized him with both hands, knocked his hat off, and tugged hard at his hair. The lad howled, and the old woman reviled him. Avdyeeich ran out into the street.

The old woman was tugging at the lad's hair and wanted to drag him off to the police, while the boy fought and kicked.

"I didn't take it," said he. "What are you whacking me for? Let me go!"

Avdyeeich came up and tried to part them. He seized the lad by the arm and said: "Let him go, little mother! Forgive him for Christ's sake!"

"I'll forgive him so that he sha'n't forget the taste of fresh birch-rods. I mean to take the rascal to the police station."

Avdyeeich began to entreat with the old woman.

"Let him go, little mother; he will not do so any more. Let him go for Christ's sake."

The old woman let him go. The lad would have bolted, but Avdyeeich held him fast.

"Beg the little mother's pardon," said he, "and don't do such things any more. I saw thee take them."

Then the lad began to cry and beg pardon.

"Well, that's all right! And now, there's an apple for thee." And Avdyeeich took one out of the basket and gave it to the boy. "I'll pay thee for it, little mother," he said to the old woman.

"Thou wilt ruin them that way, the blackguards," said the old woman. "If I had the rewarding of him, he should not be able to sit down for a week."

"Oh, little mother, little mother!" cried Avdyeeich, "that is our way of looking at things, but it is not God's way. If he ought to be whipped so for the sake of one apple, what do we deserve for our sins?"

The old woman was silent.

And Avdyeeich told the old woman about the parable of the master who forgave his servant a very great debt, and how that servant immediately went out and caught his fellow-servant by the throat because he was his debtor. The old woman listened to the end, and the lad listened, too.

"God bade us forgive," said Avdyeeich, "otherwise He will not forgive us. We must forgive everyone, especially the thoughtless."

The old woman shook her head and sighed.

"That's all very well," she said, "but they are spoiled enough already."

"Then it is for us old people to teach them better," said Avdyeeich.

"So say I," replied the old woman. "I had seven of them at one time, and now I have but a single daughter left." And the old woman began telling him where and how she lived with her daughter, and how many grandchildren she had. "I'm not what I was," she said, "but I work all I can. I am sorry for my grandchildren, and good children they are, too. No one is so glad to see me as they are. Little Aksyutka will go to none but me. 'Grandma dear! darling grandma!'" and the old woman was melted to tears. "As for him," she added, pointing to the lad, "boys will be boys, I suppose. Well, God be with him!"

Now just as the old woman was about to hoist the sack on to her shoulder, the lad rushed forward and said:

"Give it here and I'll carry it for thee, granny! It is all in my way."

The old woman shook her head, but she did put the sack on the lad's shoulder.

And so they trudged down the street together side by side. And the old woman forgot to ask Avdyeeich for the money for the apple. Avdyeeich kept standing and looking after them, and heard how they talked to each other, as they went, about all sorts of things.

Avdyeeich followed them with his eyes till they were out of sight; then he turned homewards and found his glasses on the steps (they were not broken), picked up his awl, and sat down to work again. He worked away for a little while, but soon he was scarcely able to distinguish the stitches, and saw the lamplighter going round to light the lamps. "I see it is time to light up," thought he; so he trimmed his little lamp, lighted it, and again sat down to work. He finished one boot completely, turned it round and inspected it. "Good!" he cried. He put away his tools, swept up the cuttings, removed the brushes and tips, put away the awl, took down the lamp, placed it on the table, and took down the Gospels from the shelf. He wanted to find the passage where he had last evening placed a strip of morocco leather by way of marker, but he lit upon another place. And just as Avdyeeich opened the Gospel, he recollected his dream of yesterday evening. And no sooner did he call it to mind than it seemed to him as if some persons were moving about and shuffling with their feet behind him. Avdyeeich glanced round and saw that somebody was indeed standing in the dark corner—yes, someone was really there, but who he could not exactly make out. Then a voice whispered in his ear:

"Martin! Martin! dost thou not know me?"

"Who art thou?" cried Avdyeeich.

"'Tis I," cried the voice, "lo, 'tis I!" And forth from the dark corner stepped Stepanuich. He smiled, and it was as though a little cloud were breaking, and he was gone.

"It is I!" cried the voice, and forth from the corner stepped a woman with a little child; and the woman smiled and the child laughed, and they also disappeared.

"And it is I!" cried the voice, and the old woman and the lad with the apple stepped forth, and both of them smiled, and they also disappeared.

And the heart of Avdyeeich was glad. He crossed himself, put on his glasses, and began to read the Gospels at the place where he had opened them. And at the top of the page he read these words: "And I was an hungered and thirsty, and ye gave Me to drink. I was a stranger, and ye took Me in."

And at the bottom of the page he read this: "Inasmuch as ye have done it to the least of these My brethren, ye have done it unto Me."

And Avdyeeich understood that his dream had not deceived him, and that the Savior had really come to him that day, and he had really received Him.

THE FATHER

By Björnstjerne Björnson

[Björnstjerne Björnson (1832–1910) is one of the two great names in Norwegian literature of recent times. The other is Henrik Ibsen. Björnson was the son of a village clergyman. He was well educated in the University of Christiania, Norway, and later at Copenhagen, Denmark. His fame as a literary man is due to his work as poet, novelist, and dramatist. His novels depict Norwegian peasant life chiefly. His early work as novelist comprises *Arne* (1858), *A Happy Boy* (1860), and *The Fisher Maiden* (1868). In later life he wrote *Flags Are Flying in Town and Harbor*, and *In God's Way*. A long list of short stories and dramatic pieces add to his fame. For many years he was a leading figure in the dramatic, literary, and political life of Norway. He was director of the Christiania theater from 1865 to 1867. In 1903 he was awarded the Nobel Prize in literature.

The translation of *The Father* (written in 1860) was made by Professor R. B. Anderson and appeared in the volume of Björnson's *Works* entitled *The Bridal March* (1881).]

THE man whose story is here to be told was the wealthiest and most influential person in his parish; his name was Thord Overaas. He appeared in the priest's study one day, tall and earnest.

"I have got a son," said he, "and I wish to present him for baptism."

"What shall his name be?"

"Finn—after my father."

"And the sponsors?"

They were mentioned, and proved to be the best men and women of Thord's relations in the parish.

"Is there anything else?" inquired the priest, and looked up.

The peasant hesitated a little.

"I should like very much to have him baptized by himself," said he, finally.

"That is to say on a week-day?"

"Next Saturday, at twelve o'clock noon."

"Is there anything else?" inquired the priest.

"There is nothing else;" and the peasant twirled his cap, as though he were about to go.

Then the priest rose. "There is yet this, however," said he, and walking toward Thord, he took him by the hand and looked gravely into his eyes: "God grant that the child may become a blessing to you!"

One day sixteen years later, Thord stood once more in the priest's study.

"Really, you carry your age astonishingly well, Thord," said the priest; for he saw no change whatever in the man.

"That is because I have no troubles," replied Thord.

To this the priest said nothing, but after a while he asked: "What is your pleasure this evening?"

"I have come this evening about that son of mine who is to be confirmed tomorrow."

"He is a bright boy."

"I did not wish to pay the priest until I heard what number the boy would have when he takes his place in church tomorrow."

"He will stand number one."

"So I have heard; and here are ten dollars for the priest."

"Is there anything else I can do for you?" inquired the priest, fixing his eyes on Thord.

"There is nothing else."

Thord went out.

Eight years more rolled by, and then one day a noise was heard outside of the priest's study, for many men were approaching, and at their head was Thord, who entered first.

The priest looked up and recognized him.

"You come well attended this evening, Thord," said he.

"I am here to request that the banns may be published for my son; he is about to marry Karen Storliden, daughter of Gudmund, who stands here beside me."

"Why, that is the richest girl in the parish."

"So they say," replied the peasant, stroking back his hair with one hand.

The priest sat a while as if in deep thought, then entered the names in his book, without making any comments, and the men wrote their signatures underneath. Thord laid three dollars on the table.

"One is all I am to have," said the priest.

"I know that very well; but he is my only child. I want to do it handsomely."

The priest took the money.

"This is now the third time, Thord, that you have come here on your son's account."

"But now I am through with him," said Thord, and folding up his pocket-book he said farewell and walked away.

The men slowly followed him.

A fortnight later, the father and son were rowing across the lake, one calm, still day, to Storliden to make arrangements for the wedding.

"This thwart is not secure," said the son, and stood up to straighten the seat on which he was sitting.

At the same moment the board he was standing on slipped from under him; he threw out his arms, uttered a shriek, and fell overboard.

"Take hold of the oar!" shouted the father, springing to his feet and holding out the oar.

But when the son had made a couple of efforts he grew stiff.

"Wait a moment!" cried the father, and began to row toward his son.

Then the son rolled over on his back, gave his father one long look, and sank.

Thord could scarcely believe it; he held the boat still, and stared at the spot where his son had gone down, as though he must surely come to the surface again. There rose some bubbles, then some more, and finally one large one that burst; and the lake lay there as smooth and bright as a mirror again.

For three days and three nights people saw the father rowing round and round the spot, without taking either food or sleep; he was dragging the lake for the body of his son. And toward morning of the third day he found it, and carried it in his arms up over the hills to his gard.

It might have been about a year from that day, when the priest, late one autumn evening, heard someone in the passage outside of the door, carefully trying to find the latch. The priest opened the door, and in walked a tall, thin man, with bowed form and white hair. The priest looked long at him before he recognized him. It was Thord.

"Are you out walking so late?" said the priest, and stood still in front of him.

"Ah, yes! it is late," said Thord, and took a seat.

The priest sat down also, as though waiting. A long, long silence followed. At last Thord said:

"I have something with me that I should like to give to the poor; I want it to be invested as a legacy in my son's name."

He rose, laid some money on the table, and sat down again. The priest counted it.

"It is a great deal of money," said he.

"It is half the price of my gard. I sold it today."

The priest sat long in silence. At last he asked, but gently:

"What do you propose to do now, Thord?"

"Something better."

They sat there for a while, Thord with downcast eyes, the priest with his eyes fixed on Thord. Presently the priest said, slowly and softly:

"I think your son has at last brought you a true blessing."

"Yes, I think so myself," said Thord, looking up, while two big tears coursed slowly down his cheeks.

THE DARLING

By *Anton Pavlovich Chekhov*

[Anton Chekhov (1860–1904), one of the greatest of Russian dramatists and writers of fiction, was educated as a physician, but soon devoted all of his time to literature. Among his famous plays are *Uncle
Vanya*, *The Seagull*, and *The Cherry Orchard*. His short story masterpieces are generally regarded as the finest "atmosphere" stories of all
time. Perhaps the most widely known of these stories is *The Darling*
(1898), the presentation in very brief form of a human life, stirred and
wrought upon by the ordinary events of existence.

The Darling is reprinted from Thomas Seltzer's *Best Russian Short
Stories*, by permission of The Modern Library, Inc., publishers.]

OLENKA, the daughter of the retired collegiate assessor Plemyani-
kov, was sitting on the back-door steps of her house doing nothing.
It was hot, the flies were nagging and teasing, and it was pleasant to
think that it would soon be evening. Dark rain clouds were gathering
from the east, wafting a breath of moisture every now and then.

Kukin, who roomed in the wing of the same house, was standing in the
yard looking up at the sky. He was the manager of the Tivoli, an open-
air theatre.

"Again," he said despairingly. "Rain again. Rain, rain, rain! Every
day rain! As though to spite me. I might as well stick my head into a
noose and be done with it. It's ruining me. Heavy losses every day!"
He wrung his hands, and continued, addressing Olenka: "What a life,
Olga Semyonovna! It's enough to make a man weep. He works, he does
his best, his very best, he tortures himself, he passes sleepless nights, he
thinks and thinks and thinks how to do everything just right. And
what's the result? He gives the public the best operetta, the very best
pantomime, excellent artists. But do they want it? Have they the least
appreciation of it? The public is rude. The public is a great boor. The
public wants a circus, a lot of nonsense, a lot of stuff. And there's the
weather. Look! Rain almost every evening. It began to rain on the
tenth of May, and it's kept it up through the whole of June. It's simply
awful. I can't get any audiences, and don't I have to pay rent? Don't I
have to pay the actors?"

The next day towards evening the clouds gathered again, and Kukin
said with an hysterical laugh:

"Oh, I don't care. Let it do its worst. Let it drown the whole theatre,
and me, too. All right, no luck for me in this world or the next. Let the

365

actors bring suit against me and drag me to court. What's the court? Why not Siberia at hard labor, or even the scaffold? Ha, ha, ha!"

It was the same on the third day.

Olenka listened to Kukin seriously, in silence. Sometimes tears would rise to her eyes. At last Kukin's misfortune touched her. She fell in love with him. He was short, gaunt, with a yellow face, and curly hair combed back from his forehead, and a thin tenor voice. His features puckered all up when he spoke. Despair was ever inscribed on his face. And yet he awakened in Olenka a sincere, deep feeling.

She was always loving somebody. She couldn't get on without loving somebody. She had loved her sick father, who sat the whole time in his armchair in a darkened room, breathing heavily. She had loved her aunt, who came from Brianska once or twice a year to visit them. And before that, when a pupil at the progymnasium, she had loved her French teacher. She was a quiet, kind-hearted, compassionate girl, with a soft gentle way about her. And she made a very healthy, wholesome impression. Looking at her full, rosy cheeks, at her soft white neck with the black mole, and at the good naïve smile that always played on her face when something pleasant was said, the men would think, "Not so bad," and would smile too; and the lady visitors, in the middle of the conversation would suddenly grasp her hand and exclaim, "You darling!" in a burst of delight.

The house, hers by inheritance, in which she had lived from birth, was located at the outskirts of the city on the Gypsy Road, not far from the Tivoli. From early evening till late at night she could hear the music in the theatre and the bursting of the rockets; and it seemed to her that Kukin was roaring and battling with his fate and taking his chief enemy, the indifferent public, by assault. Her heart melted softly, she felt no desire to sleep, and when Kukin returned home towards morning, she tapped on her window-pane, and through the curtains he saw her face and one shoulder and the kind smile she gave him.

He proposed to her, and they were married. And when he had a good look of her neck and her full vigorous shoulders, he clapped his hands and said:

"You darling!"

He was happy. But it rained on their wedding-day, and the expression of despair never left his face.

They got along well together. She sat in the cashier's box, kept the theatre in order, wrote down the expenses and paid out the salaries. Her rosy cheeks, her kind naïve smile, like a halo around her face, could be seen at the cashier's window, behind the scenes, and in the café. She began to tell her friends that the theatre was the greatest, the most important, the most essential thing in the world, that it was the only place to obtain true enjoyment in and become humanised and educated.

"But do you suppose the public appreciates it?" she asked. "What the public wants is the circus. Yesterday boxes were empty. If we had given some silly nonsense, I assure you, the theatre would have been overcrowded. Tomorrow we'll put *Orpheus in Hades* on. Do come."

Whatever Kukin said about the theatre and the actors, she repeated. She spoke, as he did, with contempt of the public, of its indifference to art, of its boorishness. She meddled in the rehearsals, corrected the actors, watched the conduct of the musicians; and when an unfavorable criticism appeared in the local paper, she wept and went to the editor to argue with him.

The actors were fond of her and called her "Vanichka and I" and "the darling." She was sorry for them and lent them small sums. When they bilked her, she never complained to her husband; at the utmost she shed a few tears.

In winter, too, they got along nicely together. They leased a theatre in the town for the whole winter and sublet it for short periods to a Little Russian theatrical company, to a conjuror, and to the local amateur players.

Olenka grew fuller and was always beaming with contentment; while Kukin grew thinner and yellower and complained of his terrible losses, though he did fairly well the whole winter. At night he coughed, and she gave him raspberry syrup and lime water, rubbed him with eau de Cologne, and wrapped him up in soft coverings.

"You are my precious sweet," she said with perfect sincerity, stroking his hair. "You are such a dear."

At Lent he went to Moscow to get his company together, and, while without him, Olenka was unable to sleep. She sat at the window the whole time, gazing at the stars. She likened herself to the hens that are also uneasy and unable to sleep when their rooster is out of the coop. Kukin was detained in Moscow. He wrote he would be back during Easter Week, and in his letters discussed arrangements already for the Tivoli. But late one night, before Easter Monday, there was an ill-omened knocking at the wicket-gate. It was like knocking on a barrel—boom, boom, boom! The sleepy cook ran barefooted, plashing through the puddles, to open the gate.

"Open the gate, please," said some one in a hollow bass voice. "I have a telegram for you."

Olenka had received telegrams from her husband before; but this time, somehow, she was numbed with terror. She opened the telegram with trembling hands and read:

"Ivan Petranovich died suddenly today. Awaiting propt orders for wuneral Tuesday."

That was the way the telegram was written—"wuneral"—and another unintelligible word—"propt." The telegram was signed by the manager of the opera company.

"My dearest!" Olenka burst out sobbing. "Vanichka, my dearest, my sweetheart. Why did I ever meet you? Why did I ever get to know you and love you? To whom have you abandoned your poor Olenka, your poor, unhappy Ólenka?"

Kukin was buried on Tuesday in the Vagankov Cemetery in Moscow. Olenka returned home on Wednesday; and as soon as she entered her house she threw herself on her bed and broke into such loud sobbing that she could be heard in the street and in the neighboring yards.

"The darling!" said the neighbors, crossing themselves. "How Olga Semyonovna, the poor darling, is grieving!"

Three months afterwards Olenka was returning home from mass, downhearted and in deep mourning. Beside her walked a man also returning from church, Vasily Pustovalov, the manager of the merchant Babakayev's lumber-yard. He was wearing a straw hat, a white vest with a gold chain, and looked more like a landowner than a business man.

"Everything has its ordained course, Olga Semyonovna," he said sedately, with sympathy in his voice. "And if any one near and dear to us dies, then it means it was God's will and we should remember that and bear it with submission."

He took her to the wicket-gate, said good-bye and went away. After that she heard his sedate voice the whole day; and on closing her eyes she instantly had a vision of his dark beard. She took a great liking to him. And evidently he had been impressed by her, too; for, not long after, an elderly woman, a distant acquaintance, came in to have a cup of coffee with her. As soon as the woman was seated at table she began to speak about Pustovalov—how good he was, what a steady man, and any woman could be glad to get him as a husband. Three days later Pustovalov himself paid Olenka a visit. He stayed only about ten minutes, and spoke little, but Olenka fell in love with him, fell in love so desperately that she did not sleep the whole night and burned as with fever. In the morning she sent for the elderly woman. Soon after, Olenka and Pustovalov were engaged, and the wedding followed.

Pustovalov and Olenka lived happily together. He usually stayed in the lumber-yard until dinner, then went out on business. In his absence Olenka took his place in the office until evening, attending to the book-keeping and despatching the orders.

"Lumber rises twenty per cent every year nowadays," she told her customers and acquaintances. "Imagine, we used to buy wood from our forests here. Now Vasichka has to go every year to the government of Mogilev to get wood. And what a tax!" she exclaimed, covering her cheeks with her hands in terror. "What a tax!"

She felt as if she had been dealing in lumber for ever so long, that the most important and essential thing in life was lumber. There was something touching and endearing in the way she pronounced the words, "beam," "joist," "plank," "stave," "lath," "gun-carriage," "clamp." At night she dreamed of whole mountains of boards and planks, long, endless rows of wagons conveying the wood somewhere, far, far from the city. She dreamed that a whole regiment of beams, 36 ft. x 5 in., were advancing in an upright position to do battle against the lumber-yard; that the beams and joists and clamps were knocking against each other, emitting the sharp crackling reports of dry wood, that they were all falling and then rising again, piling on top of each other. Olenka cried out in her sleep, and Pustovalov said to her gently:

"Olenka, my dear, what is the matter? Cross yourself."

Her husband's opinions were all hers. If he thought the room was too hot, she thought so too. If he thought business was dull, she thought business was dull. Pustovalov was not fond of amusements and stayed home on holidays; she did the same.

"You are always either at home or in the office," said her friends. "Why don't you go to the theatre or to the circus, darling?"

"Vasichka and I never go to the theatre," she answered sedately. "We have work to do, we have no time for nonsense. What does one get out of going to the theatre?"

On Saturdays she and Pustovalov went to vespers, and on holidays to early mass. On returning home they walked side by side with rapt faces, an agreeable smell emanating from both of them, and her silk dress rustling pleasantly. At home they drank tea with milk-bread and various jams, and then ate pie. Every day at noontime there was an appetising odor in the yard and outside the gate of cabbage soup, roast mutton, or duck; and, on fast days, of fish. You couldn't pass the gate without being seized by an acute desire to eat. The samovar was always boiling on the office table, and customers were treated to tea and biscuits. Once a week the married couple went to the baths and returned with red faces, walking side by side.

"We are getting along very well, thank God," said Olenka to her friends. "God grant that all should live as well as Vasichka and I."

When Pustovalov went to the government of Mogilev to buy wood, she was dreadfully homesick for him, did not sleep nights, and cried. Sometimes the veterinary surgeon of the regiment, Smirnov, a young man who lodged in the wing of her house, came to see her evenings. He related incidents, or they played cards together. This distracted her. The most interesting of his stories were those of his own life. He was married and had a son; but he had separated from his wife because she had deceived him, and now he hated her and sent her forty rubles a month for his son's support. Olenka sighed, shook her head, and was sorry for him.

"Well, the Lord keep you," she said, as she saw him off to the door by candlelight. "Thank you for coming to kill time with me. May God give you health. Mother in Heaven!" She spoke very sedately, very judiciously, imitating her husband. The veterinary surgeon had disappeared behind the door when she called out after him: "Do you know,

Vladimir Platonych, you ought to make up with your wife. Forgive her, if only for the sake of your son. The child understands everything, you may be sure."

When Pustovalov returned, she told him in a low voice about the veterinary surgeon and his unhappy family life; and they sighed and shook their heads, and talked about the boy who must be homesick for his father. Then, by a strange association of ideas, they both stopped before the sacred images, made genuflections, and prayed to God to send them children.

And so the Pustovalovs lived for full six years, quietly and peaceably, in perfect love and harmony. But once in the winter Vasily Andreyich, after drinking some hot tea, went out into the lumber-yard without a hat on his head, caught a cold and took sick. He was treated by the best physicians, but the malady progressed, and he died after an illness of four months. Olenka was again left a widow.

"To whom have you left me, my darling?" she wailed after the funeral. "How shall I live now without you, wretched creature that I am? Pity me, good people, pity me, fatherless and motherless, all alone in the world!"

She went about dressed in black and weepers, and she gave up wearing hats and gloves for good. She hardly left the house except to go to church and to visit her husband's grave. She almost led the life of a nun.

It was not until six months had passed that she took off the weepers and opened her shutters. She began to go out occasionally in the morning to market with her cook. But how she lived at home and what went on there, could only be surmised. It could be surmised from the fact that she was seen in her little garden drinking tea with the veterinarian while he read the paper out loud to her, and also from the fact that once on meeting an acquaintance at the post-office, she said to her:

"There is no proper veterinary inspection in our town. That is why there is so much disease. You constantly hear of people getting sick from the milk and becoming infected by the horses and cows. The health of domestic animals ought really to be looked after as much as that of human beings."

She repeated the veterinarian's words and held the same opinions as he about everything. It was plain that she could not exist a single year without an attachment, and she found her new happiness in the wing of her house. In any one else this would have been condemned; but no one could think ill of Olenka. Everything in her life was so transparent. She and the veterinary surgeon never spoke about the change in their relations. They tried, in fact, to conceal it, but unsuccessfully; for Olenka could have no secrets. When the surgeon's colleagues from the regiment came to see him, she poured tea, and served the supper, and talked to them about the cattle plague, the foot and mouth disease, and the municipal slaughter houses. The surgeon was dreadfully embarrassed, and after the visitors had left, he caught her hand and hissed angrily:

"Didn't I ask you not to talk about what you don't understand? When we doctors discuss things, please don't mix in. It's getting to be a nuisance."

She looked at him in astonishment and alarm, and asked:

"But Volodichka, what *am* I to talk about?"

And she threw her arms around his neck, with tears in her eyes, and begged him not to be angry. And they were both happy.

But their happiness was of short duration. The veterinary surgeon went away with his regiment to be gone for good, when it was transferred to some distant place almost as far as Siberia, and Olenka was left alone.

Now she was completely alone. Her father had long been dead, and his armchair lay in the attic covered with dust and minus one leg. She got thin and homely, and the people who met her on the street no longer looked at her as they had used to, nor smiled at her. Evidently her best years were over, past and gone, and a new, dubious life was to begin which it were better not to think about.

In the evening Olenka sat on the steps and heard the music playing and the rockets bursting in the Tivoli; but it no longer aroused any response in her. She looked listlessly into the yard, thought of nothing, wanted nothing, and when night came on, she went to bed and dreamed of nothing but an empty yard. She ate and drank as though by compulsion.

And what was worst of all, she no longer held any opinions. She saw and understood everything that went on around her, but she could not form an opinion about it. She knew of nothing to talk about. And how dreadful not to have opinions! For instance, you see a bottle, or you see that it is raining, or you see a muzhik riding by in a wagon. But what the bottle or the rain or the muzhik are for, or what the sense of them all is, you cannot tell—you cannot tell, not for a thousand rubles. In the days of Kukin and Pustovalov and then of the veterinary surgeon, Olenka had had an explanation for everything, and would have given her opinion freely no matter about what. But now there was the same emptiness in her heart and brain as in her yard. It was as galling and bitter as a taste of wormwood.

Gradually the town grew up all around. The Gypsy Road had become a street, and where the Tivoli and the lumber-yard had been, there were now houses and a row of side streets. How quickly time flies! Olenka's house turned gloomy, the roof rusty, the shed slanting. Dock and thistles overgrew the yard. Olenka herself had aged and grown homely. In the summer she sat on the steps, and her soul was empty and dreary and bitter. When she caught the breath of spring, or when the wind wafted the chime of the cathedral bells, a sudden flood of memories would pour over her, her heart would expand with a tender warmth and the tears would stream down her cheeks. But that lasted only a moment. Then would come emptiness again, and the feeling, What is the use of living? The black kitten Bryska rubbed up against her and purred softly, but the little creature's caresses left Olenka untouched. That was not what she needed. What she needed was a love that would give her ideas, an object in life, that would warm her ageing blood. And she shook the black kitten off her skirt angrily, saying:

"Go away! What are you doing here?"

And so day after day, year after year, not a single joy, not a single opinion. Whatever Marva, the cook, said was all right.

One hot day in July, towards evening, as the town cattle were being driven by, and the whole yard was filled with clouds of dust, there was suddenly a knocking at the gate. Olenka herself went to open it, and was dumbfounded to behold the veterinarian Smirnov. He had turned gray and was dressed as a civilian. All the old memories flooded into her soul, she could not restrain herself, she burst out crying, and laid her head on Smirnov's breast without saying a word. So overcome was she that she was totally unconscious of how they walked into the house and seated themselves to drink tea.

"My darling!" she murmured, trembling with joy. "Vladimir Platonych, from where has God sent you?"

"I want to settle here for good," he told her. "I have resigned my position and have come here to try my fortune as a free man and lead a settled life. Besides, it's time to send my boy to the gymnasium. He is grown up now. You know, my wife and I have become reconciled."

"Where is she?" asked Olenka.

"At the hotel with the boy. I am looking for lodgings."

"Good gracious, bless you, take my house. Why won't my house do? Oh, dear! Why, I won't ask any rent of you," Olenka burst out in the greatest excitement, and began to cry again. "You live here, and the wing will be enough for me. Oh, Heavens, what a joy!"

The very next day the roof was being painted and the walls whitewashed, and Olenka, arms akimbo, was going about the yard superintending. Her face brightened with her old smile. Her whole being revived and freshened, as though she had awakened from a long sleep. The veterinarian's wife and child arrived. She was a thin, plain woman, with a crabbed expression. The boy Sasha, small for his ten years of age, was a chubby child, with clear blue eyes and dimples in his cheeks. He made for the kitten the instant he entered the yard, and the place rang with his happy laughter.

"Is that your cat, auntie?" he asked Olenka. "When she has little kitties, please give me one. Mamma is awfully afraid of mice."

Olenka chatted with him, gave him tea, and there was a sudden warmth in her bosom and a soft gripping at her heart, as though the boy were her own son.

In the evenings, when he sat in the dining-room studying his lessons, she looked at him tenderly and whispered to herself:

"My darling, my pretty. You are such a clever child, so good to look at."

"An island is a tract of land entirely surrounded by water," he recited.

"An island is a tract of land," she repeated—the first idea asseverated with conviction after so many years of silence and mental emptiness.

She now had her opinions, and at supper discussed with Sasha's parents how difficult the studies had become for the children at the gymnasium, but how, after all, a classical education was better than a commercial course, because when you graduated from the gymnasium, then the road was open to you for any career at all. If you chose to, you could become a doctor, or, if you wanted to, you could become an engineer.

Sasha began to go to the gymnasium. His mother left on a visit to her sister in Kharkov and never came back. The father was away every day inspecting cattle, and sometimes was gone three whole days at a time, so that Sasha, it seemed to Olenka, was utterly abandoned, was treated as if he were quite superfluous, and must be dying of hunger. So she transferred him into the wing along with herself and fixed up a little room for him there.

Every morning Olenka would come into his room and find him sound asleep with his hand tucked under his cheek, so quiet that he seemed not to be breathing. What a shame to have to wake him, she thought.

"Sashenka," she said sorrowingly, "get up, darling. It's time to go to the gymnasium."

He got up, dressed, said his prayers, then sat down to drink tea. He drank three glasses of tea, ate two large cracknels and half a buttered roll. The sleep was not yet out of him, so he was a little cross.

"You don't know your fable as you should, Sashenka," said Olenka, looking at him as though he were departing on a long journey. "What a lot of trouble you are! You must try hard and learn, dear, and mind your teachers."

"Oh, let me alone, please," said Sasha.

Then he went down the street to the gymnasium, a little fellow wearing a large cap and carrying a satchel on his back. Olenka followed him noiselessly.

"Sashenka," she called.

He looked around and she shoved a date or a caramel into his hand. When he reached the street of the gymnasium, he turned around and said, ashamed of being followed by a tall, stout woman:

"You had better go home, aunt. I can go the rest of the way myself."

She stopped and stared after him until he had disappeared into the school entrance.

Oh, how she loved him! Not one of her other ties had been so deep. Never before had she given herself so completely, so disinterestedly, so cheerfully as now that her maternal instincts were all aroused. For this boy, who was not hers, for the dimples in his cheeks and for his big cap, she would have given her life, given it with joy and with tears of rapture. Why? Ah, indeed, why?

When she had seen Sasha off to the gymnasium, she returned home quietly, content, serene, overflowing with love. Her face, which had grown younger in the last half year, smiled and beamed. People who met her were pleased as they looked at her.

"How are you, Olga Semyonovna, darling? How are you getting on, darling?"

"The gymnasium course is very hard nowadays," she told at the market. "It's no joke. Yesterday the first class had a fable to learn by heart, a Latin translation, and a problem. How is a little fellow to do all that?"

And she spoke of the teacher and the lessons and the textbooks, repeating exactly what Sasha said about them.

At three o'clock they had dinner. In the evening they prepared the lessons together, and Olenka wept with Sasha over the difficulties. When she put him to bed, she lingered a long time making the sign of the cross over him and muttering a prayer. And when she lay in bed, she dreamed of the far-away, misty future when Sasha would finish his studies and become a doctor or an engineer, have a large house of his own, with horses and a carriage, marry and have children. She would fall asleep still thinking of the same things, and tears would roll down her cheeks from her closed eyes. And the black cat would lie at her side purring: "Mrr, mrr, mrr."

Suddenly there was a loud knocking at the gate. Olenka woke up breathless with fright, her heart beating violently. Half a minute later there was another knock.

"A telegram from Kharkov," she thought, her whole body in a tremble. "His mother wants Sasha to come to her in Kharkov. O, great God!"

She was in despair. Her head, her feet, her hands turned cold. There was no unhappier creature in the world, she felt. But another minute passed, she heard voices. It was the veterinarian coming home from the club.

"Thank God," she thought. The load gradually fell from her heart, she was at ease again. And she went back to bed, thinking of Sasha who lay fast asleep in the next room and sometimes cried out in his sleep:

"I'll give it to you! Get away! Quit your scrapping!"

THE REVOLT OF "MOTHER"

By Mary E. Wilkins Freeman

[Mary E. Wilkins Freeman (1862–1930) was born in Randolph, Massachusetts, and was educated at Mount Holyoke. For some years she was secretary to Oliver Wendell Holmes. In 1902 she married Dr. C. M. Freeman and spent the remaining years of her life at Metuchen, N. J. *A New England Nun and Other Stories* (1891) contains some of her best known work, but she was the author of nearly 250 short stories which were collected in some 20 or more volumes. She was also the author of several widely read novels, among which two of the best were *Jerome: A Poor Man* (1897) and *The Portion of Labor* (1901).

The Revolt of "Mother" was first published in Harper's Magazine (1890), and later included in *A New England Nun and Other Stories*. It is here reprinted by permission of Harper & Brothers, publishers.]

"FATHER!"

"What is it?"

"What are them men diggin' over there in the field for?"

There was a sudden dropping and enlarging of the lower part of the old man's face, as if some heavy weight had settled therein; he shut his mouth tight, and went on harnessing the great bay mare. He hustled the collar on to her neck with a jerk.

"Father!"

The old man slapped the saddle upon the mare's back.

"Look here, father, I want to know what them men are diggin' over in the field for, an' I'm goin' to know."

"I wish you'd go into the house, mother, an' 'tend to your own affairs," the old man said then. He ran his words together, and his speech was almost as inarticulate as a growl.

But the woman understood; it was her most native tongue. "I ain't goin' into the house till you tell me what them men are doin' over there in the field," said she.

Then she stood waiting. She was a small woman, short and straight-waisted like a child in her brown cotton gown. Her forehead was mild and benevolent between the smooth curves of gray hair; there were meek downward lines about her nose and mouth; but her eyes, fixed upon the old man, looked as if the meekness had been the result of her own will, never of the will of another.

They were in the barn, standing before the wide open doors. The spring air, full of the smell of growing grass and unseen blossoms, came

375

in their faces. The deep yard in front was littered with farm wagons and piles of wood; on the edges, close to the fence and the house, the grass was a vivid green, and there were some dandelions.

The old man glanced doggedly at his wife as he tightened the last buckles on the harness. She looked as immovable to him as one of the rocks in his pasture-land, bound to the earth with generations of black-berry vines. He slapped the reins over the horse, and started forth from the barn.

"*Father!*" said she.

The old man pulled up. "What is it?"

"I want to know what them men are diggin' over there in that field for."

"They're diggin' a cellar, I s'pose, if you've got to know."

"A cellar for what?"

"A barn."

"A barn? You ain't goin' to build a barn over there where we was goin' to have a house, father?"

The old man said not another word. He hurried the horse into the farm wagon, and clattered out of the yard, jouncing as sturdily on his seat as a boy.

The woman stood a moment looking after him, then she went out of the barn across a corner of the yard to the house. The house, standing at right angles with the great barn and a long reach of sheds and out-buildings, was infinitesimal compared with them. It was scarcely as commodious for people as the little boxes under the barn eaves were for doves.

A pretty girl's face, pink and delicate as a flower, was looking out of one of the house windows. She was watching three men who were digging over in the field which bounded the yard near the road line. She turned quietly when the woman entered.

"What are they digging for, mother?" said she. "Did he tell you?"

"They're diggin' for—a cellar for a new barn."

"Oh, mother, he ain't going to build another barn?"

"That's what he says."

A boy stood before the kitchen glass combing his hair. He combed slowly and painstakingly, arranging his brown hair in a smooth hillock over his forehead. He did not seem to pay any attention to the con-versation.

"Sammy, did you know father was going to build a new barn?" asked the girl.

The boy combed assiduously.

"Sammy!"

He turned, and showed a face like his father's under his smooth crest of hair. "Yes, I s'pose I did," he said, reluctantly.

"How long have you known it?" asked his mother.

"'Bout three months, I guess."

"Why didn't you tell of it?"

"Didn't think 'twould do no good."

"I don't see what father wants another barn for," said the girl, in her sweet, slow voice. She turned again to the window, and stared out at the digging men in the field. Her tender, sweet face was full of a gentle distress. Her forehead was as bald and innocent as a baby's, with the light hair strained back from it in a row of curl-papers. She was quite large, but her soft curves did not look as if they covered muscles.

Her mother looked sternly at the boy. "Is he goin' to buy more cows?" said she.

The boy did not reply; he was tying his shoes.

"Sammy, I want you to tell me if he's goin' to buy more cows."

"I s'pose he is."

"How many?"

"Four, I guess."

His mother said nothing more. She went into the pantry, and there was a clatter of dishes. The boy got his cap from a nail behind the door, took an old arithmetic from the shelf, and started for school. He was lightly built, but clumsy. He went out of the yard with a curious spring in the hips, that made his loose home-made jacket tilt up in the rear.

The girl went to the sink, and began to wash the dishes that were piled up there. Her mother came promptly out of the pantry, and shoved her aside. "You wipe 'em," said she; "I'll wash. There's a good many this mornin'."

The mother plunged her hands vigorously into the water, the girl wiped the plates slowly and dreamily. "Mother," said she, "don't you think it's too bad father's going to build that new barn, much as we need a decent house to live in?"

Her mother scrubbed a dish fiercely. "You ain't found out yet we're women-folks, Nanny Penn," said she. "You ain't seen enough of men-folks yet to. One of these days you'll find it out, an' then you'll know that we know only what men-folks think we do, so far as any use of it goes, an' how we'd ought to reckon men-folks in with Providence, an' not complain of what they do any more than we do of the weather."

"I don't care; I don't believe George is anything like that, anyhow," said Nanny. Her delicate face flushed pink, her lips pouted softly, as if she were going to cry.

"You wait an' see. I guess George Eastman ain't no better than other men. You hadn't ought to judge father, though. He can't help it, 'cause he don't look at things jest the way we do. An' we've been pretty comfortable here, after all. The roof don't leak—ain't never but once—that's one thing. Father's kept it shingled right up."

"I do wish we had a parlor."

"I guess it won't hurt George Eastman any to come to see you in a nice clean kitchen. I guess a good many girls don't have as good a place as this. Nobody's ever heard me complain."

"I ain't complained either, mother."

"Well, I don't think you'd better, a good father an' a good home as you've got. S'pose your father made you go out an' work for your livin'? Lots of girls have to that ain't no stronger an' better able to than you be."

Sarah Penn washed the frying-pan with a conclusive air. She scrubbed the outside of it as faithfully as the inside. She was a masterly keeper of her box of a house. Her one living-room never seemed to have in it any of the dust which the friction of life with inanimate matter produces. She swept, and there seemed to be no dirt to go before the broom; she cleaned, and one could see no difference. She was like an artist: so perfect that he has apparently no art. Today she got out a mixing bowl and a board, and rolled some pies, and there was no more flour upon her than upon her daughter who was doing finer work. Nanny was to be married in the fall, and she was sewing on some white cambric and embroidery. She sewed industriously while her mother cooked; her soft, milk-white hands and wrists showed whiter than her delicate work.

"We must have the stove moved out in the shed before long," said Mrs. Penn. "Talk about not havin' things, it's been a real blessin' to be able to put a stove up in that shed in hot weather. Father did one good thing when he fixed that stove-pipe out there."

Sarah Penn's face as she rolled her pies had that expression of meek vigor which might have characterized one of the New Testament saints. She was making mince-pies. Her husband, Adoniram Penn, liked them better than any other kind. She baked twice a week. Adoniram often liked a piece of pie between meals. She hurried this morning. It had been later than usual when she began, and she wanted to have a pie baked for dinner. However deep a resentment she might be forced to hold against her husband, she would never fail in sedulous attention to his wants.

Nobility of character manifests itself at loop-holes when it is not provided with large doors. Sarah Penn's showed itself today in flaky dishes of pastry. So she made the pies faithfully, while across the table she could see, when she glanced up from her work, the sight that rankled in her patient and steadfast soul—the digging of the cellar of the new barn in the place where Adoniram forty years ago had promised her their new house should stand.

The pies were done for dinner. Adoniram and Sammy were home a few minutes after twelve o'clock. The dinner was eaten with serious haste. There was never much conversation at the table in the Penn family. Adoniram asked a blessing, and they ate promptly, then rose up and went about their work.

Sammy went back to school, taking soft sly lopes out of the yard like a rabbit. He wanted a game of marbles before school, and feared his father would give him some chores to do. Adoniram hastened to the door and called after him, but he was out of sight.

"I don't see what you let him go for, mother," said he. "I wanted him to help me unload that wood."

Adoniram went to work out in the yard, unloading wood from the wagon. Sarah put away the dinner dishes, while Nanny took down her curl-papers and changed her dress. She was going down to the store to buy some more embroidery and thread.

When Nanny was gone, Mrs. Penn went to the door. "Father!" she called.

"Well, what is it!"

"I want to see you jest a minute, father."

"I can't leave this wood nohow. I've got to git it unloaded an' go for a load of gravel afore two o'clock. Sammy had ought to help me. You hadn't ought to let him go to school so early."

"I want to see you jest a minute."

"I tell ye I can't, nohow, mother."

"Father, you come here." Sarah Penn stood in the door like a queen; she held her head as if it bore a crown; there was that patience which makes authority royal in her voice. Adoniram went.

Mrs. Penn led the way into the kitchen, and pointed to a chair. "Sit down, father," said she; "I've got somethin' I want to say to you."

He sat down heavily; his face was quite stolid, but he looked at her with restive eyes. "Well, what is it, mother?"

"I want to know what you're buildin' that new barn for, father?"

"I ain't got nothin' to say about it."

"It can't be you think you need another barn?"

"I tell ye I ain't got nothin' to say about it, mother; an' I ain't goin' to say nothin'."

"Be you goin' to buy more cows?"

Adoniram did not reply; he shut his mouth tight.

"I know you be, as well as I want to. Now, father, look here"—Sarah Penn had not sat down; she stood before her husband in the humble fashion of a Scripture woman—"I'm goin' to talk real plain to you; I never have since I married you, but I'm goin' to now. I ain't never complained, an' I ain't goin' to complain now, but I'm goin' to talk plain. You see this room here, father; you look at it well. You see there ain't no carpet on the floor, an' you see the paper is all dirty, an' droppin' off the walls. We ain't had no new paper on it for ten year, an' then I put it on myself, an' it didn't cost but ninepence a roll. You see this room, father; it's all the one I've had to work in an' eat in an' sit in sence we was married. There ain't another woman in the whole town whose husband ain't got half the means you have but what's got better. It's all the room Nanny's got to have her company in; an' there ain't one of her mates but what's got better, an' their fathers not so able as hers is. It's all the room she'll have to be married in. What would you have thought, father, if we had had our weddin' in a room no better than this? I was married in my mother's parlor, with a carpet on the floor, an' stuffed furniture, an' a mahogany card-table. An' this is all the room my daughter will have to be married in. Look here, father!"

Sarah Penn went across the room as though it were a tragic stage. She flung open a door and disclosed a tiny bedroom, only large enough for a bed and bureau, with a path between. "There, father," said she— "there's all the room I've had to sleep in forty year. All my children were born there—the two that died, an' the two that's livin'. I was sick with a fever there."

She stepped to another door and opened it. It led into the small, ill-lighted pantry. "Here," said she, "is all the buttery I've got—every place I've got for my dishes, to set away my victuals in, an' to keep my milk-pans in. Father, I've been takin' care of the milk of six cows in this place, an' now you're goin' to build a new barn, an' keep more cows, an' give me more to do in it."

She threw open another door. A narrow crooked flight of stairs wound upward from it. "There, father," said she, "I want you to look at the stairs that go up to them two unfinished chambers that are all the places our son an' daughter have had to sleep in all their lives. There ain't a prettier girl in town nor a more ladylike one than Nanny, an' that's the place she has to sleep in. It ain't so good as your horse's stall; it ain't so warm an' tight."

Sarah Penn went back and stood before her husband. "Now, father," said she, "I want to know if you think you're doin' right an' accordin' to what you profess. Here, when we was married, forty year ago, you promised me faithful that we should have a new house built in that lot over in the field before the year was out. You said you had money enough, an' you wouldn't ask me to live in no such place as this. It is forty year now, an' you've been makin' more money, an' I've been savin' of it for you ever since, an' you ain't built no house yet. You've built sheds an' cow-houses an' one new barn, an' now you're goin' to build another. Father, I want to know if you think it's right. You're lodgin' your dumb beasts better than you are your own flesh an' blood. I want to know if you think it's right."

"I ain't got nothin' to say."

"You can't say nothin' without ownin' it ain't right, father. An' there's another thing—I ain't complained; I've got along forty year, an' I s'pose I should forty more, if it wa'n't for that—if we don't have another house. Nanny, she can't live with us after she's married. She'll have to go somewhere else to live away from us, an' it don't seem as if I could have it so, noways, father. She wa'n't ever strong. She's got considerable color, but there wa'n't never any backbone to her. I've always took the heft of everything off her, an' she ain't fit to keep house an' do everything herself. She'll be all worn out inside of a year. Think of her doin' all the washin' an' ironin' an' bakin' with them soft white hands an' arms, an' sweepin'! I can't have it so, noways, father."

Mrs. Penn's face was burning; her mild eyes gleamed. She had pleaded her little cause like a Webster; she had ranged from severity to pathos; but her opponent employed that obstinate silence which makes eloquence futile with mocking echoes. Adoniram arose clumsily.

"Father, ain't you got nothin' to say?" said Mrs. Penn.

"I've got to go off after that load of gravel. I can't stan' here talkin' all day."

"Father, won't you think it over, an' have a house built there instead of a barn?"

"I ain't got nothin' to say."

Adoniram shuffled out. Mrs. Penn went into her bedroom. When she came out, her eyes were red. She had a roll of unbleached cotton cloth. She spread it out on the kitchen table, and began cutting out some shirts for her husband. The men over in the field had a team to help them this afternoon; she could hear their halloos. She had a scanty pattern for the shirts; she had to plan and piece the sleeves.

Nanny came home with her embroidery, and sat down with her needlework. She had taken down her curl-papers, and there was a soft roll of fair hair like an aureole over her forehead; her face was as delicately fine and clear as porcelain. Suddenly she looked up, and the tender red flamed all over her face and neck. "Mother," said she.

"What say?"

"I've been thinking—I don't see how we're goin' to have any—wedding in this room. I'd be ashamed to have his folks come if we didn't have anybody else."

"Mebbe we can have some new paper before then; I can put it on. I guess you won't have no call to be ashamed of your belongin's."

"We might have the wedding in the new barn," said Nanny, with gentle pettishness. "Why, mother, what makes you look so?"

Mrs. Penn had started, and was staring at her with a curious expression. She turned again to her work, and spread out a pattern carefully on the cloth. "Nothin', " said she.

Presently Adoniram clattered out of the yard in his two-wheeled dump cart, standing as proudly upright as a Roman charioteer. Mrs. Penn opened the door and stood there a minute looking out; the halloos of the men sounded louder.

It seemed to her all through the spring months that she heard nothing but the halloos and the noises of saws and hammers. The new barn grew fast. It was a fine edifice for this little village. Men came on pleasant Sundays, in their meeting suits and clean shirt bosoms, and stood around it admiringly. Mrs. Penn did not speak of it, and Adoniram did not mention it to her, although sometimes, upon a return from inspecting it, he bore himself with injured dignity.

"It's a strange thing how your mother feels about the new barn," he said, confidentially, to Sammy one day.

Sammy only grunted after an odd fashion for a boy; he had learned it from his father.

The barn was all completed ready for use by the third week in July. Adoniram had planned to move his stock in on Wednesday; on Tuesday he received a letter which changed his plans. He came in with it early in the morning. "Sammy's been to the post-office," said he, "an' I've got a letter from Hiram." Hiram was Mrs. Penn's brother, who lived in Vermont.

"Well," said Mrs. Penn, "what does he say about the folks?"

"I guess they're all right. He says he thinks if I come up country right off there's a chance to buy jest the kind of a horse I want." He stared reflectively out of the window at the new barn.

Mrs. Penn was making pies. She went on clapping the rolling-pin into the crust, although she was very pale, and her heart beat loudly.

"I dun' know but what I'd better go," said Adoniram. "I hate to go off jest now, right in the midst of hayin', but the ten-acre lot's cut, an' I guess Rufus an' the others can git along without me three or four days. I can't get a horse round here to suit me, nohow, an' I've got to have another for all that wood-haulin' in the fall. I told Hiram to watch out, an' if he got wind of a good horse to let me know. I guess I'd better go."

"I'll get out your clean shirt an' collar," said Mrs. Penn calmly.

She laid out Adoniram's Sunday suit and his clean clothes on the bed in the little bedroom. She got his shaving-water and razor ready. At last she buttoned on his collar and fastened his black cravat.

Adoniram never wore his collar and cravat except on extra occasions. He held his head high, with a rasped dignity. When he was all ready, with his coat and hat brushed, and a lunch of pie and cheese in a paper bag, he hesitated on the threshold of the door. He looked at his wife, and his manner was defiantly apologetic. "*If* them cows come today," Sammy can drive 'em into the new barn," said he; "an' when they bring the hay up, they can pitch it in there."

"Well," replied Mrs. Penn.

Adoniram set his shaven face ahead and started. When he had cleared the doorstep, he turned and looked back with a kind of nervous solemnity. "I shall be back by Saturday if nothin' happens," said he.

"Do be careful, father," returned his wife.

She stood in the door with Nanny at her elbow and watched him out of sight. Her eyes had a strange, doubtful expression in them; her peaceful forehead was contracted. She went in, and about her baking again. Nanny sat sewing. Her wedding-day was drawing nearer, and she was getting pale and thin with her steady sewing. Her mother kept glancing at her.

"Have you got that pain in your side this mornin'?" she asked.

"A little."

Mrs. Penn's face, as she worked, changed, her perplexed forehead smoothed, her eyes were steady, her lips firmly set. She formed a maxim for herself, although incoherently with her unlettered thoughts. "Unsolicited opportunities are the guide-posts of the Lord to the new roads of life," she repeated in effect, and she made up her mind to her course of action.

"S'posin' I *had* wrote to Hiram," she muttered once, when she was in the pantry—"s'posin' I had wrote, an' asked him if he knew of any horse? But I didn't, an' father's goin' wa'n't none of my doin'. It looks like a providence." Her voice rang out quite loud at the last.

"What you talkin' about, mother?" called Nanny.

"Nothin'."

Mrs. Penn hurried her baking; at eleven o'clock it was all done. The load of hay from the west field came slowly down the cart track, and drew up at the new barn. Mrs. Penn ran out. "Stop!" she screamed—"stop!"

The men stopped and looked; Sammy upreared from the top of the load, and stared at his mother.

"Stop!" she cried out again. "Don't you put the hay in that barn; put it in the old one."

"Why, he said to put it in here," returned one of the haymakers, wonderingly. He was a young man, a neighbor's son, whom Adoniram hired by the year to help on the farm.

"Don't you put the hay in the new barn; there's room enough in the old one, ain't there?" said Mrs. Penn.

"Room enough," returned the hired man, in his thick, rustic tones. "Didn't need the new barn, nohow, far as room's concerned. Well, I s'pose he changed his mind." He took hold of the horses' bridles.

Mrs. Penn went back to the house. Soon the kitchen windows were darkened, and a fragrance like warm honey came into the room.

Nanny laid down her work. "I thought father wanted them to put the hay into the new barn?" she said, wonderingly.

"It's all right," replied her mother.

Sammy slid down from the load of hay, and came in to see if dinner was ready.

"I ain't goin' to get a regular dinner today, as long as father's gone," said his mother. "I've let the fire go out. You can have some bread an' milk an' pie. I thought we could get along." She set out some bowls of milk, some bread, and a pie on the kitchen table. "You'd better eat your dinner now," said she. "You might jest as well get through with it. I want you to help me afterward."

Nanny and Sammy stared at each other. There was something strange in their mother's manner. Mrs. Penn did not eat anything herself. She went into the pantry, and they heard her moving dishes while they ate. Presently she came out with a pile of plates. She got the clothes-basket out of the shed, and packed them in it. Nanny and Sammy watched. She brought out cups and saucers, and put them in with the plates.

"What you goin' to do, mother?" inquired Nanny, in a timid voice. A sense of something unusual made her tremble, as if it were a ghost. Sammy rolled his eyes over his pie.

"You'll see what I'm goin' to do," replied Mrs. Penn. "If you're through, Nanny, I want you to go up-stairs an' pack up your things; an' I want you, Sammy, to help me take down the bed in the bedroom."

"Oh, mother, what for?" gasped Nanny.

"You'll see."

During the next few hours a feat was performed by this simple, pious New England mother which was equal in its way to Wolfe's storming of the Heights of Abraham. It took no more genius and audacity of bravery for Wolfe to cheer his wondering soldiers up those steep precipices, under the sleeping eyes of the enemy, than for Sarah Penn, at the head of her children, to move all their little household goods into the new barn while her husband was away.

Nanny and Sammy followed their mother's instructions without a murmur; indeed, they were overawed. There is a certain uncanny and superhuman quality about all such purely original undertakings as their mother's was to them. Nanny went back and forth with her light loads, and Sammy tugged with sober energy.

At five o'clock in the afternoon the little house in which the Penns had lived for forty years had emptied itself into the new barn.

Every builder builds somewhat for unknown purposes, and is in a measure a prophet. The architect of Adoniram Penn's barn, while he designed it for the comfort of four-footed animals, had planned better than he knew for the comfort of humans. Sarah Penn saw at a glance its possibilities. Those great box-stalls, with quilts hung before them, would make better bedrooms than the one she had occupied for forty years, and there was a tight carriage-room. The harness-room, with its chimney and shelves, would make a kitchen of her dreams. The great middle space would make a parlor, by-and-by, fit for a palace. Up stairs there was as much room as down. With partitions and windows, what a house would there be! Sarah looked at the row of stanchions before the allotted space for cows, and reflected that she would have her front entry there.

At six o'clock the stove was up in the harness-room, the kettle was boiling, and the table set for tea. It looked almost as home-like as the abandoned house across the yard had ever done. The young hired man milked, and Sarah directed him calmly to bring the milk to the new barn. He came gaping, dropping little blots of foam from the brimming pails on the grass. Before the next morning he had spread all over the little village the story of Adoniram Penn's wife moving into the new barn. Men assembled in the store and talked it over, women with shawls over their heads scuttled into each other's houses before their work was done. Any deviation from the ordinary course of life in this quiet town was enough to stop all progress in it. Everybody paused to look at the staid, independent figure on the side track. There was a difference of opinion with regard to her. Some held her to be insane; some, of a lawless and rebellious spirit.

Friday the minister went to see her. It was in the forenoon, and she was at the barn door shelling peas for dinner. She looked up and returned his salutation with dignity; then she went on with her work. She did not invite him in. The saintly expression of her face remained fixed, but there was an angry flush over it.

The minister stood awkwardly before her, and talked. She handled the peas as if they were bullets. At last she looked up, and her eyes showed the spirit that her meek front had covered for a lifetime.

"There ain't no use talkin', Mr. Hersey," said she. "I've thought it all over an' over, an' I believe I'm doin' what's right. I've made it the subject of prayer, an' it's betwixt me an' the Lord an' Adoniram. There ain't no call for nobody else to worry about it."

"Well, of course, if you have brought it to the Lord in prayer, and feel satisfied that you are doing right, Mrs. Penn," said the minister, helplessly. His thin, gray-bearded face was pathetic. He was a sickly man; his youthful confidence had cooled; he had to scourge himself up to some of his pastoral duties as relentlessly as a Catholic ascetic, and then he was prostrated by the smart.

"I think it's right jest as much as I think it was right for our forefathers to come over from the old country 'cause they didn't have what belonged to 'em," said Mrs. Penn. She arose. The barn threshold might have been Plymouth Rock from her bearing. "I don't doubt you mean well, Mr. Hersey," said she, "but there are things people hadn't ought to interfere with. I've been a member of the church for over forty year. I've got my own mind an' my own feet, an' I'm goin' to think my own thoughts an' go my own ways, an' nobody but the Lord is goin' to dictate to me unless I've a mind to have him. Won't you come in an' set down? How is Mis' Hersey?"

"She is well, I thank you," replied the minister. He added some more perplexed apologetic remarks; then he retreated.

He could expound the intricacies of every character study in the Scriptures; he was competent to grasp the Pilgrim Fathers and all historical innovators; but Sarah Penn was beyond him. He could deal with primal cases, but parallel ones worsted him. But, after all, although it was aside from his province, he wondered more how Adoniram Penn would deal with his wife than how the Lord would. Everybody shared the wonder. When Adoniram's four new cows arrived, Sarah ordered three to be put in the old barn, the other in the house shed where the cooking-stove had stood. That added to the excitement. It was whispered that all four cows were domiciled in the house.

Towards sunset on Saturday, when Adoniram was expected home, there was a knot of men in the road near the new barn. The hired man had milked, but he still hung around the premises. Sarah Penn had supper all ready. There were brown-bread and baked beans and a custard pie; it was the supper that Adoniram loved on a Saturday night. She had on a clean calico, and she bore herself imperturbably. Nanny and Sammy kept close at her heels. Their eyes were large, and Nanny was full of nervous tremors. Still, there was to them more pleasant excitement than anything else. An inborn confidence in their mother over their father asserted itself.

Sammy looked out of the harness-room window. "There he is," he announced, in an awed whisper. He and Nanny peeped around the casing. Mrs. Penn kept on about her work. The children watched Adoniram leave the new horse standing in the drive while he went to the house door. It was fastened. Then he went around to the shed. That door was seldom locked, even when the family was away. The thought how her father would be confronted by the cow flashed upon Nanny. There was a hysterical sob in her throat. Adoniram emerged from the shed and stood looking about in a dazed fashion. His lips moved; he was saying something, but they could not hear what it was. The hired man was peeping around a corner of the old barn, but nobody saw him.

Adoniram took the new horse by the bridle and led him across the yard to the new barn. Nanny and Sammy slunk close to their mother. The barn doors rolled back, and there stood Adoniram, with the long mild face of the great Canadian farm horse looking over his shoulder.

Nanny kept behind her mother, but Sammy stepped suddenly forward, and stood in front of her.

Adoniram stared at the group. "What on airth you all down here for?" said he. "What's the matter over to the house?"

"We've come here to live, father," said Sammy. His shrill voice quavered out bravely.

"What"—Adoniram sniffed—"what is it smells like cookin'?" said he. He stepped forward and looked in the open door of the harness-room. Then he turned to his wife. His old bristling face was pale and frightened. "What on airth does this mean, mother?" he gasped.

"You come in here, father," said Sarah. She led the way into the harness-room and shut the door. "Now, father," said she, "you needn't be scared. I ain't crazy. There ain't nothin' to be upset over. But we've come here to live, an' we're goin' to live here. We've got jest as good a right here as new horses an' cows. The house wa'n't fit for us to live in any longer, an' I made up my mind I wa'n't goin' to stay there. I've done my duty by you forty year, an' I'm goin' to do it now; but I'm goin' to live here. You've got to put in some windows and partitions; an' you'll have to buy some furniture."

"Why, mother!" the old man gasped.

"You'd better take your coat off an' get washed—there's the wash-basin—an' then we'll have supper."

"Why, mother!"

Sammy went past the window, leading the new horse to the old barn. The old man saw him, and shook his head speechlessly. He tried to take off his coat, but his arms seemed to lack the power. His wife helped him. She poured some water into the tin basin, and put in a piece of soap. She got the comb and brush, and smoothed his thin gray hair after he had washed. Then she put the beans, hot bread, and tea on the table. Sammy came in and the family drew up. Adoniram sat looking dazedly at his plate, and they waited.

"Ain't you goin' to ask a blessin', father?" said Sarah.

And the old man bent his head and mumbled.

All through the meal he stopped eating at intervals, and stared furtively at his wife; but he ate well. The home food tasted good to him, and his old frame was too sturdily healthy to be affected by his mind. But after supper he went out, and sat down on the step of the smaller door at the right of the barn, through which he had meant his Jerseys to pass in stately file, but which Sarah designed for her front house door, and he leaned his head on his hands.

After the supper dishes were cleared away and the milk-pans washed, Sarah went out to him. The twilight was deepening. There was a clear green glow in the sky. Before them stretched the smooth level of field; in the distance was a cluster of haystacks like the huts of a village; the air was very cool and calm and sweet. The landscape might have been an ideal one of peace.

Sarah bent over and touched her husband on one of his thin, sinewy shoulders. "Father!"

The old man's shoulders heaved; he was weeping.

"Why, don't do so, father," said Sarah.

"I'll—put up the —partitions, an'—everything you—want, mother."

Sarah put her apron up to her face; she was overcome by her own triumph.

Adoniram was like. a fortress whose walls had no active resistance, and went down the instant the right besieging tools were used. "Why, mother," he said, hoarsely, "I hadn't no idee you was so set on't as all this comes to."

THE SNOW STORY

By Chauncey Thomas

[Most of the "Western" stories of the pulp magazines fall short of representing the West as it is. Many of them romance about the old West as the writers suppose it to have been or as Eastern readers want to believe it actually was. To find a well constructed short story about mountain life or ranch life in the Rocky Mountain West, written by one who knows the West by having lived in it long enough to get the "feel" of the country, is a rare thing. This story pictures Berthoud Pass as it then was, and as it essentially is today except for the wonderfully graded automobile road that makes possible a trip from Empire to Hot Sulphur Springs in an hour or two.

Mr. Thomas was born in Denver in 1872 and still lives there. His experience covers newspaper and magazine writing and the life as a cowboy and rancher. Needless to say, the incidents and observations in *The Snow Story* come out of personal experience. A peak in the Rocky Mountains is officially named Mt. Chauncey in honor of this story which drew admiring letters from a great many readers, including Rudyard Kipling. Mr. Thomas is an expert pistol shot, and is often called into court to testify as an expert witness on ballistics.

The Snow Story, under the title *Why the Hot Sulphur Mail Was Late*, first appeared in *McClure's Magazine* (November, 1901). The final and considerably revised version of the story is reprinted here by permission of the author.]

One touch of Nature makes the whole world kin.—SHAKESPEARE.

BERTHOUD Pass is a mighty pass. It is the crest of a solid wave of granite two miles high, just at timber line. Berthoud is a vertebra in the backbone of the continent. It is the gigantic aerial gateway to Middle Park, Colorado—a park one-fifth as large as all England. The mail for this empire is carried by one man—my friend Mason.

On Berthoud is a pebble. One summer a raindrop fell upon that pebble, splashed in two and each half rolled away; one danced down the Platte-Missouri-Mississippi, the longest river on the globe, to the Atlantic; the other tumbled down the Fraser, rolled along the Grand, thence through the greatest gorge on earth, the Grand Cañon of the Colorado, where the stars shine by day, to the Pacific. In the clasp of the Berthoud-born raindrop there were Europe and Asia one way, two oceans and the two Americas the other. Then from the two oceans the nebulized half-drops arose, sun-drawn, miles into the zenith and rode the upper winds straight back to Berthoud Pass. There they united and crystallized into a snow-flake. And with it came the Cold. There, far above the Pass, the frost spirit hung in Damoclean deadliness over a creeping speck below—Mason, the mail carrier.

The rising sun glorified the snowflake; but away down there in Clear Creek cañon, where other waters gurgled and strangled under the ice, it was still a blue dark. Mason and the sun began to climb. The morning light started down Berthoud just as Mason started up. The snow-flake watched the crawling atom, then blew across the Pass, and from all along the range gathered unto itself the storm. On Berthoud was all the power of the Arctic. But the intelligent dot climbed on.

Eleven months of every year there is snow on Berthoud; only in July are the flowers safe. Even then, in shades that the sun cannot reach—packed by the centuries—is snow that fell on the rocks before they were cold. How black, how sharp the shadows are on the heights— and how cold! In them for ages has lurked ice from the continent-grinding glaciers of the North. Silent Christmas finds Berthoud hung with avalanches. At Easter these white thunderbolts come to life; and, leaning over the valleys, are so exquisitely held that they are launched even by an echo touch. Up there in long, wavering lines and tiny whirls the gritty snow blows like sugar. Shrub-like, the tops of pines bend under locks and beards of alabaster moss, their trunks frigid for seventy feet in the crusted depths. Airy crystals float as on the breath of Polar fairies; the sunlight is alive with blue sparkles; the twig splitting in the cold sends a puff of frosty feathers; in the gale white shot sings in level volleys. Nature on Berthoud in winter is not dead, but alive. She is congealed into a new life. The very air seeming to snap, is thinner as if about to solidify. A mist, frozen to a transparent blue, quivers with its own chill. Water is not ice, but glass. When the black, solid lakes burst and shatter in the awful cold, ice splinters fly and burn like slivers of white-hot iron. Ice powder, hard, dry and sharp, grinds the web of snow-shoes like steel filings. On Berthoud at night the stars are near; they silently crackle and spit colors like electric sparks.

In the valley just then the morning star paled as if frozen, and with a spiteful snap winked out. The line of sunlight, halfway down the Pass, met Mason, halfway up. The blue-gray cold melted to a flood of heaven's own warmth. It would be warmer soon, then hot, then blister-ing there on the snow. Mason stopped to rest, panting steam; peeled off his coat and put on his veil.

To climb Berthoud in winter is the work of a man. It is too much for an engine. The man was at his work. Up, slowly up, the east side, around the Big Bend, up to the now deserted mail barn, labored the mail carrier. The summit was a mile farther on and a quarter of mile farther up. No arranged postal car, warm, light and convenient, was the lot of Mason. The car was on his back, a bag of mail. Contrary to regulations, devised by easy-chair postal officials in far-off Washington, the papers and packages had been held at Empire. Only the letters went over.

"They'll keep," had said the Empire postmaster, a man of vast common sense, as he filled his pipe from Mason's pouch. Then he and Mason had hidden the bag of 2nd-class under the hay in the manger of the mail team back in Empire until the thaw was over. So Mason traveled light—only sixty-four pounds on his back and twenty pounds of wet snow on each web a foot beneath the surface. By the bleak, now empty, halfway station slouched Mason.

"Only zero! Hot. Whe-ew-w!" he gasped, as he wiped the sweat from his eyes with his shirt-sleeve. Mason meant it. Twelve feet of frigid white was between him and the earth; in the shadow the mercury was solid in the split tubes, yet in the sunlight the surface was slush. Mason was in his shirt-sleeves with fur mittens on his hands. Icicles hung from his eyelashes, yet his cheeks were frying. His nose was a blister, though his face was veiled as heavily as Milady's on an escapade. In the sun the snow was mush—in the shadow it was marble. Such is sunlight and shade on the southeastern snow banks at timberline. No wind. And the air was thin. Silence. The only sound was the carrier's bellowsed breath, and the sock-rasp-splosh of the shoes. And Mason came to the summit—and the shadow. Noon. Here the mercury falls a degree a minute when the sun goes down. A hundred and four at noon, an inch of ice at sundown. The ground is frozen for five hundred and forty feet. Such is the summer summit.

But this was winter. Up the south gorge of the Fraser, from the Pacific side of the Pass, like the burst of a volcano, so cold that the smoke was snow-dust, roared the storm. Mason saw it—looked with the indifferent interest of long experience, and put on his short fur coat. As he retied his snowshoes he looked back—and down. Below him lay the west fork of Clear Creek, green in the coming spring. Mason stood on the rampart of winter. On either side the Pass towered pinnacles of storm-eaten rock, bleak as the Poles themselves. From their tops white powder streamed in the wind like crests, and floured down on the back-turned pigmy at their feet. The carrier was taking with his eyes from the Atlantic side a swift, silent good-bye of the infant summer. Straight to the south flamed the sun, so low in the clear sky that Mason, standing on Berthoud, felt that it was below him—infernal—and that he stood alone on the tip of the Universe. Behind him the swirling heavens were murky. The world was black, white and thin blue—silent, motionless, and cold, lit, but unwarmed, by the open furnace-door of hell.

But the cold was creeping for Mason's heart, and he flung his arms. "Good for the legs," he remarked to a stump that in summer was a dead pine tree. "Track looks like a hobbled elephant's. Well—here goes." And down into the gorge went Mason.

That gale had started in Alaska and swept two-thirds of a continent to the southwest. In Montana it had torn the anemometer, the official whirligig, from the signal station, but left the register, and the needle pointed to eighty-five miles an hour. It was faster now. Caught by the wide mouth of the south fork of the Fraser and jammed into the upright narrowing of the rocky defile, the white fiend roared straight into the air a league and back over itself—chaos with flying chains. Into this walked Mason.

A single snow-flake, a bunch of frozen needle points, struck his fore-head, but glanced away into the white pandemonium. Snow-sand cut his veil as if blown from a gun. Instantly his breath was sucked from his lungs and sent twenty thousand feet—four miles above the sea. Mason whirled, his back to the flinty sleet, and the storm fell upon the United States mail. But no snow storm can stop the United States mail. With a belly-jerk Mason wrenched a breath from the torrent.

"Quite a Colorado zephyr," he yelled, but could not hear himself. There was almost perfect silence around him, because he could hear nothing—only a leaden roar. No slush here; the surface was sand paper. Zip-zip-zip, with his head low, Mason butted down the gulch. Then it eased up. The wind dropped to a mile a minute, and cleared greatly. Mason could see ten feet ahead. Easier now, he loped over the crust, down, down, down, leaving no track—not even a whiff of snow was blown from the trail. The snow was as hard, sharp, and glittering in the white night as the surface of broken steel. A blast of snow-sand caught the flying, dropping carrier square in the face. The ground ice cut like powdered glass shot from a battery. Mason, his arms before his head, ran into and leaned against a crackling pine. Amid these convulsions of the Wilderness he seemed like a frightened child.

Suddenly the pine straightened with a snap, quivering as if tired. Mason lowered his arms; all was still, quiet, pleasant. The snow was smiling; the sun was shining; there was no wind. But a mile—now two—boiling in the air—white hell churned.

"Lovely, ain't it? Snowslide gone off wrong end up," said a voice.

Mason jumped. A quick sweep of the near distance showed nothing human but himself.

"Did I say that?" he muttered. "This bucking snow is about as good on a man's savey as herding sheep. I'll be as locoed as a swell-necked buck if I keep this up—Hello!"

"Howdy?" answered the voice, and from under a sheltering ledge, crusted over but filled soft and dry with icy down as if banked from a featherbed, heaved a sheeted figure and shook itself. It fairly rattled.

"Nice little blow, wasn't it? I had an idea I was the only pack animal of the long-eared breed on the Range—but I see I have company; baggage and all. Glad to see you, though. By-the-way, sorry to trouble you, but I'll have to ask you for those shoes—and that coat; also any spare change you've got, your ticker, and that mail bag. Now don't go off half-cocked and empty, or we'll have trouble."

He of the voice had leveled a long six-shooter, white with frost and snow, at the mail carrier.

Mason was not startled. What was the use? But he was annoyed—this lack of mountain courtesy. Then he grinned.

"Not this trip, pardner. Your artillery's as full of snow as the Arctic circle; while this instrument I have—"

A burst of flame, smoke and steam exploded between the two men. As it floated upward Mason saw the stranger bend double and squeeze his right hand between his knees. Blood was dripping over his felt boots and overshoes. A splintered six-shooter rang on the ice twenty feet away.

"I told you you'd have fireworks if you turned that ice jam loose. No wonder she exploded. What'd you expect? You're too experienced a man by the looks of you to throw such a kid trick as that. Thought I wasn't heeled, hey? And you'd work a bluff on me, did you? Going to spear me on an icicle. Now, you fool"—Mason's tone became dry, metallic—"you wiggle a hair and I'll kill you. My gun has not been out all winter; it is ready for business. Just off the hip; hot as buckwheat. Now don't do the stage-eye act on me, nor try any foot-ball dives—and leave that sticker of yours alone. You might cut somebody with it. No, thank you, I'll help myself. Straighten up now; and turn your back. See here— Are you going to do as I tell you, or shall I fix your hide so that they'll tan it for chair bottoms? Jump lively now, or I'll fill you so full of lead that you'll assay for Georgetown ore and it'll take the coroner's jury twenty-four hours to count the holes. Still I don't want to kill you. It's a dirty job, and I would rather walk you into town than haul you there on your back. Oh, don't go frothing now and sass me back like that. Of course I'm festive. Who wouldn't be with a five-thousand-dollar winner—Hold on there. Five-thousand-dollar gold mine, as I was a say'en, in your own self as a standing reward for Salarado —N-No. My dear sir, a single jump into my latitude and I'll plug you. Postoffice robber, ugh? And gathered in by Uncle Sam himself in the person of your humble striker. Lord. I ain't talked so much since speech-makin' over good luck come into fashion. Oh, yes; I know you. No; it isn't any lie, either. I have your circular description here in my pocket, right next my heart, to tack up in every mail window in Empire and Hot Sulphur. You're wanted, wanted bad; five thousand dollars' worth of bad, too; and I've got you—and incidentally I intend to keep you. Now drop that cleaver of your'n and shinny on down the trail there, or we'll have troub—"

A mile above a concussion jolted the cliff; a terrific echo to the pistol-shot. Down came the slide—gently at first—so far away it seemed only as wide as one's hand. In an instant the snow shot from under the two men. A mile of snow, bristling hairlike with root-torn pines, thundered down the slope. Mason and Salarado, forgetful of each other, were whirled into the air, and fell back on a huge slab of ice that crashed down that tumbling mountainside unbroken by the mass of fighting logs around it. This piece of ice on which they lay was thick and solid, laced and interlaced with tough brushwood frozen in. This woven acre rode the avalanche like a sled. A crag a quarter of a mile, ten feet, ahead, passed with a roar. A huge pine whipped by faster yet. That rocky spur half a mile down—now behind—was a pain in the ear. Faster, faster, dropping, falling, sailing—they are standing still; but on either side, up from below, the air and the mountains pour—then blackness.

An hour later a mountain lion sneaked over the wreck. A hill of snow, ice, broken stone and splintered logs dammed the gulch. Away to the top of the Range the track of the slide lay like a scald. Miles away, high in the air, a cloud of white dust was floating. An eighth of a mile up the opposing slope had shot a huge piece of ice, and lay half buried in the debris. All Nature was hushed as if frightened. A screeching eagle went flapping far away. From under the ruin a wolf howled dismally; then weaker and weaker—a piteous whine—and silence. The frozen wind went up a gulch of naked, fire-blackened pines crooning a requiem. But the music from that wild cathedral breathed not of eternal rest and peace; it chilled the heart in icy triumph. Berthoud had struck a mountainous blow; and humanity—Where were the men?

The panther was hunting; his nose had found them, but not his jaws. Settling himself, he dug. As the famished brute raked a log to one side with his gaunt jaw, he heard a groan within an inch of his ear—whirling he flashed up the mountainside a streak of yellow. But his work was done.

From the shallow hole reared the mail sack, and the head and arms of Mason, all chalk white but his face, which was a ghastly blue. He struggled carefully, then desperately, to free himself; but when he stopped exhausted, only his head and shoulders appeared above the snow.

"Pinned down—dead—my last trip—and yet not hurt. Freeze like a cockroach in the ice-house. Cool, my boy, cool—keep cool. Don't lose your head—don't get rattled, or you're a dead man. Now's when you need all your brains. Keep cool—though you will be cool enough all too soon."

Mason's head disappeared in the panther-dug hole. Slowly the end of a small log ten feet away rose into the air and fell aside. Upstraightened the grizzly head of Salarado, one side daubed with a red slush.

"Well—I—be—damned. This don't look much like hell; still it's a pretty good imitation," growled the desperado as he gazed around the piled confusion. He noticed the straining mail-sack. Salarado waited silently till Mason's haggard face again came above the rim. The two men looked into each other's eyes.

"Hurt?" asked Mason.

"Don't think so. Both feet fast. How's yourself?" answered Salarado.

"One leg in a vise—can't move it. What d'you think?"

"We're done for."

"Guess you're right. How's the snow 'round you?"

"None 't all—all ice. Solid."

"Hold still. I've got one foot a little loose," and Mason stamped on a log far below.

"Same log," said the thief. "Got us both."

Nothing more was said. They went to work. Mason unslung the mailsack and laid it carefully aside. For an hour both men strained, pulled, twisted, and dug at their white irons with bare fingers till the purple ends were raw. Great red finger scratches stained the snow around them. Human fingers are not panther claws. Both men were packed tight up to their arm-pits in solid snow. Four feet below the surface of the ruin their legs were fast between two parallel logs as in a steel trap. An inch closer and their ankles would have cracked like pipe-stems; an inch wider and the two men would have been free. They were not hurt; merely held. Berthoud had been kind only to be cruel.

"No use," panted Mason. "My trail ends here."

"Mine don't. I wish it did," murmured Salarado. The hard tone was gone; the voice was almost gentle. "Hell's ahead of me. You are an honest man, Señor, and have nothing to fear from death; while I"— and there was silence for many minutes. "Many's the time I've faced it, but not when I had to think it over—like this," he continued to himself.

Then they waited. A camp-robber, that bird of winter timberline, came like the blue angel of death, and hopped and scolded within a yard of them, and mocked them.

"Lucky jay; you've got what I would give the world for," mused Salarado. Mason said nothing. He was thinking of a little rawhide dugout down in the hot sands of New Mexico where Mexie lay basking in the sun; and over this picture like a haze crept the scene of a great fire in the night, with Indians about it, and a cauldron of boiling water steaming furiously. With a start Mason looked about him and recognized where he was. This was the cañon where so many years before he had fought the Colorow Utes.

"What is it, Señor?" asked Salarado.

"Nothing," answered Mason.

Mason was brave; yet he did not want to die. Life held so much for him to live and to work for, yet he waited calmly, his brain as cold as his freezing foot. At intervals the men struggled, wrenched their muscles with no hope of getting out, but to keep warm. The thirst-fever that comes from pain had dried Mason's tongue. He longed for water. A mouthful of snow burned like hot cinders; he spat it out and pressed his rigid jaw with stiff, bare hands to warm the aching teeth. He looked about for water. Fifty feet up the mountain, in the lee of a boulder, was a spring, but it was solid ink banked with crystal milk. The breeze was gently keen. Mason's clothes grew cold. He felt nude and shrank from them. His skin became small and tight, and smarted as though blistered. A chill shook him. Blunt pains worked along the bones and met in the joints. Each particular finger and toe seemed about to burst. His scalp stiffened. His chin was numb. The cold, gnawing between his shoulders, was biting for his heart. Only the wedged foot was warm, and strangely comfortable. Webs of spidery ice floated and vanished in the cheerful sunlight. Flashing wiggles swarmed before the man's angular eyes like joyous worms, and disappeared only to come again. Mason was freezing. Away in the sky loomed Berthoud Pass hoary with ice ermine and wrapped in fleecy clouds. To Mason's hopeless eyes the wreath-veils seemed smoke and steam, curiously warm. He shuddered, locked his rattling jaws and grimly faced the end.

Up there on the summit the clouds were of gold; the very top was red. In oblivious majesty eternal rose the Pass; but over and about the two heads sticking in the snow a living spangle, a single snow-flake, flashing, dazzling, glittering, wafted like a dancing diamond. It tickled the cold flesh of Mason's face, then tumbled into the air in a very ecstasy of whirls. The man's head drooped, drooped, dipped, jerked back; drooped again; and hung pendulous. Mason was asleep, warm and comfortable. With a dull yell of pain he awoke. Salarado had hit him in the ear with a snowball.

"Hang on, Señor. Keep a scrape'n. Don't give up," were the rough words of cheer.

Mason knotted his muscles, shook off the torpor as if it were the tightening coils of a cold snake, and rubbed his burning ear.

"What's the use? We'll both be stiff in three hours. Might as well have it over with," replied Mason as if speaking of a card game.

Aroused, he freed his feet of the webs and pulled some feeling into the clutched one. From his pocket he took his lunch, until now forgotten, and silently tossed half to his fellow prisoner. The camp-robber captured a piece of meat in the air and flew squawking to a limb. Salarado swore at the bird in profane amusement. Mason re-divided his piece of pork and threw it over. The holdup protested, raked it in, and tossed it back. Mason chewed down his own share, but this piece of meat he put back in his pocket. Salarado looked at him:

"Say, pardner, you're a man."

The fires of life, rekindled, flamed up anew in the desperado.

"I will get loose," he snarled with set teeth as he tore frightfully at the snow around his waist.

"Try this; my hands are too stiff to use it," and Mason threw his watch to Salarado.

"Ah, Señor, a regular snow-plough," grunted the other as he sprang open the lid with his teeth and began to scrape.

"Sa-ay"—the yell rang up the Pass—"here's my knife."

Buried tight in the snow was the knife—Life itself—within easy reach, yet frozen fast. Mason did not answer, but waited. Just then Salarado's dead hands dropped the watch. It vanished along his leg into the black hole that held him, and then faintly clinked on a stone under the log-jam. With a curse the life-long criminal clawed viciously at the snow with scarlet fingers. Ten minutes of bloody scratching cleared the handle and hilt of the heavy bowie; and Salarado's head and shoulders arose triumphant, his gory right hand flourishing the priceless steel. The light from that blade flashed to the very top of Berthoud. Mason writhed to keep warm.

The shadows were growing longer now. In another two hours the sun would be down, and their lives would go out like candles. Salarado jabbed, ripped, strained and from his burrow hurled ice, snow and splintered wood. Iron against water, with men for stakes! In thirty minutes he was free all but his feet. Both ankles were held between two logs; one thick as his waist, the other a mere pole. Hack, slice, split. In five minutes more Salarado crawled painfully, sweating and breathless, from the hole.

He tried to stand, but tottered and fell as if on stilts. He rubbed, he pounded, he rolled and twisted his numbed calves and feet; the thick, black blood turned bright and throbbed again. Salarado stood erect, danced sorely, and except for his skinless fingers and a scalp wound, now staunched with a frozen plaster of bloody hair, he was as well as ever. The bruised shoulder was unheeded. A lusterless snowflake dropped weakly at the man's feet. He stepped on it as he picked up the knife and clambered over the snow and logs to Mason.

Salarado looked at Mason, and Mason looked at Salarado. Mason's lips were without motion, but in his eyes was the look of a paw-fast grizzly. The multi-murderer seated himself on a broken spruce branch not six feet from Mason, rested his hands on his knees and thought. He stared at the carrier. Here was a man whom two hours before he had tried to kill; who in turn stood ready to kill him; and even started him at the muzzle of his six-shooter on that short, sure road to a living death, the penitentiary for life, or the noose. Leave him there—why not? No crime—he had not put him there. What if it were a crime? Who would know? And what if they did? Far from being his first. In the spring—perhaps not for years—they would find the skeleton; and fleshless jaws say little. Dig him out—then what? Was it not to set free a messenger sure to start all the machinery of the law to land the rescuer in a cage—a cage—where nothing could come but insanity and death? Why again seek from what he has just escaped? And entirely by his own efforts, too— The watch? But the other's hands had been— still were—too cold to use it; so it could have done him no good. Salarado thought these things, seated there on the log-end in the snow-slide that frigid February day, facing his enemy—that enemy now harmless; but all-powerful when free. Why reverse their positions? Salarado looked at the Range ahead. In the setting sun the Pass was banked high with frozen blood. Hard, almost fatal it was. Why add a vindictive posse from behind? It was good just to be alive—and free. Then he looked once more at Mason, silent, waiting Mason—then at the empty hole, splotched with his own blood. Why not kill him quickly? One thrust and the cold-tortured man would be out of his misery—surely an act of mercy. Was not this enough? The stage-robber, murderer, desperado —reckless, careless of life and death, hunted by thirty millions, a bounty on his head—thoroughly understood the situation. So did his victim. The camp-robber flickered into the air and away homeward to a distant ranch. This winged freedom fascinated the criminal. He watched the bird float beyond the pine tops, looked again at the Range, stiffened to his feet, picked up the bowie, glanced behind him, and gazed down at the helpless, freezing man.

"I would not trade places with you," curled from Mason's lips, but Salarado was looking at the pocketed piece of meat. Then Salarado took the knife by the blade and handed it to Mason.

The light in Mason's eyes cannot be put into words. He tried to speak. Salarado smiled, and with wooden fingers tried to roll a cigarette. Mason bent into his dead-fall to hide his tears—and to work. A half hour and Salarado pulled Mason from the hole. A minute more and the two men, the morally white with black spots, the morally black with white spots, stood face to face. Mason put out his hand. Salarado took it— still smoking.

"Pardner, you're a square man. Thanks. Here—" Mason peeled off his fur jacket, his cap and his overshoes, "take these, and this," he added, as he handed the desperado two bills and some silver. Then he hesitated—but with a jerk unbuckled his cartridge belt and, with its dangling holster full of snow, handed it to Salarado. "You'll find the gun in the hole; I felt it with my foot. Don't use it unless you have to. She's sighted to a hair and has a soft trigger—but I want this knife. Good-bye. Mexico is the place for you. Less snow there." Both men smiled grimly. "Take straight down the gulch on the other side—it'll be frozen by the time you get there—and a freight is due at Empire at two in the morning—usually late, though. You can make it if you hump yourself. The shoes are in the hole there. I kicked them off. Eat that bacon when you get on top. It'll limber up your legs. Leave the tracks at the mouth of the cañon—she slows up there for the switch—for Golden is right ahead, and your picture is in the Post Office there. Cut to your right across the saddle-back you'll see about four miles to the southeast; then straight on southeast fifteen or twenty miles till you cross the Platte, and you'll hit the Santa Fe tracks going south. Jump 'em, and a week from now you'll cross the Rio Grande—*quien sabe?* Go to the Three Triangle outfit in Chihuahua; tell the foreman, Pete Miller, he is known down there, I sent you and he'll give you a job punching. He'll do it 'cause I snaked him out of the Republican two years ago with his chaps on, and she was a boomin'—runnin' ice. I'd help you fish out those webs, but I got a case of cold feet and guess I'll have to quit ya."

Salarado breathed a slow curl of smoke and murmured, "Your foot's frozen, Señor? Maybeso I go with you—part way?"

"No. No need of that; only frosted; all right now. I can stump it in all right. These dutch socks'll last me till I reach Chipmunk's. You've no time to lose, pardner, so *adios*. Good luck to you. And—" Mason stopped, embarrassed—"and—if I were you, I'd quit this business. Don't pay."

"Si, Señor, you're right. I made up my mind to that in that hole there—just before I found the knife. If I hadn't—you—" Salarado left the sentence as it was; but Mason knew. He gripped the desperado's hand again, but its five bloody fingers made him think of five one-thousand-dollar bills and half a score of murdered men.

"Well, be good to yourself. The mail must go through," Mason replied as he swung the sack to his shoulders. Then with the knife held like a sword, Mason saluted the other and left him. Salarado's face gave a white-fanged smile, but said nothing.

On darkening Berthoud the snow had turned to ashes. At the edge of the timber Mason turned and once more waved the bowie. Salarado swung his cap. Then Mason passed beneath the pines. Looking back between the trunks, now out of the other's sight, he saw a puff of snow and a piece of brush go into the air from the hole. It was Salarado digging for the shoes.

Three hours late Mason limped into Chipmunk's. Ten feet on the level had buried the station in December. Only the plumed chimney showed. During that tramp Mason had been thinking; the inevitable reaction had set in, and he staggered under his load, for it seemed to him as if that sack held the mail of the nation; his brain was boiling with conflicting thoughts and warring emotions; and his conscience was divided against itself, for Mason was an honest man and Salarado was everything that was bad. One word to those in the cabin he was approaching and by midnight Salarado, the most dangerous criminal in the

West, would be behind the bars—or lynched. Lynched? Mason shivered, and pushed open the hinge-complaining door. Gansen was swearing—had been for two hours.

"What's the trouble?" he demanded. "Think I'm going to hold the team here a week and drive it all night? With the spirit thermometer fifty-two below at the Springs this morning? If I miss the Coulter connection, Glenn won't do a thing but come up the line with a meat-ax for the whole outfit. The mails has got to go through. What's the trouble? You look as if you and a mowing machine had been havin' an argument."

"Oh, nothing," said Mason, "bucked into a little slide iust above High Bridge. We mixed, and I lost my goods and chattels, but acquired a whole museum of bumps and such things, besides a choice set of refrigerated toes. But here's the mail. No. No second-class at Empire at all. Guess it's delayed in Denver, or else good people don't mail papers in the winter time."

"Where did you get that bowie?" grinned Gansen. "Regular yearling sword—some toothpick. Fine can opener. Will it cut anything? Overgrown rooster spur, isn't it? Going to mow some hay? Better wait till the snow pulls out, and the grass comes up."

"Ugh. Maybeso," and Mason thumbed the still frosted edge. "Swapped my sixgun for it some time ago. Nothing to shoot on the Range now. Better to chop wood with. Might use it for a sawmill sometime. Or dig a prospect hole while I'm taking a siesta and letting the snowshoes cool off, or let the wind out of something. Questions break friendships, and comments are worse. That's why angels go on the warpath."

Gansen eyed that foot of chilled steel quizzically, opened his mouth to say something, then closed it.

"No noise," chuckled old Chipmunk into his whiskers.

"See here, Chipmunk, you old gorilla," continued Mason as he sheathed the knife, "I want you to let up on trappin' along my trail. I don't like it. Found a marten in one of your infernal machines, and I turned him loose. Threw the Newhouse about forty miles somewheres off into the timber. I don't want any more of it. Savey?

"Well, *adios*, Jim. Give my apologies to the folks in Hot Sulphur 'cause their mail is late. It won't happen next time—perhaps not for a thousand years. Tell Mark I'll be down to the dance sure. Ask the Coulter school-marm to save me a waltz. Sure, now. Ta-ta."

"Say, Chip! Get a wiggle on ya. Got any coffee? I'm tired. W-whew." And Mason lifted the pot off the stove. On the fire he put a bunch of circulars. They soon had the coffee boiling.

THE YELLOW WALLPAPER

By *Charlotte Perkins Gilman*

[*The Yellow Wallpaper* may be regarded as a study in abnormal psychology. It follows the steps of the mental deterioration and final collapse in hopeless insanity of an admirable woman. One may call it a study of insanity, but the total impression of the story is one of horror. It has few rivals in the class of horror stories.

Mrs. Gilman was born in Hartford, Connecticut, in 1860, and lives at present at Norwichtown, Connecticut. Literature has not been her chief occupation. She has been a lecturer on ethics, economics, and sociology, and has been prominently identified with labor and feminist movements.

The Yellow Wallpaper, first published in 1892, is reprinted by permission of the author.]

IT is very seldom that mere ordinary people like John and myself secure ancestral halls for the summer.

A colonial mansion, a hereditary estate, I would say a haunted house, and reach the height of romantic felicity—but that would be asking too much of fate!

Still I will proudly declare that there is something queer about it.

Else, why should it be let so cheaply? And why have stood so long untenanted?

John laughs at me, of course, but one expects that.

John is practical in the extreme. He has no patience with faith, an intense horror of superstition, and he scoffs openly at any talk of things not to be felt and seen and put down in figures.

John is a physician, and *perhaps*—(I would not say it to a living soul, of course, but this is dead paper and a great relief to my mind)—*perhaps* that is one reason I do not get well faster.

You see he does not believe I am sick! And what can one do?

If a physician of high standing, and one's own husband, assures friends and relatives that there is really nothing the matter with one but temporary nervous depression—a slight hysterical tendency—what is one to do?

My brother is also a physician, and also of high standing, and he says the same thing.

So I take phosphates or phosphites—whichever it is—and tonics, and air and exercise, and journeys, and am absolutely forbidden to "work" until I am well again.

Personally, I disagree with their ideas.

Personally, I believe that congenial work, with excitement and change, would do me good.

But what is one to do?

I did write for a while in spite of them; but it *does* exhaust me a good deal—having to be so sly about it, or else meet with heavy opposition.

I sometimes fancy that in my condition if I had less opposition and more society and stimulus—but John says the very worst thing I can do is to think about my condition, and I confess it always makes me feel bad.

So I will let it alone and talk about the house.

The most beautiful place! It is quite alone, standing well back from the road, quite three miles from the village. It makes me think of English places that you read about, for there are hedges and walls and gates that lock, and lots of separate little houses for the gardeners and people.

There is a *delicious* garden! I never saw such a garden—large and shady, full of box-bordered paths, and lined with long grape-covered arbors with seats under them.

There were greenhouses, but they are all broken now.

There was some legal trouble, I believe, something about the heirs and co-heirs; anyhow the place has been empty for years.

That spoils my ghostliness, I am afraid, but I don't care—there is something strange about the house—I can feel it.

I even said so to John one moonlight evening, but he said what I felt was a draught, and shut the window.

I get unreasonably angry with John sometimes. I'm sure I never used to be so sensitive. I think it is due to this nervous condition.

But John says if I feel so I shall neglect proper self-control; so I take pains to control myself—before him, at least, and that makes me very tired.

I don't like our room a bit. I wanted one downstairs that opened on the piazza and had roses all over the window, and such pretty old-fashioned chintz hangings! But John would not hear of it.

He said there was only one window and not room for two beds, and no near room for him if he took another.

He is very careful and loving, and hardly lets me stir without special direction.

I have a schedule prescription for each hour in the day; he takes all care from me, and so I feel basely ungrateful not to value it more.

He said he came here solely on my account, that I was to have perfect rest and all the air I could get. "Your exercise depends on your strength, my dear," said he, "and your food somewhat on your appetite; but air you can absorb all the time." So we took the nursery at the top of the house.

It is a big, airy room, the whole floor nearly, with windows that look all ways, and air and sunshine galore. It was nursery first, and then playroom and gymnasium, I should judge; for the windows are barred for little children, and there are rings and things in the walls.

The paint and paper look as if a boys' school had used it. It is stripped off—the paper—in great patches all around the head of my bed, about as far as I can reach, and in a great place on the other side of the room low down. I never saw a worse paper in my life.

One of those sprawling, flamboyant patterns committing every artistic sin.

It is dull enough to confuse the eye in following, pronounced enough constantly to irritate and provoke study, and when you follow the lame uncertain curves for a little distance they suddenly commit suicide—plunge off at outrageous angles, destroy themselves in unheard-of contradictions.

The color is repellant, almost revolting; a smouldering unclean yellow, strangely faded by the slow-turning sunlight.

It is a dull yet lurid orange in some places, a sickly sulphur tint in others.

No wonder the children hated it! I should hate it myself if I had to live in this room long.

There comes John, and I must put this away—he hates to have me write a word.

We have been here two weeks, and I haven't felt like writing before, since that first day.

I am sitting by the window now, up in this atrocious nursery, and there is nothing to hinder my writing as much as I please, save lack of strength.

John is away all day, and even some nights when his cases are serious.

I am glad my case is not serious!

But these nervous troubles are dreadfully depressing.

John does not know how much I really suffer. He knows there is no *reason* to suffer, and that satisfies him.

Of course it is only nervousness. It does weigh on me so not to do my duty in any way!

I meant to be such a help to John, such a real rest and comfort, and here I am a comparative burden already!

Nobody would believe what an effort it is to do what little I am able—to dress and entertain, and order things.

It is fortunate Mary is so good with the baby. Such a dear baby!

And yet I *cannot* be with him, it makes me so nervous.

I suppose John never was nervous in his life. He laughs at me so about this wallpaper!

At first he meant to repaper the room, but afterward he said that I was letting it get the better of me, and that nothing was worse for a nervous patient than to give way to such fancies.

He said that after the wallpaper was changed it would be the heavy bedstead, and then the barred windows, and then that gate at the head of the stairs, and so on.

"You know the place is doing you good," he said, "and really, dear, I don't care to renovate the house just for a three months' rental."

"Then do let us go downstairs," I said, "there are such pretty rooms there."

Then he took me in his arms and called me a blessed little goose, and said he would go down cellar, if I wished, and have it whitewashed into the bargain.

But he is right enough about the beds and windows and things.

It is an airy and comfortable room as any one need wish, and, of course, I would not be so silly as to make him uncomfortable just for a whim.

I'm really getting quite fond of the big room, all but that horrid paper.

Out of one window I can see the garden, those mysterious deep-shaded arbors, the riotous old-fashioned flowers, and bushes and gnarly trees.

Out of another I get a lovely view of the bay and a little private wharf belonging to the estate. There is a beautiful shaded lane that runs down there from the house. I always fancy I see people walking in these numerous paths and arbors, but John has cautioned me not to give way to fancy in the least. He says that with my imaginative power and habit of story-making, a nervous weakness like mine is sure to lead to all manner of excited fancies, and that I ought to use my will and good sense to check the tendency. So I try.

I think sometimes that if I were only well enough to write a little, it would relieve the press of ideas and rest me.

But I find I get pretty tired when I try.

It is so discouraging not to have any advice and companionship about my work. When I get really well, John says we will ask Cousin Henry and Julia down for a long visit; but he says he would as soon put fireworks in my pillow-case as to let me have those stimulating people about now.

I wish I could get well faster.

But I must not think about that. This paper looks to me as if it *knew* what a vicious influence it had!

There is a recurrent spot where the pattern lolls like a broken neck and two bulbous eyes stare at you upside down.

I get positively angry with the impertinence of it and the everlasting-ness. Up and down and sideways they crawl and those absurd, un-blinking eyes are everywhere. There is one place where two breadths didn't match, and the eyes go all up and down the line, one a little higher than the other.

I never saw so much expression in an inanimate thing before, and we all know how much expression they have! I used to lie awake as a child and get more entertainment and terror out of black walls and plain furniture than most children could find in a toy-store.

I remember what a kindly wink the knobs of our big, old bureau used to have, and there was one chair that always seemed like a strong friend.

I used to feel that if any of the other things looked too fierce I could always hop into that chair and be safe.

The furniture in this room is no worse than inharmonious, however, for we had to bring it all from downstairs. I suppose when this was used as a playroom they had to take the nursery things out, and no wonder! I never saw such ravages as the children have made here.

The wallpaper, as I said before, is torn off in spots, and it sticketh closer than a brother—they must have had perseverance as well as hatred.

Then the floor is scratched and gouged and splintered, the plaster itself is dug out here and there, and this great heavy bed which is all we found in the room, looks as if it had been through the wars.

But I don't mind it a bit—only the paper.

There comes John's sister. Such a dear girl as she is, and so careful of me! I must not let her find me writing.

She is a perfect and enthusiastic housekeeper, and hopes for no better profession. I verily believe she thinks it is the writing which made me sick!

But I can write when she is out, and see her a long way off from these windows.

There is one that commands the road, a lovely shaded winding road, and one that just looks off over the country. A lovely country, too, full of great elms and velvet meadows.

This wallpaper has a kind of sub-pattern in a different shade, a particularly irritating one, for you can only see it in certain lights, and not clearly then.

But in the places where it isn't faded and where the sun is just so— I can see a strange, provoking, formless sort of figure, that seems to skulk about behind that silly and conspicuous front design.

There's sister on the stairs!

Well, the Fourth of July is over! The people are all gone and I am tired out. John thought it might do me good to see a little company, so we just had mother and Nellie and the children down for a week.

Of course I didn't do a thing. Jennie sees to everything now.

But it tired me all the same.

John says if I don't pick up faster he shall send me to Weir Mitchell in the fall.

But I don't want to go there at all. I had a friend who was in his hands once, and she says he is just like John and my brother, only more so!

Besides, it is such an undertaking to go so far.

I don't feel as if it was worth while to turn my hand over for anything, and I'm getting dreadfully fretful and querulous.

I cry at nothing, and cry most of the time.

Of course I don't when John is here, or anybody else, but when I am alone.

And I am alone a good deal just now. John is kept in town very often by serious cases, and Jennie is good and lets me alone when I want her to.

So I walk a little in the garden or down that lovely lane, sit on the porch under the roses, and lie down up here a good deal.

I'm getting really fond of the room in spite of the wallpaper. Perhaps *because* of the wallpaper.

It dwells in my mind so!

I lie here on this great immovable bed—it is nailed down, I believe—and follow that pattern about by the hour. It is as good as gymnastics, I assure you. I start, we'll say, at the bottom, down in the corner over there where it has not been touched, and I determine for the thousandth time that I *will* follow that pointless pattern to some sort of a conclusion.

I know a little of the principle of design, and I know this thing was not arranged on any laws of radiation, or alternation, or repetition, or symmetry, or anything else that I ever heard of.

It is repeated, of course, by the breadths, but not otherwise.

Looked at in one way each breadth stands alone, the bloated curves and flourishes—a kind of "debased Romanesque" with delirium tremens—go waddling up and down in isolated columns of fatuity.

But, on the other hand, they connect diagonally, and the sprawling outlines run off in great slanting waves of optic horror, like a lot of wallowing sea-weeds in full chase.

The whole thing goes horizontally, too, at least it seems so, and I exhaust myself trying to distinguish the order of its going in that direction.

They have used a horizontal breadth for a frieze, and that adds wonderfully to the confusion.

There is one end of the room where it is almost intact, and there, when the crosslights fade and the low sun shines directly upon it, I can almost fancy radiation after all—the interminable grotesque seems to form around a common centre and rush off in headlong plunges of equal distraction.

It makes me tired to follow it. I will take a nap, I guess.

I don't know why I should write this.

I don't want to.

I don't feel able.

And I know John would think it absurd. But I *must* say what I feel and think in some way—it is such a relief!

But the effort is getting to be greater than the relief.

Half the time now I am awfully lazy, and lie down ever so much. John says I mustn't lose my strength, and has me take cod liver oil and lots of tonics and things, to say nothing of ale and wine and rare meat.

Dear John! He loves me very dearly, and hates to have me sick. I tried to have a real earnest, reasonable talk with him the other day, and tell him how I wish he would let me go and make a visit to Cousin Henry and Julia.

But he said I wasn't able to go, nor able to stand it after I got there; and I did not make out a very good case for myself, for I was crying before I had finished.

It is getting to be a great effort for me to think straight. Just this nervous weakness, I suppose.

And dear John gathered me up in his arms, and just carried me upstairs and laid me on the bed, and sat by me and read to me till it tired my head.

He said I was his darling and his comfort and all he had, and that I must take care of myself for his sake, and keep well.

He says no one but myself can help me out of it, that I must use my will and self-control and not let any silly fancies run away with me.

There's one comfort, the baby is well and happy, and does not have to occupy this nursery with the horrid wallpaper.

If we had not used it, that blessed child would have! What a fortunate escape! Why, I wouldn't have a child of mine, an impressionable little thing, live in such a room for worlds.

I never thought of it before, but it is lucky that John kept me here after all. I can stand it so much easier than a baby, you see.

Of course I never mention it to them any more—I am too wise—but I keep watch for it all the same.

There are things in that wallpaper that nobody knows about but me, or ever will.

Behind that outside pattern the dim shapes get clearer every day.

It is always the same shape, only very numerous.

And it is like a woman stooping down and creeping about behind that pattern. I don't like it a bit. I wonder—I begin to think—I wish John would take me away from here!

It is so hard to talk with John about my case, because he is so wise, and because he loves me so.

But I tried it last night.

It was moonlight. The moon shines in all around just as the sun does.

I hate to see it sometimes, it creeps so slowly, and always comes in by one window or another.

John was asleep and I hated to waken him, so I kept still and watched the moonlight on that undulating wallpaper till I felt creepy.

The faint figure behind seemed to shake the pattern, just as if she wanted to get out.

I got up softly and went to feel and see if the paper *did* move, and when I came back John was awake.

"What is it, little girl?" he said. "Don't go walking about like that —you'll get cold."

I thought it was a good time to talk so I told him that I really was not gaining here, and that I wished he would take me away.

"Why darling!" said he, "our lease will be up in three weeks, and I can't see how to leave before.

"The repairs are not done at home, and I cannot possibly leave town just now. Of course if you were in any danger, I could and would, but you really are better, dear, whether you can see it or not. I am a doctor, dear, and I know. You are gaining flesh and color, your appetite is better, I feel really much easier about you."

"I don't weigh a bit more," said I, "nor as much; and my appetite may be better in the evening when you are here, but it is worse in the morning when you are away!"

"Bless her little heart!" said he with a big hug, "she shall be as sick as she pleases! But now let's improve the shining hours by going to sleep and talk about it in the morning!"

"And you won't go away?" I asked gloomily.

"Why, how can I, dear? It is only three weeks more, and then we will take a nice little trip of a few days while Jennie is getting the house ready. Really, dear, you are better!"

"Better in body perhaps—" I began, and stopped short, for he sat up straight and looked at me with such a stern, reproachful look that I could not say another word.

"My darling," said he, "I beg of you, for my sake and for our child's sake, as well as for your own, that you will never for one instant let that idea enter your mind! There is nothing so dangerous, so fascinating, to a temperament like yours. It is a false and foolish fancy. Can you not trust me as a physician when I tell you so?"

So of course I said no more on that score, and we went to sleep before long. He thought I was asleep first, but I wasn't, and lay there for hours trying to decide whether that front pattern and the back pattern really did move together or separately.

On a pattern like this, by daylight, there is a lack of sequence, a defiance of law, that is a constant irritant to a normal mind.

The color is hideous enough, and unreliable enough, and infuriating enough, but the pattern is torturing.

You think you have mastered it, but just as you get well underway in following, it turns a back-somersault and there you are. It slaps you in the face, knocks you down, and tramples upon you. It is like a bad dream.

The outside pattern is a florid arabesque, reminding one of a fungus. If you can imagine a toadstool in joints, an interminable string of toadstools, budding and sprouting in endless convolutions—why, that is something like it.

That is, sometimes!

There is one marked peculiarity about this paper, a thing nobody seems to notice but myself, and that is that it changes as the light changes.

When the sun shoots in through the east window—I always watch for that first, long, straight ray—it changes so quickly that I never can quite believe it.

That is why I watch it always.

By moonlight—the moon shines in all night when there is a moon—I wouldn't know it was the same paper.

At night in any kind of light, in twilight, candlelight, lamplight, and worst of all by moonlight, it becomes bars! The outside pattern I mean, and the woman behind it is as plain as can be.

I didn't realize for a long time what the thing was that showed behind, that dim sub-pattern, but now I am quite sure it is a woman.

By daylight she is subdued, quiet. I fancy it is the pattern that keeps her so still. It is so puzzling. It keeps me quiet by the hour.

I lie down ever so much now. John says it is good for me, and to sleep all I can.

Indeed he started the habit by making me lie down for an hour after each meal.

It is a very bad habit, I am convinced, for you see I don't sleep.

And that cultivates deceit, for I don't tell them I'm awake—O, no!

The fact is I am getting a little afraid of John.

He seems very queer sometimes, and even Jennie has an inexplicable look.

It strikes me occasionally, just as a scientific hypothesis, that perhaps it is the paper!

I have watched John when he did not know I was looking, and come into the room suddenly on the most innocent excuses, and I've caught him several times *looking at the paper!* And Jennie too. I caught Jennie with her hand on it once.

She didn't know I was in the room, and when I asked her in a quiet, a very quiet voice, with the most restrained manner possible, what she was doing with the paper—she turned around as if she had been caught stealing, and looked quite angry—asked me why I should frighten her so!

Then she said that the paper stained everything it touched, that she had found yellow smooches on all my clothes and John's, and she wished we would be more careful!

Did not that sound innocent? But I know she was studying that pattern, and I am determined that nobody shall find it out but myself!

Life is very much more exciting now than it used to be. You see I have something more to expect, to look forward to, to watch. I really do eat better, and am more quiet than I was.

John is so pleased to see me improve! He laughed a little the other day, and said I seemed to be flourishing in spite of my wallpaper.

I turned it off with a laugh. I had no intention of telling him it was *because* of the wallpaper—he would make fun of me. He might even want to take me away.

I don't want to leave now until I have found it out. There is a week more, and I think that will be enough.

I'm feeling so much better!

I don't sleep much at night, for it is so interesting to watch developments; but I sleep a good deal during the daytime.

In the daytime it is tiresome and perplexing.

There are always new shoots on the fungus, and new shades of yellow all over it. I cannot keep count of them, though I have tried conscientiously.

It is the strangest yellow, that wallpaper! It makes me think of all the yellow things I ever saw—not beautiful ones like buttercups, but old foul, bad yellow things.

But there is something else about that paper—the smell! I noticed it the moment we came into the room, but with so much air and sun it was not bad. Now we have had a week of fog and rain and whether the windows are open or not, the smell is here.

It creeps all over the house.

I find it hovering in the dining-room, skulking in the parlor, hiding in the hall, lying in wait for me on the stairs.

It gets into my hair.

Even when I go to ride, if I turn my head suddenly and surprise it—there is that smell!

Such a peculiar odor, too! I have spent hours in trying to analyze it, to find what it smelled like.

It is not bad—at first, and very gentle, but quite the subtlest, most enduring odor I ever met.

In this damp weather it is awful. I wake up in the night and find it hanging over me.

It used to disturb me at first. I thought seriously of burning the house—to reach the smell.

But now I am used to it. The only thing I can think of that it is like is the *color* of the paper! A yellow smell.

There is a very funny mark on this wall, low down, near the mop-board. A streak that runs round the room. It goes behind every piece of furniture, except the bed, a long, straight, even *smooch*, as if it had been rubbed over and over.

I wonder how it was done and who did it, and what they did it for. Round and round and round—round and round and round—it makes me dizzy!

I really have discovered something at last.

Through watching so much at night, when it changes so, I have finally found out.

The front pattern *does* move—and no wonder! The woman behind shakes it!

Sometimes I think there are a great many women behind, and sometimes only one, and she crawls around fast, and her crawling shakes it all over.

Then in the very bright spots she keeps still, and in the very shady spots she just takes hold of the bars and shakes them hard.

And she is all the time trying to climb through. But nobody could climb through that pattern—it strangles so; I think that is why it has so many heads.

They get through, and then the pattern strangles them off and turns them upside down, and makes their eyes white!

If those heads were covered or taken off it would not be half so bad.

I think that woman gets out in the daytime!

And I'll tell you why—privately—I've seen her!

I can see her out of every one of my windows!

It is the same woman, I know, for she is always creeping, and most women do not creep by daylight.

I see her in that long shaded lane, creeping up and down. I see her in those dark grape arbors, creeping all around the garden.

I see her on that long road under the trees, creeping along, and when a carriage comes she hides under the blackberry vines.

I don't blame her a bit. It must be very humiliating to be caught creeping by daylight!

I always lock the door when I creep by daylight. I can't do it at night, for I know John would suspect something at once.

And John is so queer now, that I don't want to irritate him. I wish he would take another room! Besides, I don't want anybody to get that woman out at night but myself.

I often wonder if I could see her out of all the windows at once.

But, turn as fast as I can, I can only see out of one at one time.

And though I always see her, she *may* be able to creep faster than I can turn! I have watched her sometimes away off in the open country, creeping as fast as a cloud shadow in a wind.

If only that top pattern could be gotten off from the under one! I mean to try it, little by little.

I have found out another funny thing, but I shan't tell it this time! It does not do to trust people too much.

There are only two more days to get this paper off, and I believe John is beginning to notice. I don't like the look in his eyes.

And I heard him ask Jennie a lot of professional questions about me. She had a very good report to give.

She said I slept a good deal in the daytime.

John knows I don't sleep very well at night, for all I'm so quiet!

He asked me all sorts of questions, too, and pretended to be very loving and kind.

As if I couldn't see through him!

Still, I don't wonder he acts so, sleeping under this paper for three months.

It only interests me, but I feel sure John and Jennie are affected by it.

Hurrah! This is the last day, but it is enough. John is to stay in town over night, and won't be out until this evening.

Jennie wanted to sleep with me—the sly thing; but I told her I should undoubtedly rest better for a night all alone.

That was clever, for really I wasn't alone a bit! As soon as it was moonlight and that poor thing began to crawl and shake the pattern, I got up and ran to help her.

I pulled and she shook, I shook and she pulled, and before morning we had peeled off yards of that paper.

A strip about as high as my head and half around the room.

And then when the sun came and that awful pattern began to laugh at me, I declared I would finish it today!

We go away tomorrow, and they are moving all my furniture down again to leave things as they were before.

Jennie looked at the wall in amazement, but I told her merrily that I did it out of pure spite at the vicious thing.

She laughed and said she wouldn't mind doing it herself, but I must not get tired.

How she betrayed herself that time!

But I am here, and no person touches this paper but Me—not *alive!*

She tried to get me out of the room—it was too patent! But I said it was so quiet and empty and clean now that I believed I would lie down again and sleep all I could; and not to wake me even for dinner— I would call when I woke.

So now she is gone, and the servants are gone, and the things are gone, and there is nothing left but that great bedstead nailed down, with the canvas mattress we found on it.

We shall sleep downstairs tonight, and take the boat home tomorrow.

I quite enjoy the room, now it is bare again.

How those children did tear about here!

This bedstead is fairly gnawed!

But I must get to work.

I have locked the door and thrown the key down into the front path.

I don't want to go out, and I don't want to have anybody come in, till John comes.

I want to astonish him.

I've got a rope up here that even Jennie did not find. If that woman does get out, and tries to get away, I can tie her!

But I forgot I could not reach far without anything to stand on!

This bed will *not* move!

I tried to lift and push it until I was lame, and then I got so angry I bit off a little piece at one corner—but it hurt my teeth.

Then I peeled off all the paper I could reach standing on the floor. It sticks horribly and the pattern just enjoys it! All those strangled heads and bulbous eyes and waddling fungus growths just shriek with derision!

I am getting angry enough to do something desperate. To jump out of the window would be admirable exercise, but the bars are too strong even to try.

Besides I wouldn't do it. Of course not. I know well enough that a step like that is improper and might be misconstrued.

I don't like to *look* out of the windows even—there are so many of those creeping women, and they creep so fast.

I wonder if they all come out of that wallpaper as I did?

But I am securely fastened now by my well-hidden rope—you don't get *me* out in the road there!

I suppose I shall have to get back behind the pattern when it comes night, and that is hard!

It is so pleasant to be out in this great room and creep around as I please!

I don't want to go outside. I won't, even if Jennie asks me to.

For outside you have to creep on the ground, and everything is green instead of yellow.

But here I can creep smoothly on the floor, and my shoulder just fits in that long smooch around the wall, so I cannot lose my way.

Why there's John at the door!

It is no use, young man, you can't open it!

How he does call and pound!

Now he's crying to Jennie for an axe.

It would be a shame to break down that beautiful door!

"John, dear!" said I in the gentlest voice, "the key is down by the front steps, under a plantain leaf!"

That silenced him for a few moments.

Then he said, very quietly indeed, "Open the door, my darling!"

"I can't," said I. "The key is down by the front door under a plantain leaf!" And then I said it again, several times, very gently and slowly, and said it so often that he had to go and see, and he got it of course, and came in. He stopped short by the door.

"What is the matter?" he cried. "For God's sake, what are you doing!"

I kept on creeping just the same, but I looked at him over my shoulder.

"I've got out at last," said I, "in spite of you and Jane. And I've pulled off most of the paper, so you can't put me back!"

Now, why should that man have fainted? But he did, and right across my path by the wall, so that I had to creep over him every time!

KING SOLOMON OF KENTUCKY

By James Lane Allen

[The South has produced some of the best of the American short story writers, and most of these have written excellent stories of the Southern scene. While Poe was reared in Virginia, his stories do not in any way reflect the South. A few of the outstanding short story writers who have lived in the South and written about Southern scenes, characters, manners and problems are: Thomas Nelson Page, George W. Cable, Armistead C. Gordon, Ruth McEnery Stuart, Harry Stillwell Edwards, Irvin S. Cobb, and William Faulkner, to mention only a representative seven out of the dozen or more who are worthy of notice here.

James Lane Allen (1849–1925) was a Kentuckian born near Lexington. As a young man he was a teacher in Kentucky University, and in Bethany College, West Virginia. There he taught Latin. After he was thirty-seven he gave all his time to writing and made his home in New York. The most noted of his novels is *The Choir Invisible* (1897).

King Solomon of Kentucky is one of the best of Allen's short stories, and is built definitely around a theme. One might almost call its dominating idea a "moral." In it the author makes a picture of an apparently worthless character inspired to heroic action by a great need and a compelling opportunity.

King Solomon of Kentucky is reprinted from *Flute and Violin* (1891), the volume that contains the best of Allen's short stories, by permission of The Macmillan Company, publishers.]

I

IT HAD been a year of strange disturbances—a desolating drought, a hurly-burly of destructive tempests, killing frosts in the tender valleys, mortal fevers in the tender homes. Now came tidings that all day the wail of myriads of locusts was heard in the green woods of Virginia and Tennessee; now that Lake Erie was blocked with ice on the very verge of summer, so that in the Niagara new rocks and islands showed their startling faces. In the Blue-grass Region of Kentucky countless caterpillars were crawling over the ripening apple orchards and leaving the trees as stark as when tossed in the thin air of bitter February days.

Then, flying low and heavily through drought and tempest and frost and plague, like the royal presence of disaster, that had been but heralded by its mournful train, came nearer and nearer the dark angel of the pestilence.

M. Xaupi had given a great ball only the night before in the dancing-rooms over the confectionery of M. Giron—that M. Giron who made the tall pyramids of méringues and macaroons for wedding suppers, and spun around them a cloud of candied webbing as white and misty as the veil of the bride. It was the opening cotillon party of the summer. The men came in blue cloth coats with brass buttons, buff waistcoats, and laced and ruffled shirts; the ladies came in white satins with ethereal silk overdresses, embroidered in the figure of a gold beetle or an oak leaf of green. The walls of the ballroom were painted to represent landscapes of blooming orange-trees, set here and there in clustering tubs; and the chandeliers and sconces were lighted with innumerable wax-candles, yellow and green and rose.

Only the day before, also, Clatterbuck had opened for the summer a new villa-house, six miles out in the country, with a dancing-pavilion in a grove of maples and oaks, a pleasure-boat on a sheet of crystal water, and a cellar stocked with old sherry, Sauterne, and Château Margaux wines, with anisette, "Perfect Love," and Guigholet cordials.

Down on Water Street, near where now stands a railway station, Hugh Lonney, urging that the fear of cholera was not the only incentive to cleanliness, had just fitted up a sumptuous bath-house, where cold and shower baths might be had at twelve and a half cents each, or hot ones at three for half a dollar.

Yes, the summer of 1833 was at hand, and there must be new pleasures, new luxuries; for Lexington was the Athens of the West and the Kentucky Birmingham.

Old Peter Leuba felt the truth of this, as he stepped smiling out of his little music-store on Main Street, and, rubbing his hands briskly together, surveyed once more his newly-arranged windows, in which were displayed gold and silver epaulets, bottles of Jamaica rum, garden seeds from Philadelphia, drums and guitars and harps. Dewees & Grant felt it in their drug-store on Cheapside, as they sent off a large order for calomel and superior Maccoboy, rappee, and Lancaster snuff. Bluff little Daukins Tegway felt it, as he hurried on the morning of that day to the office of the *Observer and Reporter*, and advertised that he would willingly exchange his beautiful assortment of painted muslins and Dunstable bonnets for flax and feathers. On the threshold he met a florid farmer, who had just offered ten dollars' reward for a likely runaway boy with a long fresh scar across his face; and tomorrow the paper would contain one more of those tragical little cuts, representing an African slave scampering away at the top of his speed, with a stick swung across his shoulder and a bundle dangling down his back. In front of Postle-thwaite's Tavern, where now stands the Phœnix Hotel, a company of idlers, leaning back in Windsor chairs and planting their feet against the opposite wall on a level with their heads, smoked and chewed and yawned, as they discussed the administration of Jackson and arranged for the coming of Daniel Webster in June, when they would give him a great barbecue, and roast in his honor a buffalo bull taken from the herd emparked near Ashland. They hailed a passing merchant, who, however, would hear nothing of the bull, but fell to praising his Rocky Mountain beaver and Goose Creek salt; and another, who turned a dead ear to Daniel Webster, and invited them to drop in and examine his choice essences of peppermint, bergamot, and lavender.

But of all the scenes that might have been observed in Lexington on that day, the most remarkable occurred in front of the old court-house at the hour of high noon. On the mellow stroke of the clock in the steeple above, the sheriff stepped briskly forth, closely followed by a man of powerful frame, whom he commanded to station himself on the pavement several feet off. A crowd of men and boys had already collected in anticipation, and others came quickly up as the clear voice of the sheriff was heard across the open public square and old market-place.

He stood on the topmost of the court-house steps, and for a moment looked down on the crowd with the usual air of official severity.

"Gentlemen," he then cried out sharply, "by an ordah of the cou't I now offah this man at public sale to the highes' biddah. He is able-bodied but lazy, without visible property or means of suppoht, an' of dissolute habits. He is therefoh adjudged guilty of high misdemeanahs, an' is to be sole into labah foh a twelve-month. How much, then, am I offahed foh the vagrant? How much am I offahed foh ole King Sol'mon?"

Nothing was offered for old King Solomon. The spectators formed themselves into a ring around the big vagrant and settled down to enjoy the performance.

"Staht 'im, somebody."

Somebody started a laugh, which rippled around the circle.

The sheriff looked on with an expression of unrelaxed severity, but catching the eye of an acquaintance on the outskirts, he exchanged a lightning wink of secret appreciation. Then he lifted off his tight beaver hat, wiped out of his eyes a little shower of perspiration which rolled suddenly down from above, and warmed a degree to his theme.

"Come, gentlemen," he said, more suasively, "it's too hot to stan' heah all day. Make me an offah! You all know ole King Sol'mon; don't wait to be interduced. How much, then, to staht 'im? Say fifty dollahs! Twenty-five! Fifteen! Ten! Why, gentlemen! Not *ten* dollahs? Remembah this is the Blue-grass Region of Kentucky—the land of Boone an' Kenton, the home of Henry Clay!" he added, in an oratorical *crescendo*.

"He ain't wuth his victuals," said an oily little tavern-keeper, folding his arms restfully over his own stomach and cocking up one piggish eye into his neighbor's face. "He ain't wuth his 'taters."

"Buy 'im foh 'is rags!" cried a young law-student, with a Blackstone under his arm, to the town rag-picker opposite, who was unconsciously ogling the vagrant's apparel.

"I *might* buy 'im foh 'is *scalp*," drawled a farmer, who had taken part in all kinds of scalp contests and was now known to be busily engaged in collecting crow scalps for a match soon to come off between two rival counties.

"I think I'll buy 'im foh a hat-sign," said a manufacturer of ten-dollar Castor and Rhorum hats. This sally drew merry attention to the vagrant's hat, and the merchant felt rewarded.

"You'd bettah say the town ought to buy 'im an' put 'im up on top of the cou't-house as a scarecrow foh the cholera," said some one else.

"What news of the cholera did the stagecoach bring this mohning?" quickly inquired his neighbor in his ear; and the two immediately fell into low, grave talk, forgot the auction, and turned away.

"Stop, gentlemen, stop!" cried the sheriff, who had watched the rising tide of good-humor, and now saw his chance to float in on it with spreading sails. "You're runnin' the price in the wrong direction—down, not up. The law requires that he be sole to the highes' biddah, not the lowes'. As loyal citizens, uphole the constitution of the commonwealth of Kentucky an' make me an offah; the man is really a great bargain. In the first place, he would cos' his ownah little or nothin', because, as you see, he keeps himself in cigahs an' clo'es; then, his main article of diet is whisky—a supply of which he always has on han'. He don't even need a bed, foh you know he sleeps jus' as well on any dooh-step; noh a chair, foh he prefers to sit roun' on the curbstones. Remembah, too, gentlemen, that ole King Sol'mon is a Virginian—from the same neighbouhhood as Mr. Clay. Remembah that he is well educated, that he is an *awful* Whig, an' that he has smoked mo' of the stumps of Mr. Clay's cigahs than any other man in existence. If you don't b'lieve *me*, gentlemen, yondah goes Mr. Clay now; call *him* ovah an' ask 'im foh yo'se'ves."

He paused, and pointed with his right forefinger towards Main Street, along which the spectators, with a sudden craning of necks, beheld the familiar figure of the passing statesman.

"But you don't need *any*body to tell you these fac's, gentlemen," he continued. "You merely need to be reminded that ole King Sol'mon is no ohdinary man. Mo'ovah he has a kine heaht, he nevah spoke a rough wohd to anybody in this worl', an' he is as proud as Tecumseh of his good name an' charactah. An', gentlemen," he added, bridling with an air of mock gallantry and laying a hand on his heart, "if anythin' fu'thah is required in the way of a puffect encomium, we all know that there isn't anothah man among us who cuts as wide a swath among the ladies. The'foh, if you have any appreciation of virtue, any magnanimity of heaht; if you set a propah valuation upon the descendants of Virginia, that mothah of Presidents; if you believe in the pure laws of Kentucky as the pioneer bride of the Union; if you love America an' love the worl'— make me a gen'rous, high-toned offah foh ole King Sol'mon!"

He ended his peroration amid a shout of laughter and applause, and, feeling satisfied that it was a good time for returning to a more practical treatment of his subject, proceeded in a sincere tone:

"He can easily earn from one to two dollahs a day, an' from three to six hundred a yeah. There's not anothah white man in town capable of doin' as much work. There's not a niggah han' in the hemp factories with such muscles an' such a chest. *Look* at 'em! An', if you don't b'lieve me, step fo'wahd and *feel* 'em. How much, then, is bid foh 'im?"

"One dollah!" said the owner of a hemp factory, who had walked forward and felt the vagrant's arm, laughing, but coloring up also as the eyes of all were quickly turned upon him. In those days it was not an unheard-of thing for the muscles of a human being to be thus examined when being sold into servitude to a new master.

"Thank you!" cried the sheriff, cheerily. "One precinc' heard from! One dollah! I am offahed one dollah foh ole King Sol'mon. One dollah foh the king! Make it a half. One dollah an' a half. Make it a half. One dol-dol-dol-dollah!"

Two medical students, returning from lectures at the old Medical Hall, now joined the group, and the sheriff explained:

"One dollah is bid foh the vagrant ole King Sol'mon, who is to be sole into labah foh a twelvemonth. Is there any othah bid? Are you all done? One dollah, once——"

"Dollah and a half," said one of the students, and remarked half jestingly under his breath to his companion, "I'll buy him on the chance of his dying. We'll dissect him."

"Would you own his body if he *should* die?"

"If he dies while bound to me, I'll arrange *that*."

"One dollah an' a half," resumed the sheriff; and falling into the tone of a facile auctioneer he rattled on:

"One dollah an' a half foh ole Sol'mon—sol, sol, sol,—do, re, mi, fa, sol—do, re, mi, fa, sol! Why, gentlemen, you can set the king to music!"

All this time the vagrant had stood in the centre of that close ring of jeering and humorous bystanders—a baffling text from which to have preached a sermon on the infirmities of our imperfect humanity. Some years before, perhaps as a master-stroke of derision, there had been given to him that title which could but heighten the contrast of his personality and estate with every suggestion of the ancient sacred magnificence; and never had the mockery seemed so fine as at this moment, when he was led forth into the streets to receive the lowest sentence of the law upon his poverty and dissolute idleness. He was apparently in the very prime of life—a striking figure, for nature at least had truly done some royal work on him. Over six feet in height, erect, with limbs well shaped and sinewy, with chest and neck full of the lines of great power, a large head thickly covered with long reddish hair, eyes blue, face beardless, complexion fair but discolored by low passions and excesses—such was old King Solomon. He wore a stiff, high, black Castor hat of the period, with the crown smashed in and the torn rim hanging down over one ear; a black cloth coat in the old style, ragged and buttonless; a white cotton shirt, with the broad collar crumpled, wide open at the neck and down his sunburnt bosom; blue jeans pantaloons, patched at the seat and the knees; and ragged cotton socks that fell down over the tops of his dusty shoes, which were open at the heels.

In one corner of his sensual mouth rested the stump of a cigar. Once during the proceedings he had produced another, lighted it, and continued quietly smoking. If he took to himself any shame as the central figure of this ignoble performance, no one knew it. There was something almost royal in his unconcern. The humor, the badinage, the open contempt, of which he was the public target, fell thick and fast upon him, but as harmlessly as would balls of pith upon a coat of mail. In truth, there was that in his great, lazy, gentle, good-humored bulk and bearing which made the gibes seem all but despicable. He shuffled from one foot to the other as though he found it a trial to stand up so long, but all the while looking the spectators full in the eyes without the least impatience. He suffered the man of the factory to walk round him and push and pinch his muscles as calmly as though he had been the show bull at a country fair. Once only, when the sheriff had pointed across the street at the figure of Mr. Clay, he had looked quickly in that direction with a kindling light in his eye and a passing flush on his face. For the rest, he seemed like a man who has drained his cup of human life and has nothing left him but to fill again and drink without the least surprise or eagerness.

The bidding between the man of the factory and the student had gone slowly on. The price had reached ten dollars. The heat was intense, the sheriff tired. Then something occurred to revivify the scene. Across the market-place and towards the steps of the courthouse there suddenly came trundling along in breathless haste a huge old negress, carrying on one arm a large shallow basket containing apple crab-lanterns and fresh gingerbread. With a series of half-articulate grunts and snorts she approached the edge of the crowd and tried to force her way through. She coaxed, she begged, she elbowed and pushed and scolded, now laughing, and now with the passion of tears in her thick, excited voice. All at once, catching sight of the sheriff, she lifted one ponderous brown arm, naked to the elbow, and waved her hand to him above the heads of those in front.

"Hole on, marster! Hole on!" she cried, in a tone of humorous entreaty. "Don' knock 'im off till I come! Gim *me* a bid at 'im!"

The sheriff paused and smiled. The crowd made way tumultuously, with broad laughter and comment.

"Stan' aside theah an' let Aun' Charlotte in!"

"*Now* you'll see biddin'!"

"Get out of the way foh Aun' Charlotte!"

"Up, my free niggah! Hurrah foh Kentucky!"

A moment more and she stood inside the ring of spectators, her basket on the pavement at her feet, her hands plumped akimbo into her fathomless sides, her head up, and her soft, motherly eyes turned eagerly upon the sheriff. Of the crowd she seemed unconscious, and on the vagrant before her she had not cast a single glance.

She was dressed with perfect neatness. A red and yellow Madras kerchief was bound about her head in a high coil, and another was crossed over the bosom of her stiffly starched and smoothly ironed blue cottonade dress. Rivulets of perspiration ran down over her nose, her temples, and around her ears, and disappeared mysteriously in the creases of her brown neck. A single drop accidentally hung glistening like a diamond on the circlet of one of her large brass ear-rings.

The sheriff looked at her a moment, smiling, but a little disconcerted. The spectacle was unprecedented.

"What do you want heah, Aun' Charlotte?" he asked, kindly. "You can't sell yo' pies an' gingerbread heah."

"I don' *wan'* sell no pies en gingerbread," she replied, contemptuously. "I wan' bid on *him*," and she nodded sidewise at the vagrant.

"White folks allers sellin' niggahs to wuk fuh *dem*; I gwine buy a white man to wuk fuh *me*. En he gwine t' git a mighty hard mistiss, you heah *me!*"

The eyes of the sheriff twinkled with delight.

"Ten dollahs is offahed foh ole King Sol'mon. Is theah any othah bid? Are you all done?"

"'Leben," she said.

Two young ragamuffins crawled among the legs of the crowd up to her basket and filched pies and cake beneath her very nose.

"Twelve!" cried the student, laughing.

"Thirteen!" she laughed too, but her eyes flashed.

"*You are bidding against a niggah*," whispered the student's companion in his ear.

"So I am; let's be off," answered the other, with a hot flush on his proud face.

Thus the sale was ended, and the crowd variously dispersed. In a distant corner of the courtyard the ragged urchins were devouring their unexpected booty. The old negress drew a red handkerchief out of her bosom, untied a knot in a corner of it, and counted out the money to the sheriff. Only she and the vagrant were now left on the spot.

"You have bought me. What do you want me to do?" he asked quietly.

"Lohd, honey!" she answered, in a low tone of affectionate chiding, "I don' wan' you to do *nothin'!* I wuzn' gwine t' 'low dem white folks to buy you. Dey'd wuk you till you dropped dead. You go 'long en do ez you please."

She gave a cunning chuckle of triumph in thus setting at naught the ends of justice, and, in a voice rich and musical with affection, she said, as she gave him a little push:

"You bettah be gittin' out o' dis blazin' sun. G' on home! I be 'long by-en-by."

He turned and moved slowly away in the direction of Water Street, where she lived; and she, taking up her basket, shuffled across the market-place towards Cheapside, muttering to herself the while:

"I come mighty nigh gittin' dah too late, foolin' 'long wid dese pies. Sellin' *him* 'ca'se he don' wuk! Umph! If all de men in dis town dat don' wuk wuz to be tuk up en sole, d' wouldn' be 'nough money in de town to buy 'em! Don' I see 'em settin' 'roun' dese taverns f'om mohnin' till night?"

She snorted out her indignation and disgust, and sitting down on the sidewalk, under a Lombardy poplar, uncovered her wares and kept the flies away with a locust bough, not discovering in her alternating good and ill humor, that half of them had been filched by her old tormentors.

This was the memorable scene enacted in Lexington on that memorable day of the year 1833—a day that passed so briskly. For whoever met and spoke together asked the one question: Will the cholera come to Lexington? And the answer always gave a nervous haste to business— a keener thrill to pleasure. It was of the cholera that the negro woman heard two sweet passing ladies speak as she spread her wares on the sidewalk. They were on their way to a little picture-gallery just opened opposite M. Giron's ball-room, and in one breath she heard them discussing their toilets for the evening and in the next several portraits by Jouett.

So the day passed, the night came on, and M. Xaupi gave his brilliant ball. Poor old Xaupi—poor little Frenchman! whirled as a gamin of Paris through the mazes of the Revolution, and lately come all the way to Lexington to teach the people how to dance. Hop about blithely on thy dry legs, basking this night in the waxen radiance of manners and melodies and graces! Where will be thy tunes and airs to-morrow! Ay, smile and prompt away! On and on! Swing corners, ladies and gentlemen! Form the basket! Hands all round!

While the bows were still darting across the strings, out of the low, red east there shot a long, tremulous bow of light up towards the zenith. And then, could human sight have beheld the invisible, it might have seen hovering over the town, over the ball-room, over M. Xaupi, the awful presence of the plague.

But knowing nothing of this, the heated revellers went merrily home in the chill air of the red and saffron dawn. And knowing nothing of it also, a man awakened on the door-step of a house opposite the ball-room, where he had long since fallen asleep. His limbs were cramped and a shiver ran through his frame. Staggering to his feet, he made his way down to the house of Free Charlotte, mounted to his room by means of a stairway opening on the street, threw off his outer garments, kicked off his shoes, and taking a bottle from a closet pressed it several times to his lips with long outward breaths of satisfaction. Then, casting his great white bulk upon the bed, in a minute more he had sunk into a heavy sleep—the usual drunken sleep of old King Solomon.

He, too, had attended M. Xaupi's ball, in his own way and in his proper character, being drawn to the place for the pleasure of seeing the fine ladies arrive and float in, like large white moths of the summer night, of looking in through the open windows at the many-colored waxen lights and the snowy arms and shoulders, of having blown out to him the perfume and the music; not worthy to go in, being the lowest of the low, but attending from a door-step of the street opposite—with a certain rich passion in his nature for splendor and revelry and sensuous beauty.

II

About 10 o'clock the sunlight entered through the shutters and awoke him. He threw one arm up over his eyes to intercept the burning rays. As he lay outstretched and stripped of grotesque rags, it could be better seen in what a mould nature had cast his figure. His breast, bare and tanned, was barred by full, arching ribs and knotted by crossing muscles; and his shirt-sleeve, falling away to the shoulder from his bent arm, revealed its crowded muscles in the high relief of heroic bronze. For, although he had been sold as a vagrant, old King Solomon had in earlier years followed the trade of a digger of cellars, and the strenuous use of mattock and spade had developed every sinew to the utmost. His whole person, now half naked and in repose, was full of the suggestions of unspent power. Only his face, swollen and red, only his eyes, bloodshot and dull, bore the impress of wasted vitality. There, all too plainly stamped, were the passions long since raging and still on fire.

The sunlight had stirred him to but a low degree of consciousness, and some minutes passed before he realized that a stifling, resinous fume impregnated the air. He sniffed it quickly; through the window seemed to come the smell of burning tar. He sat up on the edge of the bed and vainly tried to clear his thoughts.

The room was a clean but poor habitation—uncarpeted, whitewashed, with a piece or two of the cheapest furniture, and a row of pegs on one wall, where usually hung those tattered coats and pantaloons, miscellaneously collected, that were his purple and fine linen. He turned his eyes in this direction now and noticed that his clothes were missing. The old shoes had disappeared from their corner; the cigar stumps, picked up here and there in the streets according to his wont, were gone from the mantelpiece. Near the door was a large bundle tied up in a sheet. In a state of bewilderment, he asked himself what it all meant. Then a sense of the silence in the street below possessed him. At this hour he was used to hear noises enough—from Hugh Lonney's new bathhouse on one side, from Harry Sikes's barber shop on the other.

A mysterious feeling of terror crept over and helped to sober him. How long had he lain asleep? By degrees he seemed to remember that two or three times he had awakened far enough to drink from the bottle under his pillow, only to sink again into heavier stupefaction. By degrees, too, he seemed to remember that other things had happened—a driving of vehicles this way and that, a hurrying of people along the street. He had thought it the breaking-up of M. Xaupi's ball. More than once had not some one shaken and tried to arouse him? Through the wall of Harry Sikes's barber shop had he not heard cries of pain—sobs of distress?

He staggered to the window, threw open the shutters, and, kneeling at the sill, looked out. The street was deserted. The houses opposite were closed. Cats were sleeping in the silent door-ways. But as he looked up and down he caught sight of people hurrying along cross-streets. From a distant lumber yard came the muffled sound of rapid hammerings. On the air was the faint roll of vehicles—the hush and the vague noises of a general terrifying commotion.

In the middle of the street below him a keg was burning, and, as he looked, the hoops gave way, the tar spread out like a stream of black lava, and a cloud of inky smoke and deep-red furious flame burst upward through the sagging air. Just beneath the window a common cart had been backed close up to the door of the house. In it had been thrown a few small articles of furniture, and on the bottom bedclothes had been spread out as if for a pallet. While he looked old Charlotte hurried out with a pillow.

He called down to her in a strange, unsteady voice:

"What is the matter? What are you doing, Aunt Charlotte?"

She uttered a cry, dropped the pillow, and stared up at him. Her face looked dry and wrinkled.

"My God! De chol'ra's in town! I'm waitin' on you! Dress, en come down en fetch de bun'le by de dooh." And she hurried back into the house.

But he continued leaning on his folded arms, his brain stunned by the shock of the intelligence. Suddenly he leaned far out and looked down at the closed shutters of the barber shop. Old Charlotte reappeared.

"Where is Harry Sikes?" he asked.

"Dead en buried."

"When did he die?"

"Yestidd'y evenin'."

"What day is this?"

"Sadd'y."

M. Xaupi's ball had been on Thursday evening. That night the cholera had broken out. He had lain in his drunken stupor ever since. Their talk had lasted but a minute, but she looked up anxiously and urged him.

"D' ain' no time to was'e, honey! D' ain' no time to was'e. I done got dis cyart to tek you 'way in, en I be ready to start in a minute. Put yo' clo'es on en bring de bun'le wid all yo' yudder things in it."

With incredible activity she climbed into the cart and began to roll up the bedclothes. In reality she had made up her mind to put him into the cart, and the pallet had been made for him to lie and finish his drunken sleep on, while she drove him away to a place of safety.

Still he did not move from the window-sill. He was thinking of Harry Sikes, who had shaved him many a time for nothing. Then he suddenly called down to her:

"Have many died of the cholera? Are there many cases in town?"

She went on with her preparations and took no notice of him. He repeated the question. She got down quickly from the cart and began to mount the staircase. He went back to bed, pulled the sheet up over him, and propped himself up among the pillows. Her soft, heavy footsteps slurred on the stairway as though her strength were failing, and as soon as she entered the room she sank into a chair, overcome with terror. He looked at her with a sudden sense of pity.

"Don't be frightened," he said, kindly. "It might only make it the worse for you."

"I can't he'p it, honey," she answered, wringing her hands and rocking herself to and fro; "de ole niggah can' he'p it. If de Lohd jes spah me to git out'n dis town wid you! Honey, ain' you able to put on yo' clo'es?"

"You've tied them all up in the sheet."

"De Lohd he'p crazy ole niggah!"

She started up and tugged at the bundle, and laid out a suit of his clothes, if things so incongruous could be called a suit.

"Have many people died of the cholera?"

"Dey been dyin' like sheep ev' since yestidd'y mohnin'—all day, en all las' night, en dis mohnin'! De man he done lock up de huss, en dey been buryin' 'em in cyarts. En de grave-diggah he done run away, en hit look like d' ain' nobody to dig de graves."

She bent over the bundle, tying again the four corners of the sheet. Through the window came the sound of the quick hammers driving nails. She threw up her arms into the air, and then seizing the bundle dragged it rapidly to the door.

"You heah dat? Dey nailin' up cawfins in de lumbah-yahd! Put on yo' clo'es, honey, en come on."

A resolution had suddenly taken shape in his mind.

"Go on away and save your life. Don't wait for me; I'm not going. And good-bye, Aunt Charlotte, in case I don't see you any more. You've been very kind to me—kinder than I deserved. Where have you put my mattock and spade?"

He said this very quietly, and sat up on the edge of the bed, his feet hanging down, and his hand stretched out towards her.

"Honey," she explained, coaxingly, from where she stood, "can't you sobah up a little en put on yo' clo'es? I gwine to tek you 'way to de country. You don' wan' no tools. You can' dig no cellahs now. De chol'ra's in town en de people's dyin' like sheep."

"I expect they will need me," he answered.

She perceived now that he was sober. For an instant her own fear was forgotten in an outburst of resentment and indignation.

"Dig graves fuh 'em, when dey put you up on de block en sell you same ez you wuz a niggah! Dig graves fuh 'em, when dey allers callin' you names on de street en makin' fun o' you!"

"They are not to blame. I have brought it on myself."

"But we can' stay heah en die o' de chol'ra!"

"You mustn't stay. You must go away at once."

"But if I go, who gwine tek cyah o' *you?*"

"Nobody."

She came quickly across the room to the bed, fell on her knees, clasped his feet to her breast, and looked up into his face with an expression of imploring tenderness. Then, with incoherent cries and with sobs and tears, she pleaded with him—pleaded for dear life; his and her own.

It was a strange scene. What historian of the heart will ever be able to do justice to those peculiar ties which bound the heart of the negro in years gone by to a race of not always worthy masters? This old Virginia nurse had known King Solomon when he was a boy playing with her young master, till that young master died on the way to Kentucky.

At the death of her mistress she had become free with a little property. By thrift and industry she had greatly enlarged this. Years passed and she became the only surviving member of the Virginian household, which had emigrated early in the century to the Blue-grass Region. The same wave of emigration had brought in old King Solomon from the same neighborhood. As she had risen in life, he had sunk. She sat on the sidewalks selling her fruits and cakes; he sat on the sidewalks more idle, more ragged and dissolute. On no other basis than these facts she began to assume a sort of maternal pitying care of him, patching his rags, letting him have money for his vices, and when, a year or two before, he had ceased working almost, entirely, giving him a room in her house and taking in payment what he chose to pay.

He brushed his hand quickly across his eyes as she knelt before him now, clasping his feet to her bosom. From coaxing him as an intractable child she had, in the old servile fashion, fallen to imploring him, with touching forgetfulness of their real relations:

"O my marseter! O my marseter Solomon! Go 'way en save yo' life, en tek yo' po' ole niggah wid you!"

But his resolution was formed, and he refused to go. A hurried footstep paused beneath the window and a loud voice called up. The old nurse got up and went to the window. A man was standing by the cart at her door.

"For God's sake, let me have this cart to take my wife and little children away to the country! There is not a vehicle to be had in town. I will pay you—" He stopped, seeing the distress on her face.

"Is he dead?" he asked, for he knew of her care of old King Solomon.

"He *will* die!" she sobbed. "Tilt de t'ings out on de pavement. I gwine t' stay wid 'im en tek cyah o' 'im."

III

A little later, dressed once more in grotesque rags and carrying on his shoulder a rusty mattock and a rusty spade, old King Solomon appeared in the street below and stood looking up and down it with an air of anxious indecision. Then shuffling along rapidly to the corner of Mill Street, he turned up towards Main.

Here a full sense of the terror came to him. A man, hurrying along with his head down, ran full against him and cursed him for the delay:

"Get out of my way, you old beast!" he cried. "If the cholera would carry you off, it would be a blessing to the town."

Two or three little children, already orphaned and hungry, wandered past, crying and wringing their hands. A crowd of negro men with the muscles of athletes, some with naked arms, some naked to the waist, their eyes dilated, their mouths hanging open, sped along in tumultuous disorder. The plague had broken out in the hemp factory and scattered them beyond control.

He grew suddenly faint and sick. His senses swam, his heart seemed to cease beating, his tongue burned, his throat was dry, his spine like ice. For a moment the contagion of deadly fear overcame him, and, unable to stand, he reeled to the edge of the sidewalk and sat down.

Before him along the street passed the flying people—men on horseback with their wives behind and children in front, families in carts and wagons, merchants in two-wheeled gigs and sulkies. A huge red and yellow stagecoach rolled ponderously by, filled within, on top, in front, and behind with a company of riotous students of law and of medicine. A rapid chorus of voices shouted to him as they passed:

"Good-bye, Solomon!"

"The cholera'll have you befoah sunset!"

"Better be diggin' yoah grave, Solomon! That'll be yoah last cellah."

"Dig us a big wine cellah undah the Medical Hall while we are away."

"And leave yo' body there! We want yo' skeleton."

"Good-bye, old Solomon!"

A wretched carry-all passed with a household of more wretched women; their tawdry and gay attire, their haggard and painted and ghastly faces, looking horrible in the blaze of the pitiless sunlight. They, too, simpered and hailed him and spent upon him their hardened and degraded badinage. Then there rolled by a high-swung carriage, with the most luxurious of cushions, upholstered with morocco, with a coat-of-arms, a driver and a footman in livery, and drawn by sparkling, prancing horses. Lying back on the satin cushions a fine gentleman; at the window of the carriage two rosy children, who pointed their fingers at the vagrant and turned and looked into their father's face, so that he leaned forward, smiled, leaned back again, and was whirled away to a place of safety.

Thus they passed him, as he sat down on the sidewalk—even physicians from their patients, pastors from their stricken flocks. Why should not he flee? He had no ties, except the faithful affection of an old negress. Should he not at least save her life by going away, seeing that she would not leave him?

The orphaned children wandered past again, sobbing more wearily. He called them to him.

"Why do you not go home? Where is your mother?" he asked.

"She is dead in the house," they answered; "and no one has come to bury her."

Slowly down the street was coming a short funeral train. It passed—a rude cortège: a common cart, in the bottom of which rested a box of plain boards containing the body of the old French dancing-master; walking behind it, with a cambric handkerchief to his eyes, the old French confectioner; at his side, wearing the robes of his office and carrying an umbrella to ward off the burning sun, the beloved Bishop Smith; and behind them, two by two and with linked arms, perhaps a dozen men, most of whom had been at the ball.

No head was lifted or eye turned to notice the vagrant seated on the sidewalk. But when the train had passed he rose, laid his mattock and spade across his shoulder, and, stepping out into the street, fell into line at the end of the procession.

They moved down Short Street to the old burying-ground, where the Baptist churchyard is today. As they entered it, two grave-diggers passed out and hurried away. Those before them had fled. They had been at work but a few hours. Overcome with horror at the sight of the dead arriving more and more rapidly, they, too, deserted that post of peril. No one was left. Here and there in the churchyard could be seen bodies awaiting interment. Old King Solomon stepped quietly forward and, getting down into one of the half-finished graves, began to dig.

The vagrant had happened upon an avocation.

IV

All summer long, Clatterbuck's dancing-pavilion was as silent in its grove of oaks as a temple of the Druids, and his pleasure-boat nestled in its moorings, with no hand to feather an oar in the little lake. All summer long, no athletic young Kentuckians came to bathe their white bodies in Hugh Lonney's new bathhouse for twelve and a half cents, and no one read Daukins Tegway's advertisement that he was willing to exchange his Dunstable bonnets for flax and feathers. The likely runaway boy, with a long, fresh scar across his face, was never found, nor the buffalo bull roasted for Daniel Webster, and Peter Leuba's guitars were never thrummed on any moonlit verandas. Only Dewees and Grant were busy, dispensing, not snuff, but calomel.

Grass grew in the deserted streets. Gardens became little wildernesses of rank weeds and riotous creepers. Around shut window-lattices roses clambered and shed their perfume into the poisoned air, or dropped their faded petals to strew the echoless thresholds. In darkened rooms family portraits gazed on sad vacancy or looked helplessly down on rigid sheeted forms.

In the trees of poplar and locust along the streets the unmolested birds built and brooded. The oriole swung its hempen nest from a bough over the door of the spider-tenanted factory, and in front of the old Medical Hall the blue-jay shot up his angry crest and screamed harshly down at the passing bier. In a cage hung against the wall of a house in a retired street a mocking-bird sung, beat its breast against the bars, sung more passionately, grew silent and dropped dead from its perch, never knowing that its mistress had long since become a clod to its full-throated requiem.

Famine lurked in the wake of the pestilence. Markets were closed. A few shops were kept open to furnish necessary supplies. Now and then some old negro might have been seen, driving a meat-wagon in from the country, his nostrils stuffed with white cotton saturated with camphor. Oftener the only visible figure in the streets was that of a faithful priest going about among his perishing fold, or that of the bishop moving hither and thither on his ceaseless ministrations.

But over all the ravages of that terrible time there towered highest the solitary figure of that powerful grave-digger, who, nerved by the spectacle of the common misfortune, by one heroic effort rose for the time above the wrecks of his own nature. In the thick of the plague, in the very garden spot of the pestilence, he ruled like an unterrified king. Through days unnaturally chill with grey cloud and drizzling rain, or unnaturally hot with the fierce sun and suffocating damps that appeared to steam forth from subterranean cauldrons, he worked unfaltering, sometimes with a helper, sometimes with none. There were times when, exhausted, he would lie down in the half-dug graves and there sleep until able to go on; and many a midnight found him under the spectral moon, all but hidden by the rank nightshade as he bent over to mark out the lines of one of those narrow mortal cellars.

Nature soon smiles upon her own ravages and strews our graves with flowers, not as memories, but for other flowers when the spring returns.

It was one cool, brilliant morning late in that autumn. The air blew fresh and invigorating, as though on the earth there were no corruption, no death. Far southward had flown the plague. A spectator in the open court-square might have seen many signs of life returning to the town. Students hurried along, talking eagerly. Merchants met for the first time and spoke of the winter trade. An old negress, gayly and neatly dressed, came into the market-place, and sitting down on a sidewalk displayed her yellow and red apples and fragrant gingerbread. She hummed to herself an old cradle-song, and in her soft, motherly black eyes shone a mild, happy radiance. A group of young ragamuffins eyed her longingly from a distance. Court was to open for the first time since the spring. The hour was early, and one by one the lawyers passed slowly in. On the steps of the court-house three men were standing: Thomas Brown, the sheriff, old Peter Leuba, who had just walked over from his music-store on Main Street; and little M. Giron, the French confectioner. Each wore mourning on his hat, and their voices were low and grave.

"Gentlemen," the sheriff was saying, "it was on this very spot the day befoah the cholera broke out that I sole 'im as a vagrant. An' I did the meanes' thing a man can evah do. I hel' 'im up to public ridicule foh his weaknesses an' made spoht of 'is infirmities. I laughed at 'is povahty an' 'is ole clo'es. I delivahed on 'im as complete an oration of sarcastic detraction as I could prepare on the spot, out of my own meanness an' with the vulgah sympathies of the crowd. Gentlemen, if I only had that crowd heah now, an' old King Sol'mon standin' in the midst of it, that I might ask 'im to accept a humble public apology, offahed from the heaht of one who feels himself unworthy to shake 'is han'! But, gentlemen, that crowd will nevah reassemble. Neahly ev'ry man of them is dead, an' ole King Sol'mon buried them."

"He buried my friend Adolphe Xaupi," said François Giron, touching his eyes with his handkerchief.

"There is a case of my best Jamaica rum for him whenever he comes for it," said old Leuba, clearing his throat.

"But, gentlemen, while we are speakin' of ole King Sol'mon we ought not to fohget who it is that has suppohted 'im. Yondah she sits on the sidewalk, sellin' 'er apples an' gingerbread."

The three men looked in the direction indicated.

"Heah comes old King Sol'mon now," exclaimed the sheriff.

Across the open square the vagrant was seen walking slowly along with his habitual air of quiet, unobtrusive preoccupation. A minute more and he had come over and passed into the court-house by a side door.

"Is Mr. Clay to be in court today?"

"He is expected, I think."

"Then let's go in; there will be a crowd."

"I don't know; so many are dead."

They turned and entered and found seats as quietly as possible; for a strange and sorrowful hush brooded over the court-room. Until the bar assembled, it had not been realized how many were gone. The silence was that of a common overwhelming disaster. No one spoke with his neighbor, no one observed the vagrant as he entered and made his way to a seat on one of the meanest benches, a little apart from the others. He had not sat there since the day of his indictment for vagrancy. The judge took his seat and, making a great effort to control himself, passed his eyes slowly over the court-room. All at once he caught sight of old King Solomon sitting against the wall in an obscure corner; and before any one could know what he was doing, he hurried down and walked up to the vagrant and grasped his hand. He tried to speak, but could not. Old King Solomon had buried his wife and daughter—buried them one clouded midnight, with no one present but himself.

Then the oldest member of the bar started up and followed the example; and then the other members, rising by a common impulse, filed slowly back and one by one wrung that hard and powerful hand. After them came the other persons in the court-room. The vagrant, the grave-digger, had risen and stood against the wall, at first with a white face and a dazed expression, not knowing what it meant; afterwards, when he understood it, his head dropped suddenly forward and his tears fell thick and hot upon the hands that he could not see. And his were not the only tears. Not a man in the long file but paid his tribute of emotion as he stepped forward to honor that image of sadly eclipsed but still effulgent humanity. It was not grief, it was not gratitude, nor any sense of making reparation for the past. It was the softening influence of an act of heroism, which makes every man feel himself a brother hand in hand with every other—such power has a single act of moral greatness to reverse the relations of men, lifting up one, and bringing all others to do him homage.

It was the coronation scene in the life of old King Solomon of Kentucky.

HEART OF DARKNESS

By Joseph Conrad

[Joseph Conrad (1857–1924) was a native of Poland, who chose England as his home and the English tongue as his literary language. He was born in 1857, and as a boy chose the life of the sea as his calling. At the age of nineteen he entered the English merchant service and soon rose through the ranks of apprentice and mate to that of master, and thus followed the sea for nineteen years. When he began his first book, he had to choose between French, a language he had known from boyhood, and English, a tongue acquired in early manhood. He chose English. *Almayer's Folly* was that first book. It was begun in 1890 and written at odd times afloat and ashore during the next five years. Mr. Conrad left the sea soon after his literary success had become an assured fact and made his home in the south of England until his death in 1924, living near Canterbury and enjoying the friendship of many noted literary men.

Among his best known books are: *Almayer's Folly* (1895), *An Outcast of the Islands* (1896), *The Nigger of the Narcissus* (1897), *Tales of Unrest* (1898), *Lord Jim* (1900), *Youth, and Other Tales* (1902), *Typhoon* (1903), *Nostromo* (1904), *The Mirror of the Sea* (1906), and *The Secret Agent* (1907).

Heart of Darkness is in reality a novelette. It is one of the three narratives included in the volume entitled *Youth*. Conrad's style is individual and his technique different from that of the usual short story writer. Instead of deliberate plot-making he appears to be telling a story from first-hand experience. He lets us have the details as they recur to him, and the effect is tremendously like life. Apparently he is not concerned with ethical or philosophical themes. He mirrors a phase of life and lets it sink home, carrying whatever meaning it will. *Heart of Darkness* is a terrible condemnation of the commercial policy of those who exploit the tropics; but one feels that Mr. Conrad's chief concern is to depict the sinking of a great soul back into elemental savagery under the compelling spell of the torrid jungle. It is the story of the reversion of the soul of Mr. Kurtz.

The chief external difference between a short story and a novelette is in the observance of economy of means. There are tales that do not admit of economy. The writer deals with many people in extensive spaces and seeks to produce results which cannot be held within the compass of a few thousand words. Such a tale is *Heart of Darkness*, which is here reprinted from *Youth* (copyright, 1902) by permission of Doubleday, Doran and Company, publishers.]

I

THE *Nellie*, a cruising yawl, swung to her anchor without a flutter of the sails, and was at rest. The flood had made, the wind was nearly calm, and being bound down the river, the only thing for it was to come to and wait for the turn of the tide.

The sea-reach of the Thames stretched before us like the beginning of an interminable waterway. In the offing the sea and the sky were welded together without a joint, and in the luminous space the tanned sails of the barges drifting up with the tide seemed to stand still in red clusters of canvas sharply peaked, with gleams of varnished sprits. A haze rested on the low shores that ran out to sea in vanishing flatness. The air was dark above Gravesend, and farther back still seemed condensed into a mournful gloom, brooding motionless over the biggest, and the greatest, town on earth.

The Director of Companies was our captain and our host. We four affectionately watched his back as he stood in the bows looking to seaward. On the whole river there was nothing that looked half so nautical. He resembled a pilot, which to a seaman is trustworthiness personified. It was difficult to realize his work was not out there in the luminous estuary, but behind him, within the brooding gloom.

Between us there was, as I have already said somewhere, the bond of the sea. Besides holding our hearts together through long periods of separation, it had the effect of making us tolerant of each other's yarns—and even convictions. The Lawyer—the best of old fellows— had, because of his many years and many virtues, the only cushion on deck, and was lying on the only rug. The Accountant had brought out already a box of dominoes, and was toying architecturally with the bones. Marlow sat cross-legged right aft, leaning against the mizzen-mast. He had sunken cheeks, a yellow complexion, a straight back, an ascetic aspect, and, with his arms dropped, the palms of hands outwards, resembled an idol. The director, satisfied the anchor had good hold, made his way aft and sat down amongst us. We exchanged a few words lazily. Afterwards there was silence on board the yacht. For some reason or other we did not begin that game of dominoes. We felt meditative, and fit for nothing but placid staring. The day was ending in a serenity of still and exquisite brilliance. The water shone pacifically; the sky, without a speck, was a benign immensity of unstained light; the very mist on the Essex marshes was like a gauzy and radiant fabric, hung from the wooded rises inland, and draping the low shores in diaphanous folds. Only the gloom to the west, brooding over the upper reaches, became more somber every minute, as if angered by the approach of the sun.

And at last, in its curved and imperceptible fall, the sun sank low, and from glowing white changed to a dull red without rays and without heat, as if about to go out suddenly, stricken to death by the touch of that gloom brooding over a crowd of men.

Forthwith a change came over the waters, and the serenity became less brilliant but more profound. The old river in its broad reach rested unruffled at the decline of day, after ages of good service done to the race that peopled its banks, spread out in the tranquil dignity of a waterway leading to the uttermost ends of the earth. We looked at the venerable stream not in the vivid flush of a short day that comes and departs forever, but in the august light of abiding memories. And indeed nothing is easier for a man who has, as the phrase goes, "followed the sea" with reverence and affection, than to evoke the great spirit of the past upon the lower reaches of the Thames. The tidal current runs to and fro in its unceasing service, crowded with memories of men and ships it had borne to the rest of home or to the battles of the sea. It had known and served all the men of whom the nation is proud, from Sir Francis Drake to Sir John Franklin, knights all, titled and untitled—the great knights-errant of the sea. It had borne all the ships whose names are like jewels flashing in the night of time, from the *Golden Hind* returning with her round flanks full of treasure, to be visited by the Queen's Highness and thus pass out of the gigantic tale, to the *Erebus* and *Terror*, bound on other conquests—and that never returned. It had known the ships and the men. They had sailed from Deptford, from Greenwich, from Erith—the adventurers and the settlers; kings' ships and the ships of men on 'Change; captains, admirals, the dark "interlopers" of the Eastern trade, and the commissioned "generals" of East India fleets. Hunters for gold or pursuers of fame, they all had gone out on that stream, bearing the sword, and often the torch, messengers of the might within the land, bearers of a spark from the sacred fire. What greatness had not floated on the ebb of that river into the mystery of an unknown earth! . . . The dreams of men, the seed of commonwealths, the germs of empires.

The sun set; the dusk fell on the stream, and lights began to appear along the shore. The Chapman lighthouse, a three-legged thing erect on a mud-flat, shone strongly. Lights of ships moved in the fairway—a great stir of lights going up and going down. And farther west on the upper reaches the place of the monstrous town was still marked ominously on the sky, a brooding gloom in sunshine, a lurid glare under the stars.

"And this also," said Marlow suddenly, "has been one of the dark places on the earth."

He was the only man of us who still "followed the sea." The worst that could be said of him was that he did not represent his class. He was a seaman, but he was a wanderer, too, while most seamen lead, if one may so express it, a sedentary life. Their minds are of the stay-at-home order, and their home is always with them—the ship; and so is their country—the sea. One ship is very much like another, and the sea is always the same. In the immutability of their surroundings the foreign shores, the foreign faces, the changing immensity of life, glide past, veiled not by a sense of mystery but by a slightly disdainful ignorance; for there is nothing mysterious to a seaman unless it be the sea itself, which is the mistress of his existence and as inscrutable as Destiny. For the rest, after his hours of work, a casual stroll or a casual spree on shore suffices to unfold for him the secret of a whole continent, and generally he finds the secret not worth knowing. The yarns of seamen have a direct simplicity, the whole meaning of which lies within the shell of a cracked nut. But Marlow was not typical (if his propensity to spin yarns be excepted), and to him the meaning of an episode was not inside like a kernel but outside, enveloping the tale which brought it out only as a glow brings out a haze, in the likeness of one of these misty halos that sometimes are made visible by the spectral illumination of moonshine.

His remark did not seem at all surprising. It was just like Marlow. It was accepted in silence. No one took the trouble to grunt even; and presently he said, very slow—

"I was thinking of very old times, when the Romans first came here, nineteen hundred years ago—the other day. . . . Light came out of this river since—you say Knights? Yes; but it is like a running blaze on a plain, like a flash of lightning in the clouds. We live in the flicker—may it last as long as the old earth keeps rolling! But darkness was here yesterday. Imagine the feelings of a commander of a fine—what d'ye call 'em?—trireme in the Mediterranean, ordered suddenly to the north; run overland across the Gauls in a hurry; put in charge of one of these craft the legionaries—a wonderful lot of handy men they must have been, too—used to build, apparently by the hundred, in a month or two, if we may believe what we read. Imagine him here—the very end of the world, a sea the color of lead, a sky the color of smoke, a kind of ship about as rigid as a concertina—and going up this river with stores, or orders, or what you like. Sand-banks, marshes, forests, savages—precious little to eat fit for a civilized man, nothing but Thames water to drink. No Falernian wine here, no going ashore. Here and there a military camp lost in a wilderness, like a needle in a bundle of hay—cold, fog, tempests, disease, exile, and death,—death skulking in the air, in the water, in the bush. They must have been dying like flies here. Oh, yes—he did it. Did it very well, too, no doubt, and without thinking much about it either, except afterwards to brag of what he had gone through in his time, perhaps. They were men enough to face the darkness. And perhaps he was cheered by keeping his eye on a chance of promotion to the fleet at Ravenna by and by, if he had good friends in Rome and survived the awful climate. Or think of a decent young citizen in a toga—perhaps too much dice, you know—coming out here in the train of some prefect, or tax-gatherer, or trader even, to mend his fortunes. Land in a swamp, march through the woods, and in some inland post feel the savagery, the utter savagery, had closed round him, —all that mysterious life of the wilderness that stirs in the forest, in the jungles, in the hearts of wild men. There's no initiation either into such mysteries. He has to live in the midst of the incomprehensible, which is also detestable. And it has a fascination, too, that goes to work upon him. The fascination of the abomination—you know, imagine the growing regrets, the longing to escape, the powerless disgust, the surrender, the hate."

He paused.

"Mind," he began again, lifting one arm from the elbow, the palm of the hand outwards, so that, with his legs folded before him, he had the pose of a Buddha preaching in European clothes and without a lotus-flower— "Mind, none of us would feel exactly like this. What saves us is efficiency—the devotion to efficiency. But these chaps were not much account, really. They were no colonists; their administration was merely a squeeze, and nothing more, I suspect. They were conquerors, and for that you want only brute force—nothing to boast of, when you have it, since your strength is just an accident arising from the weakness of others. They grabbed what they could get for the sake of what was to be got. It was just robbery with violence, aggravated murder on a great scale, and men going at it blind—as is very proper for those who tackle a darkness. The conquest of the earth, which mostly means the taking it away from those who have a different complexion or slightly flatter noses than ourselves, is not a pretty thing when you look into it too much. What redeems it is the idea only. An idea at the back of it; not a sentimental pretense but an idea; and an unselfish belief in the idea—something you can set up, and bow down before, and offer a sacrifice to. . . ."

He broke off. Flames glided in the river, small green flames, red flames, white flames, pursuing, overtaking, joining, crossing each other— then separating slowly or hastily. The traffic of the great city went on in the deepening night upon the sleepless river. We looked on, waiting patiently—there was nothing else to do till the end of the flood; but it was only after a long silence, when he said, in a hesitating voice, "I suppose you fellows remember I did once turn fresh-water sailor for a bit," that we knew we were fated, before the ebb began to run, to hear about one of Marlow's inconclusive experiences.

"I don't want to bother you much with what happened to me personally," he began, showing in this remark the weakness of many tellers of tales who seem so often unaware of what their audience would best like to hear; "yet to understand the effect of it on me you ought to know how I got out there, what I saw, how I went up that river to the place where I first met the poor chap. It was the farthest point of navigation and the culminating point of my experience. It seemed somehow to throw a kind of light on everything about me—and into my thoughts. It was somber enough, too—and pitiful—not extraordinary in any way—not very clear either. No, not very clear. And yet it seemed to throw a kind of light.

"I had then, as you remember, just returned to London after a lot of Indian Ocean, Pacific, China Seas—a regular dose of the East—six years or so, and I was loafing about, hindering you fellows in your work and invading your homes, just as though I had got a heavenly mission to civilize you. It was very fine for a time, but after a bit I did get tired of resting. Then I began to look for a ship—I should think the hardest work on earth. But the ships wouldn't even look at me. And I got tired of that game, too.

"Now when I was a little chap I had a passion for maps. I would look for hours at South America, or Africa, or Australia, and lose myself in all the glories of exploration. At that time there were many blank spaces on the earth, and when I saw one that looked particularly inviting on a map (but they all look that) I would put my finger on it and say, When I grow up I will go there. The North Pole was one of these places, I remember. Well, I haven't been there yet, and shall not try now. The glamor's off. Other places were scattered about the Equator, and in every sort of latitude all over the two hemispheres. I have been in some of them, and . . . well, we won't talk about that. But there was one yet—the biggest, the most blank, so to speak—that I had a hankering after.

"True, by this time it was not a blank space any more. It had got filled since my boyhood with rivers and lakes and names. It had ceased to be a blank space of delightful mystery—a white patch for a boy to dream gloriously over. It had become a place of darkness. But there was in it one river especially, a mighty big river, that you could see on the map, resembling an immense snake uncoiled, with its head in the sea, its body at rest curving afar over a vast country, and its tail lost in the depths of the land. And as I looked at the map of it in a shop-window, it fascinated me as a snake would a bird—a silly little bird. Then I remembered there was a big concern, a Company for trade on that river. Dash it all! I thought to myself, they can't trade without using some kind of craft on that lot of fresh water—steamboats! Why shouldn't I try to get charge of one? I went on along Fleet Street, but could not shake off the idea. The snake had charmed me.

"You understand it was a Continental concern, that Trading society; but I have a lot of relations living on the Continent, because it's cheap and not so nasty as it looks, they say.

"I am sorry to own I began to worry them. This was already a fresh departure for me. I was not used to getting things that way, you know. I always went my own road and on my own legs where I had a mind to go. I wouldn't have believed it of myself; but, then—you see—I

felt somehow I must get there by hook or by crook. So I worried
them. The men said 'My dear fellow,' and did nothing. Then—would
you believe it?—I tried the women. I, Charlie Marlow, set the women to
work—to get a job. Heavens! Well, you see, the notion drove me. I
had an aunt, a dear enthusiastic soul. She wrote: 'It will be delightful.
I am ready to do anything, anything for you. It is a glorious idea. I
know the wife of a very high personage in the Administration, and
also a man who has lots of influence with,' etc., etc. She was determined to make no end of fuss to get me appointed skipper of a river
steamboat, if such was my fancy.

"I got my appointment—of course; and I got it very quick. It appears the Company had received news that one of their captains had
been killed in a scuffle with the natives. This was my chance, and it
made me the more anxious to go. It was only months and months afterwards, when I made the attempt to recover what was left of the body,
that I heard the original quarrel arose from a misunderstanding about
some hens. Yes, two black hens. Fresleven—that was the fellow's name,
a Dane—thought himself wronged somehow in the bargain, so he went
ashore and started to hammer the chief of the village with a stick.
Oh, it didn't surprise me in the least to hear this, and at the same time
to be told that Fresleven was the gentlest, quietest creature that ever
walked on two legs. No doubt he was; but he had been a couple of
years already out there engaged in the noble cause, you know, and he
probably felt the need at last of asserting his self-respect in some way.
Therefore he whacked the old nigger mercilessly, while a big crowd of
his people watched him, thunderstruck, till some man—I was told the
chief's son—in desperation at hearing the old chap yell, made a tentative
jab with a spear at the white man—and of course it went quite easy between the shoulder-blades. Then the whole population cleared into the
forest, expecting all kinds of calamities to happen, while, on the other
hand, the steamer Fresleven commanded left also in a bad panic, in
charge of the engineer, I believe. Afterwards nobody seemed to trouble
much about Fresleven's remains, till I got out and stepped into his shoes.
I couldn't let it rest, though; but when an opportunity offered at last
to meet my predecessor, the grass growing through his ribs was tall
enough to hide his bones. They were all there. The supernatural being
had not been touched after he fell. And the village was deserted, the
huts gaped black, rotting, all askew within the fallen enclosures. A
calamity had come to it, sure enough. The people had vanished. Mad
terror had scattered them, men, women, and children, through the bush,
and they had never returned. What became of the hens I don't know
either. I should think the cause of progress got them, anyhow. However, through this glorious affair I got my appointment, before I had
fairly begun to hope for it.

"I flew around like mad to get ready, and before forty-eight hours I was crossing the Channel to show myself to my employers, and sign the contract. In a very few hours I arrived in a city that always makes me think of a whited sepulchre. Prejudice no doubt. I had no difficulty in finding the Company's offices. It was the biggest thing in the town, and everybody I met was full of it. They were going to run an over-sea empire, and make no end of coin by trade.

"A narrow and deserted street in deep shadow, high houses, innumerable windows with venetian blinds, a dead silence, grass sprouting between the stones, imposing carriage archways right and left, immense double doors standing ponderously ajar. I slipped through one of these cracks, went up a swept and ungarnished staircase, as arid as a desert, and opened the first door I came to. Two women, one fat and the other slim, sat on straw-bottomed chairs, knitting black wool. The slim one got up and walked straight at me—still knitting with down-cast eyes—and only just as I began to think of getting out of her way, as you would for a somnambulist, stood still, and looked up. Her dress was as plain as an umbrella-cover, and she turned round without a word and preceded me into a waiting-room. I gave my name, and looked about. Deal table in the middle, plain chairs all around the walls, on one end a large shining map marked with all the colors of a rainbow. There was a vast amount of red—good to see at any time, because one knows that some real work is done in there, a deuce of a lot of blue, a little green, smears of orange, and, on the East Coast, a purple patch, to show where the jolly pioneers of progress drink the jolly lager-beer. However, I wasn't going into any of these. I was going into the yellow. Dead in the center. And the river was there—fascinating—deadly— like a snake. Ough! A door opened, a white-haired secretarial head, but wearing a compassionate expression, appeared, and a skinny forefinger beckoned me into the sanctuary. Its light was dim, and a heavy writing-desk squatted in the middle. From behind that structure came out an impression of pale plumpness in a frock-coat. The great man himself. He was five feet six, I should judge, and had his grip on the handle-end of ever so many millions. He shook hands, I fancy, murmured vaguely, was satisfied with my French. *Bon voyage.*

"In about forty-five seconds I found myself again in the waiting-room with the compassionate secretary, who, full of desolation and sympathy, made me sign some document. I believe I undertook amongst other things not to disclose any trade secrets. Well, I am not going to.

"I began to feel slightly uneasy. You know I am not used to such ceremonies, and there was something ominous in the atmosphere. It was just as though I had been let into some conspiracy—I don't know— something not quite right; and I was glad to get out. In the outer room the two women knitted black wool feverishly. People were arriving, and the younger one was walking back and forth introducing them. The old one sat on her chair. Her flat cloth slippers were propped up on a foot-warmer, and a cat reposed on her lap. She wore a starched white affair on her head, had a wart on one cheek, and silver-rimmed spectacles hung on the tip of her nose. She glanced at me above the glasses. The swift and indifferent placidity of that look troubled me. Two youths with foolish and cheery countenances were being piloted over, and she threw at them the same quick glance of unconcerned wisdom. She seemed to know all about them, and about me, too. An eerie feeling came over me. She seemed uncanny and fateful. Often far away from there I thought of these two, guarding the door of Darkness, knitting black wool as for a warm pall, one introducing, introducing continuously to the unknown, the other scrutinizing the cheery and foolish faces with unconcerned old eyes. *Ave!* Old knitter of black wool. *Morituri te salutant.* Not many of those she looked at ever saw her again—not half, by a long way.

"There was yet a visit to the doctor. 'A simple formality,' assured me the secretary, with an air of taking an immense part in all my sorrows. Accordingly a young chap wearing his hat over the left eyebrow, some clerk I suppose,—there must have been clerks in the business, though the house was as still as a house in a city of the dead—came from somewhere upstairs, and led me forth. He was shabby and careless, with inkstains on the sleeves of his jacket, and his cravat was large and billowy, under a chin shaped like the toe of an old boot. It was a little too early for the doctor, so I proposed a drink, and thereupon he developed a vein of joviality. As we sat over our vermuths he glorified the Company's business, and by and by I expressed casually my surprise at him not going out there. He became very cool and collected all at once. 'I am not such a fool as I look, quoth Plato to his disciples,' he said sententiously, emptied his glass with great resolution, and we rose.

"The old doctor felt my pulse, evidently thinking of something else the while. 'Good, good for there,' he mumbled, and then with a certain eagerness asked me whether I would let him measure my head. Rather surprised, I said Yes, when he produced a thing like calipers and got the dimensions back and front and every way, taking notes carefully. He was an unshaven little man in a threadbare coat like a gaberdine, with his feet in slippers, and I thought him a harmless fool. 'I always ask leave, in the interests of science, to measure the crania of those going out there,' he said. 'And when they come back, too?' I asked. 'Oh, I never see them,' he remarked; 'and, moreover, the changes take place inside, you know.' He smiled, as if at some quiet joke. 'So you are going out there. Famous. Interesting, too.' He gave me a searching glance, and made another note. 'Ever any madness in your family?' he asked, in a matter-of-fact tone. I felt very annoyed. 'Is that question in the interests of science, too?' 'It would be,' he said, without taking notice of my irritation, 'interesting for science to watch the mental changes of individuals, on the spot, but . . .' 'Are you an alienist?' I interrupted. 'Every doctor should be—a little,' answered that original, imperturbably. 'I have a little theory which you Messieurs who go out there must help me to prove. This is my share in the advantages my country shall reap from the possession of such a magnificent dependency. The mere wealth I leave to others. Pardon my questions, but you are the first Englishman coming under my observation . . .' I hastened to assure him I was not in the least typical. 'If I were,' I said, 'I wouldn't be talking like this with you.' 'What you say is rather profound, and probably erroneous,' he said, with a laugh. 'Avoid irritation more than exposure to the sun. Adieu. How do you English say, eh? Good-bye. Ah! Good-bye. Adieu. In the tropics one must before everything keep calm.' . . . He lifted a warning forefinger. . . . '*Du calme, du calme. Adieu.*'

"One thing more remained to do—say good-bye to my excellent aunt. I found her triumphant. I had a cup of tea—the last decent cup of tea for many days—and in a room that most soothingly looked just as you would expect a lady's drawing-room to look, we had a long quiet chat by the fireside. In the course of these confidences it became quite plain to me I had been represented to the wife of the high dignitary, and goodness knows to how many more people besides, as an exceptional and gifted creature—a piece of good fortune for the Company—a man you don't get hold of every day. Good heavens! and I was going to take charge of a two-penny-half-penny river-steamboat with a penny whistle attached! It appeared, however, I was also one of the Workers, with a capital—you know. Something like an emissary of light, something like a lower sort of apostle. There had been a lot of such rot let loose in print and talk just about that time, and the excellent woman, living right in the rush of all that humbug, got carried off her feet. She talked about 'weaning those ignorant millions from their horrid ways,' till, upon my word, she made me quite uncomfortable. I ventured to hint that the Company was run for profit.

"'You forget, dear Charlie, that the laborer is worthy of his hire,' she said brightly. It's queer how out of touch with truth women are. They live in a world of their own, and there has never been anything like it, and never can be. It is too beautiful altogether, and if they were to set it up it would go to pieces before the first sunset. Some confounded fact we men have been living contentedly with ever since the day of creation would start up and knock the whole thing over.

"After this I got embraced, told to wear flannel, be sure to write often, and so on—and I left. In the street—I don't know why—a queer feeling came to me that I was an impostor. Odd thing that I, who used to clear out for any part of the world at twenty-four hours' notice, with less thought than most men give to the crossing of a street, had a moment— I won't say of hesitation, but of startled pause, before this commonplace affair. The best way I can explain it to you is by saying that, for a second or two, I felt as though, instead of going to the center of a continent, I were about to set off for the center of the earth.

"I left in a French steamer, and she called in every blamed port they have out there, for, as far as I could see, the sole purpose of landing soldiers and custom-house officers. I watched the coast. Watching a coast as it slips by the ship is like thinking about an enigma. There it is before you—smiling, frowning, inviting, grand, mean, insipid, or savage, and always mute with an air of whispering, Come and find out. This one was almost featureless, as if still in the making, with an aspect of monotonous grimness. The edge of a colossal jungle, so dark-green as to be almost black, fringed with white surf, ran straight, like a ruled line, far, far away along a blue sea whose glitter was blurred by a creeping mist. The sun was fierce, the land seemed to glisten and drip with steam. Here and there grayish-whitish specks showed up clustered inside the white surf, with a flag flying above them perhaps. Settlements some centuries old, and still no bigger than pinheads on the untouched expanse of their background. We pounded along, stopped, landed soldiers; went on, landed custom-house clerks to levy toll in what looked like a God-forsaken wilderness, with a tin shed and a flag-pole lost in it; landed more soldiers—to take care of the custom-house clerks, presumably. Some, I heard, got drowned in the surf; but whether they did or not, nobody seemed particularly to care. They were just flung out there, and on we went. Every day the coast looked the same, as though we had not moved; but we passed various places—trading places—with names like Gran' Bassam, Little Popo; names that seemed to belong to some sordid farce acted in front of a sinister back-cloth. The idleness of a passenger, my isolation amongst all these men with whom I had no point of contact, the oily and languid sea, the uniform somberness of the coast, seemed to keep me away from the truth of things, within the toil of a mournful and senseless delusion. The voice of the surf heard now and then was a positive pleasure, like the speech of a brother. It was something natural, that had its reason, that had a meaning. Now and then a boat from the shore gave one a momentary contact with reality. It was paddled by black fellows. You could see from afar the white of their eyeballs glistening. They shouted, sang; their bodies streamed with perspiration; they had faces like grotesque masks—these chaps; but they had bone, muscle, a wild vitality, an intense energy of movement, that was as natural and true as the surf along their coast. They wanted no excuse for being there. They were a great comfort to look at. For a time I would feel I belonged still to a world of straightforward facts; but the feeling would not last long. Something would turn up to scare it away. Once, I remember, we came upon a man-of-war anchored off the coast. There wasn't even a shed there, and she was shelling the bush. It appears the French had one of their wars going on thereabouts.

Her ensign dropped limp like a rag; the muzzles of the long six-inch guns stuck out all over the low hull; the greasy, slimy swell swung her up lazily and let her down, swaying her thin masts. In the empty immensity of earth, sky, and water, there she was, incomprehensible, firing into a continent. Pop, would go one of the six-inch guns; a small flame would dart and vanish, a little white smoke would disappear, a tiny projectile would give a feeble screech—and nothing happened. Nothing could happen. There was a touch of insanity in the proceeding, a sense of lugubrious drollery in the sight; and it was not dissipated by somebody on board assuring me earnestly there was a camp of natives—he called them enemies!—hidden out of sight somewhere.

"We gave her her letters (I heard the men in that lonely ship were dying of fever at the rate of three a day) and went on. We called at some more places with farcical names, where the merry dance of death and trade goes on in a still and earthy atmosphere as of an overheated catacomb; all along the formless coast bordered by dangerous surf, as if Nature herself had tried to ward off intruders; in and out of rivers, streams of death in life, whose banks were rotting into mud, whose waters, thickened into slime, invaded the contorted mangroves, that seemed to writhe at us in the extremity of an impotent despair. Nowhere did we stop long enough to get a particularized impression, but the general sense of vague and oppressive wonder grew upon me. It was like a weary pilgrimage amongst hints for nightmares.

"It was upward of thirty days before I saw the mouth of the big river. We anchored off the seat of the government. But my work would not begin till some two hundred miles farther on. So as soon as I could I made a start for a place thirty miles higher up.

"I had my passage on a little sea-going steamer. Her captain was a Swede, and knowing me for a seaman, invited me on the bridge. He was a young man, lean, fair, and morose, with lanky hair and a shuffling gait. As we left the miserable little wharf, he tossed his head contemptuously at the shore. 'Been living there?' he asked. I said, 'Yes.' 'Fine lot these government chaps—are they not?' he went on, speaking English with great precision and considerable bitterness. 'It is funny what some people will do for a few francs a month. I wonder what becomes of that kind when it goes up-country?' I said to him I expected to see that soon. 'So-o-o!' he exclaimed. He shuffled athwart, keeping one eye ahead vigilantly. 'Don't be too sure,' he continued. 'The other day I took up a man who hanged himself on the road. He was a Swede, too.' 'Hanged himself! Why, in God's name?' I cried. He kept on looking out watchfully. 'Who knows? The sun was too much for him, or the country perhaps.'

"At last we opened a reach. A rocky cliff appeared, mounds of turned-up earth by the shore, houses on a hill, others with iron roofs, amongst a waste of excavations, or hanging to the declivity. A continuous noise of the rapids above hovered over this scene of inhabited devastation. A lot of people, mostly black and naked, moved about like ants. A jetty projected into the river. A blinding sunlight drowned all this at times in a sudden recrudescence of glare. 'There's your Company's station,' said the Swede, pointing to three wooden barrack-like structures on the rocky slope. 'I will send your things up. Four boxes did you say? So. Farewell.'

"I came upon a boiler wallowing in the grass, then found a path leading up the hill. It turned aside for the bowlders, and also for an under-sized railway-truck lying there on its back with its wheels in the air. One was off. The thing looked as dead as the carcass of some animal. I came upon more pieces of decaying machinery, a stack of rusty rails. To the left a clump of trees made a shady spot, where dark things seemed to stir feebly. I blinked, the path was steep. A horn tooted to the right, and I saw the black people run. A heavy and dull detonation shook the ground, a puff of smoke came out of the cliff, and that was all. No change appeared on the face of the rock. They were building a railway. The cliff was not in the way or anything; but this objectless blasting was all the work going on.

"A slight clinking behind me made me turn my head. Six black men advanced in a file, toiling up the path. They walked erect and slow, balancing small baskets full of earth on their heads, and the clink kept time with their footsteps. Black rags were wound round their loins, and the short ends behind waggled to and fro like tails. I could see every rib, the joints of their limbs were like knots in a rope; each had an iron collar on his neck, and all were connected together with a chain whose bights swung between them, rhythmically clinking. Another report from the cliff made me think suddenly of that ship of war I had seen firing into a continent. It was the same kind of ominous voice; but these men could by no stretch of imagination be called enemies. They were called criminals, and the outraged law, like bursting shells, had come to them, an insoluble mystery from the sea. All their meager breasts panted together, the violently dilated nostrils quivered, the eyes stared stonily up-hill. They passed me within six inches, without a glance, with that complete, deathlike indifference of unhappy savages. Behind this raw matter one of the reclaimed, the product of the new forces at work, strolled despondently, carrying a rifle by its middle. He had a uniform jacket with one button off, and seeing a white man on the path, hoisted his weapon to his shoulder with alacrity. This was simple prudence, white men being so much alike at a distance that he could not tell who I might be. He was speedily reassured, and with a large, white, rascally grin, and a glance at his charge, seemed to take me into partnership in his exalted trust. After all, I also was a part of the great cause of these high and just proceedings.

"Instead of going up, I turned and descended to the left. My idea was to let that chain-gang get out of sight before I climbed the hill. You know I am not particularly tender; I've had to strike and to fend off. I've had to resist and to attack sometimes—that's only one way of resisting—without counting the exact cost, according to the demands of such sort of life as I had blundered into. I've seen the devil of violence, and the devil of greed, and the devil of hot desire; but, by all the stars! these were strong, lusty, red-eyed devils, that swayed and drove men—men, I tell you. But as I stood on this hillside, I foresaw that in the blinding sunshine of that land I would become acquainted with a flabby, pretending, weak-eyed devil of a rapacious and pitiless folly. How insidious he could be, too, I was only to find out several months later and a thousand miles farther. For a moment I stood appalled, as though by a warning. Finally I descended the hill, obliquely, towards the trees I had seen.

"I avoided a vast artificial hole somebody had been digging on the slope, the purpose of which I found it impossible to divine. It wasn't a quarry or a sandpit, anyhow. It was just a hole. It might have been connected with the philanthropic desire of giving the criminals something to do. I don't know. Then I nearly fell into a very narrow ravine, almost no more than a scar in the hillside. I discovered that a lot of imported drainage-pipes for the settlement had been tumbled in there. There wasn't one that was not broken. It was a wanton smash-up. At last I got under the trees. My purpose was to stroll into the shade for a moment; but no sooner within than it seemed to me I had stepped into the gloomy circle of some Inferno. The rapids were near, and an uninterrupted, uniform, headlong, rushing noise filled the mournful stillness of the grove, where not a breath stirred, not a leaf moved, with a mysterious sound—as though the tearing pace of the launched earth had suddenly become audible.

"Black shapes crouched, lay, sat between the trees leaning against the trunks, clinging to the earth, half coming out, half effaced within the dim light, in all the attitudes of pain, abandonment, and despair. Another mine on the cliff went off, followed by a slight shudder of the soil under my feet. The work was going on. The work! And this was the place where some of the helpers had withdrawn to die.

"They were dying slowly—it was very clear. They were not enemies, they were not criminals, they were nothing earthly now,—nothing but black shadows of disease and starvation, lying confusedly in the greenish gloom. Brought from all the recesses of the coast in all the legality of time contracts, lost in uncongenial surroundings, fed on unfamiliar food, they sickened, became inefficient, and were then allowed to crawl away and rest. These moribund shapes were free as air—and nearly as thin. I began to distinguish the gleam of the eyes under the trees. Then, glancing down, I saw a face near my hand. The black bones reclined at full length with one shoulder against the tree, and slowly the eyelids rose and the sunken eyes looked up at me, enormous and vacant, a kind of blind, white flicker in the depths of the orbs, which died out slowly. The man seemed young—almost a boy—but you know with them it's hard to tell. I found nothing else to do but to offer him one of my good Swede's ship's biscuits I had in my pocket. The fingers closed slowly on it and held—there was no other movement and no other glance. He had tied a bit of white worsted round his neck—Why? Where did he get it? Was it a badge—an ornament—a charm—a propitiatory act? Was there any idea at all connected with it? It looked startling round his black neck, this bit of white thread from beyond the seas.

"Near the same tree two more bundles of acute angles sat with their legs drawn up. One, with his chin propped on his knees, stared at nothing, in an intolerable and appalling manner: his brother phantom rested its forehead, as if overcome with a great weariness; and all about others were scattered in every pose of contorted collapse, as in some picture of a massacre or a pestilence. While I stood horror-struck, one of these creatures rose to his hands and knees, and went off on all-fours towards the river to drink. He lapped out of his hand, then sat up in the sunlight, crossing his shins in front of him, and after a time let his woolly head fall on his breastbone.

"I didn't want any more loitering in the shade, and I made haste towards the station. When near the buildings I met a white man, in such an unexpected elegance of get-up that the first moment I took him for a sort of vision. I saw a high starched collar, white cuffs, a light alpaca jacket, snowy trousers, a clean necktie, and varnished boots. No hat. Hair parted, brushed, oiled, under a green-lined parasol held in a big white hand. He was amazing, and had a penholder behind his ear.

"I shook hands with this miracle, and I learned he was the Company's chief accountant, and that all the book-keeping was done at this station. He had come out for a moment, he said, 'to get a breath of fresh air.' The expression sounded wonderfully odd, with its suggestion of sedentary desk-life. I wouldn't have mentioned the fellow to you at all, only it was from his lips that I first heard the name of the man who is so indissolubly connected with the memories of that time. Moreover, I respected the fellow. Yes; I respected his collars, his vast cuffs, his brushed hair. His appearance was certainly that of a hairdresser's dummy; but in the great demoralization of the land he kept up his appearance. That's backbone. His starched collars and got-up shirt-fronts were achievements of character. He had been out nearly three years; and, later, I could not help asking him how he managed to sport such linen. He had just the faintest blush, and said modestly, 'I've been teaching one of the native women about the station. It was difficult. She had a distaste for the work.' Thus this man had verily accomplished something. And he was devoted to his books, which were in apple-pie order.

"Everything else in the station was in a muddle,—heads, things, buildings. Strings of dusty niggers with splay feet arrived and departed; a stream of manufactured goods, rubbishy cottons, beads, and brass-wire set into the depths of darkness, and in return came a precious trickle of ivory.

"I had to wait in the station for ten days—an eternity. I lived in a hut in the yard, but to be out of the chaos I would sometimes get into the accountant's office. It was built of horizontal planks, and so badly put together that, as he bent over his high desk, he was barred from neck to heels with narrow strips of sunlight. There was no need to open the big shutter to see. It was hot there, too; big flies buzzed fiendishly, and did not sting, but stabbed. I sat generally on the floor, while, of fault-less appearance (and even slightly scented), perching on a high stool, he wrote, he wrote. Sometimes he stood up for exercise. When a truckle-bed with a sick man (some invalid agent from up-country) was put in there, he exhibited a gentle annoyance. 'The groans of this sick person,' he said, 'distract my attention. And without that it is extremely difficult to guard against clerical errors in this climate.'

"One day he remarked, without lifting his head, 'In the interior you will no doubt meet Mr. Kurtz.' On my asking who Mr. Kurtz was, he said he was a first-class agent; and seeing my disappointment at this information, he added slowly, laying down his pen, 'He is a very remark-able person.' Further questions elicited from him that Mr. Kurtz was at present in charge of a trading post, a very important one, in the true ivory-country, at 'the very bottom of there. Sends in as much ivory as all the others put together. . . .' He began to write again. The sick man was too ill to groan. The flies buzzed in a great peace.

"Suddenly there was a growing murmur of voices and a great tramp-ing of feet. A caravan had come in. A violent babble of uncouth sounds burst out on the other side of the planks. All the carriers were speaking together, and in the midst of the uproar the lamentable voice of the chief agent was heard 'giving it up' tearfully for the twentieth time that day. . . . He rose slowly. 'What a frightful row,' he said. He crossed the room gently to look at the sick man, and returning, said to me, 'He does not hear.' 'What! Dead?' I asked, startled. 'No, not yet,' he answered, with great composure. Then, alluding with a toss of the head to the tumult in the station-yard, 'When one has got to make correct entries, one comes to hate those savages—hate them to the death.' He remained thoughtful for a moment. 'When you see Mr. Kurtz,' he went on, 'tell him for me that everything here'—he glanced at the desk—'is very satisfactory. I don't like to write to him—with those messengers of ours you never know who may get hold of your letter—at that Central Station.' He stared at me for a moment with his mild, bulging eyes. 'Oh, he will go far, very far,' he began again. 'He will be a somebody in the Administration before long. They, above—the Council in Europe, you know—mean him to be.'

"He turned to his work. The noise outside had ceased, and presently in going out I stopped at the door. In the steady buzz of flies the home-ward-bound agent was lying flushed and insensible; the other, bent over his books, was making correct entries of perfectly correct trans-actions; and fifty feet below the doorstep I could see the still tree-tops of the grove of death.

"Next day I left that station at last, with a caravan of sixty men, for a two-hundred-mile tramp.

"No use telling you much about that. Paths, paths, everywhere; a stamped-in network of paths spreading over the empty land, through long grass, through burnt grass, through thickets, down and up chilly ravines, up and down stony hills ablaze with heat; and a solitude, a solitude, nobody, not a hut. The population had cleared out a long time ago. Well, if a lot of mysterious niggers armed with all kinds of fearful weapons suddenly took to traveling on the road between Deal and Gravesend, catching the yokels right and left to carry heavy loads for them, I fancy every farm and cottage thereabouts would get empty very soon. Only here the dwellings were gone, too. Still I passed through several abandoned villages. There's something pathetically childish in the ruins of grass walls. Day after day, with the stamp and shuffle of sixty pair of bare feet behind me, each pair under a sixty-lb. load. Camp, cook, sleep, strike camp, march. Now and then a carrier dead in harness, at rest in the long grass near the path, with an empty water-gourd and his long staff lying by his side. A great silence around and above. Perhaps on some quiet night the tremor of far-off drums, sink-ing, swelling, a tremor vast, faint; a sound weird, appealing, suggestive, and wild—and perhaps with as profound a meaning as the sound of bells in a Christian country. Once a white man in an unbuttoned uniform, camping on the path with an armed escort of lank Zanzibaris, very hos-pitable and festive—not to say drunk. Was looking after the upkeep of the road, he declared. Can't say I saw any road or any upkeep, unless the body of a middle-aged negro, with a bullet-hole in the fore-head, upon which I absolutely stumbled three miles farther on, may be considered as a permanent improvement. I had a white companion, too, not a bad chap, but rather too fleshy and with the exasperating habit of fainting on the hot hill-sides, miles away from the least bit of shade and water. Annoying, you know, to hold your own coat like a parasol over a man's head while he is coming-to. I couldn't help asking him once what he meant by coming there at all. 'To make money, of course. What do you think?' he said, scornfully. Then he got fever, and had to be carried in a hammock slung under a pole. As he weighed sixteen stone I had no end of rows with the carriers. They jibbed, ran away, sneaked off with their loads in the night—quite a mutiny. So, one evening, I made a speech in English with gestures, not one of which was lost to the sixty pairs of eyes before me, and the next morning I started the hammock off in front all right. An hour afterwards I came upon the whole concern wrecked in a bush—man, hammock, groans, blankets, horrors. The heavy pole had skinned his poor nose. He was very anxious for me to kill somebody, but there wasn't the shadow of a carrier near. I remembered the old doctor—'It would be interesting for science to watch the mental changes of individuals, on the spot.' I felt I was becoming scientifically interesting. However, all that is to no purpose. On the fifteenth day I came in sight of the big river again, and hobbled into the Central Station. It was on a back water surrounded by scrub and forest, with a pretty border of smelly mud on one side, and on the three others enclosed by a crazy fence of rushes. A neglected gap was all the gate it had, and the first glance at the place was enough to let you see the flabby devil was running that show. White men with long staves in their hands appeared languidly from amongst the buildings, strolling up to take a look at me, and then retired out of sight somewhere. One of them, a stout, excitable chap with black mustaches, informed me with great volubility and many digressions, as soon as I told him who I was, that my steamer was at the bottom of the river. I was thunderstruck. What, how, why? Oh, it was 'all right.' The 'manager himself' was there. All quite correct. 'Everybody had behaved splendidly! splendidly!'—'you must,' he said in agitation, 'go and see the general manager at once. He is waiting!'

"I did not see the real significance of that wreck at once. I fancy I see it now, but I am not sure—not at all. Certainly the affair was too stupid—when I think of it—to be altogether natural. Still . . . But at the moment it presented itself simply as a confounded nuisance. The steamer was sunk. They had started two days before in a sudden hurry up the river with the manager on board, in charge of some volunteer skipper, and before they had been out three hours they tore the bottom out of her on stones, and she sunk near the south bank. I asked myself what I was to do there, now my boat was lost. As a matter of fact, I had plenty to do in fishing my command out of the river. I had to set about it the very next day. That, and the repairs when I brought the pieces to the station, took some months.

"My first interview with the manager was curious. He did not ask me to sit down after my twenty-mile walk that morning. He was commonplace in complexion, in feature, in manners, and in voice. He was of middle size and of ordinary build. His eyes, of the usual blue, were perhaps remarkably cold, and he certainly could make his glance fall on one as trenchant and heavy as an axe. But even at these times the rest of his person seemed to disclaim the intention. Otherwise there was only an indefinable, faint expression of his lips, something stealthy—

a smile—not a smile—I remember it, but I can't explain. It was unconscious, this smile was, though just after he had said something it got
intensified for an instant. It came at the end of his speeches like a seal
applied on the words to make the meaning of the commonest phrase
appear absolutely inscrutable. He was a common trader, from his youth
up employed in these parts—nothing more. He was obeyed, yet he inspired neither love nor fear, nor even respect. He inspired uneasiness.
That was it! Uneasiness. Not a definite mistrust—just uneasiness—
nothing more. You have no idea how effective such a . . . a . . . faculty
can be. He had no genius for organizing, for initiative, or for order even.
That was evident in such things as the deplorable state of the station.
He had no learning, and no intelligence. His position had come to him—
why? Perhaps because he was never ill . . . He had served three terms
of three years out there . . . Because triumphant health in the general
rout of constitutions is a kind of power in itself. When he went home on
leave he rioted on a large scale—pompously. Jack ashore—with a
difference—in externals only. This one could gather from his casual
talk. He originated nothing, he could keep the routine going—that's
all. But he was great. He was great by this little thing that it was impossible to tell what could control such a man. He never gave that
secret away. Perhaps there was nothing within him. Such a suspicion
made one pause—for out there there were no external checks. Once
when various tropical diseases had laid low almost every 'agent' in
the station, he was heard to say, 'Men who come out here should have
no entrails.' He sealed the utterance with that smile of his, as though
it had been a door opening into a darkness he had in his keeping. You
fancied you had seen things—but the seal was on. When annoyed at
meal-times by the constant quarrels of the white men about precedence,
he ordered an immense round table to be made, for which a special house
had to be built. This was the station's mess-room. Where he sat was
the first place—the rest were nowhere. One felt this to be his unalterable
conviction. He was neither civil nor uncivil. He was quiet. He allowed
his 'boy'—an overfed young negro from the coast—to treat the white
men, under his very eyes, with provoking insolence.

"He began to speak as soon as he saw me. I had been very long on
the road. He could not wait. Had to start without me. The up-river
stations had to be relieved. There had been so many delays already
that he did not know who was dead and who was alive, and how they
got on—and so on, and so on. He paid no attention to my explanations,
and, playing with a stick of sealing-wax, repeated several times that the
situation was 'very grave, very grave.' There were rumors that a very
important station was in jeopardy, and its chief, Mr. Kurtz, was ill.
Hoped it was not true. Mr. Kurtz was . . . I felt weary and irritable.
Hang Kurtz, I thought. I interrupted him by saying I had heard of Mr.
Kurtz on the coast. 'Ah! So they talk of him down there,' he murmured

to himself. Then he began again, assuring me Mr. Kurtz was the best agent he had, an exceptional man, of the greatest importance to the Company; therefore I could understand his anxiety. He was, he said, 'very, very uneasy.' Certainly he fidgeted on his chair a good deal, exclaimed, 'Ah, Mr. Kurtz!' broke the stick of sealing-wax and seemed dumbfounded by the accident. Next thing he wanted to know 'how long it would take to' . . . I interrupted him again. Being hungry, you know, and kept on my feet too, I was getting savage. 'How can I tell?' I said. 'I haven't even seen the wreck yet—some months, no doubt.' All this talk seemed to me so futile. 'Some months,' he said. 'Well, let us say three months before we can make a start. Yes. That ought to do the affair.' I flung out of his hut (he lived all alone in a clay hut with a sort of veranda) muttering to myself my opinion of him. He was a chattering idiot. Afterwards I took it back when it was borne in upon me startlingly with what extreme nicety he had estimated the time requisite for the 'affair.'

"I went to work the next day, turning, so to speak, my back on that station. In that way only it seemed to me I could keep my hold on the redeeming facts of life. Still, one must look about sometimes; and then I saw this station, these men strolling aimlessly about in the sunshine of the yard. I asked myself sometimes what it all meant. They wandered here and there with their absurd long staves in their hands, like a lot of faithless pilgrims bewitched inside a rotten fence. The word 'ivory' rang in the air, was whispered, was sighed. You would think they were praying to it. A taint of imbecile rapacity blew through it all, like a whiff from some corpse. By Jove! I've never seen anything so unreal in my life. And outside, the silent wilderness surrounding this cleared speck on the earth struck me as something great and invincible, like evil or truth, waiting patiently for the passing away of this fantastic invasion.

"Oh, these months! Well, never mind. Various things happened. One evening a grass shed full of calico, cotton prints, beads, and I don't know what else, burst into a blaze so suddenly that you would have thought the earth had opened to let an avenging fire consume all that trash. I was smoking my pipe quietly by my dismantled steamer, and saw them all cutting capers in the light, with their arms lifted high, when the stout man with mustaches came tearing down to the river, a tin pail in his hand, assured me that everybody was 'behaving splendidly, splendidly,' dipped about a quart of water and tore back again. I noticed there was a hole in the bottom of his pail.

"I strolled up. There was no hurry. You see the thing had gone off like a box of matches. It had been hopeless from the very first. The flame had leaped high, driven everybody back, lighted up everything— and collapsed. The shed was already a heap of embers glowing fiercely. A nigger was being beaten near by. They said he had caused the fire in some way; be that as it may, he was screeching most horribly. I saw him, later, for several days, sitting in a bit of shade looking very sick and trying to recover himself: afterwards he arose and went out—and the wilderness without a sound took him into its bosom again. As I approached the glow from the dark I found myself at the back of two men, talking. I heard the name of Kurtz pronounced, then the words, 'take advantage of this unfortunate accident.' One of the men was the manager. I wished him a good evening. 'Did you ever see anything like it—eh? it is incredible,' he said, and walked off. The other man remained. He was a first-class agent, young, gentlemanly, a bit reserved, with a forked little beard and a hooked nose. He was stand-offish with the other agents, and they on their side said he was the manager's spy upon them. As to me, I had hardly ever spoken to him before. We got into talk, and by and by we strolled away from the hissing ruins. Then he asked me to his room, which was in the main building of the station. He struck a match, and I perceived that this young aristocrat had not only a silver-mounted dressing-case but also a whole candle all to himself. Just at that time the manager was the only man sup- posed to have any right to candles. Native mats covered the clay walls; a collection of spears, assegais, shields, knives was hung up in trophies. The business intrusted to this fellow was the making of bricks—so I had been informed; but there wasn't a fragment of a brick anywhere in the station, and he had been there more than a year— waiting. It seems he could not make bricks without something, I don't know what—straw maybe. Anyways, it could not be found there, and as it was not likely to be sent from Europe, it did not appear clear to me what he was waiting for. An act of special creation perhaps. How- ever, they were all waiting—all the sixteen or twenty pilgrims of them —for something; and upon my word it did not seem an uncongenial occupation, from the way they took it, though the only thing that ever came to them was disease—as far as I could see. They beguiled the time by backbiting and intriguing against each other in a foolish kind of way. There was an air of plotting about that station, but nothing came of it, of course. It was as unreal as everything else—as the philanthropic pretense of the whole concern, as their talk, as their government, as their show of work. The only real feeling was a desire to get appointed to a trading-post where ivory was to be had, so that they could earn percentages. They intrigued and slandered and hated each other only on that account,—but as to effectually lifting a little finger—oh, no. By heavens! there is something after all in the world allowing one man to steal a horse while another must not look at a halter. Steal a horse straight out. Very well. He has done it. Perhaps he can ride. But there is a way of looking at a halter that would pro- voke the most charitable of saints into a kick.

"I had no idea why he wanted to be sociable, but as we chatted in

there it suddenly occurred to me the fellow was trying to get at something—in fact, pumping me. He alluded constantly to Europe, to the
people I was supposed to know there—putting leading questions as to
my acquaintances in the sepulchral city, and so on. His little eyes
glittered like mica discs—with a curiosity—though he tried to keep up
a bit of superciliousness. At first I was astonished, but very soon I
became awfully curious to see what he would find out from me. I
couldn't possibly imagine what I had in me to make it worth his while.
It was very pretty to see how he baffled himself, for in truth my body
was full only of chills, and my head had nothing in it but that wretched
steamboat business. It was evident he took me for a perfectly shameless
prevaricator. At last he got angry, and, to conceal a movement of
furious annoyance, he yawned. I rose. Then I noticed a small sketch
in oils, on a panel, representing a woman, draped and blindfolded,
carrying a lighted torch. The background was somber—almost black.
The movement of the woman was stately, and the effect of the torch-
light on the face was sinister.

"It arrested me, and he stood by civilly, holding an empty half-pint
champagne bottle (medical comforts) with the candle stuck in it. To
my question he said Mr. Kurtz had painted this—in this very station
more than a year ago—while waiting for means to go to his trading-
post. 'Tell me, pray,' I said, 'who is this Mr. Kurtz?'

" 'The chief of the Inner Station,' he answered in a short tone, looking
away. 'Much obliged,' I said, laughing. 'And you are the brickmaker
of the Central Station.   Everyone knows that.' He was silent for a
while. 'He is a prodigy,' he said at last. 'He is an emissary of pity, and
science, and progress, and devil knows what else. We want,' he began
to declaim suddenly, 'for the guidance of the cause intrusted to us by
Europe, so to speak, higher intelligence, wide sympathies, a singleness
of purpose.' 'Who says that?' I asked. 'Lots of them,' he replied.
'Some even write that; and so *he* comes here, a special being, as you
ought to know.' 'Why ought I to know?' I interrupted, really surprised.
He paid no attention. 'Yes. Today he is chief of the best station, next
year he will be assistant-manager, two years more and . . . but I daresay you know what he will be in two years' time. You are of the new
gang—the gang of virtue. The same people who sent him specially also
recommended you. Oh, don't say no. I've my own eyes to trust.'
Light dawned upon me. My dear aunt's influential acquaintances were
producing an unexpected effect upon that young man. I nearly burst
into a laugh. 'Do you read the Company's confidential correspondence?'
I asked. He hadn't a word to say. It was great fun. 'When Mr. Kurtz,'
I continued severely, 'is General Manager, you won't have the opportunity.'

"He blew the candle out suddenly, and we went outside. The moon
had risen. Black figures strolled about listlessly, pouring water on the

glow, whence proceeded a sound of hissing; steam ascended in the moonlight, the beaten nigger groaned somewhere. 'What a row the brute makes!' said the indefatigable man with the mustaches, appearing near us. 'Serves him right. Transgression—punishment—bang! Pitiless, pitiless. That's the only way. This will prevent all conflagrations for the future. I was just telling the manager . . .' He noticed my companion, and became crestfallen all at once. 'Not in bed yet,' he said, with a kind of servile heartiness; 'it's so natural. Ha! Danger— agitation.' He vanished. I went on to the river-side, and the other followed me. I heard a scathing murmur at my ear. 'Heap of muffs— go to.' The pilgrims could be seen in knots gesticulating, discussing. Several had still their staves in their hands. I verily believe they took these sticks to bed with them. Beyond the fence the forest stood up spectrally in the moonlight, and through the dim stir, through the faint sounds of that lamentable courtyard, the silence of the land went home to one's very heart—its mystery, its greatness, the amazing reality of its concealed life. The hurt nigger moaned feebly somewhere near by, and then fetched a deep sigh that made me mend my pace away from there. I felt a hand introducing itself under my arm. 'My dear sir,' said the fellow, 'I don't want to be misunderstood, and especially by you, who will see Mr. Kurtz long before I can have that pleasure. I wouldn't like him to get a false idea of my disposition. . . .'

"I let him run on, this papier-mâché Mephistopheles, and it seemed to me that if I tried I could poke my forefinger through him, and would find nothing inside but a little loose dirt, maybe. He, don't you see, had been planning to be assistant-manager by and by under the present man, and I could see that the coming of that Kurtz had upset them both not a little. He talked precipitately, and I did not try to stop him. I had my shoulders against the wreck of my steamer, hauled up on the slope like a carcass of some big river animal. The smell of mud, of primeval mud, by Jove! was in my nostrils, the high stillness of primeval forest was before my eyes; there were shiny patches on the black creek. The moon had spread over everything a thin layer of silver—over the rank grass, over the mud, upon the wall of matted vegetation standing higher than the wall of a temple, over the great river I could see through a somber gap glittering, glittering, as it flowed broadly by without a murmur. All this was great, expectant, mute, while the man jabbered about himself. I wondered whether the stillness on the face of the immensity looking at us two were meant as an appeal or as a menace. What were we who had strayed in here? Could we handle that dumb thing, or would it handle us? I felt how big, how confoundedly big, was that thing that couldn't talk, and perhaps was deaf as well. What was in there? I could see a little ivory coming out from there, and I had heard Mr. Kurtz was in there. I had heard enough about it, too—God knows! Yet somehow it didn't bring any image with it—no more than if I had been told an angel or a fiend was in there. I believed it in the same way one of you might believe there are inhabitants in the planet Mars. ¡I knew once a Scotch sailmaker who was certain, dead sure, there were people in Mars. If you asked him for some idea how they looked and behaved, he would get shy and mutter something about 'walking on all-fours.' If you as much as smiled, he would—though a man of sixty—offer to fight you. I would not have gone so far as to fight for Kurtz, but I went for him near enough to a lie. You know I hate, detest, and can't bear a lie, not because I am straighter than the rest of us, but simply because it appalls me. There is a taint of death, a flavor of mortality in lies—which is exactly what I hate and detest in the world—what I want to forget. It makes me miserable and sick, like biting something rotten would do. Temperament, I suppose. Well, I went near enough to it by letting the young fool there believe anything he liked to imagine as to my influence in Europe. I became in an instant as much of a pretense as the rest of the bewitched pilgrims. This simply because I had a notion it somehow would be of help to that Kurtz whom at the time I did not see—you understand. He was just a word for me. I did not see the man in the name any more than you do. Do you see him? Do you see the story? Do you see anything? It seems to me I am trying to tell you a dream—making a vain attempt, because no relation of a dream can convey the dream-sensation, that commingling of absurdity, that notion of being captured by the incredible which is of the very essence of dreams. . . ."

He was silent for a while.

". . . No, it is impossible; it is impossible to convey the life-sensation of any given epoch of one's existence—that which makes its truth, its meaning—its subtle and penetrating essence. It is impossible. We live, as we dream—alone. . . ."

He paused again as if reflecting, then added—

"Of course in this you fellows see more than I could then. You see me, whom you know. . . ."

It had become so pitch dark that we listeners could hardly see one another. For a long time already he, sitting apart, had been no more to us than a voice. There was not a word from anybody. The others might have been asleep, but I was awake. I listened, I listened on the watch for the sentence, for the word, that would give me the clew to the faint uneasiness inspired by this narrative that seemed to shape itself without human lips in the heavy night-air of the river.

". . . Yes—I let him run on," Marlow began again, "and think what he pleased about the powers that were behind me. I did! And there was nothing behind me. There was nothing but that wretched, old, mangled steamboat I was leaning against, while he talked fluently about 'the necessity for every man to get on.' 'And when one comes out here, you conceive, it is not to gaze at the moon.' Mr. Kurtz was a 'universal genius,' but even a genius would find it easier to work with 'adequate tools—intelligent men.' He did not make bricks—why, there was a physical impossibility in the way—as I was well aware; and if he did secretarial work for the manager, it was because 'no sensible man rejects wantonly the confidence of his superiors.' Did I see it? I saw it. What more did I want? What I really wanted was rivets, by heaven! Rivets. To get on with the work—to stop the hole. Rivets I wanted. There were cases of them down at the coast—cases—piled up—burst—split! You kicked a loose rivet at every second step in that station yard on the hillside. Rivets had rolled into the grove of death. You could fill your pockets with rivets for the trouble of stooping down—and there wasn't one rivet to be found where it was wanted. We had plates that would do, but nothing to fasten them with. And every week the messenger, a lone negro, letter-bag on shoulder and staff in hand, left our station for the coast. And several times a week a coast caravan came in with trade goods—ghastly glazed calico that made you shudder only to look at it; glass beads, value about a penny a quart, confounded spotted cotton handkerchiefs. And no rivets. Three carriers could have brought all that was wanted to set that steamboat afloat.

"He was becoming confidential now, but I fancy my unresponsive attitude must have exasperated him at last, for he judged it necessary to inform me he feared neither God nor devil, let alone any mere man. I said I could see that very well, but what I wanted was a certain quantity of rivets—and rivets were what really Mr. Kurtz wanted, if he had only known it. Now letters went to the coast every week. . . . 'My dear sir,' he cried, 'I write from dictation.' I demanded rivets. There was a way—for an intelligent man. He changed his manner; became very cold, and suddenly began to talk about a hippopotamus; wondered whether sleeping on board the steamer (I stuck to my salvage night and day) I wasn't disturbed. There was an old hippo that had the habit of getting out on the bank and roaming at night over the station grounds. The pilgrims used to turn out in a body and empty every rifle they could lay hands on at him. Some even had sat up o' nights for him. All this energy was wasted, though. 'That animal has a charmed life,' he said; 'but you can say this only of brutes in this country. No man—you apprehend me?—no man here bears a charmed life.' He stood there for a moment in the moonlight with his delicate hooked nose set a little askew, and his mica eyes glittering without a wink, then, with a curt Good-night, he strode off. I could see he was disturbed and considerably puzzled, which made me feel more hopeful than I had been for days. It was a great comfort to turn from that chap to my influential friend, the battered, twisted, ruined, tin-pot steamboat. I clambered on board. She rang under my feet like an empty Huntley & Palmer biscuit-tin kicked along a gutter; she was nothing so solid in make, and rather less pretty in shape, but I had expended enough hard work on her to make me love her. No influential friend would have served me better. She had given me a chance to come out a bit—to find out what I could do. No, I don't like work. I had rather laze about and think of all the fine things that can be done. I don't like work—no man does—but I like what is in the work—the chance to find yourself. Your own reality—for yourself, not for others—what no other man can ever know. They can only see the mere show, and never can tell what it really means.

"I was not surprised to see somebody sitting aft, on the deck, with his legs dangling over the mud. You see I rather chummed with the few mechanics there were in that station, whom the other pilgrims naturally despised—on account of their imperfect manners, I suppose. This was the foreman—a boiler-maker by trade—a good worker. He was a lank, bony, yellow-faced man, with big intense eyes. His aspect was worried, and his head was as bald as the palm of my hand; but his hair in falling seemed to have stuck to his chin, and had prospered in the new locality, for his beard hung down to his waist. He was a widower with six young children (he had left them in charge of a sister of his to come out there), and the passion of his life was pigeon-flying. He was an enthusiast and a connoisseur. He would rave about pigeons. After work hours he used sometimes to come over from his hut for a talk about his children and his pigeons; at work, when he had to crawl in the mud under the bottom of the steamboat, he would tie up that beard of his in a kind of white serviette he brought for the purpose. It had loops to go over his ears. In the evening he could be seen squatted on the bank rinsing that wrapper in the creek with great care, then spreading it solemnly on a bush to dry.

"I slapped him on the back and shouted, 'We shall have rivets!' He scrambled to his feet exclaiming, 'No! Rivets!' as though he couldn't believe his ears. Then in a low voice, 'You . . . eh?' I don't know why we behaved like lunatics. I put my finger to the side of my nose and nodded mysteriously. 'Good for you!' he cried, snapped his fingers above his head, lifting one foot. I tried a jig. We capered on the iron deck. A frightful clatter came out of that hulk, and the virgin forest on the other bank of the creek sent it back in a thundering roll upon the sleeping station. It must have made some of the pilgrims sit up in their hovels. A dark figure obscured the lighted doorway of the manager's hut, vanished, then, a second or so after, the doorway itself vanished, too. We stopped, and the silence driven away by the stamping of our feet flowed back again from the recesses of the land. The great wall of vegetation, an exuberant and entangled mass of trunks, branches, leaves, boughs, festoons, motionless in the moonlight, was like a rioting invasion of soundless life, a rolling wave of plants, piled up, crested, ready to topple over the creek, to sweep every little man of us out of his little existence. And it moved not. A deadened burst of mighty splashes and snorts reached us from afar, as though an ichthyosaurus had been taking a bath of glitter in the great river. 'After all,' said the boiler-maker in a reasonable tone, 'why shouldn't we get the rivets?' Why not, indeed! I did not know of any reason why we shouldn't. 'They'll come in three weeks,' I said, confidently.

"But they didn't. Instead of rivets there came an invasion, an inflic-tion, a visitation. It came in sections during the next three weeks, each section headed by a donkey carrying a white man in new clothes and tan shoes, bowing from that elevation right and left to the impressed pil-grims. A quarrelsome band of footsore sulky niggers trod on the heels of the donkey; a lot of tents, campstools, tin boxes, white cases, brown bales would be shot down in the courtyard, and the air of mystery would deepen a little over the muddle of the station. Five such installments came, with their absurd air of disorderly flight with the loot of innumer-able outfit shops and provision stores, that, one would think, they were lugging, after a raid, into the wilderness for equitable division. It was an inextricable mess of things decent in themselves but that human folly made look like the spoils of thieving.

"This devoted band called itself the Eldorado Exploring Expedition, and I believe they were sworn to secrecy. Their talk, however, was the talk of sordid buccaneers; it was reckless without hardihood, greedy without audacity, and cruel without courage; there was not an atom of foresight or of serious intention in the whole batch of them, and they did not seem aware these things are wanted for the work of the world. To tear treasure out of the bowels of the land was their desire, with no more moral purpose at the back of it than there is in burglars breaking into a safe. Who paid the expenses of the noble enterprise I don't know; but the uncle of our manager was leader of that lot.

"In exterior he resembled a butcher in a poor neighborhood, and his eyes had a look of sleepy cunning. He carried his fat paunch with osten-tation on his short legs, and during the time his gang infested the station spoke to no one but his nephew. You could see these two roaming about all day long with their heads close together in an everlasting confab.

"I had given up worrying myself about the rivets. One's capacity for that kind of folly is more limited than you would suppose. I said Hang! —and let things slide. I had plenty of time for meditation, and now and then I would give some thought to Kurtz. I wasn't very interested in him. No. Still, I was curious to see whether this man, who had come out equipped with moral ideas of some sort, would climb to the top after all and how he would set about his work when there."

II

"One evening as I was lying flat on the deck of my steamboat, I heard voices approaching—and there were the nephew and the uncle strolling along the bank. I laid my head on my arm again, and had nearly lost myself in a doze, when somebody said in my ear, as it were: 'I am as harmless as a little child, but I don't like to be dictated to. Am I the manager—or am I not? I was ordered to send him there. It's incredible.' . . . I became aware that the two were standing on the shore alongside the forepart of the steamboat, just below my head. I did not move; it did not occur to me to move: I was sleepy. 'It *is* unpleasant,' grunted the uncle. 'He has asked the Administration to be sent there,' said the other, 'with the idea of showing what he could do; and I was instructed accordingly. Look at the influence that man must have. Is it not frightful?' They both agreed it was frightful, then made several bizarre remarks: 'Make rain and fine weather—one man—the Council—by the nose'—bits of absurd sentences that got the better of my drowsiness, so that I had pretty near the whole of my wits about me when the uncle said, 'The climate may do away with this difficulty for you. Is he alone there?' 'Yes,' answered the manager; 'he sent his assistant down the river with a note to me in these terms: "Clear this poor devil out of the country, and don't bother sending more of that sort. I had rather be alone than have the kind of men you can dispose of with me." It was more than a year ago. Can you imagine such impudence!' 'Anything since then?' asked the other, hoarsely. 'Ivory,' jerked the nephew; 'lots of it—prime sort—lots—most annoying, from him.' 'And with that?' questioned the heavy rumble. 'Invoice,' was the reply fired out, so to speak. Then silence. They had been talking about Kurtz.

"I was broad awake by this time, but, lying perfectly at ease, remained still, having no inducement to change my position. 'How did that ivory come all this way?' growled the elder man, who seemed very vexed. The other explained that it had come with a fleet of canoes in charge of an English half-caste clerk Kurtz had with him; that Kurtz had apparently intended to return himself, the station being by that time bare of goods and stores, but after coming three hundred miles, had suddenly decided to go back, which he started to do alone in a small dugout with four paddlers, leaving the half-caste to continue down the river with the ivory. The two fellows there seemed astounded at anybody attempting such a thing. They were at a loss for an adequate motive. As to me, I seemed to see Kurtz for the first time. It was a distinct glimpse: the dugout, four paddling savages, and the lone white man turning his back suddenly on the headquarters, on relief, on thoughts of home—perhaps; setting his face towards the depths of the wilderness, towards his empty and desolate station. I did not know the motive. Perhaps he was just simply a fine fellow who stuck to his work for its own sake. His name, you understand, had not been pronounced once. He was 'that man.' The half-caste, who, as far as I could see, had conducted a difficult trip with great prudence and pluck, was invariably alluded to as 'that scoundrel.' The 'scoundrel' had reported that the 'man' had been very ill—had recovered imperfectly. . . . The two below me moved away then a few paces, and strolled back and forth at some little distance. I heard: 'Military post—doctor—two hundred miles— quite alone now—unavoidable delays—nine months—no news—strange rumors.' They approached again, just as the manager was saying, 'No one, as far as I know, unless a species of wandering trader—a pestilential fellow, snapping ivory from the natives.' Who was it they were talking about now? I gathered in snatches that this was some man supposed to be in Kurtz's district, and of whom the manager did not approve. 'We will not be free from unfair competition till one of these fellows is hanged for an example,' he said. 'Certainly,' grunted the other; 'get him hanged! Why not? Anything—anything can be done in this country. That's what I say; nobody here, you understand, *here*, can endanger your position. And why? You stand the climate—you outlast them all. The danger is in Europe; but there before I left I took care to—' They moved off and whispered, then their voices rose again. 'The extraordinary series of delays is not my fault. I did my best.' The fat man sighed. 'Very sad.' 'And the pestiferous absurdity of his talk,' continued the other; 'he bothered me enough when he was here. "Each station should be like a beacon on the road towards better things, a center for trade, of course, but also for humanizing, improving, instructing." Conceive you—that ass! And he wants to be manager! No, it's—' Here he got choked by excessive indignation, and I lifted my head the least bit. I was surprised to see how near they were—right under me. I could have spat upon their hats. They were looking on the ground, absorbed in thought. The manager was switching his leg with a slender twig: his sagacious relative lifted his head. 'You have been well since you came out this time?' he asked. The other gave a start. 'Who? I? Oh! Like a charm—like a charm. But the rest—oh, my goodness! All sick. They die so quick, too, that I haven't the time to send them out of the country—it's incredible!' 'H'm. Just so,' grunted the uncle. 'Ah! my boy, trust to this—I say, trust to this.' I saw him extend his short flipper of an arm for a gesture that took in the forest, the creek, the mud, the river,—seemed to beckon with a dishonoring flourish before the sunlit face of the land a treacherous appeal to the lurking death, to the hidden evil, to the profound darkness of its heart. It was so startling that I leaped to my feet and looked back at the edge of the forest, as though I had expected an answer of some sort to that black display of confidence. You know the foolish notions that come to one sometimes. The high stillness confronted these two figures with its ominous patience, waiting for the passing away of a fantastic invasion.

"They swore aloud together—out of sheer fright, I believe—then pretending not to know anything of my existence, turned back to the station. The sun was low; and leaning forward side by side, they seemed to be tugging painfully uphill their two ridiculous shadows of unequal

length, that trailed behind them slowly over the tall grass without
bending a single blade.

"In a few days the Eldorado Expedition went into the patient wilderness, that closed upon it as the sea closes over a diver. Long afterwards
the news came that all the donkeys were dead. I know nothing as to the
fate of the less valuable animals. They, no doubt, like the rest of us,
found what they deserved. I did not inquire. I was then rather excited
at the prospect of meeting Kurtz very soon. When I say very soon I
mean it comparatively. It was just two months from the day we left
the creek when we came to the bank below Kurtz's station.

"Going up that river was like traveling back to the earliest beginnings
of the world, when vegetation rioted on the earth and the big trees were
kings. An empty stream, a great silence, an impenetrable forest. The
air was warm, thick, heavy, sluggish. There was no joy in the brilliance
of sunshine. The long stretches of the waterway ran on, deserted, into
the gloom of overshadowed distances. On silvery sandbanks hippos and
alligators sunned themselves side by side. The broadening waters
flowed through a mob of wooded islands; you lost your way on that
river as you would in a desert, and butted all day long against shoals,
trying to find the channel, till you thought yourself bewitched and cut
off forever from everything you had known once—somewhere—far
away—in another existence perhaps. There were moments when one's
past came back to one, as it will sometimes when you have not a moment
to spare to yourself; but it came in the shape of an unrestful and noisy
dream, remembered with wonder amongst the overwhelming realities of
this strange world of plants, and water, and silence. And this stillness
of life did not in the least resemble a peace. It was the stillness of an
implacable force brooding over an inscrutable intention. It looked at
you with a vengeful aspect. I got used to it afterwards; I did not see it
any more; I had no time. I had to keep guessing at the channel; I had
to discern, mostly by inspiration, the signs of hidden banks; I watched
for sunken stones; I was learning to clap my teeth smartly before my
heart flew out, when I shaved by a fluke some infernal sly old snag
that would have ripped the life out of the tin-pot steamboat and
drowned all the pilgrims; I had to keep a look-out for the signs of dead
wood we could cut up in the night for next day's steaming. When you
have to attend to things of that sort, to the mere incidents of the surface,
the reality—the reality, I tell you—fades. The inner truth is hidden—
luckily, luckily. But I felt it all the same; I felt often its mysterious
stillness watching me at my monkey tricks, just as it watches you fellows
performing on your respective tight-ropes for—what is it? half-a-crown
a tumble—"

"Try to be civil, Marlow," growled a voice, and I knew there was at
least one listener awake besides myself.

"I beg your pardon. I forgot the heartache which makes up the rest of the price. And indeed what does the price matter, if the trick be well done? You do your tricks very well. And I didn't do badly either, since I managed not to sink that steamboat on my first trip. It's a wonder to me yet. Imagine a blindfolded man set to drive a van over a bad road. I sweated and shivered over that business considerably, I can tell you. After all, for a seaman, to scrape the bottom of the thing that's supposed to float all the time under his care is the unpardonable sin. No one may know of it, but you never forget the thump—eh? A blow on the very heart. You remember it, you dream of it, you wake up at night and think of it—years after—and go hot and cold all over. I don't pretend to say that steamboat floated all the time. More than once she had to wade for a bit, with twenty cannibals splashing around and pushing. We had enlisted some of these chaps on the way for a crew. Fine fellows—cannibals—in their place. They were men one could work with, and I am grateful to them. And, after all, they did not eat each other before my face: they had brought along a provision of hippo-meat which went rotten, and made the mystery of the wilderness stink in my nostrils. Phoo! I can sniff it now. I had the manager on board and three or four pilgrims with their staves—all complete. Sometimes we came upon a station close by the bank, clinging to the skirts of the unknown, and the white men rushing out of a tumble-down hovel, with great gestures of joy and surprise and welcome, seemed very strange—had the appearance of being held there captive by a spell. The word 'ivory' would ring in the air for a while—and on we went again into the silence, along empty reaches, round the still bends, between the high walls of our winding way, reverberating in hollow claps the ponderous beat of the stern-wheel. Trees, trees, millions of trees, massive, immense, running up high; and at their foot, hugging the bank against the stream, crept the little begrimed steamboat, like a sluggish beetle crawling on the floor of a lofty portico. It made you feel very small, very lost, and yet it was not altogether depressing, that feeling. After all, if you were small, the grimy beetle crawled on—which was just what you wanted it to do. Where the pilgrims imagined it crawled to I don't know. To some place where they expected to get something, I bet! For me it crawled towards Kurtz—exclusively; but when the steam-pipes started leaking we crawled very slowly. The reaches opened before us and closed behind, as if the forest had stepped leisurely across the water to bar the way for our return. We penetrated deeper and deeper into the heart of darkness. It was very quiet there. At night sometimes the roll of drums behind the curtain of trees would run up the river and remain sustained faintly, as if hovering in the air high over our heads, till the first break of day. Whether it meant war, peace, or prayer we could not tell. The dawns were heralded by the descent of a chill stillness; the wood-cutters slept, their fires burned low; the snapping of a twig would make you start. We were wanderers on a prehistoric earth, on an earth that wore the aspect of an unknown planet. We could have fancied ourselves the first of men taking possession of an accursed inheritance, to be subdued at the cost of profound anguish and of excessive toil. But suddenly, as we struggled round a bend, there would be a glimpse of rush walls, of peaked grass-roofs, a burst of yells, a whirl of black limbs, a mass of hands clapping, of feet stamping, of bodies swaying, of eyes rolling, under the droop of heavy and motionless foliage. The steamer toiled along slowly on the edge of a black and incomprehensible frenzy. The prehistoric man was cursing us, praying to us, welcoming us—who could tell? We were cut off from the comprehension of our surroundings; we glided past like phantoms, wondering and secretly appalled, as sane men would be before an enthusiastic outbreak in a madhouse. We could not understand because we were too far and could not remember, because we were traveling in the night of first ages, of those ages that are gone, leaving hardly a sign—and no memories.

"The earth seemed unearthly. We are accustomed to look upon the shackled form of a conquered monster, but there—there you could look at a thing monstrous and free. It was unearthly, and the men were—No, they were not inhuman. Well, you know, that was the worst of it—this suspicion of their not being inhuman. It would come slowly to one. They howled and leaped, and spun, and made horrid faces; but what thrilled you was just the thought of their humanity—like yours—the thought of your remote kinship with this wild and passionate uproar. Ugly. Yes, it was ugly enough; but if you were man enough you would admit to yourself that there was in you just the faintest trace of a response to the terrible frankness of that noise, a dim suspicion of there being a meaning in it which you—you so remote from the night of first ages—could comprehend. And why not? The mind of man is capable of anything—because everything is in it, all the past as well as all the future. What was there after all? Joy, fear, sorrow, devotion, valor, rage—who can tell?—but truth—truth stripped of its cloak of time. Let the fool gape and shudder—the man knows, and can look on without a wink. But he must at least be as much of a man as these on the shore. He must meet that truth with his own true stuff—with his own inborn strength. Principles won't do. Acquisitions, clothes, pretty rags—rags that would fly off at the first good shake. No; you want a deliberate belief. An appeal to me in this fiendish row—is there? Very well; I hear; I admit, but I have a voice, too, and for good or evil mine is the speech that cannot be silenced. Of course, a fool, what with sheer fright and fine sentiments, is always safe. Who's that grunting? You wonder I didn't go ashore for a howl and a dance? Well, no—I didn't. Fine sentiments, you say? Fine sentiments, be hanged! I had no time. I had to mess about with white-lead and strips of woolen blanket helping to put bandages on those leaky steam-pipes—I tell you. I had to watch the steering, and circumvent those snags, and get the tin-pot along by hook or by crook. There was surface-truth enough in these things to save a wiser man. And between whiles I had to look after the savage who was fireman. He was an improved specimen; he could fire up a vertical boiler. He was there below me, and, upon my word, to look at him was as edifying as seeing a dog in a parody of breeches and a feather hat, walking on his hind legs. A few months of training had done for that really fine chap. He squinted at the steam-gauge and at the water-gauge with an evident effort of intrepidity—and he had filed teeth, too, the poor devil, and the wool of his pate shaved into queer patterns, and three ornamental scars on each of his cheeks. He ought to have been clapping his hands and stamping his feet on the bank, instead of which he was hard at work, a thrall to strange witchcraft, full of improving knowledge. He was useful because he had been instructed; and what he knew was this—that should the water in that transparent thing disappear, the evil spirit inside the boiler would get angry through the greatness of his thirst, and take a terrible vengeance. So he sweated and fired up and watched the glass fearfully (with an impromptu charm, made of rags, tied to his arm, and a piece of polished bone, as big as a watch, stuck flatways through his lower lip), while the wooded banks slipped past us slowly, the short noise was left behind, the interminable miles of silence—and we crept on, towards Kurtz. But the snags were thick, the water was treacherous and shallow, the boiler seemed indeed to have a sulky devil in it, and thus neither that fireman nor I had any time to peer into our creepy thoughts.

"Some fifty miles below the Inner Station we came upon a hut of reeds, an inclined and melancholy pole, with the unrecognizable tatters of what had been a flag of some sort flying from it, and a neatly stacked woodpile. This was unexpected. We came to the bank, and on the stack of firewood found a flat piece of board with some faded pencil-writing on it. When deciphered it said: 'Wood for you. Hurry up. Approach cautiously.' There was a signature, but it was illegible—not Kurtz—a much longer word. 'Hurry up.' Where? Up the river? 'Approach cautiously.' We had not done so. But the warning could not have been meant for the place where it could be only found after approach. Something was wrong above. But what—and how much? That was the question. We commented adversely upon the imbecility of that telegraphic style. The bush around said nothing, and would not let us look very far, either. A torn curtain of red twill hung in the doorway of the hut, and flapped sadly in our faces. The dwelling was dismantled; but we could see a white man had lived there not very long ago. There remained a rude table—a plank on two posts; a heap of rubbish reposed in a dark corner, and by the door I picked up a book. It had lost its covers, and the pages had been thumbed into a state of extremely dirty softness; but the back had been lovingly stitched afresh with white cotton thread, which looked clean yet. It was an extraordinary find. Its title was, *An Inquiry into some Points of Seamanship*, by a man Towser, Towson—some such name—Master in his Majesty's Navy. The matter looked dreary reading enough, with illustrative diagrams and repulsive tables of figures, and the copy was sixty years old. I handled this amazing antiquity with the greatest possible tenderness, lest it should dissolve in my hands. Within, Towson or Towser was inquiring earnestly into the breaking strain of ships' chains and tackle, and other such matters. Not a very enthralling book; but at the first glance you could see there a singleness of intention, an honest concern for the right way of going to work, which made these humble pages, thought out so many years ago, luminous with another than a professional light. The simple old sailor, with his talk of chains and purchases, made me forget the jungle and the pilgrims in a delicious sensation of having come upon something unmistakably real. Such a book being there was wonderful enough; but still more astounding were the notes penciled in the margin, and plainly referring to the text. I couldn't believe my eyes! They were in cipher! Yes, it looked like cipher. Fancy a man lugging with him a book of that description into this nowhere and studying it—and making notes—in cipher at that! It was an extravagant mystery.

"I had been dimly aware for some time of a worrying noise, and when I lifted my eyes I saw the woodpile was gone, and the manager, aided by all the pilgrims, was shouting at me from the river-side. I slipped the book into my pocket. I assure you to leave off reading was like tearing myself away from the shelter of an old and solid friendship.

"I started the lame engine ahead. 'It must be this miserable trader—this intruder,' exclaimed the manager, looking back malevolently at the place we had left. 'He must be English,' I said. 'It will not save him from getting into trouble if he is not careful,' muttered the manager darkly. I observed with assumed innocence that no man was safe from trouble in this world.

"The current was more rapid now, the steamer seemed at her last gasp, the stern-wheel flopped languidly, and I caught myself listening on tiptoe for the next beat of the boat, for in sober truth I expected the wretched thing to give up every moment. It was like watching the last flickers of a life. But still we crawled. Sometimes I would pick out a tree a little way ahead to measure our progress towards Kurtz by, but I lost it invariably before we got abreast. To keep the eyes so long on one thing was too much for human patience. The manager displayed a beautiful resignation. I fretted and fumed and took to arguing with myself whether or no I would talk openly with Kurtz; but before I could come to any conclusion it occurred to me that my speech or my silence, indeed any action of mine, would be a mere futility. What did it matter who was manager? One gets sometimes such a flash of insight. The essentials of this affair lay deep under the surface, beyond my reach, and beyond my power of meddling.

"Towards the evening of the second day we judged ourselves about eight miles from Kurtz's station. I wanted to push on; but the manager looked grave, and told me the navigation up there was so dangerous that it would be advisable, the sun being very low already, to wait where we were till next morning. Morever, he pointed out that if the warning to approach cautiously were to be followed, we must approach in daylight—not at dusk, or in the dark. This was sensible enough. Eight miles meant nearly three hours' steaming for us, and I could also see suspicious ripples at the upper end of the reach. Nevertheless, I was annoyed beyond expression at the delay, and most unreasonably, too, since one night more could not matter much after so many months. As we had plenty of wood, and caution was the word, I brought up in the middle of the stream. The reach was narrow, straight, with high sides like a railway cutting. The dusk came gliding into it long before the sun had set. The current ran smooth and swift, but a dumb immobility sat on the banks. The living trees, lashed together by the creepers and every living bush of the undergrowth, might have been changed into stone, even to the slenderest twig, to the lightest leaf. It was not sleep— it seemed unnatural, like a state of trance. Not the faintest sound of any kind could be heard. You looked on amazed, and began to suspect yourself of being deaf—then the night came suddenly, and struck you blind as well. About three in the morning some large fish leaped, and the loud splash made me jump as though a gun had been fired. When the sun rose there was a white fog, very warm and clammy, and more blinding than the night. It did not shift or drive; it was just there, standing all round you like something solid. At eight or nine, perhaps, it lifted as a shutter lifts. We had a glimpse of the towering multitude of trees, of the immense matted jungle, with the blazing little ball of the sun hanging over it—all perfectly still—and then the white shutter came down again, smoothly, as if sliding in greased grooves. I ordered the chain, which we had begun to heave in, to be paid out again. Before it stopped running with a muffled rattle, a cry, a very loud cry, as of infinite desolation, soared slowly in the opaque air. It ceased. A complaining clamor, modulated in savage discords, filled our ears. The sheer unexpectedness of it made my hair stir under my cap. I don't know how it struck the others: to me it seemed as though the mist itself had screamed, so suddenly, and apparently from all sides at once, did this tumultuous and mournful uproar arise. It culminated in a hurried outbreak of almost intolerably excessive shrieking, which stopped short, leaving us stiffened in a variety of silly attitudes, and obstinately listening to the nearly as appalling and excessive silence. 'Good God! What is the meaning—' stammered at my elbow one of the pilgrims,—a little fat man, with sandy hair and red whiskers, who wore side-spring boots, and pink pajamas tucked into his socks. Two others remained openmouthed a whole minute, then dashed into the little cabin, to rush out incontinently and stand darting scared glances, with Winchesters at 'ready' in their hands. What we could see was just the steamer we were on, her outlines blurred as though she had been on the point of dissolving, and a misty strip of water, perhaps two feet broad, around her—and that was all. The rest of the world was nowhere, as far as our eyes and ears were concerned. Just nowhere. Gone, disappeared; swept off without leaving a whisper or a shadow behind.

"I went forward, and ordered the chain to be hauled in short, so as to be ready to trip the anchor and move the steamboat at once if necessary. 'Will they attack?' whispered an awed voice. 'We will be all butchered in this fog,' murmured another. The faces twitched with the strain, the hands trembled slightly, the eyes forgot to wink. It was very curious to see the contrast of expressions of the white men and of the black fellows of our crew, who were as much strangers to that part of the river as we, though their homes were only eight hundred miles away. The whites, of course greatly discomposed, had besides a curious look of being painfully shocked by such an outrageous row. The others had an alert, naturally interested expression; but their faces were essentially quiet, even those of the one or two who grinned as they hauled at the chain. Several exchanged short, grunting phrases, which seemed to settle the matter to their satisfaction. Their headman, a young, broad-chested black, severely draped in dark-blue fringed cloths, with fierce nostrils and his hair all done up artfully in oily ringlets, stood near me. 'Aha!' I said, just for good fellowship's sake. 'Catch 'im,' he snapped, with a bloodshot widening of his eyes and a flash of sharp teeth—'catch 'im. Give 'im to us.' 'To you, eh?' I asked; 'what would you do with them?' 'Eat 'im!' he said, curtly, and leaning his elbow on the rail, looked out into the fog in a dignified and profoundly pensive attitude. I would no doubt have been properly horrified, had it not occurred to me that he and his chaps must be very hungry: that they must have been growing increasingly hungry for at least this month past. They had been engaged for six months (I don't think a single one of them had any clear idea of time, as we at the end of countless ages have. They still belonged to the beginnings of time—had no inherited experience to teach them as it were), and of course, as long as there was a piece of paper written over in accordance with some farcical law or other made down the river, it didn't enter anybody's head to trouble how they would live. Certainly they had brought with them some rotten hippo-meat, which couldn't have lasted very long, anyway, even if the pilgrims hadn't, in the midst of a shocking hullabaloo, thrown a considerable quantity of it overboard. It looked like a high-handed proceeding; but it was really a case of legitimate self-defense. You can't breathe dead hippo waking, sleeping, and eating, and at the same time keep your precarious grip on existence. Besides that, they had given them every week three pieces of brass wire, each about nine inches long; and the theory was they were to buy their provisions with that currency in river-side villages. You can see how *that* worked. There were either no villages, or the people were hostile, or the director, who like the rest of us fed out of tins, with an occasional old he-goat thrown in, didn't want to stop the steamer for some more or less recondite reason. So, unless they swallowed the wire itself, or made loops of it to snare the fishes with, I don't see what good their extravagant salary could be to them. I must say it was paid with a regularity worthy of a large and honorable trading company. For the rest, the only thing to eat—though it didn't look eatable in the least—I saw in their possession was a few lumps of some stuff like half-cooked dough, of a dirty lavender color, they kept wrapped in leaves, and now and then swallowed a piece of, but so small that it seemed done more for the looks of the thing than for any serious purpose of sustenance. Why in the name of all the gnawing devils of hunger they didn't go for us—they were thirty to five—and have a good tuck-in for once, amazes me now when I think of it. They were big powerful men, with not much capacity to weigh the consequences, with courage, with strength, even yet, though their skins were no longer glossy and their muscles no longer hard. And I saw that something re-straining, one of those human secrets that baffle probability, had come into play there. I looked at them with a swift quickening of interest—not because it occurred to me I might be eaten by them before very long, though I own to you that just then I perceived—in a new light, as it were—how unwholesome the pilgrims looked, and I hoped, yes, I positively hoped, that my aspect was not so—what shall I say?—so—unappetizing: a touch of fantastic vanity which fitted well with the dream-sensation that pervaded all my days at that time. Perhaps I had a little fever, too. One can't live with one's finger everlastingly on one's pulse. I had often 'a little fever,' or a little touch of other things—the playful paw-strokes of the wilderness, the preliminary trifling before the more serious onslaught which came in due course. Yes; I looked at them as you would on any human being, with a curiosity of their im-pulses, motives, capacities, weaknesses, when brought to the test of an inexorable physical necessity. Restraint! What possible restraint? Was it superstition, disgust, patience, fear—or some kind of primitive honor? No fear can stand up to hunger, no patience can wear it out, disgust simply does not exist where hunger is; and as to superstition, beliefs, and what you may call principles, they are less than chaff in a breeze. Don't you know the devilry of lingering starvation, its exasper-ating torment, its black thoughts, its somber and brooding ferocity? Well, I do. It takes a man all his inborn strength to fight hunger prop-erly. It's really easier to face bereavement, dishonor, and the perdition of one's soul—than this kind of prolonged hunger. Sad, but true. And these chaps, too, had no earthly reason for any kind of scruple. Re-straint! I would just as soon have expected restraint from a hyena prowling amongst the corpses of a battlefield. But there was the fact facing me—the fact dazzling, to be seen, like the foam on the depths of the sea, like a ripple on an unfathomable enigma, a mystery greater— when I thought of it—than the curious, inexplicable note of desperate grief in this savage clamor that had swept by us on the river-bank, behind the blind whiteness of the fog.

"Two pilgrims were quarreling in hurried whispers as to which bank. 'Left.' 'No, no; how can you? Right, right, of course.' 'It is very serious,' said the manager's voice behind me; 'I would be desolated if anything should happen to Mr. Kurtz before we came up.' I looked at him, and had not the slightest doubt he was sincere. He was just the kind of man who would wish to preserve appearances. That was his restraint. But when he muttered something about going on at once, I did not even take the trouble to answer him. I knew, and he knew, that it was impossible. Were we to let go our hold of the bottom, we would be absolutely in the air—in space. We wouldn't be able to tell where we were going to—whether up or down stream, or across—till we fetched against one bank or the other,—and then we wouldn't know at first which it was. Of course I made no move. I had no mind for a smash-up. You couldn't imagine a more deadly place for a shipwreck. Whether drowned at once or not, we were sure to perish speedily in one way or another. 'I authorize you to take all the risks,' he said, after a short silence. 'I refuse to take any,' I said, shortly; which was just the answer he expected, though its tone might have surprised him. 'Well, I must defer to your judgment. You are captain,' he said, with marked civility. I turned my shoulder to him in sign of my appreciation, and looked into the fog. How long would it last? It was the most hopeless look-out. The approach to this Kurtz grubbing for ivory in the wretched bush was beset by as many dangers as though he had been an enchanted princess sleeping in a fabulous castle. 'Will they attack, do you think?' asked the manager, in a confidential tone.

"I did not think they would attack, for several obvious reasons. The thick fog was one. If they left the bank in their canoes they would get lost in it, as we would be if we attempted to move. Still, I had also judged the jungle of both banks quite impenetrable—and yet eyes were in it, eyes that had seen us. The river-side bushes were certainly very thick; but the undergrowth behind was evidently penetrable. However, during the short lift I had seen no canoes anywhere in the reach—cer- tainly not abreast of the steamer. But what made the idea of attack inconceivable to me was the nature of the noise—of the cries we had heard. They had not the fierce character boding immediate hostile in- tention. Unexpected, wild, and violent as they had been, they had given me an irresistible impression of sorrow. The glimpse of the steamboat had for some reason filled those savages with unrestrained grief. The danger, if any, I expounded, was from our proximity to a great human passion let loose. Even extreme grief may ultimately vent itself in violence—but more generally takes the form of apathy. . . .

"You should have seen the pilgrims stare! They had no heart to grin, or even to revile me: but I believe they thought me gone mad—with fright, maybe. I delivered a regular lecture. My dear boys, it was no good bothering. Keep a look-out? Well, you may guess I watched the fog for the signs of lifting as a cat watches a mouse; but for anything else our eyes were of no more use to us than if we had been buried miles deep in a heap of cotton-wool. It felt like it, too—choking, warm, stifling. Besides, all I said, though it sounded extravagant, was absolutely true to fact. What we afterwards alluded to as an attack was really an attempt at repulse. The action was very far from being aggressive— it was not even defensive, in the usual sense: it was undertaken under the stress of desperation, and in its essence was purely protective.

"It developed itself, I should say, two hours after the fog lifted, and its commencement was at a spot, roughly speaking, about a mile and a half below Kurtz's station. We had just floundered and flopped round a bend, when I saw an islet, a mere grassy hummock of bright green, in the middle of the stream. It was the only thing of the kind; but as we opened the reach more, I perceived it was the head of a long sandbank, or rather of a chain of shallow patches stretching down the middle of the river. They were discolored, just awash, and the whole lot was seen just under the water, exactly as a man's backbone is seen running down the middle of his back under the skin. Now, as far as I did see, I could go to the right or to the left of this. I didn't know either channel, of course. The banks looked pretty well alike, the depth appeared the same; but as I had been informed the station was on the west side, I naturally headed for the western passage.

"No sooner had we fairly entered it than I became aware it was much narrower than I had supposed. To the left of us there was the long uninterrupted shoal, and to the right a high, steep bank heavily overgrown with bushes. Above the bush the trees stood in serried ranks. The twigs overhung the current thickly, and from distance to distance a large limb of some tree projected rigidly over the stream. It was then well on in the afternoon, the face of the forest was gloomy, and a broad strip of shadow had already fallen on the water. In this shadow we steamed up—very slowly, as you may imagine. I sheered her well inshore—the water being deepest near the bank, as the sounding-pole informed me.

"One of my hungry and forbearing friends was sounding in the bows just below me. This steamboat was exactly like a decked scow. On the deck, there were two little teakwood houses, with doors and windows. The boiler was in the fore-end, and the machinery right astern. Over the whole there was a light roof, supported on stanchions. The funnel projected through that roof, and in front of the funnel a small cabin built of light planks served for a pilot-house. It contained a couch, two camp-stools, a loaded Martini-Henry leaning in one corner, a tiny table, and the steering-wheel. It had a wide door in front and a broad shutter at each side. All these were always thrown open, of course. I spent my days perched up there on the extreme fore-end of that roof, before the door. At night I slept, or tried to, on the couch. An athletic black belonging to some coast tribe, and educated by my poor predecessor, was the helmsman. He sported a pair of brass earrings, wore a blue cloth wrapper from the waist to the ankles, and thought all the world of himself. He was the most unstable kind of fool I had ever seen. He steered with no end of a swagger while you were by; but if he lost sight of you, he became instantly the prey of an abject funk, and would let that cripple of a steamboat get the upper hand of him in a minute.

"I was looking down at the sounding-pole, and feeling much annoyed to see at each try a little more of it stick out of that river, when I saw my poleman give up the business suddenly, and stretch himself flat on the deck, without even taking the trouble to haul his pole in. He kept hold on it though, and it trailed in the water. At the same time the fireman, whom I could also see below me, sat down abruptly before his furnace and ducked his head. I was amazed. Then I had to look at the river mighty quick, because there was a snag in the fairway. Sticks, little sticks, were flying about—thick: they were whizzing before my nose, dropping below me, striking behind me against my pilot-house. All this time the river, the shore, the woods, were very quiet— perfectly quiet. I could only hear the heavy splashing thump of the stern-wheel and the patter of these things. We cleared the snag clumsily. Arrows, by Jove! We were being shot at! I stepped in quickly to close the shutter on the land-side. That fool-helmsman, his hands on the spokes, was lifting his knees high, stamping his feet, champing his mouth, like a reined-in horse. Confound him! And we were staggering within ten feet of the bank. I had to lean right out to swing the heavy shutter, and I saw a face amongst the leaves on the level with my own, looking at me very fierce and steady; and then suddenly, as though a veil had been removed from my eyes, I made out, deep in the tangled gloom, naked breasts, arms, legs, glaring eyes,—the bush was swarming with human limbs in movement, glistening, of bronze color. The twigs shook, swayed, and rustled, the arrows flew out of them, and then the shutter came to. 'Steer her straight,' I said to the helmsman. He held his head rigid, face forward; but his eyed rolled, he kept on lifting and setting down his feet gently, his mouth foamed a little. 'Keep quiet!' I said in a fury. I might just as well have ordered a tree not to sway in the wind. I darted out. Below me there was a great scuffle of feet on the iron deck; confused exclamations; a voice screamed, 'Can you turn back?' I caught sight of a V-shaped ripple on the water ahead. What? another snag! A fusillade burst out under my feet. The pilgrims had opened with their Winchesters, and were simply squirting lead into that bush. A deuce of a lot of smoke came up and drove slowly forward. I swore at it. Now I couldn't see the ripple or the snag either. I stood in the doorway, peering, and the arrows came in swarms. They might have been poisoned, but they looked as though they wouldn't kill a cat. The bush began to howl. Our woodcutters raised a warlike whoop; the report of a rifle just at my back deafened me. I glanced over my shoulder, and the pilot-house was yet full of noise and smoke when I made a dash at the wheel. The fool-nigger had dropped everything, to throw the shutter open and let off that Martini-Henry. He stood before the wide opening, glaring, and I yelled at him to come back, while I straightened the sudden twist out of that steamboat. There was no room to turn even if I had wanted to, the snag was somewhere very near ahead in that confounded smoke, there was no time to lose, so I just crowded her into the bank—right into the bank, where I knew the water was deep.

"We tore slowly along the overhanging bushes in a whirl of broken twigs and flying leaves. The fusillade below stopped short, as I had foreseen it would when the squirts got empty. I threw my head back to a glinting whizz that traversed the pilot-house, in at one shutter-hole and out at the other. Looking past that mad helmsman, who was shaking the empty rifle and yelling at the shore, I saw vague forms of men running bent double, leaping, gliding, distinct, incomplete, evanescent. Something big appeared in the air before the shutter, the rifle went overboard, and the man stepped back swiftly, looked at me over his shoulder in an extraordinary, profound, familiar manner, and fell upon my feet. The side of his head hit the wheel twice, and the end of what appeared a long cane clattered round and knocked over a little campstool. It looked as though after wrenching that thing from somebody ashore he had lost his balance in the effort. The thin smoke had blown away, we were clear of the snag, and looking ahead I could see that in another hundred yards or so I would be free to sheer off, away from the bank; but my feet felt so very warm and wet that I had to look down. The man had rolled on his back and stared straight up at me; both his hands clutched that cane. It was the shaft of a spear that, either thrown or lunged through the opening, had caught him in the side just below the ribs; the blade had gone in out of sight, after making a frightful gash; my shoes were full; a pool of blood lay very still, gleaming dark-red under the wheel; his eyes shone with an amazing luster. The fusillade burst out again. He looked at me anxiously, gripping the spear like something precious, with an air of being afraid I would try to take it away from him. I had to make an effort to free my eyes from his gaze and attend to steering. With one hand I felt above my head for the line of the steam whistle, and jerked out screech after screech hurriedly. The tumult of angry and warlike yells was checked instantly, and then from the depths of the woods went out such a tremulous and prolonged wail of mournful fear and utter despair as may be imagined to follow the flight of the last hope from the earth. There was a great commotion in the bush; the shower of arrows stopped, a few dropping shots rang out sharply—then silence, in which the languid beat of the stern-wheel came plainly to my ears. I put the helm hard a-starboard at the moment when the pilgrim in pink pajamas, very hot and agitated, appeared in the doorway. 'The manager sends me—,' he began in an official tone, and stopped short. 'Good God.' he said, glaring at the wounded man.

"We two whites stood over him, and his lustrous and inquiring glance enveloped us both. I declare it looked as though he would presently put to us some question in an understandable language; but he died without uttering a sound, without moving a limb, without twitching a muscle. Only in the very last moment, as though in response to some sign we could not see, to some whisper we could not hear, he frowned heavily, and that frown gave to his black death-mask an inconceivably somber, brooding, and menacing expression. The luster of inquiring glance faded swiftly into vacant glassiness. 'Can you steer?' I asked the agent eagerly. He looked very dubious; but I made a grab at his arm. and he understood at once I meant him to steer whether or no. To tell you the truth, I was morbidly anxious to change my shoes and socks. 'He is dead,' murmured the fellow, immensely impressed. 'No doubt about it,' said I, tugging like mad at the shoe-laces. 'And by the way, I suppose Mr. Kurtz is dead as well by this time.'

"For the moment that was the dominant thought. There was a sense of extreme disappointment, as though I had found out I had been striving after something altogether without a substance. I couldn't have been more disgusted if I had traveled all this way for the sole purpose of talking with Mr. Kurtz. Talking with . . . I flung one shoe overboard, and became aware that that was exactly what I had been looking forward to—a talk with Kurtz. I made the strange discovery that I had never imagined him as doing, you know, but as discoursing. I didn't say to myself, 'Now I will never see him,' or 'Now I will never shake him by the hand,' but, 'Now I will never hear him.' The man presented himself as a voice. Not of course that I did not connect him with some sort of action. Hadn't I been told in all the tones of jealousy and admiration that he had collected, bartered, swindled, or stolen more ivory than all the other agents together? That was not the point. The point was in his being a gifted creature, and that of all his gifts the one that stood out preëminently, that carried with it a sense of real presence, was his ability to talk, his words—the gift of expression, the bewildering, the illuminating, the most exalted and the most contemptible, the pulsating stream of light, or the deceitful flow from the heart of an impenetrable darkness.

"The other shoe went flying unto the devil-god of that river. I thought,

By Jove! it's all over. We are too late; he has vanished—the gift has vanished, by means of some spear, arrow, or club. I will never hear that chap speak after all,—and my sorrow had a startling extravagance of emotion, even such as I had noticed in the howling sorrow of these savages in the bush. I couldn't have felt more lonely desolation somehow, had I been robbed of a belief or had missed my destiny in life. . . . Why do you sigh in this beastly way, somebody? Absurd? Well, absurd. Good Lord! mustn't a man ever—Here, give me some tobacco." . . .

There was a pause of profound stillness, then a match flared, and Marlow's lean face appeared, worn, hollow, with downward folds and dropped eyelids, with an aspect of concentrated attention; and as he took vigorous draws at his pipe, it seemed to retreat and advance out of the night in the regular flicker of the tiny flame. The match went out.

"Absurd!" he cried. "This is the worst of trying to tell. . . . Here you all are, each moored with two good addresses, like a hulk with two anchors, a butcher round one corner, a policeman round another, excellent appetites, and temperature normal—you hear—normal from year's end to year's end. And you say, Absurd! Absurd be—exploded! Absurd! My dear boys, what can you expect from a man who out of sheer nervousness had just flung overboard a pair of new shoes! Now I think of it, it is amazing I did not shed tears. I am, upon the whole, proud of my fortitude. I was cut to the quick at the idea of having lost the inestimable privilege of listening to the gifted Kurtz. Of course I was wrong. The privilege was waiting for me. Oh, yes, I heard more than enough. And I was right, too. A voice. He was very little more than a voice. And I heard—him—it—this voice—other voices—all of them were so little more than voices—and the memory of that time itself lingers around me, impalpable, like a dying vibration of one immense jabber, silly, atrocious, sordid, savage, or simply mean, without any kind of sense. Voices, voices—even the girl herself—now—"

He was silent for a long time.

"I laid the ghost of his gifts at last with a lie," he began, suddenly. "Girl! What? Did I mention a girl? Oh, she is out of it—completely. They—the women I mean—are out of it—should be out of it. We must help them to stay in that beautiful world of their own, lest ours gets worse. Oh, she had to be out of it. You should have heard the disinterred body of Mr. Kurtz saying, 'My Intended.' You would have perceived directly then how completely she was out of it. And the lofty frontal bone of Mr. Kurtz! They say the hair goes on growing sometimes, but this—ah—specimen, was impressively bald. The wilderness had patted him on the head, and, behold, it was like a ball—an ivory ball; it had caressed him, and—lo!—he had withered; it had taken him, loved him, embraced him, got into his veins, consumed his flesh, and sealed his soul to its own by the inconceivable ceremonies of some devilish

initiation. He was its spoiled and pampered favorite. Ivory? I should
think so. Heaps of it, stacks of it. The old mud shanty was bursting
with it. You would think there was not a single tusk left either above or
below the ground in the whole country. 'Mostly fossil,' the manager
had remarked, disparagingly. It was no more fossil than I am; but they
call it fossil when it is dug up. It appears that these niggers do bury the
tusks sometimes—but evidently they couldn't bury this parcel deep
enough to save the gifted Mr. Kurtz from his fate. We filled the steamboat with it, and had to pile a lot on the deck. Thus he could see and
enjoy as long as he could see, because the appreciation of this favor had
remained with him to the last. You should have heard him say, 'My
ivory.' Oh, yes, I heard him, 'My Intended, my ivory, my station, my
river, my—' everything belonged to him. It made me hold my breath in
expectation of hearing the wilderness burst into a prodigious peal of
laughter that would shake the fixed stars in their places. Everything
belonged to him—but that was a trifle. The thing was to know what he
belonged to, how many powers of darkness claimed him for their own.
That was the reflection that made you creepy all over. It was impossible
—it was not good for one either—trying to imagine. He had taken a
high seat amongst the devils of the land—I mean literally. You can't
understand. How could you?—with solid pavement under your feet,
surrounded by kind neighbors ready to cheer you or to fall on you, stepping delicately between the butcher and the policeman, in the holy
terror of scandal and gallows and lunatic asylums—how can you imagine
what particular region of the first ages a man's untrammeled feet may
take him into by the way of solitude—utter solitude without a policeman—by the way of silence—utter silence, where no warning voice of
a kind neighbor can be heard whispering of public opinion? These
little things make all the great difference. When they are gone you must
fall back upon your own innate strength, upon your own capacity for
faithfulness. Of course you may be too much of a fool to go wrong—too
dull even to know you are being assaulted by the powers of darkness. I
take it, no fool ever made a bargain for his soul with the devil: the fool
is too much of a fool, or the devil too much of a devil—I don't know
which. Or you may be such a thunderingly exalted creature as to be
altogether deaf and blind to anything but heavenly sights and sounds.
Then the earth for you is only a standing place—and whether to be like
this is your loss or your gain I won't pretend to say. But most of us are
neither one nor the other. The earth for us is a place to live in, where we
must put up with sights, with sounds, with smells, too, by Jove!—
breathe dead hippo, so to speak, and not be contaminated. And there,
don't you see? your strength comes in, the faith in your ability for the
digging of unostentatious holes to bury the stuff in—your power of
devotion, not to yourself, but to an obscure, back-breaking business.
And that's difficult enough. Mind, I am not trying to excuse or even

explain—I am trying to account to myself for—for—Mr. Kurtz—for the shade of Mr. Kurtz. This initiated wraith from the back of Nowhere honored me with its amazing confidence before it vanished altogether. This was because it could speak English to me. The original Kurtz had been educated partly in England, and—as he was good enough to say himself—his sympathies were in the right place. His mother was half English, his father was half French. All Europe contributed to the making of Kurtz; and by and by I learned that, most appropriately, the International Society for the Suppression of Savage Customs had intrusted him with the making of a report, for its future guidance. And he had written it, too. I've seen it. I've read it. It was eloquent, vibrating with eloquence, but too high-strung, I think. Seventeen pages of close writing he had found time for! But this must have been before his—let us say—nerves, went wrong, and caused him to preside at certain midnight dances ending with unspeakable rites, which—as far as I reluctantly gathered from what I heard at various times—were offered up to him—do you understand?—to Mr. Kurtz himself. But it was a beautiful piece of writing. The opening paragraph, however, in the light of later information, strikes me now as ominous. He began with the argument that we whites, from the point of development we had arrived at, 'must necessarily appear to them [savages] in the nature of supernatural beings—we approach them with the might as of a deity,' and so on, and so on. 'By the simple exercise of our will we can exert a power for good practically unbounded,' etc., etc. From that point he soared and took me with him. The peroration was magnificent, though difficult to remember, you know. It gave me the notion of an exotic Immensity ruled by an august Benevolence. It made me tingle with enthusiasm. This was the unbounded power of eloquence—of words— of burning noble words. There were no practical hints to interrupt the magic current of phrases, unless a kind of note at the foot of the last page, scrawled evidently much later, in an unsteady hand, may be re- garded as the exposition of a method. It was very simple, and at the end of that moving appeal to every altruistic sentiment it blazed at you, luminous and terrifying, like a flash of lightning in a serene sky: 'Exterminate all the brutes!' The curious part was that he had ap- parently forgotten all about that valuable postscriptum, because, later on, when he in a sense came to himself, he repeatedly entreated me to take good care of 'my pamphlet' (he called it), as it was sure to have in the future a good influence upon his career. I had full information about all these things, and, besides, as it turned out, I was to have the care of his memory. I've done enough for it to give me the indisputable right to lay it, if I choose, for an everlasting rest in the dust-bin of prog- ress, amongst all the sweepings and, figuratively speaking, all the dead cats of civilization. But then, you see, I can't choose. He won't be forgotten. Whatever he was, he was not common. He had the power to charm or frighten rudimentary souls into an aggravated witch-dance in his honor; he could also fill the small souls of the pilgrims with bitter misgivings: he had one devoted friend at least, and he had conquered one soul in the world that was neither rudimentary nor tainted with self-seeking. No; I can't forget him, though I am not prepared to affirm the fellow was exactly worth the life we lost in getting to him. I missed my late helmsman awfully,—I missed him even while his body was still lying in the pilot-house. Perhaps you will think it passing strange this regret for a savage who was no more account than a grain of sand in a black Sahara. Well, don't you see, he had done something, he had steered; for months I had him at my back—a help—an instrument. It was a kind of partnership. He steered for me—I had to look after him, I worried about his deficiencies, and thus a subtle bond had been created, of which I only became aware when it was suddenly broken. And the intimate profundity of that look he gave me when he received his hurt remains to this day in my memory—like a claim of distant kinship affirmed in a supreme moment.

"Poor fool! If he had only left that shutter alone. He had no restraint, no restraint—just like Kurtz—a tree swayed by the wind. As soon as I had put on a dry pair of slippers, I dragged him out, after first jerking the spear out of his side, which operation I confess I performed with my eyes shut tight. His heels leaped together over the little door-step; his shoulders were pressed to my breast; I hugged him from behind desperately. Oh! he was heavy, heavy; heavier than any man on earth, I should imagine. Then without more ado I tipped him overboard. The current snatched him as though he had been a wisp of grass, and I saw the body roll over twice before I lost sight of it forever. All the pilgrims and the manager were then congregated on the awning-deck about the pilot-house, chattering at each other like a flock of excited magpies, and there was a scandalized murmur at my heartless promptitude. What they wanted to keep that body hanging about for I can't guess. Embalm it, maybe. But I had also heard another, and a very ominous, murmur on the deck below. My friends the wood-cutters were likewise scandalized, and with a better show of reason—though I admit that the reason itself was quite inadmissible. Oh, quite! I had made up my mind that if my late helmsman was to be eaten, the fishes alone should have him. He had been a very second-rate helmsman while alive, but now he was dead he might have become a first-class temptation, and possibly cause some startling trouble. Besides, I was anxious to take the wheel, the man in pink pajamas showing himself a hopeless duffer at the business.

"This I did directly the simple funeral was over. We were going half-speed, keeping right in the middle of the stream, and I listened to the talk about me. They had given up Kurtz, they had given up the station; Kurtz was dead, and the station had been burnt—and so on—

and so on. The red-haired pilgrim was beside himself with the thought that at least this poor Kurtz had been properly avenged. 'Say! We must have made a glorious slaughter of them in the bush. Eh? What do you think? Say?' He positively danced, the bloodthirsty little gingery beggar. And he had nearly fainted when he saw the wounded man! I could not help saying, 'You made a glorious lot of smoke, any-how.' I had seen, from the way the tops of the bushes rustled and flew, that almost all the shots had gone too high. You can't hit anything unless you take aim and fire from the shoulder; but these chaps fired from the hip with their eyes shut. The retreat, I maintained—and I was right—was caused by the screeching of the steam-whistle. Upon this they forgot Kurtz, and began to howl at me with indignant pro-tests.

"The manager stood by the wheel murmuring confidentially about the necessity of getting well away down the river before dark at all events, when I saw in the distance a clearing on the river-side and the outlines of some sort of building. 'What's this?' I asked. He clapped his hands in wonder. 'The station!' he cried. I edged in at once, still going half-speed.

"Through my glasses I saw the slope of a hill interspersed with rare trees and perfectly free from undergrowth. A long decaying building on the summit was half buried in the high grass; the large holes in the peaked roof gaped black from afar; the jungle and the woods made a background. There was no enclosure or fence of any kind; but there had been one apparently, for near the house half-a-dozen slim posts remained in a row, roughly trimmed, and with their upper ends orna-mented with round carved balls. The rails, or whatever there had been between, had disappeared. Of course the forest surrounded all that. The river-bank was clear, and on the water-side I saw a white man under a hat like a cart-wheel beckoning persistently with his whole arm. Examining the edge of the forest above and below, I was almost certain I could see movements—human forms gliding here and there. I steamed past prudently, then stopped the engines and let her drift down. The man on the shore began to shout, urging us to land. 'We have been attacked,' screamed the manager. 'I know—I know. It's all right,' yelled back the other, as cheerful as you please. 'Come along. It's all right. I am glad.'

"His aspect reminded me of something I had seen—something funny I had seen somewhere. As I maneuvered to get alongside, I was asking myself, 'What does this fellow look like?' Suddenly I got it. He looked like a harlequin. His clothes had been made of some stuff that was brown holland probably, but it was covered with patches all over, with bright patches, blue, red, and yellow—patches on the back, patches on the front, patches on elbows, on knees; colored binding around his jacket, scarlet edging at the bottom of his trousers; and the sunshine made him

look extremely gay and wonderfully neat withal, because you could see
how beautifully all this patching had been done. A beardless, boyish
face, very fair, no features to speak of, nose peeling, little blue eyes,
smiles and frowns chasing each other over that open countenance like
sunshine and shadow on a wind-swept plain. 'Look out, captain!' he
cried; 'there's a snag lodged in here last night.' What! Another snag?
I confess I swore shamefully, I had nearly holed my cripple, to finish
off that charming trip. The harlequin on the bank turned his little pug-
nose up to me. 'You English?' he asked, all smiles. 'Are you?' I
shouted from the wheel. The smiles vanished, and he shook his head
as if sorry for my disappointment. Then he brightened up. 'Never
mind!' he cried, encouragingly. 'Are we in time?' I asked. 'He is up
there,' he replied, with a toss of the head up the hill, and becoming
gloomy all of a sudden. His face was like the autumn sky, overcast one
moment and bright the next.

"When the manager, escorted by the pilgrims, all of them armed to
the teeth, had gone to the house this chap came on board. 'I say, I
don't like this. These natives are in the bush,' I said. He assured me
earnestly it was all right. 'They are simple people,' he added; 'well, I
am glad you came. It took me all my time to keep them off.' 'But you
said it was all right,' I cried. 'Oh, they meant no harm,' he said; and as
I stared he corrected himself, 'Not exactly.' Then vivaciously, 'My
faith, your pilot-house wants a clean-up!' In the next breath he advised
me to keep enough steam on the boiler to blow the whistle in case of
any trouble. 'One good screech will do more for you than all your rifles.
They are simple people,' he repeated. He rattled away at such a rate he
quite overwhelmed me. He seemed to be trying to make up for lots of
silence, and actually hinted, laughing, that such was the case. 'Don't
you talk with Mr. Kurtz?' I said. 'You don't talk with that man—you
listen to him,' he exclaimed with severe exaltation. 'But now—' He
waved his arm, and in the twinkling of an eye was in the uttermost
depths of despondency. In a moment he came up again with a jump,
possessed himself of both my hands, shook them continuously, while
he gabbled: 'Brother sailor . . . honor . . . pleasure . . . delight . . . introduce myself . . . Russian . . . son of an arch-priest . . . Government
of Tambov . . . What? Tobacco! English tobacco; the excellent English tobacco! Now, that's brotherly. Smoke? Where's a sailor that
does not smoke?'

"The pipe soothed him, and gradually I made out he had run away
from school, had gone to sea in a Russian ship; ran away again; served
some time in English ships; was now reconciled with the arch-priest.
He made a point of that. 'But when one is young one must see things,
gather experience, ideas; enlarge the mind.' 'Here!' I interrupted.
'You can never tell! Here I met Mr. Kurtz,' he said, youthfully solemn
and reproachful. I held my tongue after that. It appears he had per-

suaded a Dutch trading-house on the coast to fit him out with stores and goods, and had started for the interior with a light heart, and no more idea of what would happen to him than a baby. He had been wandering about that river for nearly two years alone, cut off from everybody and everything. 'I am not so young as I look. I am twenty-five,' he said. 'At first old Van Shuyten would tell me to go to the devil,' he narrated with keen enjoyment; 'but I stuck to him, and talked and talked, till at last he got afraid I would talk the hind-leg off his favorite dog, so he gave me some cheap things and a few guns, and told me he hoped he would never see my face again. Good old Dutchman, Van Shuyten. I've sent him one small lot of ivory a year ago, so that he can't call me a little thief when I get back. I hope he got it. And for the rest I don't care. I had some wood stacked for you. That was my old house. Did you see?'

"I gave him Towson's book. He made as though he would kiss me, but restrained himself. 'The only book I had left, and I thought I had lost it,' he said, looking at it ecstatically. 'So many accidents happen to a man going about alone, you know. Canoes get upset sometimes— and sometimes you've got to clear out so quick when the people get angry.' He thumbed the pages. 'You made notes in Russian?' I asked. He nodded. 'I thought they were written in cipher,' I said. He laughed, then became serious. 'I had lots of trouble to keep these people off,' he said. 'Did they want to kill you?' I asked. 'Oh, no!' he cried, and checked himself. 'Why did they attack us?' I pursued. He hesitated, then said shamefacedly, 'They don't want him to go.' 'Don't they?' I said, curiously. He nodded a nod full of mystery and wisdom. 'I tell you,' he cried, 'this man has enlarged my mind.' He opened his arms wide, staring at me with his little blue eyes that were perfectly round."

III

"I looked at him, lost in astonishment. There he was before me, in motley, as though he had absconded from a troupe of mimes, enthusiastic, fabulous. His very existence was improbable, inexplicable, and altogether bewildering. He was an insoluble problem. It was inconceivable how he had existed, how he had succeeded in getting so far, how he had managed to remain—why he did not instantly disappear. 'I went a little farther,' he said, 'then still a little farther—till I had gone so far that I don't know how I'll ever get back. Never mind. Plenty time. I can manage. You take Kurtz away quick—quick—I tell you.' The glamor of youth enveloped his particolored rags, his destitution, his loneliness, the essential desolation of his futile wanderings. For months—for years—his life hadn't been worth a day's purchase; and there he was gallantly, thoughtlessly alive, to all appearance indestructible solely by the virtue of his few years and of his unreflecting audacity.

I was seduced into something like admiration—like envy. Glamor urged him on, glamor kept him unscathed. He surely wanted nothing from the wilderness but space to breathe in and to push on through. His need was to exist, and to move onwards at the greatest possible risk, and with a maximum of privation. If the absolutely pure, uncalculating, unpractical spirit of adventure had ever ruled a human being, it ruled this be-patched youth. I almost envied him the possession of this modest and clear flame. It seemed to have consumed all thought of self so completely, that, even while he was talking to you, you forgot that it was he —the man before your eyes—who had gone through these things. I did not envy him his devotion to Kurtz, though. He had not meditated over it. It came to him, and he accepted it with a sort of eager fatalism. I must say that to me it appeared about the most dangerous thing in every way he had come upon so far.

"They had come together unavoidably, like two ships becalmed near each other, and lay rubbing sides at last. I suppose Kurtz wanted an audience, because on a certain occasion, when encamped in the forest, they had talked all night, or more probably Kurtz had talked. 'We talked of everything,' he said, quite transported at the recollection. 'I forgot there was such a thing as sleep. The night did not seem to last an hour. Everything! Everything! . . . Of love too.' 'Ah, he talked to you of love!' I said, much amused. 'It isn't what you think,' he cried, almost passionately. 'It was in general. He made me see things— things.'

"He threw his arms up. We were on deck at the time, and the headman of my wood-cutters, lounging near by, turned upon him his heavy and glittering eyes. I looked around, and I don't know why, but I assure you that never, never before, did this land, this river, this jungle, the very arch of this blazing sky, appear to me so hopeless and so dark, so impenetrable to human thought, so pitiless to human weakness. 'And, ever since, you have been with him, of course?' I said.

"On the contrary. It appears their intercourse had been very much broken by various causes. He had, as he informed me proudly, managed to nurse Kurtz through two illnesses (he alluded to it as you would to some risky feat), but as a rule Kurtz wandered alone, far in the depths of the forest. 'Very often coming to this station, I had to wait days and days before he would turn up,' he said. 'Ah, it was worth waiting for!— sometimes.' 'What was he doing? exploring or what?' I asked. 'Oh, yes, of course;' he had discovered lots of villages, a lake, too—he did not know exactly in what direction; it was dangerous to inquire too much— but mostly his expeditions had been for ivory. 'But he had no goods to trade with by that time,' I objected. 'There's a good lot of cartridges left even yet,' he answered, looking away. 'To speak plainly, he raided the country,' I said. He nodded. 'Not alone, surely!' He muttered something about the villages round that lake. 'Kurtz got the tribe to follow him, did he?' I suggested. He fidgeted a little. 'They adored him,' he said. The tone of these words was so extraordinary that I looked at him searchingly. It was curious to see his mingled eagerness and reluctance to speak of Kurtz. The man filled his life, occupied his thoughts, swayed his emotions. 'What can you expect?' he burst out; 'he came to them with thunder and lightning, you know—and they had never seen anything like it—and very terrible. He could be very terrible. You can't judge Mr. Kurtz as you would an ordinary man. No, no, no! Now—just to give you an idea—I don't mind telling you, he wanted to shoot me, too, one day—but I don't judge him.' 'Shoot you!' I cried. 'What for?' 'Well, I had a small lot of ivory the chief of that village near my house gave me. You see I used to shoot game for them. Well, he wanted it, and wouldn't hear reason. He declared he would shoot me unless I gave him the ivory and then cleared out of the country, because he could do so, and had a fancy for it, and there was nothing on earth to prevent him killing whom he jolly well pleased. And it was true, too. I gave him the ivory. What did I care! But I didn't clear out. No, no. I couldn't leave him. I had to be careful, of course, till we got friendly again for a time. He had his second illness then. Afterwards I had to keep out of the way; but I didn't mind. He was living for the most part in those villages on the lake. When he came down to the river, sometimes he would take to me, and sometimes it was better for me to be careful. This man suffered too much. He hated all this, and somehow he couldn't get away. When I had a chance I begged him to try and leave while there was time; I offered to go back with him. And he would say yes, and then he would remain; go off on another ivory hunt; disappear for weeks; forget himself amongst these people—forget himself— you know.' 'Why! he's mad,' I said. He protested indignantly. Mr. Kurtz couldn't be mad. If I had heard him talk, only two days ago, I wouldn't dare hint at such a thing. . . . I had taken up my binoculars while we talked and was looking at the shore, sweeping the limit of the forest at each side and at the back of the house. The consciousness of there being people in that bush, so silent, so quiet—as silent and quiet as the ruined house on the hill—made me uneasy. There was no sign on the face of nature of this amazing tale that was not so much told as suggested to me in desolate exclamations, completed by shrugs, in interrupted phrases, in hints ending in deep sighs. The woods were unmoved, like a mask—heavy, like the closed door of a prison—they looked with their air of hidden knowledge, of patient expectation, of unapproachable silence. The Russian was explaining to me that it was only lately that Mr. Kurtz had come down to the river, bringing along with him all the fighting men of that lake tribe. He had been absent for several months— getting himself adored, I suppose—and had come down unexpectedly, with the intention to all appearance of making a raid either across the river or down stream. Evidently the appetite for more ivory had got the better of the—what shall I say?—less material aspirations. However, he had got much worse suddenly. 'I heard he was lying helpless, and so I came up—took my chance,' said the Russian. 'Oh, he is bad, very bad.' I directed my glass to the house. There were no signs of life, but there was the ruined roof, the long mud wall peeping above the grass, with three little square window-holes, no two of the same size; all this brought within reach of my hand, as it were. And then I made a brusque movement, and one of the remaining posts of that vanished fence leaped up in the field of my glass. You remember I told you I had been struck at the distance by certain attempts at ornamentation, rather remarkable in the ruinous aspect of the place. Now I had suddenly a nearer view, and its first result was to make me throw my head back as if before a blow. Then I went carefully from post to post with my glass, and I saw my mistake. These round knobs were not ornamental but symbolic; they were expressive and puzzling, striking, and disturbing—food for thought and also for the vultures if there had been any looking down from the sky; but at all events for such ants as were industrious enough to ascend the pole. They would have been even more impressive, those heads on the stakes, if their faces had not been turned to the house. Only one, the first I had made out, was facing my way. I was not so shocked as you may think. The start back I had given was really nothing but a movement of surprise. I had expected to see a knob of wood there, you know. I returned deliberately to the first I had seen—and there it was, black, dried, sunken, with closed eyelids—a head that seemed to sleep at the top of that pole, and, with the shrunken dry lips showing a narrow white line of the teeth, was smiling, too, smiling continuously at some endless and jocose dream of that eternal slumber.

"I am not disclosing any trade secrets. In fact, the manager said afterwards that Mr. Kurtz's methods had ruined the district. I have no opinion on that point, but I want you clearly to understand that there was nothing exactly profitable in these heads being there. They only showed that Mr. Kurtz lacked restraint in the gratification of his various lusts, that there was something wanting in him—some small matter which, when the pressing need arose, could not be found under his magnificent eloquence. Whether he knew of this deficiency himself I can't say. I think the knowledge came to him at last—only at the very last. But the wilderness had found him out early, and had taken on him a terrible vengeance for the fantastic invasion. I think it had whispered to him things about himself which he did not know, things of which he had no conception till he took counsel with this great solitude—and the whisper had proved irresistibly fascinating. It echoed loudly within him because he was hollow at the core. . . . . I put down the glass, and the head that had appeared near enough to be spoken to seemed at once to have leaped away from me into inaccessible distance.

"The admirer of Mr. Kurtz was a bit crestfallen. In a hurried, indistinct voice he began to assure me he had not dared to take these—say, symbols—down. He was not afraid of the natives; they would not stir till Mr. Kurtz gave the word. His ascendency was extraordinary. The camps of these people surrounded the place, and the chiefs came every day to see him. They would crawl. . . . 'I don't want to know anything of the ceremonies used when approaching Mr. Kurtz,' I shouted. Curious, this feeling that came over me that such details would be more intolerable than those heads drying on the stakes under Mr. Kurtz's windows. After all, that was only a savage sight, while I seemed at one bound to have been transported into some lightless region of subtle horrors, where pure, uncomplicated savagery was a positive relief, being something that had a right to exist—obviously—in the sunshine. The young man looked at me with surprise. I suppose it did not occur to him Mr. Kurtz was no idol of mine. He forgot I hadn't heard any of these splendid monologues on, what was it? on love, justice, conduct of life— or what not. If it had come to crawling before Mr. Kurtz, he crawled as much as the veriest savage of them all. I had no idea of the conditions, he said: these heads were the heads of rebels. I shocked him excessively by laughing. Rebels! What would be the next definition I was to hear? There had been enemies, criminals, workers—and these were rebels. Those rebellious heads looked very subdued to me on their sticks. 'You don't know how such a life tries a man like Kurtz,' cried Kurtz's last disciple. 'Well, and you?' I said. 'I! I! I am a simple man. I have no great thoughts. I want nothing from anybody. How can you compare me to . . .?' His feelings were too much for speech, and suddenly he broke down. 'I don't understand,' he groaned. 'I've been doing my best to keep him alive, and that's enough. I had no hand in all this. I have no abilities. There hasn't been a drop of medicine or a mouthful of invalid food for months here. He was shamefully abandoned. A man like this, with such ideas. Shamefully! Shamefully! I—I—haven't slept for the last ten nights. . . . '

"His voice lost itself in the calm of the evening. The long shadows of the forest had slipped down hill while we talked, had gone far beyond the ruined hovel, beyond the symbolic row of stakes. All this was in the gloom, while we down there were yet in the sunshine, and the stretch of the river abreast of the clearing glittered in a still and dazzling splendor, with a murky and overshadowed bend above and below. Not a living soul was seen on the shore. The bushes did not rustle.

"Suddenly round the corner of the house a group of men appeared, as though they had come up from the ground. They waded waist-deep in the grass, in a compact body, bearing an improvised stretcher in their midst. Instantly, in the emptiness of the landscape, a cry arose whose shrillness pierced the still air like a sharp arrow flying straight to the very heart of the land; and, as if by enchantment, streams of human beings— of naked human beings—with spears in their hands, with bows, with shields, with wild glances and savage movements, were poured into the clearing by the dark-faced and pensive forest. The bushes shook, the grass swayed for a time, and then everything stood still in attentive immobility.

"'Now, if he does not say the right thing to them we are all done for,' said the Russian at my elbow. The knot of men with the stretcher had stopped, too, half-way to the steamer, as if petrified. I saw the man on the stretcher sit up, lank and with an uplifted arm, above the shoulders of the bearers. 'Let us hope that the man who can talk so well of love in general will find some particular reason to spare us this time,' I said. I resented bitterly the absurd danger of our situation, as if to be at the mercy of that atrocious phantom had been a dishonoring necessity. I could not hear a sound, but through my glasses I saw the thin arm extended commandingly, the lower jaw moving, the eyes of that apparition shining darkly far in its bony head that nodded with grotesque jerks. Kurtz—Kurtz—that means *short* in German—don't it? Well, the name was as true as everything else in his life—and death. He looked at least seven feet long. His covering had fallen off, and his body emerged from it pitiful and appalling as from a winding-sheet. I could see the cage of his ribs all astir, the bones of his arm waving. It was as though an animated image of death carved out of old ivory had been shaking its hand with menaces at a motionless crowd of men made of dark and glittering bronze. I saw him open his mouth wide—it gave him a weirdly voracious aspect, as though he had wanted to swallow all the air, all the earth, all the men before him. A deep voice reached me faintly. He must have been shouting. He fell back suddenly. The stretcher shook as the bearers staggered forward again, and almost at the same time I noticed that the crowd of savages was vanishing without any perceptible movement of retreat, as if the forest that had ejected these beings so suddenly had drawn them in again as the breath is drawn in a long aspiration.

"Some of the pilgrims behind the stretcher carried his arms—two shot-guns, a heavy rifle, and a light revolver-carbine—the thunderbolts of that pitiful Jupiter. The manager bent over him murmuring as he walked beside his head. They laid him down in one of the little cabins— just a room for a bed-place and a camp-stool or two, you know. We had brought his belated correspondence, and a lot of torn envelopes and open letters littered his bed. His hand roamed feebly amongst these papers. I was struck by the fire of his eyes and the composed languor of his expression. It was not so much the exhaustion of disease. He did not seem in pain. This shadow looked satiated and calm, as though for the moment it had had its fill of all the emotions.

"He rustled one of the letters, and looking straight in my face said, 'I am glad.' Somebody had been writing to him about me. These special recommendations were turning up again. The volume of tone he emitted without effort, almost without the trouble of moving his lips, amazed me. A voice! a voice! It was grave, profound, vibrating, while the man did not seem capable of a whisper. However, he had enough strength in him—factitious no doubt—to very nearly make an end of us, as you shall hear directly.

"The manager appeared silently in the doorway; I stepped out at once and he drew the curtain after me. The Russian, eyed curiously by the pilgrims, was staring at the shore. I followed the direction of his glance.

"Dark human shapes could be made out in the distance, flitting indistinctly against the gloomy border of the forest, and near the river two bronze figures, leaning on tall spears, stood in the sunlight under fantastic head-dresses of spotted skins, warlike and still in statuesque repose. And from right to left along the lighted shore moved a wild and gorgeous apparition of a woman.

"She walked with measured steps, draped in striped and fringed cloths, treading the earth proudly, with a slight jingle and flash of barbarous ornaments. She carried her head high; her hair was done in the shape of a helmet; she had brass leggings to the knee, brass wire gauntlets to the elbow, a crimson spot on her tawny cheek, innumerable necklaces of glass beads on her neck; bizarre things, charms, gifts of witchmen, that hung about her, glittered and trembled at every step. She must have had the value of several elephant tusks upon her. She was savage and superb, wild-eyed and magnificent; there was something ominous and stately in her deliberate progress. And in the hush that had fallen suddenly upon the whole sorrowful land, the immense wilderness, the colossal body of the fecund and mysterious life seemed to look at her, pensive, as though it had been looking at the image of its own tenebrous and passionate soul.

"She came abreast of the steamer, stood still, and faced us. Her long shadow fell to the water's edge. Her face had a tragic and fierce aspect of wild sorrow and of dumb pain mingled with the fear of some struggling, half-shaped resolve. She stood looking at us without a stir and like the wilderness itself, with an air of brooding over an inscrutable purpose. A whole minute passed, and then she made a step forward. There was a low jingle, a glint of yellow metal, a sway of fringed draperies, and she stopped as if her heart had failed her. The young fellow by my side growled. The pilgrims murmured at my back. She looked at us all as if her life had depended upon the unswerving steadiness of her glance. Suddenly she opened her bared arms and threw them up rigid above her head, as though in an uncontrollable desire to touch the sky, and at the same time the swift shadows darted out on the earth, swept around on the river, gathering the steamer into a shadowy embrace. A formidable silence hung over the scene.

"She turned away slowly, walked on, following the bank, and passed into the bushes to the left. Once only her eyes gleamed back at us in the dusk of the thickets before she disappeared.

"'If she had offered to come aboard I really think I would have tried to shoot her,' said the man of patches, nervously. 'I have been risking my life every day for the last fortnight to keep her out of the house. She got in one day and kicked up a row about those miserable rags I picked up in the storeroom to mend my clothes with. I wasn't decent. At least it must have been that, for she talked like a fury to Kurtz for an hour, pointing at me now and then. I don't understand the dialect of this tribe. Luckily for me, I fancy Kurtz felt too ill that day to care, or there would have been mischief. I don't understand. . . . No—it's too much for me. Ah, well, it's all over now.'

"At the moment I heard Kurtz's deep voice behind the curtain, 'Save me!—save the ivory, you mean. Don't tell me. Save *me!* Why, I've had to save you. You are interrupting my plans now. Sick! Sick! Not so sick as you would like to believe. Never mind. I'll carry my ideas out yet—I will return. I'll show you what can be done. You with your little peddling notions—you are interfering with me. I will return. I. . . .'

"The manager came out. He did me the honor to take me under the arm and lead me aside. 'He is very low, very low,' he said. He considered it necessary to sigh, but neglected to be consistently sorrowful. 'We have done all we could for him—haven't we? But there is no disguising the fact, Mr. Kurtz has done more harm than good to the Company. He did not see the time was not ripe for vigorous action. Cautiously, cautiously—that's my principle. We must be cautious yet. The district is closed to us for a time. Deplorable! Upon the whole, the trade will suffer. I don't deny there is a remarkable quantity of ivory—mostly fossil. We must save it, at all events—but look how precarious the position is—and why? Because the method is unsound.' 'Do you,' said I, looking at the shore, 'call it "unsound method"?' 'Without doubt,' he exclaimed, hotly. 'Don't you?' . . . 'No method at all,' I murmured after a while. 'Exactly,' he exulted. 'I anticipated this. Shows a complete want of judgment. It is my duty to point it out in the proper quarter.' 'Oh,' said I, 'that fellow—what's his name?—the brickmaker, will make a readable report for you.' He appeared confounded for a moment. It seemed to me I had never breathed an atmosphere so vile, and I turned mentally to Kurtz for relief—positively for relief. 'Nevertheless I think Mr. Kurtz is a remarkable man,' I said with emphasis. He started, dropped on me a cold, heavy glance, said very quietly, 'He *was*,' and turned his back on me. My hour of favor was over; I found myself lumped along with Kurtz as a partisan of methods for which the time was not ripe: I was unsound! Ah! but it was something to have at least a choice of nightmares.

"I had turned to the wilderness really, not to Mr. Kurtz, who, I was ready to admit, was as good as buried. And for a moment it seemed to me as if I also were buried in a vast grave full of unspeakable secrets. I felt an intolerable weight oppressing my breast, the smell of the damp earth, the unseen presence of victorious corruption, the darkness of an impenetrable night. . . . The Russian tapped me on the shoulder. I heard him mumbling and stammering something about 'brother sea- man—couldn't conceal—knowledge of matters that would affect Mr. Kurtz's reputation.' I waited. For him evidently Mr. Kurtz was not in his grave; I suspect that for him Mr. Kurtz was one of the immortals. 'Well!' said I at last, 'speak out. As it happens, I am Mr. Kurtz's friend—in a way.'

"He stated with a good deal of formality that had we not been 'of the same profession,' he would have kept the matter to himself without re- gard to consequences. 'He suspected there was an active ill will towards him on the part of these white men that——' 'You are right,' I said, remembering a certain conversation I had overheard. 'The manager thinks you ought to be hanged.' He showed a concern at this intelligence which amused me at first. 'I had better get out of the way quietly,' he said, earnestly. 'I can do no more for Kurtz now, and they would soon find some excuse. What's to stop them? There's a military post three hundred miles from here.' 'Well, upon my word,' said I, 'perhaps you had better go if you have any friends amongst the savages near by.' 'Plenty,' he said. 'They are simple people—and I want nothing, you know.' He stood biting his lip, then: 'I don't want any harm to happen to these whites here, but of course I was thinking of Mr. Kurtz's reputa- tion—but you are a brother seaman and——' 'All right,' said I, after a time. 'Mr. Kurtz's reputation is safe with me.' I did not know how truly I spoke.

"He informed me, lowering his voice, that it was Kurtz who had ordered the attack to be made on the steamer. 'He hated sometimes the idea of being taken away—and then again. . . . But I don't understand these matters. I am a simple man. He thought it would scare you away —that you would give it up, thinking him dead. I could not stop him. Oh, I had an awful time of it this last month.' 'Very well,' I said. 'He is all right now.' 'Ye-e-es,' he muttered, not very convinced apparently. 'Thanks,' said I; 'I shall keep my eyes open.' 'But quiet—eh?' he urged, anxiously. 'It would be awful for his reputation if anybody here——' I promised a complete discretion with great gravity. 'I have a canoe and three black fellows waiting not very far. I am off. Could you give me a few Martini-Henry cartridges?' I could, and did, with proper secrecy. He helped himself, with a wink at me, to a handful of my tobacco. 'Be- tween sailors—you know—good English tobacco.' At the door of the pilot-house he turned round—'I say, haven't you a pair of shoes you could spare?' He raised one leg. 'Look.' The soles were tied with knotted strings sandal-wise under his bare feet. I rooted out an old pair, at which he looked with admiration before tucking it under his left arm. One of his pockets (bright red) was bulging with cartridges;

from the other (dark blue) peeped 'Towson's Inquiry,' etc., etc. He seemed to think himself excellently well equipped for a renewed encounter with the wilderness. 'Ah! I'll never, never meet such a man again. You ought to have heard him recite poetry—his own, too, it was, he told me. Poetry!' He rolled his eyes at the recollection of these delights. 'Oh, he enlarged my mind!' 'Good-bye,' said I. He shook hands and vanished in the night. Sometimes I ask myself whether I had ever really seen him—whether it was possible to meet such a phenomenon!...

"When I woke up shortly after midnight his warning came to my mind with its hint of danger that seemed, in the starred darkness, real enough to make me get up for the purpose of having a look round. On the hill a big fire burned, illuminating fitfully a crooked corner of the station-house. One of the agents with a picket of a few of our blacks, armed for the purpose, was keeping guard over the ivory; but deep within the forest, red gleams that wavered, that seemed to sink and rise from the ground amongst confused columnar shapes of intense blackness, showed the exact position of the camp where Mr. Kurtz's adorers were keeping their uneasy vigil. The monotonous beating of a big drum filled the air with muffled shocks and a lingering vibration. A steady droning sound of many men chanting each to himself some weird incantation came out from the black, flat wall of the woods as the humming of bees comes out of a hive, and had a strange narcotic effect upon my half-awake senses. I believe I dozed off leaning over the rail, till an abrupt burst of yells, an overwhelming outbreak of a pent-up and mysterious frenzy, woke me up in a bewildered wonder. It was cut short all at once, and the low droning went on with an effect of audible and soothing silence. I glanced casually into the little cabin. A light was burning within, but Mr. Kurtz was not there.

"I think I would have raised an outcry if I had believed my eyes. But I didn't believe them at first—the thing seemed so impossible. The fact is I was completely unnerved by a sheer blank fright, pure abstract terror, unconnected with any distinct shape of physical danger. What made this emotion so overpowering was—how shall I define it?—the moral shock I received, as if something altogether monstrous, intolerable to thought and odious to the soul, had been thrust upon me unexpectedly. This lasted of course the merest fraction of a second, and then the usual sense of commonplace, deadly danger, the possibility of a sudden onslaught and massacre, or something of the kind, which I saw impending, was positively welcome and composing. It pacified me, in fact, so much, that I did not raise an alarm.

"There was an agent buttoned up inside an ulster and sleeping on a chair on deck within three feet of me. The yells had not awakened him; he snored very slightly; I left him to his slumbers and leaped ashore. I did not betray Mr. Kurtz—it was ordered I should never betray him— it was written I should be loyal to the nightmare of my choice. I was anxious to deal with this shadow by myself alone,—and to this day I don't know why I was so jealous of sharing with anyone the peculiar blackness of that experience.

"As soon as I got on the bank I saw a trail—a broad trail through the grass. I remember the exultation with which I said to myself, 'He can't walk—he is crawling on all-fours—I've got him.' The grass was wet with dew. I strode rapidly with clenched fists. I fancy I had some vague notion of falling upon him and giving him a drubbing. I don't know. I had some imbecile thoughts. The knitting old woman with the cat obtruded herself upon my memory as a most improper person to be sitting at the other end of such an affair. I saw a row of pilgrims squirting lead in the air out of Winchesters held to the hip. I thought I would never get back to the steamer, and imagined myself living alone and unarmed in the woods to an advanced age. Such silly things—you know. And I remember I confounded the beat of the drum with the beating of my heart, and was pleased at its calm regularity.

"I kept to the track though—then stopped to listen. The night was very clear: a dark blue space, sparkling with dew and starlight, in which black things stood very still. I thought I could see a kind of motion ahead of me. I was strangely cocksure of everything that night. I actually left the track and ran in a wide semicircle (I verily believe chuckling to myself) so as to get in front of that stir, of that motion I had seen—if indeed I had seen anything. I was circumventing Kurtz as though it had been a boyish game.

"I came upon him, and, if he had not heard me coming, I would have fallen over him, too, but he got up in time. He rose, unsteady, long, pale, indistinct, like a vapor exhaled by the earth, and swayed slightly, misty and silent before me; while at my back the fires loomed between the trees, and the murmur of many voices issued from the forest. I had cut him off cleverly; but when actually confronting him I seemed to come to my senses, I saw the danger in its right proportion. It was by no means over yet. Suppose he began to shout? Though he could hardly stand, there was still plenty of vigor in his voice. 'Go away—hide yourself,' he said, in that profound tone. It was very awful. I glanced back. We were within thirty yards from the nearest fire. A black figure stood up, strode on long black legs, waving long black arms, across the glow. It had horns—antelope horns, I think—on its head. Some sorcerer, some witch-man, no doubt: it looked fiend-like enough. 'Do you know what you are doing?' I whispered. 'Perfectly,' he answered, raising his voice for that single word: it sounded to me far off and yet loud, like a hail through a speaking-trumpet. If he makes a row we are lost, I thought to myself. This clearly was not a case for fisticuffs, even apart from the very natural aversion I had to beat that Shadow—this wandering and tormented thing. 'You will be lost,' I said—'utterly lost.' One gets sometimes such a flash of inspiration, you know. I did say the right thing, though indeed he could not have been more irretrievably lost than he was at this very moment, when the foundations of our intimacy were being laid—to endure—to endure—even to the end—even beyond.

"'I had immense plans,' he muttered irresolutely. 'Yes,' said I; 'but if you try to shout I'll smash your head with——' there was not a stick or a stone near. 'I will throttle you for good,' I corrected myself. 'I was on the threshold of great things,' he pleaded, in a voice of longing, with a wistfulness of tone that made my blood run cold. 'And now for this stupid scoundrel——' 'Your success in Europe is assured in any case,' I affirmed, steadily. I did not want to have the throttling of him, you understand—and indeed it would have been very little use for any practical purpose. I tried to break the spell—the heavy, mute spell of the wilderness—that seemed to draw him to its pitiless breast by the awakening of forgotten and brutal instincts, by the memory of gratified and monstrous passions. This alone, I was convinced, had driven him out to the edge of the forest, to the bush, towards the gleam of fires, the throb of drums, the drone of weird incantations; this alone had beguiled his unlawful soul beyond the bounds of permitted aspirations. And, don't you see, the terror of the position was not in being knocked on the head—though I had a very lively sense of that danger, too—but in this, that I had to deal with a being to whom I could not appeal in the name of anything high or low. I had, even like the niggers, to invoke him—himself—his own exalted and incredible degradation. There was nothing either above or below him, and I knew it. He had kicked himself loose of the earth. Confound the man! he had kicked the very earth to pieces. He was alone, and I before him did not know whether I stood on the ground or floated in the air. I've been telling you what we said—repeating the phrases we pronounced—but what's the good? They were common everyday words—the familiar, vague sounds exchanged on every waking day of life. But what of that? They had behind them, to my mind, the terrific suggestiveness of words heard in dreams, of phrases spoken in nightmares. Soul! If anybody had ever struggled with a soul, I am the man. And I wasn't arguing with a lunatic either. Believe me or not, his intelligence was perfectly clear—concentrated, it is true, upon himself with horrible intensity, yet clear; and therein was my only chance—barring, of course, the killing him there and then, which wasn't so good, on account of unavoidable noise. But his soul was mad. Being alone in the wilderness, it had looked within itself, and, by heavens! I tell you, it had gone mad. I had—for my sins, I suppose—to go through the ordeal of looking into it myself. No eloquence could have been so withering to one's belief in mankind as his final burst of sincerity. He struggled with himself, too. I saw it—I heard it. I saw the inconceivable mystery of a soul that knew no restraint, no faith, and no fear, yet struggling blindly with itself. I kept my head pretty well; but when I had him at last stretched on the couch,

I wiped my forehead, while my legs shook under me as though I had carried half a ton on my back down that hill. And yet I had only supported him, his bony arm clasped round my neck—and he was not much heavier than a child.

"When next day we left at noon, the crowd, of whose presence behind the curtain of trees I had been acutely conscious all the time, flowed out of the woods again, filled the clearing, covered the slope with a mass of naked, breathing, quivering, bronze bodies. I steamed up a bit, then swung downstream, and two thousand eyes followed the evolutions of the splashing, thumping, fierce river-demon beating the water with its terrible tail and breathing black smoke into the air. In front of the first rank, along the river, three men, plastered with bright red earth from head to foot, strutted to and fro restlessly. When we came abreast again, they faced the river, stamped their feet, nodded their horned heads, swayed their scarlet bodies; they shook towards the fierce river-demon a bunch of black feathers, a mangy skin with a pendent tail—something that looked like a dried gourd; they shouted periodically together strings of amazing words that resembled no sounds of human language; and the deep murmurs of the crowd, interrupted suddenly, were like the responses of some satanic litany.

"We had carried Kurtz into the pilot-house: there was more air there. Lying on the couch, he stared through the open shutter. There was an eddy in the mass of human bodies, and the woman with helmeted head and tawny cheeks rushed out to the very brink of the stream. She put out her hands, shouted something, and all that wild mob took up the shout in a roaring chorus of articulated, rapid, breathless utterance.

"'Do you understand this?' I asked.

"He kept on looking out past me with fiery, longing eyes, with a mingled expression of wistfulness and hate. He made no answer, but I saw a smile, a smile of indefinable meaning, appear on his colorless lips that a moment after twitched convulsively. 'Do I not?' he said slowly, gasping, as if the words had been torn out of him by a supernatural power.

"I pulled the string of the whistle, and I did this because I saw the pilgrims on deck getting out their rifles with an air of anticipating a jolly lark. At the sudden screech there was a movement of abject terror through that wedged mass of bodies. 'Don't! don't you frighten them away,' cried someone on deck disconsolately. I pulled the string time after time. They broke and ran, they leaped, they crouched, they swerved, they dodged the flying terror of the sound. The three red chaps had fallen flat, face down on the shore, as though they had been shot dead.. Only the barbarous and superb woman did not so much as flinch, and stretched tragically her bare arms after us over the somber and glittering river.

"And then that imbecile crowd down on the deck started their little fun, and I could see nothing more for smoke.

"The brown current ran swiftly out of the heart of darkness, bearing us down towards the sea with twice the speed of our upward progress; and Kurtz's life was running swiftly, too, ebbing, ebbing out of his heart into the sea of inexorable time. The manager was very placid, he had no vital anxieties now, he took us both in with a comprehensive and satisfied glance: the 'affair' had come off as well as could be wished. I saw the time approaching when I would be left alone of the party of 'unsound method.' The pilgrims looked upon me with disfavor. I was, so to speak, numbered with the dead. It is strange how I accepted this unforeseen partnership, this choice of nightmares forced upon me in the tenebrous land invaded by these mean and greedy phantoms.

"Kurtz discoursed. A voice! a voice! It rang deep to the very last. It survived his strength to hide in the magnificent folds of eloquence the barren darkness of his heart. Oh, he struggled! he struggled! The wastes of his weary brain were haunted by shadowy images now— images of wealth and fame revolving obsequiously round his unextinguishable gift of noble and lofty expression. My Intended, my station, my career, my ideas—these were the subjects for the occasional utterances of elevated sentiments. The shade of the original Kurtz frequented the bedside of the hollow sham, whose fate it was to be buried presently in the mold of primeval earth. But both the diabolic love and the unearthly hate of the mysteries it had penetrated fought for the possession of that soul satiated with primitive emotion, avid of lying fame, of sham distinction, of all the appearances of success and power.

"Sometimes he was contemptibly childish. He desired to have kings meet him at railway-stations on his return from some ghastly Nowhere, where he intended to accomplish great things. 'You show them you have in you something that is really profitable, and then there will be no limits to the recognition of your ability,' he would say. 'Of course you must take care of the motives—right motives—always.' The long reaches that were like one and the same reach, monotonous bends that were exactly alike, slipped past the steamer with their multitude of secular trees looking patiently after this grimy fragment of another world, the forerunner of change, of conquest, of trade, of massacres, of blessings. I looked ahead—piloting. 'Close the shutter,' said Kurtz suddenly one day; 'I can't bear to look at this.' I did so. There was silence. 'Oh, but I will wring your heart yet!' he cried at the invisible wilderness.

"We broke down—as I had expected—and had to lie up for repairs at the head of an island. This delay was the first thing that shook Kurtz's confidence. One morning he gave me a packet of papers and a photograph—the lot tied together with a shoe-string. 'Keep this for me,' he said. 'This noxious fool' (meaning the manager) 'is capable of prying into my boxes when I am not looking.' In the afternoon I saw him. He was lying on his back with closed eyes, and I withdrew quietly, but I heard him mutter, 'Live rightly, die, die . . .' I listened. There was nothing more. Was he rehearsing some speech in his sleep, or was it a fragment of a phrase from some newspaper article? He had been writing for the papers and meant to do so again, 'for the furthering of my ideas. It's a duty.'

"His was an impenetrable darkness. I looked at him as you peer down at a man who is lying at the bottom of a precipice where the sun never shines. But I had not much time to give him, because I was helping the engine-driver to take to pieces the leaky cylinders, to straighten a bent connecting-rod, and in other such matters. I lived in an infernal mess of rust, filings, nuts, bolts, spanners, hammers, ratchet-drills— things I abominate, because I don't get on with them. I tended the little forge we fortunately had aboard; I toiled wearily in a wretched scrap-heap—unless I had the shakes too bad to stand.

"One evening coming in with a candle I was startled to hear him say a little tremulously, 'I am lying here in the dark waiting for death.' The light was within a foot of his eyes. I forced myself to murmur, 'Oh, nonsense!' and stood over him as if transfixed.

"Anything approaching the change that came over his features I have never seen before, and hope never to see again. Oh, I wasn't touched. I was fascinated. It was as though a veil had been rent. I saw on that ivory face the expression of somber pride, of ruthless power, of craven terror—of an intense and hopeless despair. Did he live his life again in every detail of desire, temptation, and surrender during that supreme moment of complete knowledge? He cried in a whisper at some image, at some vision—he cried out twice, a cry that was no more than a breath—

"'The horror! The horror!'

"I blew the candle out and left the cabin. The pilgrims were dining in the mess-room, and I took my place opposite the manager, who lifted his eyes to give me a questioning glance, which I successfully ignored. He leaned back, serene, with that peculiar smile of his sealing the unexpressed depths of his meanness. A continuous shower of small flies streamed upon the lamp, upon the cloth, upon our hands and faces. Suddenly the manager's boy put his insolent black head in the doorway, and said in a tone of scathing contempt—

"'Mistah Kurtz—he dead.'

"All the pilgrims rushed out to see. I remained, and went on with my dinner. I believe I was considered brutally callous. However, I did not eat much. There was a lamp in there—light, don't you know—and outside it was so beastly, beastly dark. I went no more near the remarkable man who had pronounced a judgment upon the adventures of his soul on this earth. The voice was gone. What else had been there? But I am of course aware that next day the pilgrims buried something in a muddy hole.

"And then they very nearly buried me.

"However, as you see, I did not go to join Kurtz there and then. I did not. I remained to dream the nightmare out to the end, and to show my loyalty to Kurtz once more. Destiny. My destiny! Droll thing life is—that mysterious arrangement of merciless logic for a futile purpose. The most you can hope from it is some knowledge of yourself—that comes too late—a crop of unextinguishable regrets. I have wrestled with death. It is the most unexciting contest you can imagine. It takes place in an impalpable grayness, with nothing underfoot, with nothing around, without spectators, without clamor, without glory, without the great desire of victory, without the great fear of defeat, in a sickly atmosphere of tepid skepticism, without much belief in your own right, and still less in that of your adversary. If such is the form of ultimate wisdom, then life is a greater riddle than some of us think it to be. I was within a hair's breadth of the last opportunity for pronouncement, and I found with humiliation that probably I would have nothing to say. This is the reason why I affirm that Kurtz was a remarkable man. He had something to say. He said it. Since I had peeped over the edge myself, I understood better the meaning of his stare, that could not see the flame of the candle, but was wide enough to embrace the whole universe, piercing enough to penetrate all the hearts that beat in the darkness. He had summed up—he had judged. 'The horror!' He was a remarkable man. After all, this was the expression of some sort of belief; it had candor, it had conviction, it had a vibrating note of revolt in its whisper, it had the appalling face of a glimpsed truth—the strange commingling of desire and hate. And it is not my own extremity I remember best—a vision of grayness without form filled with physical pain, and a careless contempt for the evanescence of all things—even of this pain itself. No! It is his extremity that I seem to have lived through. True, he had made that last stride, he had stepped over the edge, while I had been permitted to draw back my hesitating foot. And perhaps in this is the whole difference; perhaps all the wisdom, and all truth, and all sincerity, are just compressed into that inappreciable moment of time in which we step over the threshold of the invisible. Perhaps! I like to think my summing-up would not have been a word of careless contempt. Better his cry—much better. It was an affirmation, a moral victory paid for by innumerable defeats, by abominable terrors, by abominable satisfactions. But it was a victory! That is why I have remained loyal to Kurtz to the last, and even beyond, when a long time after I heard once more, not his own voice, but the echo of his magnificent eloquence thrown to me from a soul as translucently pure as a cliff of crystal.

"No, they did not bury me, though there is a period of time which I remember mistily, with a shuddering wonder, like a passage through some inconceivable world that had no hope in it and no desire. I found myself back in the sepulchral city resenting the sight of people hurrying through the streets to filch a little money from each other, to devour their infamous cookery, to gulp their unwholesome beer, to dream their insignificant and silly dreams. They trespassed upon my thoughts. They were intruders whose knowledge of life was to me an irritating pretense, because I felt so sure they could not possibly know the things I knew. Their bearing, which was simply the bearing of commonplace individuals going about their business in the assurance of perfect safety, was offensive to me like the outrageous flauntings of folly in the face of a danger it is unable to comprehend. I had no particular desire to enlighten them, but I had some difficulty in restraining myself from laughing in their faces, so full of stupid importance. I daresay I was not very well at that time. I tottered about the streets—there were various affairs to settle—grinning bitterly at perfectly respectable persons. I admit my behavior was inexcusable, but then my temperature was seldom normal in those days. My dear aunt's endeavors to 'nurse up my strength' seemed altogether beside the mark. It was not my strength that wanted nursing, it was my imagination that wanted soothing. I kept the bundle of papers given me by Kurtz, not knowing exactly what to do with it. His mother had died lately, watched over, as I was told, by his Intended. A clean-shaved man, with an official manner and wearing gold-rimmed spectacles, called on me one day and made inquiries, at first circuitous, afterwards suavely pressing, about what he was pleased to denominate certain 'documents.' I was not surprised, because I had had two rows with the manager on the subject out there. I had refused to give up the smallest scrap out of that package, and I took the same attitude with the spectacled man. He became darkly menacing at last, and with much heat argued that the Company had the right to every bit of information about its 'territories.' And, said he, 'Mr. Kurtz's knowledge of unexplored regions must have been necessarily extensive and peculiar—owing to his great abilities and to the deplorable circumstances in which he had been placed: therefore ——' I assured him Mr. Kurtz's knowledge, however extensive, did not bear upon the problems of commerce or administration. He invoked then the name of science. 'It would be an incalculable loss if,' etc., etc. I offered him the report on the 'Suppression of Savage Customs,' with the postscriptum torn off. He took it up eagerly, but ended by sniffing at it with an air of contempt. 'This is not what we had a right to expect,' he remarked. 'Expect nothing else,' I said. 'There are only private letters.' He withdrew upon some threat of legal proceedings, and I saw him no more; but another fellow, calling himself Kurtz's cousin, appeared two days later, and was anxious to hear all the details about his dear relative's last moments. Incidentally he gave me to understand that Kurtz had been essentially a great musician. 'There was the making of an immense success,' said the man, who was an organist,

I believe, with lank gray hair flowing over a greasy coat-collar. I had
no reason to doubt his statement; and to this day I am unable to say
what was Kurtz's profession, whether he ever had any—which was the
greatest of his talents. I had taken him for a painter who wrote for the
papers, or else for a journalist who could paint—but even the cousin
(who took snuff during the interview) could not tell me what he had
been—exactly. He was a universal genius—on that point I agreed with
the old chap, who thereupon blew his nose noisily into a large cotton
handkerchief and withdrew in senile agitation, bearing off some family
letters and memoranda without importance. Ultimately a journalist
anxious to know something of the fate of his 'dear colleague' turned up.
This visitor informed me Kurtz's proper sphere ought to have been
politics 'on the popular side.' He had furry straight eyebrows, bristly
hair cropped short, an eye-glass on a broad ribbon, and, becoming ex-
pansive, confessed his opinion that Kurtz really couldn't write a bit—
'but heavens! how that man could talk! He electrified large meetings.
He had faith—don't you see?—he had the faith. He could get himself
to believe anything—anything. He would have been a splendid leader
of an extreme party.' 'What party?' I asked. 'Any party,' answered
the other. 'He was an—an—extremist.' Did I not think so? I assented.
Did I know, he asked, with a sudden flash of curiosity, 'what it was that
had induced him to go out there?' 'Yes,' said I, and forthwith handed
him the famous Report for publication, if he thought fit. He glanced
through it hurriedly, mumbling all the time, judged 'it would do,' and
took himself off with this plunder.

"Thus I was left at last with a slim packet of letters and the girl's
portrait. She struck me as beautiful—I mean she had a beautiful expression. I know that the sunlight can be made to lie, too, yet one felt
that no manipulation of light and pose could have conveyed the delicate
shade of truthfulness upon those features. She seemed ready to listen
without mental reservation, without suspicion, without a thought for
herself. I concluded I would go and give her back her portrait and those
letters myself. Curiosity? Yes; and also some other feeling perhaps. All
that had been Kurtz's had passed out of my hands: his soul, his body,
his station, his plans, his ivory, his career. There remained only his
memory and his Intended—and I wanted to give that up, too, to the
past, in a way—to surrender personally all that remained of him with
me to that oblivion which is the last word of our common fate. I don't
defend myself. I had no clear perception of what it was I really wanted.
Perhaps it was an impulse of unconscious loyalty, or the fulfilment of
one of these ironic necessities that lurk in the facts of human existence.
I don't know. I can't tell. But I went.

"I thought his memory was like the other memories of the dead that
accumulate in every man's life—a vague impress on the brain of shadows
that had fallen on it in their swift and final passage; but before the high

and ponderous door, between the tall houses of a street as still and decorous as a well-kept alley in a cemetery, I had a vision of him on the stretcher, opening his mouth voraciously, as if to devour all the earth with all its mankind. He lived then before me; he lived as much as he had ever lived—a shadow insatiable of splendid appearances, of frightful realities; a shadow darker than the shadow of the night, and draped nobly in the folds of a gorgeous eloquence. The vision seemed to enter the house with me—the stretcher, the phantom-bearers, the wild crowd of obedient worshippers, the gloom of the forests, the glitter of the reach between the murky bends, the beat of the drum, regular and muffled like the beating of a heart—the heart of a conquering darkness. It was a moment of triumph for the wilderness, an invading and vengeful rush which, it seemed to me, I would have to keep back alone for the salvation of another soul. And the memory of what I had heard him say afar there, with the horned shapes stirring at my back, in the glow of fires, within the patient woods, those broken phrases came back to me, were heard again in their ominous and terrifying simplicity. I remembered his abject pleading, his abject threats, the colossal scale of his vile desires, the meanness, the torment, the tempestuous anguish of his soul. And later on I seemed to see his collected languid manner, when he said one day, 'This lot of ivory now is really mine. The Company did not pay for it. I collected it myself at a very great personal risk. I am afraid they will try to claim it as theirs though. H'm. It is a difficult case. What do you think I ought to do—resist? Eh? I want no more than justice.' . . . He wanted no more than justice—no more than justice. I rang the bell before a mahogany door on the first floor, and while I waited he seemed to stare at me out of the glassy panel—stare with that wide and immense stare embracing, condemning, loathing all the universe. I seemed to hear the whispered cry, 'The horror! The horror!'

"The dusk was falling. I had to wait in a lofty drawing-room with three long windows from floor to ceiling that were like three luminous and bedraped columns. The bent gilt legs and backs of the furniture shone in indistinct curves. The tall marble fireplace had a cold and monumental whiteness. A grand piano stood massively in a corner, with dark gleams on the flat surfaces like a somber and polished sarcophagus. A high door opened—closed. I rose.

"She came forward, all in black, with a pale head, floating towards me in the dusk. She was in mourning. It was more than a year since his death, more than a year since the news came; she seemed as though she would remember and mourn forever. She took both my hands in hers and murmured, 'I had heard you were coming.' I noticed she was not very young—I mean not girlish. She had a mature capacity for fidelity, for belief, for suffering. The room seemed to have grown darker, as if all the sad light of the cloudy evening had taken refuge on her forehead. This fair hair, this pale visage, this pure brow, seemed surrounded by an ashy halo from which the dark eyes looked out at me. Their glance was guileless, profound, confident, and trustful. She carried her sorrowful head as though she were proud of that sorrow, as though she would say, I—I alone know how to mourn for him as he deserves. But while we were still shaking hands, such a look of awful desolation came upon her face that I perceived she was one of those creatures that are not the playthings of Time. For her he had died only yesterday. And, by Jove! the impression was so powerful that for me, too, he seemed to have died only yesterday—nay, this very minute. I saw her and him in the same instant of time—his death and her sorrow—I saw her sorrow in the very moment of his death. Do you understand? I saw them together—I heard them together. She had said, with a deep catch of the breath, 'I have survived' while my strained ears seemed to hear distinctly, mingled with her tone of despairing regret, the summing-up whisper of his eternal condemnation. I asked myself what I was doing there, with a sensation of panic in my heart as though I had blundered into a place of cruel and absurd mysteries not fit for a human being to behold. She motioned me to a chair. We sat down. I laid the packet gently on the little table, and she put her hand over it. . . . 'You knew him well,' she murmured, after a moment of mourning silence.

"'Intimacy grows quickly out there,' I said. 'I knew him as well as it is possible for one man to know another.'

"'And you admired him,' she said. 'It was impossible to know him and not to admire him. Was it?'

"'He was a remarkable man,' I said, unsteadily. Then before the appealing fixity of her gaze, that seemed to watch for more words on my lips, I went on, 'It was impossible not to——'

"'Love him,' she finished eagerly, silencing me into an appalled dumbness. 'How true! how true! But when you think that no one knew him so well as I! I had all his noble confidence. I knew him best.'

"'You knew him best,' I repeated. And perhaps she did. But with every word spoken the room was growing darker, and only her forehead, smooth and white, remained illumined by the unextinguishable light of belief and love.

"'You were his friend,' she went on. 'His friend.' she repeated, a little louder. 'You must have been, if he had given you this, and sent you to me. I feel I can speak to you—and oh! I must speak. I want you —you who have heard his last words—to know I have been worthy of him. . . . It is not pride. . . . Yes! I am proud to know I understood him better than anyone on earth—he told me so himself. And since his mother died I have had no one—no one—to—to——'

"I listened. The darkness deepened. I was not even sure whether he had given me the right bundle. I rather suspect he wanted me to take care of another batch of his papers which, after his death, I saw the manager examining under the lamp. And the girl talked, easing her pain in the certitude of my sympathy; she talked as thirsty men drink. I had heard that her engagement with Kurtz had been disapproved by her people. He wasn't rich enough or something. And indeed I don't know whether he had not been a pauper all his life. He had given me some reason to infer that it was his impatience of comparative poverty that drove him out there.

"'. . . Who was not his friend who had heard him speak once?' she was saying. 'He drew men towards him by what was best in them.' She looked at me with intensity. 'It is the gift of the great,' she went on, and the sound of her low voice seemed to have the accompaniment of all the other sounds, full of mystery, desolation, and sorrow, I had ever heard— the ripple of the river, the soughing of the trees swayed by the wind, the murmurs of wild crowds, the faint ring of incomprehensible words cried from afar, the whisper of a voice speaking from beyond the threshold of an eternal darkness. 'But you have heard him! You know!' she cried.

"'Yes, I know,' I said with something like despair in my heart, but bowing my head before the faith that was in her, before that great and saving illusion that shone with an unearthly glow in the darkness, in the triumphant darkness from which I could not have defended her—from which I could not even defend myself.

"'What a loss to me—to us!'—she corrected herself with beautiful generosity; then added in a murmur, 'To the world.' By the last gleams of twilight I could see the glitter of her eyes, full of tears—of tears that would not fall.

"'I have been very happy—very fortunate—very proud,' she went on. 'Too fortunate. Too happy for a little while. And now I am un-happy for—for life.'

"She stood up; her fair hair seemed to catch all the remaining light in a glimmer of gold. I rose too.

"'And of all this,' she went on, mournfully, 'of all his promise, and of all his greatness, of his generous mind, of his noble heart, nothing re-mains—nothing but a memory. You and I——'

"'We shall always remember him,' I said, hastily.

"'No!' she cried. 'It is impossible that all this should be lost—that such a life should be sacrificed to leave nothing—but sorrow. You know what vast plans he had. I knew of them too—I could not perhaps under-stand—but others knew of them. Something must remain. His words, at least, have not died.'

"'His words will remain,' I said.

"'And his example,' she whispered to herself. 'Men looked up to him —his goodness shone in every act. His example——'

"'True,' I said; 'his example, too. Yes, his example. I forgot that.'

"'But I do not. I cannot—I cannot believe—not yet. I cannot believe that I shall never see him again, that nobody will see him again, never, never, never.'

"She put out her arms as if after a retreating figure, stretching them back and with clasped pale hands across the fading and narrow sheen of the window. Never see him! I saw him clearly enough then. I shall see this eloquent phantom as long as I live, and I shall see her, too, a tragic and familiar Shade, resembling in this gesture another one, tragic also, and bedecked with powerless charms, stretching bare brown arms over the glitter of the infernal stream, the stream of darkness. She said suddenly very low, 'He died as he lived.'

"'His end,' said I, with dull anger stirring in me, 'was in every way worthy of his life.'

"'And I was not with him,' she murmured. My anger subsided before a feeling of infinite pity.

"'Everything that could be done——' I mumbled.

"'Ah, but I believed in him more than anyone on earth—more than his own mother, more than—himself. He needed me! Me! I would have treasured every sigh, every word, every sign, every glance.'

"I felt a chill grip my chest. 'Don't,' I said, in a muffled voice.

"'Forgive me. I—I—have mourned so long in silence—in silence.
. . . You were with him—to the last? I think of his loneliness. Nobody near to understand him as I would have understood. Perhaps no one to hear. . . .'

"'To the very end,' I said, shakily. 'I heard his very last words. . . .' I stopped in a fright.

"'Repeat them,' she murmured in a heart-broken tone. 'I want—I want—something—something—to—to live with.'

"I was on the point of crying at her, 'Don't you hear them?' The dusk was repeating them in a persistent whisper all around us, in a whisper that seemed to swell menacingly like the first whisper of a rising wind. 'The horror! the horror!'

"'His last word—to live with,' she murmured. 'Don't you understand I loved him—I loved him—I loved him!'

"I pulled myself together and spoke slowly.

"'The last word he pronounced was—your name,'

"I heard a light sigh, and then my heart stood still, stopped dead short by an exulting and terrible cry, by the cry of inconceivable triumph and of unspeakable pain. 'I knew it—I was sure!' . . . She knew. She was sure. I heard her weeping; she had hidden her face in her hands. It seemed to me that the house would collapse before I could escape, that the heavens would fall upon my head. But nothing happened. The heavens do not fall for such a trifle. Would they have fallen, I wonder, if I had rendered Kurtz that justice which was his due? Hadn't he said he wanted only justice? But I couldn't. I could not tell her. It would have been too dark—too dark altogether. . . ."

Marlow ceased, and sat apart, indistinct and silent, in the pose of a meditating Buddha. Nobody moved for a time. "We have lost the first of the ebb," said the Director, suddenly. I raised my head. The offing was barred by a black bank of clouds, and the tranquil waterway leading to the uttermost ends of the earth flowed somber under an overcast sky—seemed to lead into the heart of an immense darkness.

ON THE STAIRS

By *Arthur Morrison*

[Arthur Morrison (1863–) is an English writer. His works consist of novels, stories, plays, and art criticism. His realistic portrayals of
life in the meaner sections of London have met with high approval.

On the Stairs is from the volume of stories entitled *Tales of Mean
Streets* (1894) and is here reprinted by permission of the author.]

THE house had been "genteel." When trade was prospering in the
East End, and the ship-fitter or block-maker thought it no shame
to live in the parish where his workshop lay, such a master had lived
here. Now, it was a tall, solid, well-bricked, ugly house, grimy and
paintless in the joinery, cracked and patched in the windows: where
the front door stood open all day long; and the womankind sat on the
steps, talking of sickness and deaths and the cost of things; and treacherous holes lurked in the carpet of road-soil on the stairs and in the
passage. For when eight families live in a house, nobody buys a door-
mat, and the street was one of those streets that are always muddy. It
smelt, too, of many things, none of them pleasant (one was fried fish);
but for all that it was not a slum.

Three flights up, a gaunt woman with bare forearms stayed on her
way to listen at a door which, opening, let out a warm, fetid waft from
a close sick-room. A bent and tottering old woman stood on the threshold, holding the door behind her.

"An' is 'e no better now, Mrs. Curtis?" the gaunt woman asked,
with a nod at the opening.

The old woman shook her head, and pulled the door closer. Her jaw
wagged loosely in her withered chaps: "Nor won't be; till 'e's gone."
Then after a certain pause, "'E's goin'," she said.

"Don't doctor give no 'ope?"

"Lor' bless ye, I don't want to ast no doctors," Mrs. Curtis replied,
with something not unlike a chuckle. "I've seed too many on 'em. The
boy's a-goin', fast; I can see that. An' then"—she gave the handle
another tug, and whispered—"he's been called." She nodded amain.
"Three seprit knocks at the bed-head las' night; an' I know what *that*
means!"

The gaunt woman raised her brows, and nodded. "Ah, well," she
said, "we all on us comes to it some day, sooner or later. An' it's often
a 'appy release."

The two looked into space beyond each other, the elder with a nod and a croak. Presently the other pursued, "'E's been a very good son, ain't 'e?"

"Ay, ay, well enough son to me," responded the old woman, a little peevishly; "an' I'll 'ave 'im put away decent, though there's on'y the Union for me after. I can do that, thank Gawd!" she added, meditatively, as chin on fist she stared into the thickening dark over the stairs.

"When I lost my pore 'usband," said the gaunt woman, with a certain brightening, "I give 'im a 'ansome funeral. 'E was a Oddfeller, an' I got twelve pound. I 'ad a oak caufin an' a open 'earse. There was a kerridge for the fam'ly an' one for 'is mates—two 'orses each, an' feathers, an' mutes; an' it went the furthest way round to the cimitry. 'Wotever 'appens, Mrs. Manders,' says the undertaker, 'you'll feel as you've treated 'im proper; nobody can't reproach you over that.' An' they couldn't. 'E was a good 'usband to me, an' I buried 'im respectable."

The gaunt woman exulted. The old, old story of Manders's funeral fell upon the other one's ears with a freshened interest, and she mumbled her gums ruminantly. "Bob'll 'ave a 'ansome buryin', too," she said. "I can make it up, with the insurance money, an' this an' that. On'y I donno about mutes. It's a expense."

In the East End, when a woman has not enough money to buy a thing much desired, she does not say so in plain words; she says the thing is an "expense," or a "great expense." It means the same thing, but it sounds better. Mrs. Curtis had reckoned her resources, and found that mutes would be an "expense." At a cheap funeral mutes cost half-a-sovereign and their liquor. Mrs. Manders said as much.

"Yus, yus, 'arf-a-sovereign," the old woman assented. Within, the sick man feebly beat the floor with a stick. "I'm a-comin'," she cried shrilly; "yus, 'arf-a-sovereign, but it's a lot, an' I don't see 'ow I'm to do it—not at present." She reached for the door-handle again, but stopped and added, by after-thought, "Unless I don't 'ave no plooms."

"It 'ud be a pity not to 'ave plooms. I 'ad—"

There were footsteps on the stairs: then a stumble and a testy word. Mrs. Curtis peered over into the gathering dark. "Is it the doctor, sir?" she asked. It was the doctor's assistant; and Mrs. Manders tramped up to the next landing as the door of the sick-room took him in.

For five minutes the stairs were darker than ever. Then the assistant, a very young man, came out again, followed by the old woman with a candle. Mrs. Manders listened in the upper dark. "He's sinking fast," said the assistant. "He *must* have a stimulant. Dr. Mansell ordered port wine. Where is it?" Mrs. Curtis mumbled dolorously. "I tell you he *must* have it," he averred with unprofessional emphasis (his qualification was only a month old). "The man can't take solid food, and his strength must be kept up somehow. Another day may make all the difference. Is it because you can't afford it?" "It's a expense—sich a expense, doctor," the old woman pleaded. "An' wot with 'arf-pints o' milk an'—" She grew inarticulate, and mumbled dismally.

"But he must have it, Mrs. Curtis, if it's your last shilling: it's the only way. If you mean you absolutely haven't the money—" and he paused a little awkwardly. He was not a wealthy young man—wealthy young men do not devil for East End doctors—but he was conscious of a certain haul of sixpences at nap the night before; and, being inexperienced, he did not foresee the career of persecution whereon he was entering at his own expense and of his own motion. He produced five shillings: "If you absolutely haven't the money, why—take this and get a bottle—good: not at a public house. But mind, *at once*. He should have had it before."

It would have interested him, as a matter of coincidence, to know that his principal had been guilty of the selfsame indiscretion—even the amount was identical—on that landing the day before. But, as Mrs. Curtis said nothing of this, he floundered down the stair and out into the wetter mud, pondering whether or not the beloved son of a Congregational minister might take full credit for a deed of charity on the proceeds of sixpenny nap. But Mrs. Curtis puffed her wrinkles, and shook her head sagaciously as she carried in her candle. From the room came a clink as of money falling into a teapot. And Mrs. Manders went about her business.

The door was shut, and the stair a pit of blackness. Twice a lodger passed down, and up and down, and still it did not open. Men and women walked on the lower flights, and out at the door, and in again. From the street a shout or a snatch of laughter floated up the pit. On the pavement footsteps rang crisper and fewer, and from the bottom passage there were sounds of stagger and sprawl. A demented old clock buzzed divers hours at random, and was rebuked every twenty minutes by the regular tread of a policeman on his beat. Finally, somebody shut the street-door with a great bang, and the street was muffled. A key turned inside the door on the landing, but that was all. A feeble light shone for hours along the crack below, and then went out. The crazy old clock went buzzing on, but nothing left that room all night. Nothing that opened the door. . . .

When next the key turned, it was to Mrs. Manders' knock, in the full morning; and soon the two women came out on the landing together, Mrs. Curtis with a shapeless clump of bonnet. "Ah, 'e's a lovely corpse," said Mrs. Manders. "Like wax. So was my 'usband."

"I must be stirrin'," croaked the old woman, "an' go about the insurance an' the measurin' an' that. There's lots to do."

"Ah, there is. 'Oo are you goin' to 'ave—Wilkins? I 'ad Wilkins. Better than Kedge, I think: Kedge's mutes dresses rusty, an' their trousis is frayed. If you was thinkin' of 'avin' mutes—"

"Yus, yus,"—with a palsied nodding—"I'm a-goin' to 'ave mutes: I can do it respectable, thank Gawd!"

"And the plooms?"

"Ay, yus, an' the plooms too. They ain't sich a great expense, after all."

MARTHA'S FIREPLACE

By Hamlin Garland

[Hamlin Garland (1860–   ) has been a recognized interpreter of the Middle West in American fiction. His principal medium of expression is the novel, but he made his early reputation with a series of realistic short stories published in the volume entitled *Main-Traveled Roads*. These are serious stories depicting farm and village life on the prairies of Iowa and among the coollies of Wisconsin. Among Mr. Garland's notable publications may be mentioned the following: *A Spoil of Office* (1892), *Prairie Folks* (1892), *Rose of Dutcher's Coolly* (1895), *The Captain of the Gray Horse Troop* (1902), *Hesper* (1903), *The Shadow World* (1908), *Cavanagh, Forest Ranger* (1909), *A Son of the Middle Border* (1917), and *A Daughter of the Middle Border* (1921).

Martha's Fireplace, written in 1905, is reprinted by permission of the author.]

STEPHEN THURBER had no notion of falling in with a great sociologic movement when he decided to sell his farm in Wet Coolly and move into Bluff Siding; he merely yielded to the importunities of his wife and daughter, who looked away to the prim little village down the valley as a shining land of leisure and of possible social triumph.

It *was* a lonely place for the women—that Stephen generously admitted. A long ridge, some five hundred feet high, cut them off from the railway, and all the young people were leaving, by twos and threes as fast as they grew up, and the roads were very bad, and visitors few.

So at last he sighed and said, "All right, mother, we'll go; but I'll declare I hate to give up the farm—I don't know what in time I'll do with myself."

He sold the place soon afterward for a sum which seemed enormous to his wife, and bought a naked, angular little "wing house," which occupied a fifty-foot lot on one of the new streets in Bluff Siding. It was painted in blue and pink, stood indecently close to the board-walk, and it had only a half-dozen elms the size of broomsticks to shield it from the sun and wind. "The parlor is skursely large enough to contain the family, let alone company," Stephen sighfully remarked; "but if it suits you women, it suits me."

He seemed quite cheerful about it at the time, but the old farm looked so much more comfortable, so much more home-like on his return, that his heart failed him. The dignity, the amplitude of the buildings overwhelmed him with joy and pride—and sorrow. Every tree about the yard he had planted—some of them while Martha (his first wife and his first love) stood by to watch him tramp the earth about their roots. Now they rose far, far above the roof, like guardian soldiers, faithful and strong. Their branches had come to be like hands upraised in blessing in summer—like warding spear points in winter. Even the phloxes and the lilacs of the lawn were descendants of those his first love had planted.

And the house! How broad and generous and homey it seemed in contrast with that trig little town cottage. He had built it for Martha in the flush of prosperity which followed the great Civil War, and it still remained the most imposing dwelling in Wet Coolly. It was a big, square frame building, New England in type, and had a fine, old-fashioned fireplace in the sitting-room—the only fireplace in the township, so far as he knew.

This curious "notion," this singular extravagance, had made the Thurber place renowned throughout the entire county. To have had a fireplace left over from pioneer days would have been excusable; but to put one in a new house was considered an act of folly lying just this side of dementia. Nevertheless, all the carpers came again and again to toast their shins in its glow, and the young folks were unanimous in their praise of it. They flocked to its blaze on winter nights with joy, and many a lively dance ended an evening of unforgetable cheer in its hospitable shine.

The mantel, as Martha loved to tell, had been carved by her grandfather and came from the old homestead in the State of Maine. She loved it for its associations, and in that love had taken it from its place in the Kittredge homestead and brought it West as a kind of shrine or family totem. She had brought also the ancient andirons, the tongs and the shovel; even the old crane, almost as dear as the mantel, had been set in and completed her equipment.

Stephen, now that he was about to lose his treasures, recalled Martha's delight as she watched the workmen set the old oaken slab in its place. He re-lived the party she gave when the first fire was laid, and thrilled to remember how pretty she looked as she touched a match to the shavings and recited a little verse from *The Hanging of the Crane*. She was cheerful and, Stephen believed, happy; but when she went away he began to realize that she had never really taken root in the West, and now that he was growing old, he himself began to dwell more and more in the land of his youth. His thoughts returned often to his rocky New Hampshire intervale.

Yes, it was hardest of all to loose the tendrils of his heart from the hearth, for though Serilla had rearranged and redecorated after her own heart, Martha's fireplace remained unchanged.

"I'll let you have your way in most things, Serilly, but I want this room to look as it does now, just as she left it."

As the time for the migration drew near, Stephen stole away from the disordered kitchen to muse sadly before the fire. He had consented to a "vandue," and was willing Serilla should sell all the furniture they had, except a few pieces that had been Martha's, and as there was no demand for the irons and brasses around the fireplace, he expected to box them up as keepsakes.

The new owner was to take possession on the first of April, and so on the last day of March (a cold, gray day), having parted with all his live-stock, and the larger number of his implements, Stephen Thurber, after nearly forty years of life on his Coolly farm, took solemn leave of the trees he had planted, the barns he had built and the house which had been Martha's. The last thing he did before leaving was to visit the empty living-room, where his last fire was still blazing on the hearth. "I want to leave the room bright and warm, anyhow," he said to his wife and daughter. "I don't want to remember it all cold and dark."

"Good gracious! You talk as you were going away a thousand miles," exclaimed his wife.

"I never expect to see the inside of that house again," he said, with a pathos too deep for her to comprehend.

The cottage in town seemed to grow smaller after they moved into it; but Serilla and Cariss were delighted with its snugness, and went about extolling its "advantages" with fluent tongues. "It's small, of course; but what do we want with a big house? It's just that much less work to take care of. Besides, here we have a pump right in the kitchen, and a furnace, and a bath room, and everything is as neat as a pin—no cracks or dark corners."

"I kind o' like dark corners," said Stephen. He felt its lack of homi-ness; but could not otherwise express it.

For the first month he was busy getting feed and other necessaries down from the farm. "By jocks, I never thought I'd have to cross that hill so many times during my whole natural course of life," he said to his family, and each trip left him gloomier, and at last he sent a hired teamster. "I can't go it again," he explained, bitterly; "it makes me sick to see that sloven spoil the place. He hain't cleaned up the lawn, and he's fencing off a part of the orchard for his pigs." This was like the desecration of an altar to him, but he said no more about it. During May he spent a good deal of time in his little seven-by-twelve garden, and in taking care of his little red barn, all of which seemed like a joke, like playing farmer. "Makes me feel as if I'd come back to second child-hood, by jocks if it don't; and that truck-patch o' mine—well, if the cat should get loose she'd eat up the whole bilin' mess of it. It's so little I hate to step on it—feel like puttin' it in the barn nights."

By June he was settled into a certain daily groove. "You want to just lay back and rest," said Hiram Fox, another veteran of the plow; "that's what the rest of us are doin', an' we're doin' it conscientiously. The town is full of 'tired farmers' like us."

And sure enough, as Stephen began to comprehend his neighbors, he found himself surrounded by a score or more of gnarled old grubbers like himself, men who knew how to swing the axe, the cradle, and the scythe, pioneers who had uprooted the great oaks of the hillsides and ripped the sod of the meadow into strips in order to sow their wheat—men whose muscles had once been as steel bands and whose hearts were still the hearts of warriors. They were all old now, old and weather-worn, and heavy and slow, and taking their ease heroically while their work-bent wives fussed about their houses in a sort of automatic frenzy, toiling to pass the long days of summer, rising early to make the nights of winter short. They mostly lived as lonely couples, for their sons and daughters, impatient of the narrow opportunities and the slow round of life in the valley, had gone to the city or to the farther West.

Stephen, without knowing it, was passing through precisely the same phases, computing the same problems. For one thing, he could not break himself of the habit of early rising. He lay awake so long and so still each morning that his bones ached, and when he could endure the strain no longer, he slipped out of bed, built the fire, put on the teakettle for his wife, and filled the bucket with water before going to feed his horse. Even then, upon his return to the house he often found the kettle boiling away and no one astir. Sometimes he went to milk their meek little cow, and had time to take her to the pasture before breakfast was even a prophecy. All this was mighty discouraging, for the days were long even after his coffee.

Breakfast over, he made as much work as possible watering the horse and feeding his ten chickens, and then—was stumped! There was nothing to do, nothing to oversee, no one to "boss," and no soul to talk to around the place, for the women were busy with their own affairs and apparently quite contented.

For all these reasons he soon fell into the habit of "going up street" like the other "time-killers," to see what was going on.

The Chicago mail got in at ten, bringing the morning papers, and the post-office swarmed with the slow-moving gray-beards, all jocularly reviling each other about their lazy bones and rheumatic joints.

"I'd be ashamed to loaf around town the way you fellows do," Pilcher would say. "Here's corn-plantin' in full drive; beautiful weather, too, and you boys hangin' around town. I bet you didn't, any one o' you, have breakfast this morning till long after sun-up."

Or again Hiram would say, "Hello, Steve, why ain't you out in the meadow with your scythe this morning? Timothy is just in the purple."

Then Stephen would reply, "Remember the time I hired you to help me put up hay on my north field? By jocks, that was a hot neck o' the woods. I laid you under a bush that day."

"Yes, you did! I see you now, flat on your back, under that wild plum tree, pantin' like a lizard on a hot log."

In this way they followed the seasons, and in imagination took part in the farm duties, bragging with hearty frankness of what they were able once to do—in those far days when the land was new and they were all young. Each man listened patiently to the other, for their tales were faithful to the fact. They had truly been giants in those days.

The half-jocular, half-serious greetings over, they talked quite animatedly concerning the price of pork and cream, or touched lightly (and with decent respect) upon each other's political prejudices, and when the mail was distributed, each man put his paper under his arm, together with a parcel of steak for dinner, and trudged away homeward, intent on a certain easy chair beside a chosen window, where the light fell pleasantly, just of the right mind to enjoy the reflected tumult of the far-off wars and conflagrations of the outer world.

Stephen's cosy corner was in the sitting-room beside the west window, and his chair (one he had bought for Martha when she was ill the first time) was a plain old piece of walnut and cane, deep-seated and comfortable, which no one else presumed to sit in. He was firm on that point, and he insisted also on having a little table to himself on which his papers and his spectacles always lay ready to hand when he came from the garden or the street.

He generally took an hour for his paper; but this left some forty minutes to be filled in before dinner. Most of the veterans took naps at this hour, but Stephen had never been able to sleep in the middle of the day, so he usually went out and wandered around the garden, coddling the plants till he was on speaking terms with every potato blossom and beet top within his enclosure. These forty minutes were like hours to him, for his appetite was prodigious.

After dinner on pleasant days he hitched up his horse and drove about the country lanes. Serilla was always too busy to go, and Cariss considered it "slow." So he often took some crony, and together they jogged from farm to farm, following the progress of the crops, endlessly discussing the "left-handed way" in which the Germans did their work.

After these trips he usually tinkered around the house and re-read his paper till his eyes ached, and then, tired and sad, sat down to ponder the past with an occasional wistful, uneasy glimpse into the future. He began to wonder what it all meant, this life here on earth, for his was a deep and tender soul, sweet and kindly, holding something of the poet in solution. He both loved and feared the magic of these dreams of the past. As the nights lengthened and the cold deepened, he began to definitely long for the old fireplace. He mused much on the joy he used to feel as he came in from corn husking or rail splitting, wet and cold, to find the fire blazing on the hearth in the old log house. He minutely re-lived the days when the crane was newly hung and Martha sat beside him in the glow of the embers, her hand in his, while they spoke lovingly of the two little ones that died before they could speak.

He recalled her sickness and shuddered at the remembered loneliness of the old house after her death. Then Serilla came, and later two robust sons. How they loved the old hearth, on which they were content to bask like puppies, snuggling against his feet, asking for more bear stories. The winters of that far time were made as cheery as summers by the blaze of the hearth, and the roar of the branches outside carried no chill to his heart.

As he awoke from such a dream and looked around Serilla's sitting-room, Stephen wondered what Martha would say of it. He began to consider how much a fireplace would mean to him; he even went so far as to slyly measure between the two west windows to see if one could not be set in, but the space was too narrow for anything but a hard-coal grate, and this he despised.

Sometimes at night, when his wife thought him dozing, he was really back in the old Coolly house watching the blazing logs, his mind filled with a delicious sadness, his eyes wet with tears. What was it that had gone out of his life? Here he sat in a perfectly comfortable room, possessing a horse and a carriage, with an abundance to eat and no cares—and yet the past, with all its toil, so called to him that his throat ached at the thought of it. Oh, if he could only re-live it all!

In those dear days the wind was fierce, the woods of winter desolate; but Martha's face shone like a star, and the old hearth rendered each night with his children a poem. Work was hard in those days; but rest was sweet. Hunger was keen; but eating brought no illness in its train.

He was loyal to Serilla, the mother of his children; but Martha was the wife of his youth, the one chosen wholly of his heart—and her fireplace came to typify all that was sweetest and most poetic in his life and in the lives of his children. It was an altar. Around it they had gathered when the corn was cribbed and the cattle housed for the night. In its light they had danced when the threshing was over and at Thanksgiving time.

He awoke with a start to the present.

"What will we do on Thanksgiving Day and at Christmas?" he asked, one night. "We can't all get into this little box of a place. There ain't a room in the house we can all sit down in; and if we could, we'd have nothing but the floor to look at. I declare it clean disheartens me."

Serilla was a little dashed, but replied, comfortably, "We'll manage somehow, I guess. We can't have but a part of the children at a time, that's all. We can bid your folks for Thanksgiving and my folks for Christmas."

This rankled in Stephen's mind, and thereafter he despised his toy house. It was a good enough tenement—a place to rent for awhile, but as a *home* in which to grow old, it was revolting in spite of its shining paint and spick and span new furniture.

In reality it held out no charm, no poetry, no associations; it was as rectangular as a dry-goods box, and as hopelessly prosaic as a "golden oak" wash-stand. A child born in such a house is cheated out of its birthright of dim, wide rooms lit up by the dancing firelight; robbed of the sagas the great trees chant as they roar outside in the wild wind—deprived of all shadow, all suggestion. Something of this flitted through Stephen's thought, though he could not give it voice.

"Mother," he said one day, "I wish we had one room big enough to turn round in, and a rag carpet and some old-fashioned chairs and a fireplace—"

"There you go again about that fireplace," exclaimed his wife irritably. "Nobody has fireplaces now, and how are you going to have a big room in this house?"

"I'll build one, if you say so."

"Nonsense. This house is all right, plenty big enough for us—with Cariss likely to go off any minute. And as for Thanksgiving and Christmas, we can go to the hotel and get dinner, or take 'em in squads here at home."

"That wouldn't do," he protested. "It wouldn't do at all. It wouldn't seem natural or right for us to go to a hotel on such days. We'd ought'o have all such meals at home."

"Well, you wouldn't build a big house just to use for Thanksgiving, would you?"

"I d'know but I would," he answered, sturdily. "I d'know but it would be jest about as good a way to spend our money as any other. I'm sick o' this little coop. Let's buy the Merrill place and have room to dance a jig if we want to."

"No, sirree! You don' ketch me livin' on the edge of town, with no sidewalks. I want to be right in the center of things, where we can have our telephone, 'lectric lights an' all."

"I could put in the telephone—"

"I won't hear of it, Steve. I came away from the farm to live in town, and I don't want no half-way business in mine."

Stephen surrendered to her will and made no further complaint.

They took their Thanksgiving dinner at the hotel—and on the way home Serilla said, "There! For once in our lives, Cariss, we don't have to think of Thanksgiving dinner dishes."

"That's right," answered Cariss, "and yet it doesn't seem a bit like Thanksgiving, does it, pa?"

Stephen did not answer, for he was far away in the holidays of the past.

It is a tragic thing to grow old in daily labor, but it is almost as sad to grow old with nothing to do—and homeless. Among all his fellows Stephen alone began to perceive that to seek comfort for the body in new things left the mind filled with longing for old things—left it comfortless and unhoused.

So, while outwardly he remained the same, inwardly he was filled with recollections which made him tremble with their power. He greeted his neighbors with a smile which grew each month a little more absent-minded—a little more wistful—and when he wrote to his son in Chicago, he said: "Our house is about as big as your hat, and it's nice and neat, but we can't have any Christmas this year—no place to set a table for more'n six. I'm trying hard to pass the time;" and as he wrote his glasses grew misty with his tears.

But one day while he was sitting alone by his window at sunset, when the blue-jays were in flight, and the butter-nut leaves were falling, Stephen permitted himself a most heroic dream. In imagination he said to a contractor, "I want my old house across the hill. I don't care what it costs. I'm worth thirty thousand dollars, and if it takes half of it, I want my home. My women folks will never go back to the Coolly with me, and I can't live there alone, so you must bring the old house—fire-place and all—across the ridge and put it up under the trees somewhere. I want it just as it was—can you do this?"

In this imagined conversation he was able to express himself easily; so he went on to say, "I ain't got but a little while to stay here, and I want to spend my days in peace—I want to be comfortable *in my mind*—and my mind ain't easy in this little box; I want a roomy room with shadows in the corners and a fire to watch when I don't want to read or talk—I want the old room—"

And when his wife broke in on his magical revery, he looked up with eyes so scared and pleading that she wondered and sharply cried out, "What's the matter, Stephen? You look as if you'd seen a ghost."

"There, mother—there! mebbe I have," he answered, and turned away to hide the quiver of his lips.

One day he came in from his usual trip up town visibly excited, and after he had taken off his coat and hung up his hat, he began:

"Well, somebody has bought the Merrill place."

Serilla looked up from her sewing.

"Who?"

"Hiram said that he heard that a man from Tyre, a contractor, had bought it and was going to build on speculation."

The Merrill place, as it was called, was the remnant of a fine farm which had once been the pride of old Abner Merrill. The house, standing among magnificent elms, commanded ten acres of land—all the rest had been sold away by the heirs. The outbuildings were in decay and the yard was littered with rusty machinery, but it was a beautiful site, and Stephen had long admired it. He never passed it without planning what he would do if he owned it. Now he said: "Well, I am glad somebody is goin' to improve it, but I wish you had let me buy it."

To this Serilla made no answer.

Stephen had been "kind o' dauncy" all through the hot weather, but the work going forward on the Merrill place seemed to interest him. He fell into the habit of walking down there of a morning, and Serilla was glad of it, though she took her fling at him and his cronies.

"It's a wonder to me that you and Hiram and old man Pilcher don't get a tent and camp out in the Merrill yard. Seems to me if I was that builder I'd order you off the premises."

"He considers our advice valuable, mother."

"I'll *bet* he does!" she scornfully replied.

A few days later old Hiram reported to "the Committee on the Universe," that Mr. Hill, the builder was putting in a big chimney and fireplace. "He says all the city people have them these days."

"Well, now, Steve," said Pilcher, "you better go right down and give him a little help—you bein' an authority on fireplaces. We all hung our stockings in chimney corners back East, but I'll be dinged if I can remember just how you put 'em in."

"It's a funny thing to me," said Hiram. "In the days when we all had fireplaces we were crazy for stoves, and now when we are all pervided with furnaces some people want fireplaces. You'd think a family that had nigh about froze to death in front of a hole in the wall would fight shy of 'em thereafter."

"But they have their good pints," said Stephen, eagerly. "Recollect the mug o' cider on the hob, and the chestnuts in the ashes, and the apple parin's and the dances—I tell you there's nothin' takes the place of a good old—"

"Well you can have hot cider and apple bees without a hole in the wall you can sling a yearling through. What's the matter with a base-burner?"

Stephen was stubborn. "Won't do. A base burner is such a sullen sort o' thing. No, sir. You've got to have the flames a-leapin' an' a-crackin.' I'll admit you need other heat," he added, "when the weather's too cold; but I just believe we'd all be healthier if we went back to the drafty old fireplaces. It did keep the room ventilated—the bad air was all swept up the chimney."

"Yes, 'long with the cat and the almanac and the weekly newspaper," remarked Hiram. "My stars! but the draft in our old chimney would draw nails out of oak planks. We had to put a stun on the Bible."

"But we didn't have consumption in those days—"

"We had somethin' worse," piped Pilcher.

"What's that?"

"Chilblains, by cracky!"

And then they all cackled together, and the committee broke up.

"What's this I hear?" inquired Serilla, sharply, a few days later. "Has the owner of the Merrill place asked Jane Kittredge to go into that house?"

"I guess that's right, mother."

Serilla snorted, "Well, that's a fool thing to do—how come it? Did you advise it?"

"Well, no—Mr. Hill was sort o' inquirin' 'round for someone, and as Amos was sick and Jane—"

"I knew it! I knew you had a hand in that!"

"Well, why not? Amos is my brother-in-law—I've a right to help him—and Jane's a good housekeeper; you can't deny that!"

Serilla turned away. She and Jane were a little "aidgewise" toward each other—partly because Amos was Stephen's first wife's brother and partly because Jane herself was quite as sharp-tongued as anyone.

Serilla had grazed her husband's larger secret, but had not really touched it—and he went out to the barn to think the situation over.

The truth was that all this buying, planning, and building were stanzas in a poem of Stephen Thurber's imagination. He was the "owner"; Mr. Hill was merely his confederate, his blind.

To the sympathetic young fellow he had gone (while on a visit to Tyre) and to him had explained his needs. "Now, I can't move the old house over from the Coolly; that's out of the question, but I want you to go and look it over and build me another exactly like it. Make it just as it was when I went into it for the first time, so that when I sit down by the fire I can jest imagine I'm home again." He paused there, for his voice failed him.

This was his secret pain—a sense of homelessness. All the subtle charm of his life, all the poetry of the past, was associated with the home beyond the ridge, and the sense of loss grew in power of appeal day by day as his palms softened with idleness and his cheeks lost their coat of tan. He was bitterly unhappy in his present, and in consequence his face turned more and more fully toward the lovelit days of his youth. The thought of growing old on a fifty-foot lot in a cramped, high-colored, little house appalled him; and so, after weeks of burning desire and irresolution, he had broken ground.

No one suspected his connection with the building—his plan was too audacious, too far removed from the practical, everyday life of Bluff Siding to be imagined by anyone; and yet he was tormented with dread of the storm of shrill astonishment and protest which would encircle him when his secret should be disclosed.

His hope and comfort lay in the belief that a visit to the new house all complete and ready to move into would subdue and win his wife. Of Cariss he had no fear. He also, covertly, depended upon the sympathy and support of his "Chicago Boy," as he called John; but Albert, who was a hard-working dentist in Tyre, with a large and annually increasing family (and who was casting forward very definitely to his share of the estate)—Albert would look with disfavor on the expenditure of so much money in so foolish a fashion. As for Pilcher and old Hiram and the rest of the boys he was prepared to weather their laughter, for it would be good-natured—and, besides, the joke would be partly on them, for could he not say, "I fooled ye, though, every man jack of ye!"

But the strain of his duplicity wore upon him, and Serilla grew so concerned about his silence, his abstraction, that she wrote to John to come up and see what was the matter with his father.

John came, and in answer to his questions, Stephen said: "There's nothin' the matter with me, my son, only I ain't got nothin' to do. I miss the old place."

"Well, you are in *snug* quarters," John admitted, as he looked about the little house. "It's all very nice, mother, but it isn't a bit like home."

Serilla was defiant. "Did you s'pose I was goin' to end my days in Wet Coolly, twelve miles from the railroad?

"I was just as sorry to leave the old house as he was. But, my stars! I couldn't stand the strain. It's all right for you to talk; you can come and go, but I had to stay there winter and summer—"

John was generous enough to acknowledge that it was a lonesome place for a woman in winter.

"Lonesome! You might as well be buried."

"I s'pose you're right, mother. It's all a part of a sorrowful exodus;" and leaving a prescription for his father he went back to the city, quite uninstructed in the real cause of his father's loss of health.

The point toward which Stephen was definitely working was a grand house-warming on New Year's Day; and he wished to surprise John especially, for *he* would certainly understand.

It was a time of anxiety, but it was a time of great joy. Each day as the house took shape he rode by or sat in the yard to feast upon it. From the porch in front to the little garden fence on its roof it was exactly like the old house—the windows were the same, the chimney rose through the shingles at the same point. Sometimes he went inside, but the litter there troubled him, and besides, he wanted to wait until all was completed, in order that the impression might come to him in fulness of power.

His notion in getting Jane and her husband in was at first due to his desire to have someone to put the place to rights pending his confession to Serilla—a confession which became each day more difficult—for as the days slipped by and the house neared completion, he became absorbed in the idea of restoring the furnishings of the house as it was when Martha was alive, an idea which came to him as he sat with Amos and his wife among their furniture. He was surprised to find a number of pieces of Martha's furniture which he had given them after her death, and he asked Jane to see if she could find the armchair he had let her sister have.

As the day for warming the hearth drew near, Stephen fairly trembled with joyous excitement. The builder was paid up and gone; the yard was "slick as a whistle"; and the big new house stood cold and white and grand under the bare branches of the elms. The andirons and the mantel were in place, but Stephen had not yet permitted himself the luxury of sitting down before the fire—he wanted to wait till the room was furnished and Martha's rugs in place.

He was up early that day in order "to help Amos move in," he explained to his wife.

It was a raw day—cloudy with a strong north wind, and winter seemed in the air—and when the night began to fall and Jane's furniture was sparsely distributed (Jane herself being busy in the kitchen), Stephen lit the fire on his hearth and sat down before it with a thrill of satisfaction.

As he gazed the spell of that which he had wrought fell upon him. The first stanza of his poem was being sung by the roaring flames. On the white walls the golden light was flickering—and along the ceiling the shadows of the tall andirons danced grotesquely, familiarly, as of old. The mantel with its carven figures and its candles and vases seemed unchanged. The song of the elms outside was the same.

Tears dimmed his eyes; a big lump filled his throat. For a moment he had the exaltation of the artist. He seemed to have triumphed over time's decrees as the poet does. It appeared that he had actually restored his home, reconstructed the past, so that Martha might at any moment steal into the room, light of step as of old, to sit on the arm of his chair and to ask with that tenderness of sympathy which always melted his heart, "Tired, Stephen?" and lay her cheek against his shoulder.

He loved Serilla; he honored and cared for her as the mother of his children; but Martha was the wife of his youth, the Madonna of his dreams. She was associated with the mystery of his life, the dew of its morning. The whole earth was young that marvelous May when they two adventured into this suave and fertile land. The perfume of wild honey, the song of larks in flowery meadows lay in her name, and around her fireplace still lingered such heartiness of cheer, such neighborliness as the world no longer knew. Oh, those glorious pioneer days!

He sat so long in dreams that the red sky and fire grew gray and the good people in the kitchen became uneasy, and Amos came and brought a lamp, and then with an absent-minded smile the dreamer rose, stiff with the chill of age, and went back to his acknowledged home, to the wife of his present.

He came again the next day, and the next, and the next, re-perusing with inarticulate pain and pleasure his story in stone and steel, his epic in pungent pine, basking in the glow of his fire, forgetting his gray hair and nerveless limbs in the magic of the flame. From these secret delicious excursions into the past, these communions with the dead, he returned to his wife and daughter with reluctance, with a certain guilty fear. Without meaning to be disloyal, he began to find Serilla's brusque ways intolerable, and had moments when he resolved to keep his secret. He shrank from her sharp voice, her prosaic and harsh comment. He was like a bridegroom, jealous of the very name of his love.

He was loath to share his fire with anyone. It was so sweet to have this refuge, this place of dreams all to himself, to be absolute master of his hearth. The disclosure of his ownership would end all that, would whelm him with intrusive and discordant voices.

So he waited and dreamed while the edge of curiosity dulled, and the days went by swiftly like great birds blown southward by the sounding wind.

Amos had guessed Stephen's proprietorship of the house, but being a man of perception, he had cautioned his wife to yield no hint of their secret knowledge; and Jane was not merely discreet; she was sympathetic. She added in many little ways to Stephen's enjoyment of his home. The fire was always blazing on the hearth when he came in, and he was left alone for the most part; only upon invitation did she enter the room to sit with him before his shrine.

This understanding was mutual. Stephen knew that they were in possession of his secret, but he gave no outward sign; indeed, he kept up the fiction by greeting them as his hosts, and even went so far as to discuss the coming of "the owner" in the spring. He always expressed gratitude for a chance to sit against the fire.

"I don't know what I'll do when you move out," he said once. "Well, I'll have one comfortable winter, anyway," he ended.

Serilla deeply resented his truancy, which she ascribed to the influence of Jane Kittredge, and a barrier of distrust and defense had risen between them. Cariss, involved with the young life of the village, gave very little thought to the matter, though she occasionally defended her father. "If he gets any fun out of Aunt Jane, let him," she rather flippantly remarked; and the tone of her plea did not incline Stephen to confide in her. John would understand, but he hesitated about writing. "I'll wait till he comes up a-Christmas," he decided.

His old cronies found him distinctly less companionable, more remote. A settled sadness, a growing reserve difficult of analysis, had come into his daily greeting. He told fewer stories, he was less often at the grocery store, and his laugh was seldom heard.

All this change they referred to ill health, and their comment was gentle and commiserating.

"Stephen is failin' fast," remarked Pilcher, one day. "The cold weather seems to grip him. It wouldn't surprise me to hear any day that he was taken flat down. I doubt if he stands many more of these winters."

Hiram looked up with a smile which was at once defiant and wistful. "We're all in the same boat and driftin' the same way," he said; and then they spoke with resolute cheer of the weather and the price of firewood.

November passed without any change of plan on Stephen's part, and December was half-way gone before he broke silence. Being moved by a letter from John, he suddenly said one night, quite in his old, hearty way, "I tell you what you do, Amos. You and Jane send out invitations to John and Albert's folks and to all of Serilla's kin bidding 'em all to a Christmas dinner. Say to the boys that, seein's their mother hain't got room enough, I'm kindo' goin' in with you here. You can say I'm helpin' out on the turkey and things, and the children's stockin's, and that they can stay here—part of 'em at least. We can all get together here in this big room—" A lump came into his throat and he did not finish.

Jane and Amos fell in with the suggestion quite as if it were a command, and withdrew to write out the letters of invitation, leaving Stephen alone in the glow of the fire, for the walk that day had been a stern battle with both wind and snow, and he seemed older and feebler.

"It looks like he was planning to let 'em all know—don't you think so?" asked Amos.

"If he does, he'll be sorry. Albert will be furious, and so will Serill'. It will all be a foolish waste of money to them. She never'll come here in this world to live."

"I can see he kindo' dreads it; he does take such a power o' comfort in it—he's entitled to a little fun, seems to me."

A couple of hours later, as they went down-stairs to lock the doors and put out the lights, Jane said, "Look in and see how the fire in the big room is, while I see to the furnace. My, hear that wind!"

Amos opened the door, but paused on the threshold and beckoned with a smile. "Come here, Jane," he whispered. "I thought I didn't hear him go out." Jane looked over his shoulder with a word of surprise.

The fire had burned low. In a deep bed of ashes a big oaken gnarl still smouldered, sending up now and again a single leaping jet of flame, and by its fitful light Stephen was intermittently revealed, deep-sunk in his armchair, his gray head turned laxly aside, his gaunt hands hanging emptily by his side.

"Better wake him," said Jane. "He'll take a chill. He'd better sleep here tonight."

Amos went over and touched the sleeper on the shoulder. He did not respond. Amos laid his hand against the grizzled cheek, and turned with a start toward his wife, a look of awe on his face—a look, a gesture which told his story instantly and with completeness.

Stephen was with Martha, and the past and the present were to him as the morning and the evening of one day.

THE ADVENTURE OF THE SPECKLED BAND

By A. Conan Doyle

[Sir Arthur Conan Doyle (1859–1930) was a Scotch physician, born in Edinburgh. He was educated in Edinburgh University both in the arts and in medicine. His university also gave him the honorary degree of Doctor of Laws. He was knighted in 1902. He began active life as a practicing physician, but after a few years devoted much of his time to writing fiction. His travels were extensive and his interest in public affairs was wide. The Boer War drew him to South Africa.

Dr. Doyle began his literary work in 1887 with the publication of *A Study in Scarlet*. His reputation as a literary man was largely due to his happy creations of the characters of the famous detective, Sherlock Holmes, and his companion and foil, Dr. Watson, and to the application of literary methods to the detective story in *The Adventures of Sherlock Holmes* (1891). A second volume, *The Memoirs of Sherlock Holmes*, followed in 1893. Of his thirty or more novels, collections of stories, and plays a few of the best known are: *Micah Clarke* (1888), *The Sign of Four* (1889), *The White Company* (1890), *Round the Red Lamp* (1894), *Rodney Stone* (1896), *The Hound of the Baskervilles* (1902), and *The Return of Sherlock Holmes* (1905).

The Adventure of the Speckled Band appeared first in the *Strand Magazine*, and was later included in *The Adventures of Sherlock Holmes* (1891). It is reprinted here by permission granted by the author.]

IN glancing over my notes of the seventy-odd cases in which I have, during the last eight years, studied the methods of my friend, Sherlock Holmes, I find many tragic, some comic, a large number merely strange, but none commonplace; for, working as he did rather for the love of his art than for the acquirement of wealth, he refused to associate himself with any investigation which did not tend toward the unusual, and even the fantastic. Of all these varied cases, however, I cannot recall any which presented more singular features than that which was associated with the well-known Surrey family of the Roylotts of Stoke Moran. The events in question occurred in the early days of my association with Holmes, when we were sharing rooms as bachelors in Baker Street. It is possible that I might have placed them upon record before, but a promise of secrecy was made at the time, from which I have only been freed during the last month by the untimely death of the lady to whom the pledge was given. It is perhaps as well that the facts should now come to light, for I have reasons to know that there are wide-spread rumors as to the death of Dr. Grimesby Roylott which tend to make the matter even more terrible than the truth.

It was early in April in the year '83 that I woke one morning to find Sherlock Holmes standing, fully dressed, by the side of my bed. He was a late riser as a rule, and as the clock on the mantel-piece showed me that it was only a quarter past seven, I blinked up at him in some surprise, and perhaps just a little resentment, for I was myself regular in my habits.

"Very sorry to knock you up, Watson," said he, "but it's the common lot this morning. Mrs. Hudson has been knocked up; she retorted upon me; and I on you."

"What is it, then—a fire?"

"No; a client. It seems that a young lady has arrived in a considerable state of excitement, who insists upon seeing me. She is waiting now in the sitting-room. Now, when young ladies wander about the metropolis at this hour of the morning, and knock sleepy people up out of their beds, I presume that it is something very pressing which they have to communicate. Should it prove to be an interesting case, you would, I am sure, wish to follow it from the outset. I thought, at any rate, that I should call you and give you the chance."

"My dear fellow, I would not miss it for anything."

I had no keener pleasure than in following Holmes in his professional investigations, and in admiring the rapid deductions, as swift as intuitions, and yet always founded on a logical basis, with which he unraveled the problems which were submitted to him. I rapidly threw on my clothes, and was ready in a few minutes to accompany my friend down to the sitting-room. A lady dressed in black and heavily veiled, who had been sitting in the window, rose as we entered.

"Good-morning, madam," said Holmes, cheerily. "My name is Sherlock Holmes. This is my intimate friend and associate, Dr. Watson, before whom you can speak as freely as before myself. Ha!—I am glad to see that Mrs. Hudson has had the good sense to light the fire. Pray draw up to it, and I shall order you a cup of hot coffee, for I observe that you are shivering."

"It is not cold which makes me shiver," said the woman, in a low voice, changing her seat as requested.

"What then?"

"It is fear, Mr. Holmes. It is terror." She raised her veil as she spoke, and we could see that she was indeed in a pitiable state of agitation, her face all drawn and gray, with restless, frightened eyes, like those of some hunted animal. Her features and figure were those of a woman of thirty, but her hair was shot with premature gray, and her expression was weary and haggard. Sherlock Holmes ran her over with one of his quick, all-comprehensive glances.

"You must not fear," said he, soothingly, bending forward and patting her forearm. "We shall soon set matters right, I have no doubt. You have come in by train this morning, I see."

"You know me, then?"

"No, but I observe the second half of a return ticket in the palm of your left glove. You must have started early, and yet you had a good drive in a dog-cart, along heavy roads, before you reached the station."

The lady gave a violent start, and stared in bewilderment at my companion.

"There is no mystery, my dear madam," said he, smiling.

"The left arm of your jacket is spattered with mud in no less than seven places. The marks are perfectly fresh. There is no vehicle save a dog-cart which throws up mud in that way, and then only when you sit on the left-hand side of the driver."

"Whatever your reasons may be, you are perfectly correct," said she. "I started from home before six, reached Leatherhead at twenty past, and came in by the first train to Waterloo. Sir, I can stand this strain no longer; I shall go mad if it continues. I have no one to turn to—none, save only one, who cares for me, and he, poor fellow, can be of little aid. I have heard of you, Mr. Holmes; I have heard of you from Mrs. Farintosh, whom you helped in the hour of her sore need. It was from her that I had your address. Oh, sir, do you not think that you could help me, too, and at least throw a little light through the dense darkness which surrounds me? At present it is out of my power to reward you for your services, but in a month or six weeks I shall be married, with the control of my own income, and then at least you shall not find me ungrateful."

Holmes turned to his desk, and unlocking it, drew out a small casebook, which he consulted.

"Farintosh," said he. "Ah, yes, I recall the case; it was concerned with an opal tiara. I think it was before your time, Watson. I can only say, madam, that I shall be happy to devote the same care to your case as I did to that of your friend. As to reward, my profession is its own reward; but you are at liberty to defray whatever expenses I may be put to, at the time which suits you best. And now I beg that you will lay before us everything that may help us in forming an opinion upon the matter."

"Alas!" replied our visitor, "the very horror of my situation lies in the fact that my fears are so vague, and my suspicions depend so entirely upon small points, which might seem trivial to another, that even he, to whom of all others I have a right to look for help and advice, looks upon all that I tell him about it as the fancies of a nervous woman. He does not say so, but I can read it from his soothing answers and averted eyes. But I have heard, Mr. Holmes, that you can see deeply into the manifold wickedness of the human heart. You may advise me how to walk amid the dangers which encompass me."

"I am all attention, madam."

"My name is Helen Stoner, and I am living with my step-father, who is the last survivor of one of the oldest Saxon families in England, the Roylotts of Stoke Moran, on the western border of Surrey."

Holmes nodded his head. "The name is familiar to me," said he.

"The family was at one time among the richest in England, and the estates extended over the borders into Berkshire in the north, and Hampshire in the west. In the last century, however, four successive heirs were of a dissolute and wasteful disposition, and the family ruin was eventually completed by a gambler in the days of the Regency. Nothing was left save a few acres of ground, and the two-hundred-year-old house, which is itself crushed under a heavy mortgage. The last squire dragged out his existence there, living the horrible life of an aristocratic pauper; but his only son, my step-father, seeing that he must adapt himself to the new conditions, obtained an advance from a relative, which enabled him to take a medical degree, and went out to Calcutta, where, by his professional skill and his force of character, he established a large practice. In a fit of anger, however, caused by some robberies which had been perpetrated in the house, he beat his native butler to death, and narrowly escaped a capital sentence. As it was, he suffered a long term of imprisonment, and afterward returned to England a morose and disappointed man.

"When Dr. Roylott was in India he married my mother, Mrs. Stoner, the young widow of Major-General Stoner, of the Bengal Artillery. My sister Julia and I were twins, and we were only two years old at the time of my mother's remarriage. She had a considerable sum of money—not less than 1,000 pounds a year—and this she bequeathed to Dr. Roylott entirely while we resided with him, with a provision that a certain annual sum should be allowed to each of us in the event of our marriage. Shortly after our return to England my mother died—she was killed eight years ago in a railway accident near Crewe. Dr. Roylott then abandoned his attempts to establish himself in practice in London, and took us to live with him in the old ancestral house at Stoke Moran. The money which my mother had left was enough for all our wants, and there seemed to be no obstacle to our happiness.

"But a terrible change came over our step-father about this time. Instead of making friends and exchanging visits with our neighbors, who had at first been overjoyed to see a Roylott of Stoke Moran back in the old family seat, he shut himself up in his house, and seldom came out save to indulge in ferocious quarrels with whoever might cross his path. Violence of temper approaching to mania has been hereditary in the men of the family, and in my step-father's case it had, I believe, been intensified by his long residence in the tropics. A series of disgraceful brawls took place, two of which ended in the police-court, until at last he became the terror of the village, and the folks would fly at his approach, for he is a man of immense strength, and absolutely uncontrollable in his anger.

"Last week he hurled the local blacksmith over a parapet into a stream; and it was only by paying over all the money which I could gather together that I was able to avert another public exposure. He had no friends at all save the wandering gypsies, and he would give these vagabonds leave to encamp upon the few acres of bramble-covered land which represent the family estate, and would accept in return the hospitality of their tents, wandering away with them sometimes for weeks on end. He has a passion also for Indian animals, which are sent over to him by a correspondent, and he has at this moment a cheetah and a baboon, which wander freely over his grounds, and are feared by the villagers almost as much as their master.

"You can imagine from what I say that my poor sister Julia and I had no great pleasure in our lives. No servant would stay with us, and for a long time we did all the work of the house. She was but thirty at the time of her death, and yet her hair had already begun to whiten, even as mine has."

"Your sister is dead, then?"

"She died just two years ago, and it is of her death that I wish to speak to you. You can understand that, living the life which I have described, we were little likely to see anyone of our own age and position. We had, however, an aunt, my mother's maiden sister, Miss Honoria Westphail, who lives near Harrow, and we were occasionally allowed to pay short visits at this lady's house. Julia went there at Christmas two years ago, and met there a half-pay major of marines, to whom she became engaged. My step-father learned of the engagement when my sister returned, and offered no objection to the marriage; but within a fortnight of the day which had been fixed for the wedding, the terrible event occurred which has deprived me of my only companion."

Sherlock Holmes had been leaning back in his chair with his eyes closed and his head sunk in a cushion, but he half opened his lids now and glanced at his visitor.

"Pray be precise as to details," said he.

"It is easy for me to be so, for every event of that dreadful time is seared into my memory. The manorhouse is, as I have already said, very old, and only one wing is now inhabited. The bedrooms in this wing are on the ground floor, the sitting-rooms being in the central block of the buildings. Of these bedrooms the first is Dr. Roylott's, the second my sister's, and the third my own. There is no communication between them, but they all open out into the same corridor. Do I make myself plain?"

"Perfectly so."

"The windows of the three rooms open out upon the lawn. That fatal night Dr. Roylott had gone to his room early, though we knew that he had not retired to rest, for my sister was troubled by the smell of the strong Indian cigars, which it was his custom to smoke. She left her room, therefore, and came into mine, where she sat for some time, chatting about her approaching wedding. At eleven o'clock she rose to leave me, but she paused at the door and looked back.

"'Tell me, Helen,' said she, 'have you ever heard any one whistle in the dead of the night?'

"'Never,' said I.

"'I suppose that you could not possibly whistle, yourself, in your sleep?'

"'Certainly not. But why?'

"'Because during the last few nights I have always, about three in the morning, heard a low, clear whistle. I am a light sleeper, and it has awakened me. I cannot tell where it came from—perhaps from the next room, perhaps from the lawn. I thought that I would just ask you whether you had heard it.'

"'No, I have not. It must be those wretched gypsies in the plantation.'

"'Very likely. And yet if it were on the lawn, I wonder that you did not hear it also.'

"'Ah, but I sleep more heavily than you.'

"'Well, it is of no great consequence, at any rate.' She smiled back at me, closed my door, and a few moments later I heard her key turn in the lock."

"Indeed," said Holmes. "Was it your custom always to lock yourselves in at night?"

"Always."

"And why?"

"I think that I mentioned to you that the doctor kept a cheetah and a baboon. We had no feeling of security unless our doors were locked."

"Quite so. Pray proceed with your statement."

"I could not sleep that night. A vague feeling of impending misfortune impressed me. My sister and I, you will recollect, were twins, and you know how subtle are the links which bind two souls which are so closely allied. It was a wild night. The wind was howling outside, and the rain was beating and splashing against the windows. Suddenly, amid all the hubbub of the gale, there burst forth the wild scream of a terrified woman. I knew that it was my sister's voice. I sprang from my bed, wrapped a shawl round me, and rushed into the corridor. As I opened my door I seemed to hear a low whistle, such as my sister described, and a few moments later a clanging sound, as if a mass of metal had fallen. As I ran down the passage my sister's door was unlocked, and revolved slowly upon its hinges. I stared at it horror-stricken, not knowing what was about to issue from it. By the light of the corridor-lamp I saw my sister appear at the opening, her face blanched with terror, her hands groping for help, her whole figure swaying to and fro like that of a drunkard. I ran to her and threw my arms round her, but at that moment her knees seemed to give way and she fell to the ground. She writhed as one who is in terrible pain, and her limbs were dreadfully convulsed. At first I thought that she had not recognized me, but as I bent over her, she suddenly shrieked out, in a voice which I shall never forget: 'Oh, my God! Helen! It was the band! The speckled band!' There was something else which she would fain have said, and she stabbed with her finger into the air in the direction of the doctor's room, but a fresh convulsion seized her and choked her words. I rushed out, calling loudly for my step-father, and I met him hastening from his room in his dressing-gown. When he reached my sister's side she was unconscious, and though he poured brandy down her throat and sent for medical aid from the village, all efforts were in vain, for she slowly sank and died without having recovered her consciousness. Such was the dreadful end of my beloved sister."

"One moment," said Holmes; "are you sure about this whistle and metallic sound? Could you swear to it?"

"That was what the county coroner asked me at the inquiry. It is my strong impression that I heard it, and yet, among the crash of the gale and the creaking of an old house, I may possibly have been deceived."

"Was your sister dressed?"

"No, she was in her night-dress. In her right hand was found the charred stump of a match, and in her left a match-box."

"Showing that she had struck a light and looked about her when the alarm took place. That is important. And what conclusions did the coroner come to?"

"He investigated the case with great care, for Dr. Roylott's conduct had long been notorious in the county, but he was unable to find any satisfactory cause of death. My evidence showed that the door had been fastened upon the inner side, and the windows were blocked by old-fashioned shutters with broad iron bars, which were secured every night. The walls were carefully sounded, and were shown to be quite solid all round, and the flooring was also thoroughly examined, with the same result. The chimney is wide, but is barred up by four large staples. It is certain, therefore, that my sister was quite alone when she met her end. Besides, there were no marks of any violence upon her."

"How about poison?"

"The doctors examined her for it, but without success."

"What do you think that this unfortunate lady died of, then?"

"It is my belief that she died of pure fear and nervous shock, though what it was that frightened her I cannot imagine."

"Were there gypsies in the plantation at the time?"

"Yes, there are nearly always some there."

"Ah, and what did you gather from this allusion to a band—a speckled band?"

"Sometimes I have thought that it was merely the wild talk of delirium, sometimes that it may have referred to some band of people, perhaps to these very gypsies in the plantation. I do not know whether the spotted handkerchiefs which so many of them wear over their heads might have suggested the strange adjective which she used."

Holmes shook his head like a man who is far from being satisfied.

"These are very deep waters," said he; "pray go on with your narrative."

"Two years have passed since then, and my life had been until lately lonelier than ever. A month ago, however, a dear friend, whom I have known for many years, has done me the honor to ask my hand in marriage. His name is Armitage—Percy Armitage—the second son of Mr. Armitage, of Crane Water, near Reading. My step-father has offered no opposition to the match, and we are to be married in the course of the spring. Two days ago some repairs were started in the west wing of the building, and my bedroom wall has been pierced, so that I have had to move into the chamber in which my sister died, and to sleep in the very bed in which she slept.

"Imagine, then, my thrill of terror when last night, as I lay awake, thinking over her terrible fate, I suddenly heard in the silence of the night the low whistle which had been the herald of her own death. I sprang up and lit the lamp, but nothing was to be seen in the room. I was too shaken to go to bed again, however; so I dressed, and as soon as it was daylight I slipped down, got a dog-cart at the 'Crown Inn,' which is opposite, and drove to Leatherhead, from whence I have come on this morning with the one object of seeing you and asking your advice."

"You have done wisely," said my friend. "But have you told me all?"

"Yes, all."

"Miss Roylott, you have not. You are screening your step-father."

"Why, what do you mean?"

For answer Holmes pushed back the frill of black lace which fringed the hand that lay upon our visitor's knee. Five little livid spots, the marks of four fingers and a thumb, were printed upon the white wrist.

"You have been cruelly used," said Holmes.

The lady colored deeply and covered over her injured wrist. "He is a hard man," she said, "and perhaps he hardly knows his own strength."

There was a long silence, during which Holmes leaned his chin upon his hands and stared into the crackling fire.

"This is a very deep business," he said, at last. "There are a thousand details which I should desire to know before I decide upon our course of action. Yet we have not a moment to lose. If we were to come to Stoke Moran today, would it be possible for us to see over these rooms without the knowledge of your step-father?"

"As it happens, he spoke of coming into town today upon some most important business. It is probable that he will be away all day, and that there would be nothing to disturb you. We have a housekeeper now, but she is old and foolish, and I could easily get her out of the way."

"Excellent. You are not averse to this trip, Watson?"

"By no means."

"Then we shall both come. What are you going to do yourself?"

"I have one or two things which I would wish to do now that I am in town. But I shall return by the twelve o'clock train, so as to be there in time for your coming."

"And you may expect us early in the afternoon. I have myself some small business matters to attend to. Will you not wait and breakfast?"

"No, I must go. My heart is lightened already since I have confided my trouble to you. I shall look forward to seeing you again this afternoon." She dropped her thick black veil over her face and glided from the room.

"And what do you think of it all, Watson?" asked Sherlock Holmes, leaning back in his chair.

"It seems to me to be a most dark and sinister business."

"Dark enough and sinister enough."

"Yet if the lady is correct in saying that the flooring and walls are sound, and that the door, window, and chimney are impassable, then her sister must have been undoubtedly alone when she met her mysterious end."

"What becomes, then, of these nocturnal whistles, and what of the very peculiar words of the dying woman?"

"I cannot think."

"When you combine the ideas of whistles at night, the presence of a band of gypsies who are on intimate terms with this old doctor, the fact that we have every reason to believe the doctor has an interest in preventing his step-daughter's marriage, the dying allusion to a band, and, finally, the fact that Miss Helen Stoner heard a metallic clang, which might have been caused by one of those metal bars which secured the shutters falling back into its place, I think that there is good ground to think that the mystery may be cleared along those lines."

"But what, then, did the gypsies do?"

"I cannot imagine."

"I see many objections to any such theory."

"And so do I. It is precisely for that reason that we are going to Stoke Moran this day. I want to see whether the objections are fatal, or if they may be explained away. But what in the name of the devil!"

The ejaculation had been drawn from my companion by the fact that our door had been suddenly dashed open, and that a huge man had framed himself in the aperture. His costume was a peculiar mixture of the professional and of the agricultural, having a black top-hat, a long frock-coat, and a pair of high gaiters, with a hunting-crop swinging in his hand. So tall was he that his hat actually brushed the cross-bar of the doorway, and his breadth seemed to span it across from side to side. A large face, seared with a thousand wrinkles, burned yellow with the sun, and marked with every evil passion, was turned from one to the other of us, while his deep-set, bile-shot eyes, and his high, thin, fleshless nose, gave him somewhat the resemblance to a fierce old bird of prey.

"Which of you is Holmes?" asked this apparition.

"My name, sir; but you have the advantage of me," said my companion, quietly.

"I am Dr. Grimesby Roylott, of Stoke Moran."

"Indeed, doctor," said Holmes, blandly. "Pray take a seat."

"I will do nothing of the kind. My step-daughter has been here. I have traced her. What has she been saying to you?"

"It is a little cold for the time of the year," said Holmes.

"What has she been saying to you?" screamed the old man, furiously.

"But I have heard that the crocuses promise well," continued my companion, imperturbably.

"Ha! You put me off, do you?" said our new visitor, taking a step forward and shaking his hunting-crop. "I know you, you scoundrel! I have heard of you before. You are Holmes, the meddler."

My friend smiled.

"Holmes, the busybody!"

His smile broadened.

"Holmes, the Scotland-yard Jack-in-office!"

Holmes chuckled heartily. "Your conversation is most entertaining," said he. "When you go out, close the door, for there is a decided draught."

"I will go when I have said my say. Don't you dare to meddle with my affairs. I know that Miss Stoner has been here. I traced her! I am a dangerous man to fall foul of! See here." He stepped swiftly forward, seized the poker, and bent it into a curve with his huge brown hands.

"See that you keep yourself out of my grip," he snarled; and hurling the twisted poker into the fireplace, he strode out of the room.

"He seems a very amiable person," said Holmes, laughing. "I am not quite so bulky, but if he had remained I might have shown him that my grip was not much more feeble than his own." As he spoke he picked up the steel poker, and with a sudden effort straightened it out again.

"Fancy his having the insolence to confound me with the official detective force! This incident gives zest to our investigation, however, and I only trust that our little friend will not suffer from her imprudence in allowing this brute to trace her. And now, Watson, we shall order breakfast, and afterward I shall walk down to Doctors' Commons, where I hope to get some data which may help us in this matter."

It was nearly one o'clock when Sherlock Holmes returned from his excursion. He held in his hand a sheet of blue paper, scrawled over with notes and figures.

"I have seen the will of the deceased wife," said he. "To determine its exact meaning I have been obliged to work out the present prices of the investments with which it is concerned. The total income, which at the time of the wife's death was little short of 1,100 pounds, is now, through the fall in agricultural prices, not more than 750 pounds. Each daughter can claim an income of 250 pounds, in case of marriage. It is evident, therefore, that if both girls had married, this beauty would have had a mere pittance, while even one of them would cripple him to a very serious extent. My morning's work has not been wasted, since it has proved that he had the very strongest motives for standing in the way of anything of the sort. And now, Watson, this is too serious for dawdling, especially as the old man is aware that we are interesting ourselves in his affairs; so if you are ready, we shall call a cab and drive to Waterloo. I should be very much obliged if you would slip your revolver into your pocket. An Eley's No. 2 is an excellent argument with gentlemen who can twist steel pokers into knots. That and a toothbrush are, I think, all that we need."

At Waterloo, we were fortunate in catching a train for Leatherhead, where we hired a trap at the station inn, and drove for four or five miles through the lovely Surrey lanes. It was a perfect day, with a bright sun and a few fleecy clouds in the heavens. The trees and wayside hedges were just throwing out their first green shoots, and the air was full of the pleasant smell of the moist earth. To me at least there was a strange contrast between the sweet promise of the spring and this sinister quest upon which we were engaged. My companion sat in front of the trap, his arms folded, his hat pulled down over his eyes, and his chin sunk upon his breast, buried in the deepest thought. Suddenly, however, he started, tapped me on the shoulder, and pointed over the meadows.

"Look there!" said he.

A heavily timbered park stretched up in a gentle slope, thickening into a grove at the highest point. From amid the branches there jutted out the gray gables and high roof-tree of a very old mansion.

"Stoke Moran?" said he.

"Yes, sir, that be the house of Dr. Grimesby Roylott," remarked the driver.

"There is some building going on there," said Holmes; "that is where we are going."

"There's the village," said the driver, pointing to a cluster of roofs some distance to the left; "but if you want to get to the house, you'll find it shorter to get over this stile, and so by the foot-path over the fields. There it is, where the lady is walking."

"And the lady, I fancy, is Miss Stoner," observed Holmes, shading his eyes. "Yes, I think we had better do as you suggest."

We got off, paid our fare, and the trap rattled back on its way to Leatherhead.

"I thought it as well," said Holmes, as we climbed the stile, "that this fellow should think we had come here as architects or on some definite business. It may stop his gossip. Good-afternoon, Miss Stoner. You see that we have been as good as our word."

Our client of the morning had hurried forward to meet us with a face which spoke her joy. "I have been waiting so eagerly for you!" she cried, shaking hands with us warmly. "All has turned out splendidly. Dr. Roylott has gone to town, and it is unlikely that he will be back before evening."

"We have had the pleasure of making the doctor's acquaintance," said Holmes, and in a few words he sketched out what had occurred. Miss Stoner turned white to the lips as she listened.

"Good heavens!" she cried, "he has followed me, then."

"So it appears."

"He is so cunning that I never know when I am safe from him. What will he say when he returns?"

"He must guard himself, for he may find that there is some one more cunning than himself upon his track. You must lock yourself up from him tonight. If he is violent, we shall take you away to your aunt's at Harrow. Now, we must make the best use of our time, so kindly take us at once to the rooms which we are to examine."

The building was of gray, lichen-blotched stone, with a high central portion, and two curving wings, like the claws of a crab, thrown out on each side. In one of these wings the windows were broken, and blocked with wooden boards, while the roof was partly caved in, a picture of ruin. The central portion was in little better repair, but the right-hand block was comparatively modern, and the blinds in the windows, with the blue smoke curling up from the chimneys, showed that this was where the family resided. Some scaffolding had been erected against the end wall, and the stone-work had been broken into, but there were no signs of any workmen at the moment of our visit. Holmes walked slowly up and down the ill-trimmed lawn, and examined with deep attention the outsides of the windows.

"This, I take it, belongs to the room in which you used to sleep, the center one to your sister's, and the one next to the main building to Dr. Roylott's chamber?"

"Exactly so. But I am now sleeping in the middle one."

"Pending the alterations, as I understand. By-the-way, there does not seem to be any very pressing need for repairs at that end wall."

"There were none. I believe that it was an excuse to move me from my room."

"Ah! that is suggestive. Now, on the other side of this narrow wing runs the corridor from which these three rooms open. There are windows in it, of course?"

"Yes, but very small ones. Too narrow for any one to pass through."

"As you both locked your doors at night, your rooms were unapproachable from that side. Now, would you have the kindness to go into your room and bar your shutters."

Miss Stoner did so, and Holmes, after a careful examination through the open window, endeavored in every way to force the shutter open, but without success. There was no slit through which a knife could be passed to raise the bar. Then with his lens he tested the hinges, but they were of solid iron, built firmly into the massive masonry. "Hum!" said he, scratching his chin in some perplexity; "my theory certainly presents some difficulties. No one could pass these shutters if they were bolted. Well, we shall see if the inside throws any light upon the matter."

A small side door led into the whitewashed corridor from which the three bedrooms opened. Holmes refused to examine the third chamber, so we passed at once to the second, that in which Miss Stoner was now sleeping, and in which her sister had met with her fate. It was a homely little room, with a low ceiling and a gaping fireplace, after the fashion of old country-houses. A brown chest of drawers stood in one corner, a narrow white-counterpaned bed in another, and a dressing-table on the left-hand side of the window. These articles, with two small wicker-work chairs, made up all the furniture in the room, save for a square of Wilton carpet in the center. The boards round and the paneling of the walls were of brown, worm-eaten oak, so old and discolored that it may have dated from the original building of the house. Holmes drew one of the chairs into a corner and sat silent, while his eyes traveled round and round and up and down, taking in every detail of the apartment.

"Where does that bell communicate with?" he asked, at last, pointing to a thick bell-rope which hung down beside the bed, the tassel actually lying upon the pillow.

"It goes to the housekeeper's room."

"It looks newer than the other things?"

"Yes, it was only put there a couple of years ago."

"Your sister asked for it, I suppose?"

"No, I never heard of her using it. We used always to get what we wanted for ourselves."

"Indeed, it seemed unnecessary to put so nice a bell-pull there. You will excuse me for a few minutes while I satisfy myself as to this floor." He threw himself down upon his face with his lens in his hand, and crawled swiftly backward and forward, examining minutely the cracks between the boards. Then he did the same with the wood-work with which the chamber was paneled. Finally he walked over to the bed, and spent some time in staring at it, and in running his eye up and down the wall. Finally he took the bell-rope in his hand and gave it a brisk tug.

"Why, it's a dummy," said he.

"Won't it ring?"

"No, it is not even attached to a wire. This is very interesting. You can see now that it is fastened to a hook just above where the little opening for the ventilator is."

"How very absurd! I never noticed that before."

"Very strange!" muttered Holmes, pulling at the rope. "There are one or two very singular points about this room. For example, what a fool a builder must be to open a ventilator into another room, when, with the same trouble, he might have communicated with the outside air!"

"That is also quite modern," said the lady.

"Done about the same time as the bell-rope?" remarked Holmes.

"Yes, there were several little changes carried out about that time."

"They seem to have been of a most interesting character—dummy bell-ropes, and ventilators which do not ventilate. With your permission, Miss Stoner, we shall now carry our researches into the inner apartment."

Dr. Grimesby Roylott's chamber was larger than that of his step-daughter, but was as plainly furnished. A camp-bed, a small wooden shelf full of books, mostly of a technical character, an arm-chair beside the bed, a plain wooden chair against the wall, a round table, and a large iron safe were the principal things which met the eye.

Holmes walked slowly round and examined each and all of them with the keenest interest.

"What's in here?" he asked, tapping the safe.

"My step-father's business papers."

"Oh, you have seen inside, then?"

"Only once, some years ago. I remember that it was full of papers."

"There isn't a cat in it, for example?"

"No. What a strange idea!"

"Well, look at this!" He took up a small saucer of milk which stood on the top of it.

"No; we don't keep a cat. But there is a cheetah and a baboon."

"Ah, yes, of course! Well, a cheetah is just a big cat, and yet a saucer of milk does not go very far in satisfying its wants, I dare say. There is one point which I should wish to determine." He squatted down in front of the wooden chair, and examined the seat of it with the greatest attention.

"Thank you. That is quite settled," said he, rising and putting his lens in his pocket. "Hello!—Here is something interesting!"

The object which had caught his eye was a small doglash hung on one corner of the bed. The lash, however, was curled upon itself, and tied so as to make a loop of whip-cord.

"What do you make of that, Watson?"

"It's a common enough lash. But I don't know why it should be tied."

"That is not quite so common, is it? Ah, me! it's a wicked world, and when a clever man turns his brains to crime it is the worst of all. I think that I have seen enough now, Miss Stoner, and with your permission we shall walk out upon the lawn."

I had never seen my friend's face so grim or his brow so dark as it was when we turned from the scene of this investigation. We had walked several times up and down the lawn, neither Miss Stoner nor myself liking to break in upon his thoughts before he roused himself from his reverie.

"It is very essential, Miss Stoner," said he, "that you should absolutely follow my advice in every respect."

"I shall most certainly do so."

"The matter is too serious for any hesitation. Your life may depend upon your compliance."

"I assure you that I am in your hands."

"In the first place, both my friend and I must spend the night in your room."

Both Miss Stoner and I gazed at him in astonishment.

"Yes, it must be so. Let me explain. I believe that that is the village inn over there?"

"Yes, that is the 'Crown.'"

"Very good. Your windows would be visible from there?"

"Certainly."

"You must confine yourself to your room, on pretense of a headache, when your step-father comes back. Then when you hear him retire for the night, you must open the shutters of your window, undo the hasp, put your lamp there as a signal to us, and then withdraw quietly with everything which you are likely to want into the room which you used to occupy. I have no doubt that, in spite of the repairs, you could manage there for one night."

"Oh, yes, easily."

"The rest you will leave in our hands."

"But what will you do?"

"We shall spend the night in your room, and we shall investigate the cause of this noise which has disturbed you."

"I believe, Mr. Holmes, that you have already made up your mind," said Miss Stoner, laying her hand upon my companion's sleeve.

"Perhaps I have."

"Then, for pity's sake, tell me what was the cause of my sister's death."

"I should prefer to have clearer proofs before I speak."

"You can at least tell me whether my own thought is correct, and if she died from some sudden fright."

"No, I do not think so. I think that there was probably some more tangible cause. And now, Miss Stoner, we must leave you, for if Dr. Roylott returned and saw us, our journey would be in vain. Good-bye, and be brave, for if you will do what I have told you, you may rest assured that we shall soon drive away the dangers that threaten you."

Sherlock Holmes and I had no difficulty in engaging a bedroom and sitting-room at the "Crown Inn." They were on the upper floor, and from our window we could command a view of the avenue gate, and of the inhabited wing of Stoke Moran Manor-House. At dusk we saw Dr. Grimesby Roylott drive past, his huge form looming up beside the little figure of the lad who drove him. The boy had some slight difficulty in undoing the heavy iron gates, and we heard the hoarse roar of the doctor's voice, and saw the fury with which he shook his clenched fists at him. The trap drove on, and a few minutes later we saw a sudden light spring up among the trees as the lamp was lit in one of the sitting-rooms.

"Do you know, Watson," said Holmes, as we sat together in the gathering darkness, "I have really some scruples as to taking you to-night. There is a distinct element of danger."

"Can I be of assistance?"

"Your presence might be invaluable."

"Then I shall certainly come."

"It is very kind of you."

"You speak of danger. You have evidently seen more in these rooms than was visible to me."

"No, but I fancy that I may have deduced a little more. I imagine that you saw all that I did."

"I saw nothing remarkable save the bell-rope, and what purpose that could answer I confess is more than I can imagine."

"You saw the ventilator, too?"

"Yes, but I do not think that it is such a very unusual thing to have a small opening between two rooms. It was so small that a rat could hardly pass through."

"I knew that we should find a ventilator before ever we came to Stoke Moran."

"My dear Holmes!"

"Oh, yes, I did. You remember in her statement she said that her sister could smell Dr. Roylott's cigar. Now, of course, that suggested at once that there must be a communication between the two rooms. It could only be a small one, or it would have been remarked upon at the coroner's inquiry. I deduced a ventilator."

"But what harm can there be in that?"

"Well, there is at least a curious coincidence of dates. A ventilator is made, a cord is hung, and a lady who sleeps in the bed dies. Does not that strike you?"

"I cannot as yet see any connection."

"Did you observe anything very peculiar about that bed?"

"No."

"It was clamped to the floor. Did you ever see a bed fastened like that before?"

"I cannot say that I have."

"The lady could not move her bed. It must always be in the same relative position to the ventilator and to the rope—for so we may call it, since it was clearly never meant for a bell-pull."

"Holmes," I cried, "I seem to see dimly what you are hinting at! We are only just in time to prevent some subtle and horrible crime."

"Subtle enough and horrible enough. When a doctor does go wrong, he is the first of criminals. He has nerve, and he has knowledge. Palmer and Pritchard were among the heads of their profession. This man strikes even deeper; but I think, Watson, that we shall be able to strike deeper still. But we shall have horrors enough before the night is over; for goodness' sake let us have a quiet pipe, and turn our minds for a few hours to something more cheerful."

About nine o'clock the light among the trees was extinguished, and all was dark in the direction of the Manor-House. Two hours passed slowly away, and then, suddenly, just at the stroke of eleven, a single bright light shone out in front of us.

"That is our signal," said Holmes, springing to his feet; "it comes from the middle window."

As we passed out he exchanged a few words with the landlord, explaining that we were going on a late visit to an acquaintance, and that it was possible that we might spend the night there. A moment later we were out on the dark road, a chill wind blowing in our faces, and one yellow light twinkling in front of us through the gloom to guide us on our somber errand.

There was little difficulty in entering the grounds, for unrepaired breaches gaped in the old park wall. Making our way among the trees, we reached the lawn, crossed it, and were about to enter through the window, when out from a clump of laurel-bushes there darted what seemed to be a hideous and distorted child, who threw itself upon the grass with writhing limbs, and then ran swiftly across the lawn into the darkness.

"My God!" I whispered; "did you see it?"

Holmes was for the moment as startled as I. His hand closed like a vise upon my wrist in his agitation. Then he broke into a low laugh, and put his lips to my ear.

"It is a nice household," he murmured. "That is the baboon."

I had forgotten the strange pets which the doctor affected. There was a cheetah, too; perhaps we might find it upon our shoulders at any moment. I confess that I felt easier in my mind when, after following Holmes' example and slipping off my shoes, I found myself inside the bedroom. My companion noiselessly closed the shutters, moved the lamp onto the table, and cast his eyes round the room. All was as we had seen it in the daytime. Then creeping up to me and making a trumpet of his hand, he whispered into my ear again so gently that it was all that I could do to distinguish the words:

"The least sound would be fatal to our plans."

I nodded to show that I had heard.

"We must sit without light. He would see it through the ventilator."

I nodded again.

"Do not go asleep; your very life may depend upon it. Have your pistol ready in case we should need it. I will sit on the side of the bed, and you in that chair."

I took out my revolver and laid it on the corner of the table.

Holmes had brought up a long, thin cane, and this he placed upon the bed beside him. By it he laid the box of matches and the stump of a candle. Then he turned down the lamp, and we were left in darkness.

How shall I ever forget that dreadful vigil? I could not hear a sound, not even the drawing of a breath, and yet I knew that my companion sat open-eyed, within a few feet of me, in the same state of nervous tension in which I was myself. The shutters cut off the least ray of light, and we waited in absolute darkness. From outside came the occasional cry of a night-bird, and once at our very window a long-drawn, cat-like whine, which told us that the cheetah was indeed at liberty. Far away we could hear the deep tones of the parish clock, which boomed out every quarter of an hour. How long they seemed, those quarters! Twelve struck, and one and two and three, and still we sat waiting silently for whatever might befall.

Suddenly there was the momentary gleam of a light up in the direction of the ventilator, which vanished immediately, but was succeeded by a strong smell of burning oil and heated metal. Some one in the next room had lit a dark-lantern. I heard a gentle sound of movement, and then all was silent once more, though the smell grew stronger. For half an hour I sat with straining ears. Then suddenly another sound became audible—a very gentle, soothing sound, like that of a small jet of steam escaping continually from a kettle. The instant that we heard it, Holmes sprang from the bed, struck a match, and lashed furiously with his cane at the bell-pull.

"You see it, Watson?" he yelled. "You see it?"

But I saw nothing. At the moment when Holmes struck the light I heard a low, clear whistle, but the sudden glare flashing into my weary eyes made it impossible for me to tell what it was at which my friend lashed so savagely. I could, however, see that his face was deadly pale, and filled with horror and loathing.

He had ceased to strike, and was gazing up at the ventilator, when suddenly there broke from the silence of the night the most horrible cry to which I have ever listened. It swelled up louder and louder, a hoarse yell of pain and fear and anger all mingled in the one dreadful shriek. They say that away down in the village, and even in the distant parsonage, that cry raised the sleepers from their beds. It struck cold to our hearts, and I stood gazing at Holmes, and he at me, until the last echoes of it had died away into the silence from which it rose.

"What can it mean?" I gasped.

"It means that it is all over," Holmes answered. "And perhaps, after all, it is for the best. Take your pistol, and we will enter Dr. Roylott's room."

With a grave face he lit the lamp and led the way down the corridor. Twice he struck at the chamber door without any reply from within. Then he turned the handle and entered, I at his heels, with the cocked pistol in my hand.

It was a singular sight which met our eyes. On the table stood a dark-lantern with the shutter half open, throwing a brilliant beam of light upon the iron safe, the door of which was ajar. Beside this table, on the wooden chair, sat Dr. Grimesby Roylott, clad in a long gray dressing-gown, his bare ankles protruding beneath, and his feet thrust into red heelless Turkish slippers. Across his lap lay the short stock with the long lash which we had noticed during the day. His chin was cocked upward and his eyes were fixed in a dreadful, rigid stare at the corner of the ceiling. Round his brow he had a peculiar yellow band, with brownish speckles, which seemed to be bound tightly round his head. As we entered he made neither sound nor motion.

"The band! the speckled band!" whispered Holmes.

I took a step forward. In an instant his strange headgear began to move, and there reared itself from among his hair the squat diamond-shaped head and puffed neck of a loathsome serpent.

"It is a swamp adder!" cried Holmes; "the deadliest snake in India. He has died within ten seconds of being bitten. Violence does, in truth, recoil upon the violent, and the schemer falls into the pit which he digs for another. Let us thrust this creature back into its den, and we can then remove Miss Stoner to some place of shelter, and let the county police know what has happened."

As he spoke he drew the dog-whip swiftly from the dead man's lap, and throwing the noose round the reptile's neck, he drew it from its horrid perch, and carrying it at arm's-length, threw it into the iron safe, which he closed upon it.

Such are the true facts of the death of Dr. Grimesby Roylott, of Stoke Moran. It is not necessary that I should prolong a narrative which has already run to too great a length, by telling how we broke the sad news to the terrified girl, how we conveyed her by the morning train to the care of her good aunt at Harrow, of how the slow process of official inquiry came to the conclusion that the doctor met his fate while indiscreetly playing with a dangerous pet. The little which I had yet to learn of the case was told me by Sherlock Holmes as we traveled back next day.

"I had," said he, "come to an entirely erroneous conclusion, which shows, my dear Watson, how dangerous it always is to reason from insufficient data. The presence of the gypsies, and the use of the word 'band,' which was used by the poor girl, no doubt to explain the appearance which she had caught a hurried glimpse of by the light of her match, were sufficient to put me upon an entirely wrong scent. I can only claim the merit that I instantly reconsidered my position when, however, it became clear to me that whatever danger threatened an occupant of the room could not come either from the window or the door. My attention was speedily drawn, as I have already remarked to you, to this ventilator, and to the bell-rope which hung down to the bed. The discovery that this was a dummy, and that the bed was clamped to the floor, instantly gave rise to the suspicion that the rope was there as bridge for something passing through the hole and coming to the bed. The idea of a snake instantly occurred to me, and when I coupled it with my knowledge that the doctor was furnished with a supply of creatures from India, I felt that I was probably on the right track. The idea of using a form of poison which could not possibly be discovered by any chemical test was just such a one as would occur to a clever and ruthless man who had had an Eastern training. The rapidity with which such a poison would take effect would also, from his point of view, be an advantage. It would be a sharp-eyed coroner, indeed, who could distinguish the two little dark punctures which would show where the poison fangs had done their work. Then I thought of the whistle. Of course he must recall the snake before the morning light revealed it to the victim. He had trained it, probably by the use of the milk which we saw, to return to him when summoned. He would put it through this ventilator at the hour that he thought best, with the certainty that it would crawl down the rope and land on the bed. It might not bite the occupant, perhaps she might escape every night for a week, but sooner or later she must fall a victim.

"I had come to these conclusions before ever I had entered his room. An inspection of his chair showed me that he had been in the habit of standing on it, which of course would be necessary in order that he should reach the ventilator. The sight of the safe, the saucer of milk, and the loop of whip-cord were enough to finally dispel any doubts which may have remained. The metallic clang heard by Miss Stoner was obviously caused by her step-father hastily closing the door of his safe upon its terrible occupant. Having once made up my mind, you know the steps which I took in order to put the matter to the proof. I heard the creature hiss, as I have no doubt that you did also, and I instantly lit the light and attacked it."

"With the result of driving it through the ventilator."

"And also with the result of causing it to turn upon its master at the other side. Some of the blows of my cane came home, and roused its snakish temper, so that it flew upon the first person it saw. In this way I am no doubt indirectly responsible for Dr. Grimesby Roylott's death, and I cannot say that it is likely to weigh very heavily upon my conscience."

THE DOOR IN THE WALL

By H. G. Wells

[Herbert George Wells (1866–   ) is one of the most distinguished of the living authors of England. He was born in Kent and has lived in the neighborhood of London all his busy life. Mr. Wells was educated as a scientist, but early turned to literature. He has produced many novels dealing with social problems, government, and the like, and several that are for entertainment only. Among the best known are *Kipps* (1905), *Tono-Bungay* (1908), *The History of Mr. Polly* (1910), and *Mr. Britling Sees It Through* (1916). His *Outline of History* is well known outside of his work in prose fiction. While Mr. Wells's principal interest is in longer works of fiction, he is the author of an extended list of short stories.

The Door in the Wall, first published in 1906, is here reprinted by arrangement with the author.]

ONE confidential evening, not three months ago, Lionel Wallace told me this story of the Door in the Wall. And at the time I thought so far as he was concerned it was a true story.

He told it me with such a direct simplicity of conviction that I could not do otherwise than believe in him. But in the morning, in my own flat, I woke to a different atmosphere; and as I lay in bed and recalled the things he had told me, stripped of the glamor of his earnest slow voice, denuded of the focused, shaded table light, the shadowy atmosphere that wrapped about him and me, and the pleasant bright things, the dessert and glasses and napery of the dinner we had shared, making them for the time a bright little world quite cut off from everyday realities, I saw it all as frankly incredible. "He was mystifying!" I said, and then: "How well he did it! . . .It isn't quite the thing I should have expected him, of all people, to do well."

Afterwards, as I sat up in bed and sipped my morning tea, I found myself trying to account for the flavor of reality that perplexed me in his impossible reminiscences, by supposing they did in some way suggest, present, convey—I hardly know which word to use—experiences it was otherwise impossible to tell.

Well, I don't resort to that explanation now. I have got over my intervening doubts. I believe now, as I believed at the moment of telling, that Wallace did to the very best of his ability strip the truth of his secret for me. But whether he himself saw, or only thought he saw; whether he himself was the possessor of an inestimable privilege or the victim of a fantastic dream, I cannot pretend to guess. Even the facts of his death, which ended my doubts forever, throw no light on that.

That much the reader must judge for himself.

I forget now what chance comment or criticism of mine moved so reticent a man to confide in me. He was, I think, defending himself against an imputation of slackness and unreliability I had made in relation to a great public movement, in which he had disappointed me. But he plunged suddenly. "I have," he said, "a preoccupation——

"I know," he went on, after a pause, "I have been negligent. The fact is—it isn't a case of ghosts or apparitions—but—it's an odd thing to tell of, Redmond—I am haunted. I am haunted by something—that rather takes the light out of things, that fills me with longings. . . ."

He paused, checked by that English shyness that so often overcomes us when we would speak of moving or grave or beautiful things. "You were at Saint Athelstan's all through," he said, and for a moment that seemed to me quite irrelevant. "Well"—and he paused. Then, very haltingly at first, but afterwards more easily, he began to tell of the thing that was hidden in his life, the haunting memory of a beauty and a happiness that filled his heart with insatiable longings, that made all the interests and spectacle of worldly life seem dull and tedious and vain to him.

Now that I have the clue to it, the thing seems written visibly in his face. I have a photograph in which that look of detachment has been caught and intensified. It reminds me of what a woman once said of him—a woman who had loved him greatly. "Suddenly," she said, "the interest goes out of him. He forgets you. He doesn't care a rap for you—under his very nose. . ."

Yet the interest was not always out of him, and when he was holding his attention to a thing Wallace could contrive to be an extremely successful man. His career, indeed, is set with successes. He left me behind him long ago; he soared up over my head, and cut a figure in the world that I couldn't cut—anyhow. He was still a year short of forty, and they say now that he would have been in office and very probably in the new Cabinet if he had lived. At school he always beat me without effort—as it were by nature. We were at school together at Saint Athelstan's College in West Kensington for almost all our school-time. He came into the school as my co-equal, but he left far above me, in a blaze of scholarships and brilliant performance. Yet I think I made a fair average running. And it was at school I heard first of the Door in the Wall—that I was to hear of a second time only a month before his death.

To him at least the Door in the Wall was a real door, leading through a real wall to immortal realities. Of that I am now quite assured.

And it came into his life quite early, when he was a little fellow between five and six. I remember how, as he sat making his confession to me with a slow gravity, he reasoned and reckoned the date of it. "There was," he said, "a crimson Virginia creeper in it—all one bright uniform crimson, in a clear amber sunshine against a white wall. That came into the impression somehow, though I don't clearly remember how, and there were horse-chestnut leaves upon the clean pavement outside the green door. They were blotched yellow and green, you know, not brown nor dirty, so that they must have been new-fallen. I take it that means October. I look out for horse-chestnut leaves every year, and I ought to know.

"If I'm right in that, I was about five years and four months old."

He was, he said, rather a precocious little boy—he learned to talk at an abnormally early age, and he was so sane and "old-fashioned," as people say, that he was permitted an amount of initiative that most children scarcely attain by seven or eight. His mother died when he was two, and he was under the less vigilant and authoritative care of a nursery governess. His father was a stern, preoccupied lawyer, who gave him little attention and expected great things of him. For all his brightness he found life gray and dull, I think. And one day he wandered.

He could not recall the particular neglect that enabled him to get away, nor the course he took among the West Kensington roads. All that had faded among the incurable blurs of memory. But the white wall and the green door stood out quite distinctly.

As his memory of that childish experience ran, he did at the very first sight of that door experience a peculiar emotion, an attraction, a desire to get to the door and open it and walk in. And at the same time he had the clearest conviction that either it was unwise or it was wrong of him—he could not tell which—to yield to this attraction. He insisted upon it as a curious thing that he knew from the very beginning—unless memory has played him the queerest trick—that the door was unfastened, and that he could go in as he chose.

I seem to see the figure of that little boy, drawn and repelled. And it was very clear in his mind, too, though why it should be so was never explained, that his father would be very angry if he went in through that door.

Wallace described all these moments of hesitation to me with the utmost particularity. He went right past the door, and then, with his hands in his pockets and making an infantile attempt to whistle, strolled right along beyond the end of the wall. There he recalls a number of mean dirty shops, and particularly that of a plumber and decorator with a dusty disorder of earthenware pipes, sheet lead, ball taps, pattern books of wall paper, and tins of enamel. He stood pretending to examine these things, and *coveting*, passionately desiring, the green door.

Then, he said, he had a gust of emotion. He made a run for it, lest hesitation should grip him again; he went plump with outstretched hand through the green door and let it slam behind him. And so, in a trice, he came into the garden that has haunted all his life.

It was very difficult for Wallace to give me his full sense of that garden into which he came.

There was something in the very air of it that exhilarated, that gave one a sense of lightness and good happening and well-being; there was something in the sight of it that made all its color clean and perfect and subtly luminous. In the instant of coming into it one was exquisitely glad—as only in rare moments, and when one is young and joyful one can be glad in this world. And everything was beautiful there. . . .

Wallace mused before he went on telling me. "You see," he said, with the doubtful inflection of a man who pauses at incredible things, "there were two great panthers there. . . . Yes, spotted panthers. And I was not afraid. There was a long wide path with marble-edged flower borders on either side, and these two huge velvety beasts were playing there with a ball. One looked up and came towards me, a little curious as it seemed. It came right up to me, rubbed its soft round ear very gently against the small hand I held out, and purred. It was, I tell you, an enchanted garden. I know. And the size? Oh! it stretched far and wide, this way and that. I believe there were hills far away. Heaven knows where West Kensington had suddenly got to. And somehow it was just like coming home.

"You know, in the very moment the door swung to behind me, I forgot the road with its fallen chestnut leaves, its cabs and tradesmen's carts, I forgot the sort of gravitational pull back to the discipline and obedience of home, I forgot all hesitations and fear, forgot discretion, forgot all the intimate realities of this life. I became in a moment a very glad and wonder-happy little boy—in another world. It was a world with a different quality, a warmer, more penetrating and mellower light, with a faint clear gladness in its air, and wisps of sun-touched cloud in the blueness of its sky. And before me ran this long wide path, invitingly, with weedless beds on either side, rich with untended flowers, and these two great panthers. I put my little hands fearlessly on their soft fur, and caressed their round ears and the sensitive corners under their ears, and played with them, and it was as though they welcomed me home. There was a keen sense of home-coming in my mind, and when presently a tall, fair girl appeared in the pathway and came to meet me, smiling, and said 'Well?' to me, and lifted me and kissed me, and put me down and led me by the hand, there was no amazement, but only an impression of delightful rightness, of being reminded of happy things that had in some strange way been overlooked. There were broad red steps, I remember, that came into view between spikes of delphinium, and up these we went to a great avenue between very old and shady dark trees. All down this avenue, you know, between the red chapped stems, were marble seats of honor, and statuary, and very tame and friendly white doves. . . .

"Along this cool avenue my girl friend led me, looking down—I recall the pleasant lines, the finely-modeled chin of her sweet kind face—asking me questions in a soft, agreeable voice, and telling me things, pleasant things, I know, though what they were I was never able to recall. . . . Presently a Capuchin monkey, very clean, with a fur of ruddy brown and kindly hazel eyes, came down a tree to us and ran beside me, looking up at me and grinning, and presently leaped to my shoulder. So we two went on our way in great happiness."

He paused.

"Go on," I said.

"I remember little things. We passed an old man musing among laurels, I remember, and a place gay with paroquets, and came through a broad shaded colonnade to a spacious cool palace, full of pleasant fountains, full of beautiful things, full of the quality and promise of heart's desire. And there were many things and many people, some that still seem to stand out clearly and some that are vaguer; but all these people were beautiful and kind. In some way—I don't know how —it was conveyed to me that they all were kind to me, glad to have me there, and filling me with gladness by their gestures, by the touch of their hands, by the welcome and love in their eyes. Yes—"

He mused for a while. "Playmates I found there. That was very much to me, because I was a lonely little boy. They played delightful games in a grass-covered court where there was a sun-dial set about with flowers. And as one played one loved. . . .

"But—it's odd—there's a gap in my memory. I don't remember the games we played. I never remembered. Afterwards, as a child, I spent long hours trying, even with tears, to recall the form of that happiness. I wanted to play it all over again—in my nursery—by myself. No! All I remember is the happiness and two dear playfellows who were most with me. . . . Then presently came a sombre, dark woman, with a grave, pale face and dreamy eyes, a sombre woman, wearing a soft long robe of pale purple, who carried a book, and beckoned and took me aside with her into a gallery above a hall—though my playmates were loth to have me go, and ceased their game and stood watching as I was carried away. 'Come back to us!' they cried. 'Come back to us soon!' I looked up at her face, but she heeded them not at all. Her face was very gentle and grave. She took me to a seat in the gallery, and I stood beside her, ready to look at her book as she opened it upon her knee. The pages fell open. She pointed, and I looked, marveling, for in the living pages of that book I saw myself; it was a story about myself, and in it were all the things that had happened to me since ever I was born. . . .

"It was wonderful to me, because the pages of that book were not pictures, you understand, but realities."

Wallace paused gravely—looked at me doubtfully.

"Go on," I said. "I understand."

"They were realities—yes, they must have been; people moved and things came and went in them; my dear mother, whom I had near forgotten; then my father, stern and upright, the servants, the nursery, all the familiar things of home. Then the front door and the busy streets, with traffic to and fro. I looked and marveled, and looked half doubtfully again into the woman's face and turned the pages over, skipping this and that, to see more of this book and more, and so at last I came to myself hovering and hesitating outside the green door in the long white wall, and felt again the conflict and the fear.

"'And next?' I cried, and would have turned on, but the cool hand of the grave woman delayed me.

"'Next?' I insisted, and struggled gently with her hand, pulling up her fingers with all my childish strength, and as she yielded and the page came over she bent down upon me like a shadow and kissed my brow.

"But the page did not show the enchanted garden, nor the panthers, nor the girl who had led me by the hand, nor the playfellows who had been so loth to let me go. It showed a long gray street in West Kensington, in that chill hour of afternoon before the lamps are lit; and I was there, a wretched little figure, weeping aloud, for all that I could do to restrain myself, and I was weeping because I could not return to my dear playfellows who had called after me, 'Come back to us! Come back to us soon!' I was there. This was no page in a book, but harsh reality; that enchanted place and the restraining hand of the grave mother at whose knee I stood had gone—whither had they gone?"

He halted again, and remained for a time staring into the fire.

"Oh! the woefulness of that return!" he murmured.

"Well?" I said, after a minute or so.

"Poor little wretch I was!—brought back to this gray world again! As I realized the fulness of what had happened to me, I gave way to quite ungovernable grief. And the shame and humiliation of that public weeping and my disgraceful home-coming remain with me still. I see again the benevolent-looking old gentleman in gold spectacles who stopped and spoke to me—prodding me first with his umbrella. 'Poor little chap,' said he; 'and are you lost, then?'—and me a London boy of five and more! And he must needs bring in a kindly young policeman and make a crowd of me, and so march me home. Sobbing, conspicuous, and frightened, I came back from the enchanted garden to the steps of my father's house.

"That is as well as I can remember my vision of that garden—the garden that haunts me still. Of course, I can convey nothing of that indescribable quality of translucent unreality, that *difference* from the common things of experience that hung about it all; but that—that is what happened. If it was a dream, I am sure it was a daytime and altogether extraordinary dream. . . . H'm!—naturally there followed a terrible questioning, by my aunt, my father, the nurse, the governess—everyone. . . .

"I tried to tell them, and my father gave me my first thrashing for telling lies. When afterwards I tried to tell my aunt, she punished me again for my wicked persistence. Then, as I said, everyone was forbidden to listen to me, to hear a word about it. Even my fairy-tale books were taken away from me for a time—because I was too 'imaginative.' Eh? Yes, they did that! My father belonged to the old school. . . . And my story was driven back upon myself. I whispered it to my pillow—my pillow that was often damp and salt to my whispering lips with childish tears. And I added always to my official and less fervent prayers this one heartfelt request: 'Please God I may dream of the garden. Oh! take me back to my garden! Take me back to my garden!' I dreamt often of the garden. I may have added to it, I may have changed it; I do not know. . . . All this, you understand, is an attempt to reconstruct from fragmentary memories a very early experience. Between that and the other consecutive memories of my boyhood there is a gulf. A time came when it seemed impossible I should ever speak of that wonder glimpse again."

I asked an obvious question.

"No," he said. "I don't remember that I ever attempted to find my way back to the garden in those early years. This seems odd to me now, but I think that very probably a closer watch was kept on my movements after this misadventure to prevent my going astray. No, it wasn't till you knew me that I tried for the garden again. And I believe there was a period—incredible as it seems now—when I forgot the garden altogether—when I was about eight or nine it may have been. Do you remember me as a kid at Saint Athelstan's?"

"Rather!"

"I didn't show any signs, did I, in those days of having a secret dream?"

He looked up with a sudden smile.

"Did you ever play North-West Passage with me? . . . No, of course you didn't come my way!

"It was the sort of game," he went on, "that every imaginative child plays all day. The idea was the discovery of a North-West Passage to school. The way to school was plain enough; the game consisted in finding some way that wasn't plain, starting off ten minutes early in some almost hopeless direction, and working my way round through unaccustomed streets to my goal. And one day I got entangled among some rather low-class streets on the other side of Campden Hill, and I began to think that for once the game would be against me and that I should get to school late. I tried rather desperately a street that seemed a *cul-de-sac*, and found a passage at the end. I hurried through that with renewed hope. 'I shall do it yet,' I said, and passed a row of frowsy little shops that were inexplicably familiar to me, and behold! there was my long white wall and the green door that led to the enchanted garden!

"The thing whacked upon me suddenly. Then, after all, that garden, that wonderful garden, wasn't a dream!"

He paused.

"I suppose my second experience with the green door marks the world of difference there is between the busy life of a schoolboy and the infinite leisure of a child. Anyhow, this second time I didn't for a moment think of going in straightway. You see— For one thing, my mind was full of the idea of getting to school in time—set on not breaking my record for punctuality. I must surely have felt *some* little desire at least to try the door—yes. I must have felt that. . . . But I seem to remember the attraction of the door mainly as another obstacle to my overmastering determination to get to school. I was immensely interested by this discovery I had made, of course—I went on with my mind full of it—but I went on. It didn't check me. I ran past, tugging out my watch, found I had ten minutes still to spare, and then I was going downhill into familiar surroundings. I got to school, breathless, it is true, and wet with perspiration, but in time. I can remember hanging up my coat and hat. . . . Went right by it and left it behind me. Odd, eh?"

He looked at me thoughtfully. "Of course I didn't know then that it wouldn't always be there. Schoolboys have limited imaginations. I suppose I thought it was an awfully jolly thing to have it there, to know my way back to it; but there was the school tugging at me. I expect I was a good deal distraught and inattentive that morning, recalling what I could of the beautiful strange people I should presently see again. Oddly enough, I had no doubt in my mind that they would be glad to see me. . . . Yes, I must have thought of the garden that morning just as a jolly sort of place to which one might resort in the interludes of a strenuous scholastic career.

"I didn't go that day at all. The next day was a half-holiday, and that may have weighed with me. Perhaps, too, my state of inattention brought down impositions upon me, and docked the margin of time necessary for the *détour*. I don't know. What I do know is that in the meantime the enchanted garden was so much upon my mind that I could not keep it to myself.

"I told—what was his name?—a ferrety-looking youngster we used to call Squiff."

"Young Hopkins," said I.

"Hopkins it was. I did not like telling him. I had a feeling that in some way it was against the rules to tell him, but I did. He was walking part of the way home with me; he was talkative, and if we had not talked about the enchanted garden we should have talked of something else, and it was intolerable to me to think about any other subject. So I blabbed.

"Well, he told my secret. The next day in the play interval I found myself surrounded by half a dozen bigger boys, half teasing, and wholly curious to hear more of the enchanted garden. There was that big Fawcett—you remember him?—and Carnaby and Morley Reynolds. You weren't there, by any chance? No, you weren't; I think I should have remembered if you had been. . . .

"A boy is a creature of odd feelings. I was, I really believe, in spite of my secret self-disgust, a little flattered to have the attention of these big fellows. I remember particularly a moment of pleasure caused by the praise of Crawshaw—you remember Crawshaw major, the son of Crawshaw the composer?—who said it was the best lie he had ever heard. But at the same time there was a really painful undertow of shame at telling what I felt was indeed a sacred secret. That beast Fawcett made a joke about the girl in green—"

Wallace's voice sank with the keen memory of that shame. "I pretended not to hear," he said. "Well, then Carnaby suddenly called me a young liar, and disputed with me when I said the thing was true. I said I knew where to find the green door, could lead them all there in ten minutes. Carnaby became outrageously virtuous, and said I'd have to—and bear out my words or suffer. Did you ever have Carnaby twist your arm? Then perhaps you'll understand how it went with me. I swore my story was true. There was nobody in the school then to save a chap from Carnaby, though Crawshaw put in a word or so. Carnaby had got his game. I grew excited and red-eared, and a little frightened. I behaved altogether like a silly little chap, and the outcome of it all was that instead of starting alone for my enchanted garden, I led the way presently—cheeks flushed, ears hot, eyes smarting, and my soul one burning misery and shame—for a party of six mocking, curious, and threatening schoolfellows.

"We never found the white wall and the green door. . . ."

"You mean——?"

"I mean I couldn't find it. I would have found it if I could.

"And afterwards when I could go alone I couldn't find it. I never found it. I seem now to have been always looking for it through my school-boy days, but I never came upon it—never."

"Did the fellows—make it disagreeable?"

"Beastly. . . . Carnaby held a council over me for wanton lying. I remember how I sneaked home and upstairs to hide the marks of my blubbering. But when I cried myself to sleep at last it wasn't for Carnaby, but for the garden, for the beautiful afternoon I had hoped for, for the sweet friendly women and the waiting playfellows, and the game I had hoped to learn again, that beautiful forgotten game. . . .

"I believed firmly that if I had not told—— . . . I had bad times after that—crying at night and wool-gathering by day. For two terms I slacked and had bad reports. Do you remember? Of course you would! It was *you*—your beating me in mathematics that brought me back to the grind again."

For a time my friend stared silently into the red heart of the fire. Then he said: "I never saw it again until I was seventeen.

"It leaped upon me for the third time—as I was driving to Paddington on my way to Oxford and a scholarship. I had just one momentary glimpse. I was leaning over the apron of my hansom smoking a cigarette, and no doubt thinking myself no end of a man of the world, and suddenly there was the door, the wall, the dear sense of unforgettable and still attainable things.

"We clattered by—I too taken by surprise to stop my cab until we were well past and round a corner. Then I had a queer moment, a double and divergent movement of my will: I tapped the little door in the roof of the cab, and brought my arm down to pull out my watch. 'Yes, sir!' said the cabman, smartly. 'Er—well—it's nothing,' I cried. '*My* mistake! We haven't much time! Go on!' And he went on. . . .

"I got my scholarship. And the night after I was told of that, I sat over my fire in my little upper room, my study, in my father's house, with his praise—his rare praise—and his sound counsels ringing in my ears, and I smoked my favorite pipe—the formidable bull-dog of adolescence—and thought of that door in the long white wall. 'If I had stopped,' I thought, 'I should have missed my scholarship, I should have missed Oxford—muddled all the fine career before me!' I began to see things better! I fell musing deeply, but I did not doubt then this career of mine was a thing that merited sacrifice.

"Those dear friends and that clear atmosphere seemed very sweet to me, very fine but remote. My grip was fixing now upon the world. I saw another door opening—the door of my career."

He stared again into the fire. Its red light picked out a stubborn strength in his face for just one flickering moment, and then it vanished again.

"Well," he said, and sighed, "I have served that career. I have done —much work, much hard work. But I have dreamt of the enchanted garden a thousand dreams, and seen its door, or at least glimpsed its door, four times since then. Yes—four times. For a while this world was so bright and interesting, seemed so full of meaning and opportunity, that the half-effaced charm of the garden was by comparison gentle and remote. Who wants to pat panthers on the way to dinner with pretty women and distinguished men? I came down to London from Oxford, a man of bold promise that I have done something to redeem. Something—and yet there have been disappointments. . . .

"Twice I have been in love—I will not dwell on that—but once, as I went to some one who, I knew, doubted whether I dared to come, I took a short cut at a venture through an unfrequented road near Earl's Court, and so happened on a white wall and a familiar green door. 'Odd!' said I to myself, 'but I thought this place was on Campden Hill. It's the place I never could find somehow—like counting Stonehenge—the place of that queer daydream of mine.' And I went by it intent upon my purpose. It had no appeal to me that afternoon.

"I had just a moment's impulse to try the door, three steps aside were needed at the most—though I was sure enough in my heart that it would open to me—and then I thought that doing so might delay me on the way to that appointment in which my honor was involved. Afterwards I was sorry for my punctuality—I might at least have peeped in and waved a hand to those panthers, but I knew enough by this time not to seek again belatedly that which is not found by seeking. Yes, that time made me very sorry. . . .

"Years of hard work after that, and never a sight of the door. It's only recently it has come back to me. With it there has come a sense as though some thin tarnish had spread itself over my world. I began to think of it as a sorrowful and bitter thing that I should never see that door again. Perhaps I was suffering a little from overwork—perhaps it was what I've heard spoken of as the feeling of forty. I don't know. But certainly the keen brightness that makes effort easy has gone out of things recently, and that just at a time—with all these new political developments—when I ought to be working. Odd, isn't it? But I do begin to find life toilsome; its rewards, as I come near them, cheap. I began a little while ago to want the garden quite badly. Yes—and I've seen it three times."

"The garden?"

"No—the door! And I haven't gone in!"

He leaned over the table to me, with an enormous sorrow in his voice as he spoke. "Thrice I have had my chance—*thrice!* If ever that door offers itself to me again, I swore, I will go in, out of this dust and heat, out of this dry glitter of vanity, out of these toilsome futilities. I will go and never return. This time I will stay. . . . I swore it, and when the time came—*I didn't go.*

"Three times in one year have I passed that door and failed to enter. Three times in the last year.

"The first time was on the night of the snatch division on the Tenants' Redemption Bill, on which the Government was saved by a majority of three. You remember? No one on our side—perhaps very few on the opposite side—expected the end that night. Then the debate collapsed like eggshells. I and Hotchkiss were dining with his cousin at Brentford; we were both unpaired, and we were called up by telephone, and set off at once in his cousin's motor. We got in barely in time, and on the way we passed my wall and door—livid in the moonlight, blotched with hot yellow as the glare of our lamps lit it, but unmistakable. 'My God!' cried I. 'What?' said Hotchkiss. 'Nothing!' I answered, and the moment passed.

"'I've made a great sacrifice,' I told the whip as I got in. 'They all have,' he said, and hurried by.

"I do not see how I could have done otherwise then. And the next occasion was as I rushed to my father's bedside to bid that stern old man farewell. Then, too, the claims of life were imperative. But the third time was different; it happened a week ago. It fills me with hot remorse to recall it. I was with Gurker and Ralphs—it's no secret now, you know, that I've had my talk with Gurker. We had been dining at Frobisher's, and the talk had become intimate between us. The question of my place in the reconstructed Ministry lay always just over the boundary of the discussion. Yes—yes. That's all settled. It needn't be talked about yet, but there's no reason to keep a secret from you. . . . Yes—thanks! thanks! But let me tell you my story.

"Then, on that night things were very much in the air. My position was a very delicate one. I was keenly anxious to get some definite word from Gurker, but was hampered by Ralphs' presence. I was using the best power of my brain to keep that light and careless talk not too obviously directed to the point that concerned me. I had to. Ralphs' behavior since has more than justified my caution. . . . Ralphs, I knew, would leave us beyond the Kensington High Street, and then I could surprise Gurker by a sudden frankness. One has sometimes to resort to these little devices. . . . And then it was that in the margin of my field of vision I became aware once more of the white wall, the green door before us down the road.

"We passed it talking. I passed it. I can still see the shadow of Gurker's marked profile, his opera hat tilted forward over his prominent nose, the many folds of his muffler going before my shadow and Ralphs' as we sauntered past.

"I passed within twenty inches of the door. 'If I say good-night to them, and go in,' I asked myself, 'what will happen?' And I was all a-tingle for that word with Gurker.

"I could not answer that question in the tangle of my other problems. 'They will think me mad,' I thought. 'And suppose I vanish now!— Amazing disappearance of a prominent politician!' That weighed with me. A thousand inconceivably petty worldlinesses weighed with me in that crisis."

Then he turned on me with a sorrowful smile, and, speaking slowly, "Here I am!" he said.

"Here I am!" he repeated, "and my chance has gone from me. Three times in one year the door has been offered me—the door that goes into peace, into delight, into a beauty beyond dreaming, a kindness no man on earth can know. And I have rejected it, Redmond, and it has gone——"

"How do you know?"

"I know. I know. I am left now to work it out, to stick to the tasks that held me so strongly when my moments came. You say I have success—this vulgar, tawdry, irksome, envied thing. I have it." He had a walnut in his big hand. "If that was my success," he said, and crushed it, and held it out for me to see.

"Let me tell you something, Redmond. This loss is destroying me. For two months, for ten weeks nearly now, I have done no work at all, except the most necessary and urgent duties. My soul is full of inappeasable regrets. At nights—when it is less likely I shall be recognized—I go out. I wander. Yes. I wonder what people would think of that if they knew. A Cabinet Minister, the responsible head of that most vital of all departments, wandering alone—grieving—sometimes near audibly lamenting—for a door, for a garden!"

I can see now his rather pallid face, and the unfamiliar sombre fire that had come into his eyes. I see him very vividly tonight. I sit recalling his words, his tones; and last evening's *Westminster Gazette* still lies on my sofa, containing the notice of his death. At lunch today the club was busy with his death. We talked of nothing else.

They found his body very early yesterday morning, in a deep excavation near East Kensington Station. It is one of two shafts that have been made in connection with an extension of the railway southward. It is protected from the intrusion of the public by a hoarding upon the high road, in which a small doorway has been cut for the convenience of some of the workmen who live in that direction. The doorway was left unfastened through a misunderstanding between two gangers, and through it he made his way.

My mind is darkened with questions and riddles.

It would seem he walked all the way from the House that night—he has frequently walked home during the past Session—and so it is I figure his dark form coming along the late and empty streets, wrapped up, intent. And then did the pale electric lights near the station cheat the rough planking into a semblance of white? Did that fatal door awaken some memory?

Was there, after all, ever any green door in the wall at all?

I do not know. I have told his story as he told it to me. There are times when I believe that Wallace was no more than the victim of the coincidence between a rare but not unprecedented type of hallucination and a careless trap, but that indeed is not my profoundest belief. You may think me superstitious, if you will, and foolish; but, indeed, I am more than half convinced that he had, in truth, an abnormal gift, and a sense, something—I know not what—that in the guise of wall and door offered him an outlet, a secret and peculiar passage of escape into another and altogether more beautiful world. At any rate, you will say, it betrayed him in the end. But did it betray him? There you touch the inmost mystery of these dreamers, these men of vision and the imagination. We see our world fair and common, the hoarding and the pit. By our daylight standard he walked out of security into darkness, danger, and death.

But did he see like that?

THE RESERVED COFFIN

By Luigi Pirandello

[*The Reserved Coffin* is included in this volume as an example of the short story in Italian literature of the present time. Luigi Pirandello (1867–   ) is very well known in Italy and throughout the world as a dramatist, but he was in fact a novelist and prolific story writer long before he wrote his plays. He was born in Sicily and educated in Rome and Bonn (Germany). For thirty years he was a teacher of literature in the Normal School for Women in Rome. Among his better-known plays in America are: *Six Characters in Search of an Author*, *Right You Are*, and *As You Desire Me*. Some novels are: *The Late Mattia Pascal*, *The Outcast*, and *The Old and the Young*.

The translation that follows was made by Professor J. E. Harry and published in *The Golden Book* (January, 1926). It is used by permission of the translator.]

WHEN the cabriolet was moving along the road below the little church of San Biagio, Mèndola, coming back from the farm, thought he had better go up to the cemetery on the hill to see what truth there was in the complaints lodged with the municipality against that custodian, Nocio Pàmpina, called *Sacramento*.

City Councillor for about a year, Nino Mèndola, from the very day he had assumed office, hadn't felt very well. He suffered from attacks of dizziness. He didn't like to confess it even to himself, but he was afraid he might be struck with apoplexy any day—an ill of which all his people had died before their time. Hence he was always in a bad humor; and that sorry old nag of his that was pulling the cabriolet knew something about it, too.

And all that day, in the country, he had not felt well. Movement and diversion were futile—and finally, to brave his secret fear, he had made up his mind then and there to make that long-promised inspection of the cemetery, promised to himself and to his colleagues of the city council.

"It isn't only the living," he was thinking as he went up the hill, "even the dead give you something to think about and to do in this blessed town. Yes, indeed. The dead know whether they are guarded well or badly. Perhaps—I don't say they don't: to think that as soon as we are dead we'll be treated badly, turned over to the tender mercies of Pàmpina, stolid fellow that he is, and a drunkard to boot, furnishes food for thought—All right; now I'll see."

Pure slander.

As custodian of the cemetery, Nocio Pàmpina, called *Sacramento*, was ideal—a ghost, with a voice like a mosquito's—he seemed a corpse just come out of the grave to do as well as he could the chores about the house.

What was to be done about it then? All honest folk, up—at length—and peace.

The leaves, yes. A leaf or two fallen from the hedges encumbered the paths. A few sprouts had grown up here and there. And the sparrows—the little scamps—ignorant of the fact that the tombstones needed no punctuation marks, had sown among the magnificent and multitudinous virtues in which the inscriptions of those monuments abounded, too many commas, perhaps, and too many exclamation points.

Trifles.

Nevertheless, Mèndola, entering the hovel of the keeper at the right of the gate, stopped:

"And what's that—there?"

Nocio Pàmpina, called *Sacramento*, opened his lips to a shade of a smile and whispered:

"A coffin for a dead man, Excellency."

It was, in fact, a very beautiful coffin for a dead man. Polished chestnut, with bosses and gilding. Made really without thinking of the expense. There, almost in the middle of the little room.

"Thanks; I see it," replied Mèndola. "I mean, what's it there for?"

"It's the Cavalier Piccarone's, Excellency."

"Piccarone? And why? Why, he's not dead!"

"No, no, Excellency! Not at all!" said Pàmpina. "But your Lordship must know that his wife died last month, poor man."

"Well?"

"He accompanied her here, on foot; oldish as he is. Yes, sir. Then he called me, and said: 'Listen, Sacramento. Before another month's gone, you'll have me too.' 'But what is your Lordship saying?' says I. 'Hush!' says he. 'Listen: This coffin, my dear child, cost me more than twenty ounces. Handsome, you see that. I didn't spare expense, you understand. But now that the appearance has been made, says he, of what use will this handsome coffin be to her now, to the blessed spirit under the ground? It's a pity to waste it', says he. 'I'll tell you what we'll do. Let's lower the sainted spirit', says he, 'just as it is, in the zinc which is inside; and then put this aside, if you please: it will do for me too. One of these days, toward dusk, I'll send for it.'"

Mèndola didn't linger to hear anything more. He simply couldn't wait till he got to town to spread the news about that coffin which Piccarone had had put aside for himself.

          .   .   .   .

Famous in the town was Gerolamo Piccarone, lawyer, and, at the time of the Bourbons, Cavalier of San Gennaro, famous for his stinginess

and for his knavery. Bad pay was he. Stories were told about his
closeness that would make you stand agape. But this—Mèndola was
saying to himself—this beats all; and true, ohè, true as truth itself. He
had seen it himself, there, the coffin, with his own eyes.

He was enjoying by anticipation the bursts of laughter with which
his tale would be received, whispered in the thin voice of Pàmpina; he
didn't even notice the cloud of dust raised and the noise that the cabriolet made as his nag rushed furiously along, when lo! "Stop, stop!" he
heard somebody yell at the top of his voice from the *Hunters' Tavern*
which a man named Dolcemascolo kept there by the wayside.

Two friends, Bartolo Gaglio and Gaspare Ficarra, ardent hunters,
sitting out in front of the tavern under the pergola, had begun to shout
in that way because they thought Mèndola's horse was running off with
him.

"Running off indeed! I was running——"

"Oh! You were running, were you?" said Gaglio. "Have you got a
spare neck at home?"

"If you only knew, *cari miei!*" exclaimed Mèndola joyfully, jumping
down, and out of breath; and he told the story of the coffin to those two
friends.

They feigned, from time to time, disbelief, but only to manifest their
wonder. And then Mèndola swearing—word of honor—that he had
seen it, with his own eyes, the coffin, in Sacramento's hovel.

The other two, in turn, began to tell other well-known deeds of prowess
of Piccarone. Mèndola was for getting into his cabriolet again at once;
but they had already ordered Dolcemascolo to bring a glass for their
friend, the Councillor, and would have him drink it.

But Dolcemascolo had been standing there as if stunned.

"Dolcemascolo, ohè!" cried Gaglio.

The tavern-keeper, with his sailor fur cap aslant on his ear, without
a jacket, and his shirt sleeves rolled up on his hairy arms, roused himself, and said with a sigh:

"Pardon me," said he, "stupid man that I am, I have been standing
here like an idiot listening to this story. Only this morning, Cavalier
Piccarone's dog, Turco, that ugly old brute which comes and goes as he
pleases from the Cannatello farm up here to the little villa—say, do you
know what he did? Stole more than twenty pieces of sausage that I
had hanging out there on the balcony! It's a good thing, I say, that I
have two witnesses."

Mèndola, Gaglio, Ficarra burst out laughing. Said Mèndola:
"You like it, *caro mio!*"

Dolcemascolo raised a fist; fire darted from his eyes.

"Ah, *perdio*, no! he'll pay me for those sausages, he will! He'll pay
me for them; yes, he'll pay me," he shot back at the incredulous laughs
and at the stubborn denials of his three customers. "You gentlemen

will see. I've found the way to make' him. I know the color of his hair!"

And with a shrewd gesture, habitual with him, he winked one eye as he pulled down the lid of the other with his forefinger.

What way he had found he wouldn't state; but he did say that he was waiting for two farmers who had been present, in the morning, and had seen the theft of the sausage, and that he was going up to the villa with them before evening.

Mèndola got into his cabriolet again, not even waiting to drain his glass; Gaglio and Ficarra paid their bills; and after advising the tavern-keeper to renounce, for his own good, his famous plan of getting himself paid by Piccarone, they left.

.   .   .   .

To construct that little one-story villa, on the avenue at the edge of the town, Gerolamo Piccarone, lawyer and cavalier of San Gennaro at the time of King Bomba, had worked for more than twenty years, and rumor had it that it had not cost him a penny.

Evil tongues said that it was made of small stones found on the highway and pushed to the place, one by one, by the feet of the selfsame Piccarone.

He was, besides, a man learned in jurisprudence, and one of deep mind and profound philosophic spirit. One of his books on Gnosticism, and another on Christian Philosophy, they said, had even been translated into German.

But he was *malva di tre cotte*, was Piccarone, that is to say, an enemy of all innovations. He dressed in the style of 1821; wore a necklace beard; was thickset, coarse, baggy at the shoulders. Always frowning, his eyes half-closed, he kept continually rubbing his chin and approving his secret thoughts with frequent grunts:

"Uh—uh—uh—Italy!—they've—made Italy—what a fine thing, uh, Italy—bridges and roads—uh—illumination—army and navy—uh—uh —uh—compulsory education—taxes! and Piccarone pays——."

He paid little or nothing, in reality, for by dint of most subtle quibbles he wore out and exasperated the greatest patience. He always wound up thus:

"What have I got to do with it? Railways? I don't travel. Light? I never go out evenings. I don't ask for anything, thanks; I don't want anything. Only a little air, to breathe. Did you make the air, too? Must I pay also for the air I breathe?"

He had, in fact, withdrawn to that little villa of his and retired from his profession, which had, however, yielded him magnificent returns up to the time of his retirement a few years before. He must have laid by a snug little sum. To whom would he leave it at his death? He had no relatives, near or distant. And banknotes?—could he take them with him in that handsome coffin which he had reserved for himself? And the little villa? And the farm over there at Cannatello?

When Dolcemascolo, accompanied by the two countrymen, came up to the gate, Turco, the old ugly watch-dog, as if he understood that the tavern-keeper was coming for him, rushed furiously against the bars. The old servant ran out, but was unable to quiet him or to get him away. Piccarone, who was reading in the kiosk in the middle of the little garden, had to whistle for him and then hold him fast by the collar until the servant came to chain him up.

Dolcemascolo, who knew what was what, had put on his best Sunday clothes and, clean shaven, between those two poor country clodhoppers who were coming back dirty and tired from their work, he appeared more than commonly prosperous and lordly. His face like rose and milk—he was fair to look upon.

He entered the kiosk exclaiming, with feigned admiration:

"Fine dog! Large animal, noble and handsome! Good watchdog! Worth his weight in gold!"

Piccarone, frowning and eyes half-closed, grunted several times, nodding assent to the eulogies of Dolcemascolo; then he said:

"What do you want? Sit down."

And he pointed to the little iron stools arranged all around the kiosk. Dolcemascolo drew one up near the table, saying to the farmers:

"Sit down there, you. I come to your Lordship, a man of the law, for an opinion."

Piccarone opened his eyes.

"An opinion? But I haven't practiced law, *caro mio*, for a long time."

"I know it," Dolcemascolo hastened to add. "Your Lordship is, however, a lawyer of the old school. And my father, blessed be his soul, always used to say to me: 'Stick to the old, my son!' Now I know how conscientious your Lordship was in your profession. I have very little faith in the young pettifoggers of today. I don't want to go to law, understand, with anybody. I'd be a fool to do that—I've come simply for an opinion, which your Lordship alone can give me."

Piccarone closed his eyes:

"Speak. I am listening."

"Your Lordship knows," began Dolcemascolo. But Piccarone started and snorted:

"Uh, what do I know! What do you know? *I know, I know, he knows*—oh, come to the point, *caro mio!*"

Dolcemascolo was a little taken back, disconcerted; still he smiled and began again:

"Yes, sir. I meant that your Lordship knows that I have on the highroad, a restaurant."

"*Hunters'?* Yes: I've passed it many a time."

"Going to Cannatello, of course. And you must certainly have seen that on the balcony, under the pergola, I always have some of my wares displayed: bread, fruit, ham.''

Piccarone nodded, then added mysteriously: "Seen, and smelled too, sometimes.''

"Smelled?''

"Which smelled of sand, *figliuolo*. You understand—dust from the road—No matter. Come to the point.''

"Here it is, yes, sir," answered Dolcemascolo, swallowing. "Let us assume that I have displayed on the balcony a few—sausages, for instance. Now, your Lordship—perhaps this—of course!—I was about to repeat—it's a habit of mine—your Lordship perhaps doesn't know it, but these are the days we have quail migrating. Hence, on the road, hunters, dogs, all the time. I'm coming, I'm coming to the point! A dog passes, Signor Cavaliere, jumps up, and seizes the sausages on the balcony.''

"A dog?''

"Yes, sir. I run after him, and with me these two poor fellows who had come in to buy some victuals to take to the country with them. Is that so, yes or no? All three of us start to run after the dog; but we can't overtake him. Besides, even if we do, tell me, your Lordship, what could we do with that sausage which the dog had bitten and dragged all along the road—no good, even if we do get it back! But I recognize the dog; I know who he belongs to.''

"Uh—a moment," interrupted Piccarone. "Wasn't the owner there?''

"No, sir!" answered Dolcemascolo quickly. "It wasn't one of those hunters. The dog had evidently run away from home. Hunting dogs, you understand, smell the chase, allow themselves to be locked up; then they escape. No matter. Well, as I said, I know who owns the dog; these two friends of mine know it too, and they witnessed the theft. Now, your Lordship, a man of the law, is to tell me simply whether the owner of the dog is bound to pay me damages, *ecco!*''

Piccarone answered without hesitation:

"Of course he is bound to pay, *figliuolo*.''

Dolcemascolo leaped for joy, but quickly restrained himself, and, turning to his companions, said:

"Did you hear? The Signor lawyer says that the owner of the dog is bound to pay damages.''

"Absolutely bound, absolutely," reaffirmed Piccarone. "Did you hear me say he wasn't?''

"No, sir," replied Dolcemascolo jumping for joy and clasping his hands. "But your Lordship must pardon me if I, poor ignorant man that I am, have beat around the bush in this feeble way to come to tell you that your Lordship must pay me for the sausages, because the dog that stole it from me was your own, Turco.''

Piccarone looked at Dolcemascolo a little while as if he had gone crazy; then, all at once, he lowered his eyes—and began to read in the big book he had before him open on the table.

The two rustics looked at each other; Dolcemascolo raised a hand to make a sign to them not to breathe.

Piccarone, pretending all the time to read, rubbed his chin with one hand, grunted, and said:

"So it was Turco?"

"I can swear it, Signor Cavaliere!" exclaimed Dolcemascolo, getting up and crossing his hands over his breast.

"And you have come here," resumed Piccarone, dark and calm, "with two witnesses, eh?"

"No, sir!" said Dolcemascolo quickly. "In case your Lordship did not believe me——"

"Ah, that was the reason?" muttered Piccarone.

"But I believe you, *caro mio*. Sit down. You are a very honest man. I believe you and I'll pay you. Do I enjoy the reputation of being bad pay, eh?"

"Who says so, Signor Cavaliere?"

"Everybody says so! And you think so too, now, don't you? Two— uh—two witnesses——"

"For the truth, as much for you as for me!"

"Bravo, yes: as much for me as for you; well said. The unjust taxes, *caro mio*, I refuse to pay; but what is just, yes, I pay that willingly— have always paid that. Turco stole your sausage? Tell me, how much?"

Dolcemascolo, having come anticipating that he would have to fight God knows what kind of battles against the quibbles and snares of this old toad, when he was confronted with such meekness, lost courage, mortified.

"A trifle, Signor Cavaliere. Must have been about twenty pieces, more or less—hardly worth mentioning."

"No, no," replied Piccarone firmly. "Tell me how much I owe you and I want to pay. Tell me quickly, *figliuolo!* You work; you have suffered a loss; you must be reimbursed. How much?"

Dolcemascolo shrugged his shoulders, smiled, and said:

"Twenty pieces of those big ones—two kilos—at one lira twenty a kilo——"

"You sell them so cheap?" asked Piccarone.

"You must understand," replied Dolcemascolo, all honey, "your Lordship didn't eat them. I charge—I wouldn't—I charge you what they cost me."

"Not at all! If I didn't eat them, my dog did. So let's say—roughly —two kilos. Two lire a kilo all right?"

"As you will."

"Four lire. Good. Now tell me, *figliuolo!* twenty-five less four make how many? Twenty-one, if I mistake not. Good. You give me twenty-one lire and let's talk no more about it."

Dolcemascolo thought he had not heard aright.

"What's that?"

"Twenty-one lire," repeated Piccarone placidly.

"Here are two witnesses to the truth, as much for me as for you—all right? You come to me for an opinion. Now I, *figliuolo*, charge twenty-five lire for an opinion. Fixed price. I owe you four of them for the sausage; give me twenty-one and don't mention the matter again."

Dolcemascolo looked at Piccarone hard, perplexed, not knowing whether he should laugh or cry, unwilling to believe that Piccarone was serious; yet he did not seem to be jesting.

"I—to—to you?" he stammered.

"It seems clear to me, *figliuolo*," explained Piccarone. "Your business is keeping an inn; mine giving opinions about the law—feebly though it may be. Now, as I do not deny your right to reimbursement, so you will not deny mine for the information you asked me for, and which I gave you. *Now* you know that if a dog steals your sausage, the owner of the dog is liable for damages and is obliged to indemnify you for the loss you have sustained. You didn't know that before? No! You have to pay for knowledge, *caro mio*. I had to work and spend so much to learn it! Do you think I am jesting?"

"Yes, sir!" confessed Dolcemascolo with tears on his cheeks, lifting and opening wide his arms. "I'll forget about the sausage, Signor Cavaliere; I am a poor ignorant man; pardon me, and let's not talk about it any more, in very truth."

"Ah no, ah no, *caro mio*," exclaimed Piccarone. "I don't make reductions, *I* don't. Right is right, as much for you as for me. *I* pay, I pay, I want to pay. To pay and be paid. I was here studying, as you see; you have made me lose an hour's time. Twenty-one lire. That's my price. If you are not fully persuaded of it, give ear, *caro mio:* go to any other lawyer and ask him whether this remuneration is due me or not. I give you three days. If at the end of the third day you have not paid me, rest assured, *figliuolo*, I'll sue you."

Piccarone raised his chin, raised his hands: "I'll not listen to any excuses. I'll sue you!"

Dolcemascolo then lost the light of his eyes. Anger seized him by the hair; blinded him. What were the damages? There were no damages. He thought of the bantering he would get, the raillery which he already divined as he gazed into the faces of those two countrymen: he who considered himself so clever, so shrewd, he who had boasted he would display his cunning, and had victory almost within his grasp. Seeing himself caught in his own net, when he least expected it, made him so furious that he suddenly turned into a wild beast.

"Ah, that's the reason, is it?" said he, walking up to Piccarone with his hand raised and his fist clenched, "that's the reason your dog is such a thief? You taught him!"

Piccarone rose to his feet, turbulent, and raised an arm:

"Get out of here! You'll answer also for insults to a man of honor who——"

"Man of honor?" roared Dolcemascolo, grasping the lawyer's arm and shaking it furiously.

The two rustics rushed forward to restrain him but suddenly, before they knew it, Piccarone collapsed, inert, and fell into the violent grasp of Dolcemascolo. And as the latter, amazed, opened his arms to catch him, Piccarone dropped first to the stool, reeled to one side and slumped to the floor in a heap.

Before the terrified countrymen, the features of Dolcemascolo contracted as if by a burst of laughter. Oh—what—? Why, he hadn't even touched him!

They leaned over the man, as he lay on the floor; they moved one of his arms.

"Escape!—escape!——"

Dolcemascolo looked at them both, as if stunned. Escape?

At this point they heard the gate creak, and the coffin, which the old man had reserved for himself, appeared, borne along in triumph on the shoulders of two stalwart, panting bearers, in truth, as if it had been sent for at that very moment for immediate use.

At the apparition of the coffin the three men remained rooted to the spot; they almost fainted.

It did not occur to Dolcemascolo that Nocio Pàmpina, called *Sacramento*, after the visit and inspection of the councillor, had hastened to put himself in regular standing by forwarding the coffin to its destination; but he recalled in a flash what Mèndola had said that morning down at the restaurant; and suddenly, in that empty coffin which was waiting and which had come unexpectedly, at the very moment it was needed, as if sent for mysteriously, Dolcemascolo saw the hand of fate which had made use of his own hand.

He put his hands to his head and began to shriek:

"There it is! There it is! That was calling him! Bear witness, all of you, that I didn't even touch him! That was calling him! He had put it aside for himself! And lo! here it comes, because he was fated to die!"

And he seized the two bearers by the arms to rouse them from their stupor.

"Isn't it true? Isn't it true? Say!"

But the two bearers were not at all astonished. Since they had brought the coffin, it was the most natural thing in the world to them that they should find the lawyer dead. They shrugged their shoulders, and said:

"Why, yes, here it is."

THE SEVEN THAT WERE HANGED

By Leonid Andreyev

[Leonid Nicolaievich Andreyev (1871–1919) was one of the best of the Russian literary artists in the early years of the twentieth century. He has been described as a mournful humanist in deepest sympathy with mankind as the race lives in its "city of dreadful night." He himself lived in terror of life. As a writer he believed in making room for large ideas but clothing them in few words. Only once did he write a story of love with a happy ending—his first story. He was able to build up a considerable fortune from his writing, but lost it all by refusing to accept the fortunes of the Russians and throw in his lot with the Communists. He went to Finland in poverty and died there in 1919. His three most powerful pieces of fiction, dreadful and powerful at the same time, were directed against three social customs of his time. They are, first, *The Red Laugh* (1905), a protest against war; *The Seven That Were Hanged* (1909), a protest against capital punishment; and *S. O. S.* (1919), a protest against the Red Terror in Russia.

This piece is a novelette in its construction. If it had been written as a short story, the author would have sketched the characters of the "seven" in a few paragraphs and then would have made his story out of Sections XI and XII. The story attempts to give an answer to the question: "How does a man act when he is facing capital punishment?" Andreyev says: "It depends upon the man." And then he pictures the experiences, the mental, physical, and emotional reactions, of *seven* very different individuals, five men and two women, who are to be hanged.

This translation of *The Seven That Were Hanged* (copyright, 1925) is reprinted by permission of The Modern Library, Inc., publishers.]

I

"AT ONE O'CLOCK IN THE AFTERNOON, YOUR EXCELLENCY!"

AS the Minister was a very fat man, predisposed to apoplexy, and as it was necessary therefore to spare him every dangerous emotion, they took the minutest precautions in warning him that a serious attempt upon his life had been planned. When they saw that he received the news calmly, they gave him the details: the attempt was to be made the next day, at the moment when His Excellency was to leave the house to go to make his report. A few terrorists, armed with revolvers and bombs, whom a police spy had betrayed and who were now being watched by the police, were to meet near the steps at one o'clock in the afternoon and await the Minister's exit. There the criminals would be arrested.

"Pardon me," interrupted the Minister in surprise. "How do they know that I am to go to present my report at one o'clock in the afternoon, when I learned it myself only two days ago?"

The commander of the body-guard made a vague gesture signifying ignorance.

"At one o'clock in the afternoon, Your Excellency!"

Astonished, and at the same time satisfied with the police who had managed the affair so well, the Minister shook his head; a disdainful smile appeared on his thick red lips; quickly he made all the necessary preparations to pass the night in another palace; in no way did he wish to embarrass the police. His wife and children also were removed from the dangerous premises.

As long as the lights gleamed in this new residence, and while his familiars bustled about him expressing their indignation, the Minister felt a sensation of agreeable excitement. It seemed to him that he had just received, or was about to receive, a great and unexpected reward. But the friends went away, and the lights were put out. The intermittent and fantastic glare of the arc-lights in the street fell upon the ceiling and the walls, penetrating through the high windows, symbolizing, as it were, the fragility of all bolts and walls, the vanity of all supervision. Then, in the silence and the solitude of a strange chamber, the dignitary was seized with an unspeakable terror.

He was afflicted with a kidney trouble. Every violent emotion caused his face, feet, and hands to swell, and made him appear heavier, more massive. Now, like a heap of bloated flesh that made the bed-springs bend, he suffered the anguish of the sick as he felt his face puff up and become, as it were, something foreign to his body. His thought recurred obstinately to the cruel fate that his enemies were preparing for him. He evoked one after the other all the horrible attempts of recent date, in which bombs had been thrown against persons as noble as himself and bearing even higher titles, tearing their bodies into a thousand shreds, hurling their brains against foul brick walls, and knocking their teeth from their jaws. And, at these recollections, it seemed to him that his diseased body was another man's body suffering from the fiery shock of the explosion. He pictured to himself his arms detached from his shoulders, his teeth broken, his brain crushed. His legs, stretched out in the bed, grew numb and motionless, the feet pointing upward, like those of a dead man. He breathed noisily, coughing occasionally, to avoid all resemblance to a corpse: he moved about, that he might hear the sound of the metallic springs, the rustling of the silk coverlet. And, to prove that he was really alive, he exclaimed in a loud and clear voice:

"Brave fellows! Brave fellows!"

These words of praise were for the police, the gendarmes, the soldiers, all those who protected his life and had prevented the assassination. But in vain did he stir about, lavish his praise, and smile at the discomfiture of the terrorists; he could not yet believe that he was saved. It seemed to him that the death evoked for him by the anarchists, and which existed in their thought, was already there and would remain there, refusing to go away until the assassins should be seized, deprived of their bombs, and lodged safely in prison. There it stood, in the corner yonder, declining to leave, and unable to leave, like an obedient soldier placed on guard by an unknown will.

"At one o'clock in the afternoon, Your Excellency!" This phrase came back to him continually, uttered in all tones, now joyously and ironically, now irritably, now obstinately and stupidly. One would have said that a hundred phonographs had been placed in the chamber, and were crying one after the other, with the idiotic persistence of machines:

"At one o'clock in the afternoon, Your Excellency!"

And this "one o'clock in the afternoon" of the next day, which so short a time before was in no way to be distinguished from other hours, had taken on a menacing importance; it had stepped out of the clock-dial, and was beginning to live a distinct life, stretching itself like an immense black curtain, to divide life into two parts. Before it and after it no other hour existed; it alone, presumptuous and obsessing, was entitled to a special life.

Grinding his teeth, the Minister raised himself in his bed to a sitting posture. It was positively impossible for him to sleep.

Pressing his bloated hands against his face, he pictured to himself with terrifying clearness how he would have risen on the morrow if he had been left in ignorance; he would have taken his coffee, and dressed. And neither he, or the Swiss who would have helped him on with his fur coat, or the valet who would have served his coffee, would have understood the uselessness of breakfasting and dressing, when a few moments later everything would be annihilated by the explosion. . . . The Swiss opens the door. . . . And it is he, this good and thoughtful Swiss, with the blue eyes, and the open countenance, and the numerous military decorations—he it is who opens the terrible door with his own hands. . . .

"Ah!" suddenly exclaimed the Minister aloud; slowly he removed his hands from his face. Gazing far before him into the darkness with a fixed and attentive look, he stretched out his hand to turn on the light. Then he arose, and in his bare feet walked around the strange chamber so unfamiliar to him; finding another light, he turned that on also. The room became bright and agreeable; there was only the disordered bed and the fallen coverlet to indicate a terror that had not yet completely disappeared.

Clad in a night-shirt, his beard in a tangle, a look of irritation on his face, the Minister resembled those old people who are tormented by asthma and insomnia. One would have said that the death prepared for him by others had stripped him bare, had torn him from the luxury with which he was surrounded. Without dressing he threw himself into an arm-chair, his eyes wandered to the ceiling.

"Imbeciles!" he cried in a contemptuous tone of conviction.

"Imbeciles!" And he was speaking of the policemen whom but a few moments before he had called "brave fellows," and who, through excess of zeal, had told him all the details of the attack that had been planned.

"Evidently," he thought with lucidity, "I am afraid now because I have been warned and because I know. But, if I had been left in ignorance, I should have taken my coffee quietly. And then, evidently, this death. . . . But am I then so afraid of death? I have a kidney trouble; some day I must die of it, and yet I am not afraid, because I don't know when. And these imbeciles say to me: 'At one o'clock in the afternoon, Your Excellency!' They thought that I would be glad to know about it! . . . Instead of that, death has placed himself in the corner yonder, and does not go away! He does not go away, because I have that fixed idea! To die is not so terrible; the terrible thing is to know that one is going to die. It would be quite impossible for a man to live if he knew the hour and day of his death with absolute certainty. And yet these idiots warn me: 'At one o'clock in the afternoon, Your Excellency!'"

Recently he had been ill, and the doctors had told him that he was going to die and should make his final arrangements. He had refused to believe them; and, in fact, he did not die. Once, in his youth, it had happened to him to get beyond his depth; he had decided to put an end to his existence; he had loaded his revolver, written some letters, and even fixed the hour of his suicide; then, at the last moment, he had reconsidered. And always, at the supreme moment, something unexpected may happen; consequently no man can know when he will die.

"At one o'clock in the afternoon, Your Excellency!" these amiable idiots had said to him. They had informed him only because his death had been plotted; and yet he was terrified simply to learn the hour when it might have occurred. He admitted that they would kill him some day or other, but it would not be the next day. . . . it would not be the next day, and he could sleep quietly, like an immortal being. . . . The imbeciles! They did not know what a gulf they had dug in saying, with stupid amiability: "At one o'clock in the afternoon, Your Excellency!"

From the bitter anguish that shot through his heart, the Minister understood that he would know neither sleep, nor rest, nor joy, until this black and accursed hour, thus detached from the course of time, had passed. It was enough in itself to annihilate the light and enwrap the man in the opaque darkness of fear. Now that he was awake, the fear of death permeated his entire body, filtered into his bones, exuded from every pore.

Already the Minister had ceased to think of the assassins of the morrow: they had disappeared, forgotten in the multitude of inauspicious
things that surrounded his life. He feared the unexpected, the inevitable:
an attack of apoplexy, a laceration of the heart, the rupture of a little
artery suddenly made powerless to resist the flow of blood and splitting
like a glove on swollen hands.

His thick, short neck frightened him; he dared not look at his swollen
fingers, full of some fatal fluid. And though, just before, in the darkness,
he had been compelled to stir in order to avoid resemblance to a corpse,
now, under this bright, cold, hostile, frightful light, it seemed to him
horrible, impossible, to move even to light a cigarette or ring for a
servant. His nerves were at a tension. With red and upturned eyes and
burning head, he stifled.

Suddenly, in the darkness of the sleeping house, the electric bell just
under the ceiling, among the dust and spiders' webs, became animate.
Its little metallic tongue beat hurriedly against its sonorous edge. It
stopped for a moment, and then began to ring again in a continuous and
terrifying fashion.

People came running. Here and there lamps were lighted on the walls
and chandeliers—too few of them for intense illumination, but enough
to create shadows. On every hand appeared these shadows: they arose
in the corners and stretched out upon the ceiling, fastening upon all
projections and running along the walls. It was difficult to understand
where all these taciturn, monstrous, and innumerable shadows could
have kept themselves before—mute souls of mute things.

A thick and trembling voice said something indistinguishable. Then
they telephoned to the doctor: the Minister was ill. His Excellency's
wife was summoned also.

II

SENTENCED TO BE HANGED

The predictions of the police were realized. Four terrorists, three men
and one woman, carrying bombs, revolvers, and infernal machines, were
taken in front of the steps of the residence; a fifth accomplice was
arrested at her dwelling, where the implements had been manufactured
and the conspiracy planned. A large quantity of dynamite and many
weapons were found there. All five were very young: the eldest of the
men was twenty-eight, the younger of the women nineteen. They were
tried in the fortress where they had been imprisoned after their arrest;
they were tried quickly and secretly, as was the custom at that merciless
epoch.

Before the court all five were calm, but serious and thoughtful; their
contempt for the judges was so great that they did not care to emphasize
their fearlessness by a useless smile or a pretence of gaiety. They were

just tranquil enough to protect their souls and the deep gloom of their agony from the malevolent gaze of strangers. Some questions they refused to answer, some they answered simply, briefly, precisely, as if they were speaking, not to judges, but to statisticians desirous of completing tables of figures. Three of them, one woman and two men, gave their real names; two refused to disclose their identity, which remained unknown to the court. In everything that happened they manifested that distant and attenuated curiosity peculiar to people seriously ill or possessed by a single all-powerful idea. They cast swift glances, seized upon an interesting word in its flight, and went back to their thoughts, resuming them at the exact point where they had dropped them.

The accused placed nearest the judges had given his name as Sergey Golovin, a former officer, son of a retired colonel. He was very young, with broad shoulders, and so robust that neither the prison nor the expectation of certain death had been able to dim the color of his cheeks or the expression of happy innocence in his blue eyes. Throughout the trial he twisted his thick blond beard, to which he had not yet become accustomed, and gazed steadily at the window, knitting his brows.

It was the latter part of winter, that period into which, among snowstorms and gray, cold days, the approaching spring projects sometimes, as a forerunner, a warm and luminous day, or even a single hour, so passionately young and sparkling that the sparrows in the street become mad with joy and men seem intoxicated. Now, through the upper window, still covered with the dust of the previous summer, a very odd and beautiful sky was to be seen; at the first glance it seemed a thick and milky gray; then, upon a second examination, it appeared to be covered with azure stains, of an ever-deepening blue, a blue pure and infinite. And because it did not strip itself suddenly, but modestly draped itself in the transparent veil of clouds, it became charming, like one's *fiancée*. Sergey Golovin looked at the sky, pulled at his mustache, winked now one and now the other of his eyes behind the long, heavy eyelashes, and reflected profoundly on nobody knows what. Once, even, his fingers moved rapidly, and an expression of naïve joy appeared upon his face; but he looked around him, and his joy was extinguished like a live coal upon which one steps. Almost instantaneously, almost without transition, the redness of his cheeks gave place to a corpse-like pallor; a fine hair painfully pulled out was pressed as in a vice between his bloodless finger-ends. But the joy of life and of the spring was still stronger. A few minutes later the young face resumed its naïve expression and sought again the sky of spring.

Toward the sky also looked an unknown young girl, surnamed Musya. She was younger than Golovin, but seemed his elder because of the severity, the gravity, of her proud and loyal eyes. The delicate neck and slender arms alone revealed that intangible something which is youth itself, and which sounded so distinctly in the pure harmonious voice that resembled a costly instrument in perfect tune. Musya was very pale, of that passionate pallor peculiar to those who burn with an inner, radiant, and powerful fire. She scarcely stirred; from time to time only, with a gesture that was hardly visible, she felt for a deep trace in the third finger of her right hand—the trace of a ring recently removed. She looked at the sky with calmness and indifference; she looked at it simply because everything in this commonplace and dirty hall was hostile to her and seemed to scrutinize her face. This bit of blue sky was the only pure and true thing upon which she could look with confidence.

The judges pitied Sergey Golovin and hated Musya.

Musya's neighbor, motionless also, with hands folded between his knees and somewhat of affectation in his pose, was an unknown surnamed Werner. If one can bolt a face as one bolts a heavy door, the unknown had bolted his as if it were a door of iron. He gazed steadily at the floor, and it was impossible to tell whether he was calm or deeply moved, whether he was thinking of something or listening to the testimony of the policemen. He was rather short of stature; his features were fine and noble. He gave the impression of an immense and calm force, of a cold and audacious valor. The very politeness with which he uttered his clear and curt replies seemed dangerous on his lips. On the backs of the other prisoners the customary cloak seemed a ridiculous costume; on him it was not even noticeable, so foreign was the garment to the man. Although Werner had been armed only with a poor revolver, while the others carried bombs and infernal machines, the judges looked upon him, as the leader, and treated him with a certain respect, with the same brevity which he employed toward them.

In his neighbor, Vasily Kashirin, a frightful moral struggle was going on between the intolerable terror of death and the desperate desire to subdue this fear and conceal it from the judges. Ever since the prisoners had been taken to court in the morning, he had been stifling under the hurried beating of his heart. Drops of sweat appeared continually on his brow; his hands were moist and cold; his damp and icy shirt, sticking to his body, hindered his movements. By a superhuman effort of the will he kept his fingers from trembling, and maintained the firmness and moderation of his voice and the tranquillity of his gaze. He saw nothing around him; the sound of the voice that he heard seemed to reach him through a fog, and it was in a fog also that he stiffened himself in a desperate effort to answer firmly and aloud. But, as soon as he had spoken, he forgot the questions, as well as his own phrases; the silent and terrible struggle began again. And upon his person death was so in evidence that the judges turned their eyes away from him. It was as difficult to determine his age as that of a rotting corpse. According to his papers he was only twenty-three. Once or twice Werner touched him gently on the knee, and each time he answered briefly:

"It's nothing."

His hardest moment was when he suddenly felt an irresistible desire to utter inarticulate cries, like a hunted beast. Then he gave Werner a slight push; without raising his eyes, the latter answered in a low voice: "It's nothing, Vasya. It will soon be over!"

Consumed by anxiety, Tanya Kovalchuk, the fifth terrorist, sheltered her comrades with a maternal look. She was still very young; her cheeks seemed as highly colored as those of Sergey Golovin; and yet she seemed to be the mother of all the accused, so full of tender anxiety and infinite love were her looks, her smile, her fear. The progress of the trial did not interest her. She listened to her comrades simply to see if their voices trembled, if they were afraid, if they needed water.

But she could not look at Vasya; his anguish was too intense; she contented herself with cracking her plump fingers. At Musya and Werner she gazed with proud and respectful admiration, her face then wearing a grave and serious expression. As for Sergey Golovin, she continually tried to attract his attention by her smile.

"The dear comrade, he is looking at the sky. Look, look!" thought she, as she observed the direction of his eyes.

"And Vasya? My God! My God! . . . What can be done to comfort him? If I speak to him, perhaps it will make matters worse; suppose he should begin to weep?"

Like a peaceful pool reflecting every wandering cloud, her amiable and clear countenance showed all the feeling and all the thoughts, however fleeting, of her four comrades. She forgot that she was on trial too and would be hanged; her indifference to this was absolute. It was in her dwelling that the bombs and dynamite had been found; strange as it may seem, she had received the police with pistol shots, and had wounded one of them in the head.

The trial ended toward eight o'clock, just as the day was drawing to its close. Little by little, in the eyes of Sergey and Musya, the blue sky disappeared; without reddening, without smiling, it grew dim gently as on a summer evening, becoming grayish, and suddenly cold and wintry. Golovin heaved a sigh, stretched himself, and raised his eyes toward the window, where the chilly darkness of the night was already making itself manifest; still pulling his beard, he began to examine the judges, the soldiers, and their weapons, exchanging a smile with Tanya Kovalchuk. As for Musya, when the sun had set completely, she did not lower her gaze to the ground, but directed it toward a corner where a spider's web was swaying gently in the invisible current of warm air from the stove; and thus she remained until the sentence had been pronounced.

After the verdict, the condemned said their farewells to their lawyers, avoiding their disconcerted, pitying, and confused looks; then they grouped themselves for a moment near the door, and exchanged short phrases.

"It's nothing, Vasya! All will soon be over!" said Werner.

"But there is nothing the matter with me, brother!" answered Kashirin, in a strong, quiet, and almost joyous voice. In fact, his face had taken on a slight color, no longer resembling that of a corpse.

"The devil take them! They have hanged us all just the same!" swore Golovin naïvely.

"It was to have been expected," answered Werner, without agitation.

"Tomorrow the final judgment will be rendered, and they will put us all in the same cell," said Tanya, to console her comrades. "We shall remain together until the execution."

Silently, and with a resolute air, Musya started off.

III

"I MUST NOT BE HANGED"

A fortnight before the affair of the terrorists, in the same court, but before other judges, Ivan Yanson, a peasant, had been tried and sentenced to be hanged.

Ivan Yanson had been hired as a farm-hand by a well-to-do farmer, and was distinguished in no way from the other poor devils of his class. He was a native of Wesenberg, in Esthonia; for some years he had been advancing gradually toward the capital, passing from one farm to another. He had very little knowledge of Russian. As there were none of his countrymen living in the neighborhood, and as his employer was a Russian, named Lazaref, Yanson remained silent for almost two years. He said hardly a word to either man or beast. He led the horse to water and harnessed it without speaking to it, walking about it lazily, with short hesitating steps. When the horse began to run, Yanson did not say a word, but beat it cruelly with his enormous whip. Drink transformed his cold and wicked obstinacy into fury. The hissing of the lash and the regular and painful sound of his wooden shoes on the floor of the shed could be heard even at the farmhouse. To punish him for torturing the horse the farmer at first beat Yanson, but, not succeeding in correcting him, he gave it up.

Once or twice a month Yanson got drunk, especially when he took his master to the station. His employer once on board the train, Yanson drove a short distance away, and waited until the train had started.

Then he returned to the station, and got drunk at the buffet. He came back to the farm on the gallop, a distance of seven miles, beating the unfortunate beast unmercifully, giving it its head, and singing and shouting incomprehensible phrases in Esthonian. Sometimes silent, with set teeth, impelled by a whirlwind of indescribable fury, suffering, and enthusiasm, he was like a blind man in his mad career; he did not see the passers-by, he did not insult them, uphill and down he maintained his furious gait.

His master would have discharged him, but Yanson did not demand high wages, and his comrades were no better than he.

One day he received a letter written in Esthonian; but, as he did not know how to read or write, and as no one about him knew this language, Yanson threw it into the muck-heap with savage indifference, as if he did not understand that it brought him news from his native country. Probably needing a woman, he tried also to pay court to the girl employed on the farm. She repulsed him, for he was short and puny, and covered with hideous freckles; after that, he let her alone.

But, though he spoke little, Yanson listened continually. He listened to the desolate snow-covered fields, containing hillocks of frozen manure that resembled a series of little tombs heaped up by the snow; he listened to the bluish and limpid distance, the sonorous telegraph-poles. He alone knew what the fields and telegraph-poles were saying. He listened also to the conversations of men, the stories of murder, pillage, fire.

One night, in the village, the little church-bell began to ring in a feeble and lamentable way; flames appeared. Malefactors from nobody knew where were pillaging the neighboring farm. They killed the owner and his wife, and set fire to the house. This caused a feeling of anxiety on the farm where Yanson lived: day and night the dogs were loose; the master kept a gun within reach of his bed. He wished also to give an old weapon to Yanson, but the latter, after examining it, shook his head and refused it. The farmer did not understand that Yanson had more confidence in the efficacy of his Finnish knife than in this rusty old machine.

"It would kill me myself!" said he.

"You are only an imbecile, Ivan!"

And one winter evening, when the other farm-hand had gone to the station, this same Ivan Yanson, who was afraid of a gun, committed robbery and murder, and made an attempt at rape. He did it with an astonishing simplicity. After shutting the servant in the kitchen, lazily, like a man almost dead with sleep, he approached his master from behind, and stabbed him several times in the back. The master fell unconscious; his wife began to cry and to run about the chamber. Showing his teeth, and holding his knife in his hand, Yanson began to ransack trunks and drawers. He found the money; then, as if he had just seen the master's wife for the first time, he threw himself upon her to rape her, without the slightest premeditation. But he happened to drop his knife; and, as the woman was the stronger, she not only resisted Yanson, but half strangled him. At this moment the farmer recovered his senses, and the servant broke in the kitchen-door and came in. Yanson fled. They took him an hour later, squatting in the corner of the shed, and scratching matches which continually went out. He was trying to set fire to the farm.

A few days later the farmer died. Yanson was tried and sentenced to death. In the court one would have said that he did not understand what was going on; he viewed the large imposing hall without curiosity, and explored his nose with a shrunken finger that nothing disgusted. Only those who had seen him at church on Sunday could have guessed that he had done something in the way of making a toilet; he wore a knitted cravat of dirty red; in spots his hair was smooth and dark; in others it consisted of light thin locks, like wisps of straw on an uncultivated and devastated field.

When the sentence of death by hanging was pronounced, Yanson suddenly showed emotion. He turned scarlet, and began to untie and tie his cravat, as if it were choking him. Then he waved his arms without knowing why, and declared to the presiding judge, who had read the sentence:

"She has said that I must be hanged."

"'She'? Who?" asked the presiding judge, in a deep bass voice.

Yanson pointed at the presiding judge with his finger, and, looking at him furtively, answered angrily:

"You!"

"Well?"

Again Yanson turned his eyes toward one of the judges, in whom he divined a friend, and repeated:

"She has said that I must be hanged. I must not be hanged."

"Take away the accused."

But Yanson still had time to repeat, in a grave tone of conviction:

"I must not be hanged."

And with his outstretched finger and irritated face, to which he tried in vain to give an air of gravity, he seemed so stupid that the guard, in violation of orders, said to him in an undertone as he led him away:

"Well, you are a famous imbecile, you are!"

"I must not be hanged!" repeated Yanson, obstinately.

They shut him up again in the cell in which he had passed a month, and to which he had become accustomed, as he had become accustomed to everything: to blows, to brandy, to the desolate and snow-covered country sown with rounded hillocks resembling tombs. It even gave him pleasure to see his bed again, and his grated window, and to eat what they gave him; he had taken nothing since morning. The disagreeable thing was what had happened in court, about which he knew not what to think. He had no idea at all of what death by hanging was like.

The guard said to him, in a tone of remonstrance:

"Well, brother, there you are, hanged!"

"And when will they hang me?" asked Yanson, in a tone of incredulity. The guard reflected.

"Ah! wait, brother; you must have companions; they do not disturb themselves for a single individual, and especially for a little fellow like you."

"Then, when?" insisted Yanson.

He was not offended that they did not want to take the trouble to hang him all alone; he did not believe in this excuse, and thought they simply wanted to put off the execution, and then pardon him.

"When? When?" resumed the guard. "It is not a question of hanging a dog, which one takes behind a shed and dispatches with a single blow! Is that what you would like, imbecile?"

"Why, no, I would not like it!" said Yanson suddenly, with a joyous grimace. "'Twas she that said I must be hanged, but I, I do not want to be hanged!"

And, for the first time in his life perhaps, he began to laugh—a grinning and stupid laugh, but terribly gay. He seemed like a goose beginning to quack. The guard looked at Yanson in astonishment, and then knitted his brows: this stupid gaiety on the part of a man who was to be executed insulted the prison, the gallows itself, and made them ridiculous. And suddenly it seemed to the old guard, who had passed all his life in prison and considered the laws of the gaol as those of nature, that the prison and all of life were a sort of mad-house in which he, the guard, was the chief madman.

"The devil take you!" said he, spitting on the ground. "Why do you show your teeth? This is no wine-shop!"

"And I, I do not want to be hanged! Ha! ha! ha!"

Yanson laughed always.

"Satan!" replied the guard, crossing himself.

All the evening Yanson was calm, and even joyous. He repeated the phrase that he had uttered: "I must not be hanged," and so convincing, so irrefutable was it that he had no occasion for anxiety. He had long since forgotten his crime; sometimes he simply regretted that he had not succeeded in raping the woman. Soon he thought no more about the matter.

Every morning Yanson asked when he would be hanged, and every morning the guard answered him angrily:

"You have time enough." And he went out quickly, before Yanson began to laugh.

Thanks to this invariable exchange of words, Yanson persuaded himself that the execution would never take place; for whole days he lay upon his bed, dreaming vaguely of the desolate and snow-covered fields, of the buffet at the railway station, and also of things farther away and more luminous. He was well fed in prison, he took on flesh.

"She would love me now," he said to himself, thinking of his master's wife. "Now I am as big as her husband."

He had only one desire—to drink brandy and course madly over the roads with his horse at full gallop.

When the terrorists were arrested, the whole prison learned of it. One day, when Yanson put his customary question, the guard answered him abruptly, in an irritated voice:

"It will be soon. In a week, I think."

Yanson turned pale; the gaze of his glassy eyes became so thick that he seemed as if asleep.

"You are joking?" he asked.

"Formerly you could not await the time, today you say that I am joking. No jokes are tolerated here. It is you who like jokes, but we do not tolerate them," replied the guard with dignity; then he went out.

When evening came, Yanson had grown thin. His skin, which had become smooth again for a few days, was contracted into a thousand little wrinkles. He took no notice of anything; his movements were made slowly, as if every toss of the head, every gesture of the arm, every step, were a difficult undertaking, that must first be deeply studied. During the night Yanson lay on his camp-bed, but his eyes did not close; they remained open until morning.

"Ah!" exclaimed the guard, on seeing him the next day.

With the satisfaction of the *savant* who has made a new and a successful experiment, he examined the condemned man attentively and without haste; now everything was proceeding in the usual fashion. Satan was covered with shame; the sanctity of the prison and of the gallows was re-established. Indulgent, and even full of sincere pity, the old man asked:

"Do you want to see someone?"

"Why?"

"To say good-bye, of course . . . to your mother, for instance, or to your brother."

"I must not be hanged," said Yanson in a low voice, casting a glance sidewise at the gaoler. "I do not want to be hanged."

The guard looked at him, without saying a word.

Yanson was a little calmer in the evening. The day was so ordinary, the cloudy winter sky shone in so usual a fashion, so familiar was the sound of steps and conversations in the corridor, that he ceased to believe in the execution. Formerly the night had been to him simply the moment of darkness, the time for sleep. But now he was conscious of its mysterious and menacing essence. To disbelieve in death one must see and hear about one the customary course of life: steps, voices, light. And now everything seemed extraordinary to him; this silence, these shades, that seemed to be already the shades of death; already he felt the approach of inevitable death; in bewilderment he climbed the first steps of the gibbet.

The day, the night, brought him alternations of hope and fear; and so things went until the evening when he felt, or understood, that the inevitable death would come three days later, at sunrise.

He had never thought of death; for him it had no shape. But now he felt plainly that it had entered his cell, and was groping about in search of him. To escape it he began to run.

The room was so small that the corners seemed to push him back toward the centre. He could not hide himself anywhere. Several times he struck the walls with his body; once he hurled himself against the door. He staggered and fell, with his face upon the ground; he felt the grasp of death upon him. Glued to the floor, his face touching the dirty black asphalt, Yanson screamed with terror until help came. When they had lifted him up, seated him on his bed, and sprinkled him with cold water, he did not dare to open both eyes. He half opened one, perceived an empty and luminous corner of his cell, and began again to scream.

But the cold water had its effect. The guard, moreover, always the same old man, slapped Yanson several times on the head in a fatherly fashion. This sensation of life drove out the thought of death. Yanson slept deeply the rest of the night. He lay on his back, with mouth open, snoring loud and long. Between his half-closed eyelids appeared a whitish, flat, and dead eye, without a pupil.

Then day, night, voices, steps, the cabbage soup, everything became for him one continuous horror that plunged him into a state of wild astonishment. His weak mind could not reconcile the monstrous contradiction between, on the one hand, the bright light and the odor of the cabbage, and, on the other, the fact that two days later he must die. He thought of nothing; he did not even count the hours; he was simply the prey of a dumb terror in the presence of this contradiction that bewildered his brain: today life, tomorrow death. He ate nothing, he slept no more; he sat timidly all night long on a stool, with his legs crossed under him, or else he walked up and down his cell with furtive steps. He appeared to be in a state of open-mouthed astonishment; before taking the most commonplace article into his hands he would examine it suspiciously.

The gaolers ceased to pay attention to him. His was the ordinary condition of the condemned man, resembling, according to his gaoler who had not experienced it himself, that of an ox felled by a club.

"He is stunned; now he will feel nothing more until the moment of death," said the guard, examining him with his experienced eye. "Ivan, do you hear? Ho there, Ivan!"

"I must not be hanged!" answered Yanson, in a colorless voice; his lower jaw had dropped.

"If you had not killed, they would not hang you," reproachfully said the chief gaoler, a highly important young man, wearing a decoration. "To steal, you have killed, and you do not want to be hanged!"

"I do not want to be hanged!" replied Yanson.

"Well, you don't have to want to; that's your affair. But, instead of talking nonsense, you would do better to dispose of your possessions. You surely must have something."

"He has nothing at all! A shirt and a pair of pantaloons! And a fur cap!"

Thus time passed until Thursday. And Thursday, at midnight, a large number of people entered Yanson's cell; a man with cloth epaulets said to him:

"Get ready! it is time to start."

Always with the same slowness and the same indolence Yanson dressed himself in all that he possessed, and tied his dirty shawl around his neck. While watching him dress, the man with the epaulets, who was smoking a cigarette, said to one of the assistants:

"How warm it is today! It is spring!"

Yanson's eyes closed; he was in a complete drowse. The guard shouted:

"Come, come! Make haste! You are going to sleep!"

Suddenly Yanson ceased to move.

"I must not be hanged," said he, with indolence.

He began to walk submissively, shrugging his shoulders. In the court-yard the moist spring air had a sudden effect upon him; his nose began to run; it was thawing; close by, drops of water were falling with a joyous sound. While the gendarmes were getting into the unlighted vehicle, bending over and rattling their swords, Yanson lazily passed his finger under his running nose, or arranged his badly-tied shawl.

IV

WE OF OREL

The court that had tried Yanson sentenced to death at the same session Michael Goloubetz, known as Michka the Tzigane, a peasant of the department of Orel, district of Eletz. The last crime of which they accused him, with evidence in support of the charge, was robbery, followed by the assassination of three persons. As for his past, it was unknown. There were vague indications to warrant the belief that the Tzigane had taken part in a whole series of other murders. With absolute sincerity and frankness he termed himself a brigand, and overwhelmed with his irony those who, to follow the fashion, pompously styled themselves "expropriators"; his last crime he described willingly in all its details. But, at the slightest reference to the past, he answered:

"Go ask the wind that blows over the fields!"

And, if they persisted in questioning him, the Tzigane assumed a dignified and serious air.

"We of Orel are all hot-heads, the fathers of all the robbers of the world," said he, in a sedate and judicial tone.

They had nicknamed him Tzigane because of his physiognomy and his thieving habits. He was thin and strangely dark; yellow spots out-lined themselves upon his cheek-bones which were as prominent as those of a Tartar. He had a way of rolling the whites of his eyes, that re-minded one of a horse. His gaze was quick and keen, full of curiosity, terrifying. The things over which his swift glance passed seemed to lose something or other, and to become transformed by surrendering to him part of themselves. One hesitated to take a cigarette that he had looked at, as if it had already been in his mouth. His extraordinarily mobile nature made him seem now to coil and concentrate himself like a twisted handkerchief, now to scatter himself like a sheaf of sparks. He drank water almost by the pailful, like a horse.

When the judges questioned him, he raised his head quickly, and answered without hesitation, even with satisfaction:

"It is true!"

Sometimes, to lend emphasis, he rolled his "r's" vigorously.

Suddenly he jumped to his feet, and said to the presiding judge:

"Permit me to whistle?"

"Why?" exclaimed the judge, in astonishment.

"The witnesses say that I gave the signal to my comrades; I will show you how I did it. It is very interesting."

A little disconcerted, the judge granted the desired permission. The Tzigane quickly placed four fingers in his mouth, two of each hand; he rolled his eyes furiously. And the inanimate air of the court-room was rent by a truly savage whistle. There was everything in the pierc-ing sound, partly human, partly animal; the mortal anguish of the victim, and the savage joy of the assassin; a threat, a call, and the tragic solitude, the darkness, of a rainy autumn night.

The judge shook his head; with docility the Tzigane stopped. Like an artist who has just played a difficult air with assured success, he sat down, wiped his wet fingers on his cloak, and looked at the specta-tors with a satisfied air.

"What a brigand!" exclaimed one of the judges, rubbing his ear. But another, who had Tartar eyes, like the Tzigane's, was looking dreamily into the distance, over the brigand's head; he smiled, and replied:

"It was really interesting."

Without remorse, the judges sentenced the Tzigane to death.

"It is just!" said the Tzigane, when the sentence had been pro-nounced.

And, turning to a soldier of the guard, he added with an air of bravado:

"Well, let us be off, imbecile! And keep a good hold of your gun, lest I snatch it from you!"

The soldier looked at him seriously and timidly; he exchanged a glance with his comrade, and tested his weapon to see if it was in work-ing order. The other did the same. And all the way to the prison it seemed to the soldiers that they did not walk, but flew; they were so absorbed by the condemned man that they were unconscious of the route, of the weather, and of themselves.

Like Yanson, Michka the Tzigane remained seventeen days in prison before being executed. And the seventeen days passed as rapidly as a single day, filled with a single thought, that of flight, of liberty, of life. The turbulent and incoercible spirit of the Tzigane, stifled by the walls, the gratings, and the opaque window through which nothing could be seen, employed all its force in setting Michka's brain on fire. As in a vapor of intoxication, bright but incomplete images whirled, clashed, and mingled in his head; they passed with a blinding and irresistible rapidity, and they all tended to the same end: flight, liberty, life. For entire hours, with nostils distended like those of a horse, the Tzigane sniffed the air; it seemed to him that he inhaled the odor of hemp and flame, of dense smoke. Or else he turned in his cell like a top, examining the walls, feeling them with his fingers, measuring them, piercing the ceiling with his gaze, sawing the bars in his mind. His agitation was a source of torture to the soldier who watched him through the window; several times he threatened to fire on him.

During the night the Tzigane slept deeply, almost without stirring, in an invariable but living immobility, like a temporarily inactive spring. But, as soon as he jumped to his feet, he began again to plan, to grope, to study. His hands were always dry and hot. Sometimes his heart suddenly congealed, as if they had placed in his breast a new block of ice which did not melt, and which caused a continuous shiver to run over his skin. At these times his naturally dark complexion became darker still, taking on the blue-black shade of bronze. Then a queer tic seized him; he constantly licked his lips, as if he had eaten a dish that was much too sweet; then, with a hiss, and with set teeth, he spat upon the ground the saliva that had thus accumulated in his mouth. He left his words unfinished; his thoughts ran so fast that his tongue could no longer keep up with them.

One day the chief of the guards entered his cell, accompanied by a soldier. He squinted at the spittle with which the ground was spattered, and said rudely:

"See how he has dirtied his cell!"

The Tzigane replied quickly:

"And you, you ugly mug, you have soiled the whole earth, and I haven't said a word to you. Why do you annoy me?"

With the same rudeness the chief of the guards offered him the post of hangman. The Tzigane showed his teeth, and began to laugh:

"So they can find none! That's not bad! Go on, then, hanging people! Ah! Ah! There are necks and ropes, and nobody to do the hanging! My God, that's not bad."

"They will give your life as a reward!"

"I should say so: I could hardly play the hangman after I am dead!"

"Well, what do you say, yes or no?"

"And how do they hang here? They probably choke people secretly."

"No, they hang them to music!" retorted the chief.

"Imbecile! Of course there must be music . . . like this. . . ."

And he began to sing a captivating air.

"You have gone completely mad, my friend!" said the guard. "Come, speak seriously, what is your decision?"

The Tzigane showed his teeth.

"Are you in a hurry? Come back later, and I will tell you!"

And to the chaos of unfinished images which overwhelmed the Tzigane was added a new idea: how agreeable it would be to be the headsman! He clearly pictured to himself the square black with people, and the scaffold on which he, the Tzigane, walked back and forth, in a red shirt, with axe in hand. The sun illuminates the heads, plays gaily on the axe blade; everything is so joyous, so sumptuous, that even he whose head is to be cut off smiles. Behind the crowd are to be seen the carts and the noses of the horses; the peasants have come to town for the occasion. Still farther away fields. The Tzigane licked his lips, and spat upon the ground. Suddenly it seemed to him that his fur cap had just been pulled down over his mouth; everything became dark; he gasped for breath; and his heart changed into a block of ice, while little shivers ran through his body.

Twice more the chief came back; the Tzigane, showing his teeth again, answered:

"What a hurry you are in! Come back another time!"

Finally, one day, the gaoler cried to him, as he was passing by the window:

"You have lost your chance, my ill-favored raven. They have found another."

"The devil take you! Go, be the hangman yourself!" replied the Tzigane. And he ceased to dream of the splendors of his trade.

But toward the end, the nearer drew the day of execution, the more intolerable became the impetuosity of the torn images. The Tzigane would have liked to wait, to halt, but the furious torrent carried him on, giving him no chance to get a hold on anything; for everything was in a whirl. And his sleep became agitated; he had new and shapeless visions, as badly squared as painted blocks, and even more impetuous than his thoughts had been. It was no longer a torrent, but a continual fall from an infinite height, a whirling flight through the whole world of colors. Formerly the Tzigane had worn only a mustache tolerably well cared for; in prison he had been obliged to grow his beard, which was short, black, and stubbly; giving him a crazy look. There were moments, in fact, when the Tzigane lost his mind. He turned about in his cell all unconscious of his movements, continuing to feel for the rough and uneven walls. And he always drank great quantities of water, like a horse.

One evening, when they were lighting the lamps, the Tzigane dropped on all fours in the middle of his cell, and began to howl like a wolf. He did this very seriously, as if performing an indispensable and important act. He filled his lungs with air, and then expelled it slowly in a prolonged and trembling howl. With knit brows, he listened to himself attentively. The very trembling of the voice seemed a little affected; he did not shout indistinctly; he made each note in this wild beast's cry sound separately, full of unspeakable suffering and terror.

Suddenly he stopped, and remained silent for a few minutes, without getting up. He began to whisper, as if speaking to the ground:

"Dear friends, good friends . . . dear friends . . . good friends . . . have pit . . . friends! My friends!"

He said a word, and listened to it.

He jumped to his feet, and for a whole hour poured forth a steady stream of the worst curses.

"Go to the devil, you scoundrels!" he screamed, rolling his bloodshot eyes. "If I must be hanged, hang me, instead of . . . Ah, you blackguards!"

The soldier on guard, as white as chalk, wept with anguish and fear; he pounded the door with the muzzle of his gun, and cried in a lamentable voice:

"I will shoot you! By God, do you hear? I will shoot you!"

But he did not dare to fire; they never fire on prisoners sentenced to death, except in case of revolt. And the Tzigane ground his teeth, swore, and spat. His brain, placed on the narrow frontier that separates life from death, crumbled like a lump of dried clay.

When they came, during the night, to take him to the gallows, he regained a little of his animation. His cheeks took on some color; in his eyes the usual strategy, a little savage, sparkled again, and he asked of one of the functionaries:

"Who will hang us? The new one? Is he accustomed to it yet?"

"You needn't disturb yourself about that," answered the personage thus appealed to.

"What? Not disturb myself! It is not Your Highness that is going to be hanged, but I! At least don't spare the soap on the slip-noose; the State pays for it!"

"I beg you to hold your tongue!"

"This fellow, you see, consumes all the soap in the prison; see how his face shines," continued the Tzigane, pointing to the chief of the guards.

"Silence!"

"Don't spare the soap!"

Suddenly he began to laugh, and his legs became numb. Yet, when he arrived in the courtyard, he could still cry:

"Say, there! you fellows yonder, come forward with my carriage!"

V

"KISS HIM AND BE SILENT"

The verdict against the five terrorists was pronounced in its final form and confirmed the same day. The condemned were not notified of the day of execution. But they foresaw that they would be hanged, according to custom, the same night, or, at the latest, the night following. When they were offered the opportunity of seeing their families the next day, they understood that the execution was fixed for Friday at daybreak.

Tanya Kovalchuk had no near relatives. She knew only of some distant relatives living in Little Russia, who probably knew nothing of the trial or the verdict. Musya and Werner, not having revealed their identity, did not insist on seeing any of their people. Only Sergey Golovin and Vasily Kashirin were to see their families. The thought of this approaching interview was frightful to both of them, but they could not make up their minds to refuse a final conversation, a last kiss.

Sergey Golovin thought sadly of this visit. He was fond of his father and mother; he had seen them very recently, and he was filled with terror at the thought of what was going to happen. The hanging itself, in all its monstrosity, in its disconcerting madness, outlined itself more readily in his imagination than these few short, incomprehensible minutes that seemed apart from time, apart from life. What to do? What to say? The most simple and customary gestures—to shake hands, embrace, and say, "How do you do, father?"—seemed to him frightful in their monstrous, inhuman, insane insignificance.

After the verdict they did not put the condemned in the same cell, as Tanya expected them to do. All the morning, up to the time when he received his parents, Sergey Golovin walked back and forth in his cell, twisting his short beard, his features pitiably contracted. Sometimes he stopped suddenly, filled his lungs with air, and puffed like a swimmer who has remained too long under water. But, as he was in good health, and as his young life was solidly implanted within him, even in these minutes of atrocious suffering, the blood coursed under his skin, coloring his cheeks; his blue eyes preserved their usual brilliancy.

Everything went off better than Sergey expected; his father, Nicolas Sergiévitch Golovin, a retired colonel, was the first to enter the room where the visitors were received. Everything about him was white and of the same whiteness: face, hair, beard, hands. His old and well-brushed garment smelt of benzine; his epaulets seemed new. He entered with a firm and measured step, straightening himself up. Extending his dry, white hand, he said aloud:

"How do you do, Sergey?"

Behind him came the mother, with short steps; she wore a strange smile. But she too shook hands with her son, and repeated aloud:

"How do you do, my little Sergey?"

She kissed him and sat down without saying a word. She did not throw herself upon her son, she did not begin to weep or cry, as Sergey expected her to do. She kissed him and sat down without speaking. With a trembling hand she even smoothed the wrinkles in her black silk gown.

Sergey did not know that the colonel had spent the entire previous night in rehearsing this interview. "We must lighten the last moments of our son's life, and not make them more painful for him," the colonel had decided; and he had carefully weighed each phrase, each gesture, of the morrow's visit. But sometimes, in the course of the rehearsal, he became confused, he forgot what he had prepared himself to say, and he wept bitterly, sunk in the corner of his sofa. The next morning he had explained to his wife what she was to do.

"Above all, kiss him and be silent," he repeated. "You will be able to speak later, a little later; but, after kissing him, be silent. Do not speak immediately after kissing him, do you understand? Otherwise you will say what you should not."

"I understand, Nicolas Sergiévitch!" answered the mother, with tears.

"And do not weep! May God keep you from that! Do not weep! You will kill him if you weep, mother!"

"And why do you weep yourself?"

"Why should one not weep here with the rest of you? You must not weep, do you hear?"

"All right, Nicolas Sergiévitch."

They got into a cab and started off, silent, bent, old; they were plunged in their thoughts amid the gay roar of the city; it was the carnival season, and the streets were filled with a noisy crowd.

They sat down. The colonel assumed a suitable attitude, his right hand thrust in the front of his frock-coat. Sergey remained seated a moment; his look met his mother's wrinkled face; he rose suddenly.

"Sit down, my little Sergey!" begged the mother.

"Sit down, Sergey!" repeated the father.

They kept silence. The mother wore a strange smile.

"How many moves we have made in your behalf, Sergey! Your father . . ."

"It was useless, my little mother!"

The colonel said, firmly:

"We were in duty bound to do it that you might not think that your parents had abandoned you."

Again they became silent. They were afraid to utter a syllable, as if each word of the language had lost its proper meaning and now meant but one thing: death. Sergey looked at the neat little frock-coat smelling of benzine, and thought: "He has no orderly now; then he must have cleaned his coat himself. How is it that I have never seen him clean his coat? Probably he does it in the morning." Suddenly he asked:

"And my sister? Is she well?"

"Ninotchka knows nothing!" answered the mother, quickly.

But the colonel sternly interrupted her:

"What is the use of lying? She has read the newspaper . . . let Sergey know that . . . all . . . his own . . . have thought . . . and . . ."

Unable to continue, he stopped. Suddenly the mother's face contracted, her features became confused and wild. Her colorless eyes were madly distended; more and more she panted for breath.

"Se . . . Ser . . . Ser . . . Ser . . ." she repeated, without moving her lips; "Ser . . ."

"My little mother!"

The colonel took a step; trembling all over, without knowing how frightful he was in his corpse-like pallor, in his desperate and forced firmness, he said to his wife:

"Be silent! Do not torture him! Do not torture him! Do not torture him! He must die! Do not torture him!"

Frightened, she was silent already, and he continued to repeat, with his trembling hands pressed against his breast:

"Do not torture him!"

Then he took a step backward, and again thrust his hand into the front of his frock-coat; wearing an expression of forced calmness, he asked aloud, with pallid lips:

"When?"

"Tomorrow morning," answered Sergey.

The mother looked at the ground, biting her lips, as if she heard nothing. And she seemed to continue to bite her lips as she let fall these simple words:

"Ninotchka told me to kiss you, my little Sergey!"

"Kiss her for me!" said the condemned man.

"Good! The Chvostofs send their salutations. . . ."

"Who are they? Ah! yes. . . ."

The colonel interrupted him:

"Well, we must start. Rise, mother, it is necessary!"

The two men lifted the swooning woman.

"Bid him farewell!" ordered the colonel. "Give him your blessing!"

She did everything that she was told. But, while giving her son a short kiss and making on his person the sign of the cross, she shook her head and repeated distractedly:

"No, it is not that! No, it is not that!"

"Adieu, Sergey!" said the father. They shook hands, and exchanged a short, but earnest, kiss.

"You . . ." began Sergey.

"Well?" asked the father, spasmodically.

"No, not like that. No, no! What shall I say?" repeated the mother, shaking her head.

She had sat down again, and was tottering.

"You . . ." resumed Sergey. Suddenly his face took on a lamentable expression, and he grimaced like a child, tears filling his eyes. Through their sparkling facets he saw beside him the pale face of his father, who was weeping also.

"Father, you are a strong man!"

"What do you say? What do you say?" said the bewildered colonel. Suddenly, as if completely broken, he fell, with his head on his son's shoulder. And the two covered each other with ardent kisses, the father receiving them on his light hair, the prisoner on his cloak.

"And I?" asked suddenly a hoarse voice.

They looked: the mother was on her feet again, and, with her head thrown back, was watching them wrathfully, almost hatefully.

"What is the matter with you, mother?" cried the colonel.

"And I?" she repeated, shaking her head with an insane energy. "You embrace each other, and I? You are men, are you not? And I? And I? . . ."

"Mother!" and Sergey threw himself into her arms.

The last words of the colonel were:

"My blessing for your death, Sergey! Die with courage, like an officer!"

And they went away. . . . On returning to his cell Sergey lay upon his camp-bed, with face turned toward the wall that the soldiers might not see him, and wept a long time.

.   .   .   .

Vasily Kashirin's mother came alone to visit him. The father, a rich merchant, had refused to accompany her. When the old woman entered, Vasily was walking in his cell. In spite of the heat, he was trembling with cold. The conversation was short and painful.

"You ought not to have come, mother. Why should we two torment each other?"

"Why all this, Vasya? Why have you done this, my son? God! God!"

The old woman began to weep, drying her tears with her black silk neckerchief.

Accustomed as they were, his brothers and he, to treat their mother roughly, she being a simple woman who did not understand them, he stopped, and, in the midst of his shivering, said to her, harshly:

"That's it, I knew how it would be. You understand nothing, mama, nothing!"

"Very well, my son. What is the matter with you? Are you cold?"

"I am cold," answered Vasily, and he began to walk again, looking sidewise now and then at the old woman with the same air of irritation.

"You are cold, my son . . ."

"Ah! You speak of cold, but soon . . ." He made a gesture of desperation.

Again the mother began to sob.

"I said to your father: 'Go to see him, he is your son, your flesh; give him a last farewell.' He would not."

"The devil take him! He is not a father. All his life he has been a scoundrel. He remains one!"

"Yet, Vasya, he is your father. . . ."

And the old woman shook her head reproachfully.

It was ridiculous and terrible. This paltry and useless conversation engaged them when face to face with death. While almost weeping, so sad was the situation, Vasily cried out:

"Understand then, mother. They are going to hang me, to hang me! Do you understand, yes or no?"

"And why did you kill?" she cried.

"My God! What are you saying? Even the beasts have feelings. Am I your son or not?"

He sat down and wept. His mother wept also; but, in their incapability of communicating in the same affection in order to face the terror of the approaching death, they wept cold tears that did not warm the heart.

"You ask me if I am your mother? You heap reproaches on me; and yet I have turned completely white these last few days."

"All right, all right, forgive me. Adieu! Embrace my brothers for me."

"Am I not your mother? Do I not suffer for you?"

At last she departed. She was weeping so that she could not see her way. And, the farther she got from the prison, the more abundant became her tears. She retraced her steps, losing herself in this city in which she was born, in which she had grown up, in which she had grown old. She entered a little abandoned garden, and sat down on a damp bench.

And suddenly she understood: tomorrow they would hang her son! She sprang to her feet, and tried to shout and run, but suddenly her head turned, and she sank to the earth. The path, white with frost, was wet and slippery; the old woman could not rise again. She rested her weight on her wrists, and then fell back again. The black neckerchief slipped from her head, uncovering her dirty gray hair. It seemed to her that she was celebrating her son's wedding. Yes, they had just married him, and she had drunk a little wine; she was slightly intoxicated.

"I cannot help myself! My God, I cannot help myself!"

And, with swinging head, she said to herself that she had drunk too much, and was crawling around on the wet ground, . . . but they gave her wine to drink and wine again, and still more wine. And from her heart arose the laugh of the drunkard and the desire to abandon herself to a wild dance; . . . but they kept on lifting cups to her lips, one after another, one after another.

VI

THE HOURS FLY

In the fortress where the condemned terrorists were confined there was a steeple with an old clock. Every hour, every half-hour, every quarter of an hour, this clock struck in a tone of infinite sadness, like the distant and plaintive cry of birds of passage. In the daytime this odd and desolate music was lost in the noise of the city, of the broad and animated street that passed the fortress. The tramways rumbled, the shoes of the horses rattled, the trembling automobiles sounded their hoarse horns far into the distance. As the carnival was approaching, the peasants of the suburbs had come to town to earn some money as cabdrivers; the bells of the little Russian horses tinkled noisily. The conversations were gay, and had a flavor of intoxication, real holiday conversations. The weather harmonized with the occasion; the spring had brought a thaw, and the road was wet with dirty puddles. The trees on the squares had suddenly darkened. A slightly warm wind was blowing from the sea in copious moist puffs—a light, fresh air that seemed to have started on a joyous flight toward the infinite.

By night the street was silent under the brilliancy of the large electric suns. The immense fortress with its smooth walls was plunged in darkness and silence; a barrier of calm and shadow separated it from the ever-living city. Then they heard the striking of the hours, the slow, sad birth and death of a strange melody, foreign to the land. Like big drops of transparent glass, the hours and the minutes fell from an immeasurable height into a metallic basin that was vibrating gently. Sometimes they were like birds that passed.

Into the cells came, day and night, this single sound. It penetrated through the roof, through the thick stone walls; it alone broke the silence. Sometimes they forgot it, or did not hear it. Sometimes they awaited it with despair; they lived only by and for this sound, having learned to be distrustful of silence. The prison was reserved for criminals of note; its special, rigorous regulations were as rigid and sharp as the corners of the walls. If there is nobility in cruelty, then the solemn, deaf, dead silence that caught up every breath and every rustle was noble.

In this silence, penetrated by the desolate striking of the flying minutes, three men and two women, separated from the world, were awaiting the coming of the night, of the dawn, and of the execution; and each was preparing for it in his own fashion.

Throughout her life Tanya Kovalchuk had thought only of others, and now also it was for her comrades that she underwent suffering and torture. She pictured death to herself only because it threatened Sergey Golovin, Musya, and the others; but her thoughts did not dwell on the fact that she too would be executed.

As if to reward herself for the artificial firmness that she had shown before the judges, she wept for hours altogether. This is characteristic of old women, who have suffered much. When it occurred to her that Sergey might be unprovided with tobacco, or that Werner possibly was deprived of the tea of which he was so fond—and this at the moment when they were about to die—she suffered perhaps as much as at the idea of the execution. The execution was something inevitable, even incidental, not worthy of consideration; but that an imprisoned man should be without tobacco on the very eve of his execution was an idea absolutely intolerable. Evoking the pleasant memories of their common life, she lamented over the interview between Sergey and his parents.

For Musya she felt a special pity. For a long time it had seemed to her, mistakenly, however, that Musya was in love with Werner; she had beautiful and luminous dreams for their future. Before her arrest Musya wore a silver ring on which was engraved a skull and crossbones surrounded with a crown of thorns. Often Tanya Kovalchuk had looked at this ring sorrowfully, viewing it as a symbol of renunciation; half serious, half joking, she had asked Musya to take it off.

"No, Tanya, I will not give it to you. You will soon have another on your finger!"

Her comrades always thought that she would soon be married, which much offended her. She wanted no husband. And, as she recalled these conversations with Musya and reflected that Musya was indeed sacrificed, Tanya, full of motherly pity, felt the tears choking her. Every time the clock struck, she lifted her face, covered with tears, and listened, wondering how this plaintive and persistent summons of death was being received in the other cells.

VII

THERE IS NO DEATH

And Musya was happy!

With arms folded behind her back, dressed in a prisoner's gown that was too large for her and that made her look like a youth wearing a borrowed costume, she walked back and forth in her cell, at a regular pace, never wearying. She had tucked up the long sleeves of her gown, and her thin and emaciated arms, the arms of a child, emerged from the flaring breadths like flower-stems from a coarse and unclean pitcher. The roughness of the stuff irritated the skin of her white and slender neck; sometimes, with her two hands, she released her throat, and felt cautiously for the spot where her skin was burning.

Musya walked with a long stride, and tried blushingly to justify to herself the fact that the finest of deaths, reserved hitherto for martyrs, had been assigned to her, so young, so humble, and who had done so little. It seemed to her that, in dying upon the scaffold, she was making a pretentious show that was in bad taste.

At her last interview with her lawyer she had asked him to procure poison for her, but immediately had given up the idea: would not people think that she was actuated by fear or by ostentation? Instead of dying modestly and unnoticed, would she not cause still further scandal? And she had added, quickly:

"No, no, it is useless!"

Now her sole desire was to explain, to prove, that she was not a heroine, that it was not a frightful thing to die, and that no one need pity her or worry on her account.

Musya sought excuses, pretexts of such a nature as to exalt her sacrifice and give it a real value, as if it had actually been called in question.

"In fact," she said to herself, "I am young; I might have lived for a long time. But . . ."

Just as the gleam of a candle is effaced by the radiance of the rising sun, youth and life seem to her dull and sombre beside the magnificent and luminous halo that is about to crown her modest person.

"Is it possible?" Musya asks herself, in great confusion. "Is it possible that I am worth anybody's tears?"

And she is seized with an unspeakable joy. There is no more doubt; she has been taken into the pale. She has a right to figure among the heroes who from all countries go to heaven through flames and executions. What serene peace, what infinite happiness! An immaterial being, she believes herself hovering in a divine light.

Of what else was Musya thinking? Of many things, since for her the thread of life was not severed by death but continued to unroll in a calm and regular fashion. She was thinking of her comrades, of those who at a distance were filled with anguish at the idea of her approaching execution, of those who nearer at hand would go with her to the gallows. She was astonished that Vasily should be a prey to terror, he who had always been brave. On Tuesday morning, when they had prepared themselves to kill, and then to die themselves, Tanya Kovalchuk had trembled with emotion; they had been obliged to send her away, whereas Vasily joked and laughed and moved about amid the bombs with so little caution that Werner had said to him severely:

"One should not play with death!"

Why, then, was Vasily afraid now? And this incomprehensible terror was so foreign to Musya's soul that she soon ceased to think about it and to inquire into its cause. Suddenly she felt a mad desire to see Sergey Golovin and laugh with him.

Perhaps too her thought was unwilling to dwell long on the same subject, resembling therein a light bird that hovers before infinite horizons, all space, the caressing and tender azure, being accessible to it. The hours continued to strike. Thoughts blended in this harmonious and distant symphony; fleeting images became a sort of music. It seemed to Musya that she was travelling on a broad and easy road in a quiet night; the carriage rode easily on its springs. All care had vanished; the tired body was dissolved in the darkness; joyous and weary, the thought peacefully created vivid images, and became intoxicated on their beauty. Musya recalled three comrades who had been hanged lately; their faces were illuminated and near, nearer than those of the living. . . . So in the morning one thinks gaily of the hospitable friends who will receive you in the evening with smiles on their lips.

At last Musya became weary from walking. She lay down cautiously on the camp-bed, and continued to dream, with half-closed eyes.

"Is this really death? My God, how beautiful it is! Or is it life? I do not know, I do not know! I am going to see and hear. . . ."

From the first days of her imprisonment she had been a prey to hallucinations. She had a very musical ear; her sense of hearing, sharpened by the silence, gathered in the slightest echoes of life; the footsteps of the sentinels in the corridor, the striking of the clock, the whispering of the wind over the zinc roof, the creaking of a lantern, all blended for her in a vast and mysterious symphony. At first the hallucinations frightened Musya, and she drove them away as morbid manifestations; then, perceiving that she was in good health and had no pathological symptoms, she ceased to resist.

But now she hears very plainly the sound of the military band. She opens her eyes in astonishment, and raises her head. Through the windows she sees the night; the clock strikes. "Again!" she thought, as she closed her eyes without disturbing herself. Again the music begins. Musya clearly distinguishes the steps of the soldiers as they turn the corner of the prison; a whole regiment is passing before her windows. The boots keep time to the music on the frozen ground; one! two! one! two! Sometimes a boot squeaks; a foot slips and then recovers itself. The music draws nearer; it is playing a noisy and stirring triumphal march which Musya does not know. There is probably some festival in the fortress.

The soldiers are under her windows, and the cell is filled with joyous, regular, and harmonious sounds. A big brass trumpet emits false notes: it is not in time; now it is in advance, now it lags behind in a ridiculous fashion. Musya pictures to herself a little soldier playing this trumpet assiduously, and she laughs.

The regiment has passed; the sound of the footsteps grows fainter and fainter; one! two! one! two! In the distance the music becomes gayer and more beautiful. Several times more the trumpet sounds out of time, with its metallic, sonorous, and gay voice, and then all is quiet. Again the clock in the steeple strikes the hours.

New forms come and lean over her, surrounding her with transparent clouds and lifting her to a great height, where birds of prey are hovering. At left and right, above and below, everywhere birds are crying like heralds; they call, they warn. They spread their wings, and immensity sustains them. And on their inflated breasts that split the air is reflected the sparkling azure. The beating of Musya's heart becomes more and more regular, her respiration more and more calm and peaceful. She sleeps; her face is pale; her features are drawn; there are dark rings around her eyes. On her lips a smile. Tomorrow, when the sun shall rise, this intelligent and fine face will be deformed by a grimace in which no trace of the human will be left; the brain will be inundated with thick blood; the glassy eyes will protrude from their orbits. But today Musya sleeps quietly, and smiles in her immortality.

Musya sleeps.

And the prison continues to live its special, blind, vigilant life, a sort of perpetual anxiety. They walk. They whisper. A gun rings out. It seems as if someone cries out. Is this reality or hallucination?

The grating in the door lowers noiselessly. In the dark opening appears a sinister bearded face. For a long time the widely-opened eyes view with astonishment the sleeping Musya; then the face disappears as quietly as it came.

The bells in the steeple ring and sing interminably. One would say that the weary hours were climbing a high mountain toward midnight. The ascent grows more and more painful. They slip, fall back with a groan, and begin again to toil painfully toward the black summit.

There is a sound of footsteps. Whispering voices are heard. Already they are harnessing the horses to the sombre, unlighted vehicle.

VIII

DEATH EXISTS, AND LIFE ALSO

Sergey Golovin never thought of death. It seemed to him something incidental and foreign. He was robust, endowed with that serenity in the joy of living which causes all evil thoughts, all thoughts fatal to life, to disappear rapidly, leaving the organism intact. Just as, with him, physical wounds healed quickly, so all injuries to his soul were immediately nullified. He brought into all his acts, into his pleasures and into his preparations for crime, the same happy and tranquil gravity: everything in life was gay, everything was important, worthy of being well done.

And he did everything well; he sailed a boat admirably, he was an excellent marksman. He was as faithful in friendship as in love, and had an unshakeable confidence in the "word of honor." His comrades declared laughingly that, if one who had been proved a spy should swear to Sergey that he was not a spy, Sergey would believe him and shake hands with him. A single fault: he thought himself a good singer, whereas he sang atrociously false, even in the case of revolutionary hymns. He got angry when they laughed at him.

"Either you are all asses, or else I am an ass!" he said in a serious and offended tone. And, after a moment's reflection, the comrades declared, in a tone quite as serious:

"It is you who are an ass. You show it in your voice!"

And, as is sometimes the case with worthy people, they loved him perhaps more for his eccentricities than for his virtues.

He thought so little of death, he feared it so little, that on the fatal morning, before leaving the dwelling of Tanya Kovalchuk, he alone had breakfasted with appetite, as usual. He had taken two glasses of tea, and eaten a whole two-cent loaf. Then, looking with sadness at Werner's untouched bread, he said to him:

"Why don't you eat? Eat; it is necessary to get strength!"

"I am not hungry."

"Well, I will eat your bread! Shall I?"

"What an appetite you have, Sergey!"

By way of reply, Sergey, with his mouth full, began to sing, in a false and hollow voice:

"A hostile wind is blowing o'er our heads."

After the arrest Sergey had a moment of sadness; the plot had been badly planned. But he said to himself: "Now there is something else that must be done well: to die." And his gaiety returned. On his second day in the fortress he began gymnastic exercises, according to the extremely rational system of a German named Müller, which interested him much. He undressed himself completely; and, to the amazement of the anxious sentinel, he went carefully through the eighteen prescribed exercises.

As a propagandist of the Müller system, it gave him much satisfaction to see the soldier follow his movements. Although he knew that he would get no answer, he said to the eye that appeared at the grating:

"That is the kind of thing that does you good, brother; that gives you strength! That is what they ought to make you do in the regiment," he added, in a gentle and persuasive voice, that he might not frighten the soldier, not suspecting that his guardian took him for a madman.

The fear of death showed itself in him progressively, seemingly by shocks: it seemed to him that someone was thumping him violently in the heart from below. Then the sensation disappeared, but came back a few hours later, each time more intense and prolonged. It was beginning already to take on the vague outlines of an unendurable anguish.

"Is it possible that I am afraid?" thought Sergey, in astonishment. "How stupid!"

It was not he who was afraid; it was his young, robust, and vigorous body, which neither the gymnastics of Müller or the cold shower-baths could deceive. The stronger and fresher he became after his cold-water ablutions, the more acute and unendurable was his sensation of temporary fear. And it was in the morning, after his deep sleep and physical exercises, that this atrocious fear like something foreign appeared—exactly at the moment when formerly he had been particularly conscious of his strength and his joy in living. He noticed this, and said to himself:

"You are stupid, my friend. In order that the body may die more easily, it should be weakened, not fortified."

From that time he gave up his gymnastics and his massage. And, to explain this right-about-face, he cried to the soldier:

"Brother, the method is a good one. It is only for those who are going to be hanged that it is good for nothing."

In fact, he felt a sort of relief. He tried also to eat less in order to weaken himself, but, in spite of the lack of air and exercise, his appetite remained excellent. Sergey could not resist it, and ate everything that they brought him. Then he resorted to a subterfuge; before sitting down to table, he poured half of his soup into his bucket. And this method succeeded; a great weariness, a vague numbness, took possession of him."

"I will teach you!" he said, threatening his body; and he caressed his softening muscles sadly.

But soon the body became accustomed to this régime and the fear of death appeared again, not in so acute a form, but as a vague sensation of nausea, still harder to bear. "It is because this lasts so long," thought Sergey. "If only I could sleep all the time until the day of execution!" He tried to sleep as much as possible. His first efforts were not altogether fruitless; then insomnia set in, accompanied with obsessing thoughts and, with these, a regret that he must part with life.

"Am I, then, afraid of it?" he asked himself, thinking of death. "It is the loss of life that I regret. Life is an admirable thing, whatever the pessimists may say. What would a pessimist say if they were to hang him? Ah! I regret to lose my life, I regret it much."

When he clearly understood that for him all was over, that he had before him only a few hours of empty waiting and then death, he had a queer feeling. It seemed to him that they had stripped him naked in an extraordinary fashion. Not only had they taken away his clothes, but also sun, air, sound and light, speech and the power of action. Death had not yet arrived, and yet life seemed already absent; he felt a strange sensation, sometimes incomprehensible, sometimes intelligible, but very subtle and mysterious.

"What is it, then?" wondered Sergey, in his torment. "And I, where am I? I . . . What I?"

He examined himself attentively, with interest, beginning with his loose slippers, such as the prisoners wore, and stopping with his belly, over which hung his ample cloak. He began to walk back and forth in his cell, with arms apart, and continued to look at himself as a woman does when trying on a gown that is too long. He tried to turn his head: it turned. And what seemed to him a little terrifying was he himself, Sergey Golovin, who soon would be no more!

Everything became strange.

He tried to walk, and it seemed queer to him to walk. He tried to sit down, and he was surprised that he could do so. He tried to drink water, and it seemed queer to him to drink, to swallow, to hold the goblet, to see his fingers, his trembling fingers. He began to cough, and thought: "How curious it is! I cough."

"What is the matter? Am I going mad?" he asked himself. "That would be the last straw, indeed!"

He wiped his brow, and this gesture seemed to him equally surprising. Then he fixed himself in a motionless posture, without breathing—for entire hours, it seemed to him, extinguishing all thought, holding his breath, avoiding all motion; for every thought was madness, every gesture an aberration. Time disappeared as if transformed into space, into a transparent space in which there was no air, into an immense place containing everything—land and life and men. And one could take in everything at a glance, to the very extremity, to the edge of the unknown gulf, to death. And it was not because he saw death that Sergey suffered, but because he saw life and death at the same time. A sacrilegious hand had lifted the curtain which from all eternity had hidden the mystery of life and the mystery of death; they had ceased to be mysteries, but they were no more comprehensible than truth written in a foreign language.

"And here we are back to Müller again!" he suddenly declared aloud, in a voice of deep conviction. He shook his head, and began to laugh gaily, sincerely:

"Ah, my good Müller! My dear Müller! My worthy German! You are right, after all, Müller; as for me, brother Müller, I am only an ass!"

He quickly made the round of his cell; and, to the great astonishment of the soldier who was watching him through the grating, he entirely undressed and went through the eighteen exercises with scrupulous exactness. He bent and straightened up his young body, which had grown a little thin; he stooped, inhaling and exhaling the air; he raised himself on tiptoe, and moved his arms and legs.

"Yes, but, you know, Müller," reasoned Sergey, throwing out his chest, his ribs outlining themselves plainly under his thin, distended skin—"you know, Müller, there is still a nineteenth exercise—suspension by the neck in a fixed position. And that is called hanging. Do you understand, Müller? They take a living man, Sergey Golovin, for example; they wrap him up like a doll, and they hang him by the neck until he is dead. It is stupid, Müller, but that is the way it is; one must be resigned!"

He leaned on his right side, and repeated:

"One must be resigned, Müller!"

IX

THE HORRIBLE SOLITUDE

Under the same roof and to the same melodious chant of the indifferent hours, separated from Sergey and from Musya by a few empty cells, but as isolated as if he alone had existed in the whole universe, the unhappy Vasily Kashirin was finishing his life in anguish and terror.

Covered with sweat, his shirt adhering to his body, his formerly curly hair now falling in straight locks, he went back and forth in his cell with the jerky and lamentable gait of one suffering atrociously with the toothache. He sat down for a moment, and then began to run again; then he rested his forehead against the wall, stopped, and looked about as if in search of a remedy. He had so changed that one might think that he possessed two different faces, one of which, the younger, had gone nobody knows where, to give place to the second, a terrible face, that seemed to have come from darkness.

Fear had shown itself suddenly to him, and had seized upon his person as an exclusive and sovereign mistress. On the fatal morning, when he was marching to certain death, he had played with it; but that evening, confined in his cell, he had been carried away and lashed by a wave of mad terror. As long as he had gone freely forward to meet danger and death, as long as he had held his fate in his own hands, however terrible it might be, he had appeared tranquil and even joyous, the small amount of shameful and decrepit fear that he had felt having disappeared in a consciousness of infinite liberty, in the firm and audacious affirmation of his intrepid will, leaving no trace behind. With an infernal machine strapped around his waist, he had transformed himself into an instrument of death, he had borrowed from the dynamite its cruel reason and its flashing and homicidal power. In the street, among the busy people preoccupied with their affairs and quickly dodging the tramcars and the cabs, it seemed to him as if he came from another and an unknown world, where there was no such thing as death or fear.

Suddenly a brutal, bewildering change had taken place. Vasily no longer went where he wanted to go, but was led where others wanted him to go. He no longer chose his place; they placed him in a stone cage and locked him in, as if he were a thing. He could no longer choose between life and death; they led him to death, certainly and inevitably. He who had been for a moment the incarnation of will, of life, and of force, had become a lamentable specimen of impotence; he was nothing but an animal destined for the slaughter. Whatever he might say, they would not listen; if he started to cry out, they would stuff a rag in his mouth; and, if he even tried to walk, they would take him away and hang him. If he resisted, if he struggled, if he lay down on the ground, they would be stronger than he; they would pick him up, they would tie him, and thus they would carry him to the gallows. And his imagination gave to the men charged with his execution, men like himself, the new, extraordinary, and terrifying aspect of unthinking automata, whom nothing in the world could stop, and who seized a man, overpowered him, hanged him, pulled him by the feet, cut the rope, put the body in a coffin, carried it away, and buried it.

From the first day of his imprisonment, people and life had transformed themselves for him into an unspeakably frightful world filled with mechanical dolls. Almost mad with fear, he tried to fancy to himself that these people had tongues and spoke, but he did not succeed. Their mouths opened, something like a sound came from them; then they separated with movements of their legs, and all was over. He was in the situation of a man who, left alone in a house at night, should see all things become animate, move, and assume over him an unlimited power; suddenly the wardrobe, the chair, the sofa, the writing-table would sit in judgment upon him. He would cry out, call for help, beg, and rove from room to room; and the things would speak to each other in their own tongue; and then the wardrobe, the chair, the sofa, and the writing-table would start to hang him, the other things looking on.

In the eyes of Vasily Kashirin, sentenced to be hanged, everything took on a puerile aspect; the cell, the grated door, the striking apparatus of the clock, the fortress with its carefully modelled ceilings, and, above, the mechanical doll equipped with a musket, who walked up and down in the corridor, and the other dolls who frightened him by looking through the grating and handing him his food without a word.

A man had disappeared from the world.

In court the presence of the comrades had brought Kashirin back to himself. Again for a moment he saw people; they were there, judging him, speaking the language of men, listening, and seeming to understand. But, when he saw his mother, he felt clearly, with the terror of a man who is going mad and he knows it, that this old woman in a black neckerchief was a simple mechanical doll. He was astonished at not having suspected it before, and at having awaited this visit as something infinitely sorrowful in its distressing gentleness. While forcing himself to speak, he thought with a shudder:

"My God! But it is a doll! A doll-mother! And yonder is a doll-soldier; at home there is a doll-father, and this is the doll Vasily Kashirin."

When the mother began to weep, Vasily again saw something human in her, but this disappeared with the first words that she uttered. With curiosity and terror he watched the tears flow from the doll's eyes.

When his fear became intolerable, Vasily Kashirin tried to pray. There remained with him only a bitter, detestable, and enervating rancor against all the religious principles upon which his youth had been nourished, in the house of his father, a large merchant. He had no faith. But one day, in his childhood, he had heard some words that had made an impression upon him and that remained surrounded forever with a gentle poesy: These words were:

"Joy of all the afflicted!"

Sometimes, in painful moments, he whispered, without praying, without even accounting to himself for what he was doing: "Joy of all the afflicted!" And then he suddenly felt relieved; he had a desire to approach someone who was dear to him and complain gently:

"Our life! . . . but is it really a life? Say, my dear, is it really a life?"

And then suddenly he felt himself ridiculous; he would have liked to bare his breast and ask someone to beat it.

He had spoken to no one, not even to his best comrades, of his "Joy of all the afflicted!" He seemed to know nothing of it himself, so deeply hidden was it in his soul. And he evoked it rarely, with precaution.

Now that the fear of the unfathomable mystery which was rising before him completely covered him, as the water covers the plants on the bank when the tide is rising, he had a desire to pray. He wanted to fall upon his knees, but was seized with shame before the sentinel; so, with hands clasped upon his breast, he murmured in a low voice:

"Joy of all the afflicted!"

And he repeated with anxiety, in a tone of supplication:

"Joy of all the afflicted, descend into me, sustain me!"

Something moved softly. It seemed to him that a sorrowful and gentle force hovered in the distance and then vanished, without illuminating the shades of the agony. In the steeple the hour struck. The soldier yawned long and repeatedly.

"Joy of all the afflicted! You are silent! And you will say nothing to Vasily Kashirin!"

He wore an imploring smile, and waited. But in his soul there was the same void as around him. Useless and tormenting thoughts came to him; again he saw the lighted candles, the priest in his robe, the holy image painted on the wall, his father bending and straightening up again, praying and kneeling, casting furtive glances at Vasily to see if he too was praying or was simply amusing himself. And Kashirin was in still deeper anguish than before.

Everything disappeared.

His consciousness went out like the dying embers that one scatters on the hearth; it froze, like the body of a man just dead in which the heart is still warm while the hands and feet are already cold.

Vasily had a moment of wild terror when they came into his cell to get him. He did not even suspect that the hour of the execution had arrived; he simply saw the people and took fright, almost like a child. "I will not do it again! I will not do it again!" he whispered, without being heard; and his lips became icy as he recoiled slowly toward the rear of his cell, just as in childhood he had tried to escape the punishments of his father.

"You will have to go . . ."

They talked, they walked around him, they gave him he knew not what. He closed his eyes, staggered, and began to prepare himself painfully. Undoubtedly he had recovered consciousness; he suddenly asked a cigarette of one of the officials, who amiably extended his cigarette-case.

X

THE WALLS CRUMBLE

The unknown, surnamed Werner, was a man fatigued by struggle. He had loved life, the theatre, society, art, literature, passionately. Endowed with an excellent memory, he spoke several languages perfectly. He was fond of dress, and had excellent manners. Of the whole group of terrorists he was the only one who was able to appear in society without risk of recognition.

For a long time already, and without his comrades having noticed it, he had entertained a profound contempt for men. More of a mathematician than a poet, ecstasy and inspiration had remained so far things unknown to him; at times he would look upon himself as a madman seeking to square the circle in seas of human blood. The enemy against which he daily struggled could not inspire him with respect; it was nothing but a compact network of stupidities, treasons, falsehoods, base deceits. The thing that had finally destroyed in him forever, it seemed to him, the desire to live, was his execution of a police-spy in obedience to the order of his party. He had killed him tranquilly, but at sight of this human countenance, inanimate, calm, but still false, pitiable in spite of everything, he suddenly lost his esteem for himself and his work. He considered himself as the most indifferent, the least interesting, of beings. Being a man of will, he did not leave his party; apparently he remained the same; but from that time there was something cold and terrifying in his eyes. He said nothing to anyone.

He possessed also a very rare quality: he knew not fear. He pitied those of his comrades who had this feeling, especially Vasily Kashirin. But his pity was cold, almost official.

Werner understood that the execution was not simply death, but also something more. In any case, he was determined to meet it calmly, to live until the end as if nothing had happened or would happen. Only in this way could he express the profoundest contempt for the execution and preserve his liberty of mind. In the courtroom—his comrades, although knowing well his cold and haughty intrepidity, perhaps would not have believed it themselves—he thought not of life or of death: he played in his mind a difficult game of chess, giving it his deepest and quietest attention. An excellent player, he had begun this game on the very day of his imprisonment, and he kept it up continually. And the verdict that condemned him did not displace a single piece on the invisible board.

The idea that he probably would not finish the game did not stop Werner. On the morning of the last day he began by correcting a plan that had failed the night before. With hands pressed between his knees, he sat a long time motionless; then he arose, and began to walk, reflecting. He had a gait of his own; the upper part of his body inclined a little forward, and he brought down his heels forcibly; even when the ground was dry, he left clear foot-prints behind him. He whistled softly a rather simple Italian melody, which helped him to reflect.

But now he was shrugging his shoulders and feeling his pulse. His heart beat fast, but tranquilly and regularly, with a sonorous force. Like a novice thrown into prison for the first time, he examined attentively the cell, the bolts, the chair screwed to the wall, and said to himself:

"Why have I such a sensation of joy, of liberty? Yes, of liberty; I think of tomorrow's execution, and it seems to me that it does not exist. I look at the walls, and they seem to me not to exist either. And I feel as free as if instead of being in prison, I had just come out of another cell in which I had been confined all my life."

Werner's hands began to tremble, a thing unknown to him. His thoughts became more and more vibrant. It seemed to him that tongues of fire were moving in his head, trying to escape from his brain to lighten the still obscure distance. Finally the flame darted forth, and the horizon was brilliantly illuminated.

The vague lassitude that had tortured Werner during the last two years had disappeared at the sight of death; his beautiful youth came back as he played. It was even something more than beautiful youth. With the astonishing clearness of mind that sometimes lifts man to the supreme heights of meditation, Werner saw suddenly both life and death; and the majesty of this new spectacle struck him. He seemed to be following a path as narrow as the edge of a blade, on the crest of the loftiest mountain. On one side he saw life, and on the other he saw death; and they were like two deep seas, sparkling and beautiful, melting into each other at the horizon in a single infinite extension.

"What is this, then? What a divine spectacle!" said he slowly.

He arose involuntarily and straightened up, as if in the presence of the Supreme Being. And, annihilating the walls, annihilating space and time, by the force of his all-penetrating look, he cast his eyes into the depths of the life that he had quitted.

And life took on a new aspect. He no longer tried, as of old, to translate into words what he was; moreover, in the whole range of human language, still so poor and miserly, he found no words adequate. The paltry, dirty, and evil things that suggested to him contempt and sometimes even disgust at the sight of men had completely disappeared, just as, to people rising in a balloon, the mud and filth of the narrow streets become invisible, and ugliness changes into beauty.

With an unconscious movement Werner walked toward the table and leaned upon it with his right arm. Haughty and authoritarian by nature, he had never been seen in a prouder, freer, and more imperious attitude; never had his face worn such a look, never had he so lifted up his head, for at no previous time had he been as free and powerful as now, in this prison, on the eve of execution, at the threshold of death.

In his illuminated eyes men wore a new aspect, an unknown beauty and charm. He hovered above time, and never had this humanity, which only the night before was howling like a wild beast in the forests, appeared to him so young. What had heretofore seemed to him terrible, unpardonable, and base became suddenly touching and naïve, just as we cherish in the child the awkwardness of its behavior, the incoherent stammerings in which its unconscious genius glimmers, its laughable errors and blunders, its cruel bruises.

"My dear friends!"

Werner smiled suddenly, and his attitude lost its haughty and imposing force. Again he became the prisoner suffering in his narrow cell, weary of seeing a curious eye steadily fixed upon him through the door. He sat down, but not in his usual stiff position, and looked at the walls and the gratings with a weak and gentle smile such as his face had never worn. And something happened which had never happened to him before: he wept.

"My dear comrades!" he whispered, shedding bitter tears. "My dear comrades!"

What mysterious path had he followed to pass from a feeling of unlimited and haughty liberty to this passionate and moving pity? He did not know. Did he really pity his comrades, or did his tears hide something more passionate, something really greater? His heart, which had suddenly revived and reblossomed, could not tell him. Werner wept, and whispered:

"My dear comrades! My dear comrades!"

And in this man who wept, and who smiled through his tears, no one—not the judges, or his comrades, or himself—would have recognized the cold and haughty Werner, sceptical and insolent.

XI

ON THE WAY TO THE GALLOWS

Before getting into the vehicles, all five of the condemned were gathered in a large cold room with an arched ceiling, resembling an abandoned office or an unused reception-room. They were permitted to talk with each other.

Only Tanya Kovalchuk took immediate advantage of the permission. The others pressed in silence hands as cold as ice or as hot as fire; dumb, trying to avoid each other's gaze, they formed a confused and distracted group. Now that they were reunited, they seemed to be ashamed of what they had felt individually in the solitude. They were afraid to look at each other, afraid to show the new, special, somewhat embarrassing thing that they felt or suspected in each other.

Nevertheless, they did look, and, after a smile or two, all found themselves at ease, as before; no change revealed itself, or, if something had happened, all had taken an equal share in it, so that nothing special was noticeable in any one of them. All talked and moved in a queer and jerky fashion, impulsively, either too slowly or too quickly. Sometimes one of them quickly repeated the same words, or else failed to finish a phrase that he had begun or thought he had already spoken. But nothing of all this did they notice. All blinkingly examined the familiar objects without recognizing them, like people who have suddenly taken off their glasses. They often turned around quickly, as if someone were calling them from the rear. But they did not notice this. The cheeks and ears of Musya and Tanya were burning. At first Sergey was a little pale; he soon recovered, and appeared as usual.

Vasily alone attracted attention. Even in such a group he was extraordinary and dreadful. Werner was moved, and said in a low voice to Musya, with deep anxiety:

"What is the matter with him, Musya? Is it possible that he has . . . ? Really, we must speak to him."

Vasily looked at Werner from a distance, as if he had not recognized him; then he lowered his eyes.

"But, Vasily, what is the matter with your hair? What is the matter with you? It is nothing, brother, it will soon be over! We must control ourselves! We really must!"

Vasily did not break the silence. But, when they had already concluded that he would say absolutely nothing, there came a hollow, tardy, terribly distant reply, such as the grave might give up after a long appeal:

"But there is nothing the matter with me. I am in control of myself!"

He repeated:

"I am in control of myself!"

Werner was delighted.

"Good, good! You are a brave fellow! All is well!" But, when his eyes met the dark and heavy gaze of Vasily, he felt a momentary anguish, asking himself: "But whence does he look? whence does he speak?" In a tone of deep tenderness, he said:

"Vasily, do you hear? I love you much!"

"And I too, I love you much!" replied a tongue that moved painfully.

Suddenly Musya seized Werner by the arm, and, expressing her astonishment forcibly, like an actress on the stage, she said:

"Werner, what is the matter with you? You said: 'I love you'? You never said that to anyone before. And why is your face so sparkling and your voice so tender? What is it? What is it?"

And Werner, also in the manner of an actor dwelling upon his words, answered, as he pressed the young girl's hand:

"Yes, I love, now! Do not tell the others. I am ashamed of it, but I love my brothers passionately!"

Their eyes met and burst into flame: everything about them became extinct, just as all other lights pale in the fugitive flash of the lightning.

"Yes!" said Musya. "Yes, Werner!"

"Yes!" he answered. "Yes, Musya, yes!"

They had understood something and ratified it forever. With sparkling eyes and quick steps Werner moved on again in the direction of Sergey.

"Sergey!"

But it was Tanya Kovalchuk that answered. Full of joy, almost weeping with maternal pride, she pulled Sergey violently by the sleeve.

"Just listen, Werner! I weep on his account. I torment myself, and he, he does gymnastics!"

"The Müller system?" asked Werner, with a smile.

Sergey, somewhat confused, knit his brows.

"You do wrong to laugh, Werner! I have absolutely convinced myself . . ."

Everybody began to laugh. Gaining strength and firmness from their mutual communion, they gradually became again what they used to be; they did not notice it, and thought that they were always the same. Suddenly Werner stopped laughing; with perfect gravity he said to Sergey:

"You are right, Sergey! You are perfectly right!"

"Understand this, then!" rejoined Sergey, satisfied. "Of course we . . ."

Just then they were asked to get into the vehicles. The officials even had the amiability to allow them to place themselves in their own fashion, in pairs. In general, they were very amiable with them, even too much so; were they trying to give evidence of a little humanity, or to show that they were not responsible for what was taking place and that everything was happening of itself? It is impossible to say, but all those taking part were pale.

"Go with him, Musya!" said Werner, pointing the young girl to Vasily, who stood motionless.

"I understand!" she answered, nodding her head. "And you?"

"I? Tanya will go with Sergey, you with Vasily. As for me, I shall be alone! What matters it? I can stand it, you know!"

When they had reached the courtyard, the damp and slightly warm air fell softly upon their faces and eyes, cut their breathing, and penetrated their shivering bodies, purifying them. It was hard to believe that this stimulant was simply the wind, a spring wind, gentle and moist.

The astonishing spring night had a flavor of melted snow, of infinite space; it made the stones resound. Brisk and busy little drops of water fell rapidly, one after another, making a sonorous song. But, if one of them delayed a little or fell too soon, the song changed into a joyous splash, an animated confusion. Then a big drop fell heavily, and again the spring-like song began, rhythmical and sonorous. Above the city, higher than the walls of the fortress, was the pale halo formed by the electric lights.

Sergey Golovin heaved a deep sigh, and then held his breath, as if regretting to expel from his lungs air so pure and fresh.

"Have we had this fine weather long?" Werner inquired. "It is spring!"

"Only since yesterday!" they answered politely and promptly. "There have been many cold days."

One after another the black vehicles came up, took in two persons, and went away in the darkness, toward the spot where a lantern was swinging in the gateway. Around each vehicle were moving the gray outlines of soldiers; their horses' shoes resounded loudly; often the beasts slipped on the wet snow.

When Werner bent to get into the vehicle, a gendarme said to him, in a vague way:

"There is another in there who *goes* with you!"

Werner was astonished.

"Who *goes* where? Ah! Yes! Another one! Who is it?"

The soldier said nothing. In a dark corner something small and motionless, but alive, lay rolled up: an open eye shone under an oblique ray of the lantern. As he sat down, Werner brushed against a knee with his foot.

"Pardon me, comrade!"

There was no answer. Not until the vehicle had started did the man ask hesitatingly, in bad Russian:

"Who are you?"

"My name is Werner, sentenced to be hanged for an attempt upon the life of XX. And you?"

"I am Yanson. . . . I must not be hanged. . . ."

In two hours they would be face to face with the great mystery as yet unsolved; in two hours they would leave life for death; thither both were going, and yet they became acquainted. Life and death were marching simultaneously on two different planes, and to the very end, even in the most laughable and most stupid details, life remained life.

"What did you do, Yanson?"

"I stuck a knife into my boss. I stole money."

From the sound of his voice it seemed as if Yanson were asleep. Werner found his limp hand in the darkness, and pressed it. Yanson lazily withdrew it.

"You are afraid?" asked Werner.

"I do not want to be hanged."

They became silent. Again Werner found the Esthonian's hand, and pressed it tightly between his dry and burning palms. It remained motionless, but Yanson did not try again to release it.

They stifled in the cramped vehicle, whose musty smell mingled with the odors of the soldiers' uniforms, of the muck-heap, and of wet leather. The breath of a young gendarme, redolent of garlic and bad tobacco, streamed continually into the face of Werner, who sat opposite. But the keen fresh air came in at the windows, and thanks to this the presence of spring was felt in the little moving box even more plainly than outside. The vehicle turned now to the right, now to the left; sometimes it seemed to turn around and go back. There were moments when it appeared to the prisoners as if they had been going in a circle for hours. At first the bluish electric light came in between the heavy lowered curtains; then suddenly, after a turn, darkness set in; it was from this that the travellers gathered that they had reached the suburbs and were approaching the station of S——. Sometimes, at a sudden turn, Werner's bent and living knee brushed in a friendly way against the bent and living knee of the gendarme, and it was hard to believe in the approaching execution.

"Where are we going?" asked Yanson, suddenly. The continuous and prolonged shaking of the sombre vehicle gave him vertigo and a little nausea.

Werner answered, and pressed the Esthonian's hand more tightly than before. He would have liked to say specially friendly and kind words to this little sleeping man, whom already he loved more than anyone in the world.

"Dear friend! I think that you are in an uncomfortable position! Draw nearer to me!"

At first Yanson said nothing, but after a moment he replied:

"Thank you! I am comfortable! And you, they are going to hang you too?"

"Yes!" replied Werner, with an unlooked-for gaiety, almost laughing.

He made a free-and-easy gesture, as if they were speaking of some futile and stupid prank that a band of affectionate practical jokers were trying to play upon them.

"You have a wife?" asked Yanson.

"No! A wife! I! No, I am alone!"

"So am I! I am alone."

Werner, too, was beginning to feel the vertigo. At times it seemed to him that he was on his way to some festivity. A queer thing; almost all those who were going to the execution had the same feeling; although a prey to fear and anguish, they rejoiced vaguely in the extraordinary thing that was about to happen. Reality became intoxicated on madness, and death, coupling with life, gave birth to phantoms.

"Here we are at last!" said Werner, gay and curious, when the vehicle stopped; and he leaped lightly to the ground. Not so with Yanson, who resisted, without saying a word, very lazily it seemed, and who refused to descend. He clung to the handle of the door; the gendarme loosened his weak fingers, and grasped his arm. Ivan caught at the corner, at the door, at the high wheel, but yielded at every intervention of the gendarme. He adhered to things rather than gripped them. And it was not necessary to use much force to loosen his grasp. In short, they prevailed over him.

As always at night, the station was dark, deserted, and inanimate. The passenger trains had already passed, and for the train that was waiting on the track for the prisoners there was no need of light or activity. Werner was seized with ennui. He was not afraid, he was not in distress, but he was bored; an immense, heavy, fatiguing ennui filled him with a desire to go away no matter where, lie down, and close his eyes. He stretched himself, and yawned repeatedly.

"If only they did these things more quickly!" said he, wearily.

Yanson said nothing, and shuddered.

When the condemned passed over the deserted platform surrounded with soldiers, on their way to the poorly-lighted railway carriages, Werner found himself placed beside Sergey Golovin. The latter designated something with his hand, and began to speak; his neighbor clearly understood only the word "lamp"; the rest of the phrase was lost in a weary and prolonged yawn.

"What did you say?" asked Werner, yawning also.

"The reflector . . . the lamp of the reflector is smoking," said Sergey.

Werner turned around. It was true; the glass shades were already black.

"Yes, it is smoking!"

Suddenly he thought: "What matters it to me whether the lamp is smoking, when . . . ?" Sergey undoubtedly had the same idea. He threw a quick glance at Werner, and turned away his head. But both stopped yawning.

All walked to the train without difficulty; Yanson alone had to be led. At first he stiffened his legs, and glued the soles of his feet to the platform; then he bent his knees. The entire weight of his body fell upon the arms of the policemen; his legs dragged like those of a drunken man; and the toes of his boots ground against the wooden platform. With a thousand difficulties, but in silence, they lifted him into the railway-carriage.

Vasily Kashirin himself walked unsupported; unconsciously he imitated the movements of his comrades. After mounting the steps of the carriage, he drew back; a policeman took him by the elbow to sustain him. Then Vasily began to tremble violently and uttered a piercing cry, pushing away the policeman!

"Aie!"

"Vasily, what is the matter with you?" asked Werner, rushing toward him.

Vasily kept silence, shivering the while. The policeman, vexed and even chagrined, explained:

"I wanted to sustain him, and he—he . . . ."

"Come, Vasily, I will sustain you," said Werner.

He tried to take his comrade's arm. But the latter repulsed him, and cried louder than ever.

"Vasily, it is I, Werner!"

"I know! Don't touch me! I want to walk alone!"

And, still trembling, he entered the carriage and sat down in a corner. Werner leaned toward Musya, and asked in a low voice, designating Vasily with his eyes:

"Well, how are things with him?"

"Badly!" answered Musya, in a whisper. "He is already dead. Tell me, Werner, does death really exist?"

"I don't know, Musya; but I think not!" answered Werner in a serious and thoughtful tone.

"That is what I thought! And he? I suffered on his account during the whole ride; it seemed to me that I was travelling beside a dead man."

"I don't know, Musya. Perhaps death still exists for some. Later it will not exist at all. For me, for instance, death has existed, but now it exists no more."

The slightly pallid cheeks of Musya reddened.

"It has existed for you, Werner? For you?"

"Yes, but no more. As for you!"

They heard a sound at the door of the railway carriage; Michka the Tzigane entered spitting, breathing noisily, and making a racket with his boot-heels. He glanced about him, and stopped short.

"There is no room left, officer!" he declared to the fatigued and irritated policeman. "See to it that I travel comfortably, otherwise I will not go with you! Rather hang me right here, to the lamp-post! Oh, the scoundrels, what a carriage they have given me! Do you call this a carriage? The devil's guts, yes, but not a carriage!"

But suddenly he lowered his head, stretched out his neck, and advanced towards the other prisoners. From the frame of his bushy hair and beard his black eyes shot a savage, sharp, and rather crazy look.

"Oh, my God!" he cried; "so this is where we are! How do you do, sir!"

He sat down opposite Werner, holding out his hand; then, with a wink, he leaned over and swiftly passed his hand across his companion's neck:

"You too? Eh?"

"Yes!" smiled Werner.

"All?"

"All!"

"Oh! oh!" said the Tzigane, showing his teeth. He examined the other prisoners with a swift glance, which nevertheless dwelt longest on Musya and Yanson.

"On account of the Minister?"

"Yes. And you?"

"Oh, sir, my case is quite another story. I am not so distinguished! I, sir, am a brigand, an assassin. That makes no difference, sir; move up a little to make room for me; it is not my fault that they have put me in your company! In the other world there will be room for all."

He took the measure of all the prisoners with a watchful, distrustful, and savage gaze. But they looked at him without a word, seriously and even with evident compassion. Again he showed his teeth, and slapped Werner several times on the knee.

"So that is how it is, sir! As they say in the song:

"'Take care to make no sound, O forest of green oaks!'"

"Why do you call me sir, when all of us . . ."

"You are right!" acquiesced the Tzigane, with satisfaction. "Why should you be sir, since you are to be hanged beside me? There sits the real sir!"

He pointed his finger at the silent policeman.

"And your comrade yonder, he doesn't seem to be enjoying himself hugely!" he added, looking at Vasily. "Say there, you are afraid?"

"No!" answered a tongue that moved with difficulty.

"Well, then, don't be so disturbed; there is nothing to be ashamed of. It is only dogs that wag their tails and show their teeth when they are going to be hanged; you are a man. And this marionette, who is he? He certainly is not one of your crowd?"

His eyes danced incessantly; constantly, with a hissing sound, he spat out his abundant and sweetish saliva. Yanson, doubled up motionless in a corner, slightly shook the ears of his bald fur cap, but said nothing. Werner answered for him.

"He killed his employer."

"My God!" exclaimed the Tzigane, in astonishment. "How is it that they permit such birds as that to kill people?"

For a moment he looked at Musya stealthily; then suddenly he turned, and fixed his straight and piercing gaze upon her.

"Miss! Say there, Miss! what is the matter with you? Your cheeks are pink, and you are laughing! Look, she is really laughing! Look! Look!" And he seized Werner's knee with his hooked fingers.

Blushing and somewhat confused, Musya squarely returned the gaze of the attentive and savage eyes that questioned her. All kept silence.

The little cars bounced speedily along the narrow track. At every turn or grade-crossing the whistle blew, the engineer being afraid of crushing somebody. Was it not atrocious to think that so much care and effort, in short all human activity, was being expended in taking men to be hanged? The maddest thing in the world was being done with an air of simplicity and reasonableness. Cars were running; people were sitting in them as usual, travelling as people ordinarily travel. Then there would be a halt as usual: "Five minutes' stop."

And then would come death—eternity—the great mystery.

XII

THE ARRIVAL

The train advanced rapidly.

Sergey Golovin remembered to have spent the summer, some years before, in a little country-house along this very line. He had often travelled the road by day and by night, and knew it well. Closing his eyes, he could fancy himself returning by the last train, after staying out late at night with friends.

"I shall arrive soon," thought he, straightening up: and his eyes met the dark grated window. Around him nothing stirred. Only the Tzigane kept on spitting, and his eyes ran the length of the car, seeming to touch the doors and the soldiers.

"It is cold," said Vasily Kashirin between his thin lips, which seemed frozen.

Tanya Kovalchuk bestirred herself in a maternal fashion:

"Here's a very warm kerchief to wrap around your . . ."

"Neck?" asked Sergey, and he was frightened by his own question.

"What matters it, Vasya? Take it."

"Wrap yourself up. You will be warmer," added Werner.

He turned to Yanson, and asked him tenderly:

"And aren't you cold, too?"

"Werner, perhaps he wants to smoke. Comrade, do you want to smoke?" asked Musya. "We have some tobacco."

"Yes, I want to."

"Give him a cigarette, Sergey," said Werner.

But Sergey was already holding out his cigarette-case.

And all began to watch tenderly Yanson's clumsy fingers as they took the cigarette and struck the match, and the little curl of bluish smoke that issued from his mouth.

"Thank you," said Yanson. "It is good."

"How queer it is," said Sergey.

"How queer what is?" asked Werner.

"The cigarette," answered Sergey, unwilling to say all that he thought.

Yanson held the cigarette between his pale and living fingers. With astonishment he looked at it. And all fixed their gaze on this tiny bit of paper, on this little curl of smoke rising from the gray ashes.

The cigarette went out.

"It is out," said Tanya.

"Yes, it is out."

"The devil take it!" said Werner, looking anxiously at Yanson, whose hand, holding the cigarette, hung as if dead. Suddenly the Tzigane turned, placed his face close to Werner's, and, looking into the whites of his eyes, whispered:

"Suppose, sir, we were to attack the soldiers of the convoy? What do you think about it?"

"No," answered Werner.

"Why? It is better to die fighting. I will strike a blow, they strike back, and I shall die without noticing it."

"No, it is not necessary," said Werner. And he turned to Yanson:

"Why don't you smoke?"

Yanson's dried-up face wrinkled pitifully, as if someone had pulled the threads that moved the creases in his face. As in a nightmare, Yanson sobbed in a colorless voice, shedding no tears:

"I can't smoke. Ah! Ah! Ah! I must not be hanged. Ah! Ah! Ah!"

Everybody turned toward him. Tanya, weeping copiously, stroked his arms and readjusted his fur cap.

"My dear, my friend, don't cry, my friend! My poor friend!"

Suddenly the cars bumped into one another and began to slow up. The prisoners rose, but immediately sat down again.

"Here we are," said Sergey.

It was as if all the air had suddenly been pumped out of the car. It became difficult to breathe. Their swollen hearts became heavy in their breasts, rose to their throats, beat desperately and their blood, in its terror, seemed to revolt. Their eyes looked at the trembling floor, their ears listened to the slowly-turning wheels, which began to turn more slowly still, and gently stopped.

The train halted.

The prisoners were plunged into a strange stupor. They did not suffer. They seemed to live an unconscious life. Their corporeal being was absent; only its phantom moved about, voiceless but speaking, silent but walking. They went out. They arranged themselves in pairs, breathing in the fresh air of the woods. Like one in a dream, Yanson struggled awkwardly: they dragged him from the car.

"Are we to go on foot?" asked someone, almost gaily.

"It isn't far," answered a careless voice.

Without a word they advanced into the forest, along a damp and muddy road. Their feet slipped and sank into the snow, and their hands sometimes clung involuntarily to those of their comrades. Breathing with difficulty the soldiers marched in single file, on either side of the prisoners. An irritated voice complained:

"Could they not have cleared the road? It is difficult to advance."

A deferential voice answered:

"It was cleaned, Your Honor, but it is thawing. There is nothing to be done."

The prisoners began to recover their consciousness. Now they seemed to grasp the idea: "It is true, they could not clean the roads"; now it became obscured again, and there remained only the sense of smell, which perceived with singular keenness the strong and healthy odor of the forest; and now again all became very clear and comprehensible, the forest, and the night, and the road . . . and the certainty that very soon, in a minute, implacable death would lay its hands upon them. And little by little a whispering began:

"It is almost four o'clock."

"I told you so. We started too early."

"The sun rises at five."

"That's right, at five: we should have waited."

They halted in the twilight. Near by, behind the trees, whose huge shadows were waving on the ground, swung silently two lanterns. There the gallows had been erected.

"I have lost one of my rubbers," said Sergey.

"Well?" asked Werner, not understanding.

"I have lost it. I am cold."

"Where is Vasily?"

"I don't know. There he is."

Vasily was standing close by them, gloomy and motionless.

"Where is Musya?"

"Here I am. Is that you, Werner?"

They looked at each other, their eyes avoiding the silent and terrible significant swaying of the lanterns. At the left the thin forest seemed to be growing lighter. And beyond, something vast and gray and flat appeared, whence came a moist breeze.

"That is the sea," said Sergey, sucking in the damp air. "That is the sea."

Musya answered by a line from the song:

"My love as broad as is the sea."

"What did you say, Musya?"

"The shores of life cannot contain
My love as broad as is the sea."

"'My love as broad as is the sea,'" repeated Sergey, pensively.

"'My love as broad as is the sea,'" echoed Werner. And suddenly he exclaimed in astonishment:

"Musya, my little Musya, how young you still are!"

Just then, close to Werner's ear, sounded the breathless and passionate voice of the Tzigane:

"Sir, sir, look at the forest. My God! What is all that? And yonder! The lanterns! My God, is that the scaffold?"

Werner looked at him. The convulsed features of the unfortunate man were frightful to see.

"We must say our farewells," said Tanya.

"Wait! They still have to read the sentence. Where is Yanson?"

Yanson lay stretched in the snow, surrounded by people. A strong smell of ammonia filled the air around him.

"Well, doctor, will you soon be through?" asked someone, impatiently.

"It's nothing. A fainting fit. Rub his ears with snow. He is better already. You can read."

The light of a dark lantern fell upon the paper and the ungloved white hands. Both paper and hands trembled. The voice also.

"Gentlemen, perhaps it is better not to read. You all know the sentence."

"Do not read!" answered Werner for all; and the light immediately went out.

The condemned refused also the services of the priest. Said the Tzigane:

"No nonsense, father; you will forgive me, they will hang me."

The broad dark silhouette of the priest took a few steps backward and disappeared. The day was breaking. The snow became whiter, the faces of the condemned darker, and the forest barer and sadder.

"Gentlemen, you will go in pairs, choosing your companion. But I beg you to make haste."

Werner pointed to Yanson, who now was standing again, sustained by two soldiers.

"I will go with him. You, Sergey, take Vasily. You go first."

"All right."

"I am going with you, Musya," said Tanya. "Come, let us kiss each other!"

Quickly they kissed all round. The Tzigane kissed forcibly; they felt his teeth. Yanson kissed gently and softly, with mouth half open. He did not seem to understand what he was doing. When Sergey and Kashirin had taken a few steps, the latter stopped suddenly, and in a loud voice, which seemed strange and unfamiliar, shouted:

"Good-bye, comrades."

"Good-bye, comrade," they answered him.

The two started off again. All was quiet. The lanterns behind the trees became motionless. They expected to hear a cry, a voice, some sound or other, but there as here all was calm.

"Oh! My God!" exclaimed someone, hoarsely.

They turned around: it was the Tzigane, crying desperately:

"They are going to hang us."

He struggled, clutching the air with his hands, and cried again:

"God! Am I to be hanged alone? My God!"

His convulsive hands gripped the hand of Werner, and he continued:

"Sir, my dear sir, my good sir. You will come with me, won't you?"

Werner, his face drawn with sorrow, answered:

"I cannot; I am with Yanson."

"Oh! My God! then I shall be alone. Why? Why?"

Musya took a step toward him, and said softly:

"I will go with you."

The Tzigane drew back, and fixed his big swollen eyes upon her:

"Will you?"

"Yes."

"But you are so little! You are not afraid of me? No, I don't want you to. I will go alone."

"But I am not afraid of you."

The Tzigane grinned.

"Don't you know that I am a brigand? And you are willing to go with me? Think a moment. I shall not be angry if you refuse."

Musya was silent. And in the faint light of the dawn her face seemed to take on a luminous and mystic pallor. Suddenly she advanced rapidly toward the Tzigane, and, taking his head in her hands, kissed him vigorously. He took her by the shoulders, put her away a little, and then kissed her loudly on her cheeks and eyes.

The soldier nearest them stopped, opened his hands, and let his gun fall. But he did not stoop to pick it up. He stood still for a moment, then turned suddenly, and began to walk into the forest.

"Where are you going?" shouted his comrade, in a frightened voice. "Stay!"

But the other painfully endeavored to advance. Suddenly he clutched the air with his hands, and fell, face downward.

"Milksop, pick up your gun, or I will pick it up for you," cried the

Tzigane, firmly. "You don't know your duty. Have you never seen a man die?"

Again the lantern swung. The turn of Werner and Yanson had come.

"Good-bye, sir!" said the Tzigane, in a loud voice. "We shall meet again in the other world. When you see me there, don't turn away from me."

"Good-bye!"

"I must not be hanged," said Yanson again, in a faint voice.

But Werner grasped his hand, and Yanson took a few steps. Then he was seen to sink into the snow. They bent over him, lifted him up, and carried him, while he weakly struggled in the soldiers' arms.

And again the yellow lanterns became motionless.

"And I, Musya? Am I then to go alone?" said Tanya, sadly. "We have lived together, and now . . ."

"Tanya, my good Tanya!"

The Tzigane hotly interrupted, holding Musya as if he feared that they might tear her from him.

"Miss," he cried, "you are able to go alone. You have a pure soul. You can go alone where you like. But I cannot. I am a bandit. I cannot go alone. 'Where are you going?' they will say to me, 'you who have killed, you who have stolen?' For I have stolen horses, too, Miss. And with her I shall be as if I were with an innocent child. Do you understand?"

"Yes, I understand. Go on, then! Let me kiss you once more, Musya."

"Kiss each other! Kiss each other!" said the Tzigane. "You are women. You must say good-bye to each other."

Then came the turn of Musya and the Tzigane. The woman walked carefully, her feet slipping, lifting her skirts by force of habit. Holding her with a strong hand, and feeling the ground with his foot, the man accompanied her to death. The lights became motionless. Around Tanya all was tranquil again, and solitary. The soldiers, gray in the dawn's pale light, were silent.

"I am left alone," said Tanya. And she sighed. "Sergey is dead, Werner and Vasily are dead. And Musya is dying. I am alone. Soldiers, my little soldiers, you see, I am alone, alone . . ."

The sun appeared above the sea. . . .

They placed the bodies in boxes, and started off with them. With elongated necks, bulging eyes, and blue tongues protruding, from their mouths, the dead retraced the road by which, living, they had come.

And the snow was still soft, and the air of the forest was still pure and balmy.

On the white road lay the black rubber that Sergey had lost. . . .

Thus it was that men greeted the rising sun.

THE TRUTH OF THE OLIVER CROMWELL

By James B. Connolly

[James B. Connolly (1868–   ) was born in Boston and makes his
home there. He is a teller of sea tales, using the technique of the realist
in dealing with romantic material. He was educated chiefly in the
public and parochial schools of Boston, has served both in the army
and navy, and knows intimately the life of which he writes. Among his
volumes of thrilling stories of the sea are *The Deep Sea's Toll* (1905),
The Crested Seas (1907), *Wide Courses* (1911), *Running Free* (1917),
Tide Rips (1922), and *Gloucestermen* (1930).

The Truth of the Oliver Cromwell was first published in *Scribner's
Magazine* (January, 1905) and later included in *The Deep Sea's Toll*.
In revised form it appears in *Gloucestermen*, from which volume it is here
reprinted by permission of the author and of Charles Scribner's Sons,
publishers.]

MARTIN CARR had done a fine thing that afternoon. Martin and
John Marsh were hauling trawls, when a sea capsized their dory.
The same sea washed them both clear of the dory. John Marsh could
not swim. It looked as if he had hauled his last trawl, and so, beyond
all question, he had, but for Martin, who seized one of their buoy-kegs,
which happened to bob up near by, and pushed it into John's despairing
arms. "Hang on for your life, John," said Martin, and himself struck
out for the dory, knowing that the buoy could not support two. It was
perhaps forty feet to the bottom of the dory—not a great swim that—
but this was a winter's day on the Grand Banks, and a man beaten back
by a rough sea and borne down by the weight of heavy clothing, oilskins, and big jack-boots. When he had fought his way to the dory he
had to wait a while before he dared try to climb up on it—he was so
tired—and after he got there he found no strap to the plug, and so
nothing to hang on to. He remembered then that he and John had often
spoken of fixing up a strap for the plug—and never fixed it.

"My own neglect," muttered Martin, "and now I'm paying for it."

Clinging to the smooth planking on the bottom of the dory was hard
work that day, and becoming harder every minute, for the sea was making. And there was John to keep an eye on. "How're you making out,
Johnnie-boy?" he called.

"It's heavy dragging, but I'm all right so far," John answered.

"And how is it with you now, Johnnie-boy?" he called in a little
while again.

"I can hang on a while yet, Martin."

"Good for you," said Martin to that.

"Can you see the vessel?" then asked John after another space.

"He's giving out, and I see no vessel," thought Martin, but answered cheerily, "Aye, I see her."

"And how far away is she, and what's she doing?"

Aloud Martin said, "Five or six miles maybe, up to win'ard—and she's taking aboard all but the last dory, and there's men gone aloft to look for us." But under his breath, "And God forgive me if I go to my death with that lie on my lips—but 'tis no deeper than my lips—no deeper."

Then they waited and waited, until John said, "Martin, I'll have to go soon—I can't hang on much longer."

"Bide a while, Johnnie-boy—bide a while. Dory-mates we've been for many a trip—bide a while with me now, Johnnie."

But Martin knew that it would be for but a little while for John—for them both—if help did not come soon. Scanning the sea for whatever hope the sea might give, he saw the trawl-line floating on the water. That was the line that ran from their anchor somewhere on the bottom to the buoy keg to which John was clinging. If he could but get hold of that line he could draw John to the dory, with a better chance to talk to him—to put heart into him, for Johnnie was but a lad—no more than five and twenty.

To get the line he would have to swim; and to swim any distance in that rising and already bad sea he would have to cast off most of his clothing. And with most of his clothing gone he would not last too long. Certainly if the vessel did not get them by dark, he would never live through the night. He would freeze to death—that he knew well. But could he live through the night anyway? And even if he could—but what was the good of thinking all night over it? He pulled off his boots, untied his oilskins, hauled off his heavy outer woollens.

"Johnnie-boy, can you hang on a while longer?"

"Dunno, Martin—I dunno. Where's the vessel?"

"She's bearing down, John." And with the thought of that second lie on his lips Martin scooped off for the buoy-line, which, after a battle, he grabbed and towed back to the dory. It was a hard fight, and he would have liked well to rest a while—but there was Johnnie. So in he hauled, many a long fathom of slack ground-line, with gangings and hooks, and after that the buoy-line. He sorrowfully regarded the fine fat fish that he passed along—every hook seemed to have a fish on it. "Man, man, but 'twas only last night I baited up for ye in the cold hold of the vessel—baited with the cold, frozen squid, and my fingers nigh frost-bitten." But every hook was bringing him nearer to his dory-mate.

He felt the line tauten at last. "Have a care now, Johnnie, whilst I draw you to me," and hauled in till Johnnie was alongside.

But "Good-by," said Johnnie ere yet Martin had him safe.

"Not yet, Johnnie-boy," said Martin, and reached for him and held him up and lashed him to the buoy. "You can rest your arms now, lad," he said, and Johnnie gratefully let go.

"'Tis made of iron a man should be that goes winter trawling," said Martin, and up on the bottom of the dory he climbed again, this time with infinite difficulty.

They had had the leeward berth, the farthest from the vessel, and by now it was dark. But Martin knew the skipper would not give them up in a hurry, as he explained to John. And by and by they saw the torches from the vessel flare up.

"Wait you, John," said Martin then, "and save your strength. I'll hail when I think they're near enough to hear;" which he did, in a voice that obeyed the iron will and carried far across the waters.

Then the vessel saw them and bore down, the skipper to the wheel and the men lining the rail.

"Be easy with John," said Martin to the men who first stretched their arms out, "I'm thinking he's nigh gone."

"But all right with him soon," they said as they passed him along the deck. "And how is it with yourself, Martin?" they asked him as he was about to step over the rail.

"Fine and daisy," said Martin. "How is it yourself, boy?" stepping jauntily up, and then, unable longer to stand, fell flat on the deck.

Seeing how it had been with him, they made him go below also, which he, with shipmates helping, did; and also, later, put on the dry shift of clothes they made ready. In the middle of it all he asked, "Where's Johnnie?"

"In his bunk—and full of hot coffee—where you'll be in a minute."

"The hell I will—there's my dory yet to be hoisted in."

"Your dory, Martin? Why, she's in, drained dry and griped long ago."

"What! and me below? And dory in already? What was it? Did I fall asleep or what? Lord! but it's an old man I must be getting. I wouldn't 've believed it. In all my time to sea that's the first time ever I warn't able to lift hand to tackles and my own dory hoisting in." He made for the companion-way, but so weak was he that he fell back when he tried to climb the ladder.

But a really strong man recuperates rapidly. An hour later Martin was enjoying a fine hot supper, while the crew sat around and hove questions at him. They asked for details and he gave them, or at least such of them as had become impressed on his mind; particularly did he condemn, in crisp phrases, the botheration of boots that leaked and the need of a second plug strap on the bottom of a dory. "There ought to be a new law about plug straps," said Martin.

"Did ever a man yet come off the bottom of a dory and not speak about the plug straps?" commented one.

"And leaky boots *is* the devil," affirmed another—a notorious talker this one, who bunked up in the peak, where he could be dimly seen now —his head out of his bunk that his voice might carry the better. "I bought a pair of boots in Boston once—a Jew up on Atlantic Avenue—"

"In Heaven's name, will you shut up—you and your Atlantic Avenue boots? We'll never hear the end of those boots."

The man in the peak subsided, and he who had quelled him, near to the stove and smoking a pipe, went on for himself, "And what were you thinkin' of, Martin, when you thought you were goin'?"

"Or did you think any time that you was goin'?" asked somebody else.

"Indeed and I did, and a dozen times I thought it—and that 'twas a blessed cold kind of a day for a man to be soaking his feet in the ocean."

"And yet"—the lad in the peak was in commission again—"and yet warn't it some professor said in that book that somebody was reading out of the other day—warn't it him said that salt water ain't nigh so cold as fresh. Is it, Martin?"

"As to that," answered Martin, "I dunno. But I wish 'twas that professor's feet, not mine, was astraddle the bottom of that dory—not to wish him any harm—but a winter's day and the wind no'therly, I found it cold enough."

"I went into a Turkish bath parlor in New York one time," came the conversational voice from the peak, "and hot? My Lord—"

"The man," said the next on watch, taking his mitts from the line above the stove—"the man that'd talk about hot Turkish baths on a night like this to sea—Turkish baths, and Lord in Heaven, two good long hours up there—" He halted to take a sniff up the companion-way. "Two hours—what ought to be done with the like o' him?"

The man by the stove, who awhile before had vanquished the lad in the peak, took his pipe long enough from his mouth to observe, "And for four years now to my knowledge he's been tryin' to tell how hot 'twas in that Turkish bath."

"Hit him with a gob-stick," suggested the cook—"or this rolling-pin" —he was flattening out pie-crust.

"A gob-stick or a rolling-pin," said the next on watch, "is too good for him. Here, take this," and passed the cook's hatchet along the lockers.

The opening and closing of the hatch after the watch had gone on deck admitted a blast of air that made the man in the bunk nearest the steps draw up his legs. The flame in the lamp flared; whereat the original inquirer got up to set the lamp chimney more firmly over the base of the burner, and before he sat down put the question again. What he wanted to know was how Martin felt when he thought he was sure enough going. "The last fifteen or twenty minutes or so I bet you did some thinkin', didn't you, Martin?"

"A little," admitted Martin, and with a long arm gaffed another potato. "Toward the end of it the sea did begin to take on a gray look that I know now was grayer than any mortal sea ever could've been."

"And what were you thinkin' of then, Martin?"

"What was I thinking of? What—Lord, but these apple dumplings are great stuff, aren't they? You don't want to let any of those dumplings get past you, Johnnie. Never mind how used up you feel, come out of your bunk and try 'em. Five or six good plump dumplings inside of you and you'll forget you ever saw a dory."

"He's asleep, Martin."

"Is he? Well, maybe 'tis just as well. 'Twas a hard drag for poor John today. What was I thinking of, you asked me. Well, I'll tell you what I was thinking of. You know what store I set by a good razor. I'd go a hundred mile for a good razor—a *good* razor—any time. You all know that, don't you?"

"Yes—yes—"

"Well, this last time out I brought aboard as fine a looking razor as ever a man laid against his face. Oh, I saw you all eying it the last time I took it out. Don't pretend—I know you. It's right there in my diddy-box, and before I turn in tonight it's a good scrape I'm going to give myself with it—yes. Well, when Johnnie'd said, 'Good-by, Martin'—said it for the second time—'Good-by, Martin, don't mind me any more—look out for yourself'—said that, and I'd said, 'Hold on a little longer' to him for about the tenth time—well, about that time, when I did begin to think we were sure enough going—with it coming on dark and no sign of the vessel in sight—then it was I couldn't help wondering who in hell aboard this vessel was going to get my razor."

When everybody had done laughing, and after two or three had told how they felt when they were on the bottom of a dory, the persistent one asked again, "Martin, but you must've had some close calls in your time?"

"My share—no more." He was taking a look around the table as he spoke. A lingering, regretful look, and then he gave up any further thought of it. "Ah-h," he sighed, "but I cert'nly took the good out of that meal," and leaning against the nearest bunk-board—his own—drew out his pipe from beneath the mattress. "My share and no more," he repeated, and reached across to the shelf in his bunk and drew forth a plug of tobacco. He cut off the proper quantity and rolled it around between his palms the proper length of time before he spoke again. With the pipe between his teeth he had to speak more slowly. "Any man that's been thirty years trawling will nat'rally have a few things happen to him. Today makes the third time I've been on the bottom of a dory—and cold weather each time—just my blessed luck—cold weather each time"—three times he blew through the stem of his pipe—"and I don't want to be there the fourth. Eddie-boy, hand me a wisp out of the broom at your elbow."

While Martin was cleaning out his pipe, somebody put the question generally. Would they rather be on the bottom of a dory out to sea, or on a vessel piled up on the rocky shore somewhere?

"On the rocks for me."

"And for me."

"Yes, a chance to get ashore from a wreck, but the bottom of a dory with the sea breaking over you, and it cold maybe—cert'nly it's never any too warm—wr-r-h!"

There seemed to be no doubt of what' they would take for their choice. "And yet," commented Martin when the last word had been said, "I dunno but the closest call ever I had was when the *Oliver Cromwell* went ashore and was lost off Whitehead."

"Cripes, but I'm glad I warn't on her. A bad business that—a bad business. Hand me that plate, will you, Martin"—this from the cook.

"Sure, boy—here y'are—an armful of plates. Cook on a fisherman's the last job I'd want—you're never done. And you're right it was a bad business, cook. When you've seen nineteen men washed over one after the other, every man—every man but one, that is—putting up the divil's own fight for his life before he went—I dunno but what it must be worse than going down at sea altogether, all hands in one second— with no chance at all—though that must be hard enough, too."

Silence for a while, and then Martin continued: "If I had it to do over again"—two long puffs—"to do over and be lost instead of saved, I don't know but what I'd rather founder at sea myself. Nineteen men lost—eighteen good men—Lord, but 'twas cruel!"

Martin, with his head back, was gazing thoughtfully up at the deck-beams. A gentle leading question, and he resumed.

"We left Gloucester that trip with the skipper's—but to tell that story right a man ought to begin away back. But will you give me a match, somebody?"

He lit up again and then settled himself snugly between the edge of the table and his bunk-board, after the manner of a man who is in for a long sitting-out. Once he really started there were but few interruptions. The loss of the *Cromwell* was a serious affair, and nobody broke in thoughtlessly; and only when Martin would stop to refill his pipe, or to light up again when he found he had let it go out, did he make any halt himself.

"What the Hoodleys of Cape Ann were, and are still," began Martin, "of course all of you, or most all of you anyway, know. Or maybe some of you don't know. Well, they were a hard crowd—but didn't know it— the kind of people that whenever they got to talking about their own kind, never had any tales to prove maybe that there was even the lightest bit of wit or grace or beauty among them; no, none of that for the Hoodleys of Cape Ann. But to show you what thrifty, hard-headed fore-people they had, they could spin off, any of 'em, a hundred little yarns most any day, as if anybody on earth that knew those of them that were alive would ever doubt what the dead and gone ones must have been. Hard they were—even neighbors that didn't take life as a dream of poetry said that much of them. Hard they were—man, yes— the kind that little children never toddled up to and climbed on to their knees, nor a man in hard luck by any mistake ever asked the loan of a dollar of—the kind that never a man walked across the street to shake hands with. That's the kind they were. Take 'em all in all, I guess that the Hoodleys were about as hard a tribe as you'd find in all Essex County—surely 'tisn't possible there were any harder. And yet you couldn't pick a flaw in 'em before the law. They were honest. Every-body had to say that for them—paying their debts, their just debts—as they put it themselves—and collecting their own dues, don't fear, and a great respect for the letter of the law—for the letter of it. And I mind they used to boast that for generations their people had kept clear of the poor-houses, and that all had been church-members in good stand-ing. Well, not exactly all—for to be exact and truthful—they them-selves used to put it that way—there was one here and there that had broken away. But such had been rare, as one of them—a strong church-member—used to put it, and the devil is ever active, and speaking of the devil, this particular member'd go on, there is always the blistering pit for the unrighteous. That last I s'pose he thought he ought to put in, because everybody knew that of all the people that fell from grace, the wickedest, the most blasphemous, the most evil of all evil livers had been those of the Hoodleys that had back-slided. Once they went to the bad they cert'nly went beyond all hope; and nobody did they curse out more furiously than their own people every time they did start in.

"Well, the Hoodleys weren't a seafaring people originally. They moved over to Gloucester, y'see, at one particular time when everybody was expecting in some way to make money out of fishing. George Hoodley was a lad then—seventeen—with the hard kind of a face and the awkward body that everybody nat'rally looked for in one of his breed. And he had the kind of a mind, I callate, that his father would like a boy of his to have. Well, George signed right away for a boy's wages with a prudent master—old Sol Tucker it was—that went in the *Distant Shore* so long. They used to say that Sol wore the same pair of jack-boots out of her that he had when he first went aboard, and there was eighteen years between his first and last trips in her. I mind the jack-boots—and they were cert'nly well patched when I saw them— though no more than twelve-year-old then. That'll give you an idea of Sol. And George Hoodley put in thirteen years with Sol, and thirteen long, hard drags of years they must've been. I misdoubt that any of us here could've stood those thirteen—no, sir, not for vessel's, skipper's and hand's share together. Well, George stood it, and I don't b'lieve he ever knew he was missing anything in life. But he had something to show for it, as he'd say himself. When he left old Sol, he was able to buy a half interest and go master of a good vessel. I went with him in her—the *Harding*—two trips—just two, no more."

Martin halted to light up again, and somebody asked, "Warn't it the *Harding*, Martin, that had the small cabin?"

"Yes, the smallest, they say, that ever was seen in a fisherman. Just about room to stand between the steps and the stove and between the stove and the bulkhead again—and not much better for'ard—a forec's'le so small that the crew used to say they had to go on deck to haul on their oilskins. She was all hold. Well, while he was in the *Harding*, George made a great reputation for all kinds of carefulness. Most men that went with him said he was altogether too careful for any mortal use; and maybe that was so. But his savings kept piling up, and there was plenty of other careful men to ship with him and abide by him.

"One thing that George and his people used to boast about was that he warn't like a good many other fishermen. While a good many of them were putting in time ashore drinking, skylarking, or if it warn't no more than to spend a quiet sociable evening with their friends or their own families—during all that George was attending to business, for business it was to him. He was talking one day of those who said fishing was a venture, or even adventure, and he'd been reading somewhere, he said, of the joy that somebody thought fine strong men ought to get out of fishing. He almost smiled when he was telling it. The joy of fishing! If you had a good trip of fish and got a good price for it, why yes, fishing was good fun then. But as far as he could see it was like any other kind of work. You put in about so much time at it and took good care of your money, and at the end of the year you had about so much to show for it. And as for the fun of fighting a breeze of wind that some of them talked about, seeing how long you could hang on to your canvas without losing your spars, or how far down you could let your vessel roll before she'd capsize—none of that for him. And it was all rot, their pretending they got any fun out of it. They had the same blood and nerve and senses as any other humans, and he knew that for himself he was content to stay hove-to when it blew one of the living gales they talked about, and satisfied, too, to shorten sail in time, even if he was bound home, when it blew hard enough. Gloucester would be there when he got there—it wouldn't blow away. Cert'nly, he'd admit, the drivers'd outsail him on a passage and beat him out of the market once in a while, but in the long run his way paid best. He could name the foolish fellows that'd been lost—and the fingers of both hands wouldn't begin to name them; yes, and left families to starve, some of 'em—and he himself was alive and still bringing home the fish, and everybody in Gloucester knew what he had to show for it.

"Well, by that time, everybody in Gloucester did know what he had to show for it, and everybody in Gloucester said it was about time he began to look around for a wife, though nobody expected George Hoodley to look around for a wife after the regular manner of fishermen, who don't look around at all, so far as I c'n see. We ourselves, or most of us, anyway, liking the girl pretty well and she willing, gen'rally hurry up to get married 'bout as soon as we find ourselves with a couple of months' rent ahead.

"But not that way with George Hoodley. It wasn't until he was forty-five that he began to look around after the manner of his people for a wife. There was to be no rushing into the expenses of matrimony; but with two good vessels, and a house all clear, a man might well think of it—or leastways I imagine that's the way he thought it out—if he wasted any time thinking of it at all.

"Now, if George Hoodley had not been like other men during all the years he was fishing, if he hadn't joined in the talk of his mates on what was worth having in life—you know how fishermen gen'rally talk when they get going on some things—even if George Hoodley pretended to think that he thought they were a lot of blessed fools, yet it is more than likely that the opinions of the men he went to sea with had their influence with him just the same. It stands to reason they were bound to after years of it. And then clear back he must've come of flesh-and-blood people like anybody else, for though nobody could imagine the Hoodleys having weaknesses like other people, yet cert'nly, if you went far enough back, there must've been ancestors among 'em all—one or two—that enjoyed life the same as other people.

"Well, for a wife George took a very pretty girl who was young enough—some of you that know her know that well—young enough to have had grandchildren to him. Twenty or twenty-one, light-haired, pretty face, and a trim figure. I didn't like her eyes or her mouth myself, but everybody agreed she was pretty. She had never been so far away from home that she could not be back again the same day—and that certified to her character with some people. For other things, she would come into some money when her father died. And her father didn't object to George Hoodley. He was a thrifty man, too, and said all right—made George's way easy, in fact.

"Now, I callate that George thought that he never did a wiser thing in all his life than when he married that girl. Among the men he knew there were some that'd got pretty wives but no money; and others, money but plain-lookers. He was getting both, good looks and money, and he could laugh at them all—those who wanted her because of the money in prospect or those others who were in love with her face. And maybe he didn't laugh at some of 'em!—the sail-carriers and others who imagined that a reputation for foolishness at sea won women's hearts. It was a great stroke of business altogether. He would get his share of good living yet—he boasted of that. He had always taken the best care of himself—never drank and seldom smoked—and then only in the way of business—was in the prime of life, had a tough constitution, and his wife-to-be was young and pretty. He could laugh at all of them.

"Nearly everybody in Gloucester said nice things to George. 'My, but you're the deep one—and lucky? Oh, no, you're not a bit lucky! But you always did have a long head—' That's the way most people talked to him, and he liked it. As for the few who didn't seem pleased— the three or four who hinted, but didn't ask outright if he thought he was doing a wise thing—George said it was easy enough to place them— they'd like to get her themselves. If he was only another kind of a man he might have been warned in time, but he was that kind that no-body felt sorry for. And that's a hard thing, too.

"Well, they were married, and the wonderful thing of George letting his vessel go out a trip without him was on exhibition to the people of Gloucester. Yes, sir, she went to sea the day he was married. He stayed ashore that trip—that trip, but not the second.

"The truth was they didn't get along well together; which warn't remarkable maybe—she young and pretty, and he the age he was and more than looking it. Forty-seven's a fine age for some men, but not for George's kind—leather-skinned he was, with lean chops of jaws, a mouth as tight as a deck beam, a turkey neck—you've seen the turkey necks—and eyes that were cold as a dead haddock's.

"George, I callate, was beginning to learn that a woman was a different proposition from a vessel, and that there were things about a woman that had to be studied out. Not that I think he tried overhard to study this one out. Listening to him as I had many a time before he got married, I knew that he figured that a woman, like everything else, had her place in the universe, and she ought to know it—or be made to know it. And now here was his wife's case—a steady man for a husband, a good house to live in, grub and her clothes all found, or anyway as much clothes as he thought fit and proper for her to have. Could a woman expect more, or a man do more, than that?

"'Twarn't long after he got married that things began to go wrong, not only at home but out to sea. There was the trip he broke his ankle. Coming home, he looked maybe for a little show of grief on the part of his wife; but if he did, he didn't find it. Indeed, she even said he ought to go to a hospital instead of making it hard for her at home. 'Twas common talk that she said that.

"Going out his next trip, with his leg not yet well-knit and himself having to limp out the door, he and his wife had words. Billie Shaw, passing by, heard them. 'I don't care if I never see you again,' he said. 'And if you think I'd care if I never saw you again either, you're mis-taken. I wouldn't care if you're lost—you and your vessel—only I wouldn't like to see all the crew lost.'

"That last must have set him to thinking, for he didn't sail that day as he said he would, but put in a day talking to people around town. I know he asked me, for one, a lot of questions. I didn't know till later what he was driving at. 'Twas while he was questioning me that he coaxed me into shipping with him. 'Just this trip, Martin,' he said. 'And your cousin Dan Spring's thinking of coming out with me this time—to help me out. Two men left me suddenly today, and if you'll come out Dan'll surely come.' And so out of good-nature I said I'd go with him. It's blessed little he got out of me, though, in answer to his other questions, but he found plenty of others willing to talk.

"Well, on the passage out we all noticed he seemed an absent-minded man. We noticed, too, or thought we did, that he used to forget that his leg warn't yet very strong and that now and then he had to pull up when it seemed to hurt him bad.

"That trip—well, it was a queer one from the first. With myself and my cousin Dan, who were dory-mates, it warn't nothing but accidents. There was that after the first haul of fish when we were dropping down to come alongside. It was a bit rough—that's a fact. Some said that for so careful a man it was surprising that the skipper had ordered the dories out at all that day. However, we were just ahead of her—under the end of her bowsprit almost—and of course Dan and myself nat'rally looked for the skipper to look out for us. We were so near that Dan had taken in his oars and had the painter ready to heave aboard. I was at the oars. One stroke more, I thought, and we'll be all right, when whing! the first thing we knew around came the vessel and down on us. I couldn't do anything with the dory, she being down to her gunnels with fish. Well, Dan had time to holler to me, and I hollered to him— no more than that—when she was on us. By a miracle, you might say, we both managed to grab the bob-stay. The stem of the vessel cut the dory like it was a cracker, and then under her keel it went.

"Not knowing what to make of it all, we climbed aboard over the bow. Our faces were no more than above the knight-heads than the skipper yelled. We ran aft and asked him what was wrong. He stared at us for a second as if he couldn't understand.

"'What's it?' I asked.

"'Why, I thought you two were gone.'

"'And so we were for all of you. A man that's been to sea as long as you, George Hoodley,' I said, 'and put a wheel the wrong way! Nobody ever said you were the cleverest man out of Gloucester to handle a vessel, but cert'nly you know down from up.'

"'Martin,' he said, 'I give you my word. Just as I grabbed the wheel that time a sea came aboard, the vessel lurched and down on deck I went with my weak ankle giving way under me.'

"Well, our dory was gone, but later in the trip one of the crew, Bill Thornton, was troubled with a felon on his finger. 'Twarn't anything very bad, and Bill himself said it didn't amount to anything, but the skipper thought Bill'd better stay aboard, and his dory-mate with him. 'And, Martin, you and Dan take his dory,' says the skipper—'you two being so used to each other it'll be the best way.'

"Well, that was all right. We took their dory and gear and went out the next set—only two days after our own dory had been lost, mind you. Well, this time we got lost in the fog and were out overnight. It turned out a snowy night, and cold, with fog again in the morning. That morning, so we heard from the crew later, the skipper said, after a little jogging about, 'They must be gone—we may as well give it up.' Well, everybody aboard thought there was a good chance for us yet, and one or two hinted at that. But he wouldn't have it. 'Run her westerly,' he said, and went below. Well, to everybody's surprise we popped up just then almost under her bow. 'Twas quite a little sea on at the time, but the man at the wheel this time didn't have any bad ankle. He jibbed her over in time and we climbed aboard. One man ran down to call the skipper and tell him the news, but the skipper only swore at him. 'Do you mean to tell me that the watch shifted the course of this vessel without orders from me? I'll talk to him.' And he did talk to him, and in a most surprising way. We didn't know what to make of it. He raved. 'Discipline,' he said—he'd always been a great hand for discipline aboard his vessel, but this warn't any case for discipline—'twas men's lives.

"Well, they expected to have two or three more days of fishing aboard the *Cromwell* after that day, but I made a kick. Never again would I haul a trawl for a skipper of his kind, I said.

"'What?' asked the skipper. 'You mean to mutinize on me?'

"'Call it mutiny or what you please,' said I, 'but myself and Dan don't leave this vessel again in a dory.'

"'Don't you know I can run into the nearest port, Newf'undland or Nova Scotia, and put you ashore?'

"'I do.'

"'Or take you both back to Gloucester and have you up before the court?'

"'You can put us up before forty courts—the highest in the land, if you want—and maybe they'll sentence us to ten years in jail, or to be strung up to a yardarm somewheres. But I don't callate they will; I don't callate so—not after we tell our story. It's a fine thing fishermen have come to when their own skippers try to lose 'em.'

"'Lose you? Me try to lose you? And why in God's name would I try to lose you?'

"'Lord knows. But you do, and there's an end of it. Dan and I don't swing any dory over the rail of this vessel this trip again.'

"He said nothing to that. Only he looked at me, then a long look at Dan, and turned into his bunk again. Later in the day he drew out a quart bottle of whiskey and began to drink. That was a new thing to his crew that knew him so long. They'd pretty good reason to believe that he'd kept a bottle in his closet under lock and key for a little drink on the quiet when the dories were out and nobody by; but they knew he did it slyly so as not to have the name of it, or maybe so's not to have to ask anybody to join him, and so save expense. But everybody knew that whatever liquor he took that way was not enough to hurt him. Yes, a sober man he'd always been—everybody had to say that for him. But now he was drinking with all hands looking on, taking it down in gulps, and when the first quart was gone he brought out another, drinking by himself all the time.

"However, he warn't drunk by a good deal when in the middle of the night he ordered all hands on deck to make sail. The men thought he was crazy—but he was the skipper. If anything happened 'twas his lookout, not theirs. So they gave her the full mains'l, and then he ordered the man at the wheel to swing her off.

"'Yes, sir, and what course?'

"'What course? Didn't I say to swing her off? Put her fair before it. Jibe over your fores'l and let her run—let her run, I tell you. Whichever way she goes let her run.'

"And we let her run all that night and all next day. She was under her winter rig—in March it was—no topm'sts, but the four lower sails alone were enough for any Gloucester fisherman that second night. I mind 'twas nine o'clock that night, and Abner Tucker's watch. A staid, sober man was Abner. He'd been to sea for twenty years and been with George for ten years—stayed with him because he knew him for a prudent man, I s'pose. Well, Abner took the wheel, and getting the feel of it, cried out, 'Lord in heaven, it's like trying to steer two vessels— she's running wild!' and braced himself against the wheel, but warn't braced firm enough, or he warn't strong enough, for he let her broach, and a sea swept her quarter, burying him and the vessel both. Over the top of the house went that sea and down into the cabin by the ton. They were floated out in the cabin and came tumbling up on deck. Josh Whitaker, a bait knife in his hand, jumped to the main peak halyards.

"The skipper noticed him. 'What you goin' to do?'

"'Cut,' says Josh.

"'You cut and I'll cut you!' The skipper, too, had a bait knife, and he lunged with it for Josh. Then he stood guard by the halyards. 'Or if anybody else thinks to cut'—and we saw the rest of it in his face— dark as it was, we saw that.

"The skipper was still on guard there when Dan and myself came on deck for our watch—that was eleven o'clock. Dan went for'ard to look out and I took the wheel from Abner, and glad enough he was to turn the wheel over when he gave me the course. I looked in the binnacle to make sure he had it right.

"'Still on that course?' I asked, when I'd seen 'twas so. 'Where's the skipper?'

"'Here,' said the skipper himself from between the house and the weather rail, where he was still watching that nobody bothered the halyards, I s'pose. 'What's it?'

"'How about the course?' I asked.

"'What's wrong with the course?'

"'No'west by west half west—is it right?'

"'No'west by west half west, or whatever it is—yes. And why not?'

"'Oh, nothin', if you say it's right.'

"'And why isn't it right? Why not? Why don't you spit it out? What's wrong, anyway?'

"'What's wrong?' I said. 'Don't you know we warn't much more than three hundred miles off shore on this course when we swung her off last night, and we've been coming along now for twenty-three hours— and the clip she's been coming!'

"He said nothing to that for a while, and then it was, 'And so you don't think the course is right?'

"'No, I don't—not if you're intending to make Gloucester.'

"'That so? Not if I was intending to make Gloucester? And where in the name o' heaven am I headin' for if not Gloucester?'

"'Where?—where? Damned if I know,' says I. 'Hell, maybe.'

"'That so? Well, Gloucester or hell, drive her, you.'

"'Oh, I'll drive her.' I threw it back in his teeth that way, spat to looard, took a fresh hold of the wheel and did drive her just to let him know he couldn't scare me. Cripes, but I gave her all she wanted!

"It was wicked, though, the way she was going. She warn't a big sailer, the *Cromwell*—George Hoodley never did believe in the racing kind—but any old plug could've sailed that night. Along toward midnight it got thick o' snow, I mind, and we came near running into a vessel hove to under a fores'l—'A fisherman,' Dan for'ard called out— and as we shot by her a warning hail came to us.

"'What's that he said?' asked the skipper of Dan.

"'Something about where we're bound for,' answered Dan.

"'That so? What's it of his business?' and then he went below for a spell.

"From the wheel I could see him taking another drink under the cabin light. He had got to where he wasn't bothering to pour it into a mug, but took it straight from the bottle—long pulls, too. He came on deck again just as my watch and Dan's was up. To Charlie Feeney, who was next man to the wheel, I said that the skipper ought to be spoken to about hauling her up. So Charlie did.

"'Who in the devil's name is skipper of this vessel anyway?' was all the answer he got.

"Henry Carsick, who was Charlie's dory-mate, said he didn't know what to make of it. 'I'm blessed if ever I knew him to carry half this sail in a breeze before, and I've been with him three years,' said he to me as he went for'ard.

"Well, Dan and me hadn't more than got off our oilskins after standing watch, when a hail came from Henry on watch for'ard. 'Some kind of a roaring ahead of us,' repeated Charlie from the wheel. And just then it was that, leaping like a hound, she hit something good and hard—a check, a grinding along her bottom, a rearing of her bow. But nothing small was going to stop her the clip she was going then, and whatever it was she was clear of it. By that time the whole crew was tumbling up on deck. 'God in Heaven, what is it?' they called out one to another. Another leap of her, and it was clear white astern and on either side. 'A wall of rock ahead!' said Henry Carsick and came tumbling aft— 'a ledge of solid rock, skipper!'

"'Yes,' said the skipper, in a kind of studyin' tone—'and it *was* hell or Gloucester, warn't it'—he turned to me—'I said it'd be, didn't I?'

"'That's what you did,' said I, 'and it ain't Gloucester. You ought to be proud of yourself—nineteen men, maybe, lost for you—nineteen men. I'm not counting yourself—you ought to be lost. Will we put a dory over?'

"'Put it over if you want to. Do what you please. I'm done with this vessel—I'm done with fishing.'

"'I guess that's right,' says I. 'And I guess you ain't th' only one that gets through with fishing tonight.' Then I turned to the crew: 'What d'y' say, if we try and get a dory over and see what's around us?'

"They said all right, and we unhooked the tackles. A few heaves and up went the dory into the air. It hung there for a second or two. We tried to push it over, but the wind took it, tore it from us, and dropped it into the sea. The sea took it, tossed it up and back against the rail and on to the deck. One smash, another, another, and it was kindling wood.

"'Try another,' said Dan, who was standing by the rail to his waist in water. He had a line about his waist, and that was all kept him inboard. We hoisted another dory out of the nest, and we had to fight even as we were hoisting for a footing on her deck, it was that steep and the great seas running clean over her. Up into the air we hoisted the second dory —up and out again. Once more the howling wind and the boiling sea took it—once more 'twas kindling wood.

"'There's seven more left—try another,' said Dan. A great man, Dan. If I go to sea for forty years I never expect to see a better—I could 'most cry when I think of how he was lost that night.

"'One of my hands mashed to a pulp,' said somebody.

"'Well, we can't stop to doctor you,' I called to him. 'Let somebody take your place at the tackles. Now, then, lads. I don't know that it'll

do any good when we do get it over, but maybe we c'n take a look around
—maybe find a landing place somewheres.'

"'I'll go in her,' calls out someone. 'Give me a chance now—'

"'My chance,' said Dan—'my chance, ain't it, Martin?'

"'Yes,' says I to Dan, and looking back at it now I say, 'God forgive
you, Martin Carr,' and yet 'twarn't no fault of mine.

"Out went the dory, and when she hung for a second Dan swung himself after it. He made it and called, 'Pay out that line!' and dug in with
the oars. We could just see him. We were still paying out the line—we
could still hear his voice, when 'Haul in—I broke an oar!' he called.

"'Haul in!' said I; but when we went to haul in, there was nothing to
haul—the line had parted.

"'God, he's gone!' said somebody.

"'That's what he is,' said a voice beside me—'I was bound he would be.'

"'Twas the skipper. From by the rail he crept up to me with a
knife-blade shining—a bait knife it was, the same he'd had all night.
And then I knew what it meant—he had cut the line. I stood away
from him first, then I grabbed him and picked him up and had a mind
to heave him over the rail, and then—I don't know why—I didn't.
I dropped him on the deck. 'You'll get yours before this night's over,'
I said.

"'A devil of a lot I care,' he said.

"The rest of them, or at least those that warn't too busy with the
next dory or trying to look out for themselves, called out to ask what
was wrong with the two of us. I didn't answer, nor did the skipper.

"Dan was only the first to go that night. We kept trying to launch
dories—trying, but losing them—smashed to kindling-wood they were
—until the whole nine of them were gone. During that time four men
were washed over. One, with a line about him, made a desperate try,
but was hauled back dead, I mind. We laid his body on the house, and
afterward, when I went to look for it, it was gone—swept over. The
seas were wicked.

"The wind was blowing harder, the big combers were coming even
higher, and the gang began to be washed off her deck and lost one after
the other. We took to the rigging when we saw twarn't any more use
on deck. And in the middle of it all what d'y' think the skipper did?
What d'y' think he did—the man that was the cause of it all? Well,
while his crew were going—to heaven or hell as it might be—washed
over and lost, one after the other—he goes below and has a mug-up for
himself. Yes, sir, goes into the forec's'le and has a mug of coffee and a
piece of pie. Somebody that'd seen him going below called out to the
rest of us. The Lord's truth that. And the rest of us blasphemed to
God—we were that black with rage against him.

"Well, there was ten of us, I think, in the rigging, all hoping to be
able to last until daylight, when we thought we might be able to see

where we were. Hoping only 'twas—not expecting—for 'twas getting colder, with the spray beginning to freeze where it struck and making hard work of holding on to the rigging. 'Twas wild—her sails still up, with the reef points beating a devil's tattoo where the canvas warn't tearing up and flying out like long-tailed ghostly things in the blackness. Lashed to the rigging we must've been for all of two hours, I callate. Some began to take note of the numbness creeping over them—one or two—the most discouraged. The warmer-blooded, or the strongest, tried to keep up a cheering talk—tried to crack jokes and one thing or another.

"Well, we had hope some of us of lasting through the night, when crack! We knew what was coming then. I slipped the half-hitch that had been holding me to the shrouds and climbed higher. I was 'most to the mast-head, clear of the gaff, when over the side went her forem'st —half a dozen men clinging to the forerigging, a-swaying and shaking— and after it went the mainm'st with four more, I think, in her rigging.

"Well, sir, when the forem'st went I was thrown into clear water. I had plenty of line to my hand, with a turn of it around the mast-head, and with that I hauled myself back. I hung on to an arm of the cross-trees for a while there before I started to work my way back along the mast toward the vessel. I didn't believe then I'd ever live to reach the vessel. The sail, as I said, had been kept standing on her, and now it was lying flat on the water, now sagging down with the weight of the water over it, and now bellying into the air when a great sea would get under it. I saw a shadow of a man—hanging on to a reef point he was—go down with that sail once, then go up with it once, and then the sail split under the weight of the sea, and I never saw him again. But I heard him holler as he went. What he said I don't know—I had to keep on crawling. The hoops of the sail were around the mast, of course, and I used them and the bolt-rope of the fores'l where the sail was torn away to pull myself along. And, mind you, I had to watch out for the forem'st itself. It reared and tossed with one sea after another —me astride it most of the time—like a man on horseback, though hard riding enough I found it. The least little tap of that and I knew where I'd be—bait for the fishes that I'd baited for so often. Well, between the hoops and the bolt-rope and the rigging I hauled myself along. And the way that mast rolled! Forty times I swear I thought I was good as dead. But no. And so I dragged myself along, watching out when I went upon the crests and holding my breath when I was pulled down into the depths—hung on desperately, mindful that the quietest knock of that big spar would end me then and there, and mindful, too, that once my grip loosed I'd be swallowed up in the roaring. Tired I was—aye, and weak, but I kept on working toward the vessel's hull always.

"Against the white sails and white foam I made out two others struggling like myself. 'That you, Bill?' said one. 'Yes—that you, Mike?' I heard from the other. I knew who they were then, and called out myself. Between two seas one slipped from sight. The other still crept on. 'That you, Bill?' I called out. 'Bill's gone,' said the voice —'twas Mike Cannon. 'That's tough,' I said. 'It is that,' says Mike, 'after the fight he put up. But how're you making out yourself?' 'Pretty good—how're you?' I said. 'Kind of tired. I doubt if I'll hold out much longer—something smashed inside my oilskins. My chest and a few ribs, I think—and one arm, too. A wild night and tough going, isn't it, Martin?'

"There was no more chance to talk. Two awful seas followed, and after the second a quiet spell—the back suction. I looked around. I thought I saw Mike, but warn't sure. I guess now I didn't, for another sea, the biggest of all, tossed the whole lot of wreckage back against the hull of the *Cromwell*. There was a grinding and a battering as the spars met the hull. Myself up in the air, I looked down and found myself over her deck, and then—my guardian angel it must've been that whispered me then—I let go. 'God in heaven!' I found myself saying and fetched up on her deck, the luckiest man in all the North Atlantic.

"Against what was left of the rail I found myself, close to what was left of the forerigging. At first I warn't sure just where I was at all, but that's where I found myself when my eyes were clear to see again. And when my eyes were clear I looked around. The hull of her was heaving to every sea, moving inshore maybe a foot at a time, with her bowsprit pointing to a shadow of rock or cliff ahead. I looked around again, and, so far as I could make out, everything—house, gurry-gids, booby-hatches—everything was gone off her. Only the two stumps of her masts seemed to be left on deck. But, no—the forec's'le hatch was left. Her bow, being so much higher than her stern, saved that. I saw that and—I don't know why—toward the forec's'le I crawled. The hatches were closed. I slid them back. Down the steps I went, and when I was below—I don't know why either—I thought of the razors in my bunk. I might's well get them couple of razors, I says to myself, and starts for my bunk, which was in the peak, the same bunk, clear for'ard on the starb'd side, that the Turkish-bath lad is in now. 'Twas like swimming down there. The water by the butt of the forem'st, 'bout like where I'm sitting here tonight, was over my waist. I couldn't help thinking then how deep 'twas and getting deeper fast, with the seas pouring down the companion-way. I was thinking of that—thinking I ought to've closed the hatches after me—and was looking back toward the steps, when I heard a little noise, or thought I did, for the pounding of the seas overhead was making an awful racket and I warn't sure. But I heard it again, the clinking of crockery like, and I looked around—back behind the steps—at last, and there, behind the stove, leaning up against the cook's lockers—I'd clean forgot him—was the skipper. He was having another mug-up for himself.

"'God!' I said; 'you here?'

"He half turned, dropping a coffee mug he had in his hand. Then taking a second look: 'Man, but I thought it was the ghost of Dan Spring. But you two look something alike. Come to think, you're cousins, ain't you? Man, if you could only see yourself! Blood—blood—and bruises—and your eyes, man—your eyes! But have a mug of coffee. Warn't it lucky?—here's the coffee boiler hove up here on the lockers—and some coffee still left in it—and hot. And there's a pie in the grub locker—on the top shelf. If it'd been on the bottom shelf it'd be all wet and floating around. Ain't that luck? And look here—a good half pint of whiskey left yet. It's been an awful night, ain't it? What d'y' say?'

"He held the bottle toward me. I took it from him and smashed it on the stove. And then I gave him a bit of my mind. 'And so, George Hoodley, you're so afraid, after all, to go to your death that you must go drunk, hah? The soul that the Lord gave you—that soul is going from a drunken body straight to the God that's going to judge you. And how'll you be judged, d'y' think, for this night's work, George Hoodley? Could you listen to what was said on deck tonight and not die of fright at what you've done? Did you hear Sam Catiss? 'I'm not afraid to go, if go I must,' says Sam 'but, Lord, there's one or two things I wish I hadn't done,' says Sam. You heard him—we all heard him—and then he was swept over. And but for you, George Hoodley, maybe he'd have had time to make his peace before he went. And up in the rigging—you warn't there, I know—even you, if you'd heard what Peter Harkins said when we all knew her spars were going—when Peter heard the first crack and knew what it meant. And knowing he was going, with his last free breath he said things of you that if I had an enemy I wouldn't want him to hear—not if I hated him bad enough to want to see him in the bottom of the deepest, hottest hold of hell—'

"'Hell!' he breaks in; 'there ain't no hell—no heaven, nor God, nor anything.'

"'God forgive you for that. You—'

"'God forgive me? Martin, you talk like an old woman. I tell you, since I was no higher than one of my jack-boots I've been listening to talk of hell and heaven—mostly hell, though—and I used to believe it one time. Nobody believed it any more than I did till when—till I began to see that the very people that was talking it so hard warn't governed by what they said. What they wanted was everybody else to be governed by what they preached. I tell you I know. I've seen it in my own people—I know them better than you do. It's years now—I was one of the fools, one that never let anybody, I thought, get the best of me at anything. You're one—though you're a good man in your fool way, Martin. I had no grudge against you, not even when I tried to lose you in the dory. But I had to get rid of your dory-mate.'

"'Get rid of Dan? And why Dan?'

"'Why? There again! You mean to tell me you don't know? I looked around before I went out this trip. Nobody'd tell me, but I knew his first name was Dan—Dan something. One day when the crew was out hauling the trawls I rummaged his bunk and found part of a letter in my wife's writing under his mattress. That was the same day I ran over Dan and you in the dory. 'Twas for that chance I'd been pretending my ankle warn't better. Weak ankle, bah!' He drove the bad foot against the stove and crushed in the oven door. 'Anything weak about that foot—bah? "Dear Dan," the note read—I know my wife's handwriting, and his name's Dan.'

"'Wait a bit—wait a bit. How do you know it was this Dan? Are there no other Dans in Gloucester?'

"'How do I know? And it in his bunk—under the mattress in his bunk?'

"'That's all right. And whose bunk was it before Dan Spring got it? Another Dan's, warn't it—Dan Powell's? And didn't he leave the mattress behind him when he left this vessel trip before last? Didn't he? And warn't Dan Powell just the kind of a man that'd do a thing like that, and not Dan Spring—my own cousin? And so that's the bottom of it? Nineteen souls gone because you thought—just thought only—that one of them was fooling you. And for a woman that warn't worth Dan Spring's little finger. That's the truth, George Hoodley. But if you'd been brought up different, if you'd studied to understand the good side of people instead of the other side and how to get the best of them and to make money out of them and save it, you both might've come safe out of it. But you warn't that kind. 'Twarn't in your blood—nor in none of your people. Wrong's wrong—I got nothing to say about that—but human nature's human nature. Why should you expect, George Hoodley, to get the fine things in life? Why warn't you content with money? You'd earned that. What had you to offer a handsome young woman that liked a good time? What had you, even supposing she was the kind you could trust? Anything that women love? Not a blessed thing. You've spent your life with about one idea in your head, and that idea had nothing to do with being pleasant or kind to others, or good to anybody but yourself. Miles away from the kind of thing that women love were you all the time. You come to nigh fifty year of age—you with your hard face and hard mouth and eyes like—God, like a dead fish's eyes tonight, no less—don't you know that whoever was going to marry you warn't going to for love? You had a right to marry some lean old sour-mouthed spinster with a little money like yourself. What made you think that beauty and love was for you? But even in marrying you thought to make a good bargain—and got fooled. And by the daughter of a man of your own kind, too. D'y' s'pose her father didn't know? God help you, George Hoodley, 'twas him hooked you—

'twas him made the good bargain, not you. Why, before ever you married her 'twas common talk she warn't the girl for any man to trust. But what good is it to talk of that now? Nineteen men gone, for I don't count you—you're no man. You're a—but I won't say it. Lord, but I'm tempted to choke you where you stand. Only when I think of those fine men—and poor Dan Spring—'

"'Dan Spring? Don't tell me 'twarn't Dan Spring, the—'

"'Hold up,' I says to that—'hold up, or close as we both are to death now and soon to go, I'll choke you where you stand—I'll send you to your God, or to the devil, with the print of my fingers around your turkey gobbler's throat, if you say aught of Dan—Dan was my own kind, and I know him. Whatever faults he had—and maybe he had some—it warn't in the heart of Dan Spring to undervalue good women, or to mix with married women of any kind, let alone the wife of a man he was to go ship-mate with. No, sir, not if he didn't have a wife and children of his own—wife and children that'll have to suffer all their lives because of you, and they'll never know what brought it all about. But years from now they'll still be without food and clothing because of you. When I think of it, George Hoodley, I misdoubt they'd count it against me in the other world, where we'll both be soon with the others, if I was to take you by the throat and wind my fingers around your windpipe and choke and choke and squeeze and squeeze you till your tongue came out and your eyes popped and your face got blue and then black and you—'

"He drew back against the lockers and put his hands before his face. 'Martin, Martin, don't!' he said, for in truth I all but had hold of him in spite of myself.

"'I'm not going to,' I said. 'I have enough already to account for. There's two or three things I wish I hadn't done, and maybe if I sent you to death a few minutes sooner than you're going, I'd be sorry for it, too, later on. I'm going on deck now. This vessel won't last much longer. She's breaking as it is—and up to our chests in water here now.'

"Well, all the time we were below the big seas never let up. Some of her outside planks were working loose from their frames when I left him to go on deck again. Her deck planking, too, was coming apart. I almost fell through the opened-up deck into her hold when I was coming out of the forec's'le. I didn't know what to do quite, but climbed up on toward her bow at last, hanging on where I could, dodging seas and the loose bits of wreck they were carrying with them. At the knight-heads I looked around and ahead. Astern and to either side 'twas nothing but rocks and the white sea beating over them. Ahead I could make out a wall of rock—I guessed where I was—to the west'ard of Canso, off Whitehead. I knew that coast—and a bad coast it was. Up on the bowsprit, crawling out with the help of the foot-ropes and the stops hanging down and the wreck of the jib and stays, I began to think I had a chance—if I could only live till the daylight that was coming on. I climbed farther out. Hard work it was, and I soon cast off my boots. At the end of the bowsprit I got a better look. A dozen feet away was the ledge with a chance for a footing. If a man could jump that—but what man could—from a vessel's bowsprit? But now and then, perhaps every minute or so, the bowsprit under a more than average big sea, lifted and sagged a little nearer the cliff. At the right time a man might make the leap, I thought. But if he missed? I looked down with the thought and saw nothing but rocks and a white boiling below. 'If you miss, Martin,' I said to myself, 'maybe you'll live five seconds—maybe ten—but more likely maybe you'd keep clear of being mashed to jelly for just about a wink of your eye.' And 'twas enough to make a man wink his eyes just to look at the white boiling hell beneath. I cast off my oilskin jacket while I was thinking of it, and then my oil pants. After that went my jersey, flannel shirt and trousers. I meant to have a good try at it, anyway.

"Looking back before I should leap, who did I see but the skipper. In the noise of the sea I had not heard him. He, too, had cast off his boots and was even then unbuttoning his oilskins. He must've known I was watching him, for he said, 'Don't throw me off, Martin—don't.'

"'Who's going to?' I asked.

"'That's right—don't. Give me a chance now, Martin.'

"'Like you gave your crew?'

"'Oh, don't Martin—don't! I was crazy. All that I said about not believing in God and hell—I didn't mean that. I'm afraid of it—afraid. I was always afraid of it, but never like now, Martin—never so afraid of the burning pit as now—never—never. Help me up, Martin—I'm weak—I can hardly stand. Help me, won't you, Martin? You're twice the man I am—no man ever sailed with me had your strength, Martin— help me, won't you, Martin?'

"I lifted him up, and the two of us clung to the end of the bowsprit. He looked weak as water then, and I pitied him, and pitying him I pointed out what chance we had. 'There's the cliff and there's what's below. It's one chance in ten to a man that can leap well.'

"'I never could leap well, Martin.'

"'No, you couldn't—nor do anything much that other boys could do—no money in leaping, I s'pose. But there it is—and you c'n have your choice. Will you jump first or last?'

"'You go first Martin. If you make it, maybe you c'n help me— maybe pass me a bit of line or something. See, I've got a bit of line I took along. You go first, Martin—you go first. It's an awful jump to take, though.'

"'There's men of your crew took more awful jumps tonight, George Hoodley. They jumped from this world to the other when the spars went. Well, I'm going. Give me room to swing my arms. Now, if I miss, then I s'pose we'll be standing up and giving account together in a few minutes. I've got enough on my conscience, but I'm glad I'm not you. Stand clear of me now—when she lifts I'm going.'

"The *Cromwell* lifted. Her bowsprit rose up and up till the end of it was higher than the ledge in the wall of rock before us. I waited till the last little second—till the bowsprit swayed in toward the cliff, and then, while it balanced there, and before it started to settle again, knowing, as you all know, the power that's in the uplift of a sea, I gathered myself and jumped. And 'twas a good leap. I didn't think I could do it, cold and numb as I'd been feeling. A good leap—yes. And 'twas the wet, slippery shelf of rock I landed on, but I went a yard clear, and even when I slipped a little I checked myself before I slipped back to the edge, and was safe. Well, I lay there till I felt my nerve steady again, then stood up and called for the line from the skipper.

"'Now, when you jump,' I says, 'I'll get what brace I can here, so if you slip on the edge same's I did there'll be a chance to save you. But mind you, George Hoodley, if I find I can't hold you up—if it's to be your life or mine—it's you that's got to go. Mind that. And hurry—throw it quick, or I'll cast off the line altogether. That bowsprit won't be there in a few minutes maybe. Hurry up.'

"'But you'll hang on, won't you, Martin? You've got the strength if you want to use it.'

"'Jump, man, jump afore you lose your nerve entirely,' I hollers.

"He threw the line to me, after taking one end of it around his waist. The other end I took around my waist, my end half hitched so I could slip it in a hurry. I warn't throwing my life away for him if I knew it.

"Well, he jumped at last. And the bowsprit rose full as high and gave him full as good a chance as I'd got. But even so he fell a little short. His feet only caught the edge of the shelf. He staggered, and seeing how it was, I braced my feet well as I could and hauled. He came in, sagged away, I bracing my feet—they were slipping—in a crack in the rock of the ledge, I dug the fingers of one hand, the other hand to the line, and hung on. We were gaining, he was fairly on his feet, and I felt the strain easing, when a sea that swept up the side of the cliff like a tidal wave took him clear of everything. It would have swept me, too, but I gripped where I could get a hold with the fingers of my own loose hand in the crack in the rocks and hung on there—one hand to the crack and the other to the line—hung on so, supporting the weight of myself and the skipper until I felt my muscles getting hot and heavy and my breath coming fast. He was floundering somewhere on the edge of the cliff. I hollered to him, though feeling almost certain he was battered to pieces by then—'How is it with you, George—how is it, Man?' but there was no answer. Again I hollered, and again no answer. And then, when I was satisfied that it was only the last ounce of strength I had left, I called out, 'Help yourself, George—why don't you help yourself?' No answer.

Once more I called, and once more getting no answer, I knew then he must've been beaten to death against the rocks, and that 'twas his dead weight was hanging to me. And yet I called once more to make sure. But still getting no answer, 'The Lord have mercy on your soul, George Hoodley,' I said, and let slip the line."

Toward the end of Martin's story it had become very quiet in the forec's'le. Nobody said anything, neither broke in with a question nor offered any comment, until after a long silence, and then not until after Martin himself had repeated absently, as if to himself, and after a long indrawn breath, "And then I let slip the line," and only then did he look around and seem to realize that he was not on the ledge off White-head.

He tucked his pipe away under his mattress, slipped out of his slipshods, slacked away his suspenders and laid his length in his bunk. He was about to draw the curtain, but his eye catching the eye of the watch, who was then hauling off his wet boots, he had to ask, "What's it look like for the morning, Stevie—what'd the skipper say?"

"He says that unless it moderates a bit more than it looks as if 'twill now, we'll stay aboard in the morning."

"Well, here's one that ain't sorry to hear that. I don't mind sayin' now that it's all over, that hanging on to the bottom of that dory warn't any joke today. I'm good and tired. 'Twas a night like this we headed the *Cromwell* to the west'ard. 'Hell or Gloucester,' says he, and it warn't Gloucester. Good-night."

SAMUEL

By Jack London

[Jack London (1876–1916) was a native of California. He was born in San Francisco, educated in the University of California, and lived in California at the time of his early death. The material for his novels and stories is drawn largely from first-hand experience with life. As a novelist he is best known through *The Call of the Wild* (1903), *The Sea Wolf* (1904), and *Martin Eden* (1909). Many of his stories do not conform technically to the requirements of the short story, but are tales or pictures of life so convincingly drawn as to compel attention to the phases of life they illustrate. London once said to the editor of this volume that he regarded *Samuel* as one of his best stories.

Samuel was first published in the *Bookman* (July, 1913) and later included in *The Strength of the Strong* (The Macmillan Company, 1914). It is here reprinted by permission of Mrs. Charmian London and the Jack London Estate.]

MARGARET HENAN would have been a striking figure under any circumstances, but never more so than when I first chanced upon her, a sack of grain fully a hundred-weight on her shoulder, as she walked with sure though tottering stride from the cart-tail to the stable, pausing for an instant to gather strength at the foot of the steep steps that led to the grain-bin. There were four of these steps, and she went up them, a step at a time, slowly, unwaveringly, and with so dogged a certitude, that it never entered my mind that her strength could fail her and let that hundred-weight sack fall from the lean and withered frame that well-nigh doubled under it. For she was patently an old woman, and it was her age that made me linger by the cart and watch.

Six times she went between the cart and the stable, each time with a full sack on her back, and beyond passing the time of day with me she took no notice of my presence. Then, the cart empty, she fumbled for matches and lighted a short clay pipe, pressing down the burning surface of the tobacco with a calloused and apparently nerveless thumb. The hands were noteworthy. They were large-knuckled, sinewy, and malformed by labor, rimed with callouses, the nails blunt and broken, and with here and there cuts and bruises, healed and healing, such as are common to the hands of hard-working men. On the back were huge, upstanding veins, eloquent of age and toil. Looking at them it was hard to believe that they were the hands of the woman who had once been the belle of Island McGill. This last, of course, I learned later. At the time I knew neither her history nor her identity.

639

She wore heavy man's brogans. Her legs were stockingless, and I had noticed when she walked that her bare feet were thrust into the crinkly, iron-like shoes that sloshed about her lean ankles at every step. Her figure, shapeless and waistless, was garbed in a rough man's shirt and in a ragged flannel petticoat that had once been red. But it was her face, wrinkled, withered and weather-beaten, surrounded by an aureole of un-kept and straggling wisps of grayish hair, that caught and held me. Neither drifted hair nor serried wrinkles could hide the splendid dome of a fore-head, high and broad without verging in the slightest on the abnormal.

The sunken cheeks and pinched nose told little of the quality of the life that flickered behind those clear blue eyes of hers. Despite the minutiae of wrinkle-work that somehow failed to weazen them, her eyes were clear as a girl's—clear, out-looking, and far-seeing, and with an open and unblinking steadfastness of gaze that was disconcerting. The remarkable thing was the distance between them. It is a lucky man or woman who has the width of an eye between, but with Margaret Henan the width between her eyes was fully that of an eye and a half. Yet so symmetrically molded was her face that this remarkable feature produced no uncanny effect, and, for that matter, would have escaped the casual observer's notice. The mouth, shapeless and toothless, with down-turned corners and lips dry and parchment-like, nevertheless lacked the muscular slackness so usual with age. The lips might have been those of a mummy, save for the impression of rigid firmness they gave. Not that they were atrophied. On the contrary they seemed tense and set with a muscular and spiritual determination. There and in the eyes was the secret of the certitude with which she carried the sacks up the steep steps, with never a false step or over-balance, and emptied them in the grain-bin.

"You are an old woman to be working like this," I ventured.

She looked at me with that strange, unblinking gaze, and she thought and spoke with the slow deliberateness that characterized everything about her, as if well aware of an eternity that was hers and in which there was no need for haste. Again I was impressed by the enormous certitude of her. In this eternity that seemed so indubitably hers, there was time and to spare for safe-footing and stable equilibrium—for certitude, in short. No more in her spiritual life than in carrying the hundred-weights of grain, was there a possibility of a misstep or an overbalancing. The feeling produced in me was uncanny. Here was a human soul that, save for the most glimmering of contacts, was beyond the humanness of me. And the more I learned of Margaret Henan in the weeks that followed the more mysteriously remote she became. She was as alien as a far-journeyer from some other star, and no hint could she nor all the countryside give me of what forms of living, what heats of feeling, or rules of philosophic contemplation, actuated her in all that she had been and was.

"I wull be suvunty-two come Guid Friday a fortnight," she said in reply to my question.

"But you are an old woman to be doing this man's work, and a strong man's work at that," I insisted.

Again she seemed to immerse herself in that atmosphere of contemplative eternity, and so strangely did it affect me that I should not have been surprised to have awaked a century or so later and found her just beginning to enunciate her reply:

"The work hoz tull be done, an' I am beholden tull no one."

"But have you no children, no family relations?"

"O, ay, a plenty o' them, but they no see fut to be helpun' me."

She drew out her pipe for a moment, then added, with a nod of her head toward the house, "I luv' with meself."

I glanced at the house, straw thatched and commodious, at the large stable, and at the large array of fields I knew must belong with the place.

"It is a big bit of land for you to farm by yourself."

"O, ay, a bug bit, suvunty acres. Ut kept me old mon buzzy, along with a son an' a hired mon, tull say nought o' extra honds un the harvest an' a maid-servant un the house."

She clambered into the cart, gathered the reins in her hands, and quizzed me with her keen shrewd eyes.

"Belike ye hail from over the watter—Ameruky, I'm meanun'?"

"Yes, I'm a Yankee," I answered.

"Ye wull no be findun' mony Island McGill folk stoppun' un Ameruky?"

"No; I don't remember ever meeting one in the States."

She nodded her head.

"They are home-lovun' bodies, though I wull no be sayun' they are no fair-traveled. Yet they come home ot the last, them oz are no lost ot sea or kult by fevers an' such-like un foreign parts."

"Then your sons will have gone to sea and come home again?" I queried.

"O, ay, all savun' Samuel oz was drowned."

At the mention of Samuel I could have sworn to a strange light in her eyes, and it seemed, to me, as by some telepathic flash, that I divined in her a tremendous wistfulness, an immense yearning. It seemed to me that here was the key to her inscrutableness, the clew that if followed properly would make all her strangeness plain. It came to me that here was a contact and that for the moment I was glimpsing into the soul of her. The question was tickling on my tongue, but she forestalled me.

She *tckh'd* to the horse, and with a "Guid day tull you, sir," drove off.

A simple, homely people are the folk of Island McGill, and I doubt if a more sober, thrifty, and industrious folk is to be found in all the world.

Meeting them abroad—and to meet them abroad one must meet them on the sea, for a hybrid seafaring and farmer breed are they—one would never take them to be Irish. Irish they claim to be, speaking of North of Ireland with pride and sneering at their Scottish brothers; yet Scotch they undoubtedly are, transplanted Scotch of long ago, it is true, but none the less Scotch, with a thousand traits, to say nothing of their tricks of speech and woolly utterance, which nothing less than their Scotch clannishness could have preserved to this late day.

A narrow loch, scarcely half a mile wide, separates Island McGill from the main land of Ireland; and once across this loch, one finds himself in an entirely different country. The Scotch impression is strong, and the people, to commence with, are Presbyterians. When it is considered that there is no public house in all the island and that seven thousand souls dwell therein, some idea may be gained of the temperateness of the community. Wedded to old ways, public opinion and the ministers are powerful influences, while fathers and mothers are revered and obeyed as in few other places in this modern world. Courting lasts never later than ten at night, and no girl walks out with her young man without her parents' knowledge and consent.

The young men go down to the sea and sow their wild oats in the wicked ports, returning periodically, between voyages, to live the old intensive morality, to court till ten o'clock, to sit under the minister each Sunday, and to listen at home to the same stern precepts that the elders preached to them from the time they were laddies. Much they learned of women in the ends of the earth, these seafaring sons, yet a canny wisdom was theirs, and they never brought wives home with them. The one solitary exception to this had been the schoolmaster, who had been guilty of bringing a wife from half a mile the other side of the loch. For this he had never been forgiven, and he rested under a cloud for the remainder of his days. At his death the wife went back across the loch to her own people, and the blot on the escutcheon of Island McGill was erased. In the end the sailor-men married girls of their own homeland and settled down to become exemplars of all the virtues for which the island was noted.

Island McGill was without a history. She boasted none of the events that go to make history. There had never been any wearing of the green, any Fenian conspiracies, any land disturbances. There had been but one eviction, and that purely technical—a test case, and on advice of the tenant's lawyer. So Island McGill was without annals. History had passed her by. She paid her taxes, acknowledged her crowned rulers, and left the world alone; all she asked in return was that the world leave her alone. The world was composed of two parts—Island McGill and the rest of it. And whatever was not Island McGill was outlandish and barbarian; and well she knew, for did not her seafaring sons bring home reports of that world and its ungodly ways?

SAMUEL

It was from the skipper of a Glasgow tramp, as passenger from
Colombo to Rangoon, that I had first learned of the existence of Island
McGill; and it was from him that I had carried the letter that gave me
entrance to the house of Mrs. Ross, widow of a master mariner, with a
daughter living with her and with two sons, master mariners themselves
and out upon the sea. Mrs. Ross did not take in boarders, and it was
Captain Ross's letter alone that had enabled me to get from her, bed and
board. In the evening after my encounter with Margaret Henan, I
questioned Mrs. Ross, and I knew on the instant that I had in truth
stumbled upon mystery.

Like all Island McGill folk, as I was soon to discover, Mrs. Ross was
at first averse to discussing Margaret Henan at all. Yet it was from her
I learned that evening that Margaret Henan had once been one of the
island belles. Herself the daughter of a well-to-do farmer, she had married
Thomas Henan, equally well-to-do. Beyond the usual housewife's
tasks she had never been accustomed to work. Unlike many of the
island women, she had never lent a hand in the fields.

"But what of her children?" I asked.

"Two o' the sons, Jamie an' Tumothy uz married an' be goun' tull
sea. Thot bug house close tull the post office uz Jamie's. The daughters
thot ha'no married be luvun' wuth them as dud marry. An' the rest
be dead."

"The Samuels," Clara interpolated, with what I suspected was a
giggle.

She was Mrs. Ross's daughter, a strapping young woman with handsome features and remarkably handsome black eyes.

"'Tuz naught tull be snuckerun' ot," her mother reproved her.

"The Samuels?" I intervened. "I don't understand."

"Her four sons thot died."

"And were they all named Samuel?"

"Ay."

"Strange," I commented in the lagging silence.

"Very strange," Mrs. Ross affirmed, proceeding stolidly with the
knitting of the woolen singlet on her knees—one of the countless under-
garments that she interminably knitted for her skipper sons.

"And it was only the Samuels that died?" I queried, in further
attempt.

"The others luv'd," was the answer.

"A fine fomuly—no finer on the island. No better lods ever sailed
out of Island McGill. The munuster held them up oz models tull pottern
after. Nor was ever a whusper breathed again' the girls."

"But why is she left alone now in her old age?" I persisted. "Why
don't her own flesh and blood look after her? Why does she live alone?
Don't they ever go to see her or care for her?"

"Never a one un twunty years an' more now. She fetch't ut ontull herself. She drove them from the house just oz she drove old Tom Henan, thot was her husband, tull hus death."

"Drink?" I ventured.

Mrs. Ross shook her head scornfully, as if drink was a weakness beneath the weakest of Island McGill.

A long pause followed, during which Mrs. Ross knitted stolidly on, only nodding permission when Clara's young man, mate on one of the Shire Line sailing ships, came to walk out with her. I studied the half-dozen ostrich eggs, hanging in the corner against the wall like a cluster of some monstrous fruit. On each shell was painted precipitous and impossible seas through which full-rigged ships foamed with a lack of perspective only equaled by their sharp technical perfection. On the mantelpiece stood two large pearl shells, obviously a pair, intricately carved by the patient hands of New Caledonian convicts. In the center of the mantel was a stuffed bird of paradise, while about the room were scattered gorgeous shells from the Southern seas, delicate sprays of coral sprouting from barnacled *pi-pi* shells and cased in glass, assegais from South Africa, stone-axes from New Guinea, huge Alaskan tobacco-pouches beaded with heraldic totem designs, a boomerang from Australia, divers ships in glass bottles, a cannibal *kai-kai* bowl from the Marquesas, and fragile cabinets from China and the Indies, inlaid with mother-of-pearl and precious woods.

I gazed at this varied trove brought home by sailor sons, and pondered the mystery of Margaret Henan, who had driven her husband to his death and been forsaken by all her kin. It was not the drink. Then what was it?—some shocking cruelty? some amazing infidelity? or some fearful, old-world peasant crime?

I broached my theories, but to all Mrs. Ross shook her head.

"Ut was no thot," she said. "Margaret was a guid wife an' a guid mother, an' I doubt she would harm a fly. She brought up her fomuly God-fearun' an' decent-minded. Her trouble was thot she took lunatuc —turned eediot."

Mrs. Ross tapped significantly on her forehead to indicate a state of addlement.

"But I talked with her this afternoon," I objected, "and I found her a sensible woman—remarkably bright for one of her years."

"Ay, an' I'm grantun' all thot you say," she went on calmly. "But I am no referrun' tull thot. I am referrun' tull her wucked-headed an' vucious stubbornness. No more stubborn woman ever luv'd than Margaret Henan. Ut was all on account o' Samuel, which was the name o' her eldest an' they do say her favorut brother—hum oz died by hus own hond all through the munuster's mustake un' no registerun' the new church ot Dublin. Ut was a lesson thot the name was musfortunate, but she would no take ut, an' there was talk when she called her first child Samuel—hum thot died o' the croup. An' wuth thot what does

she do but call the next one Samuel, an' hum only three when he fell
un tull the tub o' hot watter an' was plain cooked tull death. Ut all
come, I tell you, o' her wucked-headed an' foolush stubbornness. For
a Samuel she must huv; an' ut was the death of the four of her sons.
After the first, dudna her own mother go down un the dirt tull her feet,
a-beggun' an' pleadun' wuth her no tull name her next one Samuel?
But she was no tull be turned from her purpose. Margaret Henan was
always set un her ways, an' never more so thon on thot name Samuel.

"She was fair lunatuc on Samuel. Dudna her neighbors, an' all kuth
an' kun savun' them thot luv'd un the house wuth her, get up an' walk
out ot the christenun' of the second—hum thot was cooked? Thot they
dud, an' ot the very moment the munuster asked what would the
bairn's name be. 'Samuel,' says she; an' wuth thot they got up an'
walked out an' left the house. An' ot the door dudna her Aunt Fanny,
her mother's suster, turn an' say loud for all tull hear: 'What for wull
she be wantun' tull murder the wee thung?' The munuster heard fine,
and dudna like ut, but oz he told my Larry afterward, what could he
do? Ut was the woman's wush, an' there was no law again' a mother
callun' her child accordun' tull her wush.

"And then was there no' the third Samuel? An' when he was lost ot
sea off the Cape, dudna she break all laws o' nature tull have a fourth?
She was forty-seven I'm tullun ye, an' she hod a child ot forty-seven.
Thunk on ut! At forty-seven! Ut was fair scand'lous."

From Clara, next morning, I got the tale of Margaret Henan's
favorite brother; and from here and there, in the week that followed, I
pieced together the tragedy of Margaret Henan. Samuel Dundee had
been the youngest of Margaret's four brothers, and, as Clara told me,
she had well-nigh worshiped him. He was going to sea at the time, the
skipper of one of the sailing ships of the Bank Line, when he married
Agnes Hewitt. She was described as a slender wisp of a girl, delicately
featured and with a nervous organization of the supersensitive order.
Theirs had been the first marriage in the "new" church, and after a
two weeks' honeymoon Samuel had kissed his bride good-by and sailed
in command of the *Loughbank*, a big four-masted bark.

And it was because of the "new" church that the minister's blunder
occurred. Nor was it the blunder of the minister alone, as one of the
elders later explained; for it was equally the blunder of the whole Presbytery of Coughleen, which included fifteen churches on Island McGill
and the mainland. The old church, beyond repair, had been torn down
and the new one built on the original foundation. Looking upon the
foundation stones as similar to a ship's keel, it never entered the minister's nor the Presbytery's head that the new church was legally any
other than the old church.

"An' three couples was married the first week un the new church,"

Clara said. "First of all, Samuel Dundee an' Agnes Hewitt; the next day Albert Mahan an' Minnie Duncan; an' by the week-end Eddie Troy an' Flo Mackintosh—all sailor men, an' un sux weeks' time the last of them back tull their shups an' awa', an' no one o' them dreamun' of the wuckedness they'd been ot."

The Imp of the Perverse must have chuckled at the situation. All things favored. The marriages had taken place in the first week of May, and it was not till three months later that the minister, as required by law, made his quarterly report to the civil authorities in Dublin. Promptly came back the announcement that his church had no legal existence, not being registered according to the law's demands. This was overcome by prompt registration; but the marriages were not to be so easily remedied. The three sailor husbands were away, and their wives, in short, were not their wives.

"But the munuster was no for alarmun' the bodies," said Clara. "He kept hus council an' bided hus time, waitun' for the lods tull be back from sea. Oz luck would have ut, he was away across the island tull a christenun' when Albert Mahan arrives home onexpected, hus shup just docked ot Dublin. Ut's nine o'clock ot night when the munuster, un hus sluppers an' dressun' gown, gets the news. Up he jumps an' calls for horse an' saddle, an' awa' goes like the wund for Albert Mahan's. Albert uz just goun' tull bed an' hoz one shoe off when the munuster arrives.

"'Come wuth me, the pair o'ye,' says he, breathless like. 'What for, an' me dead weary an' goun' tull bed?' says Albert. 'Tull be lawful married,' says the munuster. Albert looks black an' says, 'Now, munuster, ye wull be jokin'.' But tull himself, oz I've heard hum tell mony a time, he was wonderun' thot the munuster should a-took tull whusky ot hus time o' life.

"'We be no married?' says Minnie. He shook hus head. 'An' I om no Mussus Mahan?' 'No,' says he, 'ye are no Mussus Mahan. Ye are plain Muss Duncan.' 'But ye married us yoursel',' says she. 'I dud an' I dudna',' says he. An' wuth thot he tells them the whole upshot, an' Albert puts on hus shoe, an' they go wuth the munuster an' are married proper an' lawful, an' oz Albert Mahan says afterward mony's the time, ''Tus no every mon thot hos two weddun' nights on Island McGill.'"

Six months later, Eddie Troy came home and was promptly remarried. But Samuel Dundee was away on a three year's voyage and his ship fell overdue. Further to complicate the situation, a baby boy, past two years old, was waiting for him in the arms of his wife. The months passed, and the wife grew thin with worrying. "Ut's no meself I'm thinkun' on," she is reported to have said many times, "but ut's the puir fatherless bairn. Uf aught hoppened tull Samuel where wull the bairn stond?"

Lloyds posted the *Loughbank* as missing, and the owners ceased the monthly remittance of Samuel's half-pay to his wife. It was the question of the child's legitimacy that preyed on her mind, and when all hope of Samuel's return was abandoned, she drowned herself and the child in the loch. And here enters the greater tragedy. The *Loughbank* was not lost. By a series of sea disasters and delays too interminable to relate, she had made one of those long, unsighted passages such as occur once or twice in half a century. How the Imp must have held both his sides! Back from the sea came Samuel, and when they broke the news to him something else broke somewhere in his heart or head. Next morning they found him where he had tried to kill himself across the grave of his wife and child. Never in the history of Island McGill was there so fearful a deathbed. He spat in the minister's face and reviled him, and died blaspheming so terribly that those that tended on him did so with averted gaze and trembling hands.

And in the face of all this, Margaret Henan named her first child Samuel.

How account for the woman's stubbornness? Or was it a morbid obsession that demanded a child of hers should be named Samuel? Her third child was a girl, named after herself, and the fourth was a boy again. Despite the strokes of fate that had already bereft her, and despite the loss of friends and relatives, she persisted in her resolve to name the child after her brother. She was shunned at church by those who had grown up with her. Her mother, after a final appeal, left her house with the warning that if the child were so named she would never speak to her again. And though the old lady lived thirty odd years longer, she kept her word. The minister agreed to christen the child any name but Samuel, and every other minister on Island McGill refused to christen it by the name she had chosen. There was talk on the part of Margaret Henan of going to law at the time, but in the end she carried the child to Belfast and there had it christened Samuel.

And then nothing happened. The whole Island was confuted. The boy grew and prospered. The schoolmaster never ceased averring that it was the brightest lad he had ever seen. Samuel had a splendid constitution, a tremendous grip on life. To everybody's amazement he escaped the usual run of childish afflictions. Measles, whooping-cough, and mumps knew him not. He was armor clad against germs, immune to all diseases. Headaches and earaches were things unknown. "Never so much oz a boil or a pumple," as one of the old bodies told me, ever marred his healthy skin. He broke school records in scholarship and athletics, and whipped every boy of his size or years on Island McGill.

It was a triumph for Margaret Henan. This paragon was hers, and it bore the cherished name. With the one exception of her mother, friends and relatives drifted back and acknowledged that they had been mistaken; though there were old crones who still abided by their opinions and who shook their heads ominously over their cups of tea. The boy was too wonderful to last. There was no escaping the curse of the name his mother had wickedly laid upon him. The young generation joined Margaret Henan in laughing at them, but the old crones continued to shake their heads.

Other children followed. Margaret Henan's fifth was a boy, whom she called Jamie, and in rapid succession followed three girls, Alice, Sara, and Nora, the boy Timothy, and two more girls, Florence and Katie. Katie was the last and eleventh, and Margaret Henan, at thirty-five, ceased from her exertions. She had done well by Island McGill and the Queen. Nine healthy children were hers. All prospered. It seemed her ill luck had shot its bolt with the deaths of her first two. Nine lived, and one of them was named Samuel.

Jamie elected to follow the sea, though it was not so much a matter of election as compulsion, for the eldest sons on Island McGill remained on the land, while all the other sons went to the salt ploughing. Timothy followed Jamie, and by the time the latter had got his first command, a steamer in the Bay trade out of Cardiff, Timothy was mate of a big sailing ship. Samuel, however, did not take kindly to the soil. The farmer's life had no attraction for him. His brothers went to sea, not out of desire, but because it was the only way for them to gain their bread; and he who had no need to go envied them when, returned from far voyages, they sat by the kitchen fire and told their bold tales of the wonderlands beyond the sea rim.

Samuel became a teacher, much to his father's disgust, and even took extra certificates, going to Belfast for his examinations. When the old master retired, Samuel took over his school. Secretly, however, he studied navigation, and it was Margaret's delight when he sat by the kitchen fire, and, despite their master's tickets, tangled up his brothers in the theoretics of their profession. Tom Henan alone was outraged when Samuel, school-teacher, gentleman, and heir to the Henan farm, shipped to sea before the mast. Margaret had an abiding faith in her son's star, and whatever he did she was sure was for the best. Like everything else connected with his glorious personality, there had never been known so swift a rise as in the case of Samuel. Barely with two years' sea experience before the mast, he was taken from the forecastle and made a provisional second mate. This occurred in a fever port on the West Coast, and the committee of skippers that examined him agreed that he knew more of the science of navigation than they had remembered or forgotten. Two years later he sailed from Liverpool, mate of the *Starry Grace*, with both master's and extra master's tickets in his possession. And then it happened—the thing the old crones had been shaking their heads over for years.

It was told me by Gavin McNab, bosun of the *Starry Grace* at the time, himself an Island McGill man.

"Wull do I remember ut," he said. "We was runnun' our Eastun' down, an' makun' heavy weather of ut. Oz fine a sailor-mon oz ever walked was Samuel Henan. I remember the look of hum wull that last marnun', a-watchun' them bug seas curlun' up astern, an' a-watchun' the old girl an' seeun' how she took them—the skupper down below an' drunkun' for days. Ut was ot seven thot Henan brought her up on tull the wund, not darun' tull run longer un thot fearful sea. Ot eight, after havun' breakfast, he turns un, an' a half hour after up comes the skupper, bleary-eyed an' shaky an' holdun' on tull the companion. Ut was fair smokun', I om tellun' ye, and there he stood, blunkun' an' noddun' an' talkun' tull humsel'. 'Keep off,' says he ot last to the mon ot the wheel. 'My God!' says the second mate, standun' beside hum. The skupper never looks tull hum ot all, but keeps on mutterun' an' jabberun' tull humsel'. All of a suddent-like he straightuns up an' throws hus head back, an' says: 'Put your wheel over, me mon—now, domn ye! Are ye deef thot ye'll no be hearun' me!'

"Ut was a drunkun mon's luck, for the *Starry Grace* wore off afore that God-Almighty gale wuthout shuppun' a bucket o' watter, the second mate shoutun' orders an' the crew jumpin' like mod. An' wuth thot the skupper nods contented-like tull humsel' an' goes below after more whuskey. Ut was plain murder o' the lives o' all of us, for ut was no the time for the buggest shup afloat tull be runnun'. Run? Never hov I seen the like! Ut was beyond all thunkun', an' me goun' tull sea, boy an' mon, for forty year. I tell you ut was fair awesome.

"The face o' the second mate was white oz death, an' he stood ut alone for half an hour, when ut was too much for hum, an' he went below an' called Samuel an' the third. Ay, a fine sailor-mon thot Samuel, but ut was too much for hum. He looked an' studied, an' looked an' studied, but he could no see hus way. He durst na heave tull. She would ha' been sweeput o' all honds an' stucks an' every-thung afore she could a-fetcht up. There was nought tull do but keep on runnun'. An' uf ut worsened we were lost onyway, for soon or late that overtakun' sea was sure tull sweep us clear over poop an' all.

"Dud I say it was a God-Almighty gale? Ut was worse nor thot. The Devil himself must ha' hod a hond un the brewun' o' ut, ut was thot fearsome. I ha' looked on some sights, but I om no carun' tull look on the like o' thot again. No mon dared tull be un hus bunk. No, nor no mon on the decks. All honds of us stood on top the house an' held on an' watched. The three mates was on the poop, wuth two men ot the wheel, an' the only mon below was thot whuskey-blighted captain snorun' drunk.

"An' then I see ut comun', a mile away, risun' above all the waves like an island un the sea—the buggest wave ever I looked upon. The three mates stood tulgether an' watched ut comun', a-prayun' like we thot she would no break un passun' us. But ut was no tull be. Ot the last, when she rose up like a mountain, curlun' above the stern an' blottun' out the sky, the mates scottered, the second an' third runnun' for the mizzen-shrouds an' climbun' up, but the first runnun' tull the wheel tull lend a hond. He was a grave mon, thot Samuel Henan. He run straight un tull the face o' thot father o' all waves, no thunkun' on humsel' but thunkun' only o' the ship. The two men was lashed tull the wheel, but he would be ready tull hond un the case they was kult. An' then she took ut. We on the house could no see the poop for the thousand tons of watter that had hut ut. Thot wave cleaned them out, took everything along wuth ut—the two mates climbun' up the mizzun-riggun', Samuel Henan runnun' tull the wheel, the two men ot the wheel, ay, an' the wheel utself. We never saw aught o' them, for she broached tull, what o' the wheel goun', an' two men o' us was drowned off the house, no tull mention the carpenter thot we picked up ot the break o' the poop wuth every bone o' hus body broke tull he was like so much jelly."

And here enters the marvel of it, the miraculous wonder of that woman's heroic spirit. Margaret Henan was forty-seven when the news came home of the loss of Samuel; and it was not long after that the unbelievable rumor went around! Island McGill. I say unbelievable. Island McGill would not believe. Dr. Hall pooh-pooh'd it. Everybody laughed at it as a good joke. They traced back the gossip to Sara Dack, servant to the Henans, and who alone lived with Margaret and her husband. But Sara Dack persisted in her assertion and was called a low-mouthed liar. One or two dared question Tom Henan himself, but beyond black looks and curses for their presumption they elicited nothing from him.

The rumor died down, and the island fell to discussing in all its ramifications the loss of the *Grenoble* in the China Seas, with all her officers and half her crew born and married on Island McGill. But the rumor would not stay down. Sara Dack was louder in her assertions, the looks Tom Henan cast about him were blacker than ever, and Dr. Hall, after a visit to the Henan House, no longer pooh-pooh'd. Then Island McGill sat up, and there was a tremendous wagging of tongues. It was unnatural and ungodly. The like had never been heard. And when, as time passed, the truth of Sara Dack's utterances was manifest, the island folk decided, like the bosun of the *Starry Grace*, that only the Devil could have had a hand in so untoward a happening. And the infatuated woman, so Sara Dack reported, insisted that it would be a boy. "Eleven bairns ha' I borne," she said; "sux o' them lassies and five o' them loddies. An' sunce there be balance un all thungs, so wull there be balance wuth me. Sux o' one an' half a dozen o' the other—there uz the balance, an' oz sure oz the sun rises un' the marnun', thot sure wull ut be a boy."

And boy it was, and a prodigy. Doctor Hall raved about its unblemished perfection and massive strength, and wrote a brochure on it for the Dublin Medical Society as the most interesting case of the sort in his long career.

When Sara Dack gave the babe's unbelievable weight, Island McGill refused to believe and once again called her liar. But when Dr. Hall attested that he had himself weighed it and seen it tip that very notch, Island McGill held its breath and accepted whatever report Sara Dack made of the infant's progress or appetite. And once again Margaret Henan carried a babe to Belfast and had it christened Samuel.

"Oz good oz gold ut was," said Sara Dack to me.

Sara, at the time I met her, was a buxom, phlegmatic spinster of sixty, equipped with an experience so tragic and unusual that though her tongue ran on for decades its output would still be of imperishable interest to her cronies.

"Oz good oz gold," said Sara Dack. "Ut never fretted. Sut ut down un the sun by the hour an' never a sound ut would make oz long oz ut was no hungered. An' thot strong! The grup o' uts honds was like a mon's. I mind me when ut was but hours old, ut grupped me so mighty thot I fetcht a scream I was thot frightened. Ut was the punk o' health. Ut slept an' ate, an' grew. Ut never bothered. Never a night's sleep ut lost tull no one, nor even a munut's, an' thot wuth cuttun' uts teeth an' all. An' Margaret would dandle ut on her knee an' ask was there ever so fine a loddie un the three kingdoms.

"The way ut grew! Ut was un keepun' wuth the way ut ate. Ot a year ut was the size o' a bairn of two. Ut was slow tull walk an' talk. Exceptun' for gurgly noises un uts throat an' for creepun' on all-fours, ut dudna monage much un the walkun' and talkun' line. But thot was tull be expected from the way ut grew. Ut all went tull growun' strong an' healthy. An' even old Tom Henan cheered up ot the might of ut an' said was there ever the like o' ut un the three kingdoms. Ut was Doctor Hall thot first suspicioned, I mind me well, though ut was luttle I dreamt what he was up tull ot the time. I see hum holdun' thungs un front o' luttle Sammy's eyes, an' a-makun' noises, loud an' soft, an' far an' near, un' little Sammy's ears. An' then I see Doctor Hall go away, wrunklun' hus eyebrows an' shakun' hus head like the bairn was ailun'. But he was no ailun', oz I could swear tull, me a'seeun' hum eat an' grow. But Doctor Hall no said a word tull Margaret, an' I was no for guessun' the why he was sore puzzled.

"I mind me when luttle Sammy first spoke. He was two years old an' the size of a child o' five, though he could no monage the walkun' yet but went around on all-fours, happy an' contented-like an' makun' no trouble oz long oz he was fed promptly, whuch was onusual often. I was hangun' the wash on the line ot the time, when out he comes on all-fours, hus bug head waggun' tull an' fro an' blunkun' un the sun. An' then, suddent, he talked. I was thot took a-back I near died o' fright, an' fine I knew ut then the shakun' o' Doctor Hall's head. Talked? Never a bairn on Island McGill talked so loud an' tull such purpose. There was no mistakun' ut. I stood there all tremblun' an' shakun'. Luttle Sammy was brayun'. I tell you, sir, he was brayun' like an ass—just like thot, loud an' long an' cheerful tull ut seemed hus lungs ud crack.

"He was a eediot—a great, awful, monster eediot. Ut was after he talked thot Doctor Hall told Margaret, but she would no believe. Ut would all come right, she said. Ut was growun' too fast for aught else. Give ut time, said she, an' we would see. But old Tom Henan knew, an' he never held up hus head again. He could no abide the thung, an' would no brung humsel' tull touch ut, though I am no denyun' he was fair fascinated by ut. Mony the time I see hum watchun' of ut around a corner, lookun' ot ut tull hus eyes fair bulged wuth the horror; an' when ut brayed, old Tom ud stuch hus fungers tull hus ears an' look thot miserable I could a-puttied hum.

"An' bray ut could! Ut was the only thung ut could do beside eat an' grow. Whenever ut was hungry ut brayed, an' there was no stoppun' ut save wuth food. An' always of a marnun', when first ut crawled tull the kutchen-door an' blunked out ot the sun, ut brayed. An' ut was brayun' thot brought about uts end.

"I mind me well. Ut was three years old and ez bug oz a lod o' ten. Old Tom hod been goun' from bod tull worse, ploughun' up an' down the fields an' talkun' an' mutturun' tull humself. On the marnun' o' the day I mind me, he was suttun' on the bench outside the kutchun' a-futtun' a handle tull a puck-axe. Unbeknown, the monster eediot crawled tull the door and brayed after hus fashion ot the sun. I see old Tom start up an' look. An' there was the monster eediot waggun' uts bug head an' blunkun' an' brayun' like the great bug ass ut was. Ut was too much for Tom. Somethun' went wrong with hum suddent-like. He jumped tull his feet an' fetched the puck-handle down on the monster eediot's head. An' he hut ut again an' again like ut was a mad dog an' hum afeared o' ut. An' he went straight tull the stable an' hung humsel' tull a rafter. An' I was no for stoppun' on after such-like, an' I went tull stay along wuth me suster thot was married tull John Martin an' comfortable off."

I sat on the bench by the kitchen door and regarded Margaret Henan, while with her callous thumb she pressed down the live fire of her pipe and gazed out across the twilight-sombered fields. It was the very bench Tom Henan sat upon that last sanguinary day of life. And

Margaret sat in the doorway where the monster, blinking at the sun, had so often wagged its head and brayed. We had been talking for an hour, she with that slow certitude of eternity that so befitted her; and for the life of me I could lay no finger on the motives that ran through the tangled warp and woof of her. Was she a martyr to Truth? Did she have it in her to worship at so abstract a shrine? Had she conceived Abstract Truth to be the one high goal of human endeavor on that day of long ago when she named her first-born Samuel? Or was hers the stubborn obstinacy of the ox? the fixity of purpose of the balky horse? the stolidity of the self-willed peasant-mind? Was it whim or fancy?—the one streak of lunacy in what was otherwise an eminently rational mind? Or, reverting, was hers the spirit of a Bruno? Was she convinced of the intellectual rightness of the stand she had taken? Was hers a steady, enlightened opposition to superstition? or—and a subtler thought—was she mastered by some vaster, profounder superstition, fetish-worship of which the Alpha and Omega was the cryptic *Samuel?*

"Wull ye be tellun' me," she said, "thot uf the second Samuel hod been named Larry, thot he would no hov fell un the hot watter and drowned? Atween you an' me, sir, an' ye are untellugent-lookun' tull the eye, would the name hov made ut onyways dufferunt? Would the washun' no be done thot day uf he had been Larry or Michael? Would hot watter no be hot, an' would hot watter no burn, uf he hod hod ony other name but Samuel?"

I acknowledged the justness of her contention, and she went on.

"Do a wee but of a name change the plans o' God? Do the world run by hut or muss, an' be God a weak, shully-shallyun' creature that ud alter the fate an' destiny o' thungs because the worm Margaret Henan seen fut tull name her bairn Samuel? There be my son Jamie. He wull no sign a Rooshan-Funn un hus crew because o' believun' thot Rooshan-Funns do be monajun' the wunds an' hov the makun' o' bod weather. Wull you be thunkun' so? Wull you be thunkun' thot God thot makes the wunds tull blow wull bend hus head from on high tull lusten tull the word o' a greasy Rooshan-Funn un some dirty shup's fo'c'sle?"

I said no, certainly not; but she was not to be set aside from pressing home the point of her argument.

"Then wull you be thunkun' thot God thot directs the stars un their courses an' tull whose mighty foot the world uz but a footstool, wull you be thunkun' thot he wull take a spite again' Margaret Henan an' send a bug wave off the Cape tull wash her son un tull eternity, all because she was for namun' hum Samuel?"

"But why Samuel?" I asked.

"And thot I dinna know. I wanted ut so."

"But why did you want it so?"

"An' uz ut me thot would be answerun' a such-like question? Be there ony mon luvun' or dead thot can answer? Who can tell the *why* o' like? My Jamie was fair daft on buttermulk; he would drink ut tull, oz he said humself, hus back-teeth was awash. But my Tumothy could no abide buttermulk. I like tull lussen tull the thunder growlun', an' roarun', an rampajun'. My Katie could no abide the noise of ut, but must scream an' flutter an' go runnun' for the mudmost o' a featherbed. Never yet hov I heard the answer tull the *why* o' like. God alone hoz thot answer. You an' me be mortal an' we canna know. Enough for us tull know what we like an' what we duslike. I *like*—thot uz the first word an' the last. And behind thot *like* no mon can go and find the *why* o' ut. I like Samuel, an' I like ut wull. Ut uz a sweet name, an' there be a rollun' wonder un the sound o' ut thot passes onderstondun'."

The twilight deepened, and in the silence I gazed upon that splendid dome of a forehead which time could not mar, at the width between the eyes, and at the eyes themselves, clear, out-looking, and wide-seeing. She rose to her feet with an air of dismissing me, saying:

"Ut wull be a dark walk home; an' there wull be more thon a sprunkle o' wet on the sky."

"Have you any regrets, Margaret Henan?" I asked suddenly and without forethought.

She studied me a moment.

"Ay, thot I no ha' borne another son."

"And you would . . . ?" I faltered.

"Ay, thot I would," she answered. "Ut would ha' been hus name."

I went down the dark road between the hawthorne hedges, puzzling over the why of like, repeating *Samuel* to myself and aloud and listening to the rolling wonder in its sound that had charmed her soul and led her life in tragic places. *Samuel!* There was a rolling wonder in the sound of it. Ay, there was!

THE PRINCESS AND THE VAGABONE

By Ruth Sawyer

[Ruth Sawyer Durand (1880–   ) is an American writer who has succeeded in telling in a very delightful way the kind of Irish folk tales which the Irish dramatists have used in comedy and tragedy. She was born in Boston and now lives in Ithaca, N. Y. She has written a number of books for children, including *A Child's Year Book* (1917), *Tale of the Enchanted Bunnies* (1923), and *Four Ducks in a Pond* (1928).

The *Princess and the Vagabone* first appeared in *The Outlook* (September 9, 1911) and is reprinted by permission of the editors and of the author.]

IF you would hear a tale in Ireland, you must first tell one. So it happened, as we sat in the Hegartys' cabin on a late fall night after a cross-roads dance, that I, the stranger, found myself beginning the story-telling. The cabin was overflowing with neighbors from the hills about: girls and lads stretched tired-limbed beside the hearth, elders sitting in an outer circle. The men smoked, the women were busy with their knitting, and the old gray piper—hidden in the shadow of the chimney-corner—sat with his pipes across his knees, fingering the stops with tenderness as unconsciously as a parent's hand goes out to stroke a much-loved child. From between the curtains of the outshot bed peered the children, sleepless-eyed and laughing. The kettle hung, freshly filled, over the fire; the empty griddle stood beside it, ready for a late baking, for there would be tea and currant-bread at the end of the evening.

I remember I told the legend of the Catskills, dwelling long on Rip's shrewish wife and the fame of her sharp tongue. They liked the story; I knew well that they would, for the supernatural lies close to the Irish heart; and before ever it was finished Michael Hegarty was knocking the ashes from his pipe that he might be ready with the next tale.

"That's grand," he said at the conclusion. "Do ye know, ye've given me a great consolation? I was after thinkin' that Ireland had the exclusive rights to all the sharp-tongued, pestherin' wives," and he shook his head teasingly at the wife who sat across the firelight from him.

"Did ye, now?" she answered, her face drawn into an expression of mock solemnity. "Sure, was it because ye knew we had the run o' vagabone husbands?"

The children gurgled with appreciative merriment, but Michael pulled me gently by the sleeve.

"I have a tale—do ye know Willie Shakespeare?"

I nodded, surprised at the question.

"Well, ye may not be knowin' this: he was afther writin' a play a few hundthred years ago which he took sthraight out of a Connaught tale. Like as not he had it from an Irish nurse, or maybe he heard it from a rovin' tinker that came to his town."

"Which play do you mean?"

"Faith, I haven't the name by me handy, just, but your story put me in mind of it. I was readin' it myself once, so it's the truth I am tellin' ye. He has it changed a wee bit—turned it an' patched it an' made it up in a sthrange fashion; but 'tis the same tale, for all o' that. Sure, did ye ever know an Englishman yet that would let on to anything he'd took from an Irishman?"

A joyful murmur greeted the last.

"Tell us the tale," I said.

There was a long pause; the burning turf sifted down into "faery gold" upon the hearth and the kettle commenced to sing. Michael Hegarty smiled foolishly—

"I am afther wishin' ye had the Gaelic so as I could tell it to ye right. Ye see, I'm not good at givin' a tale in English—I haven't the words, just"; and he fumbled uneasily with his empty pipe.

"Ye can do it," said the wife, proudly.

"I can make the try," he answered, simply; and then he added, regretfully, "But I wish ye had the Gaelic."

Thus did Michael Hegarty begin the story of the Princess and the Vagabone. I marveled at first that the poetry and beauty of language should come so readily yet so unconsciously to his lips; and then I remembered that his people had once been the poets of the world, and men had come from far away to be taught by them.

This is the tale as he told it that night by the hearth—save that the soft Donegal brogue is missing, and nowhere can you hear the rhythmic click of the knitters' needles or the singing of the kettle on the crook making accompaniment.

Once, in the olden time, when an Irish king sat in every province and plenty covered the land, so that fat wee pigs ran free on the highroad, crying "Who'll eat us?" there lived in Connaught a grand old king with one daughter. She was as tall and slender as the reeds that grow by Loch Erne, and her face was the fairest in seven counties. This was more the pity, for the temper she had did not match it at all, at all; it was the blackest and ugliest that ever fell to the birthlot of a princess. She was proud, she was haughty; her tongue had the length and the sharpness of the thorns on a sidheog bush; and from the day she was born till long after she was a woman grown she was never heard to say a kind word or known to do a kind deed to a living creature.

As each year passed, the King would think to himself, "'Tis the New Year will see her better." But it was worse instead of better she grew, until one day the King found himself at the end of his patience, and he groaned aloud as he sat alone, drinking his poteen.

"Faith, another man shall have her for the next eighteen years, for, by my soul, I've had my fill of her!"

So it came about, as I am telling ye, that the King sent word to the nobles of the neighboring provinces that whosoever would win the consent of his daughter in marriage should have the half of his kingdom and the whole of his blessing. On the day that she was eighteen they came: a wonderful procession of earls, dukes, princes, and kings, riding up to the castle gate, a-courting. The air was filled with the ring of the silver trappings on their horses, and the courtyard was gay with the colors of their bratas and the long cloaks they wore, riding. The King made each welcome according to his rank; and then he sent a serving-man to his daughter, bidding her come and choose her suitor, the time being ripe for her to marry. It was a courteous message that the King sent, but the Princess heard little of it. She flew into the hall on the heels of the serving-man, like a fowl hawk after a bantam cock. Her eyes burned with the anger that was hot in her heart, while she stamped her foot in the King's face until the rafters rang with the noise of it.

"So ye will be giving me away for the asking—to any one of these blithering fools who have a rag to their backs or a castle to their names?"

The King grew crimson at her words. He was ashamed that they should all hear how sharp was her tongue; moreover, he was fearsome lest they should take to their heels and leave him with a shrew on his hands for another eighteen years. He was hard at work piecing together a speech made up of all the grand words he knew, when the Princess strode past him on to the first suitor in the line.

"At any rate, I'll not be choosin' ye, ye long-legged corn-crake," and she gave him a sound kick as she went on to the next. He was a large man with a shaggy beard; and, seeing how the first suitor had fared, he tried a wee bit of a smile on her while his hand went out coaxingly. She saw, and the anger in her grew three-fold.

She sprang at him, digging the two of her hands deep in his beard, and then she wagged his foolish head back and forth, screaming:

"Take that, and that, and that, ye old whiskered rascal!"

It was a miracle that any beard was left on his face the way that she pulled it. But she let him go free at last, and turned to a thin, sharp-faced prince with a monstrous long nose. The nose took her fancy, and she gave it a tweak, telling the prince to take himself home before he did any damage with it. The next one she called "pudding-face" and slapped his fat cheeks until they were purple, and the poor lad groaned with the sting of it.

"Go back to your trough, for I'll not marry a grunter, i' faith," said she.

She moved swiftly down the line in less time than it takes for the telling. It came to the mind of many of the suitors that they would be doing a wise thing if they betook themselves off before their turn came; so as many of them as were not fastened to the floor with fear started away. There happened to be a fat, crooked-legged prince from Leinster just making for the door when the Princess looked around. In a trice she reached out for the tongs that stood on the hearth near by, and she laid it across his shoulders, sending him spinning into the yard.

"Take that, ye old gander, and good riddance to ye!" she cried after him.

It was then that she saw looking at her a great towering giant of a man; and his eyes burned through hers, deep down into her soul. So great was he that he could have picked her up with a single hand and thrown her after the gander; and she knew it, and yet she felt no fear. He was as handsome as Nuada of the Silver Hand; and not a mortal fault could she have found with him, not if she had tried for a hundred years. The two of them stood facing each other, glaring, as if each would spring at the other's throat the next moment; but all the while the Princess was thinking how wonderful he was, from the top of his curling black hair, down the seven feet of him, to the golden clasps on his shoes. What the man was thinking I cannot be telling. Like a breath of wind on smoldering turf, her liking for him set her anger fierce-burning again. She gave him a sound cuff of the ear; then turned, and with a sob in her throat she went flying from the room, the serving-men scattering before her as if she had been a hundred million robbers on a raid.

And the King? Faith, he was dumb with rage. But when he saw the blow that his daughter had given to the finest gentleman in all Ireland, he went after her as if he had been two hundred million constables on the trail of the robbers.

"Ye are a disgrace and a shame to me," said he, catching up with her and holding firmly to her two hands; "and, what's more, ye are a disgrace and a blemish to my castle and my kingdom; I'll not keep ye in it a day longer. The first traveling vagabone who comes begging at the door shall have ye for his wife."

"Will he?" and the Princess tossed her head in the King's face and went to her chamber.

The next morning a poor singing *sthronshuch* came to the castle to sell a song for a penny or a morsel of bread. The song was sweet that he sang, and the Princess listened as Oona, the tirewoman, was winding strands of her long black hair with golden thread:

> The gay young wran sang over the moor.
> "I'll build me a nest," sang he.
> "'Twill have a thatch and a wee latched door,
> For the wind blows cold from the sea.

And I'll let no one but my true love in,
For she is the mate for me."
Sang the gay young wran.

The wee brown wran by the hedgerow cried—
"I'll wait for him here," cried she.
"For the way is far and the world is wide,
And he might miss the way to me.
Long is the time when the heart is shut,
But I'll open to none save he,"
Sang the wee brown wran.

A strange throb came to the heart of the Princess when the song was done. She pulled her hair free from the hands of the tirewoman.

"Get silver," she said; "I would throw it to him." And when she saw the wonderment grow in Oona's face, she added: "The song pleased me. Can I not pay for what I like without having ye look at me as if ye feared my wits had flown? Go, get the silver!"

But when she pushed open the grating and leaned far out to throw it, the *sthronshuch* had gone.

For the King had heard the song as well as the Princess. His rage was still with him, and when he saw who it was, he lost no time, but called him quickly inside.

"Ye are as fine a vagabone as I could wish for," he said. "Maybe ye're not knowing it, but ye are a bridegroom this day." And the King went on to tell him the whole tale. The tale being finished, he sent ten strong men to bring the Princess down.

A king's word was law in those days. The Vagabone knew this; and, what's more, he knew he must marry the Princess, whether he liked it or no. The Vagabone had great height, but he stooped so that it shortened the length of him. His hair was long, and it fell, uncombed and matted, about his shoulders. His brogues were patched, his hose were sadly worn, and with his rags he was the sorriest cut of a man that a maid ever laid her two eyes on. When the Princess came, she was dressed in a gown of gold, with jewels hanging from every thread of it, and her cap was caught with a jeweled brooch. She looked as beautiful as a May morning—with a thunder-cloud rising back of the hills; and the Vagabone held his breath for a moment, watching her. Then he pulled the King gently by the arm.

"I'll not have a wife that looks grander than myself. If I marry your daughter, I must marry her in rags—the same as my own."

The King agreed 'twas a good idea, and sent for the worst dress of rags in the whole countryside. The rags were fetched, the Princess dressed, the priest brought, and the two of them married; and, though she cried and she kicked and she cuffed and she prayed, she was the Vagabone's wife—hard and fast.

"Now take her, and good luck go with ye," said the King. Then his eyes fell on the tongs on the hearth. "Here, take these along—they may come in handy on the road; but, whatever ye do, don't let them out of your hands, for your wife is very powerful with them herself."

Out of the castle gate, across the gardens, and into the country that lay beyond went the Princess and the Vagabone. The sky was blue over their heads and the air was full of spring; each wee creature that passed them on the road seemed bursting with the joy of it. There was naught but anger in the Princess' heart, however; and what was in the heart of the Vagabone I cannot be telling. This I know—that he sang the "Song of the Wran" as they went. Often and often the Princess turned back on the road or sat down, swearing she would go no farther; and often and often did she feel the weight of the tongs across her shoulders that day.

At noon the two sat down by the cross-roads to rest.

"I am hungry," said the Princess; "not a morsel of food have I tasted this day. Ye will go get me some."

"Not I, my dear," said the Vagabone; "ye will go beg for yourself."

"Never," said the Princess.

"Then ye'll go hungry," said the Vagabone; and that was all. He lighted his pipe and went to sleep with one eye open and the tongs under him.

One, two, three hours passed, and the sun hung low in the sky. The Princess sat there until hunger drove her to her feet. She rose wearily and stumbled to the road. It might have been the sound of wheels that had startled her, I cannot be telling; but as she reached the road a great coach drawn by six black horses came galloping up. The Princess made a sign for it to stop; for though she was in rags, yet she was still so beautiful that the coachman drew in the horses and asked her what she was wanting.

"I am near to starving;" and as she spoke the tears started to her eyes, while a new soft note crept into her voice. "Do ye think your master could spare me a bit of food—or a shilling?" and the hand that had been used to strike went out for the first time to beg.

It was a prince who rode inside the coach that day, and he heard her. Reaching out a fine, big hamper through the window, he told her she was hearty welcome to whatever she found in it, along with his blessing. But as she put up her arms for it, just, she looked—and saw that the prince was none other than the fat suitor whose face she had slapped on the day before. Then anger came back to her again, for the shame of begging from him. She emptied the hamper—chicken pasty, jam, currant bread, and all—on top of his head, peering through the window, and threw the empty basket at the coachman. Away drove the coach; away ran the Princess, and threw herself, sobbing, on the ground near the Vagabone.

"'Twas a good dinner that ye lost," said the Vagabone; and that was all.

But the next coach that passed she stopped. This time it was the shaggy-bearded rascal that rode inside. She paid no heed, however, and begged again for food; but her cheeks grew crimson when he looked at her, and she had to be biting her lips fiercely to keep the sharp words back.

"Ye are a lazy good-for-naught to beg. Why don't ye work for your food?" called the rascal after her.

And the Vagabone answered: "Ye are right entirely. 'Tis a sin to beg, and tomorrow I'll be teaching her a trade, so she need never be asking charity again upon the highroad."

That night they reached a wee scrap of a cabin on the side of a hill. The Vagabone climbed the steps and opened the door. "Here we are at home, my dear," said he.

"What kind of a home do ye call that?" and the Princess stamped her foot. "Faith, I'll not live in it."

"Then ye can live outside; it's all the same to me." The Vagabone went in and closed the door after him; and in a moment he was whistling merrily the song of "The Wee Brown Wran."

The Princess sat down on the ground and nursed her poor tired knees. She had walked many a mile that day, with a heavy heart and an empty stomach—two of the worst traveling companions ye can find. The night came down, black as a raven's wing; the dew fell, heavy as rain, wetting the rags and chilling the Princess to the marrow. The wind blew fresh from the sea, and the wolves began their howling in the woods near by, and at last, what with the cold and the fear and the loneliness of it, she could bear it no longer, and she crept softly up to the cabin and went in.

"There's the creepy-stool by the fire, waiting for ye," said the Vagabone; and that was all. But late in the night he lifted her from the chimney-corner where she had dropped asleep and laid her gently on the bed, which was freshly made and clean. And he sat by the hearth till dawn, keeping the turf piled high on the fire, so that the cold would not waken her. Once he left the hearth; coming to the bedside, he stood a moment to watch her while she slept, and he stopped and kissed the wee pink palm of her hand that lay there like a half-closed loch lily.

Next morning the first thing the Princess asked was where was the breakfast, and where were the servants to wait on her, and where were some decent clothes.

"Your servants are your own two hands, and they will serve ye well when ye teach them how," was the answer she got.

"I'll have neither breakfast nor clothes if I have to be getting them myself. And shame on ye for treating a wife so," and the Princess caught up a piggin and threw it at the Vagabone.

He jumped clear of it, and it struck the wall behind him. "Have your own way, my dear," and he left her to go out on the bogs and cut turf.

That night the Princess hung the kettle and made stir-about and griddle bread for the two of them.

"'Tis the best I have tasted since I was a lad and my mother made the baking," said the Vagabone, and that was all. But often and often his lips touched the braids of her hair as she passed him in the dark; and again he sat through the night, keeping the fire and mending her wee leather brogues, that they might be whole against the morrow.

Next day he brought some sally twigs and showed her how to weave them into creels to sell on coming market-day. But the twigs cut her fingers until they bled, and the Princess cried, making the Vagabone white with rage. Never had she seen such a rage in another creature. He threw the sally twigs about the cabin, making them whirl and eddy like leaves before an autumn wind; he stamped upon the half-made creel, crushing it to pulp under his feet; and, catching up the table, he tore it to splinters, throwing the fragments into the fire, where they blazed.

"By St. Patrick, 'tis a bad bargain that ye are! I will take ye this day to the castle in the next county, where I hear they are needing a scullery-maid, and there I'll apprentice ye to the King's cook."

"I will not go," said the Princess; but even as she spoke fear showed in her eyes and her knees began to tremble under her.

"Aye, but ye will, my dear;" and the Vagabone took up the tongs quietly from the hearth.

For a month the Princess worked in the castle of the King, and all that time she never saw the Vagabone.

Often and often she said to herself, fiercely, that she was well rid of him; but often, as she sat alone after her work in the cool of the night, she would wish for the song of "The Wee Brown Wran," while a new loneliness crept deeper and deeper into her heart.

She worked hard about the kitchen, and as she scrubbed the pots and turned the spit and cleaned the floor with fresh white sand she listened to the wonderful tales the other servants had to tell of the King. They had it that he was the handsomest, aye, and the strongest, king in all Ireland; and every man and child and little creature in his kingdom worshiped him. And after the tales were told the Princess would say to herself: "If I had not been so proud and free with my tongue, I might have married such a king, and ruled his kingdom with him, learning kindness."

Now it happened one day that the Princess was told to be unusually spry and careful about her work; and there was a monstrous deal of it to be done; cakes to be iced and puddings to be boiled, fat ducks to be roasted, and a whole sucking pig put on the spit to turn.

"What's the meaning of all this?" asked the Princess.

"Ochone, ye poor feeble-minded girl!" and the cook looked at her pityingly. "Haven't ye heard the King is to be married this day to the fairest princess in seven counties?"

"Once that was I," thought the Princess, and she sighed.

"What makes ye sigh?" asked the cook.

"I was wishing, just, that I could be having a peep at her and the King."

"Faith, that's possible. Do your work well, and maybe I can put ye where ye can see without being seen."

So it came about, as I am telling ye, at the end of the day, when the feast was ready and the guests come, that the Princess was hidden behind the broidered curtains in the great hall. There, where no one could see her, she watched the hundreds upon hundreds of fair ladies and fine noblemen in their silken dresses and shining coats, all silver and gold, march back and forth across the hall, laughing and talking and making merry among themselves. Then the pipes began to play, and everybody was still. From the farthest end of the hall came two-and-twenty lads in white and gold; these were followed by two-and-twenty pipers in green and gold and two-and-twenty bowmen in saffron and gold, and, last of all, the King.

A scream, a wee wisp of a cry, broke from the Princess, and she would have fallen had she not caught one of the curtains. For the King was as tall and strong and beautiful as Nuada of the Silver Hand; and from the top of his curling black hair down the seven feet of him to the golden clasps of his shoes he was every whit as handsome as he had been that day when she had cuffed him in her father's castle.

The King heard the cry and stopped the pipers. "I think," said he, "there's a scullery-maid behind the curtains. Someone fetch her to me."

A hundred hands pulled the Princess out; a hundred more pushed her across the hall to the feet of the King, and held her there, fearing lest she should escape. "What were ye doing there?" the King asked.

"Looking at ye, and wishing I had the undoing of things I have done," and the Princess hung her head and sobbed piteously.

"Nay, sweetheart, things are best as they are," and there came a look into the King's eyes that blinded those watching, so that they turned away and left the two alone.

"Heart of mine," he went on, softly, "are ye not knowing me?"

"Ye are putting more shame on me because of my evil tongue and the blow my hand gave ye that day."

"I' faith, it is not so. Look at me."

Slowly the eyes of the Princess looked into the eyes of the King. For a moment she could not be reading them; she was as a child who pores over a strange tale after the light fades and it grows too dark to see. But bit by bit the meaning of it came to her, and her heart grew glad with the wonder of it. Out went her arms to him with the cry of loneliness that had been hers so long.

"I never dreamed that it was ye; never once."

"Can ye ever love and forgive?" asked the King.

"Hush ye!" and the Princess laid her finger on his lips.

The tirewomen were called, and she was led away. Her rags were changed for a dress that was spun from gold and woven with pearls, and her beauty shone about her like a great light.

They were married again that night, for none of the guests were knowing of that first wedding long ago.

Late o' that night a singing *sthronshuch* came under the Princess' window, and very softly the words of his song came to her:

The gay young wran sang over the moor.
"I'll build me a nest," sang he.
"'Twill have a thatch and a wee latched door,
For the wind blows cold from the sea.
And I'll let no one but my true love in,
For she is the mate for me,"
Sang the gay young wran.

The wee brown wran by the hedgerow cried—
"I'll wait for him here," cried she.
"For the way is far and the world is wide,
And he might miss the way to me.
Long is the time when the heart is shut,
But I'll open to none save he,"
Sang the wee brown wran.

The grating opened slowly; the Princess leaned far out, her eyes like stars in the night, and when she spoke there was naught but gentleness and love in her voice.

"Here is the silver I would have thrown ye on a day long gone by. Shall I throw it now, or will ye come for it?"

And that was how a princess of Connaught was won by a king who was a vagabone.

A MUNICIPAL REPORT

By O. Henry

[One of O. Henry's stories, *The Whirligig of Life*, appears earlier in this volume (p. 64) as a typical example of story structure. It shows the compact, carefully made plot. *A Municipal Report* shows another side of O. Henry. He is more deliberate, less insistent upon the well-planned framework. He gives more attention to his characters and has a dominating idea running through this story.

A Municipal Report is reprinted from *Strictly Business* (1910), by permission of Doubleday, Doran and Company, publishers.]

> *The cities are full of pride,*
> *Challenging each to each—*
> *This from her mountainside,*
> *That from her burthened beach.*
>
> R. KIPLING

Fancy a novel about Chicago or Buffalo, let us say, or Nashville, Tennessee! There are just three big cities in the United States that are "story cities"—New York, of course, New Orleans, and, best of the lot, San Francisco.—FRANK NORRIS

EAST is East, and West is San Francisco, according to Californians. Californians are a race of people; they are not merely inhabitants of a State. They are the Southerners of the West. Now, Chicagoans are no less loyal to their city; but when you ask them why, they stammer and speak of lake fish and the new Odd Fellows Building. But Californians go into detail.

Of course they have, in the climate, an argument that is good for half an hour while you are thinking of your coal bills and heavy underwear. But as soon as they come to mistake your silence for conviction, madness comes upon them, and they picture the city of the Golden Gate as the Bagdad of the New World. So far, as a matter of opinion, no refutation is necessary. But, dear cousins all (from Adam and Eve descended), it is a rash one who will lay his finger on the map and say: "In this town there can be no romance—what could happen here?" Yes, it is a bold and rash deed to challenge in one sentence history, romance, and Rand and McNally.

NASHVILLE.—A city, port of delivery, and the capital of the State of Tennessee, is on the Cumberland River and on the N. C. & St. L. and the L. & N.

railroads. This city is regarded as the most important educational centre in the South.

I stepped off the train at 8 P. M. Having searched the thesaurus in vain for adjectives, I must, as a substitution, hie me to comparison in the form of a recipe.

Take of London fog 30 parts; malaria 10 parts; gas leaks 20 parts; dewdrops gathered in a brick yard at sunrise, 25 parts; odor of honeysuckle 15 parts. Mix.

The mixture will give you an approximate conception of a Nashville drizzle. It is not so fragrant as a moth-ball nor as thick as pea-soup; but 'tis enough—'twill serve.

I went to a hotel in a tumbril. It required strong self-suppression for me to keep from climbing to the top of it and giving an imitation of Sidney Carton. The vehicle was drawn by beasts of a bygone era and driven by something dark and emancipated.

I was sleepy and tired, so when I got to the hotel I hurriedly paid it the fifty cents it demanded (with approximate lagniappe, I assure you). I knew its habits; and I did not want to hear it prate about its old "marster" or anything that happened "befo' de wah."

The hotel was one of the kind described as "renovated." That means $20,000 worth of new marble pillars, tiling, electric lights and brass cuspidors in the lobby, and a new L. & N. time table and a lithograph of Lookout Mountain in each one of the great rooms above. The management was without reproach, the attention full of exquisite Southern courtesy, the service as slow as the progress of a snail and as good-humored as Rip Van Winkle. The food was worth traveling a thousand miles for. There is no other hotel in the world where you can get such chicken livers *en brochette*.

At dinner I asked a Negro waiter if there was anything doing in town. He pondered gravely for a minute, and then replied: "Well, boss, I don't really reckon there's anything at all doin' after sundown."

Sundown had been accomplished; it had been drowned in the drizzle long before. So that spectacle was denied me. But I went forth upon the streets in the drizzle to see what might be there.

It is built on undulating grounds; and the streets are lighted by electricity at a cost of $32,470 per annum.

As I left the hotel there was a race riot. Down upon me charged a company of freedmen, or Arabs, or Zulus, armed with—no, I saw with relief that they were not rifles, but whips. And I saw dimly a caravan of black, clumsy vehicles; and at the reassuring shouts, "Kyar you anywhere in the town, boss, fuh fifty cents," I reasoned that I was merely a "fare" instead of a victim.

I walked through long streets, all leading uphill. I wondered how those streets ever came down again. Perhaps they didn't until they were "graded." On a few of the "main streets" I saw lights in stores here and there; saw street cars go by conveying worthy burghers hither and yon; saw people pass engaged in the art of conversation, and heard a burst of semi-lively laughter issuing from a soda-water and ice-cream parlor. The streets other than "main" seemed to have enticed upon their borders houses consecrated to peace and domesticity. In many of them lights shone behind discreetly drawn window shades; in a few pianos tinkled orderly and irreproachable music. There was, indeed, little "doing." I wished I had come before sundown. So I returned to my hotel.

In November, 1864, the Confederate General Hood advanced against Nashville, where he shut up a National force under General Thomas. The latter then sallied forth and defeated the Confederates in a terrible conflict.

All my life I have heard of, admired, and witnessed the fine marksmanship of the South in its peaceful conflicts in the tobacco-chewing regions. But in my hotel a surprise awaited me. There were twelve bright, new, imposing, capacious brass cuspidors in the great lobby, tall enough to be called urns and so wide-mouthed that the crack pitcher of a lady baseball team should have been able to throw a ball into one of them at five paces distant. But, although a terrible battle had raged and was still raging, the enemy had not suffered. Bright, new, imposing, capacious, untouched, they stood. But, shades of Jefferson Brick! the tile floor—the beautiful tile floor! I could not avoid thinking of the battle of Nashville, and trying to draw, as is my foolish habit, some deductions about hereditary marksmanship.

Here I first saw Major (by misplaced courtesy) Wentworth Caswell. I knew him for a type the moment my eyes suffered from the sight of him. A rat has no geographical habitat. My old friend, A. Tennyson, said, as he so well said almost everything:

> Prophet, curse me the blabbing lip,
> And curse me the British vermin, the rat.

Let us regard the word "British" as interchangeable *ad lib*. A rat is a rat.

This man was hunting about the hotel lobby like a starved dog that had forgotten where he had buried a bone. He had a face of great acreage, red, pulpy, and with a kind of sleepy massiveness like that of Buddha. He possessed one single virtue—he was very smoothly shaven. The mark of the beast is not indelible upon a man until he goes about with a stubble. I think that if he had not used his razor that day I would have repulsed his advances, and the criminal calendar of the world would have been spared the addition of one murder.

I happened to be standing within five feet of a cuspidor when Major

Caswell opened fire upon it. I had been observant enough to perceive that the attacking force was using Gatlings instead of squirrel rifles; so I side-stepped so promptly that the major seized the opportunity to apologize to a non-combatant. He had the blabbing lip. In four minutes he had become my friend and had dragged me to the bar.

I desire to interpolate here that I am a Southerner. But I am not one by profession or trade. I eschew the string tie, the slouch hat, the Prince Albert, the number of bales of cotton destroyed by Sherman, and plug chewing. When the orchestra plays Dixie I do not cheer. I slide a little lower on the leather-cornered seat and, well, order another Würzburger and wish that Longstreet had—but what's the use?

Major Caswell banged the bar with his fist, and the first gun at Fort Sumter reëchoed. When he fired the last one at Appomattox I began to hope. But then he began on family trees, and demonstrated that Adam was only a third cousin of a collateral branch of the Caswell family. Genealogy disposed of, he took up, to my distaste, his private family matters. He spoke of his wife, traced her descent back to Eve, and profanely denied any possible rumor that she may have had relations in the land of Nod.

By this time I began to suspect that he was trying to obscure by noise the fact that he had ordered the drinks, on the chance that I would be bewildered into paying for them. But when they were down he crashed a silver dollar loudly upon the bar. Then, of course, another serving was obligatory. And when I had paid for that I took leave of him brusquely; for I wanted no more of him. But before I had obtained my release he had prated loudly of an income that his wife received, and showed a handful of silver money.

When I got my key at the desk the clerk said to me courteously: "If that man Caswell has annoyed you, and if you would like to make a complaint, we will have him ejected. He is a nuisance, a loafer, and without any known means of support, although he seems to have some money most of the time. But we don't seem to be able to hit upon any means of throwing him out legally."

"Why, no," said I, after some reflection; "I don't see my way clear to making a complaint. But I would like to place myself on record as asserting that I do not care for his company. Your town," I continued, "seems to be a quiet one. What manner of entertainment, adventure, or excitement have you to offer to the stranger within your gates?"

"Well, sir," said the clerk, "there will be a show here next Thursday. It is—I'll look it up and have the announcement sent up to your room with the ice water. Good night."

After I went up to my room I looked out the window. It was only about ten o'clock, but I looked upon a silent town. The drizzle continued, spangled with dim lights, as far apart as currants in a cake sold at the Ladies' Exchange.

"A quiet place," I said to myself, as my first shoe struck the ceiling of the occupant of the room beneath mine. "Nothing of the life here that gives color and variety to the cities in the East and West. Just a good, ordinary, humdrum business town."

Nashville occupies a foremost place among the manufacturing centers of the country. It is the fifth boot and shoe market in the United States, the largest candy and cracker manufacturing city in the South, and does an enormous wholesale drygoods, grocery, and drug business.

I must tell you how I came to be in Nashville, and I assure you the digression brings as much tedium to me as it does to you. I was traveling elsewhere on my own business, but I had a commission from a Northern literary magazine to stop over there and establish a personal connection between the publication and one of its contributors, Azalea Adair.

Adair (there was no clue to the personality except the handwriting) had sent in some essays (lost art!) and poems that had made the editors swear approvingly over their one o'clock luncheon. So they had commissioned me to round up said Adair and corner by contract his or her output at two cents a word before some other publisher offered her ten or twenty.

At nine o'clock the next morning, after my chicken livers *en brochette* (try them if you can find that hotel), I strayed out into the drizzle, which was still on for an unlimited run. At the first corner I came upon Uncle Cæsar. He was a stalwart Negro, older than the pyramids, with gray wool and a face that reminded me of Brutus, and a second afterwards of the late King Cettiwayo. He wore the most remarkable coat that I ever had seen or expect to see. It reached to his ankles and had once been a Confederate gray in color. But rain and sun and age had so variegated it that Joseph's coat, beside it, would have faded to a pale monochrome. I must linger with that coat, for it has to do with the story—the story that is so long in coming, because you can hardly expect anything to happen in Nashville.

Once it must have been the military coat of an officer. The cape of it had vanished, but all adown its front it had been frogged and tasseled magnificently. But now the frogs and tassels were gone. In their stead had been patiently stitched (I surmised by some surviving "black mammy") new frogs made of cunningly twisted common hempen twine. This twine was frayed and disheveled. It must have been added to the coat as a substitute for vanished splendors, with tasteless but painstaking devotion, for it followed faithfully the curves of the long-missing frogs. And, to complete the comedy and pathos of the garment, all its buttons were gone save one. The second button from the top alone remained. The coat was fastened by other twine strings tied through the buttonholes and other holes rudely pierced in the opposite side. There was never such a weird garment so fantastically bedecked and of so many mottled hues. The lone button was the size of a half-dollar, made of yellow horn and sewed on with coarse twine.

This Negro stood by a carriage so old that Ham himself might have started a hack line with it after he left the ark, with the two animals hitched to it. As I approached he threw open the door, drew out a feather-duster, waved it without using it, and said in deep, rumbling tones:

"Step right in, suh; ain't a speck of dust in it—jus' got back from a funeral, suh."

I inferred that on such gala occasions carriages were given an extra cleaning. I looked up and down the street and perceived that there was little choice among the vehicles for hire that lined the curb. I looked in my memorandum book for the address of Azalea Adair.

"I want to go to 861 Jessamine Street," I said, and was about to step into the hack. But for an instant the thick, long, gorilla-like arm of the old Negro barred me. On his massive and saturnine face a look of sudden suspicion and enmity flashed for a moment. Then, with quickly returning conviction, he asked blandishingly: "What are you gwine there for, boss?"

"What is that to you?" I asked, a little sharply.

"Nothin', suh, jus' nothin'. Only it's a lonesome kind of part of town, and few folks ever has business out there. Step right in. The seats is clean—jes' got back from a funeral, suh."

A mile and a half it must have been to our journey's end. I could hear nothing but the fearful rattle of the ancient hack over the uneven brick paving; I could smell nothing but the drizzle, now further flavored with coal smoke and something like a mixture of tar and oleander blossoms. All I could see through the streaming windows were two rows of dim houses.

The city has an area of 10 square miles; 181 miles of streets, of which 137 miles are paved; a system of waterworks that cost $2,000,000, with 77 miles of mains.

Eight-sixty-one Jessamine Street was a decayed mansion. Thirty yards back from the street it stood out, merged in a splendid grove of trees and untrimmed shrubbery. A row of box bushes overflowed and almost hid the paling fence from sight; the gate was kept closed by a rope noose that encircled the gate post and the first paling of the gate. But when you got inside you saw that 861 was a shell, a shadow, a ghost of former grandeur and excellence. But in the story, I have not yet got inside.

When the hack had ceased from rattling and the weary quadrupeds came to a rest I handed my jehu his fifty cents with an additional quarter. feeling a glow of conscious generosity as I did so. He refused it.

"It's two dollars, suh," he said.

"How's that?" I asked. "I plainly heard you call out at the hotel: 'Fifty cents to any part of the town.'"

"It's two dollars, suh," he repeated obstinately. "It's a long ways from the hotel."

"It is within the city limits and well within them," I argued. "Don't think that you have picked up a greenhorn Yankee. Do you see those hills over there?" I went on, pointing toward the east (I could not see them, myself, for the drizzle); "well, I was born and raised on their other side. You old fool nigger, can't you tell people from other people when you see 'em?"

The grim face of King Cettiwayo softened. "Is you from the South, suh? I reckon it was them shoes of yourn fooled me. They is somethin' sharp in the toes for a Southern gen'l'man to wear."

"Then the charge is fifty cents, I suppose?" said I inexorably.

His former expression, a mingling of cupidity and hostility, returned, remained ten seconds, and vanished.

"Boss," he said, "fifty cents is right; but I *needs* two dollars, suh; I'm *obleeged* to have two dollars. I ain't *demandin'* it now, suh, after I knows whar you's from; I'm jus' sayin' that I *has* to have two dollars tonight, and business is mighty po'."

Peace and confidence settled upon his heavy features. He had been luckier than he had hoped. Instead of having picked up a greenhorn, ignorant of rates, he had come upon an inheritance.

"You confounded old rascal," I said, reaching down to my pocket, "you ought to be turned over to the police."

For the first time I saw him smile. He knew; *he knew*; HE KNEW.

I gave him two one-dollar bills. As I handed them over I noticed that one of them had seen parlous times. Its upper right-hand corner was missing, and it had been torn through in the middle, but joined again. A strip of blue tissue paper, pasted over the split, preserved its negotiability.

Enough of the African bandit for the present: I left him happy, lifted the rope and opened the creaky gate.

The house, as I said, was a shell. A paint brush had not touched it in twenty years. I could not see why a strong wind should not have bowled it over like a house of cards, until I looked again at the trees that hugged it close—the trees that saw the battle of Nashville and still drew their protecting branches around it against storm and enemy and cold.

Azalea Adair, fifty years old, white-haired, a descendant of the cavaliers, as thin and frail as the house she lived in, robed in the cheapest and cleanest dress I ever saw, with an air as simple as a queen's, received me.

The reception room seemed a mile square, because there was nothing in it except some rows of books, on unpainted white-pine bookshelves, a cracked marble-top table, a rag rug, a hairless horse-hair sofa and two or three chairs. Yes, there was a picture on the wall, a colored crayon drawing of a cluster of pansies. I looked around for the portrait of Andrew Jackson and the pine-cone hanging basket, but they were not there.

Azalea Adair and I had conversation, a little of which will be repeated to you. She was a product of the old South, gently nurtured in the sheltered life. Her learning was not broad, but was deep and of splendid originality in its somewhat narrow scope. She had been educated at home, and her knowledge of the world was derived from inference and by inspiration. Of such is the precious, small group of essayists made. While she talked to me I kept brushing my fingers, trying, unconsciously, to rid them guiltily of the absent dust from the half-calf backs of Lamb, Chaucer, Hazlitt, Marcus Aurelius, Montaigne and Hood. She was exquisite, she was a valuable discovery. Nearly everybody nowadays knows too much—oh, so much too much—of real life.

I could perceive clearly that Azalea Adair was very poor. A house and a dress she had; not much else, I fancied. So, divided between my duty to the magazine and my loyalty to the poets and essayists who fought Thomas in the valley of the Cumberland, I listened to her voice, which was like a harpsichord's, and found that I could not speak of contracts. In the presence of the nine Muses and the three Graces one hesitated to lower the topic to two cents. There would have to be another colloquy after I had regained my commercialism. But I spoke of my mission, and three o'clock of the next afternoon was set for the discussion of the business proposition.

"Your town," I said, as I began to make ready to depart (which is the time for smooth generalities), "seems to be a quiet, sedate place. A home town, I should say, where few things out of the ordinary ever happen."

It carries on an extensive trade in stoves and hollow ware with the West and South, and its flouring mills have a daily capacity of more than 2,000 barrels.

Azalea Adair seemed to reflect.

"I have never thought of it that way," she said, with a kind of sincere intensity that seemed to belong to her. "Isn't it in the still, quiet places that things do happen? I fancy that when God began to create the earth on the first Monday morning one could have leaned out one's window and heard the drops of mud splashing from His trowel as He built up the everlasting hills. What did the noisiest project in the world— I mean the building of the tower of Babel—result in finally? A page and a half of Esperanto in the *North American Review*."

"Of course," said I platitudinously, "human nature is the same everywhere; but there is more color—er—more drama and movement and—er—romance in some cities than in others."

"On the surface," said Azalea Adair. "I have traveled many times around the world in a golden airship wafted on two wings—print and dreams. I have seen (on one of my imaginary tours) the Sultan of Turkey bowstring with his own hands one of his wives who had uncovered her face in public. I have seen a man in Nashville tear up his theater tickets because his wife was going out with her face covered—with rice powder. In San Francisco's Chinatown I saw the slave girl Sing Yee dipped slowly, inch by inch, in boiling almond oil to make her swear she would never see her American lover again. She gave in when the boiling oil had reached three inches above her knee. At a euchre party in East Nashville the other night I saw Kitty Morgan cut dead by seven of her schoolmates and lifelong friends because she had married a house painter. The boiling oil was sizzling as high as her heart; but I wish you could have seen the fine little smile that she carried from table to table. Oh, yes, it is a humdrum town. Just a few miles of red brick houses and mud and stores and lumber yards."

Some one knocked hollowly at the back of the house. Azalea Adair breathed a soft apology and went to investigate the sound. She came back in three minutes with brightened eyes, a faint flush on her cheeks, and ten years lifted from her shoulders.

"You must have a cup of tea before you go," she said, "and a sugar cake."

She reached and shook a little iron bell. In shuffled a small negro girl about twelve, barefoot, not very tidy, glowering at me with thumb in mouth and bulging eyes.

Azalea Adair opened a tiny, worn purse and drew out a dollar bill, a dollar bill with the upper right-hand corner missing, torn in two pieces and pasted together again with a strip of blue tissue paper. It was one of the bills I had given the piratical negro—there was no doubt of it.

"Go up to Mr. Baker's store on the corner, Impy," she said, handing the girl the dollar bill, "and get a quarter of a pound of tea—the kind he always sends me—and ten cents worth of sugar cakes. Now, hurry. The supply of tea in the house happens to be exhausted," she explained to me.

Impy left by the back way. Before the scrape of her hard, bare feet had died away on the back porch, a wild shriek—I was sure it was hers—filled the hollow house. Then the deep, gruff tones of an angry man's voice mingled with a girl's further squeals and unintelligible words.

Azalea Adair rose without surprise or emotion and disappeared. For two minutes I heard the hoarse rumble of the man's voice; then something like an oath and a slight scuffle, and she returned calmly to her chair.

"This is a roomy house," she said, "and I have a tenant for part of it.

I am sorry to have to rescind my invitation to tea. It was impossible to get the kind I always use, at the store. Perhaps tomorrow Mr. Baker will be able to supply me."

I was sure that Impy had not had time to leave the house. I inquired concerning street-car lines and took my leave. After I was well on my way I remembered that I had not learned Azalea Adair's name. But tomorrow would do.

That same day I started in on the course of iniquity that this uneventful city forced upon me. I was in the town only two days, but in that time I managed to lie shamelessly by telegraph, and to be an accomplice—after the fact, if that is the correct legal term—to a murder.

As I rounded the corner nearest my hotel, the Afrite coachman of the polychromatic, nonpareil coat seized me, swung open the dungeony door of his peripatetic sarcophagus, flirted his feather duster and began his ritual: "Step right in, boss. Carriage is clean—jus' got back from a funeral. Fifty cents to any——"

And then he knew me and grinned broadly. "'Scuse me, boss; you is de genl'man what rid out with me dis mawnin'. Thank you kindly, suh."

"I am going out to 861 again tomorrow afternoon at three," said I, "and if you will be here, I'll let you drive me. So you know Miss Adair?" I concluded, thinking of my dollar bill.

"I belonged to her father, Judge Adair, suh," he replied.

"I judge that she is pretty poor," I said. "She hasn't much money to speak of, has she?"

For an instant I looked again at the fierce countenance of King Cettiwayo, and then he changed back to an extortionate old negro hack-driver.

"She ain't gwine to starve, suh," he said slowly. "She has reso'ces, suh; she has reso'ces."

"I shall pay you fifty cents for the trip," said I.

"Dat is puffeckly correct, suh," he answered humbly. "I jus' *had* to have dat two dollars dis mawnin', boss."

I went to the hotel and lied by electricity. I wired the magazine: "A. Adair holds out for eight cents a word."

The answer that came back was: "Give it to her quick, you duffer."

Just before dinner "Major" Wentworth Caswell bore down upon me with the greetings of a long-lost friend. I have seen few men whom I have so instantaneously hated, and of whom it was so difficult to be rid. I was standing at the bar when he invaded me; therefore I could not wave the white ribbon in his face. I would have paid gladly for the drinks, hoping, thereby, to escape another; but he was one of those despicable, roaring, advertising bibbers who must have brass bands and fireworks attend upon every cent that they waste in their follies.

With an air of producing millions he drew two one-dollar bills from a pocket and dashed one of them upon the bar. I looked once more at the dollar bill with the upper right-hand corner missing, torn through the middle, and patched with a strip of blue tissue paper. It was my dollar bill again. It could have been no other.

I went up to my room. The drizzle and the monotony of a dreary, eventless Southern town had made me tired and listless. I remember that just before I went to bed I mentally disposed of the mysterious dollar bill (which might have formed the clew to a tremendously fine detective story of San Francisco) by saying to myself sleepily: "Seems as if a lot of people here own stock in the Hack-Drivers' Trust. Pays dividends promptly, too. Wonder if—" Then I fell asleep.

King Cettiwayo was at his post the next day, and rattled my bones over the stones out to 861. He was to wait and rattle me back again when I was ready.

Azalea Adair looked paler and cleaner and frailer than she had looked on the day before. After she had signed the contract at eight cents per word she grew still paler and began to slip out of her chair. Without much trouble I managed to get her up on the antediluvian horse-hair sofa and then I ran out to the sidewalk and yelled to the coffee-colored pirate to bring a doctor. With a wisdom that I had not suspected in him, he abandoned his team and struck off up the street afoot, realizing the value of speed. In ten minutes he returned with a grave, gray-haired and capable man of medicine. In a few words (worth much less than eight cents each) I explained to him my presence in the hollow house of mystery. He bowed with stately understanding, and turned to the old negro.

"Uncle Cæsar," he said calmly, "run up to my house and ask Miss Lucy to give you a cream pitcher full of fresh milk and half a tumbler of port wine. And hurry back. Don't drive—run. I want you to get back some time this week."

It occurred to me that Dr. Merriman also felt a distrust as to the speeding powers of the land-pirate's steeds. After Uncle Cæsar was gone, lumberingly, but swiftly, up the street, the doctor looked me over with great politeness and as much careful calculation until he had decided that I might do.

"It is only a case of insufficient nutrition," he said. "In other words, the result of poverty, pride, and starvation. Mrs. Caswell has many devoted friends who would be glad to aid her, but she will accept nothing except from that old negro, Uncle Cæsar, who was once owned by her family."

"Mrs. Caswell!" said I, in surprise. And then I looked at the contract and saw that she had signed it "Azalea Adair Caswell."

"I thought she was Miss Adair," I said.

"Married to a drunken, worthless loafer, sir," said the doctor. "It is said that he robs her even of the small sums that her old servant contributes toward her support."

When the milk and wine had been brought the doctor soon revived Azalea Adair. She sat up and talked of the beauty of the autumn leaves that were then in season, and their height of color. She referred lightly to her fainting seizure as the outcome of an old palpitation of the heart. Impy fanned her as she lay on the sofa. The doctor was due elsewhere, and I followed him to the door. I told him that it was within my power and intentions to make a reasonable advance of money to Azalea Adair on future contributions to the magazine, and he seemed pleased.

"By the way," he said, "perhaps you would like to know that you have had royalty for a coachman. Old Cæsar's grandfather was a king in the Congo. Cæsar himself has royal ways, as you may have observed."

As the doctor was moving off I heard Uncle Cæsar's voice inside: "Did he git bofe of dem two dollars from you, Mis' Zalea?"

"Yes, Cæsar," I heard Azalea Adair answer weakly. And then I went in and concluded business negotiations with our contributor. I assumed the responsibility of advancing fifty dollars, putting it as a necessary formality in binding our bargain. And Uncle Cæsar drove me back to the hotel.

Here ends all of the story as far as I can testify as a witness. The rest must be only bare statements of facts.

At about six o'clock I went out for a stroll. Uncle Cæsar was at his corner. He threw open the door of his carriage, flourished his duster and began his depressing formula: "Step right in, suh. Fifty cents to anywhere in the city—hack's puffickly clean, suh—jus' got back from a funeral——"

And then he recognized me. I think his eyesight was getting bad. His coat had taken on a few more faded shades of color, the twine strings were more frayed and ragged, the last remaining button—the button of yellow horn—was gone. A motley descendant of kings was Uncle Cæsar!

About two hours later I saw an excited crowd besieging the front of a drug store. In a desert where nothing happens this was manna; so I wedged my way inside. On an extemporized couch of empty boxes and chairs was stretched the mortal corporeality of Major Wentworth Caswell. A doctor was testing him for the immortal ingredient. His decison was that it was conspicuous by its absence.

The erstwhile Major had been found dead on a dark street and brought by curious and ennuiéd citizens to the drug store. The late human being had been engaged in terrific battle—the details showed that. Loafer and reprobate though he had been, he had been also a warrior. But he had lost. His hands were yet clinched so tightly that his fingers would not be opened. The gentle citizens who had known him stood about and searched their vocabularies to find some good words, if it were possible, to speak of him. One kind-looking man said, after much thought: "When 'Cas' was about fo'teen, he was one of the best spellers in school."

While I stood there the fingers of the right hand of "the man that was," which hung down the side of a white pine box, relaxed, and dropped something at my feet. I covered it with one foot quietly, and a little later on I picked it up and pocketed it. I reasoned that in his last struggle his hand must have seized that object unwittingly and held it in a death grip.

At the hotel that night the main topic of conversation, with the possible exceptions of politics and prohibition, was the demise of Major Caswell. I heard one man say to a group of listeners:

"In my opinion, gentlemen, Caswell was murdered by some of these no-account niggers for his money. He had fifty dollars this afternoon which he showed to several gentlemen in the hotel. When he was found the money was not on his person."

I left the city the next morning at nine, and as the train was crossing the bridge over the Cumberland River I took out of my pocket a yellow horn overcoat button the size of a fifty-cent piece, with frayed ends of coarse twine hanging from it, and cast it out of the window into the slow, muddy waters below.

I wonder what's doing in Buffalo!

THE PROCURATOR OF JUDEA

By *Anatole France*

[Through the centuries there has been much speculation about the men who had a part in the condemnation and crucifixion of Jesus of Nazareth—what did they think, what did they do with themselves when they came to realize the enormity of their acts? Anatole France assumes that the crucifixion of Jesus, from the Roman point of view, was a minor administrative matter in the government of a small province a long way from the capital—a detail mixed up with local religion and politics, and of so little significance to the Roman empire that Pilate could barely remember the event a few years after his retirement from public life. Out of this idea he makes the story of *The Procurator of Judea.*

Jacques Anatole Thibault (1844–1924) assumed the pen name of Anatole France early in his career as a writer. The name became as much his as the name of Mark Twain superseded the real name of Samuel L. Clemens. France was born in Paris and made his home in or near that city all his life. In his political and religious thinking he was a liberal. The more important of his books are novels, among which may be mentioned *The Crime of Sylvestre Bonnard, The Red Lily, Thaïs, The Revolt of the Angels,* and *Penguin Island.*

Anatole France is recognized as one of the few greatest of French novelists of the last quarter of the Nineteenth Century and the first quarter of the Twentieth. He was a member of the French Academy (the "Forty Immortals"), and the recipient of the Nobel Prize in 1921.

The Procurator of Judea first appeared in *The Mother of Pearl Casket* (*L'Étuit de Nacre,* 1892). Frederic Chapman's translation is here reprinted from *Mother of Pearl* by permission of Dodd, Mead and Company, publishers.]

ÆLIUS LAMIA, born in Italy of illustrious parents, had not yet discarded the *toga prætexta* when he set out for the schools of Athens to study philosophy. Subsequently he took up his residence at Rome, and in his house on the Esquiline, amid a circle of youthful wastrels, abandoned himself to licentious courses. But being accused of engaging in criminal relations with Lepida, the wife of Sulpicius Quirinus, a man of consular rank, and being found guilty, he was exiled by Tiberius Cæsar. At that time he was just entering his twenty-fourth year. During the eighteen years that his exile lasted he traversed Syria, Palestine, Cappadocia, and Armenia, and made prolonged visits to

Antioch, Cæsarea, and Jerusalem. When, after the death of Tiberius, Caius was raised to the purple, Lamia obtained permission to return to Rome. He even regained a portion of his possessions. Adversity had taught him wisdom.

He avoided all intercourse with the wives and daughters of Roman citizens, made no efforts towards obtaining office, held aloof from public honors, and lived a secluded life in his house on the Esquiline. Occupying himself with the task of recording all the remarkable things he had seen during his distant travels, he turned, as he said, the vicissitudes of his years of expiation into a diversion for his hours of rest. In the midst of these calm employments, alternating with assiduous study of the works of Epicurus, he recognized with a mixture of surprise and vexation that age was stealing upon him. In his sixty-second year, being afflicted with an illness which proved in no slight degree troublesome, he decided to have recourse to the waters at Baiæ. The coast at that point, once frequented by the halcyon, was at this date the resort of the wealthy Roman, greedy of pleasure. For a week Lamia lived alone, without a friend in the brilliant crowd. Then one day, after dinner, an inclination to which he yielded urged him to ascend the incline, which, covered with vines that resembled bacchantes, looked out upon the waves.

Having reached the summit he seated himself by the side of a path beneath a terebinth, and let his glances wander over the lovely landscape. To his left, livid and bare, the Phlegræan plain stretched out towards the ruins of Cumæ. On his right, Cape Misenum plunged its abrupt spur beneath the Tyrrhenian Sea. Beneath his feet luxurious Baiæ, following the graceful outline of the coast, displayed its gardens, its villas thronged with statues, its porticos, its marble terraces along the shores of the blue ocean where the dolphins sported. Before him, on the other side of the bay, on the Campanian coast, gilded by the already sinking sun, gleamed the temples which far away rose above the laurels of Posilippo, whilst on the extreme horizon Vesuvius looked forth smiling.

Lamia drew from a fold of his toga a scroll containing the *Treatise upon Nature*, extended himself upon the ground, and began to read. But the warning cries of a slave necessitated his rising to allow of the passage of a litter which was being carried along the narrow pathway through the vineyards. The litter, being uncurtained, permitted Lamia to see stretched upon the cushions as it was borne nearer to him the figure of an elderly man of immense bulk, who, supporting his head on his hand, gazed out with a gloomy and disdainful expression. His nose, which was aquiline, and his chin, which was prominent, seemed desirous of meeting across his lips, and his jaws were powerful.

From the first moment Lamia was convinced that the face was familiar to him. He hesitated a moment before the name came to him. Then suddenly hastening toward the litter with a display of surprise and delight——

"Pontius Pilate!" he cried. "The gods be praised who have permitted me to see you once again!"

The old man gave a signal to the slaves to stop, and cast a keen glance upon the stranger who had addressed him.

"Pontius, my dear host," resumed the latter, "have twenty years so far whitened my hair and hollowed my cheeks that you no longer recognize your friend Lælius Lamia?"

At this name Pontius Pilate dismounted from the litter as actively as the weight of his years and the heaviness of his gait permitted him, and embraced Lælius Lamia again and again.

"Gods! what a treat it is to me to see you once more! But, alas, you call up memories of those long-vanished days when I was Procurator of Judea in the province of Syria. Why, it must be thirty years ago that I first met you. It was at Cæsarea, whither you came to drag out your weary term of exile. I was fortunate enough to alleviate it a little, and out of friendship, Lamia, you followed me to that depressing place Jerusalem, where the Jews filled me with bitterness and disgust. You remained for more than ten years my guest and my companion, and in converse about Rome and things Roman we both of us managed to find consolation—you for your misfortunes, and I for my burdens of State."

Lamia embraced him afresh.

"You forget two things, Pontius; you are overlooking the facts that you used your influence on my behalf with Herod Antipas, and that your purse was freely open to me."

"Let us not talk of that," replied Pontius, "since after your return to Rome you sent me by one of your freedmen a sum of money which repaid me with usury."

"Pontius, I could never consider myself out of your debt by the mere payment of money. But tell me, have the gods fulfilled your desires? Are you in the enjoyment of all the happiness you deserve? Tell me about your family, your fortunes, your health."

"I have withdrawn to Sicily, where I possess estates, and where I cultivate wheat for the market. My eldest daughter, my best-beloved Pontia, who has been left a widow, lives with me, and directs my household. The gods be praised, I have preserved my mental vigor; my memory is not in the least degree enfeebled. But old age always brings in its train a long procession of griefs and infirmities. I am cruelly tormented with gout. And at this very moment you find me on my way to the Phlegræan plain in search of a remedy for my sufferings. From that burning soil, whence at night flames burst forth, proceed acrid exhalations of sulphur, which, so they say, ease the pains and restore suppleness to the joints. At least, the physicians assure me that it is so."

"May you find it so in your case, Pontius! But, despite the gout and its burning torments, you scarcely look as old as myself, although in reality you must be my senior by ten years. Unmistakably you have retained a greater degree of vigor than I ever possessed, and I am overjoyed to find you looking so hale. Why, dear friend, did you retire from the public service before the customary age? Why, on resigning your governorship in Judea, did you withdraw to a voluntary exile on your Sicilian estates? Give me an account of your doings from the moment that I ceased to be a witness of them. You were preparing to suppress a Samaritan rising when I set out for Cappadocia, where I hoped to draw some profit from the breeding of horses and mules. I have not seen you since then. How did that expedition succeed? Pray tell me. Everything interests me that concerns you in any way."

Pontius Pilate sadly shook his head.

"My natural disposition," he said, "as well as a sense of duty, impelled me to fulfil my public responsibilities, not merely with diligence, but even with ardor. But I was pursued by unrelenting hatred. Intrigues and calumnies cut short my career in its prime, and the fruit it should have looked to bear has withered away. You ask me about the Samaritan insurrection. Let us sit down on this hillock. I shall be able to give you an answer in few words. Those occurrences are as vividly present to me as if they had happened yesterday.

"A man of the people, of persuasive speech—there are many such to be met with in Syria—induced the Samaritans to gather together in arms on Mount Gerizim (which in that country is looked upon as a holy place) under the promise that he would disclose to their sight the sacred vessels which in the ancient days of Evander and our father, Æneas, had been hidden away by an eponymous hero, or rather a tribal deity, named Moses. Upon this assurance the Samaritans rose in rebellion; but having been warned in time to forestall them, I dispatched detachments of infantry to occupy the mountain, and stationed cavalry to keep the approaches to it under observation.

"These measures of prudence were urgent. The rebels were already laying siege to the town of Tyrathaba, situated at the foot of Mount Gerizim. I easily dispersed them, and stifled the as yet scarcely organized revolt. Then, in order to give a forcible example with as few victims as possible, I handed over to execution the leaders of the rebellion. But you are aware, Lamia, in what strait dependence I was kept by the proconsul Vitellius, who governed Syria not in, but against the interests of Rome, and looked upon the provinces of the empire as territories which could be farmed out to tetrarchs. The head-men among the Samaritans, in their resentment against me, came and fell at his feet lamenting. To listen to them, nothing had been further from their thoughts than to disobey Cæsar. It was I who had provoked the rising, and it was purely in order to withstand my violence that they had gathered together round Tyrathaba. Vitellius listened to their complaints, and handing over the affairs of Judea to his friend Marcellus, commanded me to go and justify my proceedings before the Emperor himself. With a heart overflowing with grief and resentment I took ship. Just as I approached the shores of Italy, Tiberius, worn out with age and the cares of empire, died suddenly on the selfsame Cape Misenum, whose peak we see from this very spot magnified in the mists of evening. I demanded justice of Caius, his successor, whose perception was naturally acute, and who was acquainted with Syrian affairs. But marvel with me, Lamia, at the maliciousness of fortune, resolved on my discomfiture. Caius then had in his suite at Rome the Jew Agrippa, his companion, the friend of his childhood, whom he cherished as his own eyes. Now Agrippa favored Vitellius, inasmuch as Vitellius was the enemy of Antipas, whom Agrippa pursued with his hatred. The Emperor adopted the prejudices of his beloved Asiatic, and refused even to listen to me. There was nothing for me to do but bow beneath the stroke of unmerited misfortune. With tears for my meat and gall for my portion, I withdrew to my estates in Sicily, where I should have died of grief if my sweet Pontia had not come to console her father. I have cultivated wheat, and succeeded in producing the fullest ears in the whole province. But now my life is ended; the future will judge between Vitellius and me."

"Pontius," replied Lamia, "I am persuaded that you acted toward the Samaritans according to the rectitude of your character, and solely in the interests of Rome. But were you not perchance on that occasion a trifle too much influenced by that impetuous courage which has always swayed you? You will remember that in Judea it often happened that I who, younger than you, should naturally have been more impetuous than you, was obliged to urge you to clemency and suavity."

"Suavity toward the Jews!" cried Pontius Pilate. "Although you have lived amongst them, it seems clear that you ill understand those enemies of the human race. Haughty and at the same time base, combining an invincible obstinacy with a despicably mean spirit, they weary alike your love and your hatred. My character, Lamia, was formed upon the maxims of the divine Augustus. When I was appointed Procurator of Judea, the world was already penetrated with the majestic ideal of the *pax Romana*. No longer, as in the days of our internecine strife, were we witnesses to the sack of a province for the aggrandizement of a proconsul. I knew where my duty lay. I was careful that my actions should be governed by prudence and moderation. The gods are my witnesses that I was resolved upon mildness, and upon mildness only. Yet what did my benevolent intentions avail me? You were at my side, Lamia, when, at the outset of my career as ruler, the first rebellion came to a head. Is there any need for me to recall the details to you? The garrison had been transferred from Cæsarea to take up its winter quarters at Jerusalem. Upon the ensigns of the legionaries appeared the presentment of Cæsar. The inhabitants of Jerusalem, who did not recognize the indwelling divinity of the Emperor, were scandalized at this, as though, when obedience is compulsory, it were not less abject to obey a god than a man. The priests of their nation appeared before my tribunal imploring me with supercilious humility to have the ensigns removed from within the holy city. Out of reverence for the divine nature of Cæsar and the majesty of the empire, I refused to comply. Then the rabble made common cause with the priests, and all around the pretorium portentous cries of supplication arose. I ordered the soldiers to stack their spears in front of the tower of Antonia, and to proceed, armed only with sticks like lictors, to disperse the insolent crowd. But, heedless of blows, the Jews continued their entreaties, and the more obstinate amongst them threw themselves on the ground and, exposing their throats to the rods, deliberately courted death. You were a witness of my humiliation on that occasion, Lamia. By the order of Vitellius I was forced to send the insignia back to Cæsarea. That disgrace I had certainly not merited. Before the immortal gods I swear that never once during my term of office did I flout justice and the laws. But I am grown old. My enemies and detractors are dead. I shall die unavenged. Who will now retrieve my character?"

He moaned and lapsed into silence. Lamia replied—

"That man is prudent who neither hopes nor fears anything from the uncertain events of the future. Does it matter in the least what estimate men may form of us hereafter? We ourselves are after all our own witnesses, and our own judges. You must rely, Pontius Pilate, on the testimony you yourself bear to your own rectitude. Be content with your own personal respect and that of your friends. For the rest, we know that mildness by itself will not suffice for the work of government. There is but little room in the actions of public men for that indulgence of human frailty which the philosophers recommend."

"We'll say no more at present," said Pontius. "The sulphurous fumes which rise from the Phlegræan plain are more powerful when the ground which exhales them is still warm beneath the sun's rays. I must hasten on. Adieu! But now that I have rediscovered a friend, I should wish to take advantage of my good fortune. Do me the favor, Lælius Lamia, to give me your company at supper at my house tomorrow. My house stands on the seashore, at the extreme end of the town in the direction of Misenum. You will easily recognize it by the porch which bears a painting representing Orpheus surrounded by tigers and lions, whom he is charming with the strains from his lyre.

"Till tomorrow, Lamia," he repeated, as he climbed once more into his litter. "Tomorrow we will talk about Judea."

The following day at the supper hour Lamia presented himself at the

house of Pontius Pilate. Two couches only were in readiness for occupants. Creditably but simply equipped, the table held a silver service
in which were set out beccaficos in honey, thrushes, oysters from the
Lucrine lake, and lampreys from Sicily. As they proceeded with their
repast, Pontius and Lamia interchanged inquiries with one another
about their ailments, the symptoms of which they described at considerable length, mutually emulous of communicating the various remedies
which had been recommended to them. Then, congratulating themselves on being thrown together once more at Baiæ, they vied with one
another in praise of the beauty of that enchanting coast and the mildness of the climate they enjoyed. Lamia was enthusiastic about the
charms of the courtesans who frequented the seashore laden with golden
ornaments and trailing draperies of barbaric broidery. But the aged
Procurator deplored the ostentation with which by means of trumpery
jewels and filmy garments foreigners and even enemies of the empire
beguiled the Romans of their gold. After a time they turned to the subject of the great engineering feats that had been accomplished in the
country; the prodigious bridge constructed by Caius between Puteoli
and Baiæ, and the canals which Augustus excavated to convey the
waters of the ocean to Lake Avernus and the Lucrine lake.

"I also," said Pontius, with a sigh, "I also wished to set afoot public
works of great utility. When, for my sins, I was appointed Governor of
Judea, I conceived the idea of furnishing Jerusalem with an abundant
supply of pure water by means of an aqueduct. The elevation of the
levels, the gradient for the brazen reservoirs to which the distribution
pipes were to be fixed—I had gone into every detail, and decided everything for myself with the assistance of mechanical experts. I had drawn
up regulations for the superintendents so as to prevent individuals from
making unauthorized depredations. The architects and the workmen
had their instructions. I gave orders for the commencement of operations. But far from viewing with satisfaction the construction of that
conduit, which was intended to carry to their town upon its massive
arches not only water but health, the inhabitants of Jerusalem gave
vent to lamentable outcries. They gathered tumultuously together,
exclaiming against the sacrilege and impiousness, and, hurling themselves upon the workmen, scattered the foundation stones. Can you
picture to yourself, Lamia, a filthier set of barbarians? Nevertheless,
Vitellius decided in their favor, and I received orders to put a stop to
the work."

"It is a knotty point," said Lamia, "how far one is justified in devising
things for the common weal against the will of the populace."

Pontius Pilate continued as though he had not heard this interruption.

"Refuse an aqueduct! What madness! But whatever is of Roman
origin is distasteful to the Jews. In their eyes we are an unclean race,
and our very presence appears a profanation to them. You will remem-

ber that they would never venture to enter the pretorium for fear of defiling themselves, and that I was consequently obliged to discharge my magisterial functions in an open-air tribunal on that marble pavement your feet so often trod.

"They fear us and they despise us. Yet is not Rome the mother and warden of all those peoples who nestle smiling upon her venerable bosom? With her eagles in the van, peace and liberty have been carried to the very confines of the universe. Those whom we have subdued we look on as our friends, and we leave those conquered races, nay, we secure to them the permanence of their customs and their laws. Did Syria, aforetime rent asunder by its rabble of petty kings, ever even begin to taste of peace and prosperity until it submitted to the armies of Pompey? And when Rome might have reaped a golden harvest as the price of her good will, did she lay hands on the hoards that swell the treasuries of barbaric temples? Did she despoil the shrine of Cybele at Pessinus, or the Morimene and Cilician sanctuaries of Jupiter, or the temple of the Jewish god at Jerusalem? Antioch, Palmyra, and Apamea, secure despite their wealth, and no longer in dread of the wandering Arab of the desert, have erected temples to the genius of Rome and the divine Cæsar. The Jews alone hate and withstand us. They withhold their tribute till it is wrested from them, and obstinately rebel against military service."

"The Jews," replied Lamia, "are profoundly attached to their ancient customs. They suspected you, unreasonably I admit, of a desire to abolish their laws and change their usages. Do not resent it, Pontius, if I say that you did not always act in such a way as to disperse their unfortunate illusion. It gratified you, despite your habitual self-restraint, to play upon their fears, and more than once have I seen you betray in their presence the contempt with which their beliefs and religious ceremonies inspired you. You irritated them particularly by giving instructions for the sacerdotal garments and ornaments of their high priest to be kept in ward by your legionaries in the Antonine tower. One must admit that though they have never risen like us to an appreciation of things divine, the Jews celebrate rites which their very antiquity renders venerable."

Pontius Pilate shrugged his shoulders.

"They have very little exact knowledge of the nature of the gods," he said. "They worship Jupiter, yet they abstain from naming him or erecting a statue of him. They do not even adore him under the semblance of a rude stone, as certain of the Asiatic peoples are wont to do. They know nothing of Apollo, of Neptune, of Mars, nor of Pluto, nor of any goddess. At the same time, I am convinced that in days gone by they worshipped Venus. For even to this day their women bring doves to the altar as victims, and you know as well as I that the dealers who trade beneath the arcades of their temple supply those birds in couples for sacrifice. I have even been told that on one occasion some madman proceeded to overturn the stalls bearing these offerings, and their owners with them. The priests raised an outcry about it, and looked on it as a case of sacrilege. I am of opinion that their custom of sacrificing turtle-doves was instituted in honor of Venus. Why are you laughing, Lamia?"

"I was laughing," said Lamia, "at an amusing idea which, I hardly know how, just occurred to me. I was thinking that perchance some day the Jupiter of the Jews might come to Rome and vent his fury upon you. Why should he not? Asia and Africa have already enriched us with a considerable number of gods. We have seen temples in honor of Isis and the dog-faced Anubis erected in Rome. In the public squares, and even on the race-courses, you may run across the Bona Dea of the Syrians mounted on an ass. And did you never hear how, in the region of Tiberius, a young patrician passed himself off as the horned Jupiter of the Egyptians, Jupiter Ammon, and in this disguise procured the favors of an illustrious lady who was too virtuous to deny anything to a god? Beware, Pontius, lest the invisible Jupiter of the Jews disembark some day on the quay at Ostia!"

At the idea of a god coming out of Judea, a fleeting smile played over the severe countenance of the Procurator. Then he replied gravely—

"How would the Jews manage to impose their sacred law on outside peoples, when they are in a perpetual state of tumult amongst themselves as to the interpretation of that law? You have seen them yourself, Lamia, in the public squares, split up into twenty rival parties, with staves in their hands, abusing each other and clutching one another by the beard. You have seen them on the steps of the temple, tearing their filthy garments as a symbol of lamentation, with some wretched creature in a frenzy of prophetic exaltation in their midst. They have never realized that it is possible to discuss peacefully and with an even mind those matters concerning the divine which yet are hidden from the profane and wrapped in uncertainty. For the nature of the immortal gods remains hidden from us, and we cannot arrive at a knowledge of it. Though I am of opinion, none the less, that it is a prudent thing to believe in the providence of the gods. But the Jews are devoid of philosophy, and cannot tolerate any diversity of opinions. On the contrary, they judge worthy of the extreme penalty all those who on divine subjects profess opinions opposed to their law. And as, since the genius of Rome has towered over them, capital sentences pronounced by their own tribunals can only be carried out with the sanction of the proconsul or the procurator, they harry the Roman magistrate at any hour to procure his signature to their baleful decrees, they besiege the pretorium with their cries of 'Death!' A hundred times, at least, have I known them, mustered, rich and poor together, all united under their priests, make a furious onslaught on my ivory chair, seizing me by the skirts of my robe, by the thongs of my sandals, and all to demand of me

—nay, to exact from me—the death sentence on some unfortunate whose guilt I failed to perceive, and as to whom I could only pronounce that he was as mad as his accusers. A hundred times, do I say! Not a hundred, but every day and all day. Yet it was my duty to execute their law as if it were ours, since I was appointed by Rome not for the destruction, but for the upholding of their customs, and over them I had the power of the rod and the axe. At the outset of my term of office I endeavored to persuade them to hear reason; I attempted to snatch their miserable victims from death. But this show of mildness only irritated them the more; they demanded their prey, fighting around me like a horde of vultures with wing and beak. Their priests reported to Cæsar that I was violating their law, and their appeals, supported by Vitellius, drew down upon me a severe reprimand. How many times did I long, as the Greeks used to say, to dispatch accusers and accused in one convoy to the crows!

"Do not imagine, Lamia, that I nourish the rancor of the discomfited, the wrath of the superannuated, against a people which in my person has prevailed against both Rome and tranquillity. But I foresee the extremity to which sooner or later they will reduce us. Since we cannot govern them, we shall be driven to destroy them. Never doubt it. Always in a state of insubordination, brewing rebellion in their inflammatory minds, they will one day burst forth upon us with a fury beside which the wrath of the Numidians and the mutterings of the Parthians are mere child's play. They are secretly nourishing preposterous hopes, and madly premeditating our ruin. How can it be otherwise, when, on the strength of an oracle, they are living in expectation of the coming of a prince of their own blood whose kingdom shall extend over the whole earth? There are no half measures with such a people. They must be exterminated. Jerusalem must be laid waste to the very foundation. Perchance, old as I am, it may be granted me to behold the day when her walls shall fall and the flames shall envelop her houses, when her inhabitants shall pass under the edge of the sword, when salt shall be strown on the place where once the temple stood. And in that day I shall at length be justified."

Lamia exerted himself to lead the conversation back to a less acrimonious note.

"Pontius," he said, "it is not difficult for me to understand both your long-standing resentment and your sinister forebodings. Truly, what you have experienced of the character of the Jews is nothing to their advantage. But I lived in Jerusalem as an interested onlooker, and mingled freely with the people, and I succeeded in detecting certain obscure virtues in these rude folk which were altogether hidden from you. I have met Jews who were all mildness, whose simple manners and faithfulness of heart recalled to me what our poets have related concerning the Spartan lawgiver. And you yourself, Pontius, have seen perish beneath the cudgels of your legionaries simple-minded men who have died for a cause they believed to be just without revealing their names. Such men do not deserve our contempt. I am saying this because it is desirable in all things to preserve moderation and an even mind. But I own that I never experienced any lively sympathy for the Jews. The Jewesses, on the contrary, I found extremely pleasing. I was young then, and the Syrian women stirred all my senses to response. Their ruddy lips, their liquid eyes that shone in the shade, their sleepy gaze pierced me to the very marrow. Painted and stained, smelling of nard and myrrh, steeped in odors, their physical attractions are both rare and delightful."

Pontius listened impatiently to these praises.

"I was not the kind of man to fall into the snares of the Jewish women," he said, "and since you have opened the subject yourself, Lamia, I was never able to approve of your laxity. If I did not express with sufficient emphasis formerly how culpable I held you for having intrigued at Rome with the wife of a man of consular rank, it was because you were then enduring heavy penance for your misdoings. Marriage from the patrician point of view is a sacred tie; it is one of the institutions which are the support of Rome. As to foreign women and slaves, such relations as one may enter into with them would be of little account were it not that they habituate the body to a humiliating effeminacy. Let me tell you that you have been too liberal in your offerings to the Venus of the Market-place; and what, above all, I blame in you is that you have not married in compliance with the law and given children to the Republic, as every good citizen is bound to do."

But the man who had suffered exile under Tiberius was no longer listening to the venerable magistrate. Having tossed off his cup of Falernian, he was smiling at some image visible to his eye alone.

After a moment's silence he resumed in a very deep voice, which rose in pitch by little and little—

"With what languorous grace they dance, those Syrian women! I knew a Jewess at Jerusalem who used to dance in a poky little room, on a threadbare carpet, by the light of one smoky little lamp, waving her arms as she clanged her cymbals. Her loins arched, her head thrown back, and, as it were, dragged down by the weight of her heavy red hair, her eyes swimming with voluptuousness, eager, languishing, compliant, she would have made Cleopatra herself grow pale with envy. I was in love with her barbaric dances, her voice—a little raucous and yet so sweet—her atmosphere of incense, the semi-somnolescent state in which she seemed to live. I followed her everywhere. I mixed with the vile rabble of soldiers, conjurers, and extortioners with which she was surrounded. One day, however, she disappeared, and I saw her no more. Long did I seek her in disreputable alleys and taverns. It was more difficult to learn to do without her than to lose the taste for Greek wine. Some months after I lost sight of her, I learned by chance that she had attached herself to a small company of men and women who were followers of a young Galilean thaumaturgist. His name was Jesus; he came from Nazareth, and he was crucified for some crime, I don't quite know what. Pontius, do you remember anything about the man?"

Pontius Pilate contracted his brows, and his hand rose to his forehead in the attitude of one who probes the deeps of memory. Then after a silence of some seconds—

"Jesus?" he murmured, "Jesus—of Nazareth? I cannot call him to mind."

THE DRAKE WHO HAD MEANS OF HIS OWN

By Owen Wister

[Owen Wister (1860–   ) was born in Philadelphia and has made his home there except for brief periods in his life when temporary interests drew him away from his native city. He was educated at Harvard, and admitted to the practice of law in Philadelphia. He gave up the law for literature in a very short time. One period of his life was spent in the Rocky Mountain West, chiefly in Wyoming. Out of that experience came some excellent stories of the West, including *The Virginian* (1902), a novel of cowboy life.

The Drake Who Had Means of His Own was first published in the *Saturday Evening Post* (1911). It is here reprinted from *The Writings of Owen Wister* (11 vols., 1928), by permission of the author and of The Macmillan Company, publishers.]

SCIPIO sat beside the table—Mrs. Culloden's still very new, wedding-present table—arguing on and on, and I forgot all about him. When he slapped the Wyoming game laws for that year down on the table hard, and complained that I was not listening to him, I continued to look out of the ranch window at the pond and merely said:—

"Just hear those ducks."

He stared at me with disgust and scorn. "Ducks!" he then muttered.

"Well, but hear them," I urged.

"Well, they're quackin'," he said. "A duck does." He picked up the game laws and resumed: "As I was telling you, it says—page 12, section 25—"

But I gave him no attention and still looked out at the pond.

So then he remarked bitterly: "I suppose ducks crow back East—or bark."

He was perfectly welcome to all the satire he could invent; I was not to be turned from my curiosity about the clamor in the water outside, and as I watched I said aloud: "There's something behind it."

This brought him to the window, where, as he stood silent beside me, I could feel his impatience as definitely as if it had been a radiator. The matter was that he had his mind running on something, and I had my mind running on something—and they weren't the same things; and each of us wished the other to be interested in his own thing.

"Something behind it," echoed Scipio slightingly. "Behind every quack you'll find a duck."

To this I returned no answer.

"Maybe they have forgot themselves and laid eggs in the water," suggested Scipio.

"Do your Western ducks lay much in September?" I inquired, with chill.

The noise in the pond, which had died down for an instant, was now set up again—loud, remonstrant, voluble; the two birds sat in the middle of the water and lifted up their heads and screamed to the sky.

"That's what they've done," said Scipio; "and they can't locate the eggs. Well, it'd make me holler too. Say," he pleaded, "what's the point in your point, anyhow? I want to show you about those game laws."

"Must I hear it all over again and must I say it all over again?" I responded, not taking my eye from the pond.

"You've never heard it wunst yet, for you've never listened."

"I did. I didn't begin to wander till you began repeating the whole thing for the third time. And now I'll say, for the fourth time, it's a closed season till 1912. There they go out of the pond, single file— Duchess in the lead. The Duchess has purple in her wings; the Countess has none."

"Oh, soap fat!" said Scipio.

"And they've gone to feed on the grain in the haystack. There's Sir Francis waiting for them by the woodpile. He's the drake."

"Oh, soap fat!" repeated Scipio.

I followed the ducks until they had waddled out of sight.

"Every now and then, during the day," I said, "they go through that same performance: sit in the water and scream louder each minute, then come out and head for the haystack in the most orderly, quiet manner, just after having given every symptom of falling into convulsions. Now I'm going to find out what that means. And what I am wondering at," I continued, "is why you do not suggest that they are screaming at the game laws."

Well, we sat down then and had it out about those game laws; and it is but right to confess that they were more important to poor Scipio than the ducks were to me. First we took section 25 to pieces, dug its sentences to the bottom, and carefully lifted out every scrap which gave promise of containing sense. It was no child's task. You didn't reach the first full stop for a hundred and twelve words—nothing but commas; it was like being lost in the sagebrush—and, by the time the full stop did come, your head—but let me quote the sentence:—

"It shall be unlawful for any person or persons to kill any antelope until the open season for other game animals in 1915, when only one antelope may be killed by any person hunting legally, or to kill any moose, elk or mountain sheep until the open season for other game animals, in 1912, when only one male moose may be killed by any person hunting legally, or to kill any elk or mountain sheep in any part of this

State, except in Fremont County, Uinta County, Carbon County and that part of Bighorn County and Park County west of the Bighorn River, until the open season for game animals in 1915."

To tell you all that we said before we had finished with this would be worse than useless—it would be profane; enough that I stuck to the conclusion I had reached when I read the section in the East—no hunting anything anywhere for anybody until 1912. On the strength of it I had left my rifle at home and brought only my fishing rod.

"If it is your way," said Scipio, "what do you make of section 26? 'It shall be unlawful for any person or persons to hunt, pursue or kill any elk, deer or mountain sheep except from September twenty-fifth to November thirtieth of *each year*.'" He yelled the last two words at me.

But I merely clapped my hands to my brow.

"And if it is your way," Scipio pursued, playing his ace, "what do you make of Honey Wiggin taking a party out next Monday for six weeks?"

"Why, they'll simply be all arrested."

"No; they'll not. I've saw Honey's license with this year stamped in red figures right acrost it, just as plain as headlines."

What could one reply to that? I picked up the pamphlet and stared at the page.

Scipio ruminated. "Will you tell me," he said, "why, in a country where everybody's born equal, the legislature should be a bigger fool than anybody else?"

"It's a free country," I reminded him. "Every man has the right to be an ass here."

But Scipio still brooded. "Well," he said, "if I was a legislator—" he stopped.

"You're not qualified," said I.

"Not?"

"You haven't sufficient command of the English language."

"*What!*" cried Scipio; for vocabulary is his chief pride and I had actually touched him.

"No. You couldn't cook up two paragraphs of your mother tongue that would defy any sane human intelligence."

"They have done worse than that to me," he said ruefully. "They have lost me my season's job. The party I was to take out read them laws same as you did, and they stayed back East and made other plans. That's what I got in last night's mail."

"Well, I haven't stayed back East," I said. "The fishing's about done, but I want an excuse for another month or two of outing. My things can get here in twelve days—we'll hunt, and I'll be your season's job. And," I added, "now I shall have time to study the ducks."

We launched then into discussion of horses and camp outfit, copiously arguing what the legislature would let a man hunt, pursue, or kill in a season it declared to be open for no big game at all, until from eleven the clock went round to noon; and in the kitchen the voice of Mrs. Culloden was heard, calling clearly to her young bridegroom in the corral—calling too clearly.

"Well, Jimsy," the voice said, "are you going to get me any wood for this stove—or ain't you?"

Our discussion dropped; we sat still; it was time for Scipio to be getting back across the river to his own cabin and dinner. He rose, put on his hat, and stood looking at me for a moment. Then he took his hat off and scratched his head, glancing toward the kitchen.

"Jimsy, did you hear me telling you about that wood?" came the voice of the young bride, a trifle clearer. "I seem to have to remind you of everything."

Scipio's bleached blue eye and his long, eccentric nose turned slowly once more on me. "My, but it's turrable easy to get married," was his word. He shoved his hat on again and was out of the door and on his horse; and I watched him ride down to the river and ford it. As he grew distant, my three ducks waddled back from the haystack to the pond. The Duchess led, the Countess followed; Sir Francis brought up the rear. But how could I attend to them while the following reached me through the door from the kitchen?

"If dinner's late you can thank yourself, Jimsy."

"Why, May, I split the wood for you right after breakfast. That corral gate——"

"Split the wood and leave me to carry it!"

"Well, I've been about as busy as I could be on the ditch; and that gate needs——"

"Never mind. Wash your hands and get ready now. Kiss me first."

At this point it seemed best to go out of the sitting-room door and come presently into the kitchen by the other way, at the moment when my hostess was placing the hot food upon the table. It was good food, well cooked; and all the spoons and things were bright and clean. Bright and clean too, and very pretty, was the little bride. She was not twenty yet; Jimsy was not twenty-four; and as he sat down to his meal I saw her look at him with a look which I understood plainly: had no stranger been there to see, some more kissing would have occurred. Yet, what did she now find to say to him—she that so visibly adored him?

"Jimsy Culloden! Well, I guess you'll never learn to brush your hair!"

Jimsy suddenly grinned. "Others have enjoyed it pretty well this way," said he. "Tangled their hands all through it." And his gray eyes twinkled at me. But the little woman's blue eyes flashed and she sat up very stiff. "Before I asked you, that was," Jimsy added.

Have I ever told you how Jimsy became married? I believe not—

but it would take too long now; it will have to wait. His bachelor live-
liness had not contributed to his mother's peace of mind, but all was
now well; the poker chips had gone I don't know where; our beloved old
card-table of past years stood now in the bridal bedroom, stifled in
feminine drapery beyond recognition; the bottles that in these days lay
empty beyond the corral had contained merely tomato ketchup and
such things; and here was Jimsy Culloden a stable citizen, an anchored
man, county commissioner, selling vegetables, alfalfa, and horses,
with me for a paying boarder in that new-established Wyoming industry
which is locally termed dude-wrangling. The eastern "dude" is destined
to replace Hereford cattle in Wyoming—and sheep also.

Jimsy was an anchored man, to be sure: might he possibly some day
drag his anchor? I glanced at his blue-eyed May, so fair and so competent, and I hoped her voice would not grow much clearer. I glanced
at Jimsy, quietly eating, and wondered if a new look lately lurking in
his eye—a look of slight bewilderment—would increase or pass.

"Didn't I see Scipio Le Moyne ride away?" he asked me.

"Yes. It was dinner-time."

"Couldn't he stay here and eat?"

"There you go, Jimsy Culloden; wanting to feed this whole valley
every day, just like you was rich!"

Jimsy's gray eyes blinked and he attended to his plate. The failure
of that little joke about tangled hair was the probable cause of his present silence, and the bride appealed to me.

"Ain't that so?" she said. "You've been here before. You know
how folks loaf around up and down this valley and stop to dinner, and
stay for supper, and just eat people up!"

She was so perfectly right in principle that my only refuge from the
perilous error of taking sides was the somewhat lame remark: "Well,
Scipio isn't a dead-beat, you know."

"There!" cried Jimsy, triumphantly.

"Mr. Culloden would have fed a dead-beat just the same," returned
the lady promptly.

Again she was entirely right. From good heart and long habit Jimsy
made welcome every passing traveler and his horse. When Wyoming
was young and its ranches lay wide, desert miles apart, such hospitality
was the natural, unwritten law; but now, in this day of increasing settlements and of rainbowed folders of railroads painting a promised land
for all comers, a young ranchman could easily be kept poor by the perpetual drain on his groceries and his oats. Jimsy's wife was stepping
between him and his bachelor shiftlessness in all directions, and the
propitious signs of her influence were everywhere. Indoors and out, a
crisp, new appearance of things harbingered good fortune. Why, she
had actually started him on reforming his gates! Did you ever see the
thing they were frequently satisfied to call a gate in Wyoming? A sordid

wreck of barbed-wire and rotten wood, hung across the fence-gap by a rusty loop, raggedly dangling like the ribs of a broken umbrella.

The telephone bell called Mrs. Culloden to the sitting-room near the end of dinner.

Mrs. Sedlaw, her dear friend and schoolmate living five miles up the valley, was inviting them to dinner next day to eat roast grouse.

"Let's go," said Jimsy.

"And you quit your ditch and me quit my ironing?" answered the clear voice. "Thank you ever so much, Susie; we'd just love to, but Jimsy can't go off the ranch this week, and I'd not like to leave him all alone, even if I wasn't as busy as I can be with our wash." There followed exchange of gossip and laughter over it, and much love sent to and fro—and the receiver was hung up.

"As for grouse," I said to Jimsy, for his silence was on my nerves, "I will now go and catch you some trout superior to any bird that flies."

Sir Francis, the snow-white drake, stood by the woodpile as I crossed the enclosure on my way to the river. In the pond the lady ducks were loudly quacking, but I passed them by. I desired the solitude of Buffalo Horn, its pools, its cottonwoods, its quiet presiding mountains; and I walked up its stream for a mile, safe from that clear voice and from the bewildered eye of Jimsy, my once blithe, careless friend.

Unless it be from respect for Izaak Walton and tradition, I know not why I ever carry in my fly-book, or ever use, a brown-hackle; it has wasted hours of fishing time for me. The hours this afternoon it did not waste, because, under the spell of the large day that shone upon the valley, my thoughts dwelt not on fish, but with delicious vagueness upon matrimony, the game laws, and those ducks. With the waters of Buffalo Horn talking near by and singing far off, I watched all things rather than my line and often wholly stopped to smell the wild, clean odor of the sagebrush and draw the beauty of everything into my very depths. So from pool to pool I waded down the south fork of Buffalo Horn and had caught nothing when I reached Sheep Creek, by Scipio's ranch. Here I changed to a grizzly king and soon had killed four trout.

Scipio was out in his meadow gathering horses, and he came to the bank with a question:—

"Find the eggs them ducks laid in the water?"

"Jimsy wanted to know why you didn't stay to dinner," was my answer.

"Huh!" Scipio watched me land a half-pound fish. Then: "They ain't been married a year yet."

I cast below a sunken log and took a small trout, which I threw back, while Scipio resumed:

"Why I didn't stop to dinner! Huh! Say, when did they quit havin' several wives at wunst?"

"Who quit?"

"Why, them sheep-men back in the Bible—Laban and Solomon and them old-timers. What made 'em quit?"

"They didn't all quit. There, you've made me lose that fish. Are you thinking two wives would be twice as bad as one?"

"You'll get another fish. I'm thinking they wouldn't be half as bad as one."

Certain passages in Scipio's earlier days came into my mind, but I did not mention them to him. Possibly he was thinking of them himself.

"Two at once is not considered moral in this country," I said.

Scipio mused. "I'm not sure I've ever clearly understood about morals," he muttered. "Are you going to keep that whitefish?"

"I always keep a few for the hens. Makes 'em lay."

This caused Scipio to look frowningly across Buffalo Horn to where the Culloden Ranch buildings lay clear in the blue crystal of the afternoon light. "Marriage ain't learned in a day," he remarked, "any more than ropin' stock is. He ain't learned how to *be* married yet."

Again I thought of Scipio's past adventures and remembered that the best critics are they who have failed in art.

"Did you mean what you said about hunting with me?" Scipio now inquired.

"Sure thing!" I returned, "if you're right about Honey Wiggin."

"Oh, I'm right enough. You'll see him come by here Monday."

"Then I'll send East for my things," I said.

"Well, I'll be looking for a man to cook and horse-wrangle," said Scipio.

As I approached the ranch across the level pasture with my fish, I could hear from afar the quack of the ducks, invisible in the pond, and could see from afar the snow-white figure of the drake, stationary by the woodpile. Now for the first time the idea glimmered upon me that he had something to do with it. But what? I came to the breast of the little pond and stood upon it to watch the Countess and the Duchess. They were making a great noise; but over what? Sometimes they sat still and screamed together; a punctuation of silence would then follow. Next one or the other would take it up alone. Was it a sort of service they were holding to celebrate the sunset? I looked up at the lustrous crimson on the mountain wall—a mile of giant battlements sending forth a rose glow as if from within, like something in a legend; birds and beasts might well celebrate such a marvel—but the Countess and Duchess were doing this at other hours, when nothing particular seemed to be happening. I looked at the drake by the woodpile. He had not moved a quarter of an inch. He stood in profile, most becomingly. His neat, spotless white, his lemon-colored bill, his orange-colored legs, his benign yet confident attitude, as if of personal achievement taken for granted but not thrust forward—all this put me in mind of something, but so faintly that I could not just then make out what it was. Shouts from the Duchess at the top of her voice hastily recalled my attention to the pond.

I expected to find something sudden was wrong. Not at all. The water was without a wrinkle, the ducks floated motionless: yet there had been a note, a quality, urgent, piercingly remonstrant, in those quacks of the Duchess. She might have been calling for the constabulary, the fire brigade, and the health department. And then, without change for better or for worse in anything around us that I could see, the two birds swam placidly to land. They got out on the bank, wiggled their tails, stood on their toes to flap their wings, and, this brief drying process being over, they took their way to the drake. He stood by the wood-pile, stock-still in profile; he had not yet moved a quarter of an inch; it seemed to me—but I was not certain—that his ladies raced as they drew near him. When they reached him he turned with gravity and headed for the haystack. They fell in behind him, and the three waddled and wobbled solemnly toward their goal, squeezed under the fence and were lost to view.

I took in my trout to Mrs. Culloden, who praised their size and my skill. On the subject of giving her hens a diet of whitefish, she told me it was her great ambition so to manage that before the moulting fowls should wholly stop laying the spring pullets should have begun to lay. "Jimsy is real fond of eggs," she explained, "and I want him to have them."

I further learned that whitefish cooked were better than whitefish raw, which often tainted the eggs with a fishy taste. I stood high in the little bride's favor because I was helping her to please Jimsy. Lying abed that night in my one-room cabin, I said aloud, abruptly: "That was a protest."

I know nothing about what they call our subconscious workings, save that I am chock-full of them; I meant the Duchess. Apparently my subconscious works had been dealing with her ever since the scene at the pond. Thus a conclusion had popped out of my mouth full-fledged before I knew it was there. "Yes," I repeated; "she was protesting. They both were."

The works, however, must have stopped after that for the night—or turned to other activity—for next morning I went down to the pond with nothing beyond the two theories of yesterday: that it was protest and that the drake was somehow at the bottom of it. But I scored no advance in my knowledge. All three birds were in the water and did not come out while I remained there; nothing more of their plan of life was revealed to me. Still, I saw one new thing. Sir Francis swam about with the Duchess and Countess in a suite, following close, but never crowding him. What they did do was crowd each other. A struggle for place occurred between them from time to time; and, although all the rest of the time they were like sisters, when the struggle was on it was bitter.

I must have stayed watching them for half an hour to make sure of this, and I know that there were moments when they would have gladly killed each other. Sir Francis never took the slightest notice of it, though he must have been well aware of it, since it always went on some six inches behind his back. The Countess would attempt to swim up closer to him, at which the Duchess would instantly crook her neck sidewise at her and, savagely undulating her head, would utter quick, poisonous sounds that trembled with fury. To these the Countess would retort, crooking and undulating too; thus they would swim with their necks at right-angles, raging at each other and crowding for place. Sometimes the Duchess darted her bill out and bit the Countess, who was of a milder nature, I gradually discerned. The admirable ignorance which Sir Francis preserved of all this testified plainly to his moral balance, and filled me with curiosity and respect. Whatever was going on behind him, whether peace or war, he swam quietly on or stopped as it pleased him, with never a change in the urbanity of his eye and carriage.

It came to me that afternoon what his attitude at the woodpile essentially was. He stood there again alone—the ducks were quacking in the pond—and as I looked at his neat white body and the lemon-colored bill and orange-colored legs, all presented in the same dignified profile, I saw that his was by instinct the historical portrait attitude: Perry after Lake Erie, Webster before replying to Hayne, Washington on being notified of his appointment as Commander-in-Chief—you will understand what I mean. And if you smile at my absorption in these little straws from the farmyard, you have never known the blessing of true leisure. To drop clean out of my mind for a while the law and investment of trust funds and the self-induced hysterics of Wall Street, and study a perfectly irrelevant, unuseful trifle, such as the family life of Sir Francis and his ladies, brings a pastoral health to the spirit and to the biliary duct.

There was an error in my conclusions about the Countess and Duchess which I did not have a chance to perceive for a day or two, because our domestic harmony was mysteriously disturbed. That clear note in May's voice waked up again, this time a tone or so higher; and it was kept awake by one thing after another. It began after a wagonful of people had passed the ranch on its way down the valley to town. I was off by the river when they stopped a few minutes on the road outside the fence. One could not see who they were at that distance. Jimsy left his ditch work and talked to them, and when they had gone returned to it. At our next meal Jimsy's eye was bewildered—and something more— and May's voice was bad for digestion. As soon as my last mouthful was swallowed I sought the solitude of my cabin and read a book until bedtime. How should one connect that wagonload of people with the new and higher tide of unrest? Nothing was more the custom than this stopping of neighbors to chat over the fence. May's voice and Jimsy's eye kept me as often and as far from their neighborhood as I could get.

It was Scipio, the next time I saw him, who began at once: "Did you see Mrs. Faxon?"

"Who's she?"

"Gracious! I thought everybody in this country knowed her. She's an alfalfa widow."

"Well, I seem to have somehow missed her."

"She went down to town the other day. Pity you've missed her. Awful good-looker."

"Well, I'll try to meet her."

"Her and Jimsy used to meet a whole heap," said Scipio.

"Oh!" said I. "H'm! All the same May's a fool."

"Did she get mad? Did she get mad?" demanded Scipio, vivaciously.

"Lord!" said I, thinking of it. I told Scipio how Jimsy had talked over the fence to the scarlet fragment of his past for perhaps three minutes in the safe presence of a wagonload of witnesses, and how in consequence May had gone up into the air. "To love acceptably needs tact," I moralized; but while I expatiated on this, Scipio's attention wandered.

"You saw Honey Wiggin go up the river with his dudes?"

"Oh, yes."

"And two other parties go up?"

"Yes."

"Any further notions about the game laws?"

"Nothing—except it's the merest charity to assume they made them when they were drunk."

"Sure thing! I guess I'll have a cook when your camping stuff comes."

My stuff was due in not many days; and as I walked home from Scipio's cabin I felt gratitude to the game laws for the part they had played in delaying me in this valley, where each day seemed the essence distilled from the beauty of seven usual days. Even as I waded Buffalo Horn I stopped to look up and down the course that it made between its bordering cottonwoods. A week ago these had been green; but autumn had come one night and now here was Buffalo Horn unwinding its golden miles between the castle walls of the mountains. Amid all this august serenity I walked the slower through fear of having it marred by the voice of May. I lingered outside the house and it was the voice of the Duchess that I heard. Yes, I was grateful to the game laws. They, too, caused me to learn the whole truth about Sir Francis.

On this particular evening I saw where had been my error regarding the Countess and Duchess. I have spoken of the Countess' milder nature, which I thought always put her behind the Duchess in their struggle for precedence. It did not. Quite often she made up in skill what she lacked in force, and I now saw the first example of it. They were all coming to the pond for their evening swim, the two ducks scolding and walking with their necks at right-angles. Sir Francis was in the lead, his head gently inclined toward the water. As he got in, the Duchess made an evident miscalculation. She thought he was going to swim to the right, and she splashed hastily in that direction. But he swam to the left. The Countess was there in a flash. She got herself next to him and held her place round and round the pond, crooking her neck and quacking backward at the enraged, defeated Duchess.

Twice in the following forenoon I saw this recur; and before supper I knew that it was a part of their daily lives. Sometimes it happened on land, sometimes in the water, and always in the same way—a miscalculation as to which way the drake was going to turn. It was the duck who had been nearest to him that always made the miscalculation, and she invariably lost her place by it. Then she would rage in the rear while the other scoffed back at her. Neither of them could have been entirely a lady or they would have known how to conduct their quarrel without all this displeasing publicity. But there can be no doubt that Sir Francis was a perfect gentleman. Not only was he never aware of what was happening, but he so bore himself as wholly to avoid being made ridiculous. That the Duchess was a little near-sighted I learned when I took to feeding them with toast brought from breakfast.

My time was growing short and I began to fear that I might be gone hunting before I had penetrated the mystery of the historical portrait attitude near the woodpile and the protests of the ducks in the water. This was going on straight along, only I had never managed to see the beginning of it. Therefore I fed them on toast to draw closer to them, and I tried to give each a piece, turn about; but only too often, when toast meant for the Duchess had fallen in the water directly under her nose, she would peer helplessly about and the Countess would dip down quickly and get it. Sometimes the Duchess saw it one second too late, when their heads would literally collide, and the Duchess, under the impression she had got it, would snap her bill two or three times on nothing, and then perceive the Countess chewing the morsel. At this she always savagely bit the Countess; and still, through it all, the drake sustained his admirable ignorance. My feeding device triumphed. I did learn about the woodpile.

This is what I saw. They had been swimming for a while after eating the toast. Sir Francis had finally swallowed a last hard bit of crust after repeatedly soaking it in the water. He looked about and evidently decided it was time for the haystack. He got out on the bank, but the ladies did not. He turned and looked at them; they continued swimming. Then he walked slowly away in silence, and as he grew distant their swimming became agitated. Reaching the woodpile, he turned and stood in bland, eminent profile. Then the ducks in the pond began. The Duchess quacked; the Countess quacked; their voices rose and became positively wild. A person who did not know would have hastened to see if they needed assistance. This performance lasted four minutes by my watch—the drake statuesque by the woodpile, the ducks screaming in the water. Then, as I have before described, they succumbed to the power at the woodpile. They swam ashore, flapped to dry themselves, and made for Sir Francis like people catching a train. He did not move until they had reached him, when all sought the haystack.

So now I understood clearly that it was he who made their plans, timed all their comings and goings, and that they, bitterly as they disliked leaving the water until they were ready, nevertheless had to leave it when he was ready. Of course, if either of them had had any real mind, they would have realized long before that it was of no use to attempt to cope with him and they would have got out quickly when he did, instead of making this scene several times every day. But why did they get out at all when they didn't want to? Why didn't they let him go to the haystack by himself? What was the secret of his power? It was they who were always fighting and biting; his serenity was flawless.

I stood on the breast of the pond, turning this over. If you have outrun me and arrived at the truth, it just shows once again how superior readers are to writers in intelligence. I was not destined to fathom it. Many a problem has taken two to solve it and it was Jimsy who—but let that wait. Jimsy came across from the stable and spoke to me now:—

"What are you studying?"

"I have been studying your ducks."

He looked over at the cabin, where May could be seen moving about in the kitchen, and I saw his face grow suddenly tender. "They're hers," he said softly. "She kind o' wanted ducks round here and so one day I brought 'em to her from town. Then I made this pond for 'em— just dammed the creek across this little gully. Nothing's wrong with 'em?"

"Oh, no. But they've set me guessing."

He did not believe my story, though he listened with his gray eyes fixed on mine. "That's wonderful," he said; "but you've made it up. I'd have noticed a thing like that."

"I don't think you would. You're working all day with your stock and your ditches. Think what a loafer I am."

"It's most too extraordinary," he said, and stood looking at the woodpile. He was not really thinking about what I had told him; I could feel that.

"Well, Jimsy!"

We both started a little. It was May, who had come round the corner of the house, and the setting sun shone upon her and made her quite lovely, where she stood shading her eyes, with a little hair floating one side of her forehead.

"Well, Jimsy! Dreaming again! Do you know what time it is? The way you've took to dreaming is something terrible!"

Jimsy went into the house.

I was glad that two days more would see me out of this.

Next morning I stood justified—oh, more than justified—in Jimsy's eyes. No one could have anticipated such a performance at the pond as I was able to show him—it bore me out and surpassed anything I had told him—and no one could have foretold that it would fire Jimsy with a curiosity equal to mine.

The ceremony of the toast was in progress when Jimsy, crossing to the corral, saw me thus engaged. He stuck his hands into his pockets and strolled across to the water's edge, wearing a broad grin of indulgence.

"Awful busy, you are!" said he.

"Just watch them," said I.

"Oh, I've got a day's work to do."

"I'm aware," I retorted, "that scientific observation doesn't look like work to the ignorant."

"What're you trying to find out?"

"I told you last night. I can't see how that drake keeps those ducks in order."

"Oh, I guess he don't keep 'em in order."

"I tell you he has them under his thumb."

Jimsy cast a careless eye upon the birds. They had finished the toast and were swimming about. The quacks of the Duchess were merely quacks to him; he did not hear that she was saying to the Countess: "Hah, Hah, Hah! How do you fancy a back seat this morning?"

"One feels mortified, of course," I explained to Jimsy, "that she should betray her spite so crudely—a sad but common thing in our country."

"In the name of God, what are you talking about?" demanded Jimsy.

"Oh, I'm not in the least crazy. New York stinks with people like that."

At this moment the usual thing happened in the pond—the Duchess made a miscalculation. The drake swam suddenly left instead of right, and the Countess jumped to the favored place. Now it was she who quacked backward at her discountenanced rival.

"She is really the sweeter nature of the two," I said. But Jimsy was attending to the ducks with an awakened interest; in fact, he was now caught in the same fascination that had held me for so many days. He took his hands out of his pockets and followed the ducks keenly.

"I believe you weren't lyin' to me," he remarked presently.

"You wait! Just wait!" I exclaimed.

He watched a little longer. "D'you suppose," he said, "it's his feathers they love so?"

"His feathers?" I repeated.

"Those two curly ones in his tail. They're crooked plumb enticing, like they were saying, 'Come, girls!'"

This reminded me of Jimsy's unbrushed mound of hair and May's coldness at his reference to it. "Feathers would hardly account for everything," I said.

A last spark of doubt flickered in Jimsy. "Are you joshing about this thing?" he asked.

"Just you wait," I said again.

We did not have to wait. In the judgment of the drake it was time for the haystack; the ducks thought it too soon. All began as usual. Sir Francis had reached the woodpile and taken his attitude, the first protesting scream from the pond had risen to the sky, Jimsy's face was causing me acute pleasure, when the Duchess did an entirely new thing. She swam to the inlet and began to waddle slowly up the trickling stream. Then I perceived a few yards beyond her the cleanings of some fish which had been thrown out. It was for these she was making.

"She has ruined everything!" I lamented.

"Wait!" said Jimsy. He whispered it. His new faith was completer than mine.

The Duchess heavily proceeded. In my childhood I used sometimes to see old ladies walking slowly, shod in soft, wide, heelless things made of silk or satin—certainly not of leather, except the soles—which seem to have gone out. The Duchess trod as if she had these same mid-Victorian feet and she began gobbling the fish. If this was any strain upon the drake, he did not show it. The Countess now discerned from the pond what the Duchess was doing and she was instantly riven with contending emotions. The waves from her legs agitated the whole pond as she swam wildly; sometimes she looked at the drake, sometimes at the fish, and between the looks she quacked as if she would die. Then she, too, got out and went toward the fish. I looked apprehensively at the figure by the woodpile, but it might have been a painted figure in very truth. I think Jimsy was holding his breath. When a moral conflict becomes visible to the naked eye there is something in it that far out-matches any mere thumping of fists; here was Sir Francis battling for his empire in silence and immobility, with his ladies getting all the fish. And just then the Countess wavered. She saw Sir Francis, white and monumental, thirty yards away; and she saw the Duchess and the fish about three more steps from her nose. She stood still and then she broke down. She turned and fled back to her lord. It can not be known what the more forcible Duchess would have done but for this. As it was, she looked up and saw the Countess—and immediately went to pieces herself. I had not known that she had it in her to run so.

I can not repeat Jimsy's first oath as he stared at the triumphant drake leading his family to the haystack. After silence he turned to me. "Wouldn't that kill you?" he said very quietly: and said no more, but began to walk slowly away.

"Now," I called after him, "will you tell me how he manages to keep head of his house like that?"

If Jimsy had any hypothesis to offer then, he did not offer it, and before he had reached the corral May appeared. I'll not report her talk this time; it was the usual nursery governess affair: did Jimsy know that he had wasted half an hour when he ought to have hitched up and gone for wood up Dead Timber Creek, and didn't he know there was wood for just one day left and it would take him the whole day? I escaped to my fishing before she had done, and I took my dinner with Scipio.

It is wicked to fish in October, but we ate the trout; and I must tell you of a discovery: when artificial flies fail, and frost has finished the grasshoppers, the housefly is a deadly bait! I am glad at last to have accounted for the presence of the housefly in a universe of infinite love.

At supper I was sorry that Scipio and I had not got off to the mountains that day. Jimsy was still out. He had brought, it appeared, one load of wood from Dead Timber Creek and had gone for another.

It was May's opinion that he should have returned by now. I hardly thought so, but this made small difference to May. She was up from table and listening at the open door three times before our restless meal was over. Next she lighted a lantern and hung it out upon a gate-post of one of the outer corrals, that Jimsy might be guided home from afar. In the following thirty minutes she went out twice again to listen, and soon after this she sent me out to the lantern to make sure it was burning brightly.

"He would see the windows at any rate," I told her.

But now she had begun to be frightened and could not sit in her chair for more than a few moments at a time.

"What o'clock is it?" she asked me.

It was seven forty-five and I think she fancied it was midnight. If Jimsy had been six years old and a perfect fool to boot she could not have been more distracted than she presently became.

"Why, Mrs. Culloden," I remonstrated, "Jimsy was raised in this valley. He knows his way about."

She did not hear me and now she seized the telephone. Into the ears of one neighbor after another she poured questions up and down the valley. It was idle to remind her that Dead Timber Creek was five miles to the south of us and that the Whitlows, who lived six miles to the north, were not likely to have seen Jimsy. The whole valley quickly learned that he had not come back with his second load of wood by eight o'clock and that she was asking them all if they knew anything about it. In the space of twenty minutes with the telephone she had made him ridiculous throughout the precinct; and then at ten minutes past eight, while she was ringing up her friend Mrs. Sedlaw for the second time, in came Jimsy. The wood and the wagon were safe in the corral, he was safe in the house and hungry; and, of course, she hadn't heard him arrive because of the noise of the telephone. He had been at the stable for the last ten minutes, attending to the horses.

"And you never had the sense to tell me!" she cried.

"Tell you what?" He had not taken it in. "Gosh, but that chicken looks good! What's that lantern out there for?" He was now seated and helping himself to the food.

"And that's all you've got to say to me!" she said. And then the deluge came—not of tears, but words.

Somewhere inside of Jimsy was an angel, whatever else he contained. Throughout that foolish, galling scene made in my presence before I could escape, never a syllable of what he must have been feeling came from him, but only good-natured ejaculations—not many and rather brief, to be sure. When he learned the reason for the lantern he laughed aloud. This set her off and she rushed into the story of her telephoning. Then, and then alone, it was on the verge of being too much for him. He laid down his knife and fork and leaned back for a second, but the angel won. He resumed his meal; only a brick-red sunset of color spread from his collar to his hair—and his eyes were not gray, but black.

That was what I saw after I had got away to my cabin and was in bed: the man's black eyes fixed on his plate and the pretty girl standing by the stove and working off her needless fright in an unbearable harangue.

Audibly I sighed, sighed with audible relief, when the Culloden Ranch lay a mile behind Scipio and me and our packhorses the next day. Jimsy had been as self-controlled in the morning as on the night before —except that no man can control the color of his eyes. The murky storm that hung in Jimsy's eyes was the kind that does not blow over but breaks. Was May blind to such a sign? At breakfast she told him that the next time he went for wood she would go to see that he got back for supper! I told Scipio that if things were not different when we returned I should move over to his cabin.

"You'd never have figured a girl could get Jimsy buffaloed!" said Scipio.

"He's not buffaloed a little bit," I returned.

"Ain't he goin' to do nothin'?"

"I don't know what he'll do."

Scipio rode for a while, thinking it over. "If I had a wife," he said, "and she got to thinkin' she was my mother, I'd take a dally with her." His meaning was not clear; but he made it so: "I'd take her—well, not *on* my knee, but acrost it."

This I doubted, but said nothing. By and by we were passing the Sedlaw Ranch, and Mrs. Sedlaw came running out rather hastily—and began speaking before she reached the gate.

"Oh, howdy-do?" said she; and she stood looking at me.

"Isn't it perfect weather?" said I.

"Yes, indeed. And so you're going hunting?"

"Yes. Want to come?"

"Why, wouldn't that be nice! I thought Jimsy and May might be going with you."

"Oh, they're too busy. Good-by."

She stood looking after me for some time and I saw her walk back to the house quite slowly.

There's no need to tell of our hunting, or of the games of Cœur d'Alène Solo which Scipio and I and the useful cook played at night. In twenty days the snow drove us out of the mountains and we came down to human habitations—and to rife rumors. I don't recall what we heard at the first cabin—or the second or the others—but we heard something everywhere. The valley was agog over Jimsy and May. Amid the wealth of details, I shall never know precisely what did happen. Jimsy had left her and gone to Alaska. He hadn't gone to Alaska, but to New York, with Mrs. Faxon, the alfalfa widow. May had gone to her mother in Iowa. She hadn't gone to Iowa; she was under the protection of Mrs. Sedlaw. Jimsy and the widow were living in open shame at the ranch. The ranch was shut up and old man Birdsall had seen Jimsy in town, driving a companion who wore splendid feathers. There was more, much more, but the only certainty seemed to be that Jimsy had broken loose and gone somewhere—and over this somewhere hovered an episodic bigamy. But where was Jimsy now? And May? Had the explosion blown them asunder forever? Was their marriage lying in fragments? On our last night in camp we talked of this more than we played Cœur d'Alène Solo. If anybody could tell me the true state of things it would be Mrs. Sedlaw, and at her door I knocked as I passed the next morning.

"Oh, howdy-do?" said I; and she sat looking at me for some moments.

"What luck?" said she. "Get an elk?"

"Yes," said I. "How are things in general?"

"Elegant," said she. "Give my love to dear May."

"Thank you," said I, not very appropriately.

The lady followed me to my horse. "Seems like only yesterday you came by," were her parting words. She had certainly squared our accounts.

As we drew in sight of the Culloden Ranch you may imagine how I wondered what we should find there. A peaceful smoke rose from the kitchen chimney into the quiet air. Through the window I saw—yes, it was May!—most domestically preparing food. Outside by the pond a figure stood. It was Jimsy. He was feeding the ducks. I swung off my horse and hurried to Jimsy. Sir Francis was eating from his hand.

"How!" said he in cheerful greeting.

"How!" I returned.

"Get an elk?"

"Yes."

"Sheep?"

"Yes."

"Good!"

"You—you're—you're feeding the ducks."

"Sure thing!—Say, I've found out his game."

I pointed to Sir Francis. "His control, you mean?—how he keeps his hold?"

"Sure thing!" Jimsy pointed to the ducks. "Has 'em competin' for him. Keeps 'em a-guessing. That's his game."

It stunned me for a second. Of course he didn't know that the valley had talked to me.

"Why, how do you do?" cried May, cheerfully, coming out of the house.

Then I took it all in and I broke into scandalous, irredeemable laughter.

A bright flash came into Jimsy's eyes as *he* took it all in—then he also gave way, but he blushed heavily.

"Whatever are you two laughing at?" exclaimed May. She looked radiant. That clear note was all melted from her voice. "Mr. Le Moyne, aren't you going to stay to dinner?"

"Why, thank you!" said Scipio—polite, and embarrassed almost to stuttering.

To Sir Francis Jimsy gave the last piece of toast. It was a large one. If the drake was aware of the tie between Jimsy's marital methods and his own, he betrayed it as little as he betrayed knowledge of all things which it is best never to notice.

Yes, I am grateful to the game laws. The next legislature made them intelligible.

THE OUTLAWS

By Selma Lagerlöf

[Selma Lagerlöf (1858–) is one of the most distinguished literary artists of Sweden. She was born on the country estate of her family near Vermland, and educated in Stockholm. For ten years she was a teacher. During that period she wrote her first novel, the book by which she is still best known in the world outside of Sweden. This is *Gösta Berling's Saga* (*The Story of Gösta Berling*). In 1902 Miss Lagerlöf was asked by the Swedish National Teachers' Association to write a story which would give to school children a picture of the folklore and the geography of Sweden. The book she wrote is *The Wonderful Adventures of Nils*. This has become a classic for young people. Miss Lagerlöf is a member of the Swedish Academy, and received the Nobel Prize for literature in 1909. She makes her home on the family estate near Vermland.

Selma Lagerlöf is the author of a number of short stories of high quality, embodying careful studies of mental or emotional states. Such a story is *The Outlaws*. The translation is by Grace Isabel Colbron, by whose permission it is reprinted.]

A PEASANT had killed a monk and fled to the woods. He became an outlaw, upon whose head a price was set. In the forest he met another fugitive, a young fisherman from one of the outermost islands, who had been accused of the theft of a herring net. The two became companions, cut themselves a home in a cave, laid their nets together, cooked their food, made their arrows, and held watch one for the other. The peasant could never leave the forest. But the fisherman, whose crime was less serious, would now and then take upon his back the game they had killed, and would creep down to the more isolated houses on the outskirts of the village. In return for milk, butter, arrow-heads, and clothing he would sell his game, the black mountain cock, the moor hen, with her shining feathers, the toothsome doe, and the long-eared hare.

The cave which was their home cut down deep into a mountain-side. The entrance was guarded by wide slabs of stone and ragged thorn-bushes. High up on the hillside there stood a giant pine, and the chimney of the fireplace nestled among its coiled roots. Thus the smoke could draw up through the heavy hanging branches and fade unseen into the air. To reach their cave the men had to wade through the stream that sprang out from the hill slope. No pursuer thought of seeking their trail in this merry brooklet. At first they were hunted as wild animals are. The peasants of the district gathered to pursue them as if for a baiting of wolf or bear. The bowmen surrounded the wood while the spear carriers entered and left no thicket or ravine unsearched. The two outlaws cowered in their gloomy cave, panting in terror and listening breathlessly as the hunt passed on with noise and shouting over the mountain ranges.

For one long day the young fisherman lay motionless, but the murderer could stand it no longer and went out into the open where he could see his enemy. They discovered him and set after him, but this was far more to his liking than lying quiet in impotent terror. He fled before his pursuers, leaped the streams, slid down the precipices, climbed up perpendicular walls of rock. All his remarkable strength and skill awoke to energy under the spur of danger. His body became as elastic as a steel spring, his foot held firm, his hand grasped sure, his eye and ear were doubly sharp. He knew the meaning of every murmur in the foliage; he could understand the warning in an upturned stone.

When he had clambered up the side of a precipice he would stop to look down on his pursuers, greeting them with loud songs of scorn. When their spears sang above him in the air, he would catch them and hurl them back. As he crashed his way through tangled underbrush something within him seemed to sing a wild song of rejoicing. A gaunt, bare hilltop stretched itself through the forest, and all alone upon its crest there stood a towering pine. The red brown trunk was bare; in the thick grown boughs at the top a hawk's nest rocked in the breeze. So daring had the fugitive grown that on another day he climbed to the nest while his pursuers sought him in the woody slopes below. He sat there and twisted the necks of the young hawks as the hunt raged far beneath him. The old birds flew screaming about him in anger. They swooped past his face, they struck at his eyes with their beaks, beat at him with their powerful wings, and clawed great scratches in his weather-hardened skin. He battled with them laughing. He stood up in the rocking nest as he lunged at the birds with his knife, and he lost all thought of danger and pursuit in the joy of the battle. When recollection came again and he turned to look for his enemies, the hunt had gone off in another direction. Not one of the pursuers had thought of raising his eyes to the clouds to see the prey hanging there, doing schoolboy deeds of recklessness while his life hung in the balance. But the man trembled from head to foot when he saw that he was safe. He caught for a support with his shaking hands; he looked down giddily from the height to which he had climbed. Groaning in fear of a fall, afraid of the birds, afraid of the possibility of being seen, weakened through terror of everything and anything, he slid back down the tree trunk. He laid himself flat upon the earth and crawled over the loose stones until he reached the under-brush. There he hid among the tangled branches of the young pines, sinking down, weak and helpless, upon the soft moss. A single man might have captured him.

.   .   .   .

Tord was the name of the fisherman. He was but sixteen years old, but was strong and brave. He had now lived for a whole year in the wood.

The peasant's name was Berg, and they had called him "The Giant." He was handsome and well-built, the tallest and strongest man in the entire county. He was broad-shouldered and yet slender. His hands were delicate in shape, as if they had never known hard work; his hair was brown, his face soft-colored. When he had lived for some time in the forest his look of strength was awe-inspiring. His eyes grew piercing under bushy brows wrinkled by great muscles over the forehead. His lips were more firmly set than before, his face more haggard, with deepened hollows at the temples, and his strongly marked cheekbones stood out plainly. All the softer curves of his body disappeared, but the muscles grew strong as steel. His hair turned gray rapidly.

Tord had never seen any one so magnificent and so mighty before. In his imagination, his companion towered high as the forest, strong as the raging surf. He served him humbly, as he would have served a master; he revered him as he would have revered a god. It seemed quite natural that Tord should carry the hunting spear, that he should drag the game home, draw the water, and build the fire. Berg, the Giant, accepted all these services, but scarce threw the boy a friendly word. He looked upon him with contempt, as a common thief.

The outlaws did not live by pillage, but supported themselves by hunting and fishing. Had not Berg killed a holy man, the peasants would soon have tired of the pursuit and left them to themselves in the mountains. But they feared disaster for the villages if he who had laid hands upon a servant of God should go unpunished. When Tord took his game down into the valley they would offer him money and a pardon for himself if he would lead them to the cave of the Giant, that they might catch the latter in his sleep. But the boy refused, and if they followed him he would lead them astray until they gave up the pursuit.

Once Berg asked him whether the peasants had ever tried to persuade him to betrayal. When he learned what reward they had promised, he said scornfully that Tord was a fool not to accept such offers. Tord looked at him with something in his eyes that Berg, the Giant, had never seen before. No beautiful woman whom he had loved in the days of his youth had ever looked at him like that; not even in the eyes of his own children, or of his wife, had he seen such affection. "You are my God, the ruler I have chosen of my own free will." This was what the eyes said. "You may scorn me, or beat me, if you will, but I shall still remain faithful."

From this on Berg gave more heed to the boy and saw that he was brave in action but shy in speech. Death seemed to have no terrors for him. He would deliberately choose for his path the fresh-formed ice on the mountain pools, the treacherous surface of the morass in springtime. He seemed to delight in danger. It gave him some compensation for the wild ocean storms he could no longer go out to meet. He would tremble in the night darkness of the wood, however, and even by day the gloom of a thicket or a deeper shadow could frighten him. When Berg asked him about this he was silent in embarrassment.

Tord did not sleep in the bed by the hearth at the back of the cave, but every night, when Berg was asleep the boy would creep to the entrance and lie there on one of the broad stones. Berg discovered this, and although he guessed the reason, he asked the boy about it. Tord would not answer. To avoid further questions he slept in the bed for two nights, then returned to his post at the door.

One night, when a snow-storm raged in the tree-tops, piling up drifts even in the heart of the thickets, the flakes swirled into the cave of the outlaws. Tord, lying by the entrance, awoke in the morning to find himself wrapped in a blanket of melting snow. A day or two later he fell ill. Sharp pains pierced his lungs when he tried to draw breath. He endured the pain as long as his strength would stand it, but one evening, when he stooped to blow up the fire, he fell down and could not rise again. Berg came to his side and told him to lie in the warm bed. Tord groaned in agony, but could not move. Berg put his arm under the boy's body and carried him to the bed. He had a feeling while doing it as if he were touching a clammy snake; he had a taste in his mouth as if he had eaten unclean horseflesh, so repulsive was it to him to touch the person of this common thief. Berg covered the sick boy with his own warm bear-skin rug and gave him water. This was all he could do, but the illness was not dangerous, and Tord recovered quickly. But now that Berg had had to do his companion's work for a few days, and had had to care for him, they seemed to have come nearer to one another. Tord dared to speak to Berg sometimes, as they sat together by the fire cutting their arrows.

"You come of good people, Berg," Tord said one evening. "Your relatives are the richest peasants in the valley. The men of your name have served kings and fought in their castles."

"They have more often fought with the rebels and done damage to the king's property," answered Berg.

"Your forefathers held great banquets at Christmas time. And you held banquets, too, when you were at home in your house. Hundreds of men and women could find place on the benches in your great hall, the hall that was built in the days before St. Olaf came here to Viken for christening. Great silver urns were there, and mighty horns, filled with mead, went the rounds of your table."

Berg looked at the boy again. He sat on the edge of the bed with his head in his hands, pushing back the heavy tangled hair that hung over his eyes. His face had become pale and refined through his illness. His eyes still sparkled with fever. He smiled to himself at the pictures called up by his fancy—pictures of the great hall and of the silver urns, of the richly clad guests, and of Berg, the Giant, lording it in the place of honor. The peasant knew that even in the days of his glory no one had ever looked at him with eyes so shining in admiration, so glowing in reverence, as this boy did now, as he sat by the fire in his worn leather jacket. He was touched, and yet displeased. This common thief had no right to admire him.

"Were there no banquets in your home?" he asked.

Tord laughed: "Out there on the rocks where father and mother live? Father plunders the wrecks and mother is a witch. When the weather is stormy she rides out to meet the ships on a seal's back, and those who are washed overboard from the wrecks belong to her."

"What does she do with them?" asked Berg.

"Oh, a witch always needs corpses. She makes salves of them, or perhaps she eats them. On moonlit nights she sits out in the wildest surf and looks for the eyes and fingers of drowned children."

"That is horrible!" said Berg.

The boy answered with calm confidence: "It would be for others, but not for a witch. She can't help it."

This was an altogether new manner of looking at life for Berg. "Then thieves have to steal, as witches have to make magic?" he questioned sharply.

"Why, yes," answered the boy. "Every one has to do the thing he was born for." But a smile of sly cunning curled his lips, as he added: "There are thieves who have never stolen."

"What do you mean by that?" spoke Berg.

The boy still smiled his mysterious smile and seemed happy to have given his companion a riddle. "There are birds that do not fly; and there are thieves who have not stolen," he said.

Berg feigned stupidity, in order to trick the other's meaning: "How can any one be called a thief who has never stolen?" he said.

The boy's lips closed tight as if to hold back the words. "But if one has a father who steals—" he threw out after a short pause.

"A man may inherit house and money, but the name thief is given only to him who earns it."

Tord laughed gently. "But when one has a mother—and that mother comes and cries, and begs one to take upon one's self the father's crime— then one can laugh at the hangman and run away into the woods. A man may be outlawed for the sake of a fish net he has never seen."

Berg beat his fist upon the stone table, in great anger. Here this strong, beautiful boy had thrown away his whole life for another.

Neither love, nor riches, nor the respect of his fellow men could ever be his again. The sordid care for food and clothing was all that remained to him in life. And this fool had let him, Berg, despise an innocent man. He scolded sternly, but Tord was not frightened any more than a sick child is frightened at the scolding of his anxious mother.

. . . .

High up on one of the broad wooded hills there lay a black swampy lake. It was square in shape, and its banks were as straight, and their corners as sharp as if it had been the work of human hands. On three sides steep walls of rock rose up, with hardy mountain pines clinging to the stones, their roots as thick as a man's arm. At the surface of the lake, where the few strips of grass had been washed away, these naked roots twisted and coiled, rising out of the water like myriad snakes that had tried to escape from the waves, but had beeen turned to stone in their struggle. Or was it more like a mass of blackened skeletons of long-drowned giants which the lake was trying to throw off? The arms and legs were twisted in wild contortions, the long fingers grasped deep into the rocks, the mighty ribs formed arches that upheld ancient trees. But now and again these iron-hard arms, these steel fingers with which the climbing pines supported themselves, would loosen their hold, and then the strong north wind would hurl the tree from the ridge far out into the swamp. There it would lie, its crown burrowing deep in the muddy water. The fishes found good hiding places amid its twigs, while the roots rose up over the water like the arms of some hideous monster, giving the little lake a repulsive appearance.

The mountains sloped down on the fourth side of the little lake. A tiny rivulet foamed out here; but before the stream could find its path it twisted and turned among boulders and mounds of earth, forming a whole colony of islands, some of which scarce offered foothold, while others carried as many as twenty trees on their back.

Here, where the rocks were not high enough to shut out the sun, the lighter foliaged trees could grow. Here were the timid, gray-green alders, and the willows with their smooth leaves. Birches were here, as they always are wherever there is a chance to shut out the evergreens, and there were mountain ash and elder bushes, giving charm and fragrance to the place.

At the entrance to the lake there was a forest of rushes as high as a man's head, through which the sunlight fell as green upon the water as it falls on the moss in the true forest. There were little clearings among the reeds, little round ponds where the water lilies slumbered. The tall rushes looked down with gentle gravity upon these sensitive beauties, who closed their white leaves and their yellow hearts so quickly in their leather outer dress as soon as the sun withdrew his rays.

One sunny day the outlaws came to one of these little ponds to fish.

They waded through the reeds to two high stones, and sat there throwing out their bait for the big, green, gleaming pike that slumbered just below the surface of the water. These men, whose life was now passed entirely among the mountains and the woods, had come to be as completely under the control of the powers of nature as were the plants or the animals. When the sun shone they were open-hearted and merry, at evening they became silent, and the night, which seemed to them so all-powerful, robbed them of their strength. And now the green light that fell through the reeds and drew out from the water stripes of gold, brown, and black-green, soothed them into a sort of magic mood. They were completely shut out from the outer world. The reeds swayed gently in the soft wind, the rushes murmured, and the long, ribbon-like leaves struck them lightly in the face. They sat on the gray stones in their gray leather garments, and the shaded tones of the leather melted into the shades of the stones. Each saw his comrade sitting opposite him as quietly as a stone statue. And among the reeds they saw giant fish swimming, gleaming and glittering in all colors of the rainbow. When the men threw out their lines and watched the rings on the water widen amid the reeds, it seemed to them that the motion grew and grew until they saw it was not they themselves alone that had occasioned it. A Nixie, half human, half fish, lay sleeping deep down in the water. She lay on her back, and the waves clung so closely to her body that the men had not seen her before. It was her breath that stirred the surface. But it did not seem to the watchers that there was anything strange in the fact that she lay there. And when she had disappeared in the next moment they did not know whether her appearance had been an illusion or not.

The green light pierced through their eyes into their brains like a mild intoxication. They saw visions among the reeds, visions which they would not tell even to each other. There was not much fishing done. The day was given up to dreams and visions.

A sound of oars came from among the reeds, and they started up out of their dreaming. In a few moments a heavy boat, hewn out of a tree trunk, came into sight, set in motion by oars not much broader than walking sticks. The oars were in the hands of a young girl who had been gathering water-lilies. She had long, dark-brown braids of hair, and great dark eyes, but she was strangely pale, a pallor that was not gray, but softly pink tinted. Her cheeks were no deeper in color than the rest of her face; her lips were scarce redder. She wore a bodice of white linen and a leather belt with a golden clasp. Her skirt was of blue with a broad red hem. She rowed past close by the outlaws without seeing them. They sat absolutely quiet, less from fear of discovery than from the desire to look at her undisturbed. When she had gone, the stone statues became men again and smiled:

"She was as white as the water-lilies," said one. "And her eyes were as dark as the water back there under the roots of the pines."

They were both so merry that they felt like laughing, like really laughing as they had never laughed in this swamp before, a laugh that would echo back from the wall of rock and loosen the roots of the pines.

"Did you think her beautiful?" asked the Giant.

"I do not know, she passed so quickly. Perhaps she was beautiful."

"You probably did not dare to look at her. Did you think she was the Nixie?"

And again they felt a strange desire to laugh.

. . . .

While a child, Tord had once seen a drowned man. He had found the corpse on the beach in broad daylight, and it had not frightened him, but at night his dreams were terrifying. He had seemed to be looking out over an ocean, every wave of which threw a dead body at his feet. He saw all the rocks and islands covered with corpses of the drowned, the drowned that were dead and belonged to the sea, but that could move, and speak, and threaten him with their white, stiffened fingers.

And so it was again. The girl whom he had seen in the reeds appeared to him in his dreams. He met her again down at the bottom of the swamp lake, where the light was greener even than in the reeds, and there he had time enough to see that she was beautiful. He dreamed that he sat on one of the great pine roots in the midst of the lake while the tree rocked up and down, now under, now over the surface of the water. Then he saw her on one of the smallest islands. She stood under the red mountain ash and laughed at him. In his very last dream it had gone so far that she had kissed him. But then it was morning, and he heard Berg rising, but he kept his eyes stubbornly closed that he might continue to dream. When he did awake he was dazed and giddy from what he had seen during the night. He thought much more about the girl than he had done the day before. Toward evening it occurred to him to ask Berg if he knew her name.

Berg looked at him sharply. "It is better for you to know it at once," he said. "It was Unn. We are related to each other."

And then Tord knew that it was this pale maiden who was the cause of Berg's wild hunted life in forest and mountain. He tried to search his memory for what he had heard about her.

Unn was the daughter of a free peasant. Her mother was dead, and she ruled in her father's household. This was to her taste, for she was independent by nature, and had no inclination to give herself to any husband. Unn and Berg were cousins, and the rumor had long gone about that Berg liked better to sit with Unn and her maids than to work at home in his own house. One Christmas, when the great banquet was to be given in Berg's hall, his wife had invited a monk from Draksmark, who, she hoped, would show Berg how wrong it was that he should neglect her for another. Berg and others besides him hated this monk because of his appearance. He was very stout and absolutely white. The ring of hair around his bald head, the brows above his moist eyes, the color of his skin, of his hands, and of his garments, were all white. Many found him very repulsive to look at.

But the monk was fearless, and as he believed that his words would have greater weight if many heard them, he rose at the table before all the guests, and said: "Men call the cuckoo the vilest of birds because he brings up his young in the nest of others. But here sits a man who takes no care for his house and his children, and who seeks his pleasure with a strange woman. Him I will call the vilest of men." Unn rose in her place. "Berg, this is said to you and me," she cried. "Never have I been so shamed, but my father is not here to protect me." She turned to go, but Berg hurried after her. "Stay where you are," she said. "I do not wish to see you again." He stopped her in the corridor, and asked her what he should do that she might stay with him. Her eyes glowed as she answered that he himself should know best what he must do. Then Berg went into the hall again and slew the monk.

Berg and Tord thought on awhile with the same thoughts, then Berg said: "You should have seen her when the white monk fell. My wife drew the children about her and cursed Unn. She turned the faces of the children toward her, that they might always remember the woman for whose sake their father had become a murderer. But Unn stood there so quiet and so beautiful that the men who saw her trembled. She thanked me for the deed, and prayed me to flee to the woods at once. She told me never to become a robber, and to use my knife only in some cause equally just."

"Your deed had ennobled her," said Tord.

And again Berg found himself astonished at the same thing that had before now surprised him in the boy. Tord was a heathen, or worse than a heathen; he never condemned that which was wrong. He seemed to know no sense of responsibility. What had to come, came. He knew of God, of Christ, and the Saints, but he knew them only by name, as one knows the names of the gods of other nations. The ghosts of the Scheeren Islands were his gods. His mother, learned in magic, had taught him to believe in the spirits of the dead. And then it was that Berg undertook a task which was as foolish as if he had woven a rope for his own neck. He opened the eyes of this ignorant boy to the power of God, the Lord of all Justice, the avenger of wrong who condemned sinners to the pangs of hell everlasting. And he taught him to love Christ and His Mother, and all the saintly men and women who sit before the throne of God praying that His anger may be turned away from sinners. He taught him all that mankind has learned to do to soften the wrath of God. He told him of the long trains of pilgrims journeying to the holy places; he told him of those who scourged themselves in their remorse; and he told him of the pious monks who flee the joys of this world.

The longer he spoke the paler grew the boy and the keener his attention as his eyes widened at the visions. Berg would have stopped, but the torrent of his own thoughts carried him away. Night sank down upon them, the black forest night, where the scream of the owl shrills ghostly through the stillness. God came so near to them that the brightness of His throne dimmed the stars, and the angels of vengeance descended upon the mountain heights. And below them the flames of the underworld fluttered up to the outer curve of the earth and licked greedily at this last refuge of a race crushed by sin and woe.

. . . .

Autumn came, and with it came storm. Tord went out alone into the woods to tend the traps and snares, while Berg remained at home to mend his clothes. The boy's path led him up a wooded height along which the falling leaves danced in circles in the gust. Again and again the feeling came to him that some one was walking behind him. He turned several times, then went on again when he had seen that it was only the wind and the leaves. He threatened the rustling circles with his fist, and kept on his way. But he had not silenced the sounds of his vision. At first it was the little dancing feet of elfin children; then it was the hissing of a great snake moving up behind him. Beside the snake there came a wolf, a tall, gray creature, waiting for the moment when the adder should strike at his feet to spring upon his back. Tord hastened his steps, but the visions hastened with him. When they seemed but two steps behind him, ready for the spring, he turned. There was nothing there, as he had known all the time. He sat down upon a stone to rest. The dried leaves played about his feet. The leaves of all the forest trees were there: the little yellow birch leaves, the red-tinged mountain ash leaves, the dried, black-brown foliage of the elm, the bright red aspen leaves, and the yellow-green fringes of the willows. Faded and crumpled, broken, and scarred, they were but little like the soft, tender shoots of green that had unrolled from the buds a few months ago.

"Ye are sinners," said the boy. "All of us are sinners. Nothing is pure in the eyes of God. Ye have already been shriveled up in the flame of His wrath."

Then he went on again, while the forest beneath him waved like a sea in storm, although it was still and calm on the path around him. But he heard something he had never heard before. The wood was full of voices. Now it was like a whispering, now a gentle plaint, now a loud threat, or a roaring curse. It laughed, and it moaned. It was as the voice of hundreds. This unknown something that threatened and excited, that whistled and hissed, a something that seemed to be, and yet was not, almost drove him mad. He shivered in deadly terror, as he had shivered before, the day that he lay on the floor of his cave, and heard his pursuers rage over him through the forest. He seemed to hear again the crashing of the branches, the heavy footsteps of the men, the clanking of their arms, and their wild, bloodthirsty shouts.

It was not alone the storm that roared about him. There was something else in it, something yet more terrible; there were voices he could not understand, sounds as of a strange speech. He had heard many a mightier storm than this roar through the rigging. But he had never heard the wind playing on a harp of so many strings. Every tree seemed to have its own voice, every ravine had another song, the loud echo from the rocky wall shouted back in its own voice. He knew all these tones, but there were other stranger noises with them. And it was these that awoke a storm of voices within his own brain.

He had always been afraid when alone in the darkness of the wood. He loved the open sea and the naked cliffs. Ghosts and spirits lurked here in the shadows of the trees.

Then suddenly he knew who was speaking to him in the storm. It was God, the Great Avenger, the Lord of all Justice. God pursued him because of his comrade. God demanded that he should give up the murderer of the monk to vengeance.

Tord began to speak aloud amid the storm. He told God what he wanted to do, but that he could not do it. He had wanted to speak to the Giant and to beg him make his peace with God. But he could not find the words; embarrassment tied his tongue. "When I learned that the world is ruled by a God of Justice," he cried, "I knew that he was a lost man. I have wept through the night for my friend. I know that God will find him, no matter where he may hide. But I could not speak to him; I could not find the words because of my love for him. Do not ask that I shall speak to him. Do not ask that the ocean shall rise to the height of the mountains."

He was silent again, and the deep voice of the storm, which he knew for God's voice, was silent also. There was a sudden pause in the wind, a burst of sunshine, a sound as of oars, and the gentle rustling of stiff reeds. These soft tones brought up the memory of Unn.

Then the storm began again, and he heard steps behind him, and a breathless panting. He did not dare to turn this time, for he knew that it was the white monk. He came from the banquet in Berg's great hall, covered with blood, and with an open ax cut in his forehead. And he whispered: "Betray him. Give him up, that you may save his soul."

Tord began to run. All this terror grew and grew in him, and he tried to flee from it. But as he ran he heard behind him the deep, mighty voice, which he knew was the voice of God. It was God himself pursuing him, demanding that he should give up the murderer. Berg's crime seemed more horrible to him than ever it had seemed before. A weapon-

less man had been murdered, a servant of God cut down by the steel.
And the murderer still dared to live. He dared to enjoy the light of
the sun and the fruits of the earth. Tord halted, clinched his fists, and
shrieked a threat. Then, like a madman, he ran from the forest, the
realm of terror, down into the valley.

.   .   .   .

When Tord entered the cave the outlaw sat upon the bench of stone,
sewing. The fire gave but a pale light, and the work did not seem to
progress satisfactorily. The boy's heart swelled in pity. This superb
Giant seemed all at once so poor and so unhappy.

"What is the matter?" asked Berg. "Are you ill? Have you been
afraid?"

Then for the first time Tord spoke of his fear. "It was so strange in
the forest. I heard the voices of spirits and I saw ghosts. I saw white
monks."

"Boy!"

"They sang to me all the way up the slope to the hilltop. I ran from
them, but they ran after me, singing. Can I not lay the spirits? What
have I to do with them? There are others to whom their appearance is
more necessary."

"Are you crazy tonight, Tord?"

Tord spoke without knowing what words he was using. His shyness
had left him all at once; speech seemed to flow from his lips. "They
were white monks, as pale as corpses. And their clothes are spotted with
blood. They draw their hoods down over their foreheads, but I can see
the wound shining there. The great, yawning, red wound from the ax."

"Tord," said the giant, pale and deeply grave, "the Saints alone know
why you see wounds of ax thrusts. I slew the monk with a knife."

Tord stood before Berg trembling and wringing his hands. "They
demand you of me. They would compel me to betray you."

"Who? The monks?"

"Yes, yes, the monks. They show me visions. They show me Unn.
They show me the open, sunny ocean. They show me the camps of the
fishermen, where there is dancing and merriment. I close my eyes, and
yet I can see it all. 'Leave me,' I say to them. 'My friend has committed a murder, but he is not bad. Leave me alone, and I will talk to
him, that he may repent and atone. He will see the wrong he has done,
and he will make a pilgrimage to the Holy Grave.'"

"And what do the monks answer?" asked Berg. "They do not want
to pardon me. They want to torture me and to burn me at the stake."

"'Shall I betray my best friend?' I ask them. 'He is all that I have
in the world. He saved me from the bear when its claws were already
at my throat. We have suffered hunger and cold together. He covered
me with his own garments while I was ill. I have brought him wood and

water, I have watched over his sleep and led his enemies off the trail. Why should they think me a man who betrays his friend? My friend will go to the priest himself, and will confess to him, and then together we will seek absolution.' "

Berg listened gravely, his keen eyes searching in Tord's face. "Go to the priest yourself, and tell him the truth. You must go back again among mankind."

"What does it help if I go alone? The spirits of the dead follow me because of your sin. Do you not see how I tremble before you? You have lifted your hand against God himself. What crime is like unto yours? Why did you tell me about the just God? It is you yourself who compel me to betray you. Spare me this sin. Go to the priest yourself." He sank down on his knees before Berg.

The murderer laid his hand on his head and looked at him. He measured his sin by the terror of his comrade, and it grew and grew to monstrous size. He saw himself in conflict with the Will that rules the world. Remorse entered his heart.

"Woe unto me that I did what I did," he said. "And is not this miserable life, this life we lead here in terror, and in deprivation, is it not atonement enough? Have I not lost home and fortune? Have I not lost friends, and all the joys that make the life of a man? What more?"

As he heard him speak thus, Tord sprang up in wild terror. "You can repent!" he cried. "My words move your heart? Oh, come with me, come at once. Come, let us go while yet there is time."

Berg the Giant sprang up also. "You—did it——?"

"Yes, yes, yes. I have betrayed you. But come quickly. Come now, now that you can repent. We must escape. We will escape."

The murderer stooped to the ground where the battle-ax of his fathers lay at his feet. "Son of a thief," he hissed. "I trusted you—I loved you."

But when Tord saw him stoop for the ax, he knew that it was his own life that was in peril now. He tore his own ax from his girdle, and thrust at Berg before the latter could rise. The Giant fell headlong to the floor, the blood spurting out over the cave. Between the tangled masses of hair Tord saw the great, yawning, red wound of an ax thrust.

Then the peasants stormed into the cave. They praised his deed and told him that he should receive full pardon.

Tord looked down at his hands, as if he saw there the fetters that had drawn him on to kill the man he loved. Like the chains of the Fenris wolf, they were woven out of empty air. They were woven out of the green light amid the reeds, out of the play of shadows in the woods, out of the song of the storm, out of the rustling of the leaves, out of the magic vision of dreams. And he said aloud: "God is great."

He crouched beside the body, spoke amid his tears to the dead, and begged him to awake. The villagers made a litter of their spears, on which to carry the body of the free peasant to his home. The dead man aroused awe in their souls, they softened their voices in his presence. When they raised him on to the bier, Tord stood up, shook the hair from his eyes, and spoke in a voice that trembled:

"Tell Unn, for whose sake Berg the Giant became a murderer, that Tord the fisherman whose father plunders wrecks, and whose mother is a witch—tell her that Tord slew Berg because Berg had taught him that justice is the cornerstone of the world."

THE BEAR TAMER'S DAUGHTER

By Konrad Bercovici

[Konrad Bercovici was born in Roumania in 1882 and came to the United States at the age of thirty-four. He has lived in or near New York City since 1916. He has been a prolific writer principally in the field of the short story. Among his volumes of stories, narratives, and articles are: *Dust of New York, Ghitza, Murdo, Ileana—The Marriage Guest, Around the World in New York, Volga Boatmen, Story of the Gypsies*, and *Between Earth and Sky. Costa's Daughter* is Mr. Bercovici's contribution to the drama.

The Bear Tamer's Daughter is reprinted in this collection by permission of the author.]

COSTA, the bear tamer, was well known all along the Carpathian Mountains; on the Hungarian side of the chain of mountains as well as on the Rumanian side. Of the hundreds of gypsies, roving to and fro between the villages, dancing their bears before inns and on the market-places, more than half bought their bears from Costa.

A bear tamed by Costa was worth a fortune. It could dance on all fours and waltz on its hind legs to the sound of a tambourine or the music of a flute; it turned somersaults, could stand on its head, roll a log or an empty barrel, stand at attention and do a thousand other cute things to amuse children and grown-ups.

And Costa was continually inventing new tricks for his bears. He could teach them anything he wanted. Once in Costa's hands a bear was not let go until it was an accomplished artist and could be relied upon to do the bidding of its master.

Costa had his establishment in a gully deep down between two mountainsides, and from early spring to late in the fall in small tents that were pitched between the tall sun-hungry trees, Costa lived with his daughter, Margarita.

In a cranny at the foot of the mountain was the school. There, Costa, all alone, surrounded only by huge brown bears, man-eating beasts caught only yesterday, plied his trade.

It was Costa's custom to leave his gully early every spring as soon as the snow began to melt, to go in search of bears. With a large loaf of black bread and a piece of cheese in a carpet-bag, a bottle of whisky in the long upper of one of his boots, a sharp knife in the other, a well-oiled army revolver in his wide, red belt, a rope, a few short chains, the links of which he had himself forged during the long winter months, the

722

pointed black fur cap 'way down over his bushy brows, Costa was off among the mountains in search of bears.

Sometimes, when in luck, he returned the same day or the same night dragging at the end of the rope a huge she-bear not yet completely awakened from her winter sleep, and a little cub or two, hind paws tied to hind paws, slung on his shoulders. At other times Costa was away for days and weeks.

He never came home empty-handed and, indeed, it was a bad week when the heavily bearded, tall, black-eyed gypsy did not sell at least one fresh bearskin to some innkeeper.

But Costa was not much interested in killing bears. He needed them alive. He knew every inch of the Carpathian Mountains and knew every bear-hole. He had a thousand different tricks for catching a bear alive.

If there were no tracks about the bear's winter home, Costa would empty half his flask of whisky in an earthen dish and place it at one of the two exit-places a she-bear generally makes before going to hibernate. Then he would gather a few sticks, set them on fire, sprinkle them with sulphur, place them near the other exit and withdraw to observe developments.

If the bear was beginning to awaken from her long sleep, the smoke and the odor of sulphur would have its effect. The beast would soon come upon the bowl filled with alcohol, turn around it, smell it, taste, and finish by lapping it dry.

A while later Costa would creep in on all fours, knife between his teeth, pistol in one hand and ready rope-noose in the other. If his calculations had not gone amiss, if the whisky had been of the right kind, Costa was soon dragging a bear behind the rope.

But that was only one of a thousand ways of catching a bear alive. The real manner was determined according to conditions, whims and instinct. After catching a dozen bears or so, the schooling would begin. No matter how a freshly caught bear tugged at the chain when anyone approached it, when Costa came near the beast it would cringe and whine. In a week at the most the fiercest bear was tamed.

He would take the beast to the *cainny*, to the "private school," as he called the fissure in the mountains, and in a day or two Master Bruin was glad to do any trick demanded of him if only he had not to face again the man who had caught him.

Such was Costa. But once a bear was tamed he lost all interest in the animal, hated him, spat at him when he passed the tree to which the beast was chained. And during the long winter nights he would tell stories to the pipe-smoking peasants at the inn, stories of other days, when bears were really fierce beasts, when it took weeks of cunning to get them and months to tame them and when every bear-dancer caught and tamed his own bear, when the bears in the Carpathians were bears and men were men and not, as they are now, when bears are tame kittens and men are old women.

And it so happened that none of Costa's own sons was worthy of his father. They could teach fine enough tricks to the bears after they were tamed by the old man; they could drive a good bargain with another gypsy coming to buy a bear; but they did not have the nose, could not scent a bear's hole and never dared what their father dared. In time they all left their father and settled in a separate gully to ply his trade of bear tamer.

Costa would have despaired of life altogether because of his offspring had it not been for his only daughter, whom he had by one of his wives, a clean-limbed almost wild woman, half Tartar and half Cherkez. He had bought her from a horse-selling gypsy chief and she had died when her daughter was yet very young. And that daughter of his, Margarita, with the straight, clean limbs of her mother and the sharp, angular almost Egyptian features of her father, was Costa's pride.

She was too young to go a-hunting like her father, or accompany him, but she could tame a mature bear almost as quickly and thoroughly as he could. She had started with the cubs her father brought when she was not yet eight years old. When she was ten, cubs grown to bears, on a chain in the gully, were disgustingly easy for her, and even some of the beasts her father brought dragging at the end of a rope were unworthy of her attention, unless they were of the proper kind, fierce, and full of fight.

Then, oh, then, life held some charms!

"Come, Margarita," her father would call to her. "This looks like a real one."

Bare-legged, disheveled, the gypsy girl would face the animal, cowhide whip in her bare brown hand, and try him. And if the bear showed fight she danced for joy, she hugged and kissed her father, tore at his mustache and bit hair from his beard.

"*Tatuca, tatuca*, it's a real one this time!"

And for days and days, from early morning to late at night, it mattered not whether a dozen wild-eyed buyers clamored to see the chief, or it snowed, or brother fought brother with knives and whips, father and daughter remained with the real one in the private school.

They emerged only when the work was done. Thinner, with eyes sparkling, arms and legs scarred and with pride in work accomplished, father or daughter would call to one of the would-be buyers:

"Take him out and give him some water. He will eat out of your hands."

And he would. The sight of any two-legged animal was enough to drive fear into any graduate from the private school of Costa and his daughter.

Then the father would say to Margarita: "That was yours." Or, "It was mine."

No compliments were exchanged. There was no contradiction on that score. Instinctively each of them knew by whom and when, at what stroke of the whip, the thing was accomplished.

When Margarita was fourteen years old it so happened that her father's catches that spring had been only *mortaciunas*, dead ones, kittens. It was a pity to waste cowhide on them. The winter had been a very long one after a very wet fall and the bears were so weak from prolonged hibernation and hunger that they looked more like sheep than man-eating beasts.

Margarita had hoped every day for a "real live one." But no. *Mortaciunas* they were, every one of them. While her father was away she stalked, whip in hand, from one bear to the other, teased them, hit them, now gave them pieces of raw meat to awaken their taste for blood, lassoed the playful cubs from their mothers to stir their savagery, but to no avail.

Occasionally some female would shoot out a paw and give a tug at the chain, one end of which was dangling from a ring pierced through the nose. Margarita's hopes would rise and she would scream for joy in a dozen endearing names, yet a second application of the whip would hardly stir the bear from its place.

And when the spring came to a close and the wild bears left the gullies and valleys and climbed the tops of the mountains for sheep, deer and wild goat, father and daughter had no excitement. The taming done and most of the bears sold, Costa went a-browsing from inn to inn, from village to village, drinking, carousing, playing cards and fighting with other gypsies, sometimes on the Roumanian side of the mountains and at other times on the Hungarian side, working up some excitement for himself by outwitting the frontier guards posted on either side of the Carpathians.

He returned home once in a while to inquire how things went; if any of the bears needed private schooling. But if such a state had come to pass, Margarita had already attended to it and there was nothing more to be done.

Margarita was far from being satisfied. She could have picked quarrels with her brothers, who came occasionally to visit her, or with the husbands of her half-sisters, but they were all "old women," well-fed, satisfied traders. Nor was there any fun in quarreling with the *tziganes* who came to buy tamed bears. She threw insults to their teeth.

"Why don't you hunt for your own bears? You only want tame bears because you are tame men yourselves. You are tame men yourselves."

They did not answer her. They told her she had pretty eyes and beautiful teeth, that her arms were round and brown. Some playfully inquired how she would like it if they would buy her from her father. But that was all.

"Sell me to you? Sell me to you? Sell a tiger to a lamb? I would tear you to pieces. No, I would not. I would just spit at you. Like that *na, ptui.*"

"Well, no, I would not buy you. I would not take you for a gift," she was answered.

"Of course you would not. You are afraid. I dare you. You are afraid. You buy tame bears. This one here, I tamed him. You could eat from one plate with him now. Or better buy this one here. He was born tame. As you were. His father was a lamb as yours was. That's the kind you want. You buy them tamed. Even your women you buy tamed. Why don't you hunt for them? You are afraid. You buy them at the end of a rope. Tied, cowed."

She teased, she dared. In vain. Men looked at her from the corner of an eye but avoided her, and no one ever inquired seriously of her father whether she was for sale or not.

One early morning, the time of the year when leaves were fluttering in the brumal air, when frost, the shadow of winter, sits on the fox grapes and plums, Petrackio, the son of Ursu, the bear tamer, entered the gully where lived Costa and his daughter.

Ursu, the bear tamer, was an old competitor of Costa's. His establishment was twenty miles from there. The two bear tamers were deadly enemies, and it was known that if the two should ever meet alone in the mountains, but one would return. That Ursu's son, Petrackio, should venture to Costa's gully was the height of audacity. What brought him there was the fact that his father had been away for more than two weeks and no one had seen him.

Sure that Costa had killed him, the boy came to avenge his father. Petrackio and Margarita had never seen each other. The young gypsy prowled about the camp for a little while without perceiving anyone. It was Sunday. Suddenly Margarita came out of the tent and yawned as she stretched her arms high over her head.

"Hey, you!" he called to her. "Is your father dead or is he hibernating already?"

"No," she answered; "he is milking the goat for babies who have lost themselves in the mountains."

As she spoke she came nearer to the young gypsy and looked him straight in the eye. His was a new face. The boy stood straight, with feet well apart, neck bent forward, and lips drawn away from the teeth. Margarita was thrilled. It was a "live one," one that should fight the whole summer. She had longed for a bear who would not tame easily and she almost ran for her whip after one good look at the boy, who squared himself before her. She had never before seen a face that promised more fight, more sport, than that now before her.

"And who are you?" he asked the girl as he returned her fierce glances.

"I am Costa's daughter," she answered, without moving an inch.

"And who are you? Have you come to buy a tame bear, a very tame bear," she mocked, "one who dances as soon as you say 'martino,' like this, like that?"

"I want none of your puppets. When I want a bear I go and get him in his lair with my bare hands," the youth answered.

Then after a while he continued, narrowing his eyes as he spoke:

"So you are Margarita, Costa's daughter! So you are Margarita! So—so! The daughter of that Cherkez woman. So—so! Well, I am Petrackio, Ursu's son. And I come for revenge. Where is your father?"

Margarita knew well what the trouble was. She also knew that her father had been away to the Dobrudja more than a month and had returned only the night before. She could have said so and assured Petrackio. Instead of that she laughed loudly, tossing her head this way and that, then hissing between her teeth, with neck stretching out toward the boy:

"Why don't you wait another twenty years when my father will be lame and blind, and fight him! Why, Ursu's son, that was between old men. If you want to fight, why not fight me?"

"You, a girl?"

It drew fire. In a flash Margarita was in her tent and back. She held her whip in one hand when she returned. Her body was as taut as a steel spring.

"So, that's what you think of me? Not good enough to fight with? I will show you who I am."

Chained to a stout tree, not far from where they were, a huge brown bear was standing on its haunches and grunting. Before Petrackio had known what had happened Margarita, with one tug at the chain, had torn the ring from the nose of the bear. Bellowing from the depths of its lungs, the bleeding animal charged ahead, kicking, pawing, shaking its head viciously back and forth as it charged the girl whose only weapon was the cowhide whip in her hand.

When the bear was near enough she let the whip fall upon its head again and again. Her arm worked like a piston rod. The bear repeated its charge, yet the girl gave no ground but kept on whipping the beast over the head until it reeled and retreated to seek shelter behind its tree.

"Will you fight me now?" Margarita asked, turning savagely on the boy who had not moved from his place.

"No," he said. "I won't fight a woman."

"It is because you are afraid. You want to fight an old man."

"Afraid, I? Have you never heard of Petrackio! I will fight a dozen of your brothers. The whole tribe of your men."

"We have no men, only old women; fight me if you dare. Here, I begin," and Margarita brought her whip across the boy's face.

It was as if a thousand bees had suddenly stung the boy. It was as if a swift turning wheel had been set on fire. Before Margarita had had time to know what happened her whip had been jerked loose from her hand and she was thrown face downward in the dirt. Petrackio's knee was between her shoulders, holding her down as one holds a squirming, wriggling, stinging snake.

Margarita felt the cold steel blade as it touched the back of her neck and thought the last breath was near.

"Snake! I will not kill you. I don't kill women. I want your father to know that I have been here. You shall tell him. And lest you forget I shall take your tresses as a reminder.

When Margarita rose from the ground she felt the cold wind on her bare neck. Petrackio had cut off her tresses and was already on his horse galloping homeward at full gallop. She looked after him and screamed. She shook her fists and stamped her feet and devised a thousand tortures for him and his father as soon as she should capture them. That very night she and her father were to pounce upon them in their gully and drag them to the cranny, to the private school, and teach them to dance. Ah! He would pay dearly for that. She would chain him herself, pass a ring through his upper lip, as she did to bears, and teach him tricks.

And afterward—ah, afterward—he would know who Margarita was. She ran to her tent, looked at herself in the silver-handled mirror her father had once given her, and screamed again. He had cut off her hair! The coward! Better he had killed her!

How could she ever show herself now? She would have to stay in her hut the whole winter; avoid being seen by anyone. Oh, why had he not killed her? He would pay for that. Oh, he would pay! She stampeded the dogs and grazing horses and in her excitement tore through the camp like a whirlwind.

Presently, only too eager to start the journey of revenge, she blew the horn to call her father. But when she saw him descending the nearest mountain she went into the hut, and, covering her head with a colored shawl, a *basma*, she pretended to Costa that she had called him because she was so wretched. She did not mention Petrackio's visit.

"What's the *basma* on your head?" Costa asked.

"Washed my hair, *tatuca*."

"What do you want, Margarita? Why have you called me? Here, what is the matter with that bear there? Bleeding, I see, and loose, too. By all the devils! Margarita, what have you been up to?"

"Oh, leave him. He is like a kitten again. Leave him, father. Why don't you ever get real ones again? When spring comes I go with you hunting."

"But what has happened to the bear, Margarita? Has he thrown you? Did you call me because you were afraid now that the beast is loose? Speak, you she-devil."

"Afraid! I? Here!"

And she went close to the bear.

"But, then, why have you called me suddenly?"

"I want you to take me to the village."

"So, so; well, that's different! Let's close up this *martino* until we come back, and let us go. Saddle my horse, Margarita, while you saddle yours." As he spoke Costa roped the bear and dragged it to a fissure in the mountain for which a revolving rock served as a door.

"That's women. They are all alike when the time comes. Their feet burn. They want to go and come. She, too, like the rest," muttered Costa as he finished his job.

Father and daughter were not loquacious. Seclusion breeds silence. Margarita rode on her small horse, following at a few paces from her father's mount. As she rode on she thought of him, of Petrackio. Of course he was a real one. But was she herself a real one? How he had knocked the whip from her hand and thrown her to the ground! It had come with such suddenness and force that she did not know how it had been done.

But she still felt the grip of his fingers on her arm, the hardness of his knee between her shoulders and the quick, hot breath as he spoke to her while she was at his mercy.

"Snake! I don't kill women. I want your father to know that I have been here."

That was bravery. She would fight him, him alone. She would tame him. But not like that, not as one tames a bear. That was not the way. He was a man.

By the time they had reached the market-place of the village Margarita had reconstructed the whole episode of the morning a hundred times and had judged carefully his actions and hers. She had very little to reproach herself with. She had acted as she should. And he? He . . . No. He should have killed her. No. No. That would not have been the right thing. To cut off her hair, to provoke her father by the insult, was greater bravery.

By the time they had tethered their horses to the trees in front of the inn Margarita had weighed him carefully in her mind and decided that he was a real one.

Not a word to her father. She would take care of all that herself. All alone. Costa had a grudge to settle with Ursu. That was all his affair. The grudge between herself and Petrackio was a separate thing.

"Whoa, look who is here!" several peasants called out loudly at Costa's appearance at the inn. "Come in, come in. *Fata mare*, come in and let us look at your eyes," said the inn-keeper, being seconded by the *popa*, the priest of the village.

"Still training cubs, *fata mare?*" Popa Yancu asked, trying to pinch Margarita's arm.

"Cubs!" called out Costa. "Cubs! She is taming the wildest quite as well as I can." And, growing suddenly very proud of his daughter: "Better, even better, I say. She may sit among men at the inn and everywhere. Sit near me, Margarita, here. Bring wine, the oldest, Calin, you swindling inn-keeper, and set glasses, big glasses, Hungarian fashion, for each of us, including my daughter." And turning to Margarita, he said: "And if you want music, I will send a messenger to bring Yancu Lautauru, or anyone you like best to hear. No? As you wish it to be."

"Ursu has gone by, an hour ago," said the innkeeper Calin as he filled the glasses.

"And why do you tell me that?" broke out Costa in a rage. "Have I ever inquired about him, what?"

"No, Costa, but he was bitten by a snake while he was in the mountains. He had to cut off one of his toes—he may lose his right foot, it swells so rapidly, and he is lame, maybe forever," said the innkeeper.

"Is that so? Tell us more. What do you know about it?" the peasants asked, curious for further information.

"That's all I know. I sold him some pure brandy. It's good to have it near oneself before the end comes," the innkeeper added. "He looks old and worn, and is bent like a twig after a hailstorm."

"Well, that's different, Calin, that's different," Costa muttered as he sat down again and began to bite off the ends of his long beard as he always did when he had to suppress great rage. "And do you say he will remain lame for life, Calin?"

"Looks that way to me."

Father's and daughter's eyes met. Margarita knew how he hated Ursu. He looked at her and she understood. He was being cheated out of his revenge. He could not fight a lame man. He did not know what her look said. He was blinded by his own rage against men and bears and life itself. Life was becoming too tame an affair. Men were tame. Bears were tame. No fights. No wolves. No robbers. No women were stolen. Ursu had been the only man and now he was lame.

"Has a fine lad for a son, Ursu has," the *popa* said as he looked at Margarita and winked to the rest of the assemblage. "He is a better hunter than his father."

"That's not very much," said Costa.

They all laughed at the sally and punched the gypsy in the ribs.

"Well, no, it's not so at all," explained the *popa*. "He is as strong a boy as there is within fifty miles of here. Quiet and strong, and good, too. And he can tame a bear as well as anybody. I ought to know!"

It was only on rare occasions that the *popa* thus revealed the fact that he was himself the son of a bear tamer. It was plain that the *popa* favored Petrackio.

"Well, be that as it may," said Costa, "but I bet a gold-piece that Margarita could throw him."

"No, no, no," many voices rose at once.

"I bet a hundred gold-pieces."

"You might as well bet a thousand!" the *popa* exclaimed. "I know the boy too well. He won't wrestle with a girl."

"But I tell you that she can throw any man," Costa argued as the wine began to have its effect. He was a bad drinker and was becoming boisterous and quarrelsome after a few drinks.

"Well, Calin, it's all your fault. Giving news about some one at least one of the party is not interested in," said an old peasant as he made ready to leave the table.

"That's so. Miron is right," seconded Costa as he rose from his chair. "Here I come ready to drink and have some music, talk with friends and please my daughter, when he finds nothing else to tell me but that Ursu had gone by. Here, take your money from this gold-piece. Come, daughter. Good night, men."

And Costa stalked out of the inn before anybody else had left.

Margarita rode silently near her father. Like a flock of golden sheep the rays of the sun broke and scattered themselves on the cold, silver mountain peaks. From time to time an awkward movement of some animal disturbed some stone or bowlder which rolled down the mountainside, filling the valley with sharp echoes that died in the dull, hollow thuds as they ended in the valleys.

Suddenly Costa began to sob. He cried easily after a glass of wine. It was his weakest spot. And as he cried it seemed as if all the mountains cried with him, felt his sorrow and wept with him. Margarita, awakened from her dreams, sped her horse.

"Why have you waited twenty years?" she reproached her father, knowing the reason for his sorrow. "If I had a grudge to settle I would not wait that long. The same day, the same day, or a day later at the most."

"Oh, a bad year! A bad year," moaned Costa. "Without a wife! Bears tame as kittens and Ursu lame, lame, lame! Oh! Oh! It's a bad year, a bad year, daughter."

"You don't even catch a live one now," the daughter reproached him again. "Is it because you are getting old? Or are bears and men all tame now? You cry like a woman. Listen, the mountain cries too. Shame!"

"I old? I old? You are crazy. The bears were tame last year. Too long a winter. Too long. Without a wife, and Ursu lame," and the old man sobbed again. "Let the mountains cry with me. They understand."

It was pitch dark by the time they had reached their gully, and Costa stretched himself on the straw-pile as soon as he let the flap of his tent fall back again.

Margarita stabled, watered, and fed the horses before she thought again of herself. She touched her neck and felt again with her fingers the place where her heavy tresses had been cut off. She thought of him and cursed him for the insult.

Yet, altho it seemed to her that she still felt the grip of his steel-like fingers on her flesh, she had no desire to free herself, no desire to shake off the illusion of a sharp knee that pressed down her shoulders; and between a thousand curses and tears of rage she saw Petrackio's sharp features, the eyes set well apart, the small ears set back firmly, the mouth and nose and forehead bespeaking courage and decision.

Margarita could not sleep. As she reviewed again what had happened in the morning she regretted that she had not used the whip on Petrackio more than she had done. It would have been much better, she thought. He should know that Costa's daughter was not a plaything. He would have gone home and found his father had returned. Petrackio would have come to see her. It would have been well for him to know that Costa's daughter was not to be trifled with. She should have used the whip more rapidly. It might have saved her long tresses.

She tried to place in her memory the exact instant the boy had knocked the whip out of her hand and thrown her to the ground. She was doubtless in his power then, absolutely in his power. He could have done what he pleased with her—he could have killed her.

As she sat on the ground in front of her tent she suddenly heard the beat of a horse's hoofs at a distance. Margarita listened and when she was sure the rider came toward the gully she entered her tent. The hoof-beats soon ceased. A dog barked. After that she heard a sharp, long, penetrating whistle. Margarita's ears, accustomed to catch the sounds, soon knew that the birds in the surrounding chestnut-trees were scenting danger. The flight of the chipmunk told her the intruder was within sight of the camp.

Again the dog barked; just one short yelp and no more. Some one had thrown him a piece of raw meat. She had heard the flop of it as it fell to the ground. Then some one whistled softly from very near. Margarita could hardly contain herself for joy.

It was Petrackio. He was a real one and she was taming him! It was the old sensation of taming bears with a thousand new thrills added. She forgot all about the loss of her tresses. What did they matter when weighed against such pleasure?

Something in her urged her to rush out to the man and talk to him. But something stronger held her back, gave promise of greater pleasure if she but sat quiet and watched the taming. It was like drinking good wine in small gulps to prolong the pleasure, to satiate oneself with the exquisite taste.

She heard the whistling again and again and every time she heard the shrill sounds she thought it the sweetest music. Not the loudest howl from the fiercest bear she had ever tamed could compare with that. He, Petrackio, was a real one, and she was taming him. And not with a cowhide whip. Not with red-hot coals and a piece of sheet iron on which the bear was compelled to dance. No, no, with another weapon, an invisible weapon, a sharper and more potent one.

She would have screamed for joy but she controlled herself. Silence added to the sting of the weapon. More than that. It was the weapon.

Daylight was coming in through rents in the canvas of the tent. The few last screeches of a preying owl, then the clicking of wild pheasants proclaimed that the sun was peeping over the mountain tops, like a red-faced boy over a high garden fence. He, Petrackio, was calling her. He was calling her. But she would not answer.

There was a last appeal in an "Oho, oho!" coming from behind her tent, then there was silence for a while. After that, and before there were too many sounds in the valley, Margarita heard the hoof-beats of a departing horse. Tired, feverish, she fell asleep.

"Ho, ho, ho!" She awoke suddenly, hearing her father's voice outside her tent. "The sun has gone to Hungary and you are still sleeping! Was the wine too strong for you? What?"

"Yes, no, yes, no, *tatuca*. Let me sleep. I want to sleep. My head aches."

"That comes from washing your hair too often," the father answered before leaving. After that he muttered to himself, "When the time comes, they are all like that."

She heard her father approach her tent several times before nightfall but she made believe that she was fast asleep. He left some food near her cot. But, as in the days when they had a real one to tame, she felt no hunger, only a horrible thirst. An hour after sunset, Margarita was listening for the hoof-beats. She heard none.

Her pain was now sharper than yesterday's joy. She waited and listened until midnight. Not a sound. She went out of her tent and looked at the sky. Her whip, the weapon in which she had had so much confidence all the years, was at her feet. She scorned it now. It was a weapon as crude as a child's plaything.

After she had waited and listened for many weary hours she whistled loud and long. The sound reverberated, thrown from one mountain wall to the other and back, until it died in some distant gully. It was like the call of some wild animal.

She waited silently. There was no answer to her call. But when she lifted the flap of her tent at daybreak she found the two braided tresses lying across the cot. Startled, shocked, mad, speechless, Margarita took one of the tresses in each hand and rushed out again. Nobody to be seen. The dog was peacefully licking his chops. Wild-eyed, the girl looked around her. Seized by an uncontrollable rage, she went for her whip and began to lash the dog with its thongs.

"So, ha, ha, you will let thieves go and come as they please, will you, will you, ha? Take this and take that."

"Why do you hit the dog?" asked Costa, coming out of his tent, awakened by the animal's howls.

"Why? Why? Because, look, look! Look at my hair. Some one has entered my tent and sheared them off while I was asleep. And he did not move, did not bark, nothing."

"What? What is that?" Costa screamed. "Who did that? Who did that? If I did not know that Ursu was lame, by fire and water! Margarita—my poor girl—my poor girl—who could have done it? I will go to the end of the world to find him."

"A thief, a coward, a triple coward, one who dared not fight me in daylight," screamed Margarita at the top of her voice, knowing that Petrackio could not be too far off to hear her words.

Costa was soon on his horse.

"I shall not return before finding the thief, the coward," was all he said before riding away.

Costa was hardly out of sight when Petrackio showed himself, emerging from behind a tree only a few paces behind the girl.

"Well, I heard you calling me a while ago, so I arrived astride an eagle and dropped your tresses on your cot through the air-hole on top of your tent. Why have you called me?"

"Called you? I called you?"

"I heard your whistle!"

"That was for the dog."

"Be it as you say," Petrackio grinned. "Well then, I may go, Costa's daughter. I gave you back what I took from you." He turned to leave her. "I was sorry, afraid that your father might beat you."

"Did I ask my hair back from you? No. I did not."

"I thought you might want it back," he said banteringly, without looking at the girl, "and, as I happened to pass this way, I just dropped it in the tent."

"You lie; you came on purpose," answered Margarita.

She felt a sudden pang as she saw the deep gash her whip had cut in the boy's face. They looked each other over. The glint of his eyes gripped her eyes even more strongly than his steely fingers had gripped her a day before. The sound of a galloping horse was coming nearer and nearer. Her father was returning. She looked at Petrackio. He too had heard the hoof-beats. Her father must have entered the gully. Petrackio knew that as well as she, yet he did not move a foot. He looked at her steadily. When she had heard her father's voice talking to the horse and seen that the boy had made no move to leave, to hide between the trees, she called to him, trembling with fear:

"Hide, for God's sake, hide. He comes."

"I will wait for you on Sunday at the inn," Petrackio said quietly before vanishing behind a tree.

And as the bear tamer's daughter passed by the tree to which a bear was chained she felt that she herself was as a bear that had been tamed, or trainer that had been tamed by a real live bear, tamed to do the master's will, yet she was already unhappy, thinking of the long days and long nights between then and Sunday.

AFTER HE WAS DEAD

By Melville Davisson Post

[Melville Davisson Post (1871–1930) was born in West Virginia, educated in the liberal arts and in law in the university of his native state, and spent his whole life there as a lawyer, a literary man, and an honored and distinguished citizen. The best of his stories are in the field of mystery with solutions depending upon careful analysis of character, studies in human nature, and plots depending upon points of law. The reader should not miss his story called *The Great Tradition*.

After He Was Dead is reprinted by arrangement with George T. Bye and Company, agents for the Melville Davisson Post estate.]

AN hour before sunset the man, who had been at work all day, turned out of the cornfield. He crossed the furrows to the rail fence, with the hoe in his hands. At the bars leading into the field, a squirrel rifle, with a long wooden stock reaching to the end of the barrel, stood against the chestnut post; beside it lay a powder-horn attached to a pouch of deerskin containing bullets. The man set his hoe against the fence. He wiped his hands on the coarse foxgrass growing in the furrows, examined the sun for a moment, then took up the rifle, removed an exploded cap from the nipple, and began to load it.

He poured the black powder into his palm, and bending his palm emptied it into the barrel. The measure of powder was a sufficient charge, but he added to it half the quantity again, emptied into his palm from the horn. Then he took a handful of bullets out of the pouch, selected one of which the neck was squarely cut, and placing a tiny fragment of calico over the muzzle of the rifle, drew out the hickory ramrod and forced the bullet down. He got a percussion cap out of a paper box, examined it, placed it on the nipple, and gently pressed it down with the hammer of the lock.

When the gun was thus carefully loaded, the man threw it across his shoulder and, taking the horn and the pouch in his hand, left the field. He went along a path leading through a wood to the valley below. Midway of the wood he stopped and concealed the horn and pouch in a hollow tree. Then he continued on his way with the rifle tucked under his arm.

The country below him was one of little farms, skirted by trees lining the crests of low hills. The man traveled for several miles, keeping in the shelter of the wood. Finally, he crossed a river on a fallen tree and sat down in a thicket behind a rail fence. Beyond this fence was a

736

pasture field and a score of grazing cattle. In this field, some twenty paces from where the man sat, the earth was bare in little patches where the owner of the cattle had been accustomed to give them salt.

The sun was still visible, but great shadows were beginning to lengthen across the valley. Presently an old man, riding a gray horse, entered the field from the road. When he came through the gate, the man concealed in the brush cocked his rifle, laid the muzzle on a rail of the fence, and waited, with his jaw pressed against the stock. The old man rode leisurely across the field to the place where he had been accustomed to "salt" his cattle. There he got down, opened a bag which he carried across the pommel of his saddle, and began to drop handfuls of salt on the bare patches in the pasture. From time to time he called the cattle, and when he did so he stood with his back toward the fence, looking at the bullocks approaching slowly from another quarter of the field.

There was a sharp report. The old man turned stiffly on his heels with his arms spread out. His face was distorted with amazement, then it changed to terror. He called out something, in a thick, choked voice; then he fell with his arms doubled under him.

A thin wisp of smoke floated up from the rail fence; the horse, however, did not move; it remained standing with its bridle-rein lying on the earth. The cattle continued to approach. The man in the brush arose. The dead man had called out his name, "Henry Fuget." Of that he was certain. That he had distinctly heard. But of the other words he was not so certain. He thought the old man had said, "You shall hear from me!" But the words were choked in the throat. He might have heard incorrectly. He looked carefully about him to be sure that no one had heard his name thus called out; then he took up his rifle, crossed the river on the fallen tree, and returned toward the cornfield.

He was a stout, compactly-built man of middle life. His hair was dark, but his eyes were blue. He was evidently of Celtic origin. He walked slowly, like one who neither delays nor hurries. He got the horn and pouch from the hollow tree as he passed, reloaded his rifle, shot one or two gray squirrels out of the maple trees, took them in his hand, and went down the ridge through the little valley, to a farmhouse. He had traveled seven miles, and it was now night.

After the evening meal, which the laborer ate with the family of his employer, he went to his bed in the loft of the farmhouse. On this night Fuget ate well and slept profoundly. The stress which had attended his plan to kill Samuel Pickens, seemed now to disappear. The following morning he returned to his work in the cornfield. But as the day advanced he became curious to know if the body of Pickens had been found, and how the country had received the discovery. He had no seizure of anxiety. He had carefully concealed every act in this tragic drama. He was unknown in this part of the country. Pickens had not seen him before the shot. He had come here quietly, obtained employment as a farm laborer, under the name of Williams, located his man, watched, and killed him. True, Pickens had realized who it was who had fired the shot when the bullet entered his body, but he was dead the following moment, and before that he had believed Fuget in another part of the world.

As Fuget remembered the scene, he found himself trying to determine what, exactly, it was that Pickens had said, after he had called his name. It seemed to Fuget that he must have heard incorrectly. He labored to recall the exact sounds that had reached him. If not these words,— "You shall hear from me"—what was it that Pickens had said? And as he puzzled, he became more curious to know how Pickens had been found, and what the people were saying of the murder. Such news travels swiftly.

As the day advanced, Fuget's curiosity increased. He paused from time to time in the furrow, and remained leaning on his hoe-handle. Finally he thrust the blade of the hoe under a root, broke it at the eye, and returned to the farmhouse, with the broken hoe in his hand.

At the door he met the farmer's wife. She spread out her arms with a sudden, abrupt gesture.

"La! Mr. Williams," she said, "have you heard the news? Somebody shot ole Sam Pickens."

Fuget stopped. "Who's Sam Pickens?" he said.

"Bless my life!" said the woman; "I forgot you're a stranger. Sam Pickens? Why, he's a cattle-man that come over the mountains about two year ago. He bought the Carpenter land on the river."

Fuget had now his first moment of anxiety.

"I hope he ain't much hurt," he said.

"Hurt!" replied the woman. "Why, he's dead. They found him a-layin' in his pasture field, where he'd gone to salt his cattle."

Fuget stood for a moment, nodding his head slowly.

"Well, that's a terrible thing. Who done it?"

The woman flung up her hands.

"That's the mystery," she said. "He didn't have any enemies. He was curious, but he was a good neighbor, folks say. They liked him. He lived over there by himself."

Fuget ventured a query.

"Did they see any signs of anybody about where they found him?"

"There wouldn't be any signs in a pasture field," said the woman, "an' the person that shot him must have been standin' out in the pasture field, because he was a-layin' a-facin' the river. An' he'd been shot in the back. They could tell that for a certainty," she added, "because a bullet tears where it comes out, an' it carries in stuff with it where it goes in."

Fuget made some further comment, then he held up the pieces of the hoe.

"I come in to get another hoe," he said. "I broke the blade on a root."

Then he went out to the log barn, selected a hoe from a number hanging in the crack of the logs, and returned to the cornfield.

He had now a sense of complete security. Even chance had helped. The turning of the old man in the act of death had diverted inquiry from the direction of the river, where some broken bushes might have indicated his hiding-place. He worked the remainder of the day in the cornfield. He had the profound satisfaction of one who successfully shapes events to a plan. Nevertheless, he found himself pausing, now and then, to consider what it was that Pickens had said. The elimination of all anxieties seemed somehow to have brought this feature of the tragedy forward to the first place. It seized his attention with the persistent interest of a puzzle.

That evening at supper the farmer related the gossip of the countryside. There was nothing in this gossip that gave Fuget the slightest concern. No clue of any character had been observed, and there were no conjectures that remotely approached the truth. Fuget talked of the tragedy without the least restraint. The anxiety which he had feared to feel when the matter would come to be discussed did not present itself. The old wives' tales of tortured conscience and the like, while he had not believed them, had, nevertheless, given him a certain concern. They were like tales of ghosts, which one could laugh at, but could not disprove until one had slept in the haunted house. He now knew that they were false.

He went to bed with the greatest composure. He was even cheerful. But he did not sleep. His mind seemed unusually clear and active. It reverted to the details of the tragedy, not with any sense of anxiety, but with a sort of satisfaction, as of one who contemplates an undertaking successfully accomplished. He passed the incidents in review, until he reached the words which Pickens had uttered. And, keenly alert, like a wrestler in condition, his mind began to struggle with that enigma. He endeavored to compose himself to slumber. But he could not. He was intensely awake. His mind formulated all the expressions that might resemble in sounds those words which Pickens seemed to have said, but they were of no service. He turned about in his bed, endeavoring to dismiss the problem. But his mind seemed to go on with it against every effort of his will. He concluded that this sleeplessness was due to the coffee which he had taken at supper, and he determined to abandon the use of it. Now and then he fell asleep, but he seemed almost instantly to awaken. He was glad when the daylight began to appear.

The following night he drank no coffee, and he fell asleep. But some time in the night he awoke again to the besetting puzzle. He sat up in the bed, and determined to dismiss it. He had believed Pickens to say,

"You shall hear from me"; very well then, that was what he had said. And he lay down. But, instantly, upon that decision, there appeared another phase of the puzzle that fascinated his attention. Why had Pickens used that expression? Why should he say, "You shall hear from me"? He was in the act of death when he spoke. He knew that. The realization of it was in his face. These words were inconsistent with a sense of death.

He lay for a long time, intent upon this new aspect of the matter. Did the dying man intend this as a threat which he expected to carry out? But how could one hear from a dead man? And there arose a medley of all the tales that he had ever heard, relating to messages transmitted to the living from the spirit world. He dismissed these tales as inconsistent with the sane experiences of men. But the effect of them, which he had received as a child, he could not dismiss. Moreover, how could one be certain that, under some peculiar conditions, such messages were not transmitted? Learned men were, themselves, not absolutely sure.

And intent upon this thing he remembered that those about to die were said sometimes to catch glimpses of truths ordinarily hidden. Men plucked from death had testified to a supernal activity of the mind. And those who had watched had observed the dying to use words and gestures which indicated a sight and hearing beyond the capacities of life.

He reflected. When Pickens had said, "You shall hear from me," it was certain that he meant what he said. Men did not utter idle threats when they were being ejected out of life. The law, ordinarily so careful for the truth, recognized this fact. He had heard that the declarations of those who believed themselves in dissolution, were to be received in courts of law without the sanctity of an oath. It was the common belief that the dying did not lie. Then, if he had heard correctly, this business was not ended. But had he heard correctly? And here the abominable thing turned back upon itself. And he began again on this interminable circle, as a fly follows the inside of a bowl, from which it can never escape.

In the realities of daylight, he was able to assail this thing, and, in a measure, overcome it. The dead did not return, and their threats were harmless. But in the insecurity of darkness, it possessed him. In the vast, impenetrable, mysterious night, one could not be so certain. One seemed then on the borderland of life where things moved that did not venture out into the sun, or in the sun became invisible. And, under the cover of this darkness, the dead man might somehow be able to carry out his threat. This was the anxiety that beset him. And in spite of his disbelief and the assurance of his reason he began to expect this message. And he began to wonder from what quarter it would approach him, and at what hour, and in what form. This thing appalled him; that one, whom he did not fear from the activity of life, should thus disturb him from the impotency of death.

Fuget was preparing quietly to leave the country when, about a week later, the farmer inquired if he wished to go with him, on that morning, to the county seat. It was the day on which the circuit court convened, —"court day,"—and by custom the country people assembled in the village. The farmer had been drawn on the grand jury.

"The judge will be chargin' us about the Pickens murder," he said. "You'd better go in an' hear him; the judge is a fine speaker."

It was the custom of these circuit judges to direct the attention of the grand jury to any conspicuous crime, and they usually availed themselves of this custom to harangue the people.

That curiosity which moved Fuget to seek the earliest news of the murder now urged him to hear what the judge would say, and he went with the farmer to the village. The court-room was crowded. Fuget remained all the afternoon seated on one of the benches. After the assembling of the grand jury, the judge began his charge. He reviewed the incidents of the assassination. Fuget found himself following these details. Under the speaker's dramatic touch the thing took on a more sinister aspect.

It could not avail the assassin that no human eye had seen him at his deadly work. By this act of violence he had involved himself with mysterious agencies that would not permit him to maintain his secret. It was in vain that human ingenuity strove against these influences. One might thrust his secret into the darkness, but he could not compel the darkness to retain it. These agencies would presently expel it into the light: as one could cast the body of the dead into the sea, but could not force the sea to receive it; it would be there when he returned, ghastly on the sand. And the hideous danger was that one never could tell at what hour, or in what place, or by what means, these mysterious agencies would reveal the thing which he had hidden.

While the judge spoke, Fuget thought of the strange words which Pickens had uttered, and he felt a sense of insecurity. He moved uneasily in his seat, and the perspiration dampened his body. When the court adjourned, he hurried out. He passed through the swinging doors of the court-room, and descended the stairway into the corridor below. As he elbowed his way through the crowd, he thought some one called out his name, "Henry Fuget," and instinctively he stopped, and turned around toward the stairway. But no one in the crowd coming down seemed to regard him, and he hurried away.

He was now alarmed, and he determined to leave the country at once. He returned with the farmer. That night, alone in the loft of the farmhouse, he packed his possessions into a bundle and sat down on the bed to wait until the family below him should be asleep. He did not cease to consider this extraordinary incident. And it presently occurred to him that if some one had, in fact, recognized him, and he should now flee in the night, his guilt would be conclusively indicated. And side by side with that suggestion, there arose another. Had he, in fact, heard a human tongue call out his name? He labored to recall the sounds which he seemed to have heard, as he had labored to recall those which Pickens had uttered. The voice had seemed to him thin and high. Was it a human voice?

He rose, unpacked the bundle, and went over to the window. The night seemed strange to him. The air was hard and bright; thin clouds were moving; a pale moonlight descended now and then on the world. There was silence. Every living thing seemed to have departed out of life. He thought of all the persons whom he had this day seen alert and alive, as now no better than dead men, lying unconscious, while the earth turned under them in this ghostly light. And it seemed to him a thing of no greater wonder that the dead should appear or utter voices than that these innumerable bodies, prone and motionless, should again reënter into life.

The following morning the farmer reassured him. No witness had come before the grand jury, and the prosecuting attorney had no evidence to offer.

"I reckon nobody will ever know who killed ol' Pickens," he said. Then he added, "The grand jury's goin' to set pretty late, an' I may. have to stay in town tonight. I wish you'd go in with me, an' bring the horse home."

Fuget could not refuse, and he returned to the village. Again he sat all day in the crowded court-room. Loss of sleep and fatigue overcame him, and occasionally, in the heat of the room, in spite of his anxiety, he would almost fall asleep. And at such times he would start up, fearful lest some word or gesture should escape him. And always, when the judge turned in his chair, or an attorney spoke, he was anxious. And when any one passed the bench on which he sat, he appeared to be watching something in the opposite corner of the court-room or, by accident, to screen his face with his hat.

But as the day advanced, he became reassured; and when the court adjourned, he went out quietly with the crowd. On the stairway and in the corridor below, he was anxious lest he should again hear his name called out. But when it did not occur and he approached the exit of the court-house, his equanimity returned. On the steps, in the sun, he stopped and wiped his face with his sleeve. He seemed to have escaped out of peril, as through a door. He was glad now of the good judgment that had turned him back from flight, and of the incident that had brought him here to face the thing that he had feared. He came forth, like one who had braved a gesticulating spectre and found its threatening body to be harmless and impalpable.

He descended the long stone steps leading down from the portico of the ancient court-house, with that sense of buoyant freedom peculiar to those who are lifted out of danger. At the street, as he was about to walk away, some one touched him on the shoulder. He turned. The sheriff of the county was beside him.

"Will you just step into the Squire's office?" he said.

Fuget was appalled.

"Me!" he stammered. "What does the Squire want with me?"

But obedient to the command, he followed the sheriff into the basement of the court-house, and through a corridor into the office of the justice of the peace. Here he found himself come into the presence of the prosecuting attorney, the justice, and a little man with sharp black eyes, and a thin, clean-shaven face. He remembered having seen this man enter the court-room, on the first day, while the judge was speaking. He had carried then a pair of saddle-pockets over his arm and had seemed to be a stranger, for he had stopped at the door and looked about, as if the court-room were unfamiliar to him. Fuget had observed this incident, as with painful attention he had observed every incident occurring in the court-room during these two days of stress. He had not seen this man again. But he now distinctly recalled him.

The justice of the peace sat at a table. Before him lay a printed paper, certain blank lines of which had been written in with a pen. He put his hand on this paper: then he spoke.

"Is your name Henry Fuget?" he said.

Fuget looked around him without moving his head, swiftly, furtively, like an animal penned into a corner. The eyes of the others were on him. They seemed to know all the details of some mysterious transaction that had led up to this question, and of which he was ignorant. He felt that he had entered some obscure trap, the deadly peril of which these men had cunningly hidden that he might the more easily step into it. Nevertheless, he realized that he could not remain silent.

"No, sir," he said, "my name's Silas Williams." Then he added, "I work for Dan'l Sheets, out on the ten-mile road. You can ask him; he'll tell you."

The justice continued, as though following a certain formula,—

"Did you know Samuel Pickens?"

"No, sir."

The justice seemed to consult a memorandum in pencil on the margin of the written paper.

"Were you not convicted of arson, on the testimony of Samuel Pickens, and sentenced to the penitentiary; and have you not repeatedly threatened to kill him when your term of penal servitude should have expired?"

Fuget was now greatly alarmed. How did these exact facts come to be known in this distant community? Here Pickens alone knew them, and he was dead. He saw that his security lay in denying that he was Henry Fuget.

"No, sir," he said.

"And your name's not Henry Fuget?"

"No, sir."

The justice turned to the stranger.

"This man denies that he is Henry Fuget," he said.

Then it was that the words were uttered that dispossessed the prisoner of composure, and cast him into panic.

"If the communication which I have received from Samuel Pickens is true," said the stranger, "Henry Fuget has the scar of a gunshot wound on his right arm above the elbow."

The muscles of Fuget's face relaxed. His mouth fell into a baggy gaping. Then he faltered the query that possessed him.

"Did *you* hear from Sam Pickens?"

"Yes."

"After he was *dead?*"

The stranger reflected. "Yes," he said. "Pickens was dead then."

Fuget's mouth remained open. A sense of disaster, complete and utter, descended on him. The dead man had carried out his terrible threat. He began to stammer, unconscious that he was completing his ruin.

"That's what he said—that's what he said when I shot him—but I thought I'd hear,—I didn't think somebody else would hear."

He caught hold of the table with his hand, and lowered himself into a chair. But he continued to regard this sinister stranger. And presently he spoke again.

"How did he tell you?" he said.

A crowd had begun to gather at the door and at the windows,—a rumor had gone out.

The stranger put his hand into his pocket, and drew from it a folded paper.

"I will tell you," he said. "I am an attorney at law; my name is Gordon, and I reside in Georgia. On the third day of November, I received this paper, inclosed in an envelope, and addressed to me. It was dated in October, but when I got it, Pickens was dead." He unfolded the paper and began to read in a thin, high-pitched voice:—

In the name of God, Amen! I, Samuel Pickens, do make, publish, and declare this to be my last will and testament. I hereby appoint Horatio Gordon my executor, and I direct and charge him as follows, to wit: Henry Fuget, a convict about to be discharged from the penitentiary of Georgia, has repeatedly threatened my life. I have come here to avoid him, but I fear that he will follow and kill me. Now, therefore, if I should be found dead, be it known that Henry Fuget is the assassin, and I direct my executor to expend the sum of one thousand dollars in order to bring him to the gallows. Fuget is to be known by a scar on the fleshy part of his right arm where he was shot in an attempt to escape from the penitentiary. The residue of my estate, both real and personal, I bequeath to my beloved daughter, Selina Pickens, now Mrs. Jonathan Clayton, of Jackson, Miss.

Given under my hand and seal, Oct. 14, 1850.

SAMUEL PICKENS. (Seal).

The stranger looked up from the paper.

"When I heard that Pickens was dead," he said, "I came here immediately. The circuit court was sitting when I arrived. It occurred to me that the assassin might be present in this crowd of people. To determine that, I placed myself at the head of the stairway, and as the crowd was going out, I called the name. This man turned, and I knew then that he was Henry Fuget."

Fuget sat with his hands on the arms of the chair, his big body thrown loosely forward, his eyes on the stranger. Slowly the thing came to him. The atmosphere of ghostly and supernatural agencies receded. He saw that he had been trapped by his own fancy. The hand that had choked this confession out of him had been born of his own flesh; the bones of it, the sinews of it, he had himself provided.

And a madness seized him. He sprang up, and rushed out of the door. The crowd gave way before the bulk of this infuriated man. But the corridor was narrow, and as he fought his way, persons began to seize him. He staggered out into the courtyard. The crowd of people wedged him in, clung to him, and bore him down. He rose. Under the mass of men who had thrown themselves upon him the bones of his legs seemed about to snap; his muscles to burst; his vertebrae to crumble. For a dozen steps he advanced with this crushing burden, but every moment it increased, and finally he fell.

THE WATER HOLE

By Struthers Burt

[Maxwell Struthers Burt (1882–   ), the author of this authentic Western story, is not a native of the West. Born in Baltimore and educated in Princeton and Oxford, he became an instructor in English in Princeton for three years. His understanding of the West came as a result of hunting and travel through the Rocky Mountains and the Southwest, and finally through the ownership of some ranches in the Jackson Hole country of Wyoming at the foot of the Teton range, where Mr. Burt spent his summers for several years. His work as a writer began before his college years as a newspaper reporter in Philadelphia. He now has to his credit short stories, novels and poems.

The Water Hole, Mr. Burt's first magazine story, appeared in Scribner's Magazine (July, 1915). It was included in O'Brien's Best Short Stories of 1915 and in the collected volume, John O'May and Other Stories (1918). It is reprinted here by permission of the author and of Charles Scribner's Sons, publishers.]

SOME men are like the twang of a bow-string. Hardy was like that—short, lithe, sunburned, vivid. Into the lives of Jarrick, Hill, and myself, old classmates of his, he came and went in the fashion of one of those queer winds that on a sultry day in summer blow unexpectedly up a city street out of nowhere. His comings excited us; his goings left us refreshed and a little vaguely discontented. So many people are gray. Hardy gave one a shock of color, as do the deserts and the mountains he inhabited. It was not particularly what he said—he didn't talk much—it was his appearance, his direct, a trifle fierce, gestures, the sense of mysterious lands that pervaded him. One never knew when he was coming to New York and one never knew how long he was going to stay; he just appeared, was very busy with mining companies for a while, sat about clubs in the late afternoon, and then, one day, he was gone.

Sometimes he came twice in a year; oftener, not for two or three years at a stretch. When he did come we gave him a dinner—that is, Jarrick, Hill, and myself. And it was rather an occasion. We would procure a table in the gayest restaurant we could find, near, but not too near, the music—Hill it was who first suggested this as a dramatic bit of incongruity between Hardy and the frequenters of Broadway—and the most exotic food obtainable, for a good part of his time Hardy, we knew, lived upon camp fare. Then we would try to make him tell about his experiences. Usually he wouldn't. Impersonally, he was entertaining about South Africa, about the Caucasus, about Alaska, Mexico, anywhere you care to think; but concretely he might have been an illustrated lecture for all he mentioned himself. He was passionately fond of abstract argument. "Y' see," he would explain, "I don't get half as much of this sort of thing as I want. Of course, one does run across remarkable people—now, I met a cow-puncher once who knew Keats by heart—but as a rule I deal only with material things, mines and prospects and assays and that sort of thing." Poor chap! I wonder if he thought that we, with our brokering and our writing and our lawyering, dealt much with ideas! I remember one night when we sat up until three discussing the philosophy of prohibition over three bottles of port. I wonder how many other men have done the same thing!

But five years ago—no, it was six—Hardy really told us a real story about himself. Necessarily the occasion is memorable in our recollections. We had dined at Lamb's, and the place was practically empty, for it was long after the theatre hour—only a drowsy waiter here and there, and away over in one corner a young couple who, I suppose, imagined themselves in love. Fancy being in love at Lamb's! We had been discussing, of all things in the world, bravery and conscience and cowardice and original sin, and that sort of business, and there was no question about it that Hardy was enjoying himself hugely. He was leaning upon the table, a coffee-cup between his relaxed brown hands, listening with an eagerness highly complimentary to the banal remarks we had to make upon the subject. "This is talk!" he ejaculated once with a laugh.

Hill, against the combined attack of Jarrick and myself, was maintaining the argument. "There is no such thing as instinctive bravery," he affirmed, for the fifth time at least, "amongst intelligent men. Every one of us is naturally a coward. Of course we are. The more imagination we've got the more we can realize how pleasant life is, after all, and how rotten the adjuncts of sudden death. It's reason that does the trick—reason and tradition. Do you know of any one who is brave when he is alone—except, that is, when it is a case of self-preservation? No! Of course not. Did you ever hear of any one choosing to go along a dangerous road or to ford a dangerous river unless he had to—that is, any one of our class, any man of education or imagination? It's the greater fear of being thought afraid that makes us brave. Take a lawyer in a shipwreck—take myself! Don't you suppose he's frightened? Naturally he is, horribly frightened. It's his reason, his mind, that after a while gets the better of his poor pipe-stem legs and makes them keep pace with the sea-legs about them."

"It's condition," said Jarrick doggedly—"condition entirely. All has to do with your liver and digestion. I know; I fox-hunt, and when I was younger—yes, leave my waist alone!—I rode jumping races. When you're fit there isn't a horse alive that bothers you, or a fence, for that matter, or a bit of water."

"Ever try standing on a ship's deck, in the dark, knowing you're going to drown in about twenty minutes?" asked Hill.

Hardy leaned forward to strike a match for his cigarette. "I don't agree with you," he said.

"Well, but—" began Hill.

"Neither of you."

"Oh, of course, you're outside the argument. You lead an adventurous life. You keep in condition for danger. It isn't fair."

"No." Hardy lit his cigarette and inhaled a puff thoughtfully. "You don't understand. All you have to say does have some bearing upon things, but, when you get down to brass tacks, it's instinct—at the last gasp, it's instinct. You can't get away from it. Look at the difference between a thoroughbred and a cold-blooded horse! There you are! That's true. It's the fashion now to discount instinct, I know; well— but you can't get away from it. I've thought about the thing—a lot. Men are brave against their better reason, against their conscience. It's a mixed-up thing. It's confusing and—and sort of damnable," he concluded lamely.

"Sort of damnable!" ejaculated Hill wonderingly.

"Yes, damnable."

I experienced inspiration. "You've got a concrete instance back of that," I ventured.

Hardy removed his gaze from the ceiling. "Er—" he stammered. "Why, yes—yes. That's true."

"You'd better tell it," suggested Hill; "otherwise your argument is not very conclusive."

Hardy fumbled with the spoon of his empty coffee-cup. It was a curious gesture on the part of a man whose franknesses were as clean-cut as his silences. "Well—" he began. "I don't know. Perhaps. I did know a man, though, who saved another man's life when he didn't want to, when there was every excuse for him not to, when he had it all reasoned out that it was wrong, the very wrongest possible thing to do; and he saved him because he couldn't help it, saved him at the risk of his own life, too."

"He did!" murmured Hill incredulously.

"Go on!" I urged. I was aware that we were on the edge of a revelation.

Hardy looked down at the spoon in his hand, then up and into my eyes.

"It's such a queer place to tell it"—he smiled deprecatingly—"here, in this restaurant. It ought to be about a camp-fire, or something like that. Here it seems out of place, like the smell of bacon or sweating mules. Do you know Los Pinos? Well, you wouldn't. It was just a few shacks and a Mexican gambling-house when I saw it. Maybe it isn't there any more, at all. You know—those places! People build them and then go away, and in a year there isn't a thing, just desert again and shifting sand and maybe the little original old ranch by the one spring." He swept the table-cloth with his hand, as if sweeping something into oblivion, and his eyes sought again the spoon. "It's queer, that business. Men and women go out to lonely places and build houses, and for a while everything goes on in miniature, just as it does here—daily bread and hating and laughing—and then something happens, the gold gives out or the fields won't pay, and in no time nature is back again. It's a big fight. You lose track of it in crowded places." He raised his head and settled his arms comfortably on the table.

"I wasn't there for any particular purpose. I was on a holiday. I'd been on a big job up in Colorado and was rather done up, and, as there were some prospects in New Mexico I wanted to see, I hit south, drifting through Santa Fé and Silver City, until I found myself way down on the southern edge of Arizona. It was still hot down there—hot as blazes—it was about the first of September—and the rattlesnakes and the scorpions were still as active as crickets. I knew a chap that had a cattle outfit near the Mexican border, so I dropped in on him one day and stayed two weeks. You see, he was lonely. Had a passion for theatres and hadn't seen a play for five years. My second-hand gossip was rather a godsend. But finally I got tired of talking about Mary Mannering, and decided to start north again. He bade me good-by on a little hill near his place. 'See here!' he said suddenly, looking toward the west. 'If you go a trifle out of your way you'll strike Los Pinos, and I wish you would. It's a little bit of a dump of the United Copper Company's, no good, I'm thinking, but the fellow in charge is a friend of mine. He's got his wife there. They're nice people—or used to be. I haven't seen them for ten years. They say he drinks a little—well, we all do. Maybe you could write me how she—I mean, how he is getting on?' And he turned red. I saw how the land lay, and as a favor to him I said I would.

"It was eighty miles away, and I drifted in there one night on top of a tired cow-horse just at sundown. You know how purple—violet, really —those desert evenings are. There was violet stretching away as far as I could see, from the faint violet at my stirrups to the deep, almost black violet of the horizon. Way off to the north I could make out the shadow of some big hills that had been ahead of me all day. The town, what there was of it, lay in a little gully. Along its single street there were a few lights shining like small yellow flowers. I asked my way of a Mexican, and he showed me up to where the Whitneys—that name will do as well as any—lived, in a decent enough sort of bungalow, it would seem, above the gully. He left me there, and I went forward and rapped at the door. Light shone from between the cracks of a near-by shutter, and I could hear voices inside—a man's voice mostly, hoarse and high-pitched. Then a Chinaman opened the door for me and I had a look inside, into a big living-room beyond. It was civilized all right enough, pleasantly so to a man stepping out of two days of desert and Mexican adobes. At a glance I saw the rugs on the polished floor, and the Navajo blankets about, and a big table in the centre with a shaded lamp and magazines in rows; but the man in riding-clothes standing before the empty fireplace wasn't civilized at all, at least not at that moment. I couldn't see the woman, only the top of her head above the back of a big chair, but as I came in I heard her say, 'Hush!—Jim!—please!' and I noticed that what I could see of her hair was of that fine true gold you so seldom find. The man stopped in the middle of a sentence and swayed on his feet; then he looked over at me and came toward me with a sort of bulldog, inquiring look. He was a big, red-faced, blond chap, about forty, I should say, who might once have been handsome. He wasn't now, and it didn't add to his beauty that he was quite obviously fairly drunk. 'Well?' he said, and blocked my way.

"'I'm a friend of Henry Martin's,' I answered. 'I've got a letter for you.' I was beginning to get pretty angry.

"'Henry Martin?' He laughed unsteadily. 'You'd better give it to my wife over there. She's his friend. I hardly know him.' I don't know when I'd seen a man I disliked as much at first sight.

"There was a rustle from the other side of the room, and Mrs. Whitney came toward us. I avoided her unattractive husband and took her hand, and I understood at once whatever civilizing influences there were about the bungalow we were in. Did you ever do that—ever step out of nowhere, in a wild sort of country, and meet suddenly a man or a woman who might have come straight from a pleasant, well-bred room filled with books and flowers and quiet, nice people? It's a sensation that never loses its freshness. Mrs. Whitney was like that. I wouldn't have called her beautiful; she was better; you knew she was good and clean-cut and a thoroughbred the minute you saw her. She was lovely, too; don't misunderstand me, but you had more important things to think about when you were talking to her. Just at the moment I was wondering how any one who so evidently had been crying could all at once greet a stranger with so cordial a smile. But she was all that—all nerve; I don't think I ever met a woman quite like her—so fine, you understand."

Hardy paused. "Have any of you chaps got a cigarette?" he asked; and I noticed that his hand, usually the steadiest hand imaginable, trembled ever so slightly. "Well," he began again, "there you are! I had tumbled into about as rotten a little, pitiful a little tragedy as you can imagine, there in a God-forsaken desert of Arizona, with not a soul about but a Chinaman, a couple of Scotch stationary engineers, an Irish foreman, two or three young mining men, and a score of Mexicans. Of course, my first impulse was to get out the next morning, to cut it— it was none of my business—although I determined to drop a line to

Henry Martin; but I didn't go. I had a talk with Mrs. Whitney that night, after her attractive husband had taken himself off to bed, and somehow I couldn't leave just then. You know how it is, you drop into a place where nothing in the world seems likely to happen, and all of a sudden you realize that something *is* going to happen, and for the life of you you can't go away. That situation up on top of the hill couldn't last forever, could it? So I stayed on. I hunted out the big Irish foreman and shared his cabin. The Whitneys asked me to visit them, but I didn't exactly feel like doing so. The Irishman was a fine specimen of his race, ten years out from Dublin, and everywhere else since that time; generous, irascible, given to great fits of gayety and equally unexpected fits of gloom. He would sit in the evenings, a short pipe in his mouth, and stare up at the Whitney bungalow on the hill above.

"'That Jim Whitney's a divvle,' he confided to me once. 'Wan of these days I'll hit him over th' head with a pick and be hung for murther. Now, what in hell d'ye suppose a nice girl like that sticks by him for? If it weren't for her I'd 'a' reported him long ago. The scut!' And I remember that he spat gloomily.

"But I got to know the answer to that question sooner than I had expected. You see, I went up to the Whitneys' often, in the afternoon, or for dinner, or in the evening, and I talked to Mrs. Whitney a great deal; although sometimes I just sat and smoked and listened to her play the piano. She played beautifully. It was a treat to a man who hadn't heard music for two years. There was a little thing of Grieg's—a spring song, or something of the sort—and you've no idea how quaint and sad and appealing it was, and incongruous, with all its freshness and murmuring about water-falls and pine-trees, there, in those hot, breathless Arizona nights. Mrs. Whitney didn't talk much; she wasn't what you'd call a particularly communicative woman, but bit by bit I pieced together something continuous. It seems that she had run away with Whitney ten years before—Oh, yes! Henry Martin! That had been a schoolgirl affair. Nothing serious, you understand. But the Whitney matter had been different. She was greatly in love with him. And the family had disapproved. Some rich, stuffy Boston people, I gathered. But she had made up her mind and taken matters in her own hands. That was her way—a clean-cut sort of person—like a gold-and-white arrow; and now she was going to stick by her choice no matter what happened; owed it to Whitney. There was the quirk in her brain; we all have a quirk somewhere, and that was hers. She felt that she had ruined his career; he had been a brilliant young engineer, but her family had kicked up the devil of a row, and, as they were powerful enough, and nasty enough, had more or less hounded him out of the East. Of course, personally, I never thought he showed any of the essentials of brilliancy, but that's neither here nor there; she did, and she was satisfied that she owed him all she had. I suppose, too, there was some trace of a Puritan conscience back of it, some inherent feeling about divorce; and there was pride as well, a desire not to let that disgusting family of hers know into what ways her idol had fallen. Anyway, she was adamant—oh, yes, I made no bones about it, I up and asked her one night why she didn't get rid of the hound. So there she was, that white-and-gold woman, with her love of music, and her love of books, and her love of fine things, and her gentleness, and that sort of fiery, suppressed Northern blood, shut up on top of an Arizona dump with a beast that got drunk every night and twice a day on Sunday. It was worse even than that. One night—we were sitting out on the veranda—her scarf slipped, and I saw a scar on her arm, near her shoulder." Hardy stopped abruptly and began to roll a little pellet of bread between his thumb and his forefinger; then his tense expression faded and he sat back in his chair.

"Let me have another cigarette," he said to Jarrick. "No. Wait a minute! I'll order some."

He called a waiter and gave his instructions. "You see," he continued, "when you run across as few nice women as I do that sort of thing is more than ordinarily disturbing. And then I suppose it was the setting, and her loneliness, and everything. Anyway, I stayed on. I got to be a little bit ashamed of myself. I was afraid that Mrs. Whitney would think me prompted by mere curiosity or a desire to meddle, so after a while I gave out that I was prospecting that part of Arizona, and in the mornings I would take a horse and ride out into the desert. I loved it, too; it was so big and spacious and silent and hot. One day I met Whitney on the edge of town. He was sober, as he always was when he had to be; he was a masterful brute, in his way. He stopped me and asked if I had found anything, and when I laughed he didn't laugh back. 'There's gold here,' he said. 'Lots of gold. Did you ever hear the story of the Ten Strike Mine? Well, it's over there.' He swept with his arm the line of distant hills to the north. 'The crazy Dutchman that found it staggered into Almuda, ten miles down the valley, just before he died; and his pockets were bulging with samples—pure gold, almost. Yes, by thunder! And that's the last they ever heard of it. Lots of men have tried—lots of men. Some day I'll go myself, surer than shooting.' And he let his hands drop to his sides and stared silently toward the north, a queer, dreamy anger in his eyes. I've seen lots of mining men, lots of prospectors, in my time, and it didn't take me long to size up that look of his. 'Aha, my friend!' I said to myself. 'So you've got another vice, have you! It isn't only rum that's got a hold on you!' And I turned my horse into the town.

"But our conversation seemed to have stirred to the surface something in Whitney's brain that had been at work there a long time, for after that he would never let me alone about his Ten Strike Mine and the mountains that hid it. 'Over there!' he would say, and point to the

north. From the porch of his bungalow the sleeping hills were plainly
visible above the shimmering desert. He would chew on the end of a
cigar and consider. 'It isn't very far, you know. Two days—maybe
three. All we need's water. No water there—at least, none found. All
those fellows who've prospected are fools. I'm an expert; so are you.
I tell you, Hardy, let's do it! A couple of little old pack-mules! Eh?
How about it? Next week? I can get off. God, I'd like money!' And
he would subside into a sullen silence. At first I laughed at him; but I
can tell you that sort of thing gets on your nerves sooner or later and
either makes you bolt it or else go. At the end of two weeks I actually
found myself considering the fool thing seriously. Of course, I didn't
want to discover a lost gold-mine, that is, unless I just happened to
stumble over it; I wanted to keep away from such things; they're bad;
they get into a man's blood like drugs; but I've always had a hankering
for a new country, and those hills, shining in the heat, were compelling—
very compelling. Besides, I reflected, a trip like that might help to
straighten Whitney up a little. I hadn't much hope, to be sure, but
drowning men clutch at straws. It's curious what sophistry you use to
convince yourself, isn't it? And then—something happened that for
two weeks occupied all my mind."

Hardy paused, considered for a moment the glowing end of his cigarette, and finally looked up gravely; there was a slight hesitation, almost
an embarrassment, in his manner. "I don't exactly know how to put
it," he began. "I don't want you chaps to imagine anything wrong;
it was all very nebulous and indefinite, you understand—Mrs. Whitney
was a wonderful woman. I wouldn't mention the matter at all if it
wasn't necessary for the point of my story; in fact, it is the point of my
story. But there was a man there—one of the young engineers—and
quite suddenly I discovered that he was in love with Mrs. Whitney, and
I think—I never could be quite sure, but I think she was in love with
him. It must have been one of those sudden things, a storm out of a
clear sky, deluging two people before they were aware. I imagine it
was brought to the surface by the chap's illness. He had been out riding
on the desert and had got off to look at something, and a rattlesnake
had struck him—a big, dust-dirty thing—on the wrist, and, very faint,
he had galloped back to the Whitneys'. And what do you suppose she
had done—Mrs. Whitney, that is? Flung herself down on him and sucked the wound! Yes, without a moment's hesitation, her gold hair all
about his hand and her white dress in the dirt. Of course, it was a foolish
thing to do, and not in the least the right way to treat a wound, but she
had risked her life to do it; a slight cut on her lip—you understand; a tiny
ragged place. Afterward, she had cut the wound crosswise, so, and had
put on a ligature, and then had got the man into the house some way
and nursed him until he was quite himself again. I dare say he had
been in love with her a long while without knowing it, but that clinched

matters. Those things come overpoweringly and take a man, down in places like that—semi-tropical and lonely and lawless, with long, empty days and moonlit nights. Perhaps he told Mrs. Whitney; he never got very far, I am sure. She was a wonderful woman—but she loved him, I think. You can tell those things, you know; a gesture, an unavoidable look, a silence.

"Anyway, I saw what had happened and I was sorry, and for a fortnight I hung around, loath to go, but hating myself all the while for not doing so. And every day Whitney would come at me with his insane scheme. 'Over there! It isn't very far. Two days—maybe three. How about it? Eh?' and then that tense sweep of the arm to the north. I don't know what it was, weariness, disgust, irritation of the whole sorry plan of things, but finally, and to my own astonishment, I found myself consenting, and within two days Whitney had his crazy pack outfit ready, and on the morning of the third day we set out. Mrs. Whitney had said nothing when we unfolded our intentions to her, nor did she say anything when we departed, but stood on the porch of the bungalow, her hand up to her throat, and watched us out of sight. I wondered what she was thinking about. The Voodoos—that was the name of the mountains we were heading for—had killed a good many men in their time."

Hardy took a long and thoughtful sip from the glass in front of him before he began again. "I've knocked about a good deal in my life," he said; "I've been lost—once in the jungle; I've starved; I've reached the point where I've imagined horrors, heard voices, you understand, and seen great, bearded men mouthing at me—a man's pretty far gone when that happens to him—but that trip across the desert was the worst I've ever taken. By day it was all right, just swaying in your saddle, half asleep a good part of the time, the smell of warm dust in your nose, the three pack-mules plodding along behind; but the nights!—I tell you, I've sat about camp-fires up the Congo and watched big, oily black men eat their food, and I once saw a native village sacked, but I'd rather be tied for life to a West Coast nigger than to a man like Whitney. It isn't good for two people to be alone in a place like that and for one to hate the other as I hated him. God knows why I didn't kill him; I'd have to get up and leave the fire and go out into the night, and, mind you, I'd be shuddering like a man with the ague under that warm, soft air. And he never for a minute suspected it. His mind was scarred with drink as if a worm had bored its slow way in and out of it. I can see him now, cross-legged, beyond the flames, big, unshaven, heavy-jowled, dirty, what he thought dripping from his mouth like the bacon drippings he was too lazy to wipe away. I won't tell you what he talked about; you know, the old thing; but not the way even the most wrong-minded of ordinary men talks; there was a sodden, triumphant deviltry in him that was appalling. He cursed the country for its lack of opportunity of a certain kind; he was like a hound held in leash, gloating over what he would do when he got back to the kennels of civilization again. And all the while, at the back of my mind, was a picture of that white-and-gold woman of his, way back toward the south, waiting his return because she owed him her life for the brilliant career she had ruined. It made you sometimes almost want to laugh—insanely. I used to lie awake at night and pray whatever there was to kill him, and do it quickly. I would have turned back, but I felt that every day I could keep him away from Los Pinos was a day gained for Mrs. Whitney. He was a dangerous maniac, too. The first day he behaved himself fairly well, but the second, after supper, when we had cleaned up, he began to fumble through the packs, and finally produced a bottle of brandy.

"'Fine camping stuff!' he announced. 'Lots of results for very little weight. Have some?'

"'Are you going to drink that?' I asked.

"'Oh, go to the devil!' he snapped. 'I've been out as much as you have.' I didn't argue with him further; I hoped if he drank enough the sun would get him. But the third night he upset the water-kegs, two of them. He had been carrying on some sort of weird celebration by himself, and finally staggered out into the desert, singing at the top of his lungs, and the first thing I knew he was down among the kegs, rolling over and over, and kicking right and left. The one that was open was gone; another he kicked the plug out of, but I managed to save about a quarter of its contents. The next morning I spoke to him about it. He blinked his red eyes and chuckled.

"'Poor sort of stuff, anyway,' he said.

"'Yes,' I agreed; 'but without it you would blow out like a candle in a dust storm.' After that we didn't speak to each other except when it was necessary.

"We were in the foot-hills of the Voodoos by now, and the next day we got into the mountains themselves—great, bare ragged peaks, black and red and dirty yellow, like the cooled-off slake of a furnace. Every now and then a dry gully came down from nowheres; and the only human thing one could see was occasionally, on the sides of one of these, a shivering, miserable, half-dead piñon—nothing but that, and the steel-blue sky overhead, and the desert behind us, shimmering like a lake of salt. It was hot—good Lord! The horn of your saddle burned your hand. That night we camped in a canyon, and the next day went still higher up, following the course of a rutted stream that probably ran water once in a year. Whitney wanted to turn east, and it was all a toss-up to me; the place looked unlikely enough, anyway, although you never can tell. I had settled into the monotony of the trip by now and didn't much care how long we stayed out. One day was like another —hot little swirls of dust, sweat of mules, and great black cliffs; and the nights came and went like the passing of a sponge over a fevered face.

On the sixth day the tragedy happened. It was toward dusk, and one of the mules, the one that carried the water, fell over a cliff.

"He wasn't hurt; just lay on his back and smiled crossly; but the kegs and the bags were smashed to bits. I like mules, but I wanted to kill that one. It was quiet down there in the canyon—quiet and hot. I looked at Whitney and he looked at me, and I had the sudden, unpleasant realization that he was a coward, added to his other qualifications. Yes, a coward! I saw it in his blurred eyes and the quivering of his bloated lips—stark dumb funk. That was bad. I'm afraid I lost my nerve, too; I make no excuses; fear is infectious. At all events, we tore down out of that place as if death was after us, the mules clattering and flapping in the rear. After a time I rode more slowly, but in the morning we were nearly down at the desert again; and there it lay before us, shimmering like a lake of salt—three days back to water.

"The next two days were rather a blur, as if a man were walking on a red-hot mirror that tipped up and down and tried to take his legs from under him. There was a water hole a little to the east of the way we had come, and toward that I tried to head. One of the mules gave out, and staggered and groaned, and tried to get up again. I remember hearing him squeal, once; it was horrible. He lay there, a little black speck on the desert. Whitney and I didn't speak to each other at all, but I thought of those two kegs of water he had upset. Have you ever been thirsty—mortally thirsty, until you feel your tongue black in your mouth? It's queer what it does to you. Do you remember that little place—Zorn's—at college? We used to sit there sometimes on spring afternoons. It was cool and cavern-like, and through the open door one could see the breeze in the maple-trees. Well, I thought about that all the time; it grew to be an obsession, a mirage. I could smell the moss-like smell of bock beer; I even remembered conversations we had had. You fellows were as real to me as you are real tonight. It's strange, and then, when you come to, uncanny; you feel the sweat on you turn cold.

"We had ridden on in that way I don't know how long, snatching a couple of feverish hours of sleep in the night, Whitney groaning and mumbling horribly, when suddenly my horse gave a little snicker—low, the way they do when you give them grain—and I felt his tired body straighten up ever so little. 'Maybe,' I thought, and I looked up. But I didn't much care; I just wanted to crawl into some cool place and forget all about it and die. It was late in the afternoon. My shadow was lengthening. Too late, really, for much mirage; but I no longer put great stock in green vegetation and matters of that kind; I had seen too much of it in the last two days fade away into nothing—nothing but blistering, damned sand. And so I wouldn't believe the cool reeds and the sparkling water until I had dipped down through a little swale and was actually fighting my horse back from the brink. I knew enough to do that, mind you, and to fight back the two mules so that they drank just a little at a time—a little at a time; and all the while I had to wait, with my tongue like sand in my mouth. Over the edge of my horse's neck I could see the water just below; it looked as cool as rain. I was always a little proud of that—that holding back; it made up, in a way, for the funk of two nights earlier. When the mules and my horse were through I dismounted and, lying flat, bathed my hands, and then, a tiny sip at a time, began to drink. That was hard. When I stood up the heat seemed to have gone, and the breeze was moist and sweet with the smell of evening. I think I sang a little and waved my hands above my head, and, at all events, I remember I lay on my back and rolled a cigarette; and quite suddenly and without the slightest reason there were tears in my eyes. Then I began to wonder what had become of Whitney; I hadn't thought of him before. I got to my feet, and just as I did so I saw him come over the little rise of sand, swaying in his saddle, and trying, the fool, to make his horse run. He looked like a great scarecrow blown out from some Indian maize-field into the desert. His clothes were torn and his mask of a face was seamed and black from dust and sweat; he saw the water and let out one queer, hoarse screech and kicked at his horse with wabbling legs.

"'Look out!' I cried, and stepped in his way. I had seen this sort of thing before and knew what to expect; but he rode me down as if I hadn't been there. His horse tried to avoid me, and the next moment the sack of grain on its back was on the sands, creeping like a great, monstrous, four-legged thing toward the water. 'Stay where you are,' I said, 'and I'll bring you some.' But he only crawled the faster. I grabbed his shoulder. 'You fool!' I said. 'You'll kill yourself!'

"'Damn you!' he blubbered. 'Damn you!' And before I knew it, and with all the strength, I imagine, left in him, he was on his feet and I was looking down the barrel of his gun. It looked very round and big and black, too. Beyond it his eyes were regarding me; they were quite mad, there was no doubt about that, but, just the way a dying man achieves some of his old desire to will, there was definite purpose in them. 'You get out of my way,' he said, and began very slowly to circle me. You could hardly hear his words, his lips were so blistered and swollen.

"And now this is the point of what I am telling you." Hardy fumbled again for a match and relit his cigarette. "There we were, we two, in that desert light, about ten feet from the water, he with his gun pointing directly at my heart—and his hand wasn't trembling as much as you would imagine, either—and he was circling me step by step, and I was standing still. I suppose the whole affair took two minutes, maybe three, but in that time—and my brain was still blurred to other impressions—I saw the thing as clearly as I see it now, as clearly as I saw that great, swollen beast of a face. Here was the chance I had longed for, the hope I had lain awake at night and prayed for; between the man and death I alone stood; and I had every reason, every instinct of decency and common sense, to make me step aside. The man was a devil; he was killing the finest woman I had ever met; his presence poisoned the air he walked in; he was an active agent of evil, there was no doubt of that. I hated him as I had never hated anything else in my life, and at the moment I was sure that God wanted him to die. I knew then that to save him would be criminal; I think so still. And I saw other considerations as well; saw them as clearly as I see you sitting here. I saw the man who loved Mrs. Whitney, and I saw Mrs. Whitney herself, and in my keeping, I knew, was all her chance for happiness, the one hope that the future would make up to her for some of the horror of the past. It would have been an easy thing to do; the most ordinary caution was on my side. Whitney was far larger than I, and, even in his weakened condition—I was weak myself—stronger, and he had a gun that in a flash of light could blow me into eternity. And what would happen then? Why, when he got back to Los Pinos they would hang him; they would be only too glad of the chance; and his wife?—she would die; I knew it—just go out like a flame from the unbearableness of it all. And there wasn't one chance in a thousand that he wouldn't kill me if I made a single step toward him. I had only to let him go and in a few minutes he would be dead—as dead as his poor brute of a horse would be within the hour. I felt already the cool relief that would be mine when the black shadow of him was gone. I would ride into town and think no more of it than if I had watched a tarantula die. You see, I had it all reasoned out as clearly as could be; there was morality and common sense, the welfare of other people, the man's own good, really, and yet —well, I didn't do it."

"Didn't?" It was Jarrick who put the question a little breathlessly.

"No. I stepped toward him—so! One step, then another, very slowly, hardly a foot at a time, and all the while I watched the infernal circle of that gun, expecting it every minute to spit fire. I didn't want to go; I went against my will. I was scared, too, mortally scared; my legs were like lead—I had to think every time I lifted a foot—and in a queer, crazy way I seemed to feel two people, a man and a woman, holding me back, plucking at my sleeves. But I went. All the time I kept saying, very steady and quiet: 'Don't shoot, Whitney! D'you hear! Don't shoot or I'll kill you!' Wasn't it silly? Kill him! Why, he had me dead ten times before I got to him. But I suppose some trace of sanity was knocking at his drink-sodden brain, for he didn't shoot— just watched me, his red eyes blinking. So! One step at a time—nearer and nearer—I could feel the sweat on my forehead—and then I jumped. I had him by the legs, and we went down in a heap. He shot then; they always do! But I had him tied up with the rags of his own shirt in a trice. Then I brought him water in my hat and let him drink it, drop by drop. After a while he came to altogether. But he never thanked

me; he wasn't that kind of a brute. I got him into town the morning of
the second day and turned him over to his wife. So you see"—Hardy
hesitated and looked at the circle of our faces with an odd, appealing
look—"it *is* queer, isn't it? All mixed up. One doesn't know." He
sank back in his chair and began to scratch, absent-mindedly, at a
holder with a match.

The after-theatre crowd was beginning to come in; the sound of
laughter and talk grew steadily higher; far off an orchestra wailed
inarticulately.

"What became of them?" I asked.

Hardy looked up as if startled. "The Whitneys? Oh—she died—
Martin wrote me. Down there, within a year. One would know it
would happen. Like a flame, I suppose—suddenly."

"And the man—the fellow who was in love with her?"

Hardy stirred wearily. "I haven't heard," he said. "I suppose he
is still alive."

He leaned over to complete the striking of his match, and for an
instant his arm touched a glass; it trembled and hung in the balance,
and he shot out a sinewy hand to stop it, and as he did so the sleeve of
his dinner jacket caught. On the brown flesh of his forearm I saw a
queer, ragged white cross—the scar a snake bite leaves when it is
cicatrized. I meant to avoid his eyes, but somehow I caught them
instead. They were veiled and hurt.

THE GREAT AUK

By Irvin S. Cobb

[Irvin Shrewsbury Cobb was born in Paducah, Kentucky in 1876. He was in newspaper work there until 1904, when he began work on New York papers. He soon gained recognition as a very capable newspaper man and as a writer of humorous short stories. Many of his stories have southern settings and southern characters. Occasionally he writes a story as grim as those of Andreyev or Zola. Such a story is his *Faith, Hope, and Charity*, the title story of a collected volume of fifteen short stories, published in 1934. *The Great Auk* is a story of an extinct species—the all-round actor. The scene is New York, and the tone humorous, shading into the pathetic.

The Great Auk first appeared in the *Saturday Evening Post* (April 29, 1916). It was included in the collection, *Local Color* (copyright 1916), from which it is reprinted by permission of Doubleday, Doran and Company, publishers.]

AS regards the body of the house it lay mostly in shadows—the manmade, daytime shadows which somehow always seem denser and blacker than those that come in the night. The little jogs in the wall behind the boxes were just the same as coalholes. The pitched front of the balcony suggested a deformed upper jaw, biting down on darkness. Its stucco facings, shining dimly, like a row of teeth, added to the illusion. At the bottom of the pit, or the family circle, or whatever it was they called it at the Cosmos Theatre, where the light was somewhat better, the backs of the seats showed bumpily beneath the white cloths that covered them, like lines of graves in a pauper burying ground after a snowstorm.

A third of the way back, in this potter's field of dead-and-gone laughter, a man was hunched in a despondent posture. His attitude would make you think of a lone ghost that had answered the resurrection trump too soon and now was overcome with embarrassment at having been deceived by a false alarm. The brim of his hat rested on the bridge of his nose. Belonging, as he did, to a race that is esteemed to be essentially commercial, he had the artistic face and the imaginative eyes which, as often as not, are found in those of his breed.

His name was Sam Verba. He was general director for Cohalan & Hymen, producing managers. He was watching a rehearsal of a new play, though he did not appear to be. Seemingly, if he was interested at all, it was in the movements of two elderly chore-women, who dawdled about the place deliberately, with dust rags and brooms. Occasionally, as one of the women raised her voice shrilly to address her distant sister, he went "Sh-h! Sh-h!"—like a defective steam pipe. Following this the offender would lower her voice for a space measurable by seconds.

Border lights, burning within the proscenium arch, made the stage brightly visible, revealing it as a thing homely and nude. Stage properties were piled indiscriminately at either side. Against the bare brick wall at the back, segments of scenes were stacked any-which-way, so that a strip of a drawing-room set was superimposed on a strip of a kitchen and that in turn overlapped part of a wainscoted library, the result being as though an earthquake had come along and shaken one room of somebody's house into another room and that into another, and then had left them so. In sight were four women and nine men, who perched on chairs or tables or roosted, crow-fashion, upon the iron steps of a narrow staircase which ascended to the top tier of dressing rooms, extending along a narrow balcony above. The hour was eleven o'clock in the morning. Therefore these persons wore the injured look which people of their nocturnal profession customarily wear upon being summoned out of their beds before midday.

At a little table, teetering on rickety legs almost in the trough of the footlights, sat a man hostilely considering a typewritten script, which was so interlined, so marked and disfigured with crosses, stars, and erasures that only one person—the author of these ciphers—might read his own code, and sometimes even he couldn't. The man at the table was the director, especially engaged to put on this particular piece, which was a comedy-drama. He raised his head.

"All right, children," he said, "take the second act—from the beginning, Miss Cherry, Mrs. Morehead—come along. Stand by, everybody else, and, please, in Heaven's name, remember your cues—for once."

A young woman and a middle-aged woman detached themselves from one of the waiting groups and came downstage. The young woman moved eagerly to obey; she was an exceedingly pretty young woman. The other woman, having passed her youth, strove now to re-create it in her costume. She wore a floppy hat and a rather skimpy frock, which buttoned down her back, school-girl fashion, and ended several inches above her ankles. Under the light her dyed hair shone with the brilliancy of a new copper saucepan. There were fine, puckery lines at her eyes. Her skin, though, had the smooth texture which comes, some say, from the grease paint, and others say from plenty of sleep.

She held in one hand a flimsy, blue-backed sheaf; it was her part in the play. Having that wisdom in her calling which comes of long experience, she would read from it until automatically she had acquired it without prolonged mental effort; would let her trained and docile memory sop up the speeches by processes of absorption. Miss Cherry carried no manuscript; she didn't need it. She had been sitting up nights, studying her lines. For she, the poor thing, was newly escaped from a dramatic school. Mrs. Morehead wanted to make a living. Miss Cherry wanted to make a hit.

These two began the opening scene of the act and, between them, carried it forward. Miss Cherry as the daughter was playing it in rehearsal, exactly as she expected to play it before an audience, inflections, short catches of the breath, emotional gasps—all the illusions, all the business of the part. On the other hand, Mrs. Morehead appeared to have but one ambition in her present employment, and that was to get it over with as speedily as possible. After this contrasted fashion, then, they progressed to a certain dramatic juncture:

"But, mother," said Miss Cherry, her arms extended in a carefully-thought-out attitude of girlish bewilderment, "what am I to do?"

Mrs. Morehead glanced down, refreshing her memory by a glance into the blue booklet.

"My child," she said, "leave it to destiny."

She said this in the tone of a person of rather indifferent appetite, ordering toast and tea for breakfast.

A pause ensued here.

"My child," repeated Mrs. Morehead, glancing over her shoulder impatiently, but speaking still in the same voice, "leave it to destiny."

"Well, well—" snapped the man at the little table, "that's the cue, 'leave it to destiny!' Come on, McVey! Come a-w-n, McVey! Where's McVey?" He raised his voice fretfully.

A nervous thin man hurried down the stage.

"Oh, there you are. Go ahead, McVey. You're keeping everybody waiting. Didn't I tell you you'd have to read the grandfather's part today?"

"No, sir, you didn't," said McVey, aggrieved.

"Well, anyhow, I meant to," said his superior.

"But I'm reading Miss Gifford's part this morning," said McVey, who was the assistant stage manager. "She had to go to see about her costumes."

"You'll have to read 'em both, then," ordered the special director. "Anyhow, the parts don't conflict—they're not on the stage together during this act. Do the best you can. Now let's go back and take those last two sides over again."

Vibrantly and with the proper gesture in the proper place, Miss Cherry repeated her speech. Wearily and without gestures, Mrs. Morehead repeated hers. The flustered McVey holding the absentee Miss Gifford's part in one hand and the mythical grandfather's in the other, circled upstage and, coming hurriedly down, stepped in between them.

"No, no, no," barked the director, "don't come on that way—you'll throw both these ladies out. Come on at the upper side of that blue chair, Mac; that's the door. This is supposed to be a house. You can't walk right through the side of a house without upsetting things. You realize that, don't you? Once more—back again to 'leave it to destiny.'"

The rehearsal went on by the customary process of advancing a foot and a half, then retreating a foot, then re-advancing two feet. The novices in the cast were prodigal of their energy, but the veterans saved themselves against what they knew was coming later, when they would need all they had of strength and more, besides.

A young man let himself in through the box-office door and stood in that drafty, inky-black space which theatrical folks call the front of the house and the public call the back of the house. Coming out of the sunlight into this cave of the winds, he was blinded at first. He blinked until he peered out the shape of chairs, and he felt his way down the center aisle and slipped into a place alongside the silent, broody figure. The newcomer was the author of the play, named Offutt; his age was less than thirty; and his manner was cheerful, as befitting an author who is less than thirty and has placed a play with an established firm.

"Well," he said, "how's everything going?"

"Rotten, thank you!" said Verba, continuing to stare straight ahead. "We're still shy one grandfather, if that should be of any interest to you."

"But you had Grainger engaged—I thought that was all settled last night," said the playwright.

"That tired business man? Huh!" said Verba expressively. "By the time he'd got through fussing over the style of contract he wanted, in case he liked the part and we liked him in it, and then quarreling about the salary he was to get, and then arguing out how high up the list his name was to appear in the billing, your friend Grainger was completely exhausted.

"And then, on top of that, he discovered we were going to Chicago after the opening in Rochester, and he balked. Said his following was here in New York. Said he'd supposed we were coming right in here after the opening instead of fussing round on the road. Said he couldn't think of being kept out of New York at the beginning of the season unless he got at least seventy-five more a week. Said he'd go back to vaudeville first. Said he had a swell offer from the two-a-day shops anyhow.

"Then I said a few things to Grainger, and he walked out on me. His following!—do you get that? Grainger could carry all the following he's got in the top of his hat and still have plenty of room left for his head. So there you are, my son—within ten days of the tryout and nobody on hand to play dear old grandfather for you! And nobody in sight either—in case anybody should happen to ask you."

"Oh, we'll find somebody," said Offutt optimistically. The young of the playwrighting species are constitutionally optimistic.

"Oh, we will, will we? Well, for example, who?—since you're so confident about it?"

"That's up to you," countered Offutt, "I should worry!"

"Take it from me, young man, you'd better worry," growled Verba morosely.

"But, Verba," contended young Offutt, "there must be somebody loose who'll fit the part. What with thousands of actors looking for engagements—"

"Say, Offutt, what's the use of going over that again?" broke in Verba in a tone which indicated he was prepared to go over it again. "To begin with, there aren't thousands of actors looking for jobs. There are a few actors looking for jobs—and a few thousand others looking for jobs who only think they can act. Offhand, I can list you just three men fit to play this grandfather part—or four, if you stick in Grainger as an added starter."

He held up a long, slender hand, ticking off the names on his fingers.

"There's Warburton, and there's Pell, and there's old Gabe Clayton. Warburton's tied up in the pictures. Damn the movies! They're stealing everybody worth a hang. I got a swell offer myself yesterday from the Ziegler crowd to direct features for 'em. The letter's on my desk now. Old Gabe is in a sanitarium taking the rest cure—which means for the time being he's practically sober, but not available for us or anybody else. And Guy Pell's under contract to Fructer Brothers, and you know what a swell chance there is of their loaning him to our shop.

"That doesn't leave anybody but Grainger, who's so swelled up with conceit that he's impossible. And, anyhow he's too young. Just as I told you yesterday, I only figured him in as a last chance. I don't want a young fellow playing this part—with his face all messed up with false whiskers and an artificial squeak in his voice. I want an old man—one that looks old and talks old and can play old.

"He's got to be right or nothing's right. You may have written this piece, boy; but, by gum, I'm responsible for the way it's cast, and I want a regular, honest-to-God grandfather. Only," he added, quoting the tag of a current Broadway story, "only there ain't no such animal."

"I still insist, Verba," put in Offutt, "that you over-estimate the importance of the grandfather—he's only a character bit."

"Son," said Verba, "you talk like an author. Maybe you thought he was a bit when you wrote him in; but he's not. He's going to carry this play. He's the whole axle that the whole action turns on, and if he's wrong the whole thing's wrong. If he falls down your play falls down."

"Well, suppose he is," said Offutt, plaintively. The bruised worm was beginning to turn. "Am I to blame because I write a part so human and so lifelike that nobody's competent to do it?"

Verba gave him a sidelong glance and grinned sardonically. "Don't ask me whose fault it is," he said. "I know this: In the old days actors were actors." Verba, who was perhaps forty-four, spoke with the air of having known Edmund Kean intimately. "They bred real actors then—people who had versatility and a range. You got hold of a play and you went out and hired a bunch of troupers, and they played it for you. Now we don't have actors any more—we only have types.

"Everybody's a type. A man or a woman starts out being one kind of type, and sticks right there. Dramatists write parts for types, and managers go out and hire types for the parts. Sometimes they can't find the right type, and then there's another expensive production taking a trip to its eternal rest in the storehouse. I don't know whose fault it is—I only know it's not mine. It's hell—that's what it is—simply hell!"

Gloom choked Verba. He stared moodily ahead of him, where the broad of a wide, blue-ginghamed back showed above the draped tops of the next row of seats but one. Suddenly he smote his hands together.

"Bateman!" he exclaimed. "Old Bird Bateman!"

Up from behind the next row of seats but one rose a chore-lady with her nose in the air and her clenched fists on the places where her hips should have been—if she had any hips.

"I beg your par-r-don?" she inquired, quivering with a grand, indignant politeness; "was you referrin' to me as an ould boid?"

"Madam," said Verba, "resume your pleasures. I wasn't thinking of you."

"Thin why was you lookin' at me whin you said it? You may be the owner of this bum dump, f'r all I care, but job or no job, let me tell you this, young man—there's no black Prowtestant Jew alive kin call me out of me own name an'——"

"Oh, shut up," said Verba, without heat. He got on his feet. "Come on, Offutt, the lady thinks I'm trying to flirt with her, and between the three of us, we're breaking up rehearsals. Let's get out—I've got an idea." In the half light his eyes shone like a cat's.

Outside on the hot pavement, he took Offutt by the lapels of his coat. "Boy," he said, "did you ever hear of Burton Bateman—better known as Old Bird Bateman?"

Offutt shook his head.

"Never did," he confessed.

"You're too young at this game to remember, I guess," said Verba. "Well, then, did you ever hear of the Scudder Stock Company?"

"Of course I've heard of that," said Offutt. "It was long before my time, though."

"It was long before everybody's time," assented Verba. "Ten years is the same as a century on this street. But twenty-five years ago Burt Bateman played leads with the Scudder Stock Company—yes; and played juveniles and walking gentlemen and friends of the family and long-lost heirs and Dutchmen and Irishmen and niggers—played anything there was to play.

"He wasn't one of your single-barrelled modern types and none of your old-time ranting scenery-biters either; he was an actor. If he'd come along a little later they'd have made a star out of him and probably ruined him. You'd have remembered him then. But he never was a star. He never was featured even. He just kept right on being an actor. And gee, how he could eat up an old man's part!"

"You speak of him as though he were dead," said Offutt.

"He might as well be—he's forgotten," said Verba, unconsciously coining all Broadway's epitaph for all Broadway's tribe. "I haven't seen him for fifteen years, but I understand he's still alive—that is, he hasn't quit breathing. Somebody was telling me not long ago they'd crossed his trail 'way downtown.

"You see, Burt Bateman was a character in his way, just as old Nate Scudder was one in his way. I guess that's why they hung together so long. When the theatrical district started to move uptown, Nate wouldn't move with it. It moved from Fourteenth Street to Twenty-third, and from there to Thirty-fourth, and from there to Forty-second—and it's still headed north. But Scudder stayed where he was. And it broke him—broke his heart, too, I guess. Anyhow, he died and his organization scattered—all but Bateman. He wouldn't scatter. The heirs fell out, and the estate—what was left of it—got tied up in litigation; and it's been tied up ever since."

He turned and waved a long arm at a passing taxi. The driver curved his machine up to the curb.

"Come on!" said Verba, making to cross the sidewalk.

"Come on where?" asked Offutt.

"We're going to University Place—you and me," said Verba, quickened and alive all over with his inspiration. "We're going down to Scudder's Theatre. Didn't know there was such a theatre as Scudder's, did you? Well, there is—what's left of it. We're going down there to find Old Bird Bateman. That's where he was, last accounts. And if the booze hasn't got him, he's going to play that damn grandfather in this show of yours."

"Can he do it?"

Verba halted with one foot in the taxi.

"Can he do it? Watch him, boy—that's all! Just watch him. Say, it's a notion—digging that old boy out of the graveyard.

"You never heard of him, and I'd forgotten him; but you take a lot of these old-timers who don't think there've been any actors since Fanny Davenport and Billy Florence—they'll remember him. And you bet they'll come to see him. We'll give this town a sensation—and that's what it loves, this town—sensation."

Once upon a time—that was when he was a green reporter newly come to town—Offutt had known, more or less minutely, almost every prowlable inch of the tip of the long seamy tongue of rock that is called Manhattan Island. Now, as a story-writer and a playwriter, he only went down there when he sought for local color in Greenwich Village, or around Washington Square or on the lower East Side. As for Verba, he found his local color, ready-mixed, in scene-painters' pots and make-up boxes. Being a typical New Yorker—if there is such a thing—he was as insular, as provincial, as closely bound to his own briefened ranging ground as none but a typical New Yorker can be. To him this wasn't a metropolis of five boroughs, many bridges, and five-and-a-half millions. To him this was a strip of street, something less than two miles long, with shorter stretches of street meeting it at right angles, east and west, as ribs meet a spine. His map of New York would have resembled a codfish's skeleton, its head aiming toward far-away Harlem, the fork in its tail pointing to the distant Battery. To him therefore Twenty-third Street was Farthest South. What might lie below was in the Antarctic Circle of community life.

They crossed Twenty-third Street and invaded a district grown strange to his eyes—a district where tall loft buildings, the successors to the sweatshops of an earlier, but not very much earlier, day, mounted, floor by floor, above the humbler roofs of older houses. They crossed Fourteenth, the taxi weaving a way through dense masses of men who gabbled in strange tongues among themselves, for lunch-time had come and the garment-workers, the feather-workers and the fur-workers, deserting their work benches for an hour, had flocked into the open, packing the sidewalks and overflowing upon the asphalt, to chatter and gossip and take the air. Just below Fourteenth Street they swung eastward and turned into University Place, which is a street of past memories and present acute activities, and, in a minute, obeying Verba's instructions, their driver brought them to a standstill before a certain number.

"Give it the once-over," advised Verba as he climbed out and felt in his pocket for the fare. "You can figure for yourself how far out of the world it is—nobody's had the nerve to try to open it up as a moving-picture palace. And that's the tip-off on any shack in this burg that'll hold a crowd, a screen, and a projecting machine all at the same time."

Offutt looked and marvelled that he had never noticed this place before, since surely, covering assignments or on exploration jaunts, he must have passed it by a score of times. It stood midway of the block. On one side of it was a little pawnshop, its single grimy window filled with the strange objects which persons acquire, seemingly for pawning purposes exclusively—sword-canes and mandolins with mother-of-pearl insets in them, and moss-agate cuff buttons. On the other side was a trunk store with half of its wares cluttering the narrow-door passage, and signs everywhere displayed to inform the public that the proprietor was going out of business and must sell his stock at an enormous sacrifice, wherefore until further notice, perfectly ruinous prices would prevail. It appears to be a characteristic of all trunk stores that their proprietors are constantly going out of business and that their contents, invariably, are to be had below cost.

Between these two establishments gaped a recessed and cavernous entryway flanked by two big stone pillars of a dropsical contour and spanned over at the top by a top-heavy cornice ponderously and painfully Corinthian in aspect. The outjutting eaves rested flat on the coping stones and from there the roof gabled up sharply. Old gates, heavily chained and slanting inward, warded the opening between the pair of pillars, so that the mouth of the place was muzzled with iron, like an Elizabethan shrew's.

Above, the building was beetle-browed; below, it was dish-faced. A student of architectural criminology would pause before this façade and take notes.

The space inclosed within the skewed and bent gate pickets was a snug harbor for the dust of many a gritty day. There were little grey drifts of it at the foot of each of the five steps that led up to the flagged floor level; secretions of grime covered the barred double doors on beyond the steps, until the original color was only to be guessed at; scraps of dodgers, pieces of newspaper and tattered handbills adhered to every carved projection at the feet of the columns, like dead leaves about tree boles in the woods.

On the frieze overhead might be made out, in lettering that once had been gold-leafed, the line: Scudder's Family Theatre. The words were scarcely decipherable now. Billposters had coated every available inch of space with snipes and sheets.

Verba shook the gates until the hasps gritted and the chains clanged.

"Nobody at home," he said. "I guess the sheriff locked her up when the lawsuits started and then threw away the key. Well, let's scout round. Somebody's sure to know our man; they told me Bateman was a neighborhood character down here. A cop ought to be able to help us—only I don't see one. Maybe they don't have cops in this street."

Speculatively his eyes ranged the vista up and down the block and opposite. He pointed to a saloon diagonally across the way, next door to the first corner south.

"When in doubt," he said, "ask everybody's friend. Come on; we'll go over and brace the barkeep."

A young man, with a humorous slant to his eyebrows and dark hair combed back from the forehead in neatly ornate scallops, pulled down the front of a reasonably clean white jacket and spread both hands on the bar, awaiting their pleasure.

"Mister Wine Clerk," said Verba, using the ceremonial title of his Tenderloin range, "we're trying to find an old boy named Bateman— Burton Bateman, retired actor by profession. Ever hear of him?"

"Sure!" assented the barkeeper. "He's part of the fixtures—Old

Bird is; but he ain't about now. To ketch him, you've come an hour late."

"Lives round here somewhere, doesn't he?"

"Search me," said the young man succinctly. "I guess he don't exactly live anywhere—not in a regular lodging house or anything like that. See? I never asked him—him being sort of touchy about his private affairs—but I guess he sleeps in some hole somewhere. He mostly does his scoffin' here though—as a guest of the house."

"Does his what here?" asked Verba.

"His scoffin'—his feedin'. See?" The young man flirted a thumb in the direction of the free-lunch counter.

"Oh! He eats here?"

"You said it! The boss-man that owns this liquor store—is a kind of an old-timer round here himself. I've heard him say he knowed The Bird away back yonder when the old theatre 'crost the street was runnin' and things was breakin' better for the old boy than what they do now. So he stakes him to a drink every now and then—Old Bird won't take a piece of change, but he will take a drink—and he lets him browse off the free lunch all he's a mind to.

"He comes driftin' in here twicet a day regular and fills up on chow for nothin'! But he's been here already and left today—'bout an hour ago. I figure he won't be back now till 'long about four or five o'clock."

Verba became cognizant of a tugging at his coat. An incredibly small, incredibly ragged boy, with some draggled first editions under his arm, had wormed silently in between his legs and was looking up at him with one eye. The boy had only one eye to look with. The other eye was a flattened slit over a sunken socket.

"Mister! Say, Mister!" beseeched the gamin earnestly. "Gimme fi' cent and I'll—"

"Hey you, Blinky!" interposed the barkeeper, bending over the bar to see the small intruder. "Beat it!"

There was a scurrying thud of bare feet on the tiled floor, and the wizened intruder magically had vanished between the swinging doors.

"You gents can sit down and wait if you want to," said the barkeeper. "It's liable to be a long time, though. Or I can tell Old Bird, when he comes in, somebody's askin' for him and try to hold him for you. I could 'phone you even, if it's important, if you'll gimme your number."

"It is important—in a way," said Verba. "Suppose we do that, Offutt—give the wine clerk our telephone number."

He laid a coin and a card on the bar. The young man regarded the name and the address on the card briefly.

"All right!" he said, depositing the coin in his pocket and the card against the mirror at his back. "I won't forget. The old boy don't have many people lookin' for him. Fact is, I don't remember he ever had anybody lookin' for him before. Are you gents friends of his? . . . No? Well, anyhow, I'll fix it."

"Funny old sneezer!" he continued. "Dippy a little up here, I guess." He tapped himself on the forehead.

"If he had a habit I'd say sometimes he was hopped. F'r instance, he'll come in here and spiel off something to me 'bout havin' been in his Louie Kahn's drawin'-room,—anyhow, that's what it sounds like. The only Louie Kahn round here that I know of runs a junk shop over in Ninth Street. And it's a cinch that Louie Kahn ain't got no drawin'-room. Or he'll tell me he's been spendin' the day on the seabeach. Only yes'day he was handin' me that junk."

"Mightn't he have taken a little run down to Coney?" suggested Verba hopefully.

"Go to Coney—him!" scoffed the barkeeper. "Where'd he raise the coin for carfare down to Coney? You can take it from me, gents, Old Bird forgot what the sad sea waves sound like, long time ago. I'll lay you a little eight-to-five he ain't been a quarter of a mile away from this liquor store in ten years. . . . Well, good day, gents."

"It strikes me, Verba," began Offutt as they passed out, "that possibly we're only wasting our time. If what that gabby young drink wrestler just said is right we're—"

Something wriggled at his knees and caromed off against Verba. A single bright, greedy eye appraised them both with an upward flash.

"Mister! Mister, listen!" pleaded a voice, the owner of which managed somehow to be in the path of both of them at once. "I heard yous spielin' in there. I know where Old Boid is. I kin show yous where he is."

"Where is he?" demanded Verba.

"Gimme fi' cent—gimme ten cent—first. It's a secrut. It's worth ten cent."

"It is," agreed Verba gravely. "It's worth all of ten cents now and it'll be worth a quarter more to you, sonny, if you deliver the goods."

He tendered the advance installment of the fee, and a hand, all claws like a bird's foot, snatched it away from him.

Blinky carefully pouched the dime in some unfathomable inner recess of his rags. Having provided against any attempt to separate him from the retainer in the event of the negotiations falling through, his code of honor asserted itself.

"It's a secrut. See? They ain't nobody but me and two-t'ree udder kids wise to it. Yous gotta swear you won't tell 'im nor nobody 'twas me tipped yous off. If yous did it'd spoil me graft—he'd be sore. See? Cold nights he lets us kids bunk in there wit' 'im. And daytimes we plays audience for 'im. See?"

"You play what for him?" asked Offutt.

"C'm on, an' I'll show yous," bade Blinky. "Only yous is gotta lay dead w'ile it's comin' off. See?"

"We'll lay dead," pledged Verba.

Satisfied, Blinky led the way. Mystified, they followed. He led them back across University Place again; and on past Scudder's Family Theatre, with the lowering stone frontal bone above and, below, the wide maw, bitted and gagged by its scold's bridle of snaffled iron; and on round the corner below into a fouled, dingy cross street.

Beyond the canvas marquee of a small walled-in beer garden the child went nimbly through a broken panel in a short stretch of aged and tottery wooden fencing. Wriggling through the gap behind him they found themselves in a small inclosure paved with cracked flagging. Confronting them was a short flight of iron steps, leading up to a wide, venerable-appearing doorway, which once, as the visible proof showed, had been sealed up with plank shorings, nailed on in vertical strips.

"One of the old side entrances to Scudder's," said Verba. "Where the carriages used to wait, I guess. The plot thickens—eh, Offutt?"

Offutt nodded, his eyes being on their small guide. A little sense of adventure possessed them both. They had the feeling of being co-conspirators in a little intrigue.

"Wotcher waitin' fur?" demanded Blinky. "Stick wit' me and don't make no noise." He climbed the iron steps and shoved the nail-pocked door ajar. "Watch yer step!" he counselled as he vanished within. "It's kind o' dark in yere."

Kind o' dark was right. Straining their eyes they stumbled along a black passage, with Blinky going on ahead silently. They turned once to the left and once to the right and emerged, where the light was somewhat clearer, into the shelter of a recess just behind the lower boxes of the abandoned playhouse.

"Wow!" said Verba in a sort of reverential undertone, as though he stood in the presence of death. "I haven't been here in twenty-odd years. Why, the last time I was here I was a kid!"

Veritably he did stand in the presence of death. The place looked dead and smelled dead and was dead. The air was heavy-laden with bone-yard scents—rot and corrosion and rust and dust. With the taints of moulded leather and gangrened metal, of worm-gnawed woodwork and moth-eaten fabrics, arose also from beneath their feet that other stench which inevitably is begotten of neglect and lonesomeness within any spot inclosed by walls and a roof, provided sun and wind and human usage are excluded from it long enough. Offutt sniffed and, over Verba's shoulder, looked about him.

He could make out his immediate surroundings fairly well, for the curtains that had guarded the windows in the hip roof and round one upper side of the building were turned by decay into squares of lacework, patterned with rents and with cracks; and in some instances they had fetched away from their fastenings altogether.

Through the glass panes, and through the grime that bleared the glass, a measure of daylight filtered, slanting in pale bluish streaks, like spilt skim milk, on vistas of the faded red-plush chairs; on the scrolled and burdened decorations of the proscenium arch; on the seamy, stained curtain; on the torn and musty hangings of the boxes; on an enormous gas chandelier which, swinging low over the pit from the domed ceiling above, was so clumped with swathings of cobweb that it had become a great, dangling grey cocoon.

Curving in wide swings from above their heads to the opposite side ran three balconies, rising one above the other, and each supported by many fat pillars. The spaces beneath these galleries were shadowy and dark, seeming to stretch away endlessly. So, too, was the perspective of the lower floor, at the back, elaborated by the gloom into a vast, yawning mouth which fairly ached with its own emptiness. But at the front the screened angles of sunlight, stippled as they were with billions of dancing motes, brought out clearly enough the stage of the old theatre and, down under the lip of the stage, the railed inclosure of the orchestra and, at either side, the scarred bulkheads and fouled drapings of the stage boxes, upper tier and lower tier.

Close at hand Offutt was aware of crawling things which might be spiders, and a long grey rat which scuffled across the floor almost beneath his feet, dragging its scaled tail over the boards with a nasty rasping sound. He heard other rats squealing and gnawing in the wainscoting behind him. He was aware, also, of the dirt, which scabbed and crusted everything. And he felt as though he had invaded the vault of an ancient tomb. Sure enough, in a manner of speaking, he had done just that.

"Some place—huh, mister?" said the small gutter-sparrow proudly, and, though he spoke in a whisper, Offutt jumped. "Stick yere, yous two," ordered the child. "Somethin'll be comin' off in a minute."

Seemingly he had caught a signal or a warning not visible to the older intruders. Leaving them, he ran briskly down a side aisle, and apparently did not care now how much noise he might make, for he whooped as he ran. He flung his papers aside and perched himself in a chair at the very front of the pit. He briskly rattled the loose back of the chair in front of him, and, inserting two dirty fingers at the corners of his mouth, emitted the shrill whistle by which a gallery god, since first gallery gods were created into an echoing world, has testified to his impatient longings that amusement be vouchsafed him.

As though the whistle had been a command, the daubed old curtain shivered and swayed. A dead thing was coming to life. Creaking dolefully, it rolled up and up until it had rolled up entirely out of sight.

A back drop, lowered at a point well down front, made the stage shallow. Once upon a time this back drop had been intended to represent a stretch of beach with blue rollers breaking on beyond. Faded as it was, and stained and cracked and scaly as it was now, the design of the artist who painted it was yet discernible; for he plainly had been one who held by the pigmented principle that all sea sands be very yellow and all sea waves be very blue.

Out of the far wings came a figure of a man, crossing the narrowed space to halt midway of the stage, close up to the tin gutter where the tipless prongs of many gas-jet footlights stood up like the tines of a garden rake. Verba's hand tightened on Offutt's arm, dragging him farther back into the shadows, and Verba's voice spoke, with a soft, tense caution, in Offutt's ear: "Lord! Lord!" Verba almost breathed the words out. "'Backward, turn backward, O Time, in your—' Look yonder, Offutt! It's him!"

He might have spared the urging. Offutt was looking and, without being told, knew the man at whom he looked was the man the two of them had come here to find. The lone gamin in the pit clapped his talons of hands together, making a feeble, thin sound. To this applause, as to a rousing greeting, the figure behind the footlights bowed low, then straightened. And Offutt could see, by one of the slanting bars of tarnished daylight, which stabbed downward through the dusk of the place, that the man up there on the stage was a very old man, with a heavy, leonine face and heavy brows and deep-set, big grey eyes, and a splendid massive head mopped with long, coarse white hair; and he was dressed as a fop of sixty years ago and he carried himself so.

The slash of indifferent sunshine, slicing into the gloom like a dulled sword blade, rested its lowermost tip full upon him. It brought out the bleached pallor of his skin, for his face was free from any suggestion of make-up, and it showed the tears and frays in his costume, and the mis-shapen shoes that were on his feet, and the high-shouldered, long-tailed coat, and the soiled, collarless shirt which he wore beneath the once gorgeous velvet waistcoat.

In one hand he held, by a dainty grip on the brim, a flat-crowned derby hat, and between the fingers of the other hand twirled a slender black walking stick, with the shreds of a silken tassel adhering to it. And everything about him, barring only the shoes and the shirt, which plainly belonged to his everyday apparel, seemed fit to fall apart with age and with shabbiness.

"Ladies and gentlemen," he said—and his voice filled all the empty house by reason of its strength and its toned richness—"with your kind indulgence I shall begin this entertainment with an attempt at an imitation of the elder Sothern in his famous rôle of Lord Dundreary, depicting him as he appeared in one of the scenes from that sterling and popular comedy, 'Our American Cousin,' by Tom Taylor, Esquire."

With that, instantly stepping into character, he took a mincing, jaunty pace or two sideways. Half turning toward an imaginary confrère and addressing that mythical listener, he began a speech which, being pieced together with other speeches, at once lengthened into a kind of monologue. But he knew the lines—that was plain; and he knew the part, too, and for the moment lived and breathed it, and in all regards veritably was it. That, likewise, the watching pair of eavesdroppers could realize, though neither of them was of sufficient age to remember, even had he seen the great craftsman whose work old Bateman now was counterfeiting.

The interlopers looked on and, under the spell of a wizardry, forgot indeed they were interlopers. For before their eyes they saw, wonderfully re-created, a most notable conception, and afterward would have sworn, both of them, that all of it—the drawl and the lisp, the exaggerated walk, the gestures, the play of leg and arm, the swing of body, the skew of head, the lift of eyebrow even—was as true and as faithful to the original as any mirrored image might be to the image itself.

How long they stood and watched neither Verba nor Offutt was subsequently able to say with any reasonable exactitude. It might have been four minutes; it might have been six, or even eight. When later, taking counsel together, they sought to reckon up the time, the estimates varied so widely they gave up trying to reconcile them.

This much, though, they were sure of—that, in his mumming, old Bateman rose magically triumphant above the abundant handicaps of his own years and his own physique, his garb and his environment. Doing the undoable, he for the moment threw aside his years as one might throw aside the weight of a wornout garment, and for that moment, to suit his own designs of mimicry, made floods of strength and youthfulness course through those withered arteries.

The old man finished with a whimsical turn of his voice and a flirt of his cane to match it. He bowed himself off with the hand which held the hat at his breast, and promptly on the second he disappeared the ancient curtain began to descend, Blinky meanwhile clapping with all his puny might.

Offutt turned to his companion. Behind the shelter of the box Verba's lean, dark face was twitching.

"Is he there? Can he act? Was I right?" Verba asked himself each question, and himself answered each with a little earnest nod. "Gee, what a find!"

"Not a find, Verba," whispered Offutt—"a resurrection—maybe. We've seen a genius in his grave."

"And we're going to dig him up." In his intentness Verba almost panted it. "Wait! Wait!" he added warningly then, though Offutt had not offered to stir. "This is going to be a Protean stunt, I take it. Let's let him show some more of his goods; for, by everything that's holy, he's got 'em!"

Up once more the curtain lifted, seemingly by its own motive power; and now the seaside drop was raised, and they beheld that, behind it, the stage had been dressed for another scene—a room in a French house. A secretaire, sadly battered and marred, stood at one side; a bookcase with broken doors and gaping, empty shelves stood at the other, balancing it off. Down stage was an armchair. Its tapestry upholstering was rotted through and a freed spiral of springs uncoiled like a slender snake from its cushioned seat. All three pieces were of a pattern— "Louie-the-Something stuff," Verba would have called them.

A table, placed fronting the chair but much nearer the right lower entrance than the chair was, and covered with a faded cloth that depended almost to the floor, belonged evidently to the same set. The scenery at the back showed a balcony, with a wide French window, open, in the middle. Beyond the window dangled a drop, dingy and discolored as all the rest was, but displaying dimly a jumble of painted house-tops and, far away in the simulated distance, the Arc de Triomphe. The colors were almost obliterated, but the suggestion of perspective remained, testifying still to the skill of the creator.

From the wings where they had seen him vanish Bateman reappeared. The trousers and the shoes were those he had worn before; but now, thrown on over his shirt, was the melancholy wreck of what once had been a blue uniform coat, with huge epaulets upon the shoulders and gold braid upon the collar and the cuffs, and brass buttons to fasten it in double-breasted fashion down the front. Now, though, it hung open. Some of the buttons were missing, and the gold lacings were mere blackened wisps of rags.

Bateman came on slowly, with dragging feet, his arms and legs and head quivering in a violent palsy. He stared out of the window as he let himself down carefully into the ruined armchair. His first movement proved that he played a venerable, very decrepit man—a man near death from age and ailments; yet by his art he managed to project, through the fleshly and physical weaknesses of the character, a power of dignity, of dominance, and of mental authority. He rolled his head back wearily.

"My child," he said, addressing a make-believe shape before him, "I must help to receive our brave, victorious troops. See! I am fittingly dressed to do them honor."

His tones were pitched in the cracked cackle of senility. He paused, as though for an answer out of space. His inflection told as he, in turn, replied that this answer had been a remonstrance:

"No, no, no!" he said almost fiercely. "You must not seek to dissuade me."

The words stung Verba's memory, raising a welt of recollections there.

"I've got it!" he said exultantly, not forgetting though, to keep his voice down. "'Siege of Berlin,' by that French fellow—what's his name? —Daudet!"

"I remember the story," answered Offutt.

"I remember the play," said Verba. "Somebody dramatized it—

Lord knows who—and Scudder put it on here as a curtain raiser. I saw it myself, Offutt—think of that! Sitting up yonder in the old peanut roost—a kid no bigger than that kid down there—I saw it. And now I'm seeing it again; seeing Burt Bateman play the part of the old paralytic—you know, the old French officer who was fooled by his doctor and his granddaughter into believing the French had licked the Germans, when all the time 't was the other way and—"

"Sh-h!" counseled Offutt.

After another little wait Bateman was going on with his scene:

"Listen! Listen!" he cried, cupping a tremulous palm behind his ear. "Do you not hear them far away?—the trumpets—the trumpets of victorious France! Our forces have entered Berlin! Thank God! Thank God! All Paris will celebrate. I must greet them from the balcony."

With a mighty effort he reared himself to his feet, straightening his slanted shoulders, erecting his lolled head. His fingers fumbled at button and buttonhole, fastening his coat at the throat. He swung one arm imperiously, warding off imaginary hands.

"The trumpets! The trumpets! Hark! They come nearer and nearer! They sound for the victory of France—for a heroic army. I will go! Doctor or no doctor. I this day pay my homage to our glorious army. Stand back, *ma chérie!*"

Offutt, fifty feet away, caught himself straining his ears to hear those trumpets too. A rat ran across his foot, and Offutt never knew it.

"They come! They come!" chuckled Bateman.

He dragged himself up stage, mounted the two stairs to the balcony, and stood in the window, at attention, to salute the tri-colored flag. Nor did he forget to keep his face half turned to the body of the house.

He smiled; and the two unseen spies, staring at that profiled head, saw the joy that was in the smile. Then, in the same moment, the expression changed. Dumb astonishment came first—an unbelieving astonishment; then blank stupefaction; then the shock of horrified understanding; then unutterable rage.

Offutt recalled the tale from which the playlet had been evolved, and Verba, for his part, recalled the playlet; but, had neither known what they knew, the both of them, guided and informed only by the quality of Bateman's acting, still could have anticipated the climax now impending; and, lacking all prior acquaintance with the plot of it, yet would have read that the cripple, expecting to cheer his beloved French, saw advancing beneath the Arc de Triomphe the heads of the conquering Germans, and heard, above the calling bugles, not the Marseillaise, but the strains of a Teuton marching song. His face literally bristled with his hate. He spun about full face, a mortally stricken man. His clenched fists rose above his head in a command.

"To arms! To arms!" he screamed impotently, with the rattle already in his throat. "The Prussians! The Prus—"

He choked, tottered down the steps, reeled forward and fell headlong out into the room, rolling in the death spasm behind the draped table; and as, ten seconds later, the curtain began to unroll from above and lengthen down, Offutt found himself saying over and over again, mechanically:

"Why, he's gone, isn't he?"

"He kept the table between him and the house and crawled out behind it—trust him not to spoil his picture!" explained Verba. "And trust him to know the tricks of his trade." He tugged at Offutt's elbow. "Come on, boy; I've seen enough and so have you, I guess. Let's go sign him."

He fumbled at the wall.

"Side passageway back to the stage ought to be round here somewhere. Here it is—that's lucky!"

Guiding himself by the touching of his outstretched hands upon the walls of the opening, Verba felt his way behind the box, with Offutt stumbling along in his rear. So progressing, they came to an iron-sheathed door. Verba lifted its latch and they were in a place of rancid smells and cluttering stage duffel. Roaches fled in front of them. On their left a small wooden door stood partly ajar, and through the cranny they looked, as they passed, into a dressing room, where a pallet of old hangings covered half the floor space, and all manner of dingy stock costumings and stage trappings hung upon hooks.

"Here's where he must sleep," said Verba. "What a place for a white man to be living in!"

He felt for his handkerchief to wipe his soiled hands, and then together they saw Bateman advancing toward them from out of the extreme rear of the stage. Over his shoulders was thrown a robe of heavy ragged sacking and upon his face he had hung a long, false beard of white hair. He glared at them angrily. And then Offutt, in instantaneous appraisal, interpreted most surely the look out of those staring big grey eyes.

Verba extended his hand and opened his mouth to speak; but Bateman was already speaking.

"What business have you here?" he demanded. "Strangers are not permitted here during performances. How came the stage doorkeeper to admit you? He has been here too long, that doorkeeper, and he grows careless. I shall have him discharged."

"But, Mr. Bateman," began Verba, half puzzled, half insistent, "I'm in the business myself. I want to—"

"Stand aside!" ordered the old man almost violently. "You cannot have been long in the business, young sir, else you would be more mannerly than to interrupt an artist when his public calls for him. Out of my way, please!"

He strutted by them in stilted vanity and gripped the lifting ropes of the old curtain where they swung in the near angle of the wings, and pulled downward on them with an unexpected display of muscular force. The curtain rose; and as Blinky, still at his place, uplifted a little yell of approbation the old man, bending his shoulders, passed out into the center of the French drawing-room set and, extending a quivering hand, uttered sonorously the command:

"Blow, winds, and crack your cheeks! rage! blow!"

"The mad scene from King Lear," said Offutt.

"Sure—Shakespeare!" agreed Verba. "Old Scudder was a bug on the Bard stuff. So was Bateman. He used to know it from cover to cover—Othello, Hamlet, Lear—the whole string. . . . Anyhow, Offutt, I've found the only man to do the grandfather's part in that show of yours, haven't I?"

"I'm sorry to say it, Verba, but you're wrong," stated Offutt.

"How do you mean—I'm wrong?" demanded Verba irritably. Out of the corner of his mouth he aimed the protest at his companion; but his eyes, through the gap of the first entrance, were fixed on Bateman as he strode back and forth, and his ears drank in the splendid full-spoken snatches from the play. "He's not too old—if that's what you mean; he's just about old enough. And he's all there, even if he is old. Didn't you see the strength he had when he hoisted up that heavy curtain?"

"I think I know where that strength came from," said Offutt. "Just a minute, Verba—did you ever hear of the Great Auk?"

"He was in vaudeville, wasn't he?" asked Verba, still staring at Bateman. "A trick juggler or something?"

Offutt forgot to smile.

"The Great Auk was a bird," he said.

"Oh, I see; and I've been calling Bateman 'Old Bird,'" said Verba. "I get you."

"No, you don't get me," went on Offutt. "The Great Auk was a rare creature. It got rarer and rarer and they thought it had vanished. They sent an expedition to the Arctic Circle, or wherever it was the thing lived, to get one specimen for the museums; but they came back without it. And now the Great Auk is an extinct species."

"What the devil are you driving at?" snapped Verba, swinging on him.

"Listen yonder!" bade the dramatist. "That old man out yonder is telling you, himself, in better words than I could tell you."

He pointed a finger through the wings. Craning their necks, they heard the deep voice speak the lines:

"Pray, do not mock me:
I am a very foolish, fond old man,
Fourscore and upward, not an hour more nor less;
And, to deal plainly,
I fear I am not in my perfect mind."

Verba hearkened, and he understood. After a little he nodded in gloomy affirmation of the younger man's belief.

"I guess you're right, Offutt," he said disappointedly. "I guess I'd have seen it, too, only I was so sort of carried away. Real acting does me that way—when I see it, which ain't often."

He paused a minute in uncertainty. Then resolution came to him.

"Well," he said, "come on; there's no use of our hanging round here any longer. I'll give Blinky his quarter—he certainly earned it ten times over—and then we'll go back uptown, and I'll telephone Grainger he can have his seventy-five more a week."

"But what are we going to do about—him?" Offutt indicated whom he meant with a wave of his arm toward the stage.

It was Verba's turn. Verba knew the stage and its people and its ways as Offutt would never know them. He had been an actor, Verba had, before he turned managing director for Cohalan & Hymen.

"What are we going to do about him?" he repeated; and then, as though surprised that the other should be asking the question: "Why, nothing! Offutt, every haunted house is entitled to its ghost. This is a haunted house if ever there was one; and there's its ghost, standing out there. You mentioned an extinct species, didn't you? Well, you were dead right, son. So take your goodby look now, before we go, at the last of a great breed. There'll be no more like him, I'm thinking."

"But you can't leave him here like this!" said Offutt. "His mind is gone—you admit it yourself. They've got hospitals and asylums in this state—and homes too. It would be a mercy to take him with us."

"Mercy? It would be the dam'dest cruelty on earth!" snapped Verba. "How long do you suppose he'd live in an asylum if we tore him up by the roots and dragged him away from this place? A week? I tell you, a week would be a blamed long time. No, sir; we leave him right here. And we'll keep our mouths shut about this too. Come on!"

He tiptoed to the iron door and opened it softly. Then with his hand on the latch he halted.

Bateman was just finishing. He spoke the mad king's mad tag-line and got himself off the stage. He unreeled the stay rope from its chock. The curtain rumbled down. Through it the insistent clapping of Blinky's skinny paws could be heard.

Smiling proudly the old man listened to the sound. He forgot their presence behind him. He stood waiting. Blinky kept on applauding—Blinky was wise in his part, too. Then, still smiling, Bateman stripped off his beard, and, putting forth a bony white hand, he plucked aside the flapping curtain and stepped forth once more.

Scrouging up behind him and holding the curtain agape, they saw him bow low to the pit where Blinky was, and to the empty boxes, and to the yawning emptiness of each balcony; and they knew that to him this was not a mangy cavern of dead memories and dead traditions and dead days, peopled only by gnawing rats and crawling vermin and one lone little one-eyed street boy, but a place of living grandeurs and living triumphs. And when he spoke, then they knew he spoke, not to one but to a worshipping, clamorous host.

"Ladies and gentlemen," he began, with a bearing of splendid conceit, "I thank you for the ovation you have given me. To an artist—to an artist who values his art—such moments as this are most precious—"

"Come on, Offutt!" whispered Verba huskily. "Leave him taking his call."

THE SILENT INFARE

By *Armistead C. Gordon*

[Armistead Churchill Gordon (1855–1931) was of the generation that knew the old South. He was a native of Virginia and educated in the law at the University of Virginia. He received honorary degrees of D.Litt. and LL.D. from other Virginia universities. Mr. Gordon was a friend of Thomas Nelson Page and collaborated with him in *Echoes in Negro Dialect* (1888). He spent his life in public service and in the active practice of the law. Writing for him was an avocation, but he distinguished himself in making stories of the South of the decade before the Civil War and through the reconstruction period. He wrote also in the field of biography and state history. Mr. Gordon's home was at Staunton.

The Silent Infare was first published in *Scribner's Magazine* (March, 1916), and is reprinted from *Ommirandy—Plantation Life at Kingsmill* (1917), by permission of the author's daughter, Mary B. Gordon, and of Charles Scribner's Sons, publishers.]

OMMIRANDY accepted with a ready and unquestioning acquiescence Mis' Nancy's tacit estimate of the social importance of the family of her hostess in the little town beyond the Blue Ridge; but the old woman's suspicion of the colored population of the place was aroused from the moment when Imogen, the spry young maid servant, came into Mis' Nancy's room on the evening of their arrival to tender her services to her mistress's guest. The tender was coldly but civilly declined by the old woman.

"*I* gwi' look arfter Mis' Nancy while she here," said Ommirandy to Imogen. "I gwi' fetch her water, an' make her bed, an' wait on her. She ain't use ter no other servant but me doin' fur her."

"You don't have ter fetch no water," responded Imogen with asperity. "De water is in de pipes. See here!"

She went to the stationary basin and turned the faucet.

"Well, *I* gwi' do fur her, anyhow," responded the old woman, regarding the flowing water with a questioning look.

Imogen withdrew after Mis' Nancy had thanked her.

"I been hear dat dey ain't so many niggers over here in dis country as dey is in Tidewater," said the old woman. "I reck'n dat's howcome dey don't tote de water over here, like we-all duz at Kingsmill."

She went over to the basin and turned the stream on and off curiously.

"'Fo' de Lord, dey think dey know mo' 'bout whar water ought ter go dan de Almighty," she grumbled. "Dey makin' it run up-hill."

781

Her visit to the kitchen after supper accentuated her critical attitude toward the servants on the place.

"Dese here culluds ain't like dem in Tidewater," she said to Mis' Nancy. "Dat cook-'oman down dar in de cellar, she tell me her name is Miz' Nellins—yas'm *Miz*' Nellins—an' she ax me what was my entitle. I answer her, I ain't got no entitle 'scusin' Ommirandy. I give her ter know dat quality niggers on de t'other side o' de mount'in don't go by no name o' Miz' ur Mister, like de white folks. She primp herse'f, an' she say: 'My! Is *dat* possible?' An' I say: 'It ain't only possible, but it's so, an' also.' I say: 'Ef you was ter tell young Mars' Jeems yo' name was Miz' Nellins, he'd think you was givin' him some o' yo' instance.' Den she say: ''Scuse *me!*' An' I done so. I ax her what her sho-nuf name is, an' she say: 'Patsey.' I say: 'Patsey, you kin gimme my supper.' She 'pear ter me younger'n Philadelphy, so I say ter her: 'You kin call me Ommirandy, an' dat's enough.' She dat Immygen gal's mother."

In a day or two after their arrival Ommirandy informed Mis' Nancy that there were frequent colored visitors to the kitchen, and that among them was a young negro man who was evidently a suitor of Imogen's.

"I ain't nuver gwine ter git used ter no kitchen in de cellar, no mo'n I is ter dis here water runnin' in dis wash-basin. I ain't excusin' dese here white folks o' nothin', Mis' Nancy; but whar I been use ter all my life, dey had de kitchen out in de yard. An' dis here house is got too many long sta'r steps in it fur a duck-legged ole nigger like me. But I boun' ter go down dar ter git my meals' vittles ur starve; an' when I duz go, I sees dem Mister an' Miz' an' Miss darkies in all dey glory; an' it's wuth de trip. Dey ack like dey was all carriage-comp'ny. It's 'Mister Paul,' an' 'Miss Immygen,' an' 'Miz' Nellins.' Dat young nigger boy, he look at me, kinder curisome, an' he ain't call me nothin' yit. He 'pear ter seem like he was skeered dat I was gwi' jump on him, all spraddled-out. 'Fo' Gord, Mis' Nancy, I ain't got nothin' 'gin him, nur any o' dese town folks, 'scusin' dey ain't like my folks."

Mis' Nancy's color was not long in coming back to her cheeks in the bracing mountain atmosphere, and she soon felt better. She listened with undisguised amusement to Ommirandy's comments on the new acquaintances of her race, and wished that young Mars' Jeems might be there to hear them.

Each new day brought forth from the old woman the narrative of some incident that to her mind illustrated the inferiority of the local black people to her familiars at Kingsmill.

"Town niggers! town niggers!" she would ejaculate, as she went about her duties in Mis' Nancy's room.

"De parson was here ter dinner," Ommirandy said on the last evening of Mis' Nancy's visit. "I wish you mought 'a' seed him. Long-tail black coat like dat one Mr. Sinjinn give Jonas, beaver hat, white shirt, an' white things hangin' down over his shiny shoes like he gwi' lose some o' his underclo'es. Our rev'un' at home, he couldn' tetch him wid a forty-foot pole. He eat a fine dinner, an' two o' de deacons, dey eat wid him. When dey was gone, I sez ter Patsey: 'Looky here, Patsey, it 'pears ter me like you was feedin' seb'ral famblies out o' dis here kitchen.' 'No, marm,' she sez, 'de minister he say we don't have ter feed mo'n two outside famblies f'om no one kitchen.' Is you uver heerd de beat o' dat, Mis' Nancy?"

Mis' Nancy smiled, and the old woman continued:

"Dey's sump'n gwine on in dis here house dat dese white folks here don't know nothin' 'bout. 'Tain't none o' my bizness, an' I ain't gwi' give 'em away. I makes it a rule not to give no cullud pussons away, 'scusin' ter you an' ter young Mars' Jeems. But dey actin' mighty cur'ous, Patsey an' Immygen an' dat young Paul, an' all uv 'em."

She paused in her narrative, while Mis' Nancy listened.

"I reck'n you ain't nuver notice dat alley what runs down de side o' de house f'om de street, is you, Mis' Nancy?"

Mis' Nancy had not observed the particular alley in question, but she informed Ommirandy that many city and town houses had such alleys or areaways, in order to connect the back premises with the street.

"I dunno nothin' 'bout dat," said the old woman. "But 'fo' Gord, dat alley been swarmin' wid niggers all day. I been watchin' out o' de winder while you was drivin', an' dey been comin' an' goin' in all shapes an' sizes, men, wimmen, an' chillun. Dey wusser'n dese here little ants when you step on dey house. Most uv 'em is been fetchin' in all sorts o' bundles, wropt up in paper, ur hid in things so's you can't see what dey got. An' dat parson an' de deacons, dey's been perambulatin' an' p'radin' an' prancin' back'ards an' forruds; an' mo' cullud wimmen, whisp'rin' an' gigglin', dan uver I see git inter one small lane befo'. Dey's sump'n gwi' happen roun' here 'fo' long; but de white folks down-sta'rs, dey don't 'pear ter notice it, an' 't ain't none o' my bizness."

When Ommirandy came up to Mis' Nancy's room from her supper she was out of breath.

"Dem dar steps ter de cellar is killin' me," she said. "I thank Gord we's gwine home ter-morrer."

Then she continued:

"It's like a graveyard down dar in dat kitchen ter-night. Dar warn't none o' de outsiders in ter supper. Eben dat young Paul, he done made hisse'f skase. Patsey she nuver say two words endurin' o' de supper, an' Immygen she look glum as a wet hen wid draggled tail-feathers. I ain't nuver see no darkies vanish like dat swarm o' culluds dat was here ter-day is done vanish dis here night. Gord knows what's done become uv 'em."

"Maybe it's the calm before the storm," said Mis' Nancy, falling in with the old woman's mood. "Possibly they are going to give their minister a pound-party."

The night came on apace; and after helping to prepare her mistress for bed Ommirandy lay down on the low couch at the far end of the room with her clothes on. The busy hum of the streets subsided; and the noise of a cricket outside the window made the old woman almost fancy that she was once more at home at Kingsmill. She fell asleep, and dreamed of pleasant things at the old place in Tidewater.

Her placid slumber, after a period of indefinite and tranquil repose, was broken at length by a most unusual and startling occurrence.

She roused herself on her elbow and looked out through the open window into a cloudless and star-strewn sky.

"Name o' Gord!" she muttered under her breath. "What dat?"

She could feel the house shaking, with a faint and swaying motion that to the inhabitants of a seismic country would have seemed unmistakable. The movement lasted for a few minutes, and then ceased. Again it began and again was as perceptible and as distinct as before. A death-like silence lay over everything; and the oscillation was as regular and as rhythmic as the strophe and antistrophe of a Greek chorus.

"It's a yearthquake, sho'!" she ejaculated, rising from her couch.

She sat on the side of her low bed for a moment and listened intently. Then she laughed softly.

"Ah-yi!" she said aloud.

The cricket outside had long since ceased his jocund chirping, and the silence was so dense that Ommirandy felt that it was like a big black cake, and that she could cut it with a kitchen knife.

Then faint, far away, elusive as elfin harping, she caught the almost inaudible tones of a fiddle.

"Um-huh!" she said. "Dey ain't no doubtin' it. Dat's what 't is!"

She felt in the dark for her carpet slippers and, thrusting her feet into them, moved cautiously and carefully toward the fireplace, on the mantel of which she kept the candle and box of matches which Mis' Nancy had brought with her from Kingsmill. Securing these, she opened the door, and when she was outside in the passageway she struck a light.

The swaying motion and the elfin music had ceased together. She stood there, wondering if she might be dreaming. After a little while the notes of the violin came up to her once more from the lower regions, faint, far-away, hushed. She crept stealthily down the stairs to the street floor, and noticed that by the grandfather's clock in the hall it was ten minutes of three o'clock.

"I ain't nuver understand howcome folks in dis country has winders over de do's, inside de house. Dey ain't nuver had 'em at Kingsmill," she said to herself, as with lit candle in hand she started to descend the stairway that led down into the kitchen basement. "But, 'fo' Gord, I sees de good uv 'em, in places whar's dey 's folks dat acks like dese here town niggers acks."

She blew out the candle and paused on one of the upper steps of the basement staircase. The swaying movement of the house was now more perceptible to her than ever; and the music, though on the faintest minor key, as if muffled and disguised, was more distinctly audible than it had been when she was up-stairs.

She leaned over the balustrade and looked through the big transom over the kitchen door, through which the light shone with a radiance that made her fear that she might be seen from the room on her perch upon the steps.

"'Ha! ha!' said de fox, wid his pocket full o' rocks," she quoted to herself. "'I done kotch you!'"

The kitchen was a large room, extending the full length of the house, and from her coign of vantage Ommirandy had a good view of a large part of it.

The scene that met her gaze was an odd one; and the old woman chuckled with repressed merriment as she regarded it.

"Mis' Nancy, she done tell de trufe," she commented, "when she talk about de calm an' de storm. De storm, it done hit here in full blars'; but 'fo' Gord, it's de silentes' storm dat uver I looked at! Dey ain't no poun'-party 'bout dat!"

After watching the unconscious occupants of the kitchen for some minutes, she retraced her steps, holding on tightly to the unlit candle and the box of matches, and feeling her way back as cautiously as she had come. The strains of the fiddle were now in a diminuendo; and the old woman gave a jump, with her heart in her mouth, when the big hall clock banged the hour of three in her ear as she passed it in the black silence.

"Dis here devilish house is beyont me!" she muttered as she continued on her way up the stairs to Mis' Nancy's room. "Gord knows what's de nex' thing gwi' happen. I'se pintedly glad we-all's gwine home in de mornin'."

She slipped quietly into Mis' Nancy's room and, undressing in the dark, was soon asleep, with her last consciousness that of the faint and elusive music below and the almost imperceptible movement of the building. She dreamed that she was a child again, being gently rocked asleep in the cradle of her childhood to the crooning notes of her mother's voice, lost in the long-ended years.

In the morning she followed Mis' Nancy down to the breakfast-room, where they found the mistress of the mansion interrogating, with an appearance of considerable surprise, an unknown, neatly dressed young colored girl, who had just brought the breakfast up from the kitchen.

"Yas'm," said Amanda, the newcomer, "Imogen, she got married las' night at de Ebenezer Church ter Mr. Paul; an' Miz' Nellins, she got me ter come here ter take Imogen's place, an' wait on de table 'twel she git home f'om her weddin'-tower nex' week."

"Imogen married?" queried Mis' Nancy's hostess of Amanda. "Why didn't her mother tell me about it?"

"I dunno'm," responded Amanda. "All Miz' Nellins say was fur me ter come an' take her place."

When they were seated at the table the head of the house was interested to ask Mis' Nancy if she had been disturbed in the night by any peculiar noise or movement.

"The mountain air makes me sleep very soundly," she replied. She had noticed nothing unusual.

His attention was attracted by a smothered chuckle from Ommirandy, who lingered in the room, with the double purpose of seeing if she might serve her mistress in any way, and of ascertaining who besides herself was cognizant of the nocturnal disturbance which had aroused her from her slumbers.

"Did you hear anything, Mirandy?" he asked. "I dreamed there was an earthquake."

"Lord, Mars' Henry, you need n' ax me nothin' 'bout no yearth-quakes. I ain't nuver seed ur heerd no yearthquakes. I dunno nothin' 'bout dem things. Dey's strangers o' mine."

"Did you feel the house rocking?" he persisted.

The unrepressed grin on the old woman's usually sombre countenance, and the agitated dangling of her earhoops, attracted Mis' Nancy's attention and aroused her suspicion that Ommirandy knew more than she was willing to admit. The suspicion grew into certainty at the old woman's answer.

"'Fo' Gord, marster, I ain't got no bizness noticin' nothin' out o' de way in a gennulmun's house whar my mistis is visitin'. Ef dis here house was ter git up on its behime-legs, an' rock an' r'ar all over de street out dar, 'twudden be becomin' in Mirandy fur ter notice it. Nor, sir."

She held her peace until she and Mis' Nancy had returned to Kings-mill. Then when her mistress and young Mars' Jeems were together again, in the library at home, she told them, with hilarious freedom, the story of her midnight adventure.

"I been bustin' ter tell Mis' Nancy 'bout it, but I holt it in ontwel I got back here, so you mought hear 'bout it, likewise, young marster. It beat anything dat uver I see in my trabels, an' I'm gwine on some years.

"Young Mars' Jeems, you knows I ain't mix much wid no outside folks, 'scusin' dese here on dis plantation sence de s'rrender; an' when I went over yondah wid Mis' Nancy I war n't adzackly sho' how dem new-issue town niggers was gwineter git along wid me. I war n't dar mo'n a day 'fo' I diskiver dat dey done size me up fo' what dey call 'a white folks' nigger.' Dey was pow'ful perlite, an' dey ax me ter church, which

I did n' go; but dey kinder friz' me, Dey nuver 'sociated wid me like I was one uv 'em. But what beat dat was dey did n' appear ter 'sociate wid dey white folks none, nuther; an' I sez ter myse'f, when niggers stop 'sociatin' wid dey white ladies an' gennulmens it's good-by, niggers. I et wid 'em an' talk ter 'em; an' it 'peared ter me like harf de cullud folks in dat town come ter dat kitchen endurin' o' de time we was dar. Den ter clap de climax, I see 'em swarmin' in by de side lane ter de back o' de house, whar de kitchen was, de day befo' we come away, fetchin' bun'les an' barskets an' buckets; but I cudden fine out what it was dey was fetchin' in 'em. 'Way late in de night de house begin ter rock an' swing an' sway, like 't was gwine ter wake up ev'vybody in it; an' I heerd a fiddle dat soun' ter me like it was 'bout a mile down in de groun'. I crope down de sta'rs, an' look thoo de winder dey got over de kitchen do', an' den I seed what was gwine on. Dat dine'-room gal, Immygen, dat was de cook's daughter, she had done got married early in de night, an' de whole cong'egation—preacher, elders, deacons, an' all uv 'em—had come ter de infare. Thoo de winder I could see a table in de fur cornder o' de room, wid hams an' turkeys an' cakes an' pies piled up on it a foot high; an' out in front o' de table sot a little darky on a stool wid a fiddle. He was a' orful little-bitty nigger wid a' orful little-bitty fiddle, playin' a' orful little-bitty chune; but, bless Gord, young Mars' Jeems, he was sho' nuf a-playin' dat chune. It was 'Git yo' pardners, fus' kwattilion,' but ef he called any figgers while he was a-fiddlin' I cudden hear him call 'em. Dem culluds was so full o' de music o' dat little fiddle dey did n' 'pear ter need ter have no figgers called fur 'em. Dey look' like dey jes' knowed 'em all anyhow. Dar dey was, de whole kit'n'bile uv 'em, out in de middle o' de flo', sas-shayin' back'ards an' forruds, an' crossin' over an' swingin' pardners, an' evvy nigger man an' 'oman in de comp'ny darncin' in dey sock-feets. Dat's de Gord's trufe, young Mars' Jeems. I lay, dey ain't nothin' like it uver been seed dis side o' dem mountains. I been ter many a infare an' darnce in my day at Ole Town, an' roun' about dis here countryside; an' I been hear 'em 'ha-ha!' an' larf an' raise a racket ter 'sturb de neighborhood fur a mile. But 'fo' Gord, sir, it was de fus' time dat uver I see sich a party, down in a cellar-kitchen, wid evvy black nigger dar a-darncin' like he was gwi' break his neck in his sock-feets, an' n'ary one uv 'em makin' a soun'. But dey was havin' fun all de same. De parson, he had on white yarn socks, an' a long-tail coat, an' de coat-tails an' de socks was a-keepin' time ter de teeny little-bitty chune on de teeny little-bitty fiddle. He holt one big han', wid a brass ring on it, over his mouf, ter keep f'om larfin' out loud, an' he swing de young wimmen wid de t'other han'. De bride, she had on red stockin'-feets an' a short white skirt; an' when de parson hit de cornders wid her dar was sich a flyin' o' skirts an' coat-tails as showed up mo' red legs dan we sees down here, ur de law allows. An' all de time de darncin' was gwine on, wid de men an' de gells a-stuffin' dey pocket-hanchkers in dey moufs an' holdin' dey han's up ter dey faces fer ter keep quiet, dat house was a-rockin' an' a-swayin' an' a-rampagin' in a way ter wake de dead. Den dey stop de kwattilion, and de teeny-bitty nigger tetched up de Ole Ferginyeh Reel on his teeny-bitty fiddle. He made dat fiddle talk, mun, eben ef it was a-whisperin' ter itse'f, an' I got ter kind o' thinkin' 'bout de times I useter have at dem darnces, mighty nigh a hunnerd years ago, when Mis' fus' tuk me f'om Ole Town, 'twell it seem ter me like I wanted ter git in dat room, wid dem niggers, an' go down de middle wid de black parson in de white yarn sock-feets myse'f. I ain't nuver seed so many diffunt cullud socks ez I seed at dat infare. Gord knows what dey all done wid dey shoes; but dey war n't a livin' sinner in de gang dat had on eben so much as a slipper, 'scusin' one o' de young deacons dat had tuk supper dar a few nights befo'. I reck'n he must 'a' been skeered dat de white folks mought come down f'om up-sta'rs an' raid 'em; an' dat's howcome he had his p'yar o' number 'leben brogans tied together an' hung roun' his neck, like a string o' beads. An' it 'peared ter me like dat deacon wid de big brogans was shovin' de hefties' foot in de whole cong'egation. Lord, he could darnce!

"I watched 'em dar fur a little while, an' den I crope back up-sta'rs ter bed. I did n' wait ter see 'em git onter dat table o' perwisions; but dey must 'a' done dat as silent as dey done de darncin'. When I went down ter bre'kfus' de nex' mornin' dey wa'n't no sign o' used plate ur dish in de room. Ev'ything was jes' ez spick an' span as it was de mornin' befo', an' Patsey dat dey call Miz' Nellins, she sot dar an' po'ed out my coffee jes' as calm as ef she nuver had heerd ur drempt o' no infare.

"'Was anything importan' gwine on lars' night?' sez I ter Patsey.

"She holp herse'f ter a big plate o' baddy-bread an' harf uv a fried roe-herrin', an' she looks me in de face as cool as de middle inside seed uv any cowcumber you uver see.

"'Nor'm,' she sez, 'nuthin' 'tall, 'scusin' my daughter Immygen, she got married ter Mr. Paul at de Ebenezer Baptis' at nine P. M. lars' night,' she sez.

"'Oh, did she?' I sez. 'I think I heerd sump'n' 'bout it up-sta'rs, f'om dis young gell here dat's a stranger o' mine,' I sez, lookin' at 'Mandy dat waited on de breakfas' in de dine'-room. 'I b'lieve she did menshun it.'

"'Yas 'm,' sez Miz' Nellins, a-chawin' away on de baddy-bread an' de roe-herrin', 'dey all sez it was a reel swell weddin'.'

"'An' did de bride an' groom leave on de night train?' sez I perlitely.

"'Dey lef' on a' early train,' sez Miz' Nellins, de ole hippycrit.

"Young Mars' Jeems, I done had enough o' dem town niggers. Dey ain't like we-all is."

JETSAM

By *John Russell*

[The author of *The Fourth Man*, *The Price of a Head*, and *Jetsam* should have been born on one of the Solomon Islands. His pictures of life among the tropical islands of the South Seas are so convincing that it seems nobody but a native could have written them. John Russell was born in Davenport, Iowa, in 1885, and lives at Santa Monica, California. He has seen a good deal of the sea and land of the world and has come to understand the human beings that exist in remote and comparatively unknown spots of the earth. He is the author of several hundred stories. Among his collected volumes are *Where the Pavement Ends* (1921), *In Dark Places* (1922), and *Far Wandering Men* (1928).

Jetsam (copyright 1915) is from *Where the Pavement Ends* (Alfred A. Knopf, Inc., publishers) and is reprinted by permission of the author.]

IT is likely that at some time in his extreme youth Junius Peabody was introduced to those single-minded creatures, the ant and the bee. Doubtless he was instructed in the highly moral lessons they are supposed to illustrate to the inquiring mind of childhood. But it is certain he never profited by the acquaintance—indeed, the contemplation of such tenacious industry must have afflicted his infant consciousness with utter repugnance. By the time he was twenty-seven the only living thing that could be said to have served him as a model was the jellyfish.

Now, the jellyfish pursues a most amiable theory of life, being harmless, humorous, and decorative. It derives much enjoyment from drifting along through the glitter and froth, as chance may direct. It does no work to speak of. It never needs to get anywhere. And it never, never has to go thirsty. But some day it may get itself stranded, and then the poor jellyfish becomes an object quite worthless and fit only to be shoveled out of sight as soon as possible—because it lacks the use of its legs.

Thus it was with Junius Peabody, who awoke one morning of his twenty-eighth year on the roaring coral beach at Fufuti, below Bendemeer's place, to find that all the chances had run out and that the glitter had faded finally from a prospect as drab as the dawn spread over a butternut sea before him. . . .

Mr. Peabody sat up and looked about from under a corrugated brow, and yawned and shivered. His nerves had been reduced to shreds, and even the fiercest heat of tropic suns seemed never to warm him, a symptom familiar enough to brandy drunkards. But he had had such awakenings before, many of them, and the chill that struck through him on this particular morning was worse than any hang-over. It was the soul of Junius Peabody that felt cold and sick, and when he fumbled through his pockets—the subtle relation between the pockets and the soul is a point sadly neglected by our best little psychologists—he uncovered a very definite reason. His last penny was gone.

Under the shock of conviction Mr. Peabody sought to cast up the mental log, in the hope of determining where he was and how he came to be there.

The entries were badly blurred, but he could trace himself down through Port Said, Colombo, Singapore—his recollections here were limited to a woman's face in a balcony and the cloying aroma of anisette. He remembered a stop at Sydney, where he made the remarkable discovery that the Circular Quay was completely circular and could be circumnavigated in a night. After that he had a sketchy impression of the Shanghai race meeting and a mad sort of trip in a private yacht full of Australian sheep-something—kings, perhaps; tremendous fellows, anyway, of amazing capacity. And then Manila, of course, the place where he hired an ocean-going tug to urge a broken date on the coy ingénue of a traveling Spanish opera company. And then Macao, where he found and lost her again, as coy as ever, together with his wallet. And after that the hectic session when he and a Norwegian schooner captain hit the bank at fan-tan and swore eternal friendship amid the champagne baskets on the schooner's decks under a complicated moon. It was this same captain who had landed him finally—the baskets having been emptied—at the point of a boot on the strand where now he sat. So much was still quite clear and recent, within range of days.

Always through the maze of these memoirs ran one consistent and tragic motive—a dwindling letter of credit, the fag end of his considerable patrimony. It had expired painlessly at last, the night before if he could trust his head, for there had been a noble wake. Here called the inscrutable face of the tall white man behind the bar who had cashed it for him after a rate of exchange of his own grim devising. And he recalled, too, a waif bit of their conversation as he signed the ultimate coupon.

"You can date it Fufuti," suggested Bendemeer, and spelled the name for him.

"And where—where the devil is Fufuti?" he asked.

"Three thousand miles from the next pub," said Bendemeer, with excessively dry significance.

The phrase came back to him now. . . .

"In that case," decided Junius Peabody, aloud, "—in that case there's no use trying to borrow car-fare, and it's too far to walk. I'm stuck."

Some one sniffed beside him, and he turned to stare into a face that might have been a distortion of his own yellow, haggard image.

"Hello," he said—and then, by natural sequence: "Say, you don't happen to have a flask anywhere handy about you—what?"

His neighbor scowled aggrievedly.

"Do I *look* like I 'ad a flask?"

The belligerent whine was enough to renew the identity of the mangy little larrikin whose couch on the sand he had shared. The Sydney Duck, they called him: a descriptive title which served as well as any. Junius did not like him very well, but he had lived in his company nearly a week, and he had long forgotten to make effective distinctions. Brandy is a great democrat.

"It's my notion I'm going to have the fantods," explained Junius. "I need a bracer."

"My word, I could do with a nip meself just now," agreed Sydney. "'In't y' got no more credit with Bendemeer?"

Peabody made an effort.

"Seems to me I was thrown out of Bendemeer's last night. Is that right?"

"You was, and so was me and that big Dutchman, Willems—all thrown out. But it was your fault. You started playin' chuck farthin' among his bottles with a bunch of copper spikes. . . . I never see a man 'old his liquor worse."

"Well, I paid for it, didn't I?" inquired Junius, without heat. "And I believe you had your share. But what I'm getting at is—if he threw me out, the credit must be gone."

This was simple logic and unanswerable. "Maybe y' got something else he'll tyke for th' price," suggested Sydney. "Damn 'im—'e's keen enough to drive a tryde!"

Junius went through the form of searching, but without any great enthusiasm, nor was Sydney himself notably expectant—a fact that might have seemed to argue a rather sinister familiarity with the probable result.

"I did have some cuff links and things," said Peabody vaguely. "I wonder what's become of them."

"I wonder," echoed Sydney. As if some last possible claim upon his regard had been dissipated, he let his lips writhe in mockery. "Ah, and that's a pity too. You got to learn now what it means bein' on the beach and doin' *without* drinks—'cept as you kin cadge them off'n 'alf-caste Chinymen and such. You won't like it, you won't."

"Do you?" asked Junius.

"Me? I'm used to it. But, Lord, look at them 'ands! I'll lay you never did a day's work in your life."

"Did you?" inquired Junius Peabody equably.

"Garn!" retorted Sydney with a peculiarly unlovely sneer. "W'y, you don't know yet what you've come to, you don't. 'Jaimes, fetch me me mornin' drawft!'—that's your style. Only there 'in't no Jaimes no more, and no drawfts to be 'ad. Ho! . . . You're only a beachcomber now, mytey. A lousy beachcomber! And you needn't expect me to do none of your beggin' for you, for I won't—no fear!"

Junius observed him with attention, with rather more attention than he could remember having bestowed upon any specific object for a long time. He examined the features of the Sydney Duck, the undue prominence of nose and upper lip, the singularly sharp ridge of the whole front face—whittled, as it might have been; the thin, pink ears and the jutting teeth that gave him something of the feeble ferocity of a rat. And with new perception he saw Sydney Duck, not only as an unpleasant individual but as a type, the fitting comrade and associate for such as he.

"It's a fact," said Junius Peabody; "I've fallen pretty low. . . ."

He looked out again upon that unprofitable dawning. To right and left stretched the flat, dim monotony of the beach, lined in misty surf and hedged with slim palms like a tufted palisade. From behind drifted the smokes from scores of homely hearths. Down by Tenbow Head the first pearling luggers were putting out under silver clouds of sail. Sea and land stirred once more with the accustomed affairs of busy men, but here between land and sea was the fringe of things, the deserted domain of wreckage and cast-off remnants. Here lay a broken spar half buried in the sand, part of the complex fabric that once enabled some fair ship to skim the waves. And here among the kelp and the bodies of marine animals he saw the loosened staves of a barrel limply spread and upthrust like the fingers of some dead giant, with an empty bottle near by as if fallen from that slack grip. And here, lastly, he was aware of Junius Peabody, also on the beach, washed up at the far edge of the world like any other useless bit of jetsam: to stay and to rot.

"Pretty low," said Junius Peabody.

But Sydney took no offense, and seemed, on the contrary, to extract a certain degree of pleasure from the other's recognition of his lot.

"Oh, it 'in't so bad," he declared, with a quite human impulse to reverse the picture. "There's easy pickin' if you know 'ow. Nobody starves 'ere anyw'y, that's one thing. No nigger will let a man starve— a soft lot of flats that w'y, the niggers. Often you fall in with a weddin' or a birthday or somethin'; they're always 'avin' a feast, and *they* don't care who comes—they 'in't proud. Then you got nobody aharryin' of you up and down and askin' you wot for, that's a comfort—my word! And once in a while there's sure to be a new chum come along with a bit of brass—some flat who's willin' to stand the drinks."

"Like me," suggested Junius.

"Oh, there's plenty like you," nodded the Sydney Duck. "It's the pearlin' brings 'em, though it 'in't so soft as maybe they think, you see. When they're stony they mostly tyke a job till they find a chance to get aw'y again—that's if they're able to do anything at all."

For the first time in his life, probably, Junius Peabody considered his accomplishments with a view to estimating their value in the open market.

"I once won the fancy diving event at Travers Island," he said. "And I used to swim the four-forty in a trifle over six minutes."

"That must 'a' been several seasons back," grinned Sydney.

"Not so many," said Junius slowly. "I forgot to add that I was also an excellent judge of French brandy."

He got to his feet and began to divest himself of the spotted remains of an expensive white silk suit.

"What's the gyme now?"

"Morning bath. Have you had yours yet?"

The Sydney Duck laughed, laughter that was strangely unmirthful and so convulsive that Junius blinked at him, fearing a fit of some kind.

"You're a rare 'un," gasped the Sydney Duck. "I seen a good few, I 'ave, but none as rare as you. Mornin' bawth—and 'ave I 'ad mine yet! . . . On the beach at Fufuti!" He waggled his hands.

"Well, if it seems so queer as all that why not blow yourself?" offered Junius with perfect good nature. "You can't tell, you might like it. Come along."

"Garn!" snarled the other.

So Junius turned away and walked down the strand alone. Outward the ground swell broke and came rushing in with long-spaced undulations, and as he stood at the verge, shrinking in his nakedness, the east flamed suddenly through its great red archway and turned all the world to tinted glory. Fair across to him was flung a shining path. It seemed as if he had only to step out along that straight way of escape, and for an instant he had a yearning to try. Never in his life had he followed a single course to a definite end, and what could be better now than to choose one at last, to follow, to go on following—and not to return?

He looked down at his body and saw as a revelation the pitiful wasting of his strength—how scrawny he was of limb, how bloated about the middle, and his skin how soft and leprous white. He made an ugly figure under the clear light of the morning, like the decaying things around him, where the carrion flies were beginning to swarm in the sun. And there came upon him then a sudden physical loathing of himself, a final sense of disaster and defeat.

"If I could only begin again—" thought Junius Peabody, and stopped and laughed aloud at the wish, which is old as folly and futile as sin. But he had no relief from laughter either, for it was the same he had just heard from the Sydney Duck, a sort of hiccup. So he stopped that too, and strode forthright into the wash. . . .

Something flung against his shin and tripped him. He sprawled awkwardly from a singular impact, soft though quite solid. He could see the object floating on the next wave and was curious enough to catch it up. It was a rough lump of some substance, a dirty grayish-brown in color, the size of a boy's football. The touch of it was rather greasy.

Junius stayed with the trove in his hands and the tingling of an odd excitement in his mind. His first instinct rejected the evidence. He had a natural suspicion that events do not happen so. But while he brought to bear such knowledge as he owned, facts read or heard, he found himself still thrilled.

There was a sound from the shore, and the Sydney Duck hurried up behind him to the edge of the water, both hands clawed, his little eyes distended.

"You've got it!" He took two steps after a retreating wave, but the next drove him hopping. It was strange to see the fellow drawn by a frantic eagerness and chased again by the merest flicker of foam, lifting his feet as gingerly as a cat.

"What have I got?" asked Junius, standing at mid-thigh where the surf creamed in between them.

"It's the stuff! Chuck it over—wha-i-i!" Sydney's voice rose to a squeal as a frothing ripple caught his toes.

Junius came wading shoreward, but he did not relinquish the lump when the other felt and paddled it feverishly, babbling.

"Look at that—look at that! All smooth an' soft—an' kind of slimy, like. Oh, no, we 'in't struck it fair rich this time, nor nothin'—oh, *now!* . . . Mytey, I tell you—by Gaw', I tell you it's the real stuff!"

"But oughtn't there be an odor—a perfume?"

"Not yet—not while it's fresh. That comes after. And any'ow, what else could it be—'ey?"

Junius shook his head.

"'Ere, I'll show you, you poor flat!" The larrikin raged about like a man in a strong temper. "Where's a nail? Gimme a nail, a long nail, or a piece of wire—'ell, I'll show you!"

He snatched up a strip of planking from the sand and wrenched a rusty spike from it. With swift jerky gestures he gathered a few dry chips and splinters, whipped a match, and set them alight. In this brief blaze he heated the spike and then applied it to the lump. It sank smoothly, leaving a little melted ring around the hole.

"Ambergris!" he yelped. "Worth near two pound an ounce, right 'ere in Fufuti. . . . And the 'arf of it's mine," he added, with a startling shift to the most brazen impudence.

Junius regarded him, incredulous: "What!"

"What? That's wot! Wasn't I here? 'In't I been pallin' along of you? It's a fair divvy. W'y, damn your soul," he screamed in a sudden febrile blast of fury, "you don't think you're goin' to 'og my 'arf an' all!"

"*Your* half!" repeated Junius. "Huh—nothing small about you, is there? Why, you weren't anywhere near when I found it. Didn't you pass up the swim?"

Just here the Sydney Duck made his mistake. Had he proceeded with any finesse, with any understanding of his man, he might have done about as he pleased, and it is likely that little of moment would have transpired on Fufuti beach that morning. But he acted by his lights, which were narrow and direct, and he hit Junius Peabody suddenly in the smiling face of him and knocked him reeling backward. The next instant he was running for the nearest palms with the prize tucked under one arm.

Junius sat on the sand and blinked, and at first he felt rather hurt, for he was not used to being treated so, at least not while he was sober. And thereafter he grinned, for such was his way of turning aside a casual unpleasantness, and the thing undeniably had its humorous aspect. But finally came the throb of a strange new emotion, as if some one had planted a small, hot coal in his breast.

It is a fact worthy of note that never before had Junius Peabody known the sting of a living anger. But never before had Junius Peabody been reduced to a naked Junius Peabody, dot and carry nothing— penniless, desperate, and now cheated of a last hope. That made the difference.

"Hey!" he protested. "See here, you know—Dammit!"

He struggled up and climbed anyhow into trousers, coat, and shoes, and set off at a shambling trot, with no clear notion of what he meant to do, but keeping the larrikin in sight.

Sydney dodged in among the trees, found them too scant for cover, paused to fling a yellow snarl over his shoulder, and swung up the shore. He turned, questing here and there, shouting as he ran, and presently raised an answering shout from a hollow whence another figure started up to join him, a bearded, heavy-set rogue, whose abnormally long arms dangled like an ape's out of his sleeveless shirt. Junius recognized Willems, the third of their party the night before, and he knew where the interest of that sullen big Hollander would lie. He had a coalition of thievery against him now. The two beachcombers ran on together, footing briskly past the long boat sheds and the high white veranda of Bendemeer's place. . . .

Under this iron thatch stood the man Bendemeer himself, cool and lathy in spotless ducks, planted there, as was his morning custom, to oversee and command all his little capital. And in truth it was a kingdom's capital, the center of a trading monopoly of the old type, and chief seat of as strange and absolute a tyrant as the world still offers room for; rich, powerful, independent, fearing nothing between heaven and hell, and at once the best-loved and the best-hated individual in his sphere of influence.

Bendemeer, trader, philanthropist, and purveyor of rotgut, was one of those unclassed growths of the South Seas that almost constitute a new racial type. Nobody could have placed his nationality or his caste or his accent. His name was of a piece with the grim self-sufficiency that gave nothing and asked nothing: an obvious jest, borrowed from the Persian song of an Irish poet, but the one touch of fancy about him. Somewhere, somehow, he had taken a cynic twist or a rankling wound that had turned his white man's blood once for all. They tell stories of such cases up and down the islands, and mostly the stories are very ugly and discreditable indeed. But not so concerning Bendemeer; against whom was no scandal; only curses and bitterness. For his peculiarity took the especially irritating form of fair dealings with some thousands of brown-skinned natives and no dealings at all with any man of his own color—except to beat him at strict business and then to sell him as much villainous liquor as he could at the highest possible price. As he leaned there indolently in his doorway, with arms folded and cheroot between his thin lips, he could measure his own land as far as he could see on either side, a small part of his holdings in plantations and trading stations throughout the archipelago. Offshore, behind the only good strip of barrier reef and near the only navigable channel on the south coast, lay anchored his *Likely Jane*, flagship of a smart little navy. His gang of boys was hustling cargo out of her in surfboats, and both boys and boats were the handiest and ablest that could be found anywhere for that ticklish work. He had only to turn his head to view the satisfactory bulk of his sheds and dependencies, solid, new-painted. The house at his back was trim, broad, and comfortable, and in the storeroom underneath lay thousands of dollars' worth of assorted trade goods, all of which would eventually become copra and great wealth.

This was the man, decidedly in possession of his own legs and able to stand and to navigate on the same, to whom Junius Peabody appealed in his wretched need. . . .

Junius stumbled up to the steps. The burst had marrow-drawn him, his lungs labored pitifully as if he were breathing cotton wool. It was hot, for the sun had sprung wide like an opened furnace gate, but he had not started a pore.

"I've been robbed," he wheezed, and pointed a wavering hand. "Those chaps there—robbed——!"

Bendemeer glanced aside up the strand after the disappearing ruffians and then down at the complainant, but otherwise he did not move, only stayed considering from his lean, leathery mask, with still eyes, outward-looking.

"What do you care?" he said idly. "You'll be dead in a month anyhow."

Junius gaped toward him dizzily. The fellow was the local authority, and besides had taken his money. He could not believe that he had heard aright. "But, say—they've stolen my property!"

Bendemeer shot a blue ring of smoke into the sunshine. "In that case you've lost it. They're heading for the Rocks, and once they've gone to earth there you never could find them—you'd be torn to pieces if you did."

He flicked the ash of his cheroot in a pause. "I suppose you mean I might help you," he continued. "I might, but I won't. I've seen a good many of your kind before, drift stuff that gets washed up on the beach. You're not worth it. And now, since you have no further business with me, I'd be obliged if you'd kindly get the hell out of my front yard. You're interfering with the view. . . ."

Junius Peabody found himself groping away through the sunlight on Fufuti beach once more. A dead calm held the air. Under the steady, low organ note of the reef he could hear only the drag of his own steps, the curious, unforgettable "shr-ring" of boot leather on coral.

It was borne upon him then that he had just acquired a liberal education, that he had learned more essential facts within the last hour than he had ever gained before in his twenty-odd years—a tabloid of life—and too late to be of any use. Such abstractions are sometimes valuable to a man, but they are not the sort that brings a lump in his throat and a winking in his eyes. The thing, the sheerly heartfelt thing that Junius Peabody said to himself, sniffling, was this: "And he didn't—didn't even offer me a drink!"

There was nothing to draw him any farther—no help, no promise of success, not even a single witness to shame with a grin or to urge with an expectant stare—nothing outside himself. Fufuti beach lay stark and aching white before him. The two thieves had long since lost themselves among the palms. Down by the water's edge a couple of Bendemeer's boat boys were salvaging odds and ends lost overboard in an upset in yesterday's heavy surf. They did not waste a thought or a look on him. He was many degrees less important than a lot of other rubbish around there. He might just as well, he might much better, slump down in a sodden heap amid the rest of the jetsam. And yet he did not. . . . And he did go on. For some obscure, irrational human reason, he did go on. Perhaps because of the tiny coal in his breast, blown red by Bendemeer's blasting contempt. Perhaps because, after all, no man ever quite achieves complete resemblance to a jellyfish.

On the southern tip of Fufuti stands Tenbow Head, the end of a rough little jut of land known locally as the Rocks. To speak by the book, there is neither rock nor head, but the abyss turned in its sleep once, and shouldered half a mile of Fufuti's shore line to a height of thirty feet—enough for a mountain in this sea of humble atolls. Incidentally it smashed the elevated reefs like chalk in a mortar. Tenbow is a wreck of shattered coral terraces, clad in the eager growths which profit by its trifling rise and which alone do profit. For the rest it remains the island jungle, a section apart and untouched, almost impenetrable.

Junius Peabody began his exploration of this cheerful region by falling on his face in a gully and bruising his nose very grievously. He found no trail to guide him up the slope. It was pitted like slag, deceitful as old honeycomb. The footing crumbled; tempting beds of moss and fern slipped away at his clutch; twisting lianas caught his ankles and sent him asprawl. The very ground seemed armed against him with a malignant life of its own. He had to creep among jagged teeth that sliced his flimsy garments and his putty-soft flesh. And when a loosened mass slid gently over at a touch and caught and crushed an arm he scarcely wondered whether any personal power had directed. It was all the same.

For a long time he lay looking at his pulped fingers and the driven drops of blood from the quick of his nails, sensing the exquisite pain almost as a luxury, hugging it to him. But at length he stirred and began to wriggle forward again.

"If I'm going to die anyway," said Junius Peabody, "I'm going to die doing this." Which was an extraordinary remark on all accounts. . . .

And so by dint of following something, and still following with unlimited purpose over a limited terrain, he ran it down in the end and came to the hiding place he sought.

A rooted instinct of the potentially criminal, which prompts them to be ready to flee though no man pursueth, had moved the beachcombers of Fufuti long since to prepare their snug retreat in the heart of the Rocks. On the inward shore of the promontory they had found a level bit of shelf screened by lush vegetation, with the green-stained cliff for wall and the sapphire waters of the lagoon below for forecourt. Hither they repaired in the intervals of lesser lawbreaking and free entertainment, always secure of hearth and shelter where the broad pandanus spread its shingles. And hither, straight as merry men to their shaw, they had brought the great treasure of the morning.

A truly homelike scene was that on which Junius Peabody peered from ambush above. . . .

From the convenient branch of a tree the Sydney Duck had suspended by its middle a single stout stick. At one end of the stick he had slung the stolen lump in a fiber net. At the other he had attached a battered tin can of the kind that the beneficent enterprise of an American oil company had spread to most of the dark parts of the earth. On this balance of an ancient and primitive design he was engaged in weighing his ill-gotten gains, squatting to the task.

"A gallon of water weighs a good eight pound," he declared. "I figger five quarts an' a 'arf. And five is ten and the 'arf is one——"

Willems stood beside him in an attitude of stolid skepticism. There was no mistaking the breed of this big derelict. He had managed to assert it on a Pacific isle by fashioning himself somehow a pipe with a clay bowl and a long stem of the true drooping line. He looked quite domestic and almost paternal as he shuffled his broad feet and towered over the little larrikin. But the fists he carried in the pockets of his dungarees bulged like coconuts, and his hairy arms were looped brown cables. A tough man for an argument was Mynheer Willems.

"Yaw," he was saying. "But how you know you got five quarts and a half?"

"W'y, any fool could guess near enough!" cried Sydney, with the superfluous violence that was his caste mark. "And you—y' big Dutchman—'in't you swilled enough beer in your time to judge? Besides, the bally can 'olds three gallon—bound to. There's one sure measure. . . . I say we got, anyw'y, eleven pounds of this stuff, and I 'appen to know that Bendemeer's fair crazy after it. He'll pay big. We ought to 'ave two thousands dollars Chile to split. . . . Two thousands silver dibs!"

It was a cue to friendly feeling, that luscious phrase. The two men beamed upon it as Sydney dumped the balance and swung the fiber net. But it was also a cue of another kind, for it brought Junius Peabody on stage. He arrived by the simple process of sliding on a bundle over the brow of the cliff.

"That's mine," he announced.

The beachcombers stayed stricken, which was pardonable. Surely there never showed a less heroic figure or a stranger defiance than that of Mr. Peabody, torn, bedraggled, and besmeared. There was nothing muscular or threatening about him. He took no pose. He offered no weapon. He came on at them limping, with quivering lip and empty hands, even with open hands. And yet the incredible fact remained that he did come on at them and continued to come.

"It's mine," repeated Junius. "All mine, and I'm going to have it—all!"

Amazement held them motionless for as long as it took him to cross the ledge—pleased amazement, as they knew him better. There are few things more congenial to certain gentlemen than a chance to maul an easy victim. And here was the easiest victim that either of these gentlemen had seen in many a day. He was no match for them, could be no possible match. Since he would have it so, they accepted joyously, closed in upon him from either side and started to drag him down as a preliminary to trampling the lights out of him. . . .

But they counted without the absolute simplicity of a man who has found an objective for the first time in his life and has set himself to reach it, regardless. Mr. Peabody did not pause to fight or to wrestle. He let them get a good grip on him and then took the unexpected way by keeping right on—and, pinioning their arms, merely walking them over the edge into space.

For an instant the three seemed to hang suspended, interlocked amid smashing vines and taut creepers, and then toppled toward the lagoon.

Even before they struck, Sydney's despairing yell rang out. Their plunge drowned it and gave way to the cries of startled sea birds, knifing the air in flung white crescents and circling about the troubled spot that boiled like blue champagne. But when he came up again the unfortunate larrikin loosed shriek after bubbling shriek and floundered madly for shore, all else forgotten in his dominant terror.

Willems was made of sterner metal. He grappled Peabody as they rose and sought to use his long arms, reaching for the throat. He learned better presently, however, and he learned, too, how much chance he had against a man who had once won a fancy diving title at Travers Island. Junius took him down by the feet and held him down until there was no spring and no temper left to him, only a large and limp and very badly frightened Hollander who wanted to get out of the wet. He was quite willing to paddle after the Sydney Duck. Meanwhile Junius gathered up an object in a fiber net that was floating near by and swam on to follow his purpose. . . .

The man Bendemeer was standing behind his little zinc bar when a shadow sifted in through the doorway, and, looking up, he took a backward step that nearly cost him his stock of glassware. The man Bendemeer was not used to stepping back from anything, but the red and dripping ruin that confronted him was beyond usage of any kind. Junius Peabody looked as if he had been run through a mangle. His dress was fragmentary. Most of the skin had been flayed from the more prominent curves of his anatomy. His left arm hung useless. He crawled in and propped himself to keep from falling, and called for brandy in a voice scarcely recognizable. "Peabody—is it?" demanded Bendemeer, incredulous.

"Will you keep a customer waiting?" rasped Junius. "You needn't stare." He laughed weakly. "You can't order me off now, Bendemeer. I'm a paying customer again."

"As how?"

Junius lifted a fist and dropped the sopping net on the bar. "Ambergris—eleven pounds of it. My property."

Bendemeer inspected the brownish lump, and as he understood, his thin lips pleated and his glance quickened. "Oh, ho!" he said. "Was it *this* they robbed you of?"

Peabody nodded.

"You got it back from them—yourself?"

"There's the stuff."

"So I see. But I'm asking—did you take it away from those two cutthroats alone, without any help?"

"I did. And now I've come to talk business. It's a good proposition, Bendemeer."

The tall, grim white man studied him with a narrow regard glinting like a probe and equally cool, detached, and impersonal. He had the air of a surgeon who approaches a clinical experiment. "I'm inclined to think it may be," he decided. "Yes—a sporting risk; though I'm certain enough of the result, Peabody, mind that. I believe I might make a bit of a gamble with myself, just to see that I'm right. Come now—what do you want?"

"A thousand silver," said Junius.

"I haven't so much about me. Suppose we say a standing credit for a thousand drinks instead."

Junius stiffened against the bar.

"It amounts to the same thing, doesn't it?" continued Bendemeer: "Why should you trouble about dollars—mere tokens? You can't get away from Fufuti. The *Jane* out there, she's due to sail this morning on a round of my plantations. She's the only ship clearing for a month at least. . . . By the time you'd drunk yourself to death I'd simply have the money back again."

Peabody stared, and a streak of crimson leaped into his cheek as if a whiplash had been laid across it.

"Damn you—!" he cried shakily. "Give me that brandy—I'll pay for it. Here's the stuff. It's mine. I went after it, and I got it. I earned it myself, and fairly!"

"To what end?" Bendemeer cut in. "So you can pickle yourself before burial?"

Junius Peabody writhed. "What's it to you how I spend it afterward? I'm a free agent. I can do as I like."

"That," said Bendemeer with quiet emphasis, "is a lie."

Holding his quivering subject, impaled on his glance as it seemed, he reached a black, square bottle. He shoved a glass in front of Junius Peabody and poured a generous measure. With one hand he kept the glass covered and with the other pointed out through the doorway.

"I'll say you lie, and I'll demonstrate:

"You see my schooner out there? That's her boat on the beach. She leaves in half an hour; her captain's come now for final orders. She goes first from here to an island of mine a hundred miles away. I planted it with coconuts five years ago, and left a population of maybe a dozen Kanakas to tend them—it's going to be worth money some day. Nukava, they call it, and it's the edge of the earth, the farthest corner, and the loneliest and the driest. There's not a drop of anything on the place except water, scant and brackish at that. But a white man could live there, if he were fit to live at all, and wanted to badly enough.

"Now I'll make you an offer. I'll buy this lump of stuff from you, and I'll buy it either of two ways. A half interest in Nukava and you go there at once to take charge as agent. . . . Or else—here's your brandy, and I'll keep you perpetually drunk as long as you last."

Junius swayed on his feet. "Agent?" he stammered. "To go away——?"

"Now. And once there you can't escape. You're stuck for a year on a coral gridiron, Peabody, to sit and fry."

"What for? You—! What for?"

Bendemeer shrugged.

"Because it amuses me. Because I please. Because—I know what you'll do. I've been watching men of your sort all my life, and I know what they're worth—drift on the beaches, scraps, trash, jetsam. Regeneration, eh? Rot and drivel! You can't save yourself any more than you could lift yourself by your own boot straps. It suits me to prove it to you this way."

He lifted his hand away from the glass. Peabody's stare dropped from that cryptic regard to the waiting brandy before him, the red liquor, odorous and maddening. Peabody's lips moved, and he wet them with the tip of his tongue and gripped the bar with straining white fingers.

"You're wrong," he breathed. "You lose, Bendemeer. I can do it—I've just learned I can do it. And, by God," he added, prayerfully, "I will."

Bendemeer took up the netted lump.

"Very well," he said, offhand. "Just a moment, while I chuck this stuff in the storeroom."

He turned and tramped out through the rear without a glance behind him—and left Junius Peabody there alone before the bar.

He was gone perhaps five minutes, quite as much as that, an ample space of time. When he came back there was no glass in sight. It had vanished, and the room reeked with the fumes of a very flagrant distillation of French brandy. He looked his customer up and down and his lids lowered a trifle.

"Well, how did you like the flavor?"

The face of Junius Peabody was like a death's-head, but the eyes in his sockets blazed with a light all their own, and, standing there erect, standing square on his two legs with his feet braced apart, he swore—somewhat inexpertly, it was true, but still quite heartily; good, crisp profanity such as one able man may use with another—until Bendemeer's puzzled gaze caught the sparkle of broken glass lying in a great splash of liquid in a corner of the floor. "I'm going to Nukava!" cried Junius Peabody. "And you see—you see there are some scraps thrown up on the beach that are worth something after all, and be damned to you, Bendemeer!"

Bendemeer's grip shot out as if against his volition, and after an instant's hesitation Peabody took it. He did not yet know all the trader had done for him, perhaps would never know, but on the inscrutable front of that remarkable man was a faint glow curiously unlike a loser's chagrin.

"So it seems," acknowledged Bendemeer. "So it seems"—and smiled a little, rather oddly. . . .

Bendemeer was still smiling that way, all by himself, an hour or so later when he had watched the *Likely Jane* lay her course for Nukava with the new agent on board and had gone down into his storeroom to put the place to rights. There was a clutter of odds and ends of cargo that had been spilled from an upset surfboat the day before. Most of it had been salvaged by his Kanaka boys along shore, but a certain broken tub containing tallow had lost part of its contents. However, he was able now to restore a large lump weighing perhaps eleven pounds or so, which made the tally nearly good.

3000 MILES AWAY

By Frank R. Adams

[Writing a first-rate short story in the form of letters seems to be a very difficult thing to do. A story cannot reach the highest level of excellence without developing a certain emotional tension. The writer is very limited in the number of pages he can cover. Letters telling a story have a tendency to use many words. A number of letters, telegrams, comments, and explanations seem necessary to get the story told. If a correspondence of two or more characters is brought into the story it begins to take on length, and to lose the close-packed effect that direct narration and conversation so readily effect. And with length and the waiting for responses from letter to letter the emotion fades or fails to appear at all.

There are a few good short stories in which letters have been used most effectively. *3000 Miles Away* is admirable. Its skill lies partly in the management of the correspondence mostly from one side only, and its emotional effect upon the reader is in a considerable measure due to the effect of the incidents upon the secondary characters in the story.

Frank R. Adams (1883–   ), is an experienced writer, the author of novels, plays, and short stories since 1914. He is an American, born at Morrison, Illinois, educated at the University of Chicago, and now living in Los Angeles.

3000 Miles Away appeared in *The Red Book* in 1918. It is here reprinted by permission of the author.]

THE first letter was one of the great surprises of Catherine's life. Jerry was the last person she had ever expected to hear from again. That "again" indicates exactly the *status quo* of affairs between them. Everything had been definitely and decisively finished.

She even hesitated about opening the envelope. But it bore a superscription that was scarcely to be so flatteringly ignored. The oblong of cheap and flimsy manila paper was addressed thus:

J. B. Thomas, 2nd Lt. F.A., O.R.C.   Officer's
U.S.A.P.O. 711, A.E.F., France   Mail
　　　　　Mrs. Catherine Thomas,
　　　　　1742 St. Anne Place,
　　　　　Lorchester, N. Y.,
　　　　　U. S. A.

O.K.
J. B. Thomas
2nd Lt. F.A., O.R.C.

And besides that, there was the censor stamp of an army post office.

Letters from "overseas" cannot be destroyed without reading even if they have been written by—yes, she would open it without thinking about it for another moment.

She had not even heard that he was in the army. Her affairs had been deliberately ordered for the last few years so that she would not hear of his doings. She had even moved to a different part of the country, the better to avoid the bitterness of a possible chance meeting with him.

"Dear Kate," the letter began. At least he had the decency not to address her as "Wops," which had once been his nickname for her. As soon as she got over thinking how angry she would have been if he had, she began to feel rather sorry that he had not.

"Dear Kate:

"I've sorted over everyone I've ever known in all my life, and you are the only one I want to talk to. Of course, you are privileged not to listen. I certainly should never blame you.

"But on the other hand I rather need you as a conversational ground-wire. Close the circuit, will you, old girl, and listen in once in a while. I'll know you are there even if you never say a word.

"It's a bit desperate, being over here in France with the trenches just ahead and finding that there is only one worthwhile person in all your life. Not that I have any idea of being killed. I'm pretty sure I won't be. We all are. But at that, we're on the eve of a great adventure and lots of the inconsequential things that have happened to us have rather faded into insignificance.

"That was how I found out how big you have been in my life. Why, you dominate all my thoughts. If something funny happens, I want to run and write it to you, because I know that once you used to laugh at the same things that I did. And if some little tragedy occurs among the men of the battery, I feel that it would be a little less acute if you knew about it, because you've got such a darn fool tender heart that you would want to share some of the troubles of my boys too.

"And they have some very real griefs. I'm battery censor and have to read all the mail of the enlisted men before it goes out, so I know all about their affairs. That's a regular job for second lieutenants. Not that reading mail is the only thing a second lieutenant does. Thinking it over carefully, I can't at this moment recall anything that a second lieutenant doesn't do, from going over the top with the 'first wave' down to conducting physical drill and standing reveille. If there is anything the captain wants done, he tells the first 'loot,' and if it is anything messy or at all apt to make the back of your neck tired, the first 'loot' passes it on down to one of the second, which the same hasn't any come-back, being the lowest animal ever created by an act of Congress.

"So one of my everlasting performances is reading the letters home. It's a good deal like shelling peas in five-bushel lots. I did that once when I was a boy, and I never saw so many pods in all my life.

"Most of the letters are just about as much alike as the vegetables just mentioned. Heaven knows they have to be if they come anywhere near conforming to the A. E. F. General Orders governing overseas mail. The average man, when confronted by the list of things he must not say for fear that the German high command will plan the next western offensive on the basis of information inadvertently spilled by him, seems to suffer an acute attack of cramp colic in the imagination. Most of them do not appear to know how to put any interesting variations into the theme of their health and the weather. They do say 'I love you,' in one way or another, but they are very self-conscious about it. I suppose the censorship is responsible for that, too. It would be rather difficult to be as foolish as you knew how to be if you were sure that somebody was going to go over it later with a magnifying glass and developing chemicals to see what you really meant.

"Of course, not all the men are hampered by hobbled imaginations. We have several very accomplished liars in our outfit. We've only been in France three weeks and we're anyway two hundred miles away from the sound of a gun, but the battles we have been in already, according to their reports, make the little affair which the French pulled off at the Marne look like a preliminary debate in the high school league. They mention hostile airplanes just as if they were mosquitoes, and you'd think our boys had a bomb for breakfast every morning, instead of grape-fruit.

"But I understand that quite the contrary is the case when troops actually do go into action. Then they never say much about it, I am told, but write home only about how nice the weather is and how is the baby?

"I've got one man in my platoon who never writes home to his family without including in his letter some derogatory remark about his bunk-mate. I have never heard one man so thoroughly criticized by another as this particular 'bunkie' has been. According to these letters, which I have to read, of course, this chap—Corrigan, his name is—snores at his slumbers, chews gum with his mouth open, borrows cigarettes without returning them (a real crime in the army), asks foolish questions, fails to wash behind his ears and has unspeakable table-manners.

"Anybody who can distinguish himself by committing a noticeable breach of etiquette while eating from an army-issue mess-kit almost has my admiration. From my own experience and what I have observed of others I would be inclined to say that it could not be done. By the time you have all, officers and men, gargled soup out of your canteen-cover or cup and mixed your stew, potatoes and jam hopelessly in your meat-can, it would seem practically impossible for any one individual to perform any food juggling that would attract attention from his fellows. I must go around sometime at mess and watch this man Corrigan. He may have something up his sleeve, so to speak, in the way of food manipulation and broadsword calisthenics.

"The writer of these letters is a master of invective. I sit humbly at his feet. His name is Conroy.

"But now I have come to the real reason for writing. I know you have been wondering what it was, all the time, because you are quite sure that it was not simply to tell you about these rather trivial things.

"The real reason, aforementioned, is a letter from the heart of a man which came to me for censoring this afternoon. I'm going to take the liberty of lifting a few paragraphs to send to you.

"The letter began simply 'Dear,' which is one of the finest ways for a letter to begin if it is written by some one who really cares. The part which I particularly wanted you to know about was this:

It is not only houses which are haunted by the spirits of men. Sometimes men are haunted by the restless phantoms of once familiar homes.

By that I do not mean that we are homesick; it is only that we remember what we are coming back to. I doubt if a man who is here would be content at home so long as America's frontier is so far-flung. But many of us are stirred by the ghostly caressing fingers of breezes that are only blowing westward from the sea and the faces we meet in the streets at dusk are never at all the ones that are carried by on the clicking wooden sabots of the peasant folk who pass.

It's spring in France and I thought it would forget to come. It hardly seems possible that there can be spring anywhere that you are not. Why, they've even got violets here, heartbreaking blue ones that simply beg to be bought and given to you. No one has told them that you are thousands of miles away and they wonder why I pass them by.

And there are peonies, too, not in blossom yet, but they're going to be soon, just like the great flaming red ones that light the way up that hill to where you are.

"There, you see I couldn't bring a thing like that to anyone but you. No one else would see anything in it but sentimental mush. This fellow happens to be a real man though; I never would have guessed that he had anything like that in his system if I had not been obliged to look over his shoulder, so to speak, while he poured his soul out of his fountain pen.

"He isn't always making love to his wife, though—did I mention that the letter was addressed to Mrs. John Scarborough, Hale's Ferry, New York, and that he is Sergeant John Scarborough, doubtless of the same place?—sometimes his letters are altogether different. Here is an extract taken from another and earlier letter of his:

Friend Wife:

We've been together a long time, but I'm afraid I have taken a step which may cause discord between us. At least, it will make you question your judgment on that occasion when you let them play the excerpt from "Lohengrin" over you and me. Your mother, you remember, cried. Maybe she was right. Anyway, I have sent you a picture of me in my overseas cap. The overseas cap is the first serious reverse suffered by the American army. As far as I can see, it is one of those acts of Providence over which man has no control and which the insurance companies refuse to take into their calculations. It looks like the devil, isn't any good to keep the rain or the sun off from your face and eyes, and I don't think it will scare the Germans enough to make up for the shock to our own troops who have to see it all the time. Maybe the idea is to get us used to the horrors of war before we actually arrive at the front. One of the fellows last night called it a half-seas-over cap, and when you get my picture, you will see what he meant. What do you mean in your last letter by saying that our cat, Blackberry Smith, has left home? I'll bet the old scoundrel has joined the army. He never could seem to get enough fighting around home. I don't suppose that black kittens will be nearly so stylish among the best families in our neighborhood this spring as they were last. But you may be mistaken; Blackberry may be back by now. He was a very durable cat and I raised him to keep the faith. You remember that I especially charged him before I left not to let a single mouse annoy you while I was away. Do you suppose he got tired of waiting for me to come back and pull his tail? Maybe life got too tame for him with no one there to tease him.

Just now while I was writing, some one outside whistled and it sounded just like the whistle you used to call to me in the lifetime I lived before this, the one that came to an end six months ago. It was so vivid that I got half up off from my bunk at the urgent command of my heart before my reasonable but disagreeable common sense told me that it was only a coincidence. It brought you so close to me for an instant that I reached out to touch you. There was a wall of solid glass between.

There goes the bugle. It's uncomplimentary, but I must leave you for mess.

Your Husband"

Jerry had not even signed his name. Catherine guessed rather shrewdly that he had not known exactly how to finish his own note and so had allowed the other man's final message to go for both. It was rather a daring assumption on his part because he would know that she was as clever as he pretended to give her credit for being.

She sighed and let the letter lie folded between her hands in her lap. It had opened up memories that were both pleasant and painful. He had caused her the happiest hours in her life, as well as the most miserable. Just as he had said, there had been between them a whimsical touch-and-go understanding that she had never attained with anyone else. It was because it had been so perfect a thing that she regretted so poignantly that everything else had marred their relationship.

If he had only been a little more like this man whose letters he had quoted to her! Catherine felt a sudden envy of the woman who had inspired the home-longing of John Scarborough. Why, that woman did not live so very far away. Hale's Ferry was in New York State, anyway, although Catherine had never heard of the town. For a moment she was almost tempted to look up the other end of the skein which had come into her hands so unexpectedly and see what Mrs. John was like. But she decided against it as a foolish idea. Besides, it was none of her business. She would forget the entire affair.

But that was easier said than done. That letter from the man who had never been successfully supplanted in her life fretted the edges of consciousness for many days. It had to be re-read every once in a while to see just why it so insistently tugged at her thoughts.

And in three weeks there was another letter.

It began "Dear Kate," just as the first one had, but in this "Wops" had been written first and then thoroughly scratched out. She knew because it took her about ten minutes to erase the scratches enough to make sure just what it was that he had deleted. And she was not angry, not so long as he had scratched it out. He could not help it if he still thought of her by that name and his pen had slipped.

The letter:

"We've moved up a little nearer the front lines and we're doing a lot of firing on the practice range, but the whole thing is strangely unreal and some way it's not warlike. There is more feeling of tremendous conflict in New York than there is here. I suppose that we are absorbing the attitude of the French. Their thought of the war is the most incomprehensible thing that I have run across so far. An intensely emotional people in everything else, they are strangely phlegmatic about this most important thing in their lives. The war is the principal industry of the country, just the way that steel is the mainspring of Pittsburgh; but outside of business hours nobody makes any fuss about it. An officer comes back from the front on leave. He visits his friends, talks about the weather, plays a little bridge, goes to the theater and at the end of his time shakes hands all around and trots off to the trenches with his trousers nicely creased and his shoes shined. It's the most casual thing you can well imagine.

"Do you remember in my first letter to you that I mentioned one of my men who was always criticizing his bunk-mate in letters home? It aroused my interest to such an extent that I took the trouble to inquire into the state of affairs between the two men. According to all the other members of their section, they were inseparable companions. And Corrigan, the one who inspired all the adverse remarks, seemed to be a nice chap, quite incapable of the things ascribed to him. It rather seemed to me that Conroy, his bunk mate, was doing him an injustice, so finally I ran the matter down to Conroy himself.

"'Conroy,' I said, one day when he happened to be in the office as orderly, 'what have you got against Corrigan? Can't you two fellows be good friends?'

"He seemed to be a little puzzled and said: 'Why, Corrigan is my best pal, sir. He has already saved my life once, sir, and if I can find a good tight place to get into over here, I'm going to let him do it again.'

"That didn't hitch up with what he had said in his letters, and I expect that he could see that I was not satisfied. Finally a light broke in on him, and he asked me with a grin, 'You've been censoring the mail lately, haven't you, sir?'

"I admitted that I had.

"'Don't pay no attention to what I say in my letters, sir. According to orders I can't write any news, and I can't criticize my superior officers, and I can't kick about the way I'm treated. But just to make the folks back home what know me, feel easy, I always put in a little knock on my bunkie. If I didn't have nothing to holler about, Mother would fret for fear I was sick. And there ain't no A. E. F. orders or no game laws or anything to protect Sam.'

"That man has imagination, and I shall look forward with pleasure to seeing what he will do next.

"While we're on this topic of imagination, I might mention that we have had some improvements sprung on us by our Battery 'Private Peats.' That's what we call the mental historians who are writing their experiences in the war before their imaginations get clouded any by the smoke of actual battle. One of the best of these fountain-pen daredevils writes this to his sweetheart:

> Darling Min:
>   I am writing this by the light of a stub of a candle stuck in a bayonet, I am in a dug-out in the front line and the roof leaks a muddy stream down on this piece of board I am using for a

table. If some of the dirty, maybe bloody, water and a few drops of candle grease get on this paper, never mind. I am doing all I can to keep it clean.

"This letter goes on, ad lib., describing the terrible battle which is raging just over the writer's head, but I introduced the first paragraph so you would appreciate it when I tell you that there were several muddy stains on the paper and also three or four drippings from a paraffin candle. Now, that may sound natural to you, but it doesn't to me, because I happen to know that all these letters are written in the Y. M. C. A. hut, which at our camp is a beautiful French chateau, luxuriously furnished and lighted by electricity. The quartermaster doesn't even possess a stock of candles at this depot and this lad must have had to walk five miles to town in order to purchase the wherewithal to manufacture those three or four drops of realism.

"No officer who has ever been a company or battery censor is ever again going to have those delightful cold chills up and down the spine when he reads the war experiences of the returned heroes who are getting a dollar and a quarter each for said experiences bound in buckram. We censors know that Ananias was an old army man and that a lot of his descendants got caught in the first draft.

"Well, I O.K.'d the letter and allowed it to go through. I never heard of any A. E. F. order that says a man shall not write home the details of a battle that never happened. At that, I wonder what would happen if the Germans got hold of this lad's correspondence.

"We have French officers and noncommissioned officers instructing us in some of the work we are to do at the front. They are charming and never seem to lose patience with us no matter how stupid we are. As an officer, I am entitled to the salute of these battle-scarred sergeants, but I always feel like remonstrating when an old fellow with two or three wound stripes on his arm comes up smartly with his right hand when we pass each other. I'd like to tell him not to mind until I, too, have at least a service badge on my own arm.

"The children on the streets salute us, too, and almost all of them greet us, no matter what time of day, with a pleasant 'Good night.' I don't know what they think it means, but it appears to be the favorite phrase to learn for those who have time for only one. . . .

"I think that's all the information and personal opinion that I can crowd in before referring to John Scarborough's letter, which is my flimsy excuse for addressing you at all.

"He loves that woman so much that everyone but myself would doubt that she was his wife. Probably at home he treats her like a dog, but over here he certainly has suffered a change of heart. I can't pick out anything particular to send you from his latest imitation of Abelard, so I'll transcribe all of it. As follows:

Dear:

Would you be interested to know that the little watch you gave me when I left for France has scarcely varied an instant since the day you put it on my wrist? Personally I am a little disgusted with it. In its place I should try to hasten over the hours that we have to be apart.

I received your letter with the perfumed handkerchief in it. Of course I recognized the faint fragrance of it. I had never been conscious of that perfume at all when I was with you, but when I smelled it again, I knew what it was that I had been missing all this time. It was rather a maddening trick of yours to send me so sensory a reminder of you. Don't you know that there are laws in your country which punish those who induce soldiers to desert from Uncle Sam's army? I don't know just what they would do to you as punishment, but I do know what I will do when I catch you.

By the way, that particular brand of essence of flowers is made right here in the part of France where we are stationed. I saw some in a shop-window the other day and inquired about it in my crippled French. They told me that it was a local product. Fleur Elise is the name of it, is it not? You say that you are well. Thank God for that. Keep yourself so, dear. The bugles are just beginning to sound my nightly prayer for you—Taps. It's the loneliest call for soldiers in all the world. Good night.   John.

"Being a 'tidy pachyderm, full of satiable curiosity,' after censoring that letter I went out to the tiny *parfumerie* in the village which is over the line from our camp and bought a small bottle of Fleur Elise. It is exquisite and I know that you will like it. I have placed a drop of the haunting stuff on this sheet of paper so you may judge, too, with your patrician nose if there is not something alluring about this Mrs. Scarborough. I don't think that either she or John will mind our having eavesdropped this little bit.

"If I may, I shall write you again if I can think up a plausible excuse, or even without any if my need becomes great.

                                          "Jerry."

Of course Catherine did not answer it. She could not answer without forgiving him for the things that could never be forgiven. The mere fact that he was playing on her heartstrings again after she had thought them long since out of tune was no reason for retiring her common sense to the side-lines and becoming a sentimental schoolgirl once more.

But she wavered a little when the next letter came, quite two months later.

"Wops," it began without apology. Later, when she had read the letter through, she had not the heart to be offended. Evidently he was not thinking about trivial things, and it had not occurred to him that his pen had slipped.

"Wops:

"We're 'going in' tomorrow. There is some kind of a hurry-up call for light artillery,—that's us,—and we're to move up sooner than we expected. I suppose it means a big offensive on one side or the other. We've been within sound of the guns for a long time, but some way their rumble sounds a little more menacing tonight, a little more personal. I don't think we're exactly afraid, but perhaps we are just a little serious about it.

"The thing about which I spoke in my first letter has proven itself true. I refer to the fact that the closer the men get to the battle-line the less they say about it. Scarcely a man in the outfit has suggested a thing in his letters back home,—and there have been lots of letters, too, since we found out that we were going to move,—that would indicate to a soul the extra tension we are under.

"The only man who wrote anything at all pertinent to the situation was John Scarborough. John, apparently, has a gloomy foreboding that all is not well with the stars of his destiny. He did not say so, but I caught the undercurrent of farewell in his letter to his wife.

"But it was never sent.

"He came to me before the mail went out and asked to have his letter destroyed.

"'Why, Sergeant?' I asked.

"'You've read it, sir?' he countered.

"'Yes,' I admitted.

"'I'm a little afraid to have her get that letter, sir. There's going to be a youngster at our house pretty soon, and I'm afraid I've said something that might make her worry. I don't even want her to know if something does happen to me up in the ditch. Not for a while, anyway. I've thought it out, sir, and I've written a couple of extra letters that I wish you would take charge of and mail about two weeks apart if I should try to stop any shrapnel or shell splinters.'

"So I destroyed his letter for him and told him to run along and forget his troubles by giving the men under him a little extra dose of Hail Columbia, which the same would be good for all hands. I'm almost sorry not to be able to send you any extracts from the letter because in it he made it quite plain to that woman that he loved her. She certainly ought to have the letter herself, but John is right. If anything should happen—but we don't think of such things.

"I have to go out as liaison officer tonight to go through the preliminaries of taking over the battery position. Maybe I'll have something more interesting to write next time—if you'll let me.

"And I hope that you will.   "Jerry."

He was strangely awkward and diffident about closing his letters. It would be hard for him to be formal with her and, of course, quite impossible to step back to the old informal basis. She smiled as she thought how he must have struggled with that finish and had at last given it up and put down the lamest of conclusions.

It was curious to get that word from him, written three weeks before, as she discovered by the date and postmark, speaking about something interesting that he was going to do that night. Why, what had happened was now history. His battery had been in position for three weeks now, had probably taken part in the struggle begun by the great German drive and Foch's greater counter-offensive. Even as she read his letter, he might be living in a hell of bursting shell. Or he might be— But, as he said, people do not speak of such things. It didn't matter to her anyway, or at least she must not let it matter. That page in her life had been too thoroughly scratched out ever to be written over with original characters.

Her indifference failed her somewhat when there was no letter the following week, nor the next. She found her mind constantly and unwillingly straying to that far-off battle line where the hearts of so many American women were trying to interpose themselves as shields to those they loved. Catherine would not admit it to anyone, but she had fretted herself into a state bordering upon nervous collapse before the next letter came thirty-seven days after the last one.

It was not in his handwriting at all and was on the stationery of a base hospital, designated only by a cryptic army-post-office number.

But it was from him because it started off, "Wops, dear," and she supplied to herself, quoting, "which is one of the finest ways for a letter to begin," and went on:

"Don't be surprised because this is written by some one else. I'm slightly wounded and cannot use my right arm; so I am asking one of the nurses to write this for me, a very pretty nurse and kinder, even, than that. I put that in to tease her and to see her blush. Now I know how the boys used to feel when they were writing their letters home, knowing that I was going to censor them.

"I would have waited until I was able to write this myself, except that I knew you would be interested in the story of John Scarborough.

"Briefly, John was gassed. That doesn't sound very serious, but unfortunately it is. We, in the artillery, are especially subject to this annoying habit on the part of the Germans, because they cannot reach us so well with their shrapnel and machine-guns, bombs and other little things like that. John got a bad case, which has caused him rather intolerable agony for some time since and has destroyed his eyesight, at least temporarily.

"By a lucky chance, we were both taken to the same hospital. I call it lucky, because I think that otherwise John would never be going back to his wife, who, I trust, loves him as much as he loves her. She must love him very much now, especially for the memory of what he has been, because he never will be quite the same.

"I did not hear anything about him for several days after we were brought here. I didn't even know that he was not with the battery, in fact, until a hospital orderly came through looking for any officer from the —th Regiment, Battery C. I admitted that those were my general descriptions.

"'There's a bad case from your battery here, sir,' the orderly reported, 'and the nurse in charge had an idea that one of his officers might be able to help. The man is mighty popular with the staff, and we didn't want to let him slip if there is anything that could be done.'

"'Who is it?'

"'A sergeant by the name of Scarborough, sir—a gas case, pretty bad. Do you think you'd be able to come and see him, sir?'

"I was quite able to be around, so I trotted over to the ward. He was out of his head when I got there, so I just talked with the nurse on duty. The orderly was right. John is certainly popular with the female help around this man's hospital. The darn fool woman nearly cried when she told me about him, and that's saying a lot about a war-time nurse, which the same has to put her heart away in the brine of all her tears before she tackles her job.

"It seems that John was fretting himself into almost incurable agitation because he hadn't had any word from his wife. I didn't know this myself, but it seems that for some time before we went in he had not had a letter from home, and quite naturally all of our mail has been more or less messed up during the drive. As a consequence it had been something like two months since he had received word from his family. The nurses had done all they could by writing to regimental headquarters for his mail, but they hadn't got any action out of that and probably they won't until after the present disturbance is over and the mail clerk can do his work without keeping a bayonet in his left hand.

"And in the meantime, John was getting worse, not doing a blessed thing to help himself but spending all his energy that he needed so badly in worrying about that fool letter. The nurse put it up to me strong to do something. And I wanted to help, too. You know how much I think of John. But I couldn't see just exactly what good it would do for me to talk to him. He didn't want any good advice; what he needed was a letter from his wife.

"That nurse and I talked for some time about the problem, and I told her about the baby that John was hoping for back home, and we agreed that we couldn't blame John for worrying. 'We've got to get that letter somehow,' she said.

"I agreed with her, and being an imaginative sort of rabbit I thought out the way to do it.

"You can guess how we managed. It was only a short note; a mother would not be apt to write much the first time. It said:

> Dear:
> We two are waiting for you to bring us back our hearts from across the sea.

"That was nice and indefinite, but it conveyed the idea in a sentimental sort of way. The signature bothered me most for some time. Every wife has some little pet name that her husband has given her and that no one else ever uses just as—you know how it is—and it was a cinch that she would sign that name to that letter if to no other. You'll never guess how I got around it. I admit it was pretty good. I put a big dauby cross on the end of the letter and labeled it 'His Mark.'

"I kept away from John entirely. He doesn't know yet that I am anywhere near the hospital. But I was where I could watch when they brought him the letter.

"Of course he couldn't see it, but he held it in his hands in the envelope unopened. He wanted to believe it was from her, but he was afraid it wasn't. Finally he put it to the supreme test—raised it to his nose and *smelled of it*.

"Fortunately I had guessed that he would do just that, so the letter passed the test. I had that small bottle of Fleur Elise in my baggage, which had been sent on from the regiment, and I had put just the faintest suspicion of the scent on the paper. The way all of John Scarborough's doubts passed away before that almost indistinguishable breath of springtime was enough to make me a believer in magic.

"The rest of the letter went across like a shot. The part about having the baby's signature made a tremendous hit, and I was almost as proud as he was. He laughed until all the nurses and I cried. There is something some way affecting about watching a six-footer like John, with bandaged eyes that may never see again, sitting up in bed and laughing as if all the world were going to be one continuous springtime of comedy for him from then on.

"But it worked. The boy is getting well. He can go home sometime not so very far off, and that is helping too. A letter did come from his wife finally, but we haven't given it to him. Why? None of the rest of us has any right to open it first, and it might contradict part of our manufactured story. We know she's all right though, or else she could not have written at the date the letter is postmarked. And we have written her all the facts of the case so he need never know until he is back home and perfectly safe from any further harm that this world can do him.

"This, then, is all that I shall ever know of the story of John Scarborough. I am afraid that I shall never again find so good an excuse for writing to you. For that reason and for others, dear, which I cannot explain, I take the thread of communication between you and the man who was once your husband, here in my two hands, and break it—thus.

"Jerry."

The signature was not even Jerry's own, and yet some way the entire letter was his. It was strange that the man could project his personality to her through some one else, that some one else another woman.

And that totally unexpected shock at the end about never writing to her again. Just what did he mean by that? Why?

She read the letter through once more to see if there were something she had missed the first time. There was nothing unless you counted an occasional slight stain on the paper, stains which looked as if something had been dropped on it. There were two or three on each sheet. At first she thought that maybe he had put a few drops of Fleur Elise on her letter, too, but the faint stains were odorless.

Catherine cudgeled her brain for hours over the matter, and because she really had a brain, it finally brought forth some slight results.

One of them was that she packed up a grip and went to the railroad station. The ticket agent not only knew where Hale's Ferry was but was able to sell her a ticket to it.

When she arrived she went to the post office as the most likely place to get the information she desired.

"Does Mrs. John Scarborough get her mail here?" Catherine asked of the lady postmistress politely.

"She does not," the latter replied with some politeness and more firmness.

"I didn't think that she did," Catherine confessed blandly. "Does anyone of that name live here, or has she lived here recently?"

"No"—shortly.

"Would you be apt to know?"

"I would. I've been here tw—I've been here a long time."

"Thank you."

That was all Catherine needed to know. In fact, it was information that she had already sensed. The entire pilgrimage to Hale's Ferry had been simply for purposes of verification.

There had never been any Mrs. John Scarborough, nor any Sergeant John Scarborough, nor any baby. It had all been just a trick that Jerry had played on her. All those love letters that he had pretended to quote were simply the ones he had written to her himself but dared not send over his own name.

Catherine's eyes swam a little as she read back over his letters. For, of course, she carried them with her.

And that last one. Those stains on each page. Of a sudden she knew what they were. They were the tears of the nurse who was taking down what he dictated. For, of course, he must be pretty badly hurt himself, although he had said that he was not. He was doubtless the one who had been gassed; and blinded, too, perhaps permanently. The grim irony of his remark about teasing his nurse to see her blush!

That, then, was why he had said that he would write no more. Before, he had been hoping, but now, he was afraid, that the trail of ink might lead them together again. For her sake he had broken the thread without letting her pity him.

It did not require much deep thinking to reason out in Catherine's serviceable mind the undeniable fact that out of the rather nebulous and uncertain personality which had once been her husband, the war had fashioned and tempered something very real: a man.

And because he had turned out so and because it was a nice day and because—well, because of everything—Catherine cried about it. In fact, going home on the train, she had one of the very best cries that she had enjoyed since she was a girl in boarding-school.

But weeping was not all that she did that day. Catherine knew when she had got her cue to enter, and she proceeded to take a hand in affairs as soon as she could get to a telegraph office which would accept cablegrams for overseas.

They say that the result of her activity did more good to one of the gas patients in an American base hospital in France than all the efforts of the nurses, who were very fond of that particular case, and of the chief surgeon, who spent time when he should have been sleeping in bending over the patient's bed, trying with drugs, lances, and prayers to make him stay on this side of the great frontier.

When Jerry heard this cablegram read to him, he decided that he could not afford not to get well. So he got at it right away.

Here's the cablegram. Judge for yourself:

2nd Lt. Jerry Thomas, F.A., O.R.C.
Base Hospital No.——
A. E. F., France.

Dear: This is first of series of communications for you to censor daily until you come back to the home we never had. Mr. and Mrs. Scarborough, son and cat, Blackberry Smith, all here waiting for you, but more than all the rest,   Wops, Her Mark.

Is anybody interested in the fact that the cablegram cost twenty dollars and fifty-five cents?

THE WEAVER'S GRAVE

A STORY OF OLD MEN

By Seumas O'Kelly

[*The Weaver's Grave* is a novelette of approximately 20,000 words. The things that happen in it are of little importance, but the setting is interesting for its own sake. Character portrayal, however, is the real business of the writer in this story. The author, Seumas O'Kelly (1881–1918) was a Dublin newspaper man, and a product of the Irish literary renaissance of the twentieth century, a movement best known for its fine showing in drama and lyric poetry. The story was called to the attention of the editor of this volume by the distinguished Irish poet Æ (George William Russell), who declared it to be the best short story written by the newer Irish group. Other notable writers of the group are Sean O'Faolian, with his volume entitled *Midsummer Night's Madness*, and Frank O'Connor, author of several stories published in a volume bearing the title of its first story, *Guests of the Nation*. O'Kelly first earned a wide recognition with his drama *The Shuiler's Child* in 1909. This was followed by a volume of *Three Plays*, and other stories and dramas in the few years following. Some of these were published after his death.

The Weaver's Grave is reprinted from *The Golden Barque* (1919), by permission of the publishers, The Talbot Press, Dublin.]

I

MORTIMER HEHIR, the weaver, had died, and they had come in search of his grave to Cloon na Morav, the Meadow of the Dead. Meehaul Lynskey, the nail-maker, was first across the stile. There was excitement in his face. His long warped body moved in a shuffle over the ground. Following him came Cahir Bowes, the stone-breaker, who was so beaten down from the hips forward, that his back was horizontal as the back of an animal. His right hand held a stick which propped him up in front, his left hand clutched his coat behind, just above the small of the back. By these devices he kept himself from toppling head over heels as he walked. Mother earth was the brow of Cahir Bowes by magnetic force, and Cahir Bowes was resisting her fatal kiss to the last. And just now there was animation in the face he raised from its customary contemplation of the ground. Both old men had the air of those who had been unexpectedly let loose. For a long time they had lurked somewhere in the shadows of life, the world having no business for them, and now, suddenly, they had been remembered and called forth to perform an office which nobody else on earth could perform. The excitement in their faces as they crossed over the stile into Cloon na Morav expressed a vehemence in their belated usefulness. Hot on their heels came two dark, handsome, stoutly-built men, alike even to the cord that tied their corduroy trousers under their knees, and, being grave-diggers, they carried flashing spades. Last of all, and after a little delay, a firm white hand was laid on the stile, a dark figure followed, the figure of a woman whose palely sad face was picturesquely, almost dramatically, framed in a black shawl which hung from the crown of the head. She was the widow of Mortimer Hehir, the weaver, and she followed the others into Cloon na Morav, the Meadow of the Dead.

To glance at Cloon na Morav as you went by on the hilly road, was to get an impression of a very old burial-ground; to pause on the road and look at Cloon na Morav was to become conscious of its quiet situation, of winds singing down from the hills in a chant for the dead; to walk over to the wall and look at the mounds inside was to provoke quotations from Gray's Elegy; to make the Sign of the Cross, lean over the wall, observe the gloomy lichened background of the wall opposite, and mark the things that seemed to stray about, like yellow snakes in the grass, was to think of Hamlet moralising at the graveside of Ophelia, and hear him establish the identity of Yorick. To get over the stile and stumble about inside, was to forget all these things and to know Cloon na Morav for itself. Who could tell the age of Cloon na Morav? The mind could only swoon away into mythology, paddle about in the dotage of paganism, the toothless infancy of Christianity. How many generations, how many septs, how many clans, how many families, how many people, had gone into Cloon na Morav? The mind could only take wing on the romances of mathematics. The ground was billowy, grotesque. Several partially suppressed insurrections—a great thirsting, worming, pushing and shouldering under the sod—had given it character. A long tough growth of grass wired it from end to end, Nature, by this effort, endeavoring to control the strivings of the more daring of the insurgents of Cloon na Morav. No path here; no plan or map or register existed; if there ever had been one or the other it had been lost. Invasions and wars and famines and feuds had swept the ground and left it. All claims to interment had been based on powerful traditional rights. These rights had years ago come to an end—all save in a few outstanding cases, the rounding up of a spent generation. The overflow from Cloon na Morav had already set a new cemetery on its legs a mile away, a cemetery in which limestone headstones and Celtic crosses were springing up like mushrooms, advertising the triviality of a civilisation of men and women, who, according to their own epitaphs, had done exactly the two things they could not very well avoid doing: they had all, their obituary notices said, been born and they had all died. Obscure quotations from Scripture were sometimes added by way of apology. There was an almost unanimous expression of forgiveness to the Lord for what had happened to the deceased. None of this lack of humor in Cloon na Morav. Its monuments were comparatively few, and such of them as it had not swallowed were well within the general atmosphere. No obituary notice in the place was complete; all were either wholly or partially eaten up by the teeth of time. The monuments that had made a stout battle for existence were pathetic in their futility. The vanity of the fashionable of dim ages made one weep. Who on earth could have brought in the white marble slab to Cloon na Morav? It had grown green with shame. Perhaps the lettering, once readable upon it, had been conscientiously picked out in gold. The shrieking winds and the fierce rains of the hills alone could tell. Plain heavy stones, their shoulders rounded with a chisel, presumably to give them some off-handed resemblance to human-ity, now swooned at fantastic angles from their settings, as if the people to whose memory they had been dedicated had shouldered them away as an impertinence. Other slabs lay in fragments on the ground, filling the mind with thoughts of Moses descending from Mount Sinai and, wax-ing angry at sight of his followers dancing about false gods, casting the stone tables containing the Commandments to the ground, breaking them in pieces—the most tragic destruction of a first edition that the world has known. Still other heavy square dark slabs, surely creatures of a pagan imagination, were laid flat down on numerous short legs, look-ing sometimes like representations of monstrous black cockroaches, and again like tables at which the guests of Cloon na Morav might sit down, goblin-like, in the moon-light, when nobody was looking. Most of the legs had given way and the tables lay overturned, as if there had been a quarrel at cards the night before. Those that had kept their legs ex-hibited great cracks or fissures across their backs, like slabs of dark ice breaking up. Over by the wall, draped in its pattern of dark green lichen, certain families of dim ages had made an effort to keep up the traditions of the Eastern sepulchres. They had showed an aristocratic reluctance to take to the common clay in Cloon na Morav. They had built low casket-shaped houses against the gloomy wall, putting an enormously heavy iron door with ponderous iron rings, like the rings on a pier by the sea at one end, a tremendous lock—one wondered what Goliath kept the key—finally cementing the whole thing up and surrounding it with spiked iron railings. In these contraptions very aristocratic families locked up their dead as if they were dangerous wild animals. But these ancient vanities only heightened the general democracy of the ground. To prove a traditional right to a place in its community was to have the bond of your pedigree sealed. The act of burial in Cloon na Morav was in itself an epitaph. And it was amazing to think that there were two people still over the sod who had such a right—one Mortimer Hehir, the weaver, just passed away, the other Malachi Roohan, a cooper, still breathing. When these two survivors of a great generation got tucked under the sward of Cloon na Morav its terrific history would, for all practical purposes, have ended.

II

Meehaul Lynskey, the nailer, hitched forward his bony shoulders and cast his eyes over the ground—eyes that were small and sharp, but unaccustomed to range over wide spaces. The width and the wealth of Cloon na Morav were baffling to him. He had spent his long life on the look-out for one small object so that he might hit it. The color that he loved was the golden glowing end of a stick of burning iron; wherever he saw that he seized it in a small sconce at the end of a long handle, wrenched it off by a twitch of the wrist, hit it with a flat hammer several deft taps, dropped it into a vessel of water, out of which it came a cool and perfect nail. To do this thing several hundred times six days in the week, and pull the chain of a bellows at short intervals, Meehaul Lynskey had developed an extraordinary dexterity of sight and touch, a swiftness of business that no mortal man could exceed, and so long as he had been pitted against nail-makers of flesh and blood he had more than held his own; he had, indeed, even put up a tremendous but an unequal struggle against the competition of nail-making machinery. Accustomed as he was to concentrate on a single, glowing, definite object, the complexity and disorder of Cloon na Morav unnerved him. But he was not going to betray any of these professional defects to Cahir Bowes, the stone-breaker. He had been sent there as an ambassador by the caretaker of Cloon na Morav, picked out for his great age, his local knowledge, and his good character, and it was his business to point out to the twin grave-diggers, sons of the caretaker, the weaver's grave, so that it might be opened to receive him. Meehaul Lynskey had a knowledge of the place, and was quite certain as to a great number of grave sites, while the caretaker, being an official without records, had a profound ignorance of the whole place.

Cahir Bowes followed the drifting figure of the nail-maker over the ground, his face hitched up between his shoulders, his eyes keen and gray, glint-like as the mountains of stones he had in his day broken up as road material. Cahir, no less than Meehaul, had his knowledge of Cloon na Morav, and some of his own people were buried here. His sharp, clear eyes took in the various mounds with the eye of a prospector. He, too, had been sent there as an ambassador, and as between himself and Meehaul Lynskey he did not think there could be any two opinions; his knowledge was superior to the knowledge of the nailer. Whenever Cahir Bowes met a loose stone on the grass quite instinctively he turned it over with his stick, his sharp old eyes judging its grain with a professional swiftness, then cracking at it with his stick. If the stick were a hammer, the stone, attacked on its most vulnerable spot, would fall to pieces like glass. In stones Cahir Bowes saw not sermons but seams. Even the headstones he tapped significantly with the ferrule of his stick, for Cahir Bowes had an artist's passion for his art, though his art was far from creative. He was one of the great destroyers, the reducers, the makers of chaos, a powerful and remorseless critic of the Stone Age.

The two old men wandered about Cloon na Morav, in no hurry whatever to get through with their business. After all they had been a long time pensioned off, forgotten, neglected, by the world. The renewed sensation of usefulness was precious to them. They knew that when this business was over they were not likely to be in request for anything in this world again. They were ready to oblige the world, but the world would have to allow them their own time. The world, made up of the two grave-diggers and the widow of the weaver, gathered all this without any vocal proclamation. Slowly, mechanically as it were, they followed the two ancients about Cloon na Morav. And the two ancients wandered about with the labor of age and the hearts of children. They separated, wandered about silently as if they were picking up old acquaintances, stumbling upon forgotten things, gathering up the threads of days that were over, reviving their memories, and then drew together, beginning to talk slowly, almost casually, and all their talk was of the dead, of the people who lay in the ground about them. They warmed to it, airing their knowledge, calling up names and complications of family relationships, telling stories, reviving all virtues, whispering at past vices, past vices that did not sound like vices at all, for the long years are great mitigators and run in splendid harness with the coyest of all the virtues, Charity. The whispered scandals of Cloon na Morav were seen by the twin grave-diggers and the widow of the weaver through such a haze of antiquity that they were no longer scandals but romances. The rake and the drab, seen a good way down the avenue, merely look picturesque. The grave-diggers rested their spades in the ground, leaning on the handles in exactly the same graveyard pose, and the pale widow stood in the background, silent, apart, patient, and, like all dark, tragic looking women, a little mysterious.

The stone-breaker pointed with his quivering stick at the graves of the people whom he spoke about. Every time he raised that forward support one instinctively looked, anxious and fearful, to see if the clutch were secure on the small of the back. Cahir Bowes had the sort of shape that made one eternally fearful for his equilibrium. The nailer, who, like his friend the stone-breaker, wheezed a good deal, made short, sharp gestures, and always with the right hand; the fingers were hooked in such a way, and he shot out the arm in such a manner, that they gave the illusion that he held a hammer and that it was struck out over a very hot fire. Every time Meehaul Lynskey made this gesture one expected to see sparks flying.

"Where are we to bury the weaver?" one of the grave-diggers asked at last.

Both old men labored around to see where the interruption, the impertinence, had come from. They looked from one twin to the other, with gravity, indeed anxiety, for they were not sure which was which, or if there was not some illusion in the resemblance, some trick of youth to baffle age.

"Where are we to bury the weaver?" the other twin repeated, and the strained look on the old men's faces deepened. They were trying to fix in their minds which of the twins had interrupted first and which last. The eyes of Meehaul Lynskey fixed on one twin with the instinct of his trade, while Cahir Bowes ranged both and eventually wandered to the figure of the widow in the background, silently accusing her of impatience in a matter which it would be indelicate for her to show haste.

"We can't stay here for ever," said the first twin.

It was the twin upon whom Meehaul Lynskey had fastened his small eyes, and, sure of his man this time, Meehaul Lynskey hit him.

"There's many a better man than you," said Meehaul Lynskey, "that will stay here for ever." He swept Cloon na Morav with the hooked figures.

"Them that stays in Cloon na Morav for ever," said Cahir Bowes with a wheezing energy, "have nothing to be ashamed of—nothing to be ashamed of. Remember that, young fellow."

Meehaul Lynskey did not seem to like the intervention, the help, of Cahir Bowes. It was a sort of implication that he had not—*he*, mind you,—had not hit the nail properly on the head.

"Well, where are we to bury him, anyway?" said the twin, hoping to profit by the chagrin of the nailer—the nailer who, by implication, had failed to nail.

"You'll bury him," said Meehaul Lynskey, "where all belonging to him is buried."

"We come," said the other twin, "with some sort of intention of that kind." He drawled out the words, in imitation of the old men. The skin relaxed on his handsome dark face and then bunched in puckers of humor about the eyes; Meehaul Lynskey's gaze, wandering for once, went to the handsome dark face of the other twin and the skin relaxed and then bunched in puckers of humor about *his* eyes, so that Meehaul Lynskey had an unnerving sensation that these young grave-diggers were purposely confusing him.

"You'll bury him," he began with some vehemence, and was amazed to again find Cahir Bowes taking the words out of his mouth, snatching the hammer out of his hand, so to speak.

"—— where you're told to bury him," Cahir Bowes finished for him.

Meehaul Lynskey was so hurt that his long slanting figure moved away down the graveyard, then stopped suddenly. He had determined to do a dreadful thing. He had determined to do a thing that was worse than kicking a crutch from under a cripple's shoulder; that was like stealing the holy water out of a room where a man lay dying. He had determined to ruin the last day's amusement on this earth for Cahir Bowes and himself by prematurely and basely disclosing the weaver's grave!

"Here," called back Meehaul Lynskey, "is the weaver's grave, and here you will bury him."

All moved down to the spot, Cahir Bowes going with extraordinary spirit, the ferrule of his terrible stick cracking on the stones he met on the way.

"Between these two mounds," said Meehaul Lynskey, and already the twins raised their twin spades in a sinister movement, like swords of lancers flashing at a drill.

"Between these two mounds," said Meehaul Lynskey, "is the grave of Mortimer Hehir."

"Hold on!" cried Cahir Bowes. He was so eager, so excited, that he struck one of the grave-diggers a whack of his stick on the back. Both grave-diggers swung about to him as if both had been hurt by the one blow.

"Easy there," said the first twin.

"Easy there," said the second twin.

"Easy yourselves," cried Cahir Bowes. He wheeled about his now quivering face on Meehaul Lynskey.

"What is it you're saying about the spot between the mounds?" he demanded.

"I'm saying," said Meehaul Lynskey vehemently, "that it's the weaver's grave."

"What weaver?" asked Cahir Bowes.

"Mortimer Hehir," replied Meehaul Lynskey. "There's no other weaver in it."

"Was Julia Rafferty a weaver?"

"What Julia Rafferty?"

"The midwife, God rest her."

"How could she be a weaver if she was a midwife?"

"Not a one of me knows. But I'll tell you what I do know and know rightly: that it's Julia Rafferty is in that place and no weaver at all."

"Amn't I telling you it's the weaver's grave?"

"And amn't I telling you it's not?"

"That I may be as dead as my father but the weaver was buried there."

"A bone of a weaver was never sunk in it as long as weavers was weavers. Full of Raffertys it is."

"Alive with weavers it is."

"Heavenlyful Father, was the like ever heard: to say that a grave was alive with dead weavers."

"It's full of them—full as a tick."

"And the clean grave that Mortimer Hehir was never done boasting about—dry and sweet and deep and no way bulging at all. Did you see the burial of his father ever?"

"I did, in troth, see the burial of his father—forty year ago if it's a day."

"Forty year ago—it's fifty-one year come the sixteenth of May. It's well I remember it and it's well I have occasion to remember it, for it was the day after that again that myself ran away to join the soldiers, my aunt hot foot after me, she to be buying me out the week after, I a high-spirited fellow morebetoken."

"Leave the soldiers out of it and leave your aunt out of it and stick to the weaver's grave. Here in this place was the last weaver buried, and I'll tell you what's more. In a straight line with it is the grave of ——"

"A straight line, indeed! Who but yourself, Meehaul Lynskey, ever heard of a straight line in Cloon na Morav? No such thing was ever wanted or ever allowed in it."

"In a straight direct line, measured with a rule——"

"Measured with crooked, stumbling feet, maybe feet half reeling in drink."

"Can't you listen to me now?"

"I was always a bad warrant to listen to anything except sense. Yourself ought to be the last man in the world to talk about straight lines, you with the sight scattered in your head, with the divil of sparks flying under your eyes."

"Don't mind me sparks now, nor me sight neither, for in a straight measured line with the weaver's grave was the grave of the Cassidys."

"What Cassidys?"

"The Cassidys that herded for the O'Sheas."

"Which O'Sheas?"

"O'Shea Ruadh of Cappakelly. Don't you know anyone at all, or is it gone entirely your memory is?"

"Cappakelly *inagh!* And who cares a whistle about O'Shea Ruadh, he or his seed, breed and generations? It's a rotten lot of landgrabbers they were."

"Me hand to you on that. Striving ever they were to put their red paws on this bit of grass and that perch of meadow."

"Hungry in themselves even for the cutaway bog."

"And Mortimer Hehir a decent weaver, respecting every man's wool."

"His forehead pallid with honesty over the yarn and the loom."

"If a bit broad-spoken when he came to the door for a smoke of the pipe."

"Well, there won't be a mouthful of clay between himself and O'Shea Ruadh now."

"In the end what did O'Shea Ruadh get after all his striving?"

"I'll tell you that. He got what land suits a blind fiddler."

"Enough to pad the crown of the head and tap the sole of the foot! Now you're talking."

"And the devil a word out of him now no more than anyone else in Cloon na Morav."

"It's easy talking to us all about land when we're packed up in our timber boxes."

"As the weaver was when he got sprinkled with the holy water in that place."

"As Julia Rafferty was when they read the prayers over her in that place, she a fine, buxom, cheerful woman in her day, with great skill in her business."

"Skill or no skill, I'm telling you she's not there, wherever she is."

"I suppose you want me to take her up in my arms and show her to you?"

"We then, indeed, Cahir, I do not. 'Tisn't a very handsome pair you would make at all, you not able to stand much more hardship than Julia herself."

From this there developed a slow, labored, aged dispute between the two authorities. They moved from grave to grave, pitting memory against memory, story against story, knocking down reminiscence with reminiscence, arguing in a powerful intimate obscurity that no outsider could hope to follow, blasting knowledge with knowledge, until the whole place seemed strewn with the corpses of their arguments. The two grave-diggers followed them about in a grim silence; impatience in their movements, their glances; the widow keeping track of the grand tour with a miserable feeling, a feeling, as site after site was rejected, that the tremendous exclusiveness of Cloon na Morav would altogether push her dead man, the weaver, out of his privilege. The dispute ended, like all epics, where it began. Nothing was established, nothing settled. But the two old men were quite exhausted, Meehaul Lynskey sitting down on the back of one of the monstrous cockroaches, Cahir Bowes leaning against a tombstone that was half-submerged, its end up like the stern of a derelict at sea. Here they sat glaring at each other like a pair of grim vultures.

The two grave-diggers grew restive. Their business had to be done. The weaver would have to be buried. Time pressed. They held a consultation apart. It broke up after a brief exchange of views, a little laughter.

"Meehaul Lynskey is right," said one of the twins.

Meehaul Lynskey's face lit up. Cahir Bowes looked as if he had been slapped on the cheeks. He moved out from his tombstone.

"Meehaul Lynskey is right," repeated the other twin. They had decided to break up the dispute by taking sides. They raised their spades and moved to the site which Meehaul Lynskey had urged upon them.

"Don't touch that place," Cahir Bowes cried, raising his stick. He was measuring the back of the grave-digger again when the man spun round upon him, menace in his handsome dark face.

"Touch me with that stick," he cried, "and I'll——"

Some movement in the background, some agitation in the widow's shawl, caused the grave-digger's menace to dissolve, the words to die in his mouth, a swift flush mounting the man's face. A faint smile of gratitude swept the widow's face like a flash. It was as if she had cried out, "Ah, don't touch the poor old, cranky fellow! you might hurt him." And it was as if the grave-digger had cried back: "He has annoyed me greatly, but I don't intend to hurt him. And since you say so with your eyes I won't even threaten him."

Under pressure of the half threat, Cahir Bowes shuffled back a little way, striking an attitude of feeble dignity, leaning out on his stick while the grave-diggers got to work.

"It's the weaver's grave, surely," said Meehaul Lynskey.

"If it is," said Cahir Bowes, "remember his father was buried down seven feet. You gave in to that this morning."

"There was no giving in about it," said Meehaul Lynskey. "We all know that one of the wonders of Cloon na Morav was the burial of the last weaver seven feet, he having left it as an injunction on his family. The world knows he went down the seven feet."

"And remember this," said Cahir Bowes, "that Julia Rafferty was buried no seven feet. If she is down three feet it's as much as she went."

Sure enough, the grave-diggers had not dug down more than three feet of ground when one of the spades struck hollowly on unhealthy timber. The sound was unmistakable and ominous. There was silence for a moment. Then Cahir Bowes made a sudden short spurt up a mound beside him, as if he were some sort of mechanical animal wound up, his horizontal back quivering. On the mound he made a superhuman effort to straighten himself. He got his ears and his blunt nose into a considerable elevation. He had not been so upright for twenty years. And raising his weird countenance, he broke into a cackle that was certainly meant to be a crow. He glared at Meehaul Lynskey, his emotion so great that his eyes swam in a watery triumph.

Meehaul Lynskey had his eyes, as was his custom, upon one thing, and that thing was the grave, and especially the spot on the grave where the spade had struck the coffin. He looked stunned and fearful. His eyes slowly withdrew their gimlet-like scrutiny from the spot, and sought the triumphant crowing figure of Cahir Bowes on the mound.

Meehaul Lynskey looked as if he would like to say something, but no words came. Instead he ambled away, retired from the battle, and standing apart, rubbed one leg against the other, above the back of the ankles, like some great insect. His hooked fingers at the same time stroked the bridge of his nose. He was beaten.

"I suppose it's not the weaver's grave," said one of the grave-diggers. Both of them looked at Cahir Bowes.

"Well, you know it's not," said the stone-breaker. "It's Julia Rafferty you struck. She helped many a one into the world in her day, and it's poor recompense to her to say she can't be at rest when she left it." He turned to the remote figure of Meehaul Lynskey and cried: "Ah-ha, well you may rub your ignorant legs. And I'm hoping Julia will forgive you this day's ugly work."

In silence, quickly, with reverence, the twins scooped back the clay over the spot. The widow looked on with the same quiet, patient, mysterious silence. One of the grave-diggers turned on Cahir Bowes.

"I suppose you know where the weaver's grave is?" he asked.

Cahir Bowes looked at him with an ancient tartness, then said: "You suppose!"

"Of course, you know where it is."

Cahir Bowes looked as if he knew where the gates of heaven were, and that he might—or might not—enlighten an ignorant world. It all depended! His eyes wandered knowingly out over the meadows beyond the graveyard. He said:

"I do know where the weaver's grave is."

"We'll be very much obliged to you if you show it to us."

"Very much obliged," endorsed the other twin.

The stone-breaker, thus flattered, led the way to a new site, one nearer to the wall, where were the plagiarisms of the Eastern sepulchres. Cahir Bowes made little journeys about, measuring so many steps from one place to another, mumbling strange and unintelligible information to himself, going through an extraordinary geometrical emotion, striking the ground hard taps with his stick.

"Glory be to the Lord," cried Meehaul Lynskey, "he's like the man they had driving the water for the well in the quarry field, he whacking the ground with his magic hazel wand."

Cahir Bowes made no reply. He was too absorbed in his own emotion. A little steam was beginning to ascend from his brow. He was moving about the ground like some grotesque spider weaving an invisible web.

"I suppose now," said Meehaul Lynskey, addressing the marble monument, "that as soon as Cahir hits the right spot one of the weavers will turn about below. Or maybe he expects one of them to whistle up at him out of the ground. That's it; devil a other! When we hear the whistle we'll all know for certain where to bury the weaver."

Cahir Bowes was contracting his movements, so that he was now circling about the one spot, like a dog going to lie down.

Meehaul Lynskey drew a little closer, watching eagerly, his grim yellow face, seared with yellow marks from the fires of his workshop, tightened up in a sceptical pucker. His half-muttered words were bitter with an aged sarcasm. He cried:

"Say nothing; he'll get it yet, will the man of knowledge, the know-all, Cahir Bowes! Give him time. Give him until this day twelve month. Look at that for a right-about-turn on the left heel. Isn't the nimbleness of that young fellow a treat to see? Are they whistling to you from below, Cahir? Is it dancing to the weaver's music you are? That's it, devil a other."

Cahir Bowes was mapping out a space on the grass with his stick. Gradually it took, more or less, the outline of a grave site. He took off his hat and mopped his steaming brow with a red handkerchief, saying: "There is the weaver's grave."

"God in Heaven," cried Meehaul Lynskey, "will you look at what he calls the weaver's grave? I'll say nothing at all. I'll hold my tongue. I'll shut up. Not one word will I say about Alick Finlay, the mildest man that ever lived, a man full of religion, never at the end of his prayers! But, sure, it's the saints of God that get the worst of it in this world, and if Alick escaped during life, faith he's in for it now, with the pirates and the body-snatchers of Cloon na Morav on top of him."

A corncrake began to sing in the nearby meadow, and his rasping notes sounded like a queer accompaniment to the words of Meehaul Lynskey. The grave-diggers, who had gone to work on the Cahir Bowes site, laughed a little, one of them looking for a moment at Meehaul Lynskey, saying: "Listen to that damned old corncrake in the meadow! I'd like to put a sod in his mouth."

The man's eye went to the widow. She showed no emotion one way or the other, and the grave-digger got back to his work. Meehaul Lynskey, however, wore the cap. He said:

"To be sure! I'm to sing dumb. I'm not to have a word out of me at all. Others can rattle away as they like in this place, as if they owned it. The ancient good old stock is to be nowhere and the scruff of the hills let rampage as they will. That's it, devil a other. Castles falling and dunghills rising! Well, God be with the good old times and the good old mannerly people that used to be in it, and God be with Alick Finlay, the holiest——"

A sod of earth came through the air from the direction of the grave, and, skimming Meehaul Lynskey's head, dropped somewhere behind. The corncrake stopped his notes in the meadow, and Meehaul Lynskey stood statuesque in a mute protest, and silence reigned in the place while the clay sang up in a swinging rhythm from the grave.

Cahir Bowes, watching the operations with intensity, said:

"It was nearly going astray on me."

Meehaul Lynskey gave a little snort. He asked:

"What was?"

"The weaver's grave."

"Remember this: the last weaver is down seven feet. And remember this: Alick Finlay is down less than Julia Rafferty."

He had no sooner spoken when a fearful thing happened. Suddenly out of the soft cutting of the earth a spade sounded harsh on tinware, there was a crash, less harsh, but painfully distinct, as if rotten boards were falling together, then a distinct subsidence of the earth. The work stopped at once. A moment's fearful silence followed. It was broken by a short, dry laugh from Meehaul Lynskey. He said:

"God be merciful to us all! That's the latter end of Alick Finlay."

The two grave-diggers looked at each other. The shawl of the widow in the background was agitated. One twin said to the other:

"This can't be the weaver's grave."

The other agreed. They all turned their eyes upon Cahir Bowes. He was hanging forward in a pained strain, his head quaking, his fingers twitching on his stick. Meehaul Lynskey turned to the marble monument and said with venom:

"If I was guilty I'd go down on my knees and beg God's pardon. If I didn't I'd know the ghost of Alick Finlay, saint as he was, would leap upon me and guzzle me—for what right would I have to set anybody at him with driving spades when he was long years in his grave?"

Cahir Bowes took no notice. He was looking at the ground, searching about, and slowly, painfully, began his web-spinning again. The grave-diggers covered in the ground without a word. Cahir Bowes appeared to get lost in some fearful maze of his own making. A little whimper broke from him now and again. The steam from his brow thickened in the air, and eventually he settled down on the end of a headstone, having got the worst of it. Meehaul Lynskey sat on another stone facing him, and they glared, sinister and grotesque, at each other.

"Cahir Bowes," said Meehaul Lynskey, "I'll tell you what you are, and then you can tell me what I am."

"Have it whatever way you like," said Cahir Bowes. "What is it that I am?"

"You're a gentleman, a grand oul' stone-breaking gentleman. That's what you are, devil a other!"

The wrinkles on the withered face of Cahir Bowes contracted, his eyes stared across at Meehaul Lynskey, and two yellow teeth showed between his lips. He wheezed:

"And do you know what you are?"

"I don't."

"You're a nailer, that's what you are, a damned nailer."

They glared at each other in a quaking, grim silence.

And it was at this moment of collapse, of deadlock, that the widow spoke for the first time. At the first sound of her voice one of the twins perked his head, his eyes going to her face. She said in a tone as quiet as her whole behavior:

"Maybe I ought to go up to the Tunnel Road and ask Malachi Roohan where the grave is."

They had all forgotten the oldest man of them all, Malachi Roohan. He would be the last mortal man to enter Cloon na Morav. He had been the great friend of Mortimer Hehir, the weaver, in the days that were over, and the whole world knew that Mortimer Hehir's knowledge of Cloon na Morav was perfect. Maybe Malachi Roohan would have learned a great deal from him. And Malachi Roohan, the cooper, was so long bed-ridden that those who remembered him at all thought of him as a man who had died a long time ago.

"There's nothing else for it," said one of the twins, leaving down his spade, and immediately the other twin laid his spade beside it.

The two ancients on the headstones said nothing. Not even *they* could raise a voice against the possibilities of Malachi Roohan, the cooper. By their terrible aged silence they gave consent, and the widow turned to walk out of Cloon na Morav. One of the grave-diggers took out his pipe. The eyes of the other followed the widow, he hesitated, then walked after her. She became conscious of the man's step behind her as she got upon the stile, and turned her palely sad face upon him. He stood awkwardly, his eyes wandering, then said:

"Ask Malachi Roohan where the grave is, the exact place."

It was to do this the widow was leaving Cloon na Morav; she had just announced that she was going to ask Malachi Roohan where the grave was. Yet the man's tone was that of one who was giving her extraordinarily acute advice. There was a little half-embarrassed note of confidence in his tone. In a dim way the widow thought that, maybe, he had accompanied her to the stile in a little awkward impulse of sympathy. Men were very curious in their ways sometimes. The widow was a very well-mannered woman, and she tried to look as if she had received a very valuable direction. She said:

"I will. I'll put that question to Malachi Roohan."

And then she passed out over the stile.

III

The widow went up the road, and beyond it struck the first of the houses of the nearby town. She passed through faded streets in her quiet gait, moderately grief-stricken at the death of her weaver. She had been his fourth wife, and the widowhoods of fourth wives had not the rich abandon, the great emotional cataclysm, of first, or even second, widow-hoods. It is a little chastened in its poignancy. The widow had a nice feeling that it would be out of place to give way to any of the characteristic manifestations of normal widowhood. She shrank from drawing attention to the fact that she had been a fourth wife. People's memories become so extraordinarily acute to family history in times of death! The widow did not care to come in as a sort of dramatic surprise in the gossip of the people about the weaver's life. She had heard snatches of such gossip at the wake the night before. She was beginning to understand why people love wakes and the intimate personalities of wakehouses. People listen to, remember, and believe what they hear at wakes. It is more precious to them than anything they ever hear in school, church, or playhouse. It is hardly because they get certain entertainment at the wake. It is more because the wake is a grand review of family ghosts. There one hears all the stories, the little flattering touches, the little un-flattering bitternesses, the traditions, the astonishing records, of the clans. The woman with a memory speaking to the company from a chair beside a laid-out corpse carries more authority than the bishop allocuting from his chair. The wake is realism. The widow had heard a great deal at the wake about the clan of the weavers, and noted, without express-ing any emotion, that she had come into the story not like other women, for anything personal to her own womanhood—for beauty, or high spirit, or temper, or faithfulness, or unfaithfulness—but simply because she was a fourth wife, a kind of curiosity, the back-wash of Mortimer Hehir's romances. The widow felt a remote sense of injustice in all this. She had said to herself that widows who had been fourth wives deserved more sympathy than widows who had been first wives, for the simple reason that fourth widows had never been, and could never be, first wives! The thought confused her a little, and she did not pursue it, in-stinctively feeling that if she did accept the conventional view of her con-dition she would only crystallise her widowhood into a grievance that nobody would try to understand, and which would, accordingly, be merely useless. And what was the good of it, anyhow? The widow smoothed her dark hair on each side of her head under her shawl.

She had no bitter and no sweet memories of the weaver. There was nothing that was even vivid in their marriage. She had no complaints to make of Mortimer Hehir. He had not come to her in any fiery love impulse. It was the marriage of an old man with a woman years younger. She had recognised him as an old man from first to last, a man who had already been thrice through a wedded experience, and her temperament, naturally calm, had met his half-stormy, half-petulant character, with-out suffering any sort of shock. The weaver had tried to keep up to the illusion of a perennial youth by dyeing his hair, and marrying one wife as soon as possible after another. The fourth wife had come to him late in life. She had a placid understanding that she was a mere flattery to the weaver's truculent egoism.

These thoughts, in some shape or other, occupied, without agitating, the mind of the widow as she passed, a dark shadowy figure, through streets that were clamorous in their quietudes, painful in their lack of all the purposes for which streets have ever been created. Her only emo-tion was one which she knew to be quite creditable to her situation: a sincere desire to see the weaver buried in the grave to which the respecta-bility of his family and the claims of his ancient house fully and fairly entitled him. The proceedings in Cloon na Morav had been painful, even tragical, to the widow. The weavers had always been great authorities and zealous guardians of the ancient burial place. This function had been traditional and voluntary with them. This was especially true of the last of them, Mortimer Hehir. He had been the greatest of all authorities on the burial places of the local clans. His knowledge was scientific. He had been the grand savant of Cloon na Morav. He had policed the place. Nay, he had been its tyrant. He had over and over again prevented terrible mistakes, complications that would have appalled those concerned if they were not beyond all such concerns. The widow of the weaver had often thought that in his day Mortimer Hehir had made his solicitation for the place a passion, unreasonable, almost violent. They said that all this had sprung from a fear that had come to him in his early youth that through some blunder an alien, an inferior, even an enemy, might come to find his way into the family burial place of the weavers. This fear had made him what he was. And in his later years his pride in the family burial place became a worship. His trade had gone down, and his pride had gone up. The burial ground in Cloon na Morav was the grand proof of his aristocracy. That was the coat-of-arms, the estate, the mark of high breeding, in the weavers. And now the man who had minded everybody's grave had not been able to mind his own. The widow thought that it was one of those injustices which blacken the reputation of the whole earth. She had felt, indeed, that she had been herself slack not to have learned long ago the lie of this precious grave from the weaver himself; and that he himself had been slack in not properly instructing her. But that was the way in this miserable world! In his passion for classifying the rights of others, the weaver had obscured his own. In his long and entirely successful battle in keeping alien corpses out of his own aristocratic pit he had made his own corpse alien to every pit in the place. The living high priest was the dead pariah of Cloon na Morav. Nobody could now tell except, perhaps, Malachi Roohan, the precise spot which he had defended against the blunders and confusions of the entire community, a dead-forgetting, indifferent, slack lot!

The widow tried to recall all she had ever heard the weaver say about his grave, in the hope of getting some clue, something that might be better than the scandalous scatter-brained efforts of Meehaul Lynskey and Cahir Bowes. She remembered various detached things that the weaver, a talkative man, had said about his grave. Fifty years ago since that grave had been last opened, and it had then been opened to receive the remains of his father. It had been thirty years previous to that since it had taken in his father, that is, the newly dead weaver's father's father. The weavers were a long-lived lot, and there were not many males of them; one son was as much as any one of them begot to pass to the succession of the loom; if there were daughters they scattered, and their graves were continents apart. The three wives of the late weaver were buried in the new cemetery. The widow remembered that the weaver seldom spoke of them, and took no interest in their resting place. His heart was in Cloon na Morav and the sweet, dry, deep aristocratic bed he had there in reserve for himself. But all his talk had been generalisation. He had never, that the widow could recall, said anything about the site, about the signs and measurements by which it could be identified. No doubt, it had been well known to many people, but they had all died. The weaver had never realised what their slipping away might mean to himself. The position of the grave was so intimate to his own mind that it never occurred to him that it could be obscure to the minds of others. Mortimer Hehir had passed away like some learned and solitary astronomer who had discovered a new star, hugging its beauty, its exclusiveness, its possession to his heart, secretly rejoicing how its name would travel with his own through heavenly space for all time—and forgetting to mark its place among the known stars grouped upon his charts. Meehaul Lynskey and Cahir Bowes might now be two seasoned astronomers of venal knowledge looking for the star which the weaver, in his' love for it, had let slip upon the mighty complexity of the skies.

The thing that is clearest to the mind of a man is often the thing that is most opaque to the intelligence of his bosom companion. A saint may walk the earth in the simple belief that all the world beholds his glowing halo; but all the world does not; if it did the saint would be stoned. And Mortimer Hehir had been as innocently proud of his grave as a saint might be ecstatic of his halo. He believed that when the time came he would get a royal funeral—a funeral fitting to the last of the line of great Cloon na Morav weavers. Instead of that they had no more idea of where to bury him than if he had been a wild tinker of the roads.

The widow, thinking of these things in her own mind, was about to sigh when, behind a window pane, she heard the sudden bubble of a roller canary's song. She had reached, half absent-mindedly, the home of Malachi Roohan, the cooper.

IV

The widow of the weaver approached the door of Malachi Roohan's house with an apologetic step, pawing the threshold a little in the manner of peasant women—a mannerism picked up from shy animals—before she stooped her head and made her entrance.

Malachi Roohan's daughter withdrew from the fire a face which reflected the passionate soul of a cook. The face cooled as the widow disclosed her business.

"I wouldn't put it a-past my father to have knowledge of the grave," said the daughter of the house, adding, "The Lord a mercy on the weaver."

She led the widow into the presence of the cooper.

The room was small and low and stuffy, indifferently served with light by an unopenable window. There was the smell of old age, of decay, in the room. It brought almost a sense of faintness to the widow. She had the feeling that God had made her to move in the ways of old men— passionate, cantankerous, egoistic old men, old men for whom she was always doing something, always remembering things, from missing buttons to lost graves.

Her eyes sought the bed of Malachi Roohan with an unemotional, quietly sceptical gaze. But she did not see anything of the cooper. The daughter leaned over the bed, listened attentively, and then very deftly turned down the clothes, revealing the bust of Malachi Roohan. The widow saw a weird face, not in the least pale or lined, but ruddy, with a mahogany bald head, a head upon which the leathery skin—for there did not seem any flesh—hardly concealed the stark outlines of the skull. From the chin there strayed a grey beard, the most shaken and whipped-looking beard that the widow had ever seen; it was, in truth, a very miracle of a beard, for one wondered how it had come there, and having come there, how it continued to hang on, for there did not seem anything to which it could claim natural allegiance. The widow was as much astonished at this beard as if she saw a plant growing in a pot without soil. Through its gaps she could see the leather of the skin, the bones of a neck, which was indeed a neck. Over this head and shoulders the cooper's daughter bent and shouted into a crumpled ear. A little spasm of life stirred in the mummy. A low, mumbling sound came from the bed. The widow was already beginning to feel that, perhaps, she had done wrong in remembering that the cooper was still extant. But what else could she have done? If the weaver was buried in a wrong grave she did not believe that his soul would ever rest in peace. And what could be more dreadful than a soul wandering on the howling winds of the earth? The weaver would grieve, even in heaven, for his grave, grieve, maybe, as bitterly as a saint might grieve who had lost his halo. He was a passionate old man, such an old man as would have a turbulent spirit. He would surely——. The widow stifled the thoughts that flashed into her mind. She was no more superstitious than the rest of us, but——. These vague and terrible fears, and her moderately decent sorrow, were alike banished from her mind by what followed. The mummy on the bed came to life. And, what was more, he did it himself. His daughter looked on with the air of one whose sensibilities had become blunted by a long familiarity with the various stages of his resurrections. The widow gathered that the daughter had been well drilled; she had been taught how to keep her place. She did not tender the slightest help to her father as he drew himself together on the bed. He turned over on his side, then on his back, and stealthily began to insinuate his shoulder blades on the pillow, pushing up his weird head to the streak of light from the little window. The widow had been so long accustomed to assist the aged that she made some involuntary movement of succor. Some half-seen gesture by the daughter, a sudden lifting of the eyelids on the face of the patient, disclosing a pair of blue eyes, gave the widow instinctive pause. She remained where she was, aloof like the daughter of the house. And as she caught the blue of Malachi Roohan's eyes it broke upon the widow that here in the essence of the cooper there lived a spirit of extraordinary independence. Here, surely, was a man who had been accustomed to look out for himself, who resented the attentions, even in these days of his flickering consciousness. Up he wormed his shoulder blades, his mahogany skull, his leathery skin, his sensational eyes, his miraculous beard, to the light and to the full view of the visitor. At a certain stage of the resurrection—when the cooper had drawn two long, stringy arms from under the clothes—his daughter made a drilled movement forward, seeking something in the bed. The widow saw her discover the end of a rope, and this she placed in the hands of her indomitable father. The other end of the rope was fastened to the iron rail of the foot of the bed. The sinews of the patient's hands clutched the rope, and slowly, wonderfully, magically, as it seemed to the widow, the cooper raised himself to a sitting posture in the bed. There was dead silence in the room except for the labored breathing of the performer. The eyes of the widow blinked. Yes, there was that ghost of a man hoisting himself up from the dead on a length of rope reversing the usual procedure. By that length of rope did the cooper hang on to life, and the effort of life. It represented his connection with the world, the world which had forgotten him, which marched past his window outside without knowing the stupendous thing that went on in his room. There he was, sitting up in the bed, restored to view by his own unaided efforts, holding his grip on life to the last. It cost him something to do it, but he did it. It would take him longer and longer every day to grip along that length of rope; he would fail ell by ell, sinking back to the last helplessness on his rope, descending into eternity as a vessel is lowered on a rope into a dark, deep well. But there he was now, still able for his work, unbeholding to all, self-dependent and alive, looking a little vaguely with his blue eyes at the widow of the weaver. His daughter swiftly and quietly propped pillows at his back, and she did it with the air of one who was allowed a special privilege.

"Nan!" called the old man to his daughter.

The widow, cool-tempered as she was, almost jumped on her feet. The voice was amazingly powerful. It was like a shout, filling the little room with vibrations. For four things did the widow ever after remember Malachi Roohan—for his rope, his blue eyes, his powerful voice, and his magic beard. They were thrown on the background of his skeleton in powerful relief.

"Yes, father," his daughter replied, shouting into his ear. He was apparently very deaf. This infirmity came upon the widow with a shock. The cooper was full of physical surprises.

"Who's this one?" the cooper shouted, looking at the widow. He had the belief that he was delivering an aside.

"Mrs. Hehir."

"Mrs. Hehir—what Hehir would she be?"

"The weaver's wife."

"The weaver? Is it Mortimer Hehir?"

"Yes, father."

"In troth I know her. She's Delia Morrissey, that married the weaver; Delia Morrissey that he followed to Munster, a raving lunatic with the dint of love."

A hot wave of embarrassment swept the widow. For a moment she thought the mind of the cooper was wandering. Then she remembered that the maiden name of the weaver's first wife was, indeed, Delia Morrissey. She had heard it, by chance, once or twice.

"Isn't it Delia Morrissey herself we have in it?" the old man asked.

The widow whispered to the daughter:

"Leave it so."

She shrank from a difficult discussion with the spectre on the bed on the family history of the weaver. A sense of shame came to her that she could be the wife to a contemporary of this astonishing old man holding on to the life rope.

"I'm out!" shouted Malachi Roohan, his blue eyes lighting suddenly. "Delia Morrissey died. She was one day eating her dinner and a bone stuck in her throat. The weaver clapped her on the back, but it was all to no good. She choked to death before his eyes on the floor. I remember that. And the weaver himself near died of grief after. But he married secondly. Who's this he married secondly, Nan?"

Nan did not know. She turned to the widow for enlightenment. The widow moistened her lips. She had to concentrate her thoughts on a subject which, for her own peace of mind, she had habitually avoided. She hated genealogy. She said a little nervously:

"Sara MacCabe."

The cooper's daughter shouted the name into his ear.

"So you're Sally MacCabe, from Looscaun, the one Mortimer took off the blacksmith? Well, well, that was a great business surely, the pair of them hot-tempered men, and your own beauty going to their heads like strong drink."

He looked at the widow, a half-sceptical, half-admiring expression flickering across the leathery face. It was such a look as he might have given to Dergorvilla of Leinster, Deirdre of Uladh, or Helen of Troy.

The widow was not the notorious Sara MacCabe from Looscaun; that lady had been the second wife of the weaver. It was said they had led a stormy life, made up of passionate quarrels and partings, and still more passionate reconciliations. Sara MacCabe from Looscaun not having quite forgotten or wholly neglected the blacksmith after her marriage to the weaver. But the widow again only whispered to the cooper's daughter:

"Leave it so."

"What way is Mortimer keeping?" asked the old man.

"He's dead," replied the daughter.

The fingers of the old man quivered on the rope.

"Dead? Mortimer Hehir dead?" he cried. "What in the name of God happened him?"

Nan did not know what happened him. She knew that the widow would not mind, so, without waiting for a prompt, she replied:

"A weakness came over him, a sudden weakness."

"To think of a man being whipped off all of a sudden like that!" cried the cooper. "When that's the way it was with Mortimer Hehir what one of us can be sure at all? Nan, none of us is sure! To think of the weaver, with his heart as strong as a bull, going off in a little weakness! It's the treacherous world we live in, the treacherous world, surely. Never another yard of tweed will he put up on his old loom! Morty, Morty, you were a good companion, a great warrant to walk the hills, whistling the tunes, pleasant in your conversation and as broad-spoken as the Bible."

"Did you know the weaver well, father?" the daughter asked.

"Who better?" he replied. "Who drank more pints with him than what myself did? And indeed it's to his wake I'd be setting out, and it's under his coffin my shoulder would be going, if I wasn't confined to my rope."

He bowed his head for a few moments. The two women exchanged a quick, sympathetic glance.

The breathing of the old man was the breathing of one who slept. The head sank lower.

The widow said:

"You ought to make him lie down. He's tired."

The daughter made some movement of dissent; she was afraid to interfere. Maybe the cooper could be very violent if roused. After a time he raised his head again. He looked in a new mood. He was fresher, more wide-awake. His beard hung in wisps to the bedclothes.

"Ask him about the grave," the widow said.

The daughter hesitated a moment, and in that moment the cooper looked up as if he had heard, or partially heard. He said:

"If you wait a minute now I'll tell you what the weaver was." He stared for some seconds at the little window.

"Oh, we'll wait," said the daughter, and turning to the widow, added, "Won't we, Mrs. Hehir?"

"Indeed we will wait," said the widow.

"The weaver," said the old man suddenly, "was a dream."

He turned his head to the women to see how they had taken it.

"Maybe," said the daughter, with a little touch of laughter, "Maybe Mrs. Hehir would not give in to that."

The widow moved her hands uneasily under her shawl. She stared a little fearfully at the cooper. His blue eyes were clear as lake water over white sand.

"Whether she gives in to it, or whether she doesn't give in to it," said Malachi Roohan, "it's a dream Mortimer Hehir was. And his loom, and his shuttles, and his warping bars, and his bobbin, and the threads that he put upon the shifting racks, were all a dream. And the only thing he ever wove upon his loom was a dream."

The old man smacked his lips, his hard gums whacking. His daughter looked at him with her head a little to one side.

"And what's more," said the cooper, "every woman that ever came into his head, and every wife he married, was a dream. I'm telling you that, Nan, and I'm telling it to you of the weaver. His life was a dream, and his death is a dream. And his widow there is a dream. And all the world is a dream. Do you hear me, Nan, this world is all a dream?"

"I hear you very well, father," the daughter sang in a piercing voice.

The cooper raised his head with a jerk, and his beard swept forward, giving him an appearance of vivid energy. He spoke in a voice like a trumpet blast:

"And I'm a dream!"

He turned his blue eyes on the widow. An unnerving sensation came to her. The cooper was the most dreadful old man she had ever seen, and what he was saying sounded the most terrible thing she had ever listened to. He cried:

"The idiot laughing in the street, the King looking at his crown, the woman turning her head to the sound of a man's step, the bells ringing in the belfry, the man walking his land, the weaver at his loom, the cooper handling his barrel, the Pope stooping for his red slippers— they're all a dream. And I'll tell you why they're a dream: because this world was meant to be a dream."

"Father," said the daughter, "you're talking too much. You'll overreach yourself."

The old man gave himself a little pull on the rope. It was his gesture of energy, a demonstration of the fine fettle he was in. He said:

"You're saying that because you don't understand me."

"I understand you very well."

"You only think you do. Listen to me now, Nan. I want you to do something for me. You won't refuse me?"

"I will not refuse you, Father; you know very well I won't."

"You're a good daughter to me, surely, Nan. And do what I tell you now. Shut close your eyes. Shut them fast and tight. No fluttering of the lids now."

"Very well, Father."

The daughter closed her eyes, throwing up her face in the attitude of one blind. The widow was conscious of the woman's strong, rough features, something good-natured in the line of the large mouth. The old man watched the face of his daughter with excitement. He asked:

"What is it that you see now, Nan?"

"Nothing at all, Father."

"In troth you do. Keep them closed tight and you'll see it."

"I see nothing only——"

"Only what? Why don't you say it?"

"Only darkness, Father."

"And isn't that something to see? Isn't it easier to see darkness than to see light? Now, Nan, look into the darkness."

"I'm looking, Father."

"And think of something—anything at all—the stool before the kitchen fire outside."

"I'm thinking of it."

"And do you remember it?"

"I do well."

"And when you remember it what do you want to do—sit on it, maybe?"

"No, Father."

"And why wouldn't you want to sit on it?"

"Because—because I'd like to see it first, to make sure."

The old man gave a little crow of delight. He cried:

"There it is! You want to make sure that it is there, although you remember it well. And that is the way with everything in this world. People close their eyes and they are not sure of anything. They want to see it again before they believe. There is Nan, now, and she does not believe in the stool before the fire, the little stool she's looking at all her life, that her mother used to seat her on before the fire when she was a small child. She closes her eyes, and it is gone! And listen to me now, Nan—if you had a man of your own and you closed your eyes you wouldn't be too sure he was the man you remembered, and you'd want to open your eyes and look at him to make sure he was the man you knew before the lids dropped on your eyes. And if you had children about you and you turned your back and closed your eyes and tried to remember them you'd want to look at them to make sure. You'd be no more sure of them than you are now of the stool in the kitchen. One flash of the eyelids and everything in this world is gone."

"I'm telling you, Father, you're talking too much."

"I'm not talking half enough. Aren't we all uneasy about the world, the things in the world that we can only believe in while we're looking at them? From one season of our life to another haven't we a kind of belief that sometime we'll waken up and find everything different? Didn't you ever feel that, Nan? Didn't you think things would change, that the world would be a new place altogether, and that all that was going on around us was only a business that was doing us out of something else? We put up with it while the little hankering is nibbling at the butt of our hearts for the something else! All the men there be who believe that some day The Thing will happen, that they'll turn round the corner and waken up in the new great Street!"

"And sure," said the daughter, "maybe they are right, and maybe they will waken up."

The old man's body was shaken with a queer spasm of laughter. It began under the clothes on the bed, worked up his trunk, ran along his stringy arms, out into the rope, and the iron foot of the bed rattled. A look of extraordinarily malicious humor lit up the vivid face of the cooper. The widow beheld him with fascination, a growing sense of alarm. He might say anything. He might do anything. He might begin to sing some fearful song. He might leap out of bed.

"Nan," he said, "do you believe you'll swing round the corner and waken up?"

"Well," said Nan, hesitating a little, "I do."

The cooper gave a sort of peacock crow again. He cried:

"Och! Nan Roohan believes she'll waken up! Waken up from what? From a sleep and from a dream, from this world! Well, if you believe, that, Nan Roohan, it shows you know what's what. You know what the thing around you, called the world, is. And it's only dreamers who can hope to waken up—do you hear me, Nan; it's only dreamers who can hope to waken up."

"I hear you," said Nan.

"The world is only a dream, and a dream is nothing at all! We all want to waken up out of the great nothingness of this world."

"And, please God, we will," said Nan.

"You can tell all the world from me," said the cooper, "that it won't."

"And why won't we, Father?"

"Because," said the old man, "we ourselves are the dream. When we're over the dream is over with us. That's why."

"Father," said the daughter, her head again a little to one side, "you know a great deal."

"I know enough," said the cooper shortly.

"And maybe you could tell us something about the weaver's grave. Mrs. Hehir wants to know."

"And amn't I after telling you all about the weaver's grave? Amn't I telling you it is all a dream?"

"You never said that, Father. Indeed you never did."

"I said everything in this world is a dream, and the weaver's grave is in this world, below in Cloon na Morav."

"Where in Cloon na Morav? What part of it, Father? That is what Mrs. Hehir wants to know. Can you tell her?"

"I can tell her," said Malachi Roohan. "I was at his father's burial. I remember it above all burials, because that was the day the handsome girl, Honor Costello, fell over a grave and fainted. The sweat broke out on young Donohoe when he saw Honor Costello tumbling over the grave. Not a marry would he marry her after that, and he sworn to it by the kiss of her lips. 'I'll marry no woman that fell on a grave,' says Donohoe. 'She'd maybe have a child by me with turned-in eyes or a twisted limb.' So he married a farmer's daughter, and the same morning Honor Costello married a cattle drover. Very well, then. Donohoe's wife had no child at all. She was a barren woman. Do you hear me, Nan? A barren woman she was. And such childer as Honor Costello had by the drover! Yellow hair they had, heavy as seaweed, the skin of them clear as the wind, and limbs as clean as a whistle! It was said the drover was of the blood of the Danes, and it broke out in Honor Costello's family!"

"Maybe," said the daughter, "they were Vikings."

"What are you saying?" cried the old man testily. "Ain't I telling you it's Danes they were. Did anyone ever hear a greater miracle?"

"No one ever did," said the daughter, and both women clicked their tongues to express sympathetic wonder at the tale.

"And I'll tell you what saved Honor Costello," said the cooper. "When she fell in Cloon na Morav she turned her cloak inside out."

"What about the weaver's grave, Father? Mrs. Hehir wants to know."

The old man looked at the widow; his blue eyes searched her face and her figure; the expression of satirical admiration flashed over his features. The nostrils of the nose twitched. He said:

"So that's the end of the story! Sally MacCabe, the blacksmith's favorite, wants to know where she'll sink the weaver out of sight! Great battles were fought in Looscaun over Sally MacCabe! The weaver thought his heart would burst, and the blacksmith damned his soul for the sake of Sally MacCabe's idle hours."

"Father," said the daughter of the house, "let the dead rest."

"Ay," said Malachi Roohan, "let the foolish dead rest. The dream of Looscaun is over. And now the pale woman is looking for the black weaver's grave. Well, good luck to her!"

The cooper was taken with another spasm of grotesque laughter. The only difference was that this time it began by the rattling of the rail of the bed, travelled along the rope, down his stringy arms, dying out somewhere in his legs in the bed. He smacked his lips, a peculiar harsh sound, as if there was not much meat to it.

"Do I know where Mortimer Hehir's grave is?" he said ruminatingly. "Do I know where me rope is?"

"Where is it, then?" his daughter asked. Her patience was great.

"I'll tell you that," said the cooper. "It's under the elm tree of Cloon na Morav. That's where it is surely. There was never a weaver yet that did not find rest under the elm tree of Cloon na Morav. There they all went as surely as the buds came on the branches. Let Sally MacCabe put poor Morty there; let her give him a tear or two in memory of the days that his heart was ready to burst for her, and believe you me no ghost will ever haunt her. No dead man ever yet came back to look upon a woman!"

A furtive sigh escaped the widow. With her handkerchief she wiped a little perspiration from both sides of her nose. The old man wagged his head sympathetically. He thought she was the long dead Sally MacCabe lamenting the weaver! The widow's emotion arose from relief that the mystery of the grave had at last been cleared up. Yet her dealings with old men had taught her caution. Quite suddenly the memory of the handsome dark face of the grave-digger who had followed her to the stile came back to her. She remembered that he said something about "the exact position of the grave." The widow prompted yet another question:

"What position under the elm tree?"

The old man listened to the question; a strained look came into his face.

"Position of what?" he asked.

"Of the grave."

"Of what grave?"

"The weaver's grave."

Another spasm seized the old frame, but this time it came from no aged merriment. It gripped his skeleton and shook it. It was as if some invisible powerful hand had suddenly taken him by the back of the neck and shaken him. His knuckles rattled on the rope. They had an appalling sound. A horrible feeling came to the widow that the cooper would fall to pieces like a bag of bones. He turned his face to his daughter. Great tears had welled into the blue eyes, giving them an appearance of childish petulance, then of acute suffering.

"What are you talking to me of graves for?" he asked, and the powerful voice broke. "Why will you be tormenting me like this? It's not going to die I am, is it? Is it going to die I am, Nan?"

The daughter bent over him as she might bend over a child. She said:

"Indeed, there's great fear of you. Lie down and rest yourself. Fatigued out and out you are."

The grip slowly slackened on the rope. He sank back, quite helpless, a little whimper breaking from him. The daughter stooped lower, reaching for a pillow that had fallen in by the wall. A sudden sharp snarl sounded from the bed, and it dropped from her hand.

"Don't touch me!" the cooper cried. The voice was again restored, powerful in its command. And to the amazement of the widow she saw him again grip along the rope and rise in the bed.

"Amn't I tired telling you not to touch me?" he cried. "Have I any business talking to you at all? Is it gone my authority is in this house?"

He glared at his daughter, his eyes red with anger, like a dog crouching in his kennel, and the daughter stepped back, a wry smile on her large mouth. The widow stepped back with her, and for a moment he held the women with their backs to the wall by his angry red eyes. Another growl and the cooper sank back inch by inch on the rope. In all her experience of old men the widow had never seen anything like this old man; his resurrections and his collapse. When he was quite down the daughter gingerly put the clothes over his shoulders and then beckoned the widow out of the room.

The widow left the house of Malachi Roohan, the cooper, with the feeling that she had discovered the grave of an old man by almost killing another.

V

The widow walked along the streets, outwardly calm, inwardly confused. Her first thought was "the day is going on me!" There were many things still to be done at home; she remembered the weaver lying there, quiet at last, the candles lighting about him, the brown habit over him, a crucifix in his hands—everything as it should be. It seemed ages to the widow since he had really fallen ill. He was very exacting and peevish all that time. His death agony had been protracted, almost melodramatically violent. A few times the widow had nearly run out of the house, leaving the weaver to fight the death battle alone. But her commonsense, her good nerves, and her religious convictions had stood to her, and when she put the pennies on the weaver's eyes she was glad she had done her duty to the last. She was glad now that she had taken the search for the grave out of the hands of Meehaul Lynskey and Cahir Bowes; Malachi Roohan had been a sight, and she would never forget him, but he had known what nobody else knew. The widow, as she ascended a little upward sweep of the road to Cloon na Morav, noted that the sky beyond it was more vivid, a red band of light having struck across the grey blue, just on the horizon. Up against this red background was the dark outline of landscape, and especially Cloon na Morav. She kept her eyes upon it as she drew nearer. Objects that were vague on the landscape began to bulk up with more distinction.

She noted the back wall of Cloon na Morav, its green lichen more vivid under the red patch of the skyline. And presently, above the green wall, black against the vivid sky, she saw elevated the bulk of one of the black cockroaches. On it were perched two drab figures, so grotesque, so still, that they seemed part of the thing itself. One figure was sloping out from the end of the tombstone so curiously that for a moment the widow thought it was a man who had reached down from the table to see what was under it. At the other end of the table was a slender warped figure, and as the widow gazed upon it she saw a sign of animation. The head and face, bleak in their outlines, were raised up in a gesture of despair. The face was turned flush against the sky, so much so that the widow's eyes instinctively sought the sky too. Above the slash of red, in the west, was a single star, flashing so briskly and so freshly that it might have never shone before. For all the widow knew, it might have been a young star frolicking in the heavens with all the joy of youth. Was that, she wondered, at what the old man, Meehaul Lynskey, was gazing. He was very, very old, and the star was very, very young! Was there some protest in the gesture of the head he raised to that thing in the sky; was there some mockery in the sparkle of the thing of the sky for the face of the man? Why should a star be always young, a man aged so soon? Should not a man be greater than a star? Was it this Meehaul Lynskey was thinking? The widow could not say, but something in the thing awed her. She had the sensation of one who surprises a man in some act that lifts him above the commonplaces of existence. It was as if Meehaul Lynskey were discovered prostrate before some altar, in the throes of a religious agony. Old men were, the widow felt, very, very strange, and she did not know that she would ever understand them. As she looked at the bleak head of Meehaul Lynskey, up against the vivid patch of the sky, she wondered if there could really be something in that head which would make him as great as a star, immortal as a star? Suddenly Meehaul Lynskey made a movement. The widow saw it quite distinctly. She saw the arm raised, the hand go out, with its crooked fingers, in one, two, three quick, short taps in the direction of the star. The widow stood to watch, and the gesture was so familiar, so homely, so personal, that it was quite understandable to her. She knew then that Meehaul Lynskey was not thinking of any great things at all. He was only a nailer! And seeing the Evening Star sparkle in the sky he had only thought of his workshop, of the bellows, the irons, the fire, the sparks, and the glowing iron which might be made into a nail while it was hot! He had in imagination seized a hammer and made a blow across interstellar space at Venus! All the beauty and youth of the star frolicking on the pale sky above the slash of vivid redness had only suggested to him the making of yet another nail! If Meehaul Lynskey could push up his scarred yellow face among the stars of the sky he would only see in them the sparks of his little smithy.

Cahir Bowes was, the widow thought, looking down at the earth, from the other end of the tombstone, to see if there were any hard things there which he could smash up. The old men had their backs turned upon each other. Very likely they had another discussion since, which ended in this attitude of mutual contempt. The widow was conscious again of the unreasonableness of old men, but not much resentful of it. She was too long accustomed to them to have any great sense of revolt. Her emotion, if it could be called an emotion, was a settled, dull toleration of all their little bigotries.

She put her hand on the stile for the second time that day, and again raised her palely sad face over the graveyard of Cloon na Morav. As she did so she had the most extraordinary experience of the whole day's sensations. It was such a sensation as gave her at once a wonderful sense of the reality and the unreality of life. She paused on the stile, and had a clear insight into something that had up to this moment been obscure. And no sooner had the thing become definite and clear than a sense of the wonder of life came to her. It was all very like the dream Malachi Roohan had talked about.

In the pale grass, under the vivid colors of the sky, the two grave-diggers were lying on their backs, staring silently up at the heavens. The widow looked at them as she paused on the stile. Her thoughts of these men had been indifferent, subconscious, up to this instant. They were handsome young men. Perhaps if there had been only one of them the widow would have been more attentive. The dark handsomeness did not seem the same thing when repeated. Their beauty, if one could call it beauty, had been collective, the beauty of flowers, of dark, velvety pansies, the distinctive marks of one faithfully duplicated on the other. The good looks of one had, to the mind of the widow, somehow nullified the good looks of the other. There was too much borrowing of Peter to pay Paul in their well-favored features. The first grave-digger spoiled the illusion of individuality in the second grave-digger. The widow had not thought so, but she would have agreed if anybody whispered to her that a good-looking man who wanted to win favor with a woman should never have so complete a twin brother. It would be possible for a woman to part tenderly with a man, and, if she met his image and likeness around the corner, knock him down. There is nothing more powerful, but nothing more delicate in life than the valves of individuality. To create the impression that humanity was a thing which could be turned out like a coinage would be to ruin the whole illusion of life. The twin grave-diggers had created some sort of such impression, vague, and not very insistent, in the mind of the widow, and it had made her lose any special interest in them. Now, however, as she hesitated on the stile, all this was swept from her mind at a stroke. That most subtle and powerful of all things, personality, sprang silently from the twins and made them, to the mind of the widow, things as far apart as the poles. The two men lay at length, and exactly the same length and bulk, in the long, grey grass. But, as the widow looked upon them, one twin seemed conscious of her presence, while the other continued his absorption in the heavens above. The supreme twin turned his head, and his soft, velvety brown eyes met the eyes of the widow. There was welcome in the man's eyes. The widow read that welcome as plainly as if he had spoken his thoughts. The next moment he had sprung to his feet, smiling. He took a few steps forward, then, self-conscious, pulled up. If he had only jumped up and smiled the widow would have understood. But those few eager steps forward and then that stock stillness! The other twin rose reluctantly, and as he did so the widow was conscious of even physical differences in the brothers. The eyes were not the same. No such velvety soft lights were in the eyes of the second one. He was more sheepish. He was more phlegmatic. He was only a plagiarism of the original man! The widow wondered how she had not seen all this before. The resemblance between the twins was only skin deep. The two old men, at the moment the second twin rose, detached themselves slowly, almost painfully, from their tombstone, and all moved forward to meet the widow. The widow, collecting her thoughts, piloted her skirts modestly about her legs as she got down from the narrow stonework of the stile and stumbled into the contrariness of Cloon na Morav. A wild sense of satisfaction swept her that she had come back the bearer of useful information.

"Well," said Meehaul Lynskey, "did you see Malachi Roohan?" The widow looked at his scorched, sceptical, yellow face, and said:

"I did."

"Had he any word for us?"

"He had. He remembers the place of the weaver's grave." The widow looked a little vaguely about Cloon na Morav.

"What does he say?"

"He says it's under the elm tree."

There was silence. The stone-breaker swung about on his legs, his head making a semi-circular movement over the ground, and his sharp eyes were turned upward, as if he were searching the heavens for an elm tree. The nailer dropped his underjaw and stared tensely across the ground, blankly, patiently, like a fisherman on the edge of the shore gazing over an empty sea. The grave-digger turned his head away shyly, like a boy, as if he did not want to see the confusion of the widow; the man was full of the most delicate mannerisms. The other grave-digger settled into a stolid attitude, then the skin bunched up about his brown eyes in puckers of humor. A miserable feeling swept the widow. She had the feeling that she stood on the verge of some collapse.

"Under the elm tree," mumbled the stone-breaker.

"That's what he said," added the widow. "Under the elm tree of Cloon na Morav."

"Well," said Cahir Bowes, "when you find the elm tree you'll find the grave."

The widow did not know what an elm tree was. Nothing had ever happened in life as she knew it to render any special knowledge of trees profitable, and therefore desirable. Trees were good; they made nice firing when chopped up; timber, and all that was fashioned out of timber, came from trees. This knowledge the widow had accepted as she had accepted all the other remote phenomena of the world into which she had been born. But that trees should have distinctive names, that they should have family relationships, seemed to the mind of the widow only an unnecessary complication of the affairs of the universe. What good was it? She could understand calling fruit trees fruit trees and all other kinds simply trees. But that one should be an elm and another an ash, that there should be name after name, species after species, giving them peculiarities and personalities, was one of the things that the widow did not like. And at this moment, when the elm tree of Malachi Roohan had raised a fresh problem in Cloon na Morav, the likeness of old men to old trees—their crankiness, their complexity, their angles, their very barks, bulges, gnarled twistiness, and kinks—was very close, and brought a sense of oppression to the sorely-tried brain of the widow.

"Under the elm tree," repeated Meehaul Lynskey. "The elm tree of Cloon na Morav." He broke into an aged cackle of a laugh. "If I was any good at all at making a rhyme I'd make one about that elm tree, devil a other but I would."

The widow looked around Cloon na Morav, and her eyes, for the first time in her life, were consciously searching for trees. If there were numerous trees there she could understand how easy it might be for Malachi Roohan to make a mistake. He might have mistaken some other sort of tree for an elm—the widow felt that there must be plenty of other trees very like an elm. In fact, she reasoned that other trees, do their best, could not help looking like an elm. There must be thousands and millions of people like herself in the world who pass through life in the belief that a certain kind of tree was an elm when, in reality, it may be an ash or an oak or a chestnut or a beech, or even a poplar, a birch, or a yew. Malachi Roohan was never likely to allow anybody to amend his knowledge of an elm tree. He would let go his rope in the belief that there was an elm tree in Cloon na Morav, and that under it was the weaver's grave—that is, if Malachi Roohan had not, in some ghastly aged kink, invented the thing. The widow, not sharply, but still with an appreciation of the thing, grasped that a dispute about trees would be the very sort of dispute in which Meehaul Lynskey and Cahir Bowes would, like the very old men that they were, have revelled. Under the impulse of the message she had brought from the cooper they would have launched out into another powerful struggle from tree to tree in Cloon na Morav; they would again have strewn the place with the corpses of slain arguments, and in the net result they would not have been able to establish anything either about elm trees or about the weaver's grave. The slow, sad gaze of the widow for trees in Cloon na Morav brought to her, in these circumstances, both pain and relief. It was a relief that Meehaul Lynskey and Cahir Bowes could not challenge each other to a battle of trees; it was a pain that the tree of Malachi Roohan was nowhere in sight. The widow could see for herself that there was not any sort of a tree in Cloon na Morav. The ground was enclosed upon three sides by walls, on the fourth by a hedge of quicks. Not even old men could transform a hedge into an elm tree. Neither could they make the few struggling briars clinging about the railings of the sepulchres into anything except briars. The elm tree of Malachi Roohan was now non-existent. Nobody would ever know whether it had or had not ever existed. The widow would as soon give the soul of the weaver to the howling winds of the world as go back and interview the cooper again on the subject.

"Old Malachi Roohan," said Cahir Bowes with tolerant decision, "is doting."

"The nearest elm tree I know," said Meehaul Lynskey, "is half a mile away."

"The one above at Carragh?" questioned Cahir Bowes.

"Ay, beside the mill."

No more was to be said. The riddle of the weaver's grave was still the riddle of the weaver's grave. Cloon na Morav kept its secret. But, nevertheless, the weaver would have to be buried. He could not be housed indefinitely. Taking courage from all the harrowing aspects of the deadlock, Meehaul Lynskey went back, plump and courageously to his original allegiance.

"The grave of the weaver is there," he said, and he struck out his hooked fingers in the direction of the disturbance of the sod which the grave-diggers had made under pressure of his earlier enthusiasm.

Cahir Bowes turned on him with a withering, quavering glance.

"Aren't you afraid that God would strike you where you stand?" he demanded.

"I'm not—not a bit afraid," said Meehaul Lynskey. "It's the weaver's grave."

"You say that," cried Cahir Bowes, "after what we all saw and what we all heard?"

"I do," said Meehaul Lynskey, stoutly. He wiped his lips with the palm of his hand, and launched out into one of his arguments, arguments, as usual, packed with particulars.

"I saw the weaver's father lowered in that place. And I'll tell you, what's more, it was Father Owen MacCarthy that read over him, he a young red-haired curate in this place at the time, long before ever he became parish priest of Benelog. There was I, standing in this exact spot, a young man, too, with a light moustache, holding me hat in me hand, and there one side of me—maybe five yards from the marble stone of the Keernahans—was Patsy Curtin that drank himself to death after, and on the other side of me was Honor Costello, that fell on the grave and married the cattle drover, a big, loose-shouldered Dane."

Patiently, half absent-mindedly, listening to the renewal of the dispute, the widow remembered the words of Malachi Roohan, and his story of Honor Costello, who fell on the grave over fifty years ago. What memories these old men had! How unreliable they were, and yet flashing out astounding corroborations of each other. Maybe there was something in what Meehaul Lynskey was saying. Maybe—but the widow checked her thoughts. What was the use of it all? This grave could not be the weaver's grave; it had been grimly demonstrated to them all that it was full of stout coffins. The widow, with a gesture of agitation, smoothed her hair down the gentle slope of her head under the shawl. As she did so her eyes caught the eyes of the grave-digger; he was looking at her! He withdrew his eyes at once, and began to twitch the ends of his dark moustache with his fingers.

"If," said Cahir Bowes, "this be the grave of the weaver, what's Julia Rafferty doing in it? Answer me that, Meehaul Lynskey."

"I don't know what's she doing in it, and what's more, I don't care. And believe you my word, many a queer thing happened in Cloon na Morav that had no right to happen in it. Julia Rafferty, maybe, isn't the only one that is where she had no right to be."

"Maybe she isn't," said Cahir Bowes, "but it's there she is, anyhow, and I'm thinking it's there she's likely to stay."

"If she's in the weaver's grave," cried Meehaul Lynskey, "what I say is, out with her!"

"Very well, then, Meehaul Lynskey. Let you yourself be the powerful man to deal with Julia Rafferty. But remember this, and remember it's my word, that touch one bone in this place and you touch all."

"No fear at all have I to right a wrong. I'm no backslider when it comes to justice, and justice I'll see done among the living and the dead."

"Go ahead, then, me hearty fellow. If Julia herself is in the wrong place somebody else must be in her own place, and you'll be following one rightment with another wrongment until in the end you'll go mad with the tangle of dead men's wrongs. That's the end that's in store for you, Meehaul Lynskey."

Meehaul Lynskey spat on his fist and struck out with the hooked fingers. His blood was up.

"That I may be as dead as my father!" he began in a traditional oath, and at that Cahir Bowes gave a little cry and raised his stick with a battle flourish. They went up and down the dips of the ground, rising and falling on the waves of their anger, and the widow stood where she was, miserable and downhearted, her feet growing stone cold from the chilly dampness of the ground. The twin, who did not now count, took out his pipe and lit it, looking at the old men with a stolid gaze. The twin who now counted walked uneasily away, bit an end off a chunk of tobacco, and came to stand in the ground in a line with the widow, looking on with her several feet away; but again the widow was conscious of the man's growing sympathy.

"They're a nice pair of boyos, them two old lads," he remarked to the widow. He turned his head to her. He was very handsome.

"Do you think they will find it?" she asked. Her voice was a little nervous, and the man shifted on his feet, nervously responsive.

"It's hard to say," he said. "You'd never know what to think. Two old lads, the like of them, do be very tricky."

"God grant they'll get it," said the widow.

"God grant," said the grave-digger.

But they didn't. They only got exhausted as before, wheezing and coughing, and glaring at each other as they sat down on two mounds.

The grave-digger turned to the widow.

She was aware of the nice warmth of his brown eyes.

"Are you waking the weaver again tonight?" he asked.

"I am," said the widow.

"Well, maybe some person—some old man or woman from the country—may turn up and be able to tell where the grave is. You could make inquiries."

"Yes," said the widow, but without any enthusiasm, "I could make inquiries."

The grave-digger hesitated for a moment, and said more sympathetically, "We could all, maybe, make inquiries." There was a softer personal note, a note of adventure, in the voice.

The widow turned her head to the man and smiled at him quite frankly.

"I'm beholding to you," she said and then added with a little wounded sigh, "Everyone is very good to me."

The grave-digger twirled the ends of his moustache.

Cahir Bowes, who had heard, rose from his mound and said briskly, "I'll agree to leave it at that." His air was that of one who had made an extraordinary personal sacrifice. What he was really thinking was that he would have another great day of it with Meehaul Lynskey in Cloon na Morav tomorrow. He'd show that oul' fellow, Lynskey, what stuff Boweses were made of.

"And I'm not against it," said Meehaul Lynskey. He took the tone of one who was never to be outdone in magnanimity. He was also thinking of another day of effort tomorrow, a day that would, please God, show the Boweses what the Lynskeys were like.

With that the party came straggling out of Cloon na Morav, the two old men first, the widow next, the grave-diggers waiting to put on their coats and light their pipes.

There was a little upward slope on the road to the town, and as the two old men took it the widow thought they looked very spent after their day. She wondered if Cahir Bowes would ever be able for that hill. She would give him a glass of whiskey at home, if there was any left in the bottle. Of the two, and as limp and slack as his body looked, Meehaul Lynskey appeared the better able for the hill. They walked together, that is to say, abreast, but they kept almost the width of the road between each other, as if this gulf expressed the breach of friendship between them on the head of the dispute about the weaver's grave. They had been making liars of each other all day, and they would, please God, make liars of each other all day tomorrow. The widow, understanding the meaning of this hostility, had a faint sense of amusement at the contrariness of old men. How could she tell what was passing in the head which Cahir Bowes hung, like a fuchsia drop, over the road? How could she know of the strange rise and fall of the thoughts, the little frets, the tempers, the faint humors, which chased each other there? Nobody— not even Cahir Bowes himself—could account for them. All the widow knew was that Cahir Bowes stood suddenly on the road. Something had happened in his brain, some old memory cell long dormant had become nascent, had a stir, a pulse, a flicker of warmth, of activity, and swiftly as a flash of lightning in the sky, a glow of lucidity lit up his memory. It was as if a searchlight had suddenly flooded the dark corners of his brain. The immediate physical effect on Cahir Bowes was to cause him to stand stark still on the road, Meehaul Lynskey going ahead without him. The widow saw Cahir Bowes pivot on his heels, his head, at the end of the horizontal body, swinging round like the movement of a hand on a runaway clock. Instead of pointing up the hill homeward the head pointed down the hill and back to Cloon na Morav. There followed the most extraordinary movements—shufflings, gyrations—that the widow had ever seen. Cahir Bowes wanted to run like mad away down the road. That was plain. And Cahir Bowes believed that he was running like mad away down the road. That was also evident. But what he actually did was to make little jumps on his feet, his stick rattling the ground in front, and each jump did not bring him an inch of ground. He would have gone more rapidly in his normal shuffle. His efforts were like a terrible parody on the springs of a kangaroo. And Cahir Bowes, in a voice that was now more a scream than a cackle, was calling out unintelligible things. The widow, looking at him, paused in wonder, then over her face there came a relaxation, a color, her eyes warmed, her expression lost its settled pensiveness, and all her body was shaken with uncontrollable laughter. Cahir Bowes passed her on the road in his fantastic leaps, his abortive buck-jumps, screaming and cracking his stick on the ground, his left hand still gripped tightly on the small of his back behind, a powerful brake on the small of his back.

Meehaul Lynskey turned back and his face was shaken with an aged emotion as he looked after the stone-breaker. Then he removed his hat and blessed himself.

"The cross of Christ between us and harm," he exclaimed. "Old Cahir Bowes has gone off his head at last. I thought there was something up with him all day. It was easily known there was something ugly working in his mind."

The widow controlled her laughter and checked herself, making the sign of the Cross on her forehead, too. She said:

"God forgive me for laughing and the weaver with the habit but fresh upon him."

The grave-digger who counted was coming out somewhat eagerly over the stile, but Cahir Bowes, flourishing his stick, beat him back again and then himself re-entered Cloon na Morav. He stumbled over the grass, now rising on a mound, now disappearing altogether in a dip of the ground, travelling in a giddy course like a hooker in a storm; again, for a long time, he remained submerged, showing, however, the eternal stick, his periscope, his indication to the world that he was about his business. In a level piece of ground, marked by stones with large mottled white marks upon them, he settled and cried out to all, and calling God to witness, that this surely was the weaver's grave. There was scepticism, hesitation, on the part of the grave-diggers, but after some parley, and because Cahir Bowes was so passionate, vehement, crying and shouting, dribbling water from the mouth, showing his yellow teeth, pouring sweat on his forehead, quivering on his legs, they began to dig carefully in the spot. The widow, at this, re-arranged the shawl on her head and entered Cloon na Morav, conscious, as she shuffled over the stile, that a pair of warm brown eyes were, for a moment, upon her movements and then withdrawn. She stood a little way back from the digging and waited the result with a slightly more accelerated beating of the heart. The twins looked as if they were ready to strike something unexpected at any moment, digging carefully, and Cahir Bowes hung over the place, cackling and crowing, urging the men to swifter work. The earth sang up out of the ground, dark and rich in color, gleaming like gold, in the deepening twilight in the place. Two feet, three feet, four feet of earth came up, the spades pushing through the earth in regular and powerful pushes, and still the coast was clear. Cahir Bowes trembled with excitement on his stick. Five feet of a pit yawned in the ancient ground. The spade work ceased. One of the grave-diggers looked up at Cahir Bowes and said:

"You hit the weaver's grave this time right enough. Not another grave in the place could be as free as this."

The widow sighed a quick little sigh and looked at the face of the other grave-digger, hesitated, then allowed a remote smile of thankfulness to flit across her palely sad face. The eyes of the man wandered away over the darkening spaces of Cloon na Morav.

"I got the weaver's grave surely," cried Cahir Bowes, his old face full of a weird animation. If he had found the Philosopher's Stone he would only have broken it. But to find the weaver's grave was an accomplishment that would help him into a wisdom before which all his world would bow. He looked around triumphantly and said:

"Where is Meehaul Lynskey now; what will the people be saying at all about his attack on Julia Rafferty's grave? Julia will haunt him, and I'd sooner have anyone at all haunting me than the ghost of Julia Rafferty. Where is Meehaul Lynskey now? Is it ashamed to show his liary face he is? And what talk had Malachi Roohan about an elm tree? Elm tree, indeed! If it's trees that is troubling him now let him climb up on one of them and hang himself from it with his rope! Where is that old fellow, Meehaul Lynskey, and his rotten head? Where is he, I say? Let him come in here now to Cloon na Morav until I be showing him the weaver's grave, five feet down and not a rib or a knuckle in it, as clean and beautiful as the weaver ever wished it. Come in here, Meehaul Lynskey, until I hear the lies panting again in your yellow throat."

He went in his extraordinary movement over the ground, making for the stile all the while talking.

Meehaul Lynskey had crouched behind the wall outside when Cahir Bowes led the diggers to the new site, his old face twisted in an attentive, almost agonising emotion. He stood peeping over the wall, saying to himself:

"Whisht, will you! Don't mind that old madman. He hasn't it at all. I'm telling you he hasn't it. Whisht, will you! Let him dig away. They'll hit something in a minute. They'll level him when they find out. His brain has turned. Whisht, now, will you, and I'll have that rambling old lunatic, Cahir Bowes, in a minute. I'll leap in on him. I'll charge him before the world. I'll show him up. I'll take the gab out of him. I'll lacerate him. I'll lambaste him. Whisht, will you!"

But as the digging went on and the terrible cries of triumph arose inside Meehaul Lynskey's knees knocked together. His head bent level to the wall, yellow and grimacing, nerves twitching across it, a little yellow froth gathering at the corners of the mouth. When Cahir Bowes came beating for the stile Meehaul Lynskey rubbed one leg with the other, a little below the calf, and cried brokenly to himself:

"God in Heaven, he has it! He has the weaver's grave."

He turned about and slunk along in the shadow of the wall up the hill, panting and broken. By the time Cahir Bowes had reached the stile Meehaul Lynskey's figure was shadowily dipping down over the crest of the road. A sharp cry from Cahir Bowes caused him to shrink out of sight like a dog at whom a weapon had been thrown.

The eyes of the grave-digger who did not now count followed the figure of Cahir Bowes as he moved to the stile. He laughed a little in amusement, then wiped his brow. He came up out of the grave. He turned to the widow and said:

"We're down five feet. Isn't that enough in which to sink the weaver in? Are you satisfied?"

The man spoke to her without any pretence at fine feeling. He addressed her as a fourth wife should be addressed. The widow was conscious but unresentful of the man's manner. She regarded him calmly and without any resentment. On her part there was no resentment either, no hypocrisy, no make-believe. Her unemotional eyes followed his action as he stuck his spade into the loose mould on the ground. A cry from Cahir Bowes distracted the man, he laughed again, and before the widow could make a reply he said:

"Old Cahir is great value. Come down until we hear him handling the nailer."

He walked away down over the ground.

The widow was left alone with the other grave-digger. He drew himself up out of the pit with a sinuous movement of the body which the widow noted. He stood without a word beside the pile of heaving clay and looked across at the widow. She looked back at him and suddenly the silence became full of unspoken words, of flying, ringing emotions. The widow could see the dark green wall, above it the band of still deepening red, above that the still more pallid grey sky, and directly over the man's head the gay frolicking of the fresh star in the sky. Cloon na Morav was flooded with a deep, vague light. The widow scented the fresh wind about her, the cool fragrance of the earth, and yet a warmth that was strangely beautiful. The light of the man's dark eyes were visible in the shadow which hid his face. The pile of earth beside him was like a vague shape of miniature bronze mountains. He stood with a stillness which was tense and dramatic. The widow thought that the world was strange, the sky extraordinary, the man's head against the red sky a wonder, a poem, above it the sparkle of the great young star. The widow knew that they would be left together like this for one minute, a minute which would be as a flash and as eternity. And she knew now that sooner or later this man would come to her and that she would welcome him. Below at the stile the voice of Cahir Bowes was cackling in its aged notes. Beyond this the stillness was the stillness of heaven and earth. Suddenly a sense of faintness came to the widow. The whole place swooned before her eyes. Never was this world so strange, so like the dream that Malachi Roohan had talked about. A movement in the figure of the man beside the heap of bronze had come to her as a warning, a fear, and a delight. She moved herself a little in response, made a step backward. The next instant she saw the figure of the man spring across the open black mouth of the weaver's grave to her.

A faint sound escaped her and then his breath was hot on her face, his mouth on her lips.

Half a minute later Cahir Bowes came shuffling back, followed by the twin.

"I'll bone him yet," said Cahir Bowes. "Never you fear I'll make that old nailer face me. I'll show him up at the weaver's wake to night!"

The twin laughed behind him. He shook his head at his brother, who was standing a pace away from the widow. He said:

"Five feet."

He looked into the grave and then looked at the widow, saying: "Are you satisfied?"

There was silence for a second or two, and when she spoke the widow's voice was low but fresh, like the voice of a young girl. She said: "I'm satisfied."

ENGLAND TO AMERICA

By Margaret Prescott Montague

[The author of this story, one of the finest stories that have come
out of the tragic experiences of the World War, was born in 1878 at
White Sulphur Springs, West Virginia, and has lived there most of her
life, though at present she makes her home in Richmond, Virginia.
This story was selected as the O. Henry Memorial Prize Story for 1920.
Stories of other types and moods by the same author are: *Of Water
and the Spirit, Uncle Sam of Freedom Ridge, Deep Channel,* and *Up Eel
River.*

England to America was first published in the *Atlantic Monthly* (September, 1919), and is here reprinted by permission of the author.]

LORD, but English people are funny!
This was the perplexed mental ejaculation that young Lieutenant Skipworth Cary, of Virginia, found his thoughts constantly reiterating during his stay in Devonshire. Had he been, he wondered, a confiding fool, to accept so trustingly Chev Sherwood's suggestion that he spend a part of his leave, at least, at Bishopsthorpe, where Chev's people lived? But why should he have anticipated any difficulty here, in this very corner of England which had bred his own ancestors, when he had always hit it off so splendidly with his English comrades at the Front? Here, however, though they were all awfully kind—at least, he was sure they meant to be kind—something was always bringing him up short; something that he could not lay hold of, but which made him feel like a blind man groping in a strange place, or worse, like a bull in a china-shop. He was prepared enough to find differences in the American and English points of view. But this thing that baffled him did not seem to have to do with that; it was something deeper, something very definite, he was sure—and yet, what was it? The worst of it was that he had a curious feeling as if they were all—that is, Lady Sherwood and Gerald; not Sir Charles so much—protecting him from himself—keeping him from making breaks, as he phrased it. That hurt and annoyed him, and piqued his vanity. Was he a social blunderer, and weren't a Virginia gentleman's manners to be trusted in England without leading-strings?

He had been at the Front for several months with the Royal Flying Corps; and when his leave came, his Flight Commander, Captain Cheviot Sherwood, discovering that he meant to spend it in England where he hardly knew a soul, had said his people down in Devonshire would be jolly glad to have him stop with them; and Skipworth Cary, knowing that, if the circumstances had been reversed, his people down in Virginia would indeed have been jolly glad to entertain Captain Sherwood, had accepted unhesitatingly. The invitation had been seconded by a letter from Lady Sherwood,—Chev's mother,—and after a few days' sight-seeing in London, he had come down to Bishopsthorpe, very eager to know his friend's family, feeling as he did about Chev himself. "He's the finest man that ever went up in the air," he had written home; and to his own family's disgust, his letters had been far more full of Chev Sherwood than they had been of Skipworth Cary.

And now here he was, and he almost wished himself away—wished almost that he was back again at the Front, carrying on under Chev. There, at least, you knew what you were up against. The job might be hard enough, but it wasn't baffling and queer, with hidden undercurrents that you couldn't chart. It seemed to him that this baffling feeling of constraint had rushed to meet him on the very threshold of the drawing-room, when he made his first appearance.

As he entered, he had a sudden sensation that they had been awaiting him in a strained expectancy, and that, as he appeared, they adjusted unseen masks and began to play-act at something. "But English people don't play-act very well," he commented to himself, reviewing the scene afterwards.

Lady Sherwood had come forward and greeted him in a manner which would have been pleasant enough, if he had not, with quick sensitiveness, felt it to be forced. But perhaps that was English stiffness.

Then she had turned to her husband, who was standing staring into the fireplace, although, as it was June, there was no fire there to stare at.

"Charles," she said, "here is Lieutenant Cary"; and her voice had a certain note in it which at home Cary and his sister Nancy were in the habit of designating "mother-making-dad-mind-his-manners."

At her words the old man—and Cary was startled to see how old and broken he was—turned round and held out his hand. "How d' you do?" he said jerkily, "how d' you do?" and then turned abruptly back again to the fireplace.

"Hello! What's up? The old boy doesn't like me!" was Cary's quick, startled comment to himself.

He was so surprised by the look the other bent upon him, that he involuntarily glanced across to a long mirror to see if there was anything wrong with his uniform. But no, that appeared to be all right. It was himself, then—or his country; perhaps the old sport didn't fall for Americans.

"And here is Gerald," Lady Sherwood went on in her low remote voice, which somehow made the Virginian feel very far away.

It was with genuine pleasure, though with some surprise, that he turned to greet Gerald Sherwood, Chev's younger brother, who had been, tradition in the corps said, as gallant and daring a flyer as Chev himself, until he got his in the face five months ago.

"I'm mighty glad to meet you," he said eagerly, in his pleasant, muffled Southern voice, grasping the hand the other stretched out, and looking with deep respect at the scarred face and sightless eyes.

Gerald laughed a little, but it was a pleasant laugh, and his handclasp was friendly.

"That's real American, isn't it?" he said. "I ought to have remembered and said it first. Sorry."

Skipworth laughed too. "Well," he conceded, "we generally are glad to meet people in my country, and we don't care who says it first. But," he added, "I didn't think I'd have the luck to find you here."

He remembered that Chev had regretted that he probably wouldn't see Gerald, as the latter was at St. Dunstan's, where they were reëducating the blinded soldiers.

The other hesitated a moment, and then said rather awkwardly, "Oh, I'm just home for a little while; I only got here this morning, in fact."

Skipworth noted the hesitation. Did the old people get panicky at the thought of entertaining a wild man from Virginia, and send an S O S for Gerald, he wondered.

"We are so glad you could come to us," Lady Sherwood said rather hastily just then. And again he could not fail to note that she was prompting her husband.

The latter reluctantly turned round, and said, "Yes, yes, quite so. Welcome to Bishopsthorpe, my boy," as if his wife had pulled a string, and he responded mechanically, without quite knowing what he said. Then, as his eyes rested a moment on his guest, he looked as if he would like to bolt out of the room. He controlled himself, however, and, jerking round again to the fireplace, went on murmuring, "Yes, yes, yes," vaguely—just like the dormouse at the Mad Tea-Party, who went to sleep, saying, "Twinkle, twinkle, twinkle," Cary could not help thinking to himself.

But after all, it wasn't really funny; it was pathetic. Gosh, how doddering the poor old boy was! Skipworth wondered, with a sudden twist at his heart, if the war was playing the deuce with his home people, too. Was his own father going to pieces like this, and had his mother's gay vivacity fallen into that still remoteness of Lady Sherwood's? But of course not! The Carys hadn't suffered as the poor Sherwoods had, with their youngest son, Curtin, killed early in the war, and now Gerald knocked out so tragically. Lord, he thought, how they must all bank on Chev! And of course they would want to hear at once about him. "I left Chev as fit as anything, and he sent all sorts of messages," he reported thinking it more discreet to deliver Chev's messages thus vaguely than to repeat his actual care-free remark, which had been, "Oh, tell 'em I'm jolly as a tick."

But evidently there was something wrong with the words as they were, for instantly he was aware of that curious sense of withdrawal on their part. Hastily reviewing them, he decided that they had sounded too familiar from a stranger and a younger man like himself. He supposed he ought not to have spoken of Chev by his first name. Gee, what sticklers they were! Wouldn't his family—dad and mother and Nancy —have fairly lapped up any messages from him, even if they had been delivered a bit awkwardly? However, he added, as a concession to their point of view, "But of course you'll have had later news of Captain Sherwood."

To which, after a pause, Lady Sherwood responded, "Oh, yes," in that remote and colorless voice which might have meant anything or nothing.

At this point dinner was announced.

Lady Sherwood drew her husband away from the empty fireplace, and Gerald slipped his arm through the Virginian's, saying pleasantly, "I'm learning to carry on fairly well at St. Dunstan's, but I confess I still like to have a pilot."

To look at the tall young fellow beside him, whose scarred face was so reminiscent of Chev's untouched good looks, who had known all the immense freedom of the air, but who was now learning to carry on in the dark, moved Skipworth Cary to generous homage.

"You know my saying I'm glad to meet you isn't just American," he said half shyly, but warmly. "It's plain English, and the straight truth. I've wanted to meet you awfully. The oldsters are always holding up your glorious exploits to us newcomers. Withers never gets tired telling about that fight of yours with the four enemy planes. And besides," he rushed on eagerly, "I'm glad to have a chance to tell Chev's brother— Captain Sherwood's brother, I mean—what I think of him. Only as a matter of fact, I can't," he broke off with a laugh. "I can't put it exactly into words, but I tell you I'd follow that man straight into hell and out the other side—or go there alone if he told me to. He is the finest chap that ever flew."

And then he felt as if a cold douche had been flung in his face, for after a moment's pause, the other returned, "That's awfully good of you," in a voice so distant and formal that the Virginian could have kicked himself. What an ass he was to be so darned enthusiastic with an Englishman! He supposed it was bad form to show any pleasure over praise of a member of your family. Lord, if Chev got the V.C., he reckoned it would be awful to speak of it. Still, you would have thought Gerald might have stood for a little praise of him. But then, glancing sideways at his companion, he surprised on his face a look so strange and suffering that it came to him almost violently what it must be never to fly again; to be on the threshold of life, with endless days of blackness ahead. Good God! How cruel he had been to flaunt Chev in his face! In remorseful and hasty reparation he stumbled on, "But the old fellows are always having great discussions as to which was the best—you or your brother. Withers always maintains you were."

"Withers lies, then!" the other retorted. "I never touched Chev—never came within a mile of him, and never could have."

They reached the dinner-table with that, and young Cary found himself bewildered and uncomfortable. If Gerald hadn't liked praise of Chev, he had liked praise of himself even less, it seemed.

Dinner was not a success. The Virginian found that, if there was to be conversation, the burden of carrying it on was upon him, and gosh! they don't mind silences in this man's island, do they? he commented desperately to himself, thinking how different it was from America. Why, there they acted as if silence was an egg that had just been laid, and everyone had to cackle at once to cover it up. But here the talk constantly fell to the ground, and nobody but himself seemed concerned to pick it up. His attempt to praise Chev had not been successful, and he could understand their not wanting to hear about flying and the war before Gerald.

So at last, in desperation, he wandered off into descriptions of America, finding to his relief that he had struck the right note at last. They were glad to hear about the States, and Lady Sherwood inquired politely if the Indians still gave them much trouble; and when he assured her that in Virginia, except for the Pocahontas tribe, they were all pretty well subdued, she accepted his statement with complete innocency. And he was so delighted to find at last a subject to which they were evidently cordial, that he was quite carried away, and wound up by inviting them all to visit his family in Richmond, as soon as the war was over.

Gerald accepted at once, with enthusiasm; Lady Sherwood made polite murmurs, smiling at him in quite a warm and almost, indeed, maternal manner. Even Sir Charles, who had been staring at the food on his plate as if he did not quite know what to make of it, came to the surface long enough to mumble, "Yes, yes, very good idea. Countries must carry on together—What?"

But that was the only hit of the whole evening, and when the Virginian retired to his room, as he made an excuse to do early, he was so confused and depressed that he fell into an acute attack of homesickness.

Heavens, he thought, as he tumbled into bed, just suppose now, this was little old Richmond, Virginia, U.S.A., instead of being Bishopsthorpe, Avery Cross near Wick, and all the rest of it! And at that, he grinned to himself. England wasn't such an all-fired big country that you'd think they'd have to ticket themselves with addresses a yard long, for fear they'd get lost—now, would you? Well, anyway, suppose it was Richmond, and his train just pulling into the Byrd Street Station. He stretched out luxuriously, and let his mind picture the whole familiar scene. The wind was blowing right, so there was the mellow, homely smell of the tobacco in the streets, and plenty of people all along the way to hail him with outstretched hands and shouts of "Hey, Skip Cary, when did you get back?" "Welcome home, my boy!" "Well, will you look what the cat dragged in!" And so he came to his own front door-step, and walking straight in, surprised the whole family at breakfast; and yes—doggone it! if it wasn't Sunday, and they having waffles! And after that his obliging fancy bore him up Franklin Street, through Monroe Park, and so to Miss Sallie Berkeley's door. He was sound asleep before he reached it, but in his dreams, light as a little bird, she came flying down the broad stairway to meet him, and—

But when he waked next morning, he did not find himself in Virginia, but in Devonshire, where, to his unbounded embarrassment, a white housemaid was putting up his curtains and whispering something about his bath. And though he pretended profound slumber, he was well aware that people do not turn brick-red in their sleep. And the problem of what was the matter with the Sherwood family was still before him.

"They're playing a game," he told himself after a few days. "That is, Lady Sherwood and Gerald are—poor old Sir Charles can't make much of a stab at it. The game is to make me think they are awfully glad to have me, when in reality there's something about me, or something I do, that gets them on the raw."

He almost decided to make some excuse and get away; but after all, that was not easy. In English novels, he remembered, they always had a wire calling them to London; but darn it all! the Sherwoods knew mighty well there wasn't anyone in London who cared a hoot about him. The thing that got his goat most, he told himself, was that they apparently didn't like his friendship with Chev. Anyway they didn't seem to want him to talk about him; and whenever he tried to express his warm appreciation for all that the older man had done for him, he was instantly aware of a wall of reserve on their part, a holding of themselves aloof from him. That puzzled and hurt him, and put him on his dignity. He concluded that they thought it was cheeky of a youngster like him to think that a man like Chev could be his friend; and if that was the way they felt, he reckoned he'd jolly well better shut up about it.

But whatever it was that they didn't like about him, they most certainly did want him to have a good time. He and his pleasure appeared to be for the time being their chief consideration. And after the first day or so he began indeed to enjoy himself extremely. For one thing, he came to love the atmosphere of the old place and of the surrounding country, which he and Gerald explored together. He liked to think that ancestors of his own had been inheritors of these green lanes, and pleasant mellow stretches. Then, too, after the first few days, he could not help seeing that they really began to like him, which of course was reassuring, and tapped his own warm friendliness, which was always ready enough to be released. And, besides, he got by accident what he took to be a hint as to the trouble. He was passing the half-open door of Lady Sherwood's morning-room, when he heard Sir Charles' voice break out, "Good God, Elizabeth, I don't see how you stand it! When I see him so straight and fine-looking, and so untouched, beside our poor lad, and think—and think—"

Skipworth hurried out of earshot, but now he understood that look of aversion in the old man's eyes which had so startled him at first. Of course the poor old boy might easily hate the sight of him beside Gerald. With Gerald himself he really got along famously. He was a most delightful companion, full of anecdotes and history of the countryside, every foot of which he had apparently explored in the old days with Chev and the younger brother, Curtin. Yet even with Gerald, Cary sometimes felt that aloofness and reserve, and that older protective air that they all showed him. Take, for instance, that afternoon when they were lolling together on the grass in the park. The Virginian, running on in his usual eager manner, had plunged without thinking into an account of a particularly daring bit of flying on Chev's part, when suddenly he realized that Gerald had rolled over on the grass and buried his face in his arms, and interrupted himself awkwardly. "But of course," he said "he must have written home about it himself."

"No, or if he did, I didn't hear of it. Go on," Gerald said in a muffled voice.

A great rush of compassion and remorse overwhelmed the Virginian, and he burst out penitently, "What a brute I am! I'm always forgetting and running on about flying, when I know it must hurt like the very devil!"

The other drew a difficult breath. "Yes," he admitted, "what you say does hurt in a way—in a way you can't understand. But all the same I like to hear you. Go on about Chev."

So Skipworth went on and finished his account, winding up. "I don't believe there's another man in the service who could have pulled it off— but I tell you your brother's one in a million."

"Good God, don't I know it!" the other burst out. "We were all three the jolliest pals together," he got out presently in a choked voice, "Chev and the young un and I; and now—"

He did not finish, but Cary guessed his meaning. Now the young un, Curtin, was dead, and Gerald himself knocked out. But, heavens! the Virginian thought, did Gerald think Chev would go back on him now on account of his blindness? Well, you could everlastingly bet he wouldn't!

"Chev thinks the world and all of you!" he cried in eager defense of his friend's loyalty. "Lots of times when we're all awfully jolly together, he makes some excuse and goes off by himself; and Withers told me it was because he was so frightfully cut up about you. Withers said he told him once that he'd a lot rather have got it himself—so you can everlastingly bank on him!"

Gerald gave a terrible little gasp. "I—I knew he'd feel like that," he got out. "We've always cared such a lot for each other." And then he pressed his face harder than ever into the grass, and his long body quivered all over. But not for long. In a moment he took fierce hold on himself, muttering. "Well, one must carry on, whatever happens," and apologized disjointedly. "What a fearful fool you must think me! And—and this isn't very pippy for you, old chap." Presently, after that, he sat up, and said, brushing it all aside, "We're facing the old moat, aren't we? There's an interesting bit of tradition about it that I must tell you."

And there you were, Cary thought: no matter how much Gerald might be suffering from his misfortune, he must carry on just the same, and see that his visitor had a pleasant time. It made the Virginian feel like an outsider and very young, as if he were not old enough for them to show him their real feelings.

Another thing that he noticed was that they did not seem to want him to meet people. They never took him anywhere to call, and if visitors came to the house, they showed an almost panicky desire to get him out of the way. That again hurt his pride. What in heaven's name was the matter with him anyway!

However, on the last afternoon of his stay at Bishopsthorpe, he told himself with a rather rueful grin, that his manners must have improved a little, for they took him to tea at the rectory.

He was particularly glad to go there because, from certain jokes of Withers's who had known the Sherwoods since boyhood, he gathered that Chev and the rector's daughter were engaged. And just as he would have liked Chev to meet Sallie Berkeley, so he wanted to meet Miss Sybil Gaylord.

He had little hope of having a *tête-à-tête* with her, but as it fell out he did. They were all in the rectory garden, together, Gerald and the rector a little behind Miss Gaylord and himself, as they strolled down a long walk with high hedges bordering it. On the other side of the hedge Lady Sherwood and her hostess still sat at the tea-table, and then it was that Cary heard Mrs. Gaylord say distinctly, "I'm afraid the strain has been too much for you—you should have let us have him."

To which Lady Sherwood returned quickly, "Oh, no, that would have been impossible with—"

"Come—come this way—I must show you the view from the arbor," Miss Gaylord broke in breathlessly; and laying a hand on his arm, she turned him abruptly into a side path.

Glancing down at her, the Southerner could not but note that the overheard words referred to him, and he was so bewildered by the whole situation, that he burst out impulsively, "I say, what is the matter with me? Why do they find me so hard to put up with? Is it something I do—or don't they like Americans? Honestly, I wish you'd tell me."

She stood still at that, looking at him, her blue eyes full of distress and concern.

"Oh, I am so sorry," she cried. "They would be so sorry to have you think anything like that."

"But what is it?" he persisted. "Don't they like Americans?"

"Oh, no, it isn't that—Oh, quite the contrary!" she returned eagerly.

"Then it's something about me they don't like?"

"Oh, no, no! Least of all, that—don't think that!" she begged.

"But what am I to think then?"

"Don't think anything just yet," she pleaded. "Wait a little, and you will understand."

She was so evidently distressed, that he could not press her further; and fearing she might think him unappreciative, he said "Well, whatever it is, it hasn't prevented me from having a ripping good time. They've seen to that, and just done everything for my pleasure."

She looked up quickly, and to his relief he saw that for once he had said the right thing.

"You have enjoyed it, then?" she questioned eagerly.

"Most awfully," he assured her warmly. "I shall always remember what a happy leave they gave me."

She gave a little sigh of satisfaction. "I am so glad," she said. "They wanted you to have a good time—that was what we all wanted."

He looked at her gratefully, thinking how sweet she was in her fair English beauty, and how good to care that he should have enjoyed his leave. How different she was too from Sallie Berkeley—why she would have made two of his little girl! And how quiet! Sallie Berkeley, with her quick glancing vivacity, would have been all around her and off again like a humming-bird before she would have uttered two words. And yet he was sure that they would have been friends, just as he and Chev were. Perhaps they all would be, after the war. And then he began to talk about Chev, being sure that, had the circumstances been reversed, Sallie Berkeley would have wanted news of him. Instantly he was aware of a tense listening stillness on her part. That pleased him. Well, she did care for the old fellow all right, he thought; and though she made no response, averting her face, and plucking nervously at the leaves of the hedge as they passed slowly along, he went on pouring out his eager admiration for his friend.

At last they came to a seat in an arbor, from which one looked out upon a green beneficent landscape. It was an intimate, secluded little spot—and oh, if Sallie Berkeley were only there to sit beside him! And as he thought of this, it came to him whimsically that in all probability she must be longing for Chev, just as he was for Sallie.

Dropping down on the bench beside her, he leaned over, and said with a friendly, almost brotherly, grin of understanding, "I reckon you're wishing Captain Sherwood was sitting here, instead of Lieutenant Cary."

The minute the impulsive words were out of his mouth, he knew he had blundered, been awkward, and inexcusably intimate. She gave a little choked gasp, and her blue eyes stared up at him, wide and startled. Good heavens, what a break he had made! No wonder the Sherwoods couldn't trust him in company! There seemed no apology that he could offer in words, but at least, he thought, he would show her that he would not have intruded on her secret without being willing to share his with her. With awkward haste he put his hand into his breast-pocket, and dragged forth the picture of Sallie Berkeley he always carried there.

"This is the little girl I'm thinking about," he said, turning very red, yet boyishly determined to make amends, and also proudly confident of Sallie Berkeley's charms. "I'd like mighty well for you two to know one another."

She took the picture in silence, and for a long moment stared down at the soft little face, so fearless, so confident and gay, that smiled appealingly back at her. Then she did something astonishing,—something which seemed to him wholly un-English,—and yet he thought it the sweetest thing he had ever seen. Cupping her strong hands about the picture with a quick protectiveness, she suddenly raised it to her lips, and kissed it lightly. "O little girl!" she cried, "I hope you will be very happy!"

The little involuntary act, so tender, so sisterly and spontaneous, touched the Virginian extremely.

"Thanks awfully," he said unsteadily. "She'll think a lot of that, just as I do—and I know she'd wish you the same."

She made no reply to that, and as she handed the picture back to him, he saw that her hands were trembling, and he had a sudden conviction that, if she had been Sallie Berkeley, her eyes would have been full of tears. As she was Sybil Gaylord, however, there were no tears there, only a look that he never forgot. The look of one much older, protective, maternal almost,. and as if she were gazing back at Sallie Berkeley and himself from a long way ahead on the road of life. He supposed it was the way most English people felt nowadays. He had surprised it so often on all their faces, that he could not help speaking of it.

"You all think we Americans are awfully young and raw, don't you?" he questioned.

"Oh, no, not that," she deprecated. "Young perhaps for these days, yes—but it is more that you—that your country is so—so unsuffered. And we don't want you to suffer!" she added quickly.

Yes, that was it! He understood now, and, heavens, how fine it was!

Old England was wounded deep—deep. What she suffered herself she was too proud to show; but out of it she wrought a great maternal care for the newcomer. Yes, it was fine—he hoped his country would understand.

Miss Gaylord rose. "There are Gerald and father looking for you," she said, "and I must go now." She held out her hand. "Thank you for letting me see her picture, and for everything you said about Captain Sherwood—for everything, remember—I want you to remember."

With a light pressure of her fingers she was gone, slipping away through the shrubbery, and he did not see her again.

So he came to his last morning at Bishopsthorpe; and as he dressed, he wished it could have been different; that he were not still conscious of that baffling wall of reserve between himself and Chev's people, for whom, despite all, he had come to have a real affection.

In the breakfast-room he found them all assembled, and his last meal there seemed to him as constrained and difficult as any that had preceded it. It was over finally, however, and in a few minutes he would be leaving.

"I can never thank you enough for the splendid time I've had here," he said as he rose. "I'll be seeing Chev tomorrow, and I'll tell him all about everything."

Then he stopped dead. With a smothered exclamation, old Sir Charles had stumbled to his feet, knocking over his chair, and hurried blindly out of the room; and Gerald said, "Mother!" in a choked appeal.

As if it were a signal between them, Lady Sherwood pushed her chair back a little from the table, her long delicate fingers dropped together loosely in her lap; she gave a faint sign as if a restraining mantle slipped from her shoulders, and looking up at the youth before her, her fine pale face lighted with a kind of glory, she said, "No, dear lad, no. You can never tell Chev, for he is gone."

"Gone!" he cried.

"Yes," she nodded back at him just above a whisper; and now her face quivered, and the tears began to rush down her cheeks.

"Not dead!" he cried. "Not Chev—not that! O my God, Gerald, not that!"

"Yes," Gerald said. "They got him two days after you left."

It was so overwhelming, so unexpected and shocking, above all so terrible, that the friend he had so greatly loved and admired was gone out of his life forever, that young Cary stumbled back into his seat, and crumpling over, buried his face in his hands, making great uncouth gasps as he strove to choke back his grief.

Gerald groped hastily around the table, and flung an arm about his shoulders.

"Steady on, dear fellow, steady," he said, though his own voice broke. "When did you hear?" Cary got out at last.

"We got the official notice just the day before you came—and Withers has written us particulars since."

"And you let me come in spite of it! And stay on, when every word I said about him must have—have fairly crucified each one of you! Oh, forgive me! forgive me!" he cried distractedly. He saw it all now; he understood at last. It was not on Gerald's account that they could not talk of flying and of Chev, it was because—because their hearts were broken over Chev himself. "Oh, forgive me!" he gasped again.

"Dear lad, there is nothing to forgive," Lady Sherwood returned. "How could we help loving your generous praise of our poor darling? We loved it, and you for it; we wanted to hear it, but we were afraid. We were afraid we might break down, and that you would find out."

The tears were still running down her cheeks. She did not brush them away now; she seemed glad to have them there at last.

Sinking down on his knees, he caught her hands. "Why did you let me do such a horrible thing?" he cried. "Couldn't you have trusted me to understand? Couldn't you see I loved him just as you did—No, no!" he broke down humbly, "Of course I couldn't love him as his own people did. But you must have seen how I felt about him—how I admired him, and would have followed him anywhere—and of course if I had known, I should have gone away at once."

"Ah, but that was just what we were afraid of," she said quickly. "We were afraid you would go away and have a lonely leave somewhere. And in these days a boy's leave is so precious a thing that nothing must spoil it—nothing," she reiterated; and her tears fell upon his hands like a benediction. "But we didn't do it very well, I'm afraid," she went on presently, with gentle contrition. "You were too quick and understanding; you guessed there was something wrong. We were sorry not to manage better," she apologized.

"Oh, you wonderful, wonderful people!" he gasped. "Doing everything for my happiness, when all the time—all the time—"

His voice went out sharply, as his mind flashed back to scene after scene: to Gerald's long body lying quivering on the grass; to Sybil Gaylord wishing Sallie Berkeley happiness out of her own tragedy; and to the high look on Lady Sherwood's face. They seemed to him themselves, and yet more than themselves—shining bits in the mosaic of a great nation. Disjointedly there passed through his mind familiar words—"these are they who have washed their garments—having come out of great tribulation." No wonder they seemed older.

"We—we couldn't have done it in America," he said humbly.

He had a desperate desire to get away to himself; to hide his face in his arms, and give vent to the tears that were stifling him; to weep for his lost friend, and for this great heartbreaking heroism of theirs.

"But why did you do it?" he persisted. "Was it because I was his friend?"

"Oh, it was much more than that," Gerald said quickly. "It was a matter of the two countries. Of course, we jolly well knew you didn't belong to us, and didn't want to, but for the life of us we couldn't help a sort of feeling that you did. And when America was in at last, and you fellows began to come, you seemed like our very own come back after many years, and," he added, a throb in his voice, "we were most awfully glad to see you—we wanted a chance to show you how England felt."

Skipworth Cary rose to his feet. The tears for his friend were still wet upon his lashes. Stooping, he took Lady Sherwood's hands in his and raised them to his lips. "As long as I live, I shall never forget," he said. "And others of us have seen it too in other ways—be sure America will never forget, either."

She looked up at his untouched youth out of her beautiful sad eyes, the exalted light still shining through her tears. "Yes," she said, "you see it was—I don't know exactly how to put it—but it was England to America."

FOR THEY KNOW NOT WHAT THEY DO

By *Wilbur Daniel Steele*

[Greensboro, North Carolina, has the distinction of being the birth-place of two of America's most distinguished short story writers, William Sydney Porter (O. Henry) was born there in 1867, and Wilbur Daniel Steele in 1886. Each became the recognized leader in the short story field in his own generation. Wilbur Steele was graduated from the University of Denver and later studied music and art in Boston, New York, and Paris. His success as a story writer began in 1914 and has grown from year to year. This has been attested by his receiving the O. Henry Memorial Award a number of times since. Some of his most notable stories are: *For They Know Not What They Do, The Man Who Saw Through Heaven, When Hell Froze, Blue Murder,* and *Bubbles.*

For They Know Not What They Do is reprinted by permission of the author.]

WHEN Christopher Kain told me his story, sitting late in his dressing-room at the Philharmonic, I felt that I ought to say something, but nothing in the world seemed adequate. It was one of those times when words have no weight; mine sounded like a fly buzzing in the tomb of kings. And after all, he did not hear me; I could tell that by the look on his face as he sat there staring into the light, the lank, dark hair framing his waxen brow, his shoulders hanging forward, his lean, strong, sentient fingers wrapped around the brown neck of "Ugo," the 'cello, tightly.

Agnes Kain was a lady, as a lady was before the light of that poor worn word went out. Quiet, reserved, gracious, continent, bearing in face and form the fragile beauty of a rose petal come to its fading on a windless ledge, she moved down the years with the steadfast sweetness of the gentlewoman—gentle, and a woman.

They did not know much about her in the city, where she had come with her son. They did not need to. Looking into her eyes, into the transparent soul behind them, they could ask no other credential for the name she bore and the lavender she wore for the husband of whom she never spoke.

She spoke of him, indeed, but that was in privacy, and to her son. As Christopher grew through boyhood, she watched him; in her enveloping eagerness she forestalled the hour when he would have asked, and told him about his father, Daniel Kain.

It gave them the added bond of secret-sharers. The tale grew as the boy grew. Each night when Christopher crept into his mother's bed for the quiet hour of her voice, it was as if he crept in to another world, the wind-blown, sky-encompassed kingdom of the Kains, Daniel, his father, and Maynard, his father, another Maynard before him, and all the Kains—and the Hill and the House, the Willow Wood, the Moor Under the Cloud, the Beach where the gray seas pounded, the boundless Marsh, the Lilac-hedge standing against the stars.

He knew he would have to be a man of men to measure up to that heritage, a man strong, grave, thoughtful, kind with the kindness that never falters, brave with the courage of that dark and massive folk whose blood ran in his veins. Coming as it did, a world of legend growing up side by side with the matter-of-fact world of Concord Street, it was made to fit in with all things natural, and it never occurred to him to question. He, the boy, was not massive, strong, or brave; he saw things in the dark that frightened him, his thin shoulders were bound to droop, the hours of practice on his violin left him with no blood in his legs and a queer pallor on his brow.

Nor was he always grave, thoughtful, kind. He did not often lose his temper; the river of his young life ran too smooth and deep. But there were times when he did. Brief passions swept him, blinded him, twisted his fingers, left him sobbing, retching, and weak as death itself. He never seemed to wonder at the discrepancy in things, however, any more than he wondered at the look in his mother's eyes, as she hung over him, waiting, in those moments of nausea after rage. She had not the look of the gentlewoman then; she had more the look a thousand times, of the prisoner led through the last gray corridor in the dawn.

He saw her like that once when he had not been angry. It was on a day when he came into the front hall unexpectedly as a stranger was going out of the door. The stranger was dressed in rough, brown homespun; in one hand he held a brown velour hat, in the other a thorn stick without a ferrule. Nor was there anything more worthy of note in his face, an average-long face with hollowed cheeks, sunken gray eyes, and a high forehead, narrow, sallow, and moist.

No, it was not the stranger that troubled Christopher. It was his mother's look at his own blundering entrance, and, when the man was out of hearing, the tremulous haste of her explanation.

"He came about some papers, you know."

"You mean our Morning Posts?" Christopher asked her.

She let her breath out all at once, and color flooded her face.

"Yes," she told him. "Yes, yes."

Neither of them said anything more about it.

It was the same day, toward evening, that Christopher broke one of his long silences, reverting to a subject always near to them both.

"Mother, you've never told me where it is—on the map, I mean."

She was looking the other way. She did not turn around.

"I—Chris—I—I haven't a map in the house."

He did not press the matter. He went out into the back yard presently, under the grape-trellis, and there he stood still for a long time, staring at nothing in particular.

He was growing up.

He went away to boarding-school not long after this, taking with him the picture of his adored mother, the treasured epic of his dark, strong fathers, his narrow shoulders, his rare blind bursts of passion, his new-born wonder, and his violin. At school they thought him a queer one.

The destinies of men are unaccountable things. Five children in the village of Deer Bay came down with diphtheria. That was why the academy shut up for a week, and that was what started Christopher on his way home for an unexpected holiday. And then it was only by one chance in a thousand that he should glimpse his mother's face in the down train halted at the Junction where he himself was changing.

She did not see him till he came striding along the aisle of her coach, his arms full of his things, face flushed, eyes brimming with the surprise and pleasure of seeing her, lips trembling questions.

"Why, Mother, what on earth? Where are you going? I'm to have a week at least, Mother; and here you're going away, and you didn't tell me, and what is it, and everything?"

His eager voice trailed off. The color drained out of his face, and there was a shadow in his eyes. He drew back from her the least way.

"What is it, Mother? Mother!"

Somewhere on the platform outside the conductor's droning "—board" ran along the coaches. Agnes Kain opened her white lips.

"Get off before it's too late, Christopher. I haven't time to explain now. Go home, and Mary will see you have everything. I'll be back in a day or so. Kiss me, and go quickly. Quickly!"

He did not kiss her. He would not have kissed her for worlds. He was too bewildered, dazed, lost, too inexpressibly hurt. On the platform outside, had she turned ever so little to look she might have seen his face again for an instant as the wheels ground on the rails. Color was coming back to it again, a murky color like the shadow of a red cloud.

They must have wondered, in the coach with her, at the change in the calm, unobtrusive, well-gowned gentlewoman, their fellow-passenger. Those that were left after another two hours saw her get down at a barren station where an old man waited in a carriage. The halt was brief, and none of them caught sight of the boyish figure that slipped down from the rearmost coach to take shelter for himself and his dark, tempest-ridden face behind the shed at the end of the platform—

Christopher walked out across a broad, high, cloudy plain, following a red road, led by the dust-feather hanging over the distant carriage.

He walked for miles, creeping ant-like between the immensities of the brown plain and the tumbled sky. Had he been less implacable, less intent, he might have noticed many things: the changing conformation of the clouds, the far flight of a gull, the new perfume and texture of the wind that flowed over his hot temples. But as it was, the sea took him by surprise. Coming over a little rise, his eyes focused for another long, dun fold of the plain, it seemed for an instant as if he had lost his balance over a void; for a wink he felt the passing of a strange sickness. He went off a little way to the side of the road and sat down on a flat stone.

The world had become of a sudden infinitely simple, as simple as the inside of a cup. The land broke down under him, a long, naked slope fringed at the foot by a ribbon of woods. Through the upper branches he saw the shingles and chimneys of a pale gray village up to the left in a border flight of cliffs, showing on their crest a cluster of roofs and dull green gable-ends against the sea that lifted vast, unbroken, to the rim of the cup.

Christopher was fifteen, and queer even for that queer age. He had a streak of the girl in him at his adolescence, and, as he sat there in a huddle, the wind coming out of this huge new gulf of life seemed to pass through him, bone and tissue, and tears rolled down his face.

The carriage bearing his strange mother was gone, from sight and from mind. His eyes came down from the lilac-crowned hill to the beach, where it showed in white patches through the wood, and he saw that the wood was of willows. And he remembered the plain behind him, the wide, brown moor under the cloud. He got up on his wobbly legs. There were stones all about him in the whispering wire-grass, and like them the one he had been sitting on bore a blurred inscription. He read it aloud, for some reason, his voice borne away faintly on the river of air:

"MAYNARD KAIN, ESQUIRE
1809—1839
THIS MONUMENT ERECTED IN HIS MEMORY BY
HIS SORROWING WIDOW,
HARRIET BURNAM KAIN

'The windy Gales of the West Indies
Laid Claim to His Noble Soul
And took him on High to his Creator
Who made him Whole.'"

His gaze went on to another of those worn stones.

"HERE LIE THE EARTHLY REMAINS OF
MAYNARD KAIN, SECOND
BORN 1835—DIED 1863 FOR THE PRESERVATION
OF THE UNION"

There was no moss or lichen on this windscoured slope. In the falling dusk the old white stones stood up like the bones of the dead themselves, and the only sound was the rustle of the wire-grass creeping over them in a dry tide. The boy had taken off his cap; the sea-wind moving under the mat of his damp hair gave it the look of some somber, outlandish cowl. With the night coming on, his solemnity had an elfin quality. He found at last what he was looking for, and his fingers had to help his eyes.

> "DANIEL KAIN
> BELOVED HUSBAND OF AGNES WILLOUGHBY KAIN
> BORN 1860—DIED 1886
> 'FORGIVE THEM, FOR THEY KNOW NOT WHAT THEY DO.'"

Christopher Kain told me that he left the naked graveyard repeating it to himself, "Forgive them, for they know not what they do," conscious less of the words than of the august rhythm falling in with the pulse of his exaltation.

The velvet darkness that hangs under clouds had come down over the hill and the great marsh stretching away to the south of it. Agnes Kain stood in the open doorway, one hand on the brown wood, the other pressed to her cheek.

"You heard it that time, Nelson?"

"No, ma'am." The old man in the entrance-hall behind her shook his head. In the thin, blown light of the candelabra which he held high, the worry and doubt of her deepened on his singularly unlined face.

"And you might well catch your death in that draft, ma'am."

But she only continued to stare out between the pillars where the lilac-hedge made a wall of deeper blackness across the night.

"What am I thinking of?" she whispered, and then: "There!"

And this time the old man heard it; a nearer, wind-blown hail.

"Mother! Oh, Mother!"

The boy came striding through the gap of the gate in the hedge.

"It's I, Mother! Chris! Aren't you surprised?"

She had no answer. As he came she turned and moved away from the door, and the old man, peering from under the flat candle-flames, saw her face like wax. And he saw the boy, Christopher, in the doorway, his hands flung out, his face transfigured.

"Mother! I'm here! Don't you understand?"

He touched her shoulder. She turned to him, as it were lazily.

"Yes," she breathed. "I see."

He threw his arms about her, and felt her shaking from head to foot. But he was shaking, too.

"I knew the way!" he cried. "I knew it, Mother, I knew it! I came down from the Moor and there was the Willow Wood, and I knew the way home. And when I came, Mother, it was like the trees bowing down their branches in the dark. And when I came by the Beach, Mother, it was like a roll of drums, beating for me, and when I came to the Hill I saw the Hedge standing against the sky, and I came, and here I am!"

She expressed no wonder, asked no question.

"Yes," was all she said, and it was as if she spoke of a tree coming to its leaf, the wind to its height, the tide to its flood.

Had he been less rapt and triumphant, he must have wondered more at the icy lassitude, and at the cloak of ceremony she wrapped about her to hide a terror. It was queer to hear the chill urbanity of her: "This is Christopher, Nelson; Christopher, this is your father's servant, Nelson." It was queerer still to see the fastidious decorum with which she led him over this, the familiar house of his fathers.

He might have been a stranger, come with a guide-book in his hand. When he stood on his heels in the big drawing-room, staring up with all his eyes at the likenesses of those men he had known so well, it was strange to hear her going on with all the patter of the gallery attendant, names of painters, prices, dates. He stood before the portrait of Daniel Kain, his father, a dark-skinned, longish face with a slightly protruding nether lip, hollow temples, and a round chin, deeply cleft. As in all the others, the eyes, even in the dead pigment, seemed to shine with an odd, fixed luminosity of their own, and like the others from first to last of the line, it bore upon it the stamp of an imperishable youth. And all the while he stood there, drinking it in, detail by detail, his mother spoke, not of the face, but of the frame, some obscure and unsuspected excellence in the goldleaf on the frame.

More than once in that stately tour of halls and chambers he found himself protesting gaily, "I know, Mother! I know, I know!"

But the contagion of his glory did not seem to touch her. Nothing seemed to touch her. Only once was the fragile, bright shell of her punctilio penetrated for a moment, and that was when Christopher, lagging, turned back to a door they were about to pass and threw it open with the happy laugh of a discoverer. And then, even before she could have hushed him, the laughter on his lips died of itself.

A man lay on a bed in the room, his face as colorless and still as the pillow behind it. His eyes were open, but they did not move from the three candles burning on the high bureau, and he seemed unconscious of any intrusion.

"I didn't know!" Christopher whispered, shocked, and shamed.

When the door closed again his mother explained. She explained at length, concisely, standing quite still, with one frail, fine hand worrying the locket she wore at her throat. Nelson stood quite still too, his attention engrossed in his candle-wicks. And Christopher stood quite still, and all their shadows. . . . That man was the caretaker, the man, Christopher was to understand, who had been looking after the place.

His name was Sanderson. He had fallen ill, very ill. In fact, he was dying. And that was why his mother had to come down, post-haste, without warning. To see about some papers. Some papers. Christopher was to understand . . .

Christopher understood. Indeed there was not much to understand. And yet, when they had gone on, he was bothered by it. Already, so young he was, so ruthless, and so romantic, he had begun to be a little ashamed of that fading, matter-of-fact world of Concord Street. And it was with just that world which he wished to forget that the man lying ill in the candle-lit chamber was linked in Christopher's memory. For it was the same man he had seen in the doorway that morning months ago, with a brown hat in one hand and a thorn stick in the other.

Even a thing like that may be half put aside, tho—for a while. And by the time Christopher went to his room for the night, the thought of the interloper had retired into the back of his mind, and they were all Kains there on the Hill, inheritors of Romance. He found himself bowing to his mother with a courtliness he had never known, and an "I wish you a good night," sounding a century old on his lips. He saw the remote, patrician figure bow as gravely in return, a petal of color as hard as paint on the whiteness of either cheek. He did not see her afterward, tho—when the merciful door was closed.

Before he slept he explored the chamber, touching old objects with reverent finger-tips. He came on a leather case like an absurdly overgrown beetle, hidden in a corner, and a violoncello was in it. He had seen such things before, but he had never touched one, and when he lifted it from the case he had a moment of feeling overawed at the pit of his stomach. Sitting in his under-things on the edge of the bed, he held the wine-colored creature in the crook of his arm for a long time, the look in his round eyes, half eagerness, half pain, of one pursuing the shadow of some ghostly and elusive memory.

He touched the C-string by-and-by with an adventuring thumb. I have heard "Ugo" sing, myself, and I know what Christopher meant when he said that the sound did not come out of the instrument, but that it came in to it, sweeping home from all the walls and corners of the chamber, a slow, rich, concentric wind of tone. He felt it about him, murmurous, pulsating, like the sound of surf borne from some far-off coast.

And then it was like drums, still farther off. And then it was the feet of marching men, massive, dark, grave men with luminous eyes, and the stamp on their faces of an imperishable youth.

He sat there so lost and rapt that he heard nothing of his mother's footsteps hurrying in the hall; knew nothing till he saw her face in the open doorway. She had forgotten herself this time; that fragile defense of gentility was down. For a moment they stared at each other across a gulf of silence, and little by little the boy's cheeks grew as white as hers, his hands as cold, his lungs as empty of breath.

"What is it, Mother?"

"Oh, Christopher, Christopher. . . . Go to bed, dear."

He did not know why, but of a sudden he felt ashamed and a little frightened, and, blowing out the candle, he crept under the covers.

The afternoon was bright with a rare sun, and the world was quiet. Christopher lay full-spread on the turf, listening idly to the "clip-clip" of Nelson's shears as the old man trimmed the hedge.

"And was my father very strong?" he asked with a drowsy pride.

"No, not so very." Nelson stopped clipping and was immediately lost in the past.

"Only when he was that way five strong men couldn't turn him. I'll say that. No, if they had to get him with a shotgun that day, 'twas nobody's fault nor sin. If Guy Bullard seen Daniel there on the sand with an ax in his hand and foam-like on his lips, and the little ones cornered where he caught them between cliff and water—Guy's own baby amongst them—and knowing the sickness of the Kains as he and everybody else did—why, I'm free and willing to say 'twas his bounden duty to hold a true arm and pull a steady trigger on Daniel, man of his tho I was, and man of his poor father before him—"

Nelson was a queer fellow. His age was really greater than his un-lined face would have told, and his mind, laden with the burden of misty years, had grown tired. It is charitable to think that, once launched on the river of memory, the dreaming fellow forgot where he was and to what audience he spoke, and that audience lying quiet, so very quiet, in the deep grass behind his back.

"No, I can't make it right to lay blame on any man for it, no more than I can on them his brother officers, that broke Maynard's neck with their tent-pegs the night after Gettysburg. No, no. . . ."

It was evidently a time-worn theme, an argument, an *apologia*, accepted after years of bitterness and self-searching. He went on with the remote serenity of age, that has escaped the toils of passion, pursuing the old, worn path of his mind, his eyes buried in vacancy.

"No, 'twas a mercy to the both of them, father and son, and a man must see it so. 'Twould be better of course if they could have gone easier, same as the old Maynard went, thinking himself the Lord our God to walk on the water and calm the West Indy gale. That's better, better for all hands round. But if it had to come so, in violence and fear, then nobody need feel the sin of it on his soul—nobody excepting the old man Bickers, him that told Daniel. For 'twas from that day he began to take it on.

"I saw it myself. There was Daniel come home from other parts where his mother had kept him, out of gossip's way, bright as you please and knowing nothing wrong with the blood of the Kains. And so I say the sin lays on the loose-wagging tongue of Bickers, for from the day he let it out to Daniel, Daniel changed. 'Twas like he'd heard his doom, and went to it. Bickers is dead a long time now, but may the Lord God lay eternal damnation on his soul!"

Even then there was no heat; the curse had grown a formula. Having come to the end, the old man's eyes tumbled down painlessly out of the void and discovered the shears in his hand.

"Dear me, that's so," he said to himself. One thought was enough at a time. He fell to work again. The steady "clip-clip-clip" moved off slowly along the hedge. Not once did he remember; not once as the indefatigable worker shuffled himself out of sight around the house did he look back with any stirring of recollection at the boyish figure lying there as still as a shadow cast in the deep grass.

A faintly lop-sided moon swam in the zenith. For three days now that rare clarity had hung in the sky, and for three nights the moon had grown. Its benign, poisonous illumination flowed down steeply through the windows of the dark chamber where Christopher huddled on the bed's edge, three pale, chill islands spread on the polished floor.

Once again the boy brought the bow home across the shivering strings, and, as if ears could be thirsty as a drunkard's throat, he drank his fill of the 'cello's deep, full-membered chord. The air was heavy with the resonance of marching feet, ghostly feet marching and marching down upon him in slow, inexorable crescendo as the tides ebbed later among the sedges on the marsh and the moon grew big. And above the pulse of the march he seemed to hear another cadence, a thin laughter.

He laughed too, giving himself up to that spectral contagion. He saw the fat, iridescent bubble with the Hill in it, the House of dreams, the Beach and the Moor and Willow Wood of fancy, and all the grave, strong, gentle line of Kains to whom he had been made to bow down in worship. He saw himself taken in, soul and body, by a thin-plated fraud, a cheap trick of mother's words, as, before him, his father had been. And the faint exhalations from the moon-patches on the floor showed his face contorted with a still, set grimace of mirth.

Anger came over him in a white veil, twitching his lips and his toes and bending his fingers in knots. Through the veil a sound crept, a sound he knew well by this time, secret foot-falls in the hall, faltering, retreating, loitering, returning to lag near the door.

How he hated her! It is curious that not once did his passion turn against his blighted fathers; it was against the woman who had borne him, the babe, and lied to him, the boy—against her, and against the man, the interloper, dying in a room below.

The thought that had been willing to creep out of sight into the back-country of his mind on that first night, came out now like a red devouring cloud. Who was that man?

What was he dying of—or supposed to be dying of? What had he been doing that morning in Concord Street? What was he doing here, in the house of the men who had never grown old and of the boy who would never grow old? Why had his mother come down here, where he was, so queerly, so secretly, so frightened?

Christopher would have liked to kill that man. He shivered and licked his lips. He would have liked to do something bloody and abominable to that face with the hollow cheeks, the sunken gray eyes, and the forehead, high, sallow, and moist. He would have liked to take an ax in his hand and run along the thundering beach and catch that face in a corner somewhere between cliff and water. The desire to do this thing possessed him and blinded him like the kiss of lightning.

He found himself on the floor at the edge of the moonlight, full of weakness and nausea. He felt himself weeping as he crawled back to the bed, his cheeks and neck bathed in a flood of painless tears. He threw himself down, dazed with exhaustion.

It seemed to him that his mother had been calling a long while. "Christopher! What is it? What is it, boy?"

He had heard no footsteps, going or coming; she must have been there all the time, waiting, listening, her ear pressed to the thick, old paneling of the door. The thought was like wine; the torment of her whispering was sweet in his ears.

"Oh, Chris, Chris! You're making yourself sick!"

"Yes," he said. He lifted on an elbow and repeated it in a voice which must have sounded strange enough to the listener beyond the door. "Yes!" he said. "Yes!"

"Go away!" he cried of a sudden, making a wide, dim, imperious gesture in the dark.

"No, no," the imploring whisper crept in. "You're making yourself sick—Christopher—all over nothing—nothing in the world. It's so foolish—so foolish! Oh, if I could only tell you, Christopher—if I could tell you—"

"Tell me what?" He shuddered with the ecstasy of his own irony. "Who that man is? That 'caretaker'? What he's doing here? What you're doing here?—" He began to scream in a high, brittle voice: "Go away from that door! Go away!"

This time she obeyed. He heard her retreating, soft-footed and frightened, along the hall. She was abandoning him—without so much as trying the door, just once again, to see if it were still bolted against her.

She did not care. She was sneaking off—down the stairs—Oh, yes, he knew where.

His lips began to twitch again and his finger-nails scratched on the bed-clothes. If only he had something, some weapon, an ax, a broad, keen, glittering ax! He would show them! He was strong, incredibly strong! Five men could not have turned him back from what he was going to do—if only he had something.

His hand, creeping, groping, closed on the neck of the 'cello leaning by the bed. He laughed.

Oh, yes, he would stop her from going down there; he would hold her, just where she was on the dark stair, nerveless, breathless, as long as he liked; if he liked he would bring her back, cringing, begging.

He drew the bow, and laughed higher and louder yet to hear the booming discord rocking in upon him from the shadows. Swaying from side to side he lashed the hollow creature to madness. They came in the press of the gale, marching, marching, the wild, dark pageant of his fathers, nearer and nearer through the moon-struck night.

"Tell me what?" he laughed. "What?"

And abruptly he slept, sprawled cross-wise on the covers, half-clothed, dishevelled, triumphant.

It was not the same night, but another, whether the next or the next but one, or two, Christopher can not say. But he was out of doors.

He had escaped from the house at dusk; he knew that. He remembered the wide, hushed mystery of twilight as he paused on the doorsill between the fading pillars, the death of day running crimson in the west; in the east the still, white travail of the sea and the moon—the queer moment.

He had run away, through the hedge and down the back side of the hill, torn between the two, the death, warm and red like life, and the birth, pale, chill, and inexorable as death.

Most of that daft night-running will always be blank in Christopher's mind; moments, and moments only, like islands of clarity, remain. He brings back one vivid interval when he found himself seated on his father's gravestone among the whispering grasses, staring down into the pallid bowl of the world. And in that moment he knew what Daniel Kain had felt, and Maynard Kain before him; a passionate and contemptuous hatred for all the dullards in the world who never dreamed dreams or saw visions or sang wordless songs or ran naked-hearted in the flood of the full-blown moon. He hated them because they could not by any possibility comprehend his magnificent separation, his starry sanity, his—kinship with gods. And he had a new thirst to obliterate the whole creeping race of dust-dwellers with one wide, incomparably-bloody gesture.

It was late when he found himself back again before the house, and an ink-black cloud touched the moon's edge. After the airless evening a wind had sprung up in the east; it thrashed among the lilac-stems as he came through them and across the turf, silent-footed as an Indian. In his right hand he had a bread-knife, held butt to thumb, dagger-wise. Where he had come by the rust-bitten thing no one knows, least of all himself. In the broken light his eyes shone with a curious luminosity of their own, absorbed, introspective.

All the windows were dark, and the entrance hall, when he slipped in between the pillars; but across its floor he saw light thrown in a yellow ribbon from the half-closed door of the drawing room.

It took his attention, laid hands on his imagination. He began to struggle against it.

He would not go into that room. He was going to another room. To stay him, he made a picture of that other room in his tumbled mind— the high, bleak walls, the bureau with the three candles burning wanly, the bed, the face of the man on the bed. And when his rebellious feet, surrendering him up to the lure of that beckoning ribbon, had edged as far as the door, and he had pushed it a little further ajar to get his head in, he saw that the face itself was there in the drawing-room.

He stood there for some time, his shoulder pressed against the door-jamb, his eyes blinking.

His slow attention moved from the face to the satin pillows that wedged it in, and then to the woman that must have been his mother, kneeling beside the casket with her arms crooked on the shining cover and her head down between them. And across from her leaned "Ugo," the 'cello, come down from his chamber to stand vigil at the other shoulder of the dead.

The first thing that came into his groping mind was a bitter sense of abandonment. The little core of candle-light hanging in the gloom left him out. Its unstirring occupants, the woman, the 'cello and the clay, seemed sufficient to themselves. His mother had forgotten him. Even "Ugo," that had grown part and parcel of his madness, had forgotten him.

Bruised, sullen, moved by some deep-lying instinct of the clan, his eyes left them and sought the wall beyond, where there were those who would not forget him, come what might, blood of his blood and mind of his own queer mind. And there among the shadowed faces he searched for one in vain. As if that candle-lit tableau, somehow holy and somehow abominable, were not for the eyes of one of them, the face of Daniel, the wedded husband, had been turned to the wall.

Here was something definite, something Christopher could take hold of, and something that he would not have.

His mother seemed not to have known he was near till he flung the door back and came stalking into the light with the rusty bread-knife in his hand. None would have imagined there was blood enough left in her wasted heart, but her face went crimson when she lifted it and saw him.

It brought him up short—the blush, where he had looked for fright. It shocked him, and, shocking him, more than by a thousand labored words of explanation it opened a window in his disordered brain. He stood gawking with the effort of thought, hardly conscious of his mother's cry, "Christopher, I never meant you to know!"

He kept on staring at the ashen face between the pillows, long (as his own was long), sensitive, worn; and at the 'cello keeping incorruptible vigil over its dead. And then slowly his eyes went down to his own left hand, to which that same old wine-brown creature had come home from the first with a curious sense of fitness and authority and right.

"Who is this man?"

"Don't look at me so! Don't, Chris!"

But he did look at her. Pre-occupied as he was, he was appalled at sight of the damage the half-dozen days had done. She had been so much the lady, so perfectly the gentlewoman. To no one had the outward gesture and symbol of purity been more precious. No whisper had ever breathed against her. If there had been secrets behind her, they had been dead; if a skeleton, the closet had been closed. And now, looking down on her, he was not only appalled, he was a little sickened, as one might be to find squalor and decay creeping into a familiar and once immaculate room.

"Who is this man?" he repeated.

"He grew up with me." She half raised herself on her knees in the eagerness of her appeal. "We were boy and girl together at home in Maryland. We were meant for each other, Chris. We were always to marry—always, Chris. And when I went away, and when I married your—when I married Daniel Kain, he hunted and he searched and he found me here. He was with me, he stood by me through that awful year—and—that was how it happened. I tell you, Christopher, darling, we were meant for each other. John Sanderson and I. He loved me more than poor Daniel ever did or could, loved me enough to throw away a life of promise, just to hang on here after every one else was gone, alone with his 'cello and his one little memory. And I loved him enough to—to—Christopher, don't look at me so!"

His eyes did not waver. You must remember his age, the immaculate, ruthless, mid-Victorian 'teens; and you must remember his bringing-up.

"And so this was my father," he said. And then he went on without waiting, his voice breaking into falsetto with the fierceness of his charge. "And you would have kept on lying to me! If I hadn't happened, just happened, to find you here, now, you would have gone on keeping me in the dark! You would have stood by and seen me—well—go crazy! Yes, go crazy, thinking I was—well, thinking I was meant for it! And all to save your precious—"

She was down on the floor again, what was left of the gentlewoman, wailing. "But you don't know what it means to a woman, Chris! You don't know what it means to a woman!"

A wave of rebellion brought her up and she strained toward him across the coffin.

"Isn't it something, then, that I gave you a father with a mind? And if you think you've been sinned against, think of me! Sin! You call it sin! Well, isn't it anything at all that by my 'sin' my son's blood came down to him clean? Tell me that!"

He shook himself, and his flame turned to sullenness.

"It's not so," he glowered.

All the girl in him, the poet, the hero-worshipping boy, rebelled. His harassed eyes went to the wall beyond and the faces there, the ghosts of the doomed, glorious, youth-ridden line, priceless possessions of his dreams. He would not lose them; he refused to be robbed of a tragic birthright. He wanted some gesture puissant enough to turn back and blot out all that had been told him.

"It's not his!" he cried. And reaching out fiercely he dragged the 'cello away from the coffin's side. He stood for an instant at bay, bitter, defiant. "It's not his! It's mine! It's—it's—ours!"

And then he fled out into the dark of the entrance-hall and up the black stairs. In his room there was no moonlight now, for the cloud ran over the sky, and the rain had come.

"It isn't so, it isn't so!" It was like a sob in his throat.

He struck on the full strings. And listening—breathless—through the dying discord he heard—the liquid whispers of the rain, nothing more. He lashed with a wild bow, time and again. But something was broken, something was lost; out of the surf of sound he could no longer fashion the measure of marching feet. The mad Kains had found him out, and cast him out. No longer could he dream them in dreams or run naked-hearted with them in the flood of the moon, for he was no blood of theirs, and they were gone. And huddling down on the edge of the bed, he wept.

The tears washed his eyes and falling down bathed his strengthless hands. And beyond the fantom windows, over the Marsh and the Moor and the Hill that were not his, the graves of strangers and the lost Willow Wood, lay the healing rain. He heard it in gurgling rivulets along the gutters overhead. He heard the soft impact, like a kiss, brushing the reedy cheeks of the Marsh, the showery shouldering of branches, the aspiration of myriad drinking grasses, the far whisper of waters coming home to the waters of the sea—the long, low melody of the rain.

And by and by he found it was "Ugo," the 'cello, and he was playing.

They went home the following afternoon, he and his mother. Or, rather, she went home, and he with her as far as the Junction, where he changed for school.

They had not much to say to each other through the journey. The boy had to be given time. Five years younger, or fifteen years older, it would have been easier for him to look at his mother. You must remember what his mother had meant to him, and what, bound up still in the fierce and somber battle of adolescence, she must mean to him now.

As for Agnes Kain, she did not look at him, either. Through the changing hours her eyes rested on the transparent hands lying crossed in her lap. She seemed very tired and very white. Her hair was done up less tidily, her lace cuffs were less fresh than they had been wont to be. About her whole presence there was a troubling hint of let-down, something obscurely slatternly, a kind of awkward and unlovely nakedness.

She really spoke to him for the first time at the Junction, when he stood before her, slim and uncouth under the huge burden of "Ugo," fumbling through his leave-taking.

"Christopher," she said. "Try not to think of me—always—as—as—well, when you're older, Christopher, you'll know what I mean."

That was the last time he ever heard her speak. He saw her once again—two days later—but the telegram was delayed and his train was late, and when he came beside her bed she said nothing. She looked into his eyes searchingly—for a long while—and died.

That space stands for the interval of silence that fell after Christopher had told me the story. I thought he had quite finished. He sat motionless, his shoulders fallen forward, his eyes fixed in the heart of the incandescent globe over the dressing-table, his long fingers wrapped around the neck of the 'cello.

"And so she got me through those years," he said. "Those nip-and-tuck years that followed. By her lie."

"Insanity is a queer thing." he went on, still brooding into the light. "There's more of it about than we're apt to think. It works in so many ways. In hobbies, arts, philosophies. Music is a kind of insanity. I know. I've got mine penned up in the music now, and I think I can keep it there now, and save my soul."

"Yours?"

"Yes, mine, I know now—now that it's safe for me to know. I was down at that village by the beach a year or so ago. I'm a Kain, of course, one of the crazy Kains, after all. John Sanderson was born in the village and lived there till his death. Only once that folks could remember had he been away, and that was when he took some papers to the city for Mrs. Kain to sign. He was caretaker at the old 'Kain place' the last ten years of his life, and deaf, they said, since his tenth year—'deaf as a post.' And they told me something else. They said there was a story that before my father, Daniel, married her, my mother had been an actress. An actress! You'll understand that I needed no one to tell me that!

"One told me he had heard that she was a great actress. Dear God, if they could only know! When I think of that night and that setting, that scene! It killed her—and it got me over the wall—"

A SOURCE OF IRRITATION

By Stacy Aumonier

[This story is one of those that came out of the experiences of the
World War. Many of those stories are so terribly grim that it is a relief
and a pleasure to turn to one that is built around an interesting old
character and entertains with its humor. Mr. Stacy Aumonier (1887–
1928) was an Englishman. His father was an architectural sculptor in
London, and the son had several artistic interests outside the field of
writing. His short stories were collected in several volumes.

A Source of Irritation is reprinted from Golden Windmill and other
Stories, by permission of The Macmillan Company, publishers.]

TO look at old Sam Gates you would never suspect him of having
nerves. His sixty-nine years of close application to the needs of the
soil had given him a certain earthy stolidity. To observe him hoeing, or
thinning out a broad field of turnips, hardly attracted one's attention.
He seemed so much part and parcel of the whole scheme. He blended
into the soil like a glorified swede. Nevertheless, the half-dozen people
who claimed his acquaintance knew him to be a man who suffered from
little moods of irritability.

And on this glorious morning a little incident annoyed him unreasonably. It concerned his niece Aggie. She was a plump girl with clear blue
eyes and a face as round and inexpressive as the dumplings for which the
county was famous. She came slowly across the long sweep of the downland, and putting down the bundle wrapped up in a red handkerchief
which contained his breakfast and dinner, she said:

"Well, uncle, is there any noos?"

Now this may not appear to the casual reader to be a remark likely to
cause irritation, but it affected old Sam Gates as a very silly and unnecessary question. It was moreover the constant repetition of it which
was beginning to anger him. He met his niece twice a day. In the morning she brought his bundle of food at seven, and when he passed his
sister's cottage on the way home to tea at five she was invariably hanging
about the gate. And on each occasion she always said, in exactly the
same voice:

"Well, uncle, is there any noos?"

"Noos!" What "noos" should there be? For sixty-nine years he had
never lived further than five miles from Halvesham. For nearly sixty of
those years he had bent his back above the soil. There were indeed
historic occasions: once, for instance, when he had married Annie

886

Hachet. And there was the birth of his daughter. There was also a famous occasion when he had visited London. Once he had been to a flower-show at Market Roughborough. He either went or didn't go to church on Sundays. He had had many interesting chats with Mr. James at "The Cowman," and three years ago had sold a pig to Mrs. Waig. But he couldn't always have interesting "noos" of this sort up his sleeve. Didn't the silly gaffer know that for the last three weeks he had been thinning out turnips for Mr. Dodge on this very same field? What "noos" could there be?

He blinked at his niece, and didn't answer. She undid the parcel, and said:

"Mrs. Goping's fowl got out again last night."

He replied, "Ah!" in a non-committal manner, and began to munch his bread and bacon. His niece picked up the handkerchief and humming to herself, walked back across the field. It was a glorious morning, and a white sea-mist added to the promise of a hot day. He sat there munching, thinking of nothing in particular, but gradually subsiding into a mood of placid content. He noticed the back of Aggie disappear in the distance. It was a mile to the cottage, and a mile and a half to Halvesham. Silly things, girls! They were all alike. One had to make allowances. He dismissed her from his thoughts and took a long swig of tea out of a bottle. Insects buzzed lazily. He tapped his pocket to assure himself that his pouch of shag was there, and then he continued munching. When he had finished, he lighted his pipe and stretched himself comfortably. He looked along the line of turnips he had thinned, and then across the adjoining field of swedes. Silver streaks appeared on the sea below the mist. In some dim way he felt happy in his solitude amidst this sweeping immensity of earth and sea and sky.

And then something else came to irritate him. It was one of "these dratted airyplanes." "Airyplanes" were his pet aversion. He could find nothing to be said in their favor. Nasty, noisy, vile-smelling things that seared the heavens, and made the earth dangerous. And every day there seemed to be more and more of them. Of course "this old war" was responsible for a lot of them, he knew. The war was "a plaguey noosance." They were short-handed on the farm. Beer and tobacco were dear, and Mrs. Stevens' nephew had been and got wounded in the foot.

He turned his attention once more to the turnips. But an "airyplane" has an annoying genius for gripping one's attention. When it appears on the scene, however much we dislike it, it has a way of taking stage-center; we cannot help constantly looking at it. And so it was with old Sam Gates. He spat on his hands, and blinked up at the sky. And suddenly the aeroplane behaved in a very extraordinary manner. It was well over the sea when it seemed to lurch in a drunken manner, and skimmed the water. Then it shot up at a dangerous angle and zigzagged.

It started to go farther out, and then turned and made for the land. The engines were making a curious grating noise. It rose once more, and then suddenly dived downwards and came plump down right in the middle of Mr. Dodge's field of swedes!

Finally, as if not content with this desecration, it ran along the ground, ripping and tearing up twenty-five yards of good swedes, and then came to a stop. Old Sam Gates was in a terrible state. The aeroplane was more than a hundred yards away, but he waved his arms, and called out:

"Hi! you there, you mustn't land in they swedes! They're Mister Dodge's."

The instant the aeroplane stopped a man leapt out, and gazed quickly round. He glanced at Sam Gates, and seemed uncertain whether to address him or whether to concentrate his attention on the flying-machine. The latter arrangement appeared to be his ultimate decision. He dived under the engine, and became frantically busy. Sam had never seen any one work with such furious energy. But all the same, it was not to be tolerated. It was disgraceful. Sam shouted out across the field, almost hurrying in his indignation. When he approached within earshot of the aviator, he cried out again:

"Hi! you mustn't rest your old airyplane here. You've kicked up all Mr. Dodge's swedes. A nice thing you've done!"

He was within five yards when suddenly the aviator turned and covered him with a revolver! And, speaking in a sharp, staccato voice, he said:

"Old grandfather, you must sit down. I am very occupied. If you interfere or attempt to go away, I shoot you. So!"

Sam gazed at the horrid glittering little barrel, and gasped. Well, he never! To be threatened with murder when you're doing your duty in your employer's private property! But, still, perhaps the man was mad. A man must be more or less mad to go up in one of these crazy things. And life was very sweet on that summer morning, in spite of sixty-nine years. He sat down among the swedes.

The aviator was so busy with his cranks and machinery that he hardly deigned to pay him any attention, except to keep the revolver handy. He worked feverishly, and Sam sat watching him. At the end of ten minutes he seemed to have solved his troubles with the machine, but he still seemed very scared. He kept on glancing round and out to sea. When his repairs were completed, he straightened his back and wiped the perspiration from his brow. He was apparently on the point of springing back into the machine and going off, when a sudden mood of facetiousness, caused by relief from the strain he had endured, came to him. He turned to old Sam, and smiled; at the same time remarking:

"Well, old grandfather, and now we shall be all right, isn't it?"

He came close up to Sam, and then suddenly started back.

"Gott!" he cried. "Paul Jouperts!"

Sam gazed at him, bewildered, and the madman started talking to him in some foreign tongue. Sam shook his head.

"You no right," he remarked, "to come bargin' through they swedes of Mr. Dodge's."

And then the aviator behaved in a most peculiar manner. He came up and examined his face very closely, and gave a gentle tug at his beard and hair, as if to see whether it were real or false.

"What is your name, old man?" he said.

"Sam Gates."

The aviator muttered some words that sounded something like "mare vudish!" and then turned to his machine. He appeared to be dazed and in a great state of doubt. He fumbled with some cranks, but kept glancing at old Sam. At last he got into the car and started the engine. Then he stopped, and sat there deep in thought. At last he suddenly sprang out again, and approaching Sam, he said very deliberately:

"Old grandfather, I shall require you to accompany me "

Sam gasped.

"Eh?" he said. "What be talking' about? 'company? I got these here lines o' tarnips—I be already behoind——"

The disgusting little revolver once more flashed before his eyes.

"There must be no discussion," came the voice. "It is necessary that you mount the seat of the car without delay. Otherwise I shoot you like the dog you are. So!"

Old Sam was hale and hearty. He had no desire to die so ignominiously. The pleasant smell of the downland was in his nostrils. His foot was on his native heath. He mounted the seat of the car, contenting himself with a mutter:

"Well, that be a noice thing, I must say! Flyin' about the country with all they tarnips on'y half thinned——"

He found himself strapped in. The aviator was in a fever of anxiety to get away. The engines made a ghastly splutter and noise. The thing started running along the ground. Suddenly it shot upwards giving the swedes a last contemptuous kick. At twenty minutes to eight that morning old Sam found himself being borne right up above his fields and out to sea! His breath came quickly. He was a little frightened.

"God forgive me!" he murmured.

The thing was so fantastic and sudden, his mind could not grasp it. He only felt in some vague way that he was going to die, and he struggled to attune his mind to the change. He offered up a mild prayer to God, Who, he felt, must be very near, somewhere up in these clouds. Automatically he thought of the vicar at Halvesham, and a certain sense of comfort came to him at the reflection that on the previous day he had taken a "cooking of runner beans" to God's representative in that village. He felt calmer after that, but the horrid machine seemed to go higher and higher. He could not turn in his seat and he could see nothing but sea and sky. Of course the man was mad, mad as a March hare. Of what earthly use could *he* be to any one? Besides, he had talked pure gibberish, and called him Paul something, when he had already told him that his name was Sam. The thing would fall down into the sea soon, and they would both be drowned. Well, well! He had reached the three-score years and ten.

He was protected by a screen, but it seemed very cold. What on earth would Mr. Dodge say? There was no one left to work the land but a fool of a boy named Billy Whitehead at Deric's Cross. On, on, on they went at a furious pace. His thoughts danced disconnectedly from incidents of his youth, conversations with the vicar, hearty meals in the open, a frock his sister wore on the day of the postman's wedding, the drone of a psalm, the illness of some ewes belonging to Mr. Dodge. Everything seemed to be moving very rapidly, upsetting his sense of time. He felt outraged and yet at moments there was something entrancing in the wild experience. He seemed to be living at an incredible pace. Perhaps he was really dead, and on his way to the Kingdom of God? Perhaps this was the way they took people?

After some indefinite period he suddenly caught sight of a long strip of land. Was this a foreign country? or were they returning? He had by this time lost all feeling of fear. He became interested, and almost disappointed. The "airyplane" was not such a fool as it looked. It was very wonderful to be right up in the sky like this. His dreams were suddenly disturbed by a fearful noise. He thought the machine was blown to pieces. It dived and ducked through the air, and things were bursting all round it and making an awful din; and then it went up higher and higher. After a while these noises ceased, and he felt the machine gliding downwards. They were really right above solid land, trees, and fields, and streams, and white villages. Down, down, down they glided. This was a foreign country. There were straight avenues of poplars and canals. This was not Halvesham. He felt the thing glide gently and bump into a field. Some men ran forward and approached them, and the mad aviator called out to them. They were mostly fat men in gray uniforms, and they all spoke this foreign gibberish. Some one came and unstrapped him. He was very stiff, and could hardly move. An exceptionally gross-looking man punched him in the ribs, and roared with laughter. They all stood round and laughed at him, while the mad aviator talked to them and kept pointing at him. Then he said:

"Old grandfather, you must come with me."

He was led to a zinc-roofed building, and shut in a little room. There were guards outside with fixed bayonets. After a while the mad aviator appeared again, accompanied by two soldiers. He beckoned him to follow. They marched through a quadrangle and entered another building. They went straight into an office where a very important-looking man, covered with medals, sat in an easy-chair. There was a lot of saluting and clicking of heels.

The aviator pointed at Sam and said something, and the man with the medals started at sight of him, and then came up and spoke to him in English.

"What is your name? Where do you come from? Your age? The name and birthplace of your parents?"

He seemed intensely interested, and also pulled his hair and beard to see if they came off. So well and naturally did he and the aviator speak English that after a voluble cross-examination they drew apart, and continued the conversation in that language. And the extraordinary conversation was of this nature:

"It is a most remarkable resemblance," said the man with medals. "*Unglaublich!* But what do you want me to do with him, Hausemann?"

"The idea came to me suddenly, excellency," replied the aviator, "and you may consider it worthless. It is just this. The resemblance is so amazing. Paul Jouperts has given us more valuable information than any one at present in our service. And the English know that. There is an award of twenty-five thousand francs on his head. Twice they have captured him, and each time he escaped. All the company commanders and their staff have his photograph. He is a serious thorn in their flesh."

"Well?" replied the man with the medals.

The aviator whispered confidently:

"Suppose, your excellency, that they found the dead body of Paul Jouperts?"

"Well?" replied the big man.

"My suggestion is this. Tomorrow, as you know, the English are attacking Hill 701, which we have for tactical reasons decided to evacuate. If after the attack they find the dead body of Paul Jouperts in, say, the second lines, they will take no further trouble in the matter. You know their lack of thoroughness. Pardon me, I was two years at Oxford University. And consequently Paul Jouperts will be able to—prosecute his labors undisturbed."

The man with the medals twirled his mustache and looked thoughtfully at his colleague.

"Where is Paul at the moment?" he asked.

"He is acting as a gardener at the Convent of St. Eloise at Mailleton-en-haut, which, as you know, is one hundred meters from the headquarters of the British central army staff."

The man with the medals took two or three rapid turns up and down the room. Then he said:

"Your plan is excellent, Hausemann. The only point of difficulty is that the attack started this morning."

"This morning?" exclaimed the other.

"Yes. The English attacked unexpectedly at dawn. We have already evacuated the first line. We shall evacuate the second line at eleven-fifty. It is now ten-fifteen. There may be just time."

He looked suddenly at old Sam in the way that a butcher might look at a prize heifer at an agricultural show, and remarked casually:

"Yes, it is a remarkable resemblance. It seems a pity not to . . . do something with it."

Then, speaking in German, he added:

"It is worth trying, and if it succeeds, the higher authorities shall hear of your lucky accident and inspiration, Herr Hausemann. Instruct Over-lieutenant Schutz to send the old fool by two orderlies to the east extremity of trench 38. Keep him there till the order of evacuation is given. Then shoot him, but don't disfigure him, and lay him out face upwards."

The aviator saluted and withdrew, accompanied by his victim. Old Sam had not understood the latter part of the conversation, and he did not catch quite all that was said in English, but he felt that somehow things were not becoming too promising and it was time to assert himself. So he remarked when they got outside:

"Now, look'ee here, mister, when be I goin' back to my tarnips?"

And the aviator replied with a pleasant smile:

"Do not be disturbed, old grandfather; you shall . . . get back to the soil quite soon."

In a few moments he found himself in a large gray car, accompanied by four soldiers. The aviator left him. The country was barren and horrible, full of great pits and rents, and he could hear the roar of artillery and the shriek of shells. Overhead, aeroplanes were buzzing angrily. He seemed to be suddenly transported from the Kingdom of God to the Pit of Darkness. He wondered whether the vicar had enjoyed the runner-beans. He could not imagine runner-beans growing here, runner-beans, ay! or anything else. If this was a foreign country, give him dear old England.

Gr-r-r-r—Bang! Something exploded just at the rear of the car. The soldiers ducked, and one of them pushed him in the stomach and swore.

"An ugly-looking lout," he thought. "If I was twenty years younger I'd give him a punch in the eye that 'ud make him sit up."

The car came to a halt by a broken wall. The party hurried out and dived behind a mound. He was pulled down a kind of shaft and found himself in a room buried right underground, where three officers were drinking and smoking. The soldiers saluted and handed a typewritten dispatch. The officers looked at him drunkenly, and one came up and pulled his beard and spat in his face, and called him "an old English swine." He then shouted out some instructions to the soldiers, and they led him out into the narrow trench. One walked behind him and occasionally prodded him with the butt end of a gun. The trenches were half-full of water, and reeked of gases, powder, and decaying matter.

Shells were constantly bursting overhead, and in places the trenches had crumbled and were nearly blocked up. They stumbled on, sometimes falling, sometimes dodging moving masses, and occasionally crawling over the dead bodies of men. At last they reached a deserted-looking trench, and one of the soldiers pushed him into the corner of it and growled something, and then disappeared round the angle. Old Sam was exhausted. He lay panting against the mud wall, expecting every minute to be blown to pieces by one of those infernal things that seemed to be getting more and more insistent. The din went on for nearly twenty minutes, and he was alone in the trench. He fancied he heard a whistle amidst the din. Suddenly one of the soldiers who had accompanied him came stealthily round the corner. And there was a look in his eye old Sam did not like. When he was within five yards the soldier raised his rifle and pointed it at Sam's body. Some instinct impelled the old man at that instant to throw himself forward on his face. As he did so, he was conscious of a terrible explosion, and he had just time to observe the soldier falling in a heap near him, when he lost consciousness.

His consciousness appeared to return to him with a snap. He was lying on a plank in a building, and he heard some one say:

"I believe the old boy's English."

He looked round. There were a lot of men lying there, and others in khaki and white overalls were busy amongst them. He sat up and rubbed his head and said:

"Hi, mister, where be I now?"

Some one laughed, and a young man came up and said:

"Well, old thing, you were very nearly in hell. Who the devil are you?"

Some one else came up, and the two of them were discussing him. One of them said:

"He's quite all right. He was only knocked out. Better take him to the colonel. He may be a spy."

The other came up, and touched his shoulder, and remarked:

"Can you walk, uncle?"

He replied: "Ay, I can walk all right."

"That's an old sport!"

The young man took his arm and helped him out of the room, into a courtyard. They entered another room, where an elderly kind-faced officer was seated at a desk. The officer looked up, and exclaimed:

"Good God! Bradshaw, do you know who you've got there?"

The younger one said, "No. Who, sir?"

"By God! It's Paul Jouperts!" exclaimed the colonel.

"Paul Jouperts! Great Scott!"

The old officer addressed himself to Sam. He said:

"Well, we've got you once more, Paul. We shall have to be a little more careful this time."

The young officer said: "Shall I detail a squad, sir?"

"We can't shoot him without a court-martial," replied the kind-faced senior.

Then Sam interpolated:

"Look'ee here, sir. I'm fair sick of all this. My name bean't Paul. My name's Sam. I was a-thinnin' a line of tarnips——"

Both officers burst out laughing, and the younger one said:

"Good! damn good! Isn't it amazing, sir, the way they not only learn the language but even take the trouble to learn a dialect?"

The older man busied himself with some papers.

"Well, Sam," he remarked, "you shall be given a chance to prove your identity. Our methods are less drastic than those of your Boche masters. What part of England are you supposed to come from? Let's see how much you can bluff us with your topographical knowledge."

"Oi was a-thinnin' a loine o' tarnips this morning at 'alf-past seven on Mr. Dodge's farm at Halvesham, when one o' these 'ere airyplanes come roight down among the swedes. I tells 'e to get clear o' that, when the feller what gets owt o' the car, 'e drahs a revowler and 'e says, 'You must 'company I——'"

"Yes, yes," interrupted the senior officer; "that's all very good. Now tell me—Where is Halvesham? What is the name of the local vicar? I'm sure you'd know that."

Old Sam rubbed his chin.

"I sits under the Reverend David Pryce, mister, and a good God-fearin' man he be. I took him a cookin' o' runner-beans on'y yesterday. I works for Mr. Dodge what owns Greenway Manor and 'as a stud-farm at Newmarket they say."

"Charles Dodge?" asked the younger officer.

"Ay, Charlie Dodge. You write and ask 'un if he knows old Sam Gates."

The two officers looked at each other, and the older one looked at Sam more closely.

"It's very extraordinary," he remarked.

"Everybody knows Charlie Dodge," added the younger officer.

It was at that moment that a wave of genius swept over old Sam. He put his hand to his head, and suddenly jerked out:

"What's more, I can tell 'ee where this yere Paul is. He's actin' a gardener in a convent at——"

He puckered up his brow and fumbled with his hat, and then got out:

"Mighteno."

The older officer gasped. "Mailleton-en-haut! Good God! What makes you say that, old man?"

Sam tried to give an account of his experience, and the things he had heard said by the German officers. But he was getting tired, and he broke off in the middle to say:

"Ye haven't a bite o' somethin' to eat, I suppose, mister, and a glass o' beer? I usually 'as my dinner at twelve o'clock."

Both the officers laughed, and the older said:

"Get him some food, Bradshaw, and a bottle of beer from the mess. We'll keep this old man here. He interests me."

While the younger man was doing this, the chief pressed a button and summoned another junior officer.

"Gateshead," he remarked, "ring up G. H. Q. and instruct them to arrest the gardener in that convent at the top of the hill, and then to report."

The officer saluted and went out, and in a few minutes a tray of hot food and a large bottle of beer was brought to the old man, and he was left alone in the corner of the room to negotiate this welcome compensation. And in the execution he did himself and his country credit. In the meanwhile the officers were very busy. People were coming and going and examining maps and telephone bells were ringing furiously. They did not disturb old Sam's gastronomic operations. He cleaned up the mess tins and finished the last drop of beer. The senior officer found time to offer him a cigarette, but he replied:

"Thank 'ee kindly, but I'd rather smoke my pipe."

The colonel smiled, and said:

"Oh, all right. Smoke away."

He lighted up, and the fumes of the shag permeated the room. Some one opened another window, and the young officer who had addressed him at first suddenly looked at him and exclaimed:

"Innocent, by God! You couldn't get shag like that anywhere but in Norfolk."

It must have been over an hour later when another officer entered, and saluted.

"Message from G. H. Q., sir," he said.

"Well?"

"They have arrested the gardener at the convent of St. Eloise, and they have every reason to believe that he is the notorious Paul Jouperts."

The colonel stood up, and his eyes beamed. He came over to old Sam and shook his hand.

"Mr. Gates," he said, "you are an old brick. You will probably hear more of this. You have probably been the means of delivering something very useful into our hands. Your own honor is vindicated. A loving government will probably award you five shillings, or a Victoria Cross, or something of that sort. In the meantime, what can I do for you?"

Old Sam scratched his chin.

"Oi want to get back 'ome," he said.

"Well, even that might be arranged."

"Oi want to get back 'ome in toime for tea."

"What time do you have tea?"

"Foive o'clock or thereabouts."

"I see."

A kindly smile came into the eyes of the colonel. He turned to another officer standing by the table, and said:

"Raikes, is any one going across this afternoon with dispatches?"

"Yes, sir," replied the young officer. "Commander Jennings is leaving at three o'clock."

"You might ask him to come and see me."

Within ten minutes a young man in a flight-commander's uniform entered.

"Ah, Jennings," said the colonel, "here is a little affair which concerns the honor of the British army. My friend here, Sam Gates, has come over from Halvesham in Norfolk in order to give us valuable information. I have promised him that he shall get home to tea at five o'clock. Can you take a passenger?"

The young man threw back his head and laughed.

"Lord!" he exclaimed. "What an old sport! Yes, I expect I could just manage it. Where is the God-forsaken place?"

A large ordnance map of Norfolk (which had been captured from a German officer) was produced, and the young man studied it closely.

At three o'clock precisely old Sam, finding himself something of a hero and quite glad to escape from the embarrassment which this position entailed, once more sped skywards in an "airyplane."

At twenty minutes to five he landed once more amongst Mr. Dodge's swedes. The breezy young airman shook hands with him and departed inland. Old Sam sat down and surveyed the field.

"A noice thing, I must say," he muttered to himself, as he looked along the lines of unthinned turnips. He still had twenty minutes, and so he went slowly along and completed a line which he had commenced in the morning. He then deliberately packed up his dinner things and his tools, and started out for home.

As he came round the corner of Stillway's Meadow, and the cottage came in view, his niece stepped out of the copse with a basket on her arm.

"Well, uncle," she said, "is there any noos?"

It was then that old Sam became really irritated.

"Noos!" he said. "Noos! drat the girl! What noos should there be? Sixty-nine year I live in these here parts, hoein' and weedin' and thinnin,' and mindin' Charlie Dodge's sheep. Am I one o' these here story book folk havin' noos 'appen to me all the time? Ain't it enough, ye silly dab-faced zany, to earn enough to buy a bite o' some'at to eat, and a glass of beer, and a place to rest a's head o'night, without always wantin' noos, noos, noos! I tell 'ee, it's this that leads 'ee to 'alf the troubles in the world. Devil take the noos!"

And turning his back on her, he went fuming up the hill.

THE FAT OF THE LAND

By *Anzia Yezierska*

[The 1919 volume of O'Brien's *Best Short Stories* was dedicated to Anzia Yezierska, and *The Fat of the Land* was reprinted from the *Century Magazine* as the best short story Mr. O'Brien found in the American magazines for that year. Miss Yezierska was born in Russia in 1885, came to the United States in 1901, and became a naturalized citizen in 1912. She educated herself and learned about life as she worked in factories, shops, and private families. She has continued, since the publication of this excellent story in 1919, to write many good stories. Her stories to 1934 make up seven volumes. She has made her American home in New York and New England.

The Fat of the Land is reprinted here by permission of the author.]

IN an air-shaft so narrow that you could touch the next wall with your bare hands, Hanneh Breineh leaned out and knocked on her neighbor's window.

"Can you loan me your wash-boiler for the clothes?" she called.

Mrs. Pelz threw up the sash.

"The boiler? What's the matter with yours again? Didn't you tell me you had it fixed already last week?"

"A black year on him, the robber, the way he fixed it! If you have no luck in this world, then it's better not to live. There I spent out fifteen cents to stop up one hole, and it runs out another. How I ate out my gall bargaining with him he should let it down to fifteen cents! He wanted yet a quarter, the swindler. *Gottuniu!* my bitter heart on him for every penny he took from me for nothing!"

"You got to watch all those swindlers, or they'll steal the whites out of your eyes," admonished Mrs. Pelz. "You should have tried out your boiler before you paid him. Wait a minute till I empty out my dirty clothes in a pillow-case; then I'll hand it to you."

Mrs. Pelz returned with the boiler and tried to hand it across to Hanneh Breineh, but the soap-box refrigerator in the window was in the way.

"You got to come in for the boiler yourself," said Mrs. Pelz.

"Wait only till I tie my Sammy on to the high-chair he shouldn't fall on me again. He's so wild that ropes won't hold him."

Hanneh Breineh tied the child in the chair, stuck a pacifier in his mouth, and went in to her neighbor. As she took the boiler Mrs. Pelz said:

"Do you know Mrs. Melker ordered fifty pounds of chicken for her daughter's wedding? And such grand chickens! Shining like gold! My heart melted in me just looking at the flowing fatness of those chickens."

Hanneh Breineh smacked her thin, dry lips, a hungry gleam in her sunken eyes.

"Fifty pounds!" she gasped. "It ain't possible. How do you know?"

"I heard her with my own ears. I saw them with my own eyes. And she said she will chop up the chicken livers with onions and eggs for an appetizer, and then she will buy twenty-five pounds of fish, and cook it sweet and sour with raisins, and she said she will bake all her strudels on pure chicken fat."

"Some people work themselves up in the world," sighed Hanneh Breineh. "For them is America flowing with milk and honey. In Savel Mrs. Melker used to get shriveled up from hunger. She and her children used to live on potato peelings and crusts of dry bread picked out from the barrels; and in America she lives to eat chicken, and apple strudels soaking in fat."

"The world is a wheel always turning," philosophized Mrs. Pelz. "Those who were high go down low, and those who've been low go up higher. Who will believe me here in America that in Poland I was a cook in a banker's house? I handled ducks and geese every day. I used to bake coffee-cake with cream so thick you could cut it with a knife."

"And do you think I was a nobody in Poland?" broke in Hanneh Breineh, tears welling in her eyes as the memories of her past rushed over her. "But what's the use of talking? In America money is everything. Who cares who my father or grandfather was in Poland? Without money I'm a living dead one. My head dries out worrying how to get for the children the eating a penny cheaper."

Mrs. Pelz wagged her head, a gnawing envy contracting her features.

"Mrs. Melker had it good from the day she came," she said begrudgingly. "Right away she sent all her children to the factory, and she began to cook meat for dinner every day. She and her children have eggs and buttered rolls for breakfast each morning like millionaires."

A sudden fall and a baby's scream, and the boiler dropped from Hanneh Breineh's hands as she rushed into her kitchen, Mrs. Pelz after her. They found the high-chair turned on top of the baby.

"*Gewalt!* Save me! Run for a doctor!" cried Hanneh Breineh as she dragged the child from under the high-chair. "He's killed! He's killed! My only child! My precious lamb!" she shrieked as she ran back and forth with the screaming infant.

Mrs. Pelz snatched little Sammy from the mother's hands.

"*Meshugneh!* what are you running around like a crazy, frightening the child? Let me see. Let me tend to him. He ain't killed yet." She hastened to the sink to wash the child's face, and discovered a swelling lump on his forehead. "Have you a quarter in your house?" she asked.

"Yes, I got one," replied Hanneh Breineh, climbing on a chair. "I got to keep it on a high shelf where the children can't get it."

Mrs. Pelz seized the quarter Hanneh Breineh handed down to her.

"Now pull your left eyelid three times while I'm pressing the quarter, and you will see the swelling go down."

Hanneh Breineh took the child again in her arms, shaking and cooing over it and caressing it.

"Ah-ah-ah, Sammy! Ah-ah-ah-ah, little lamb! Ah-ah-ah, little bird! Ah-ah-ah-ah, precious heart! Oh, you saved my life; I thought he was killed," gasped Hanneh Breineh, turning to Mrs. Pelz. "*Oi-i!*" she sighed, "a mother's heart! always in fear over her children. The minute anything happens to them all life goes out of me. I lose my head and I don't know where I am any more."

"No wonder the child fell," admonished Mrs. Pelz. "You should have a red ribbon or red beads on his neck to keep away the evil eye. Wait. I got something in my machine-drawer."

Mrs. Pelz returned, bringing the boiler and a red string, which she tied about the child's neck while the mother proceeded to fill the boiler.

A little later Hanneh Breineh again came into Mrs. Pelz's kitchen, holding Sammy in one arm and in the other an apronful of potatoes. Putting the child down on the floor, she seated herself on the unmade kitchen-bed and began to peel the potatoes in her apron.

"Woe to me!" sobbed Hanneh Breineh. "To my bitter luck there ain't no end. With all my other troubles, the stove got broke. I lighted the fire to boil the clothes, and it's to get choked with smoke. I paid rent only a week ago, and the agent don't want to fix it. A thunder should strike him! He only comes for the rent, and if anything has to be fixed, then he don't want to hear nothing."

"Why comes it to me so hard?" went on Hanneh Breineh, the tears streaming down her cheeks. "I can't stand it no more. I came into you for a minute to run away from my troubles. It's only when I sit myself down to peel potatoes or nurse the baby that I take time to draw a breath, and beg only for death."

Mrs. Pelz, accustomed to Hanneh Breineh's bitter outbursts, continued her scrubbing.

"*Ut!*" exclaimed Hanneh Breineh, irritated at her neighbor's silence, "what are you tearing up the world with your cleaning? What's the use to clean up when everything only gets dirty again?"

"I got to shine up my house for the holidays."

"You've got it so good nothing lays on your mind but to clean your house. Look on this little blood-sucker," said Hanneh Breineh, pointing to the wizened child, made prematurely solemn from starvation and neglect. "Could anybody keep that brat clean? I wash him one minute, and he is dirty the minute after." Little Sammy grew frightened and began to cry. "Shut up!" ordered the mother, picking up the child to nurse it again. "Can't you see me take a rest for a minute?"

The hungry child began to cry at the top of its weakened lungs.

"*Na, na,* you glutton." Hanneh Breineh took out a dirty pacifier from her pocket and stuffed it into the baby's mouth. The grave, pasty-faced infant shrank into a panic of fear, and chewed the nipple nervously, clinging to it with both his thin little hands.

"For what did I need yet the sixth one?" groaned Hanneh Breineh, turning to Mrs. Pelz. "Wasn't it enough five mouths to feed? If I didn't have this child on my neck, I could turn myself around and earn a few cents." She wrung her hands in a passion of despair. "*Gottuniu!* the earth should only take it back before it grows up!"

"Pshaw! Pshaw!" reproved Mrs. Pelz. "Pity yourself on the child. Let it grow up already so long as it is here. See how frightened it looks on you." Mrs. Pelz took the child in her arms and petted it. "The poor little lamb! What did it done you should hate it so?"

Hanneh Breineh pushed Mrs. Pelz away from her.

"To whom can I open the wounds of my heart?" she moaned. "Nobody has pity on me. You don't believe me, nobody believes me until I'll fall down like a horse in the middle of the street. *Oi weh!* mine life is so black for my eyes! Some mothers got luck. A child gets run over by a car, some fall from a window, some burn themselves up with a match, some get choked with diphtheria; but no death takes mine away."

"God from the world! stop cursing!" admonished Mrs. Pelz. "What do you want from the poor children? Is it their fault that their father makes small wages? Why do you let it all out on them?" Mrs. Pelz sat down beside Hanneh Breineh. "Wait only till your children get old enough to go to the shop and earn money," she consoled. "Push only through those few years while they are yet small; your sun will begin to shine, you will live on the fat of the land, when they begin to bring you in the wages each week."

Hanneh Breineh refused to be comforted.

"Till they are old enough to go to the shop and earn money they'll eat the head off my bones," she wailed. "If you only knew the fights I got by each meal. Maybe I gave Abe a bigger piece of bread than Fanny. Maybe Fanny got a little more soup in her plate than Jake. Eating is dearer than diamonds. Potatoes went up a cent on a pound, and milk is only for millionaires. And once a week, when I buy a little meat for the Sabbath, the butcher weighs it for me like gold, with all the bones in it. When I come to lay the meat out on a plate and divide it up, there ain't nothing to it but bones. Before, he used to throw me in a piece of fat extra or a piece of lung, but now you got to pay for everything, even a bone to the soup."

"Never mind; you'll yet come out from all your troubles. Just as soon as your children get old enough to get their working papers the more children you got, the more money you'll have."

"Why should I fool myself with the false shine of hope? Don't I know it's already my black luck not to have it good in this world? Do you think American children will right away give everything they earn to their mother?"

"I know what is with you the matter," said Mrs. Pelz. "You didn't eat yet today. When it is empty in the stomach, the whole world looks black. Come, only let me give you something good to taste in the mouth; that will freshen you up." Mrs. Pelz went to the cupboard and brought out the saucepan of *gefülte* fish that she had cooked for dinner and placed it on the table in front of Hanneh Breineh. "Give a taste my fish," she said, taking one slice on a spoon, and handing it to Hanneh Breineh with a piece of bread. "I wouldn't give it to you on a plate because I just cleaned out my house, and I don't want to dirty up my dishes."

"What, am I a stranger you should have to serve me on a plate yet!" cried Hanneh Breineh, snatching the fish in her trembling fingers.

"*Oi weh!* how it melts through all the bones!" she exclaimed, brightening as she ate. "May it be for good luck to us all!" she exulted, waving aloft the last precious bite.

Mrs. Pelz was so flattered that she even ladled up a spoonful of gravy.

"There is a bit of onion and carrot in it," she said as she handed it to her neighbor.

Hanneh Breineh sipped the gravy drop by drop, like a connoisseur sipping wine.

"Ah-h-h! a taste of that gravy lifts me up to heaven!" As she disposed leisurely of the slice of onion and carrot she relaxed and expanded and even grew jovial. "Let us wish all our troubles on the Russian Czar! Let him burst with our worries for rent! Let him get shriveled with our hunger for bread! Let his eyes dry out of his head looking for work!

"Pshaw! I'm forgetting from everything," she exclaimed, jumping up. "It must be eleven or soon twelve, and my children will be right away out of school and fall on me like a pack of wild wolves. I better quick run to the market and see what cheaper I can get for a quarter."

Because of the lateness of her coming, the stale bread at the nearest bake-shop was sold out, and Hanneh Breineh had to trudge from shop to shop in search of the usual bargain, and spent nearly an hour to save two cents.

In the meantime the children returned from school, and, finding the door locked, climbed through the fire-escape, and entered the house through the window. Seeing nothing on the table, they rushed to the stove. Abe pulled a steaming potato out of the boiling pot, and so scalded his fingers that the potato fell to the floor; whereupon the three others pounced on it.

"It was my potato," cried Abe, blowing his burned fingers, while with the other hand and his foot he cuffed and kicked the three who were struggling on the floor. A wild fight ensued, and the potato was smashed under Abe's foot amid shouts and screams. Hanneh Breineh, on the stairs, heard the noise of her famished brood, and topped their cries with curses and invectives.

"They are here already, the savages! They are here already to shorten my life! They heard you all over the hall, in all the houses around!"

The children, disregarding her words, pounced on her market-basket, shouting ravenously: "Mama, I'm hungry! What more do you got to eat?"

They tore the bread and herring out of Hanneh Breineh's basket and devoured it in starved savagery, clamoring for more.

"Murderers!" screamed Hanneh Breineh, goaded beyond endurance. "What are you tearing from me my flesh? From where should I steal to give you more? Here I had already a pot of potatoes and a whole loaf of bread and two herrings, and you swallowed it down in the wink of an eye. I have to have Rockefeller's millions to fill your stomachs."

All at once Hanneh Breineh became aware that Benny was missing. "*Oi weh!*" she burst out, wringing her hands in a new wave of woe, "where is Benny? Didn't he come home yet from school?"

She ran out into the hall, opened the grime-coated window, and looked up and down the street; but Benny was nowhere in sight.

"Abe, Jake, Fanny, quick, find Benny!" entreated Hanneh Breineh as she rushed back into the kitchen. But the children, anxious to snatch a few minutes' play before the school-call, dodged past her and hurried out.

With the baby on her arm, Hanneh Breineh hastened to the kindergarten.

"Why are you keeping Benny here so long?" she shouted at the teacher, as she flung open the door. "If you had my bitter heart, you would send him home long ago and not wait till I got to come for him."

The teacher turned calmly and consulted her record-cards.

"Benny Safron? He wasn't present this morning."

"Not here?" shrieked Hanneh Breineh. "I pushed him out myself he should go. The children didn't want to take him, and I had no time. Woe is me! Where is my child?" She began pulling her hair and beating her breast as she ran into the street.

Mrs. Pelz was busy at a push-cart, picking over some spotted apples, when she heard the clamor of an approaching crowd. A block off she recognized Hanneh Breineh, her hair disheveled, her clothes awry, running toward her with her yelling baby in her arms, the crowd following.

"Friend mine," cried Hanneh Breineh, falling on Mrs. Pelz's neck, "I lost my Benny, the best child of all my children." Tears streamed down her red, swollen eyes as she sobbed. "Benny! mine heart, mine life! *Oi-i!*"

Mrs. Pelz took the frightened baby out of the mother's arms.

"Still yourself a little! See how you're frightening your child."

"Woe to me! Where is my Benny? Maybe he's killed already by a car. Maybe he fainted away from hunger. He didn't eat nothing all day long. *Gottuniu!* pity yourself on me!"

She lifted her hands full of tragic entreaty.

"People, my child! Get me my child! I'll go crazy out of my head! Get me my child, or I'll take poison before your eyes!"

"Still yourself a little!" pleaded Mrs. Pelz.

"Talk not to me!" cried Hanneh Breineh, wringing her hands. "You're having all your children. I lost mine. Every good luck comes to other people. But I didn't live yet to see a good day in my life. Mine only joy, mine Benny, is lost away from me."

The crowd followed Hanneh Breineh as she wailed through the streets, leaning on Mrs. Pelz. By the time she returned to her house the children were back from school; but seeing that Benny was not there, she chased them out in the street, crying:

"Out of here, you robbers, gluttons! Go find Benny!" Hanneh Breineh crumpled into a chair in utter prostration. "*Oi weh!* he's lost! Mine life; my little bird; mine only joy! How many nights I spent nursing him when he had the measles! And all that I suffered for weeks and months when he had the whooping-cough! How the eyes went out of my head till I learned him how to walk, till I learned him how to talk! And such a smart child! If I lost all the others, it wouldn't tear me so by the heart."

She worked herself up into such a hysteria, crying, and tearing her hair, and hitting her head with her knuckles, that at last she fell into a faint. It took some time before Mrs. Pelz, with the aid of neighbors, revived her.

"Benny, mine angel!" she moaned, as she opened her eyes.

Just then a policeman came in with the lost Benny.

"*Na, na,* here you got him already!" said Mrs. Pelz. "Why did you carry on so for nothing? Why did you tear up the world like a crazy?"

The child's face was streaked with tears as he cowered, frightened and forlorn. Hanneh Breineh sprang toward him, slapping his cheeks, boxing his ears, before the neighbors could rescue him from her.

"Woe on your head!" cried the mother. "Where did you lost yourself? Ain't I got enough worries on my head than to go around looking for you? I didn't have yet a minute's peace from that child since he was born."

"See a crazy mother!" remonstrated Mrs. Pelz, rescuing Benny from another beating. "Such a mouth! With one breath she blesses him when he is lost, and with the other breath she curses him when he is found."

Hanneh Breineh took from the window-sill a piece of herring covered with swarming flies, and putting it on a slice of dry bread, she filled a cup of tea that had been stewing all day, and dragged Benny over to the table to eat.

But the child, choking with tears, was unable to touch the food.

"Go eat!" commanded Hanneh Breineh. "Eat and choke yourself eating!"

"Maybe she won't remember me no more. Maybe the servant won't let me in," thought Mrs. Pelz as she walked by the brownstone house on Eighty-fourth Street where she had been told Hanneh Breineh now lived. At last she summoned up enough courage to climb the steps. She was all out of breath as she rang the bell with trembling fingers. "*Oi weh!* even the outside smells riches and plenty! Such curtains! And shades on all windows like by millionaires! Twenty years ago she used to eat from the pot to the hand, and now she lives in such a palace."

A whiff of steam-heated warmth swept over Mrs. Pelz as the door opened, and she saw her old friend of the tenements dressed in silk and diamonds like a being from another world.

"Mrs. Pelz, is it you!" cried Hanneh Breineh, overjoyed at the sight of her former neighbor. "Come right in. Since when are you back in New York?"

"We came last week," mumbled Mrs. Pelz as she was led into a richly carpeted reception-room.

"Make yourself comfortable. Take off your shawl," urged Hanneh Breineh.

But Mrs. Pelz only drew her shawl more tightly around her, a keen sense of her poverty gripping her as she gazed, abashed by the luxurious wealth that shone from every corner.

"This shawl covers up my rags," she said, trying to hide her shabby sweater.

"I'll tell you what; come right into the kitchen," suggested Hanneh Breineh. "The servant is away for this afternoon, and we can feel more comfortable there. I can breathe like a free person in my kitchen when the girl has her day out."

Mrs. Pelz glanced about her in an excited daze. Never in her life had she seen anything so wonderful as a white tiled kitchen, with its glistening porcelain sink and the aluminum pots and pans that shone like silver.

"Where are you staying now?" asked Hanneh Breineh as she pinned an apron over her silk dress.

"I moved back to Delancey Street, where we used to live," replied Mrs. Pelz as she seated herself cautiously in a white enameled chair.

"*Oi weh!* what grand times we had in that old house when we were neighbors!" sighed Hanneh Breineh, looking at her old friend with misty eyes.

"You still think on Delancey Street? Haven't you more high-class neighbors up-town here?"

"A good neighbor is not to be found every day," deplored Hanneh Breineh. "Up-town here, where each lives in his own house, nobody cares if the person next door is dying or going crazy from loneliness. It ain't anything like we used to have it in Delancey Street, when we could walk into one another's rooms without knocking, and borrow a pinch of salt or a pot to cook in."

Hanneh Breineh went over to the pantry-shelf.

"We are going to have a bite right here on the kitchen table like on Delancey Street. So long there's no servant to watch us we can eat what we please."

"*Oi!* how it waters my mouth with appetite, the smell of the herring and onion!" chuckled Mrs. Pelz, sniffing the welcome odors with greedy pleasure.

Hanneh Breineh pulled a dish-towel from the rack and threw one end of it to Mrs. Pelz.

"So long there's no servant around, we can use it together for a napkin. It's dirty, anyhow. How it freshens up my heart to see you!" she rejoiced as she poured out her tea into a saucer. "If you would only know how I used to beg my daughter to write for me a letter to you; but these American children, what is to them a mother's feelings?"

"What are you talking!" cried Mrs. Pelz. "The whole world rings with you and your children. Everybody is envying you. Tell me how began your luck?"

"You heard how my husband died with consumption," replied Hanneh Breineh. "The five-hundred-dollars lodge money gave me the first lift in life, and I opened a little grocery store. Then my son Abe married himself to a girl with a thousand dollars. That started him in a business, and now he has the biggest shirt-waist factory on West Twenty-ninth Street."

"Yes, I heard your son had a factory." Mrs. Pelz hesitated and stammered; "I'll tell you the truth. What I came to ask you—I thought maybe you would beg your son Abe if he would give my husband a job."

"Why not?" said Hanneh Breineh. "He keeps more than five hundred hands. I'll ask him he should take in Mr. Pelz."

"Long years on you, Hanneh Breineh! You'll save my life if you could only help my husband get work."

"Of course my son will help. All my children like to do good. My daughter Fanny is a milliner on Fifth Avenue, and she takes in the poorest girls in her shop and even pays them sometimes while they learn the trade." Hanneh Breineh's face lit up, and her chest filled with pride as she enumerated the successes of her children.

"And my son Benny he wrote a play on Broadway and he gave away more than a hundred free tickets for the first night."

"Benny? The one who used to get lost from home all the time? You always did love that child more than all the rest. And what is Sammy your baby doing?"

"He ain't a baby no longer. He goes to college and quarterbacks the football team. They can't get along without him.

"And my son Jake, I nearly forgot him. He began collecting rent in Delancey Street, and now he is boss of renting the swellest apartment-houses on Riverside Drive."

"What did I tell you? In America children are like money in the bank," purred Mrs. Pelz as she pinched and patted Hanneh Breineh's silk sleeve. "*Oi weh!* how it shines from you! You ought to kiss the air and dance for joy and happiness. It is such a bitter frost outside; a pail of coal is so dear, and you got it so warm with steam-heat. I had to pawn my feather-bed to have enough for the rent, and you are rolling in money."

"Yes, I got it good in some ways, but money ain't everything," sighed Hanneh Breineh.

"You ain't yet satisfied?"

"But here I got no friends," complained Hanneh Breineh.

"Friends?" queried Mrs. Pelz. "What greater friend is there on earth than the dollar?"

"*Oi!* Mrs. Pelz; if you could only look into my heart! I'm so choked up! You know they say, a cow has a long tongue, but can't talk." Hanneh Breineh shook her head wistfully, and her eyes filmed with inward brooding. "My children give me everything from the best. When I was sick, they got me a nurse by day and one by night. They bought me the best wine. If I asked for dove's milk, they would buy it for me; but—but—I can't talk myself out in their language. They want to make me over for an American lady, and I'm different." Tears cut their way under her eyelids with a pricking pain as she went on: "When I was poor, I was free, and could holler and do what I like in my own house. Here I got to lie still like a mouse under a broom. Between living up to my Fifth Avenue daughter and keeping up with the servants I am like a sinner in the next world that is thrown from one hell to another."

The door-bell rang, and Hanneh Breineh jumped up with a start.

"*Oi weh!* it must be the servant back already!" she exclaimed as she tore off her apron. "*Oi weh!* let's quickly put the dishes together in a dish-pan. If she sees I eat on the kitchen table, she will look on me like the dirt under her feet."

Mrs. Pelz seized her shawl in haste.

"I better run home quick in my rags before your servant sees me."

"I'll speak to Abe about the job," said Hanneh Breineh as she pushed a bill into the hand of Mrs. Pelz, who edged out as the servant entered.

"I'm having fried potato *lotkes* special for you, Benny," said Hanneh Breineh as the children gathered about the table for the family dinner given in honor of Benny's success with his new play. "Do you remember how you used to lick the fingers from them?"

"O Mother!" reproved Fanny. "Anyone hearing you would think we were still in the push-cart district."

"Stop your nagging, Sis, and let ma alone," commanded Benny, patting his mother's arm affectionately. "I'm home only once a month. Let her feed me what she pleases. My stomach is bomb-proof."

"Do I hear that the President is coming to your play?" said Abe as he stuffed a napkin over his diamond-studded shirt-front.

"Why shouldn't he come?" returned Benny. "The critics say it's the greatest antidote for the race hatred created by the war. If you want to know, he is coming tonight; and what's more, our box is next to the President's."

"*Nu*, Mammeh," sallied Jake, "did you ever dream in Delancey Street that we should rub sleeves with the President?"

"I always said that Benny had more head than the rest of you," replied the mother.

As the laughter died away, Jake went on:

"Honor you are getting plenty; but how much *mezummen* does this play bring you? Can I invest any of it in real estate for you?"

"I am getting ten per cent royalties of the gross receipts," replied the youthful playwright.

"How much is that?" queried Hanneh Breineh.

"Enough to buy up all your fish markets in Delancey Street," laughed Abe in good-natured raillery at his mother.

Her son's jest cut like a knife-thrust in her heart. She felt her heart ache with the pain that she was shut out from their successes. Each added triumph only widened the gulf. And when she tried to bridge this gulf by asking questions, they only thrust her back upon herself.

"Your fame has even helped me get my hat trade solid with the Four Hundred," put in Fanny. "You bet I let Mrs. Van Suyden know that our box is next to the President's. She said she would drop in to meet you. Of course she let on to me that she hadn't seen the play yet, though my designer said she saw her there on the opening night."

"Oh, gosh! the toadies!" sneered Benny. "Nothing so sickens you with success as the way people who once shoved you off the sidewalk come crawling to you on their stomachs begging you to dine with them."

"Say, that leading man of yours, he's some class!" cried Fanny. "That's the man I'm looking for. Will you invite him to supper after the theater?"

The playwright turned to his mother.

"Say, Ma," he said laughingly, "how would you like a real actor for a son-in-law?"

"She should worry," mocked Sam. "She'll be discussing with him the future of the Greek drama. Too bad it doesn't happen to be Warfield, or mother could give him tips on the 'Auctioneer.'"

Jake turned to his mother with a covert grin.

"I guess you'd have no objection if Fanny got next to Benny's leading man. He makes at least fifteen hundred a week. That wouldn't be such a bad addition to the family, would it?"

Again the bantering tone stabbed Hanneh Breineh. Everything in her began to tremble and break loose.

"Why do you ask me?" she cried, throwing her napkin into her plate. "Do I count for a person in this house? If I'll say something, will you even listen to me? What is to me the grandest man that my daughter could pick out? Another enemy in my house! Another person to shame himself from me!" She swept in her children in one glance of despairing anguish as she rose from the table. "What worth is an old mother to American children? The President is coming tonight to the theater, and none of you asked me to go." Unable to check the rising tears, she fled toward the kitchen and banged the door.

They all looked at one another guiltily.

"Say, Sis," Benny called out sharply, "what sort of frame-up is this? Haven't you told mother that she was to go with us to-night?"

"Yes—I—" Fanny bit her lips as she fumbled evasively for words. "I asked her if she wouldn't mind my taking her some other time."

"Now you have made a mess of it!" fumed Benny. "Mother'll be too hurt to go now."

"Well, I don't care," snapped Fanny. "I can't appear with mother in a box at the theater. Can I introduce her to Mrs. Van Suyden? And suppose your leading man should ask to meet me?"

"Take your time, Sis. He hasn't asked yet," scoffed Benny.

"The more reason I shouldn't spoil my chances. You know mother. She'll spill the beans that we come from Delancey Street the minute we introduce her anywhere. Must I always have the black shadow of my past trailing after me?"

"But have you no feelings for mother?" admonished Abe.

"I've tried harder than all of you to do my duty. I've *lived* with her." She turned angrily upon them. "I've borne the shame of mother while you bought her off with a present and a treat here and there. God knows how hard I tried to civilize her so as not to have to blush with shame when I take her anywhere. I dressed her in the most stylish Paris models, but Delancey Street sticks out from every inch of her. Whenever she opens her mouth, I'm done for. You fellows had your chance to rise in the world because a man is free to go up as high as he can reach up to; but I, with all my style and pep, can't get a man my equal because a girl is always judged by her mother."

They were silenced by her vehemence, and unconsciously turned to Benny.

"I guess we all tried to do our best for mother," said Benny thoughtfully. "But wherever there is growth, there is pain and heartbreak.

The trouble with us is that the Ghetto of the Middle Ages and the children of the twentieth century have to live under one roof, and—"

A sound of crashing dishes came from the kitchen, and the voice of Hanneh Breineh resounded through the dining-room as she wreaked her pent-up fury on the helpless servant.

"Oh, my nerves! I can't stand it any more! There will be no girl again for another week," cried Fanny.

"Oh, let up on the old lady," protested Abe. "Since she can't take it out on us any more, what harm is it if she cusses the servants?"

"If you fellows had to chase around employment agencies, you wouldn't see anything funny about it. Why can't we move into a hotel that will do away with the need of servants altogether?"

"I got it better," said Jake, consulting a note-book from his pocket. "I have on my list an apartment on Riverside Drive where there's only a small kitchenette; but we can do away with the cooking, for there is a dining service in the building."

The new Riverside apartment to which Hanneh Breineh was removed by her socially ambitious children was for the habitually active mother an empty desert of enforced idleness. Deprived of her kitchen, Hanneh Breineh felt robbed of the last reason for her existence. Cooking and marketing and puttering busily with pots and pans gave her an excuse for living and struggling and bearing up with her children. The lonely idleness of Riverside Drive stunned all her senses and arrested all her thoughts. It gave her that choked sense of being cut off from air, from life, from everything warm and human. The cold indifference, the each-for-himself look in the eyes of the people about her were like stinging slaps in the face. Even the children had nothing real or human in them. They were starched and stiff miniatures of their elders.

The most unendurable part of the stifling life on Riverside Drive was being forced to eat in the public dining-room. No matter how hard she tried to learn polite table manners, she always found people staring at her, and her daughter rebuking her for eating with the wrong fork or guzzling the soup or staining the cloth.

In a fit of rebellion Hanneh Breineh resolved never to go down to the public dining-room again, but to make use of the gas-stove in the kitchenette to cook her own meals. That very day she rode down to Delancey Street and purchased a new market-basket. For some time she walked among the haggling push-cart venders, relaxing and swimming in the warm waves of her old familiar past.

A fish-peddler held up a large carp in his black, hairy hand and waved it dramatically:

"Women! Women! Fourteen cents a pound!"

He ceased his raucous shouting as he saw Hanneh Breineh in her rich attire approach his cart.

"How much?" she asked, pointing to the fattest carp.

"Fifteen cents, lady," said the peddler, smirking as he raised his price.

"Swindler! Didn't I hear you call fourteen cents?" shrieked Hanneh Breineh, exultingly, the spirit of the penny chase surging in her blood. Diplomatically, Hanneh Breineh turned as if to go, and the fishman seized her basket in frantic fear.

"I should live; I'm losing money on the fish, lady," whined the peddler. "I'll let it down to thirteen cents for you only."

"Two pounds for a quarter, and not a penny more," said Hanneh Breineh, thrilling again with the rare sport of bargaining, which had been her chief joy in the good old days of poverty.

"*Nu*, I want to make the first sale for good luck." The peddler threw the fish on the scale.

As he wrapped up the fish, Hanneh Breineh saw the driven look of worry in his haggard eyes, and when he counted out for her the change from her dollar, she waved it aside.

"Keep it for your luck," she said, and hurried off to strike a new bargain at a push-cart of onions.

Hanneh Breineh returned triumphantly with her purchases. The basket under her arm gave forth the old, home-like odors of herring and garlic, while the scaly tail of a four-pound carp protruded from its newspaper wrapping. A gilded placard on the door of the apartment-house proclaimed that all merchandise must be delivered through the trade entrance in the rear; but Hanneh Breineh with her basket strode proudly through the marble-paneled hall and rang nonchalantly for the elevator.

The uniformed hall-man, erect, expressionless, frigid with dignity, stepped forward:

"Just a minute, Madam, I'll call a boy to take up your basket for you."

Hanneh Breineh, glaring at him, jerked the basket savagely from his hands.

"Mind your own business," she retorted. "I'll take it up myself. Do you think you're a Russian policeman to boss me in my own house?"

Angry lines appeared on the countenance of the representative of social decorum.

"It is against the rules, Madam," he said stiffly.

"You should sink into the earth with all your rules and brass buttons. Ain't this America? Ain't this a free country? Can't I take up in my own house what I buy with my own money?" cried Hanneh Breineh, reveling in the opportunity to shower forth the volley of invectives that had been suppressed in her for the weeks of deadly dignity of Riverside Drive.

In the midst of this uproar Fanny came in with Mrs. Van Suyden. Hanneh Breineh rushed over to her, crying:

"This bossy policeman won't let me take up my basket in the elevator."

The daughter, unnerved with shame and confusion, took the basket in her white-gloved hand and ordered the hall-boy to take it around to the regular delivery entrance.

Hanneh Breineh was so hurt by her daughter's apparent defense of the hall-man's rules that she utterly ignored Mrs. Van Suyden's greeting and walked up the seven flights of stairs out of sheer spite.

"You see the tragedy of my life?" broke out Fanny, turning to Mrs. Van Suyden.

"You poor child! You go right up to your dear, old lady mother, and I'll come some other time."

Instantly Fanny regretted her words. Mrs. Van Suyden's pity only roused her wrath the more against her mother.

Breathless from climbing the stairs, Hanneh Breineh entered the apartment just as Fanny tore the faultless millinery creation from her head and threw it on the floor in a rage.

"Mother, you are the ruination of my life! You have driven away Mrs. Van Suyden, as you have driven away all my best friends. What do you think we got this apartment for but to get rid of your fish smells and your brawls with the servants? And here you come with a basket on your arm as if you just landed from steerage! And this afternoon, of all times, when Benny is bringing his leading man to tea. When will you ever stop disgracing us?"

"When I'm dead," said Hanneh Breineh, grimly. "When the earth will cover me up, then you'll be free to go your American way. I'm not going to make myself over for a lady on Riverside Drive. I hate you and all your swell friends. I'll not let myself be choked up here by you or by that hall-boss-policeman that is higher in your eyes than your own mother."

"So that's your thanks for all we've done for you?" cried her daughter.

"All you've done for me?" shouted Hanneh Breineh. "What have you done for me? You hold me like a dog on a chain. It stands in the Talmud; some children give their mothers dry bread and water and go to heaven for it, and some give their mother roast duck and go to Gehenna because it's not given with love."

"You want me to love you yet?" raged the daughter. "You knocked every bit of love out of me when I was yet a kid. All the memories of childhood I have is your everlasting cursing and yelling that we were gluttons."

The bell rang sharply, and Hanneh Breineh flung open the door.

"Your groceries, ma'am," said the boy.

Hanneh Breineh seized the basket from him, and with a vicious fling sent it rolling across the room, strewing its contents over the Persian rugs and inlaid floor. Then seizing her hat and coat, she stormed out of the apartment and down the stairs.

Mr. and Mrs. Pelz sat crouched and shivering over their meager supper when the door opened, and Hanneh Breineh in fur coat and plumed hat charged into the room.

"I come to cry out to you my bitter heart," she sobbed. "Woe is me! It is so black for my eyes!"

"What is the matter with you, Hanneh Breineh?" cried Mrs. Pelz in bewildered alarm.

"I am turned out of my own house by the brass-buttoned policeman that bosses the elevator. *Oi-i-i-i! Weh-h-h-h!* what have I from my life? The whole world rings with my son's play. Even the President came to see it, and I, his mother, have not seen it yet. My heart is dying in me like in a prison," she went on wailing. "I am starved out for a piece of real eating. In that swell restaurant is nothing but napkins and forks and lettuce-leaves. There are a dozen plates to every bite of food. And it looks so fancy on the plate, but it's nothing but straw in the mouth. I'm starving, but I can't swallow down their American eating."

"Hanneh Breineh," said Mrs. Pelz, "you are sinning before God. Look on your fur coat; it alone would feed a whole family for a year. I never had yet a piece of fur trimming on a coat, and you are in fur from the neck to the feet. I never had yet a piece of feather on a hat, and your hat is all feathers."

"What are you envying me?" protested Hanneh Breineh. "What have I from all my fine furs and feathers when my children are strangers to me? All the fur coats in the world can't warm up the loneliness inside my heart. All the grandest feathers can't hide the bitter shame in my face that my children shame themselves from me."

Hanneh Breineh suddenly loomed over them like some ancient, heroic figure of the Bible condemning unrighteousness.

"Why should my children shame themselves from me? From where did they get the stuff to work themselves up in the world? Did they get it from the air? How did they get all their smartness to rise over the people around them? Why don't the children of born American mothers write my Benny's plays? It is I, who never had a chance to be a person, who gave him the fire in his head. If I would have had a chance to go to school and learn the language, what couldn't I have been? It is I and my mother and my mother's mother and my father and father's father who had such a black life in Poland; it is our choked thoughts and feelings that are flaming up in my children and making them great in America. And yet they shame themselves from me!"

For a moment Mr. and Mrs. Pelz were hypnotized by the sweep of her words. Then Hanneh Breineh sank into a chair in utter exhaustion. She began to weep bitterly, her body shaking with sobs.

"Woe is me! For what did I suffer and hope on my children? A bitter old age—my end. I'm so lonely!"

All the dramatic fire seemed to have left her. The spell was broken.

They saw the Hanneh Breineh of old, ever discontented, ever complaining even in the midst of riches and plenty.

"Hanneh Breineh," said Mrs. Pelz, "the only trouble with you is that you got it too good. People will tear the eyes out of your head because you're complaining yet. If I only had your fur coat! If I only had your diamonds! I have nothing. You have everything. You are living on the fat of the land. You go right back home and thank God that you don't have my bitter lot."

"You got to let me stay here with you," insisted Hanneh Breineh. "I'll not go back to my children except when they bury me. When they will see my dead face, they will understand how they killed me."

Mrs. Pelz glanced nervously at her husband. They barely had enough covering for their one bed; how could they possibly lodge a visitor?

"I don't want to take up your bed," said Hanneh Breineh. "I don't care if I have to sleep on the floor or on the chairs, but I'll stay here for the night."

Seeing that she was bent on staying, Mr. Pelz prepared to sleep by putting a few chairs next to the trunk, and Hanneh Breineh was invited to share the rickety bed with Mrs. Pelz.

The mattress was full of lumps and hollows. Hanneh Breineh lay cramped and miserable, unable to stretch out her limbs. For years she had been accustomed to hair mattresses and ample woolen blankets, so that though she covered herself with her fur coat, she was too cold to sleep. But worse than the cold were the creeping things on the wall. And as the lights were turned low, the mice came through the broken plaster and raced across the floor. The foul odors of the kitchen-sink added to the night of horrors.

"Are you going back home?" asked Mrs. Pelz as Hanneh Breineh put on her hat and coat the next morning.

"I don't know where I'm going," she replied as she put a bill into Mrs. Pelz's hand.

For hours Hanneh Breineh walked through the crowded Ghetto streets. She realized that she no longer could endure the sordid ugliness of her past, and yet she could not go home to her children. She only felt that she must go on and on.

In the afternoon a cold, drizzling rain set in. She was worn out from the sleepless night and hours of tramping. With a piercing pain in her heart she at last turned back and boarded the subway for Riverside Drive. She had fled from the marble sepulcher of the Riverside apartment to her old home in the Ghetto; but now she knew that she could not live there again. She had outgrown her past by the habits of years of physical comforts, and these material comforts that she could no longer do without choked and crushed the life within her.

A cold shudder went through Hanneh Breineh as she approached the apartment-house. Peering through the plate glass of the door, she saw the face of the uniformed hall-man. For a hesitating moment she remained standing in the drizzling rain, unable to enter and yet knowing full well that she would have to enter.

Then suddenly Hanneh Breineh began to laugh. She realized that it was the first time she had laughed since her children had become rich. But it was the hard laugh of bitter sorrow. Tears streamed down her furrowed cheeks as she walked slowly up the granite steps.

"The fat of the land!" muttered Hanneh Breineh, with a choking sob as the hall-man with immobile face deferentially swung open the door— "the fat of the land!"

THE FLY

By Katherine Mansfield

[Katherine Mansfield (1888–1923) in the few working years of her short life proved herself to be an unusually keen observer and a capable artist in the use of the short story form. She was born in New Zealand, educated in England, became the wife of the critic, J. Middleton Murry, and developed a highly individual style of writing that attracted much attention. Her stories have been collected in three volumes: *Bliss, and Other Stories* (1920), *The Garden Party, and Other Stories* (1922), and *The Dove's Nest, and Other Stories* (1923). The stories of hers that are best known in the United States are: *Marriage à la Mode*, *The Garden Party*, *The Doll's House*, *The Fly*, *A Cup of Tea*, and *The Daughters of the Late Colonel*.

The Fly is reprinted from *The Dove's Nest* (copyright 1923), by permission of Alfred A. Knopf, Inc., publishers.]

'Y'ARE very snug in here,' piped old Mr. Woodifield, and he peered out of the great, green leather arm-chair by his friend, the boss's desk, as a baby peers out of its pram. His talk was over; it was time for him to be off. But he did not want to go. Since he had retired, since his . . . stroke, the wife and the girls kept him boxed up in the house every day of the week except Tuesday. On Tuesday he was dressed up and brushed and allowed to cut back to the City for the day. Though what he did there the wife and girls couldn't imagine. Made a nuisance of himself to his friends, they supposed. . . . Well, perhaps so. All the same, we cling to our last pleasures as the tree clings to its last leaves. So there sat old Woodifield, smoking a cigar and staring almost greedily at the boss, who rolled in his office chair, stout, rosy, five years older than he, and still going strong, still at the helm. It did one good to see him.

Wistfully, admiringly, the old voice added, 'It's snug in here, upon my word!'

'Yes, it's comfortable enough,' agreed the boss, and he flipped the *Financial Times* with a paper-knife. As a matter of fact he was proud of his room; he liked to have it admired, especially by old Woodifield. It gave him a feeling of deep, solid satisfaction to be planted there in the midst of it in full view of that frail old figure in the muffler.

'I've had it done up lately,' he explained, as he had explained for the past—how many?—weeks. 'New carpet,' and he pointed to the bright red carpet with a pattern of large white rings. 'New furniture,' and he nodded towards the massive bookcase and the table with legs like twisted treacle. 'Electric heating!' He waved almost exultantly towards the five transparent, pearly sausages glowing so softly in the tilted copper pan.

But he did not draw old Woodifield's attention to the photograph over the table of a grave-looking boy in uniform standing in one of those spectral photographers' parks with photographers' storm-clouds behind him. It was not new. It had been there for over six years.

'There was something I wanted to tell you,' said old Woodifield, and his eyes grew dim remembering. 'Now what was it? I had it in my mind when I started out this morning.' His hands began to tremble, and patches of red showed above his beard.

Poor old chap, he's on his last pins, thought the boss. And, feeling kindly, he winked at the old man, and said jokingly, 'I tell you what. I've got a little drop of something here that'll do you good before you go out into the cold again. It's beautiful stuff. It wouldn't hurt a child.' He took a key off his watch-chain, unlocked a cupboard below his desk, and drew forth a dark, squat bottle. 'That's the medicine,' said he. 'And the man from whom I got it told me on the strict Q. T. it came from the cellars at Windsor Castle.'

Old Woodifield's mouth fell open at the sight. He couldn't have looked more surprised if the boss had produced a rabbit.

'It's whisky, ain't it?' he piped, feebly.

The boss turned the bottle and lovingly showed him the label. Whisky it was.

'D'you know,' said he, peering up at the boss wonderingly, 'they won't let me touch it at home.' And he looked as though he was going to cry.

'Ah, that's where we know a bit more than the ladies,' cried the boss, swooping across for two tumblers that stood on the table with the water-bottle, and pouring a generous finger into each. 'Drink it down. It'll do you good. And don't put any water with it. It's sacrilege to tamper with stuff like this. Ah!' He tossed off his, pulled out his handkerchief, hastily wiped his moustaches, and cocked an eye at old Woodifield, who was rolling his in his chaps.

The old man swallowed, was silent a moment, and then said faintly, 'It's nutty!'

But it warmed him; it crept into his chill old brain—he remembered.

'That was it,' he said, heaving himself out of his chair. 'I thought you'd like to know. The girls were in Belgium last week having a look at poor Reggie's grave, and they happened to come across your boy's. They are quite near each other, it seems.'

Old Woodifield paused, but the boss made no reply. Only a quiver of his eyelids showed that he heard.

'The girls were delighted with the way the place is kept,' piped the old voice. 'Beautifully looked after. Couldn't be better if they were at home. You've not been across, have yer?'

'No, no!' For various reasons the boss had not been across.

'There's miles of it,' quavered old Woodifield, 'and it's all as neat as a garden. Flowers growing on all the graves. Nice broad paths.' It was plain from his voice how much he liked a nice broad path.

The pause came again. Then the old man brightened wonderfully.

'D'you know what the hotel made the girls pay for a pot of jam?' he piped. 'Ten francs! Robbery, I call it. It was a little pot, so Gertrude says, no bigger than a half-crown. And she hadn't taken more than a spoonful when they charged her ten francs. Gertrude brought the pot away with her to teach 'em a lesson. Quite right, too; it's trading on our feelings. They think because we're over there having a look around we're ready to pay anything. That's what it is.' And he turned towards the door.

'Quite right, quite right!' cried the boss, though what was quite right he hadn't the least idea. He came around by his desk, followed the shuffling footsteps to the door, and saw the old fellow out. Woodifield was gone.

For a long moment the boss stayed, staring at nothing, while the grey-haired office messenger, watching him, dodged in and out of his cubby-hole like a dog that expects to be taken for a run. Then: 'I'll see nobody for half an hour, Macey,' said the boss. 'Understand? Nobody at all.'

'Very good, sir.'

The door shut, the firm, heavy steps recrossed the bright carpet, the fat body plumped down in the spring chair, and leaning forward, the boss covered his face with his hands. He wanted, he intended, he had arranged to weep. . . .

It had been a terrible shock to him when old Woodifield sprang that remark upon him about the boy's grave. It was exactly as though the earth had opened and he had seen the boy lying there with Woodifield's girls staring down at him. For it was strange. Although over six years had passed away, the boss never thought of the boy except as lying unchanged, unblemished in his uniform, asleep for ever. 'My son!' groaned the boss. But no tears came yet. In the past, in the first months and even years after the boy's death, he had only to say those words to be overcome by such grief that nothing short of a violent fit of weeping could relieve him. Time, he had declared then, he had told everybody, could make no difference. Other men perhaps might recover, might live their loss down, but not he. How was it possible? His boy was an only son. Ever since his birth the boss had worked at building up this business for him; it had no other meaning if it was not for the boy. Life itself had come to have no other meaning. How on earth could he have slaved, denied himself, kept going all those years without the promise for ever before him of the boy's stepping into his shoes and carrying on where he left off?

And that promise had been so near being fulfilled. The boy had been in the office learning the ropes for a year before the war. Every morning they had started off together; they had come back by the same train. And what congratulations he had received as the boy's father! No wonder; he had taken to it marvellously. As to his popularity with the staff, every man jack of them down to old Macey couldn't make enough of the boy. And he wasn't in the least spoiled. No, he was just his bright, natural self, with the right word for everybody, with that boyish look and his habit of saying, 'Simply splendid!'

But all that was over and done with as though it never had been. The day had come when Macey had handed him the telegram that brought the whole place crashing about his head. 'Deeply regret to inform you . . .' And he had left the office a broken man, with his life in ruins.

Six years ago, six years . . . How quickly time passed! It might have happened yesterday. The boss took his hands from his face; he was puzzled. Something seemed to be wrong with him. He wasn't feeling as he wanted to feel. He decided to get up and have a look at the boy's photograph. But it wasn't a favorite photograph of his; the expression was unnatural. It was cold, even stern-looking. The boy had never looked like that.

At that moment the boss noticed that a fly had fallen into his broad inkpot, and was trying feebly but desperately to clamber out again. Help! help! said those struggling legs. But the sides of the inkpot were wet and slippery; it fell back again and began to swim. The boss took up a pen, picked the fly out of the ink, and shook it on to a piece of blotting-paper. For a fraction of a second it lay still on the dark patch that oozed round it. Then the front legs waved, took hold, and, pulling its small sodden body up, it began the immense task of cleaning the ink from its wings. Over and under, over and under, went a leg along a wing, as the stone goes over and under the scythe. Then there was a pause, while the fly, seeming to stand on the tips of its toes, tried to expand first one wing and then the other. It succeeded at last, and sitting down, it began, like a minute cat, to clean its face. Now one could imagine that the little front legs rubbed against each other lightly, joyfully. The horrible danger was over; it had escaped; it was ready for life again.

But just then the boss had an idea. He plunged his pen back into the ink, leaned his thick wrist on the blotting-paper, and as the fly tried its wings, down came a great, heavy blot. What would it make of that? What indeed! The little beggar seemed absolutely cowed, stunned, and afraid to move because of what would happen next. But then, as if painfully, it dragged itself forward. The front legs waved, caught hold, and, more slowly the task began again.

He's a plucky little devil, thought the boss, and he felt a real admiration for the fly's courage. That was the way to tackle things; that was the right spirit. Never say die; it was only a question of . . . But the fly had again finished its laborious task, and the boss had just time to refill his pen, to shake fair and square on the new-cleaned body yet another dark drop. What about it this time? A painful moment of suspense followed. But behold, the front legs were again waving; the boss felt a rush of relief. He leaned over the fly and said to it tenderly, 'You artful little b . . .' And he actually had the brilliant notion of breathing on it to help the drying process. All the same, there was something timid and weak about its efforts now, and the boss decided that this time should be the last, as he dipped the pen into the inkpot.

It was. The last blot fell on the soaked blotting-paper, and the draggled fly lay in it and did not stir. The back legs were stuck to the body; the front legs were not to be seen.

'Come on,' said the boss. 'Look sharp!' And he stirred it with his pen—in vain. Nothing happened or was likely to happen. The fly was dead.

The boss lifted the corpse on the end of the paper-knife and flung it into the waste-paper basket, but such a grinding feeling of wretchedness seized him that he felt positively frightened. He started forward and pressed the bell for Macey.

'Bring me some fresh blotting-paper,' he said, sternly, 'and look sharp about it.' And while the old dog padded away he fell to wondering what it was he had been thinking about before. What was it? It was . . . He took out his handkerchief and passed it inside his collar. For the life of him he could not remember.

CLAY SHUTTERED DOORS

By Helen R. Hull

[Miss Helen Hull is an assistant professor of English in Columbia University, a writer of fiction and a contributor of short stories and articles to the better magazines. She is a native of Michigan.

The reader of this story needs to ask himself several questions. Was Thalia Corson killed in the accident on Brooklyn Bridge? Or is she just figuratively dead, having no active part in a living world? In either case why does she come back? Who is the little man who can bring her back? What does Mrs. Corson mean in the final section when she says, "I can never get *in* again?"

Clay Shuttered Doors appeared in *Harper's Magazine*, May, 1926. It is here reprinted by permission of the author and of Harper and Brothers, publishers.]

FOR months I have tried not to think about Thalia Corson. Anything may invoke her, with her languorous fragility, thin wrists and throat, her elusive face with its long eyelids. I can't quite remember her mouth. When I try to visualize her sharply I get soft pale hair, the lovely curve from her temple to chin, and eyes blue and intense. Her boy, Fletcher, has eyes like hers.

Today I came back to New York, and my taxi to an uptown hotel was held for a few minutes in Broadway traffic where the afternoon sunlight fused into a dazzle a great expanse of plateglass and elaborate show motor cars. The "Regal Eight"—Winchester Corson's establishment. I huddled as the taxi jerked ahead, in spite of knowledge that Winchester would scarcely peer out of that elegant setting into taxicabs. I didn't wish to see him, nor would he care to see me. But the glimpse had started the whole affair churning again, and I went through it deliberately, hoping that it might have smoothed out into some rational explanation. Sometimes things do, if you leave them alone, like logs submerged in water that float up later, encrusted thickly. This affair won't add to itself. It stays unique and smooth, sliding through the rest of life without annexing a scrap of seaweed.

I suppose, for an outsider, it all begins with the moment on Brooklyn Bridge; behind that are the years of my friendship with Thalia. Our families had summer cottages on the Cape. She was just enough older, however, so that not until I had finished college did I catch up to any intimacy with her. She had married Winchester Corson, who at that time fitted snugly into the phrase "a rising young man." During those first years, while his yeast sent up preliminary bubbles, Thalia continued to spend her summers near Boston, with Winchester coming for occasional week-ends. Fletcher was, unintentionally, born there; he began his difficult existence by arriving as a seven-months baby. Two years later Thalia had a second baby to bring down with her. Those were the summers which gave my friendship for Thalia its sturdy roots. They made me wonder, too, why she had chosen Winchester Corson. He was personable enough; tall, with prominent dark eyes and full mouth under a neat mustache, restless hands, and an uncertain disposition. He could be a charming companion, sailing the catboat with dash, managing lobster parties on the shore; or he would, unaccountably, settle into a foggy grouch, when everyone—children and females particularly—was supposed to approach only on tiptoe, bearing burnt offerings. The last time he spent a fortnight there, before he moved the family to the new Long Island estate, I had my own difficulties with him. There had always been an undertone of sex in his attitude toward me, but I had thought "that's just his male conceit." That summer he was a nuisance, coming upon me with his insistent, messy kisses, usually with Thalia in the next room. They were the insulting kind of kisses that aren't at all personal, and I could have ended them fast enough if there hadn't been the complication of Thalia and my love for her. If I made Winchester angry he'd put an end to Thalia's relation to me. I didn't, anyway, want her to know what a fool he was. Of course she did know, but I thought then that I could protect her.

There are, I have decided, two ways with love. You can hold one love, knowing that, if it is a living thing, it must develop and change. That takes maturity, and care, and a consciousness of the other person. That was Thalia's way. Or you enjoy the beginning of love and, once you're past that, you have to hunt for a new love, because the excitement seems to be gone. Men like Winchester who use all their brains on their jobs, never grow up; they go on thinking that preliminary stir and snap is love itself. Cut flowers, that was Winchester's idea, while to Thalia love was a tree.

But I said Brooklyn Bridge was the point at which the affair had its start. It seems impossible to begin there, or anywhere, as I try to account for what happened. Ten years after the summer when Winchester made himself such a nuisance—that last summer the Corsons spent at the Cape—I went down at the end of the season for a week with Thalia and the children at the Long Island place. Winchester drove out for the week-end. The children were mournful because they didn't wish to leave the shore for school; a sharp September wind brought rain and fog down the Sound, and Winchester nourished all that Sunday a disagreeable grouch. I had seen nothing of them for most of the ten intervening years, as I had been first in France and then in China, after feature-article stuff. The week had been pleasant: good servants, comfortable house, a half-moon of white beach below the drop of lawn; Thalia a stimulating listener, with Fletcher, a thin, eager boy of twelve, like her in his intensity of interest. Dorothy, a plump, pink child of ten, had no use for stories of French villages or Chinese temples. Nug, the wire-haired terrier, and her dolls were more immediate and convincing. Thalia was thin and noncommittal, except for her interest in what I had seen and done. I couldn't, for all my affection, establish any real contact. She spoke casually of the town house, of dinners she gave for Winchester, of his absorption in business affairs. But she was sheathed in polished aloofness and told me nothing of herself. She did say, one evening, that she was glad I was to be in New York that winter. Winchester, like his daughter Dorothy, had no interest in foreign parts once he had ascertained that I hadn't even seen the Chinese quarters of the motor company in which he was concerned. He had an amusing attitude toward me: careful indifference, no doubt calculated to put me in my place as no longer alluring. Thalia tried to coax him into listening to some of my best stories. "Tell him about the bandits, Mary"— but his sulkiness brought, after dinner, a casual explanation from her, untinged with apology. "He's working on an enormous project, a merging of several companies, and he's so soaked in it he can't come up for a breath."

In the late afternoon the maid set out high tea for us, before our departure for New York. Thalia suggested that perhaps one highball was enough if Winchester intended to drive over the wet roads. Win immediately mixed a second, asking if she had ever seen him in the least affected. "Be better for you than tea before a long damp drive, too." He clinked the ice in his glass. "Jazz you up a bit." Nug was begging for food and Thalia, bending to give him a corner of her sandwich, apparently did not hear Winchester. He looked about the room, a smug, owning look. The fire and candlelight shone in the heavy waxed rafters, made silver beads of the rain on the French windows. I watched him—heavier, more dominant, his prominent dark eyes and his lips sullen, as if the whiskey banked up his temper rather than appeased it.

Then Jim, the gardener, brought the car to the door; the children scrambled in. Dorothy wanted to take Nug, but her father said not if she wanted to sit with him and drive.

"How about chains, sir?" Jim held the umbrella for Thalia.

"Too damned noisy. Don't need them." Winchester slammed the door and slid under the wheel. Thalia and I, with Fletcher between us, sat comfortably in the rear.

"I like it better when Walter drives, don't you, Mother?" said Fletcher as we slid down the drive out to the road.

"Sh—Father likes to drive. And Walter likes Sunday off, too." Thalia's voice was cautious.

"It's too dark to see anything."

"I can see lots," announced Dorothy, whereupon Fletcher promptly turned the handle that pushed up the glass between the chauffeur's seat and the rear.

The heavy car ran smoothly over the wet narrow road, with an occasional rumble and flare of headlights as some car swung past. Not till we reached the turnpike was there much traffic. There Winchester had to slacken his speed for other shiny beetles slipping along through the rain. Sometimes he cut past a car, weaving back into line in the glaring teeth of a car rushing down on him, and Fletcher would turn inquiringly toward his mother. The gleaming, wet darkness and the smooth motion made me drowsy, and I paid little heed until we slowed in a congestion of cars at the approach to the bridge. Far below on the black river, spaced red and white stars suggested slow-moving tugs, and beyond, faint lights splintered in the rain hinted at the city.

"Let's look for the cliff dwellers, mother."

Thalia leaned forward, her fine, sharp profile dimly outlined against the shifting background of arches, and Fletcher slipped to his feet, his arm about her neck. "There!"

We were reaching the New York end of the bridge, and I had a swift glimpse of their cliff dwellers—lights in massed buildings, like ancient camp fires along a receding mountain side. Just then Winchester nosed out of the slow line, Dorothy screamed, the light from another car tunnelled through our windows, the car trembled under the sudden grip of brakes, and like a crazy top spun sickeningly about, with a final thud against the stone abutment. A shatter of glass, a confusion of motor horns about us, a moment while the tautness of shock held me rigid.

Around me that periphery of turmoil—the usual recriminations, "what the hell you think you're doing?"—the shriek of a siren on an approaching motorcycle. Within the circle I tried to move across the narrow space of the car. Fletcher was crying; vaguely I knew that the door had swung open, that Thalia was crouching on her knees, the rain and the lights pouring on her head and shoulders; her hat was gone, her wide fur collar looked like a drenched and lifeless animal. "Hush, Fletcher." I managed to force movement into my stiff body. "Are you hurt? Thalia—" Then outside Winchester, with the bristling fury of panic, was trying to lift her drooping head. "Thalia! My God, you aren't hurt!" Someone focussed a searchlight on the car as Winchester got his arms about her and lifted her out through the shattered door.

Over the springing line of the stone arch I saw the cliff dwellers' fires and I thought as I scrambled out to follow Winchester, "She was leaning forward, looking at those, and that terrific spin of the car must have knocked her head on the door as it lurched open."

"Lay her down, man!" An important little fellow had rushed up, a doctor evidently. "Lay her down, you fool!" Someone threw down a robe, and Winchester, as if Thalia were a drowned feather, knelt with her, laid her there on the pavement. I was down beside her and the fussy little man also. She did look drowned, drowned in that beating sea of tumult, that terrific honking of motors, unwilling to stop an instant even for—was it death? Under the white glare of headlights her lovely face had the empty shallowness, the husklikeness of death. The little doctor had his pointed beard close to her breast; he lifted one of her long eyelids. "She's just fainted, eh, doctor?" Winchester's angry voice tore at him.

The little man rose slowly. "She your wife? I'm sorry. Death must have been instantaneous. A blow on the temple."

With a kind of roar Winchester was down there beside Thalia, lifting her, her head lolling against his shoulder, his face bent over her. "Thalia! Thalia! Do you hear? Wake up!" I think he even shook her in his baffled fright and rage. "Thalia, do you hear me? I want you to open your eyes. You weren't hurt. That was nothing." And then, "Dearest, you must!" and more words, frantic, wild words, mouthed close to her empty face. I touched his shoulder, sick with pity, but he staggered up to his feet, lifting her with him. Fletcher pressed shivering against me, and I turned for an instant to the child. Then I heard Thalia's voice, blurred and queer, "You called me, Win?" and Winchester's sudden, triumphant laugh. She was standing against his shoulder, still with that husklike face, but she spoke again, "You did call me?"

"Here, let's get out of this." Winchester was again the efficient, competent man of affairs. The traffic cops were shouting, the lines of cars began to move. Winchester couldn't start his motor. Something had smashed. His card and a few words left responsibility with an officer, and even as an ambulance shrilled up, he was helping Thalia into a taxi. "You take the children, will you?" to me, and "Get her another taxi, will you?" to the officer. He had closed the taxi door after himself, and was gone, leaving us to the waning curiosity of passing cars. As we rode off in a second taxi, I had a glimpse of the little doctor, his face incredulous, his beard wagging, as he spoke to the officer.

Dorothy was, characteristically, tearfully indignant that her father had left her to me. Fletcher was silent as we bumped along under the elevated tracks, but presently he tugged at my sleeve, and I heard his faint whisper. "What is it?" I asked.

"Is my mother really dead?" he repeated.

"Of course not, Fletcher. You saw her get into the cab with your father."

"Why didn't Daddy take us too?" wailed Dorothy, and I had to turn to her, although my nerves echoed her question.

The house door swung open even as the taxi bumped the curb, and the butler hurried out with an umbrella which we were too draggled to need.

"Mr. Corson instructed me to pay the man, madam." He led us into the hall, where a waiting maid popped the children at once into the tiny elevator.

"Will you wait for the elevator, madam? The library is one flight." The butler led me up the stairs, and I dropped into a low chair near the fire, vaguely aware of the long narrow room, with the discreet gold of the walls giving back light from soft lamps. "I'll tell Mr. Corson you have come."

"Is Mrs. Corson—does she seem all right?" I asked.

"Quite, madam. It was a fortunate accident, with no one hurt."

Well, perhaps it had addled my brain! I waited in a kind of numbness for Winchester to come.

Presently he strode in, his feet silent on the thick rugs.

"Sorry," he began, abruptly. "I wanted to look the children over. Not a scratch on them. You're all right, of course?"

"Oh, yes. But Thalia—"

"She won't even have a doctor. I put her straight to bed—she's so damned nervous, you know. Hot-water bottles . . . she was cold. I think she's asleep now. Said she'd see you in the morning. You'll stay here, of course." He swallowed in a gulp the whiskey he had poured. "Have some, Mary? Or would you like something hot?"

"No, thanks. If you're sure she's all right I'll go to bed."

"Sure?" His laugh was defiant. "Did that damn fool on the bridge throw a scare into you? He gave me a bad minute, I'll say. If that car hadn't cut in on me— I told Walter last week the brakes needed looking at. They shouldn't grab like that. Might have been serious."

"Since it wasn't—" I rose, wearily, watching him pour amber liquid slowly into his glass— "if you'll have someone show me my room—"

"After Chinese bandits, a little skid ought not to matter to you." His prominent eyes gleamed hostilely at me; he wanted some assurance offered that the skidding wasn't his fault, that only his skill had saved all our lives.

"I can't see Thalia?" I said.

"She's asleep. Nobody can see her." His eyes moved coldly from my face, down to my muddy shoes. "Better give your clothes to the maid for a pressing. You're smeared quite a bit."

I woke early, with clear September sun at the windows of the room, with blue sky behind the sharp city contours beyond the windows. There was none too much time to make the morning train for Albany, where I had an engagement that day, an interview for an article. The maid who answered my ring insisted on serving breakfast to me in borrowed elegance of satin negligée. Mrs. Corson was resting, and would see me before I left. Something—the formality and luxury, the complicated household so unlike the old days at the Cape—accented the queer dread which had filtered all night through my dreams.

I saw Thalia for only a moment. The heavy silk curtains were drawn against the light and in the dimness her face seemed to gather shadows. "Are you quite all right, Thalia?" I hesitated beside her bed, as if my voice might tear apart the veils of drowsiness in which she rested.

"Why, yes—" as if she wondered. Then she added, so low that I wasn't sure what I heard, "It is hard to get back in."

"What, Thalia?" I bent toward her.

"I'll be myself once I've slept enough." Her voice was clearer. "Come back soon, won't you, Mary?" Then her eyelids closed and her face merged into the shadows of the room. I tiptoed away, thinking she slept.

It was late November before I returned to New York. Free-lancing has a way of drawing herrings across your trail and, when I might have drifted back in early November, a younger sister wanted me to come home to Arlington for her marriage. I had written to Thalia, first a note of courtesy for my week with her, and then a letter begging for news. Like many people of charm, she wrote indifferent letters, stiff and childlike, lacking in her personal quality. Her brief reply was more unsatisfactory than usual. The children were away in school, lots of cold rainy weather, everything was going well. At the end, in writing unlike hers, as if she scribbled the line in haste, "I am lonely. When are you coming?" I answered that I'd show up as soon as the wedding was over.

The night I reached Arlington was rainy, too, and I insisted upon a taxi equipped with chains. My brother thought that amusing, and at dinner gave the family an exaggerated account of my caution. I tried to offer him some futile sisterly advice and, to point up my remarks, told about that drive in from Long Island with the Corsons. I had never spoken of it before; I found that an inexplicable inhibition kept me from making much of a story.

"Well, nothing happened, did it?" Richard was triumphant.

"A great deal might have," I insisted. "Thalia was stunned, and I was disagreeably startled."

"Thalia was stunned, was she?" An elderly cousin of ours from New Jersey picked out that item. I saw her fitting it into some pigeonhole, but she said nothing until late that evening when she stopped at the door of my room.

"Have you seen Thalia Corson lately?" she asked.

"I haven't been in New York since September."

She closed the door and lowered her voice, a kind of avid curiosity riding astride the decorous pity she expressed.

"I called there, one day last week. I didn't know what was the matter with her. I hadn't heard of that accident."

I waited, an old antagonism for my proper cousin blurring the fear that shot up through my thoughts.

"Thalia was always *individual*, of course." She used the word like a reproach. "But she had *savoir faire*. But now she's—well—*queer*. Do you suppose her head was affected?"

"How is she queer?"

"She looks miserable, too. Thin and white."

"But how—"

"I am telling you, Mary. She was quite rude. First she didn't come down for ever so long, although I sent up word that I'd come up to her room if she was resting. Then her whole manner—well, I was really offended. She scarcely heard a word I said to her, just sat with her back to a window so I couldn't get a good look at her. When I said, 'You don't look like yourself,' she actually sneered. 'Myself?' she said. 'How do you know?' Imagine! I tried to chatter along as if I noticed nothing. I flatter myself I can manage awkward moments rather well. But Thalia sat there and I am sure she muttered under her breath. Finally I rose to go and I said, meaning well, 'You'd better take a good rest. You look half dead.' Mary, I wish you'd seen the look she gave me! Really I was frightened. Just then their dog came in, you know, Dorothy's little terrier. Thalia used to be silly about him. Well, she actually tried to hide in the folds of the curtain, and I don't wonder. The dog was terrified at her. He crawled on his belly out of the room. Now she must have been cruel to him if he acts like that. I think Winchester should have a specialist. I didn't know how to account for any of it; but of course a blow on the head can affect a person."

Fortunately my mother interrupted us just then, and I didn't, by my probable rudeness, give my cousin reason to suppose that the accident had affected me, too. I sifted through her remarks and decided they might mean only that Thalia found her more of a bore than usual. As for Nug, perhaps he retreated from the cousin! During the next few days the house had so much wedding turmoil that she found a chance only for a few more dribbles: one that Thalia had given up all her clubs— she had belonged to several—the other that she had sent the children to boarding schools instead of keeping them at home. "Just when her husband is doing so well, too!"

I was glad when the wedding party had departed, and I could plan to go back to New York. Personally I think a low-caste Chinese wedding in saner and more interesting than a modern American affair. My cousin "should think I could stay home with the family," and "couldn't we go to New York together, if I insisted upon gadding off?" We couldn't. I saw to that. She hoped that I'd look up Thalia. Maybe I could advise Winchester about a specialist.

I did telephone as soon as I got in. That sentence "I am lonely," in her brief note kept recurring. Her voice sounded thin and remote, a poor connection, I thought. She was sorry. She was giving a dinner for Winchester that evening. The next day.

I had piles of proof to wade through that next day, and it was late afternoon when I finally went to the Corson house. The butler looked doubtful but I insisted, and he left me in the hall while he went off with my card. He returned, a little smug in his message: Mrs. Corson was resting and had left word she must not be disturbed. Well, you can't protest to a perfect butler, and I started down the steps, indignant, when a car stopped in front of the house, a liveried chauffeur opened the door, and Winchester emerged. He glanced at me in the twilight and extended an abrupt hand.

"Would Thalia see you?" he asked.

"No." For a moment I hoped he might convoy me past the butler. "Isn't she well? She asked me to come today."

"I hoped she'd see you." Winchester's hand smoothed at his little mustache. "She's just tired from her dinner last night. She overexerted herself, was quite the old Thalia." He looked at me slowly in the dusk, and I had a brief feeling that he was really looking at me, no, *for* me, for the first time in all our meetings, as if he considered me without relation to himself for once. "Come in again, will you?" He thrust away whatever else he thought of saying. "Thalia really would like to see you. Can I give you a lift?"

"No, thanks. I need a walk." As I started off I knew the moment had just missed some real significance. If I had ventured a question . . . but, after all, what could I ask him? He had said that Thalia was "just tired." That night I sent a note to her, saying I had called and asked when I might see her.

She telephoned me the next day. Would I come in for Thanksgiving? The children would be home, and she wanted an old-fashioned day, everything but the sleigh ride New York couldn't furnish. Dinner would be at six, for the children; perhaps I could come in early. I felt a small grievance at being put off for almost a week, but I promised to come.

That was the week I heard gossip about Winchester, in the curious devious way of gossip. Atlantic City, and a gaudy lady. Someone having an inconspicuous fortnight of convalescence there had seen them. I wasn't surprised, except perhaps that Winchester chose Atlantic City. Thalia was too fine; he couldn't grow up to her. I wondered how much she knew. She must, years ago, with her sensitiveness, have discovered that Winchester was stationary so far as love went and, being stationary himself, was inclined to move the object toward which he directed his passion.

On Thursday, as I walked across Central Park, gaunt and deserted in the chilly afternoon light, I decided that Thalia probably knew more about Winchester's affairs than gossip had given me. Perhaps that was why she had sent the children away. He had always been conventionally discreet, but discretion would be a tawdry coin among Thalia's shining values.

I was shown up to the nursery, with a message from Thalia that she would join me there soon. Fletcher seemed glad to see me, in a shy, excited way, and stood close to my chair while Dorothy wound up her phonograph for a dance record and pirouetted about us with her doll.

"Mother keeps her door tight locked all the time," whispered Fletcher doubtfully. "We can't go in. This morning I knocked and knocked but no one answered."

"Do you like your school?" I asked cheerfully.

"I like my home better." His eyes, so like Thalia's with their long, arched lids, had young bewilderment under their lashes.

"See me!" called Dorothy. "Watch me do this!"

While she twirled I felt Fletcher's thin body stiffen against my arm, as if a kind of panic froze him. Thalia stood in the doorway. Was the boy afraid of her? Dorothy wasn't. She cried, "See me, Mother! Look at me!" and in her lusty confusion, I had a moment to look at Thalia before she greeted me. She was thin, but she had always been that. She did not heed Dorothy's shrieks, but watched Fletcher, a kind of slanting dread on her white, proud face. I had thought, that week on Long Island, that she shut herself away from me, refusing to restore the intimacy of ten years earlier. But now a stiff loneliness hedged her as if she were rimmed in ice and snow. She smiled. "Dear Mary," she said. At the sound of her voice I lost my slightly cherished injury that she had refused earlier to see me. "Let's go down to the library," she went on. "It's almost time for the turkey." I felt Fletcher break his intent watchfulness with a long sigh, and as the children went ahead of us, I caught at Thalia's arm. "Thalia—" She drew away, and her arm, under the soft flowing sleeve of dull blue stuff, was so slight it seemed brittle. I thought suddenly that she must have chosen that gown because it concealed so much beneath its lovely embroidered folds. "You aren't well, Thalia. What *is* it?"

"Well enough! Don't fuss about me." And even as I stared reproachfully she seemed to gather vitality, so that the dry pallor of her face became smooth ivory, and her eyes were no longer hollow and distressed. "Come."

The dinner was amazingly like one of our old holidays. Winchester wore his best mood, the children were delighted and happy. Thalia, under the gold flames of the tall black candles, was a gracious and lovely hostess. I almost forgot my troublesome anxiety, wondering whether my imagination hadn't been playing me tricks.

We had coffee by the library fire and some of Winchester's old Chartreuse. Then he insisted upon exhibiting his new radio. Thalia demurred, but the children begged for a concert. "This is their party, Tally!" Winchester opened the doors of the old teakwood cabinet which housed the apparatus. Thalia sank back into the shadows of a wing chair, and I watched her over my cigarette. Off guard, she had relaxed into strange apathy. Was it the firelight or my unaccustomed Chartreuse? Her features seemed blurred as if a clumsy hand trying to trace a drawing made uncertain outlines. Strange groans and whirrs from the radio.

"Win, I can't stand it!" Her voice dragged from some great distance. "Not tonight." She swayed to her feet, her hands restless under the loose sleeves.

"Static," growled Winchester. "Wait a minute."

"No!" Again it was as if vitality flowed into her. "Come, children. You have had your party. Time to go upstairs. I'll go with you."

They were well trained, I thought. Kisses for their father, a curtsy from Dorothy for me, and a grave little hand extended by Fletcher. Then Winchester came toward the fire as the three of them disappeared.

"You're good for Thalia," he said, in an undertone. "She's—well, what do you make of her?"

"Why?" I fenced, unwilling to indulge him in my vague anxieties.

"You saw how she acted about the radio. She has whims like that. Funny, she was herself at dinner. Last week she gave a dinner for me, important affair, pulled it off brilliantly. Then she shuts herself up and won't open her door for days. I can't make it out. She's thin—"

"Have you had a doctor?" I asked, banally.

"That's another thing. She absolutely refuses. Made a fool of me when I brought one here. Wouldn't unlock her door. Says she just wants to rest. But—" he glanced toward the door—"do you know that fool on the bridge . . . that little runt? The other night, I swear I saw him rushing down the steps as I came home. Thalia just laughed when I asked about it."

Something clicked in my thoughts, a quick suspicion, drawing a parallel between her conduct and that of people I had seen in the East. Was it some drug? That lethargy, and the quick spring into vitality? Days behind a closed door—

"I wish you'd persuade her to go off for a few weeks. I'm frightfully pressed just now, in an important business matter, but if she'd go off—maybe you'd go with her?"

"Where, Winchester?" We both started, with the guilt of conspirators. Thalia came slowly into the room. "Where shall I go? Would you suggest—Atlantic City?"

"Perhaps. Although some place farther south this time of year—" Winchester's imperturbability seemed to me far worse than some slight sign of embarrassment; it marked him as so rooted in successful deceit whether Thalia's inquiry were innocent or not. "If Mary would go with you. I can't get away just now."

"I shall not go anywhere until your deal goes through. Then—" Thalia seated herself again in the wing chair. The hand she lifted to her cheek, fingers just touching her temple beneath the soft drift of hair, seemed transparent against the firelight. "Have you told Mary about your deal? Winchester plans to be the most important man on Automobile Row." Was there mockery in her tone? "I can't tell you the details, but he's buying out all the rest."

"Don't be absurd. Not all of them. It's a big merging of companies, that's all."

"We entertain the lords at dinner, and in some mysterious way that smooths the merging. It makes a wife almost necessary."

"Invite Mary to the next shebang, and let her see how well you do it." Winchester was irritated. "For all your scoffing, there's as much politics to being president of such a concern as of the United States."

"Yes, I'll invite Mary. Then she'll see that you don't really want to dispense with me—yet."

"Good God, I meant for a week or two."

As Winchester, lighting a cigarette, snapped the head from several matches in succession, I moved my chair a little backward, distressed. There was a thin wire of significance drawn so taut between the two that I felt at any moment it might splinter in my face.

"It's so lucky—" malice flickered on her thin face—"that you weren't hurt in that skid on the bridge, Mary. Winchester would just have tossed you in the river to conceal your body."

"If you're going over that again!" Winchester strode out of the room. As Thalia turned her head slightly to watch him, her face and throat had the taut rigidity of pain so great that it congeals the nerves.

I was silent. With Thalia I had never dared intrude except when she admitted me. In another moment she too had risen. "You'd better go home, Mary," she said, slowly. "I might tell you things you wouldn't care to live with."

I tried to touch her hand, but she retreated. If I had been wiser or more courageous, I might have helped her. I shall always have that regret, and that can't be much better to live with than whatever she might have told me. All I could say was stupidly, "Thalia, if there's anything I can do! You know I love you."

"Love? That's a strange word," she said, and her laugh in the quiet room was like the shrilling of a grasshopper on a hot afternoon. "One thing I will tell you." (She stood now on the stairway above me.) "Love has no power. It never shouts out across great space. Only fear and self-desire are strong."

Then she had gone, and the butler appeared silently, to lead me to the little dressing room.

"The car is waiting for you, madam," he assured me, opening the door. I didn't want it, but Winchester was waiting, too, hunched angrily in a corner.

"That's the way she acts," he began. "Now you've seen her I'll talk about it. Thalia never bore grudges, you know that."

"It seems deeper than a grudge," I said cautiously.

"That reference to the . . . the accident. That's a careless remark I made. I don't even remember just what I said. Something entirely inconsequential. Just that it was damned lucky no one was hurt when I was putting this merger across. You know if it'd got in the papers it would have queered me. Wrecking my own car . . . there's always a suspicion you've been drinking. She picked it up and won't drop it. It's like a fixed idea. If you can suggest something. I want her to see a nerve specialist. What does she do behind that locked door?"

"What about Atlantic City?" I asked, abruptly. I saw his dark eyes bulge, trying to ferret out my meaning, there in the dusky interior of the car.

"A week there with you might do her good." That was all he would say, and I hadn't courage enough to accuse him, even in Thalia's name.

"At least you'll try to see her again," he said, as the car stopped in front of my apartment house.

I couldn't sleep that night. I felt that just over the edge of my squirming thoughts there lay clear and whole the meaning of it all, but I couldn't reach past thought. And then, stupidly enough, I couldn't get up the next day. Just a feverish cold, but the doctor insisted on a week in bed and subdued me with warnings about influenza.

I had begun to feel steady enough on my feet to consider venturing outside my apartment when the invitation came, for a formal dinner at the Corson's. Scrawled under the engraving was a line, "Please come. T." I sent a note, explaining that I had been ill, and that I should come —the dinner was a fortnight away—unless I stayed too wobbly.

I meant that night to arrive properly with the other guests, but my watch, which had never before done anything except lose a few minutes a day, had gained an unsuspected hour. Perhaps the hands stuck— perhaps—Well, I was told I was early, Thalia was dressing, and only the children, home for the Christmas holidays, were available. So I went again to the nursery. Dorothy was as plump and unconcerned as ever, but Fletcher had a strained, listening effect, and he looked too thin and white for a little boy. They were having their supper on a small table, and Fletcher kept going to the door, looking out into the hall. "Mother promised to come up," he said.

The maid cleared away their dishes, and Dorothy, who was in a beguiling mood, chose to sit on my lap and entertain me with stories. One was about Nug the terrier; he had been sent out to the country because Mother didn't like him any more.

"I think," interrupted Fletcher, "she likes him, but he has a queer notion about her."

"She doesn't like him," repeated Dorothy. Then she dismissed that subject, and Fletcher too, for curiosity about the old silver chain I wore. I didn't notice that the boy had slipped away, but he must have gone down stairs; for presently his fingers closed over my wrist, like a frightened bird's claw, and I turned to see him, trembling, his eyes dark with terror. He couldn't speak but he clawed at me, and I shook Dorothy from my knees and let him pull me out to the hall.

"What is it, Fletcher?" He only pointed down the stairway, toward his mother's door, and I fled down those stairs. *What* had the child seen?

"The door wasn't locked—" he gasped behind me— "I opened it very still and went in—"

I pushed it ajar. Thalia sat before her dressing table, with the threefold mirrors reiterating like a macabre symphony her rigid, contorted face. Her gown, burnished blue and green like peacock's feathers, sheathed her gaudily, and silver, blue, and green chiffon clouded her shoulders. Her hands clutched at the edge of the dressing table. For an instant I could not move, thrust through with a terror like the boy's. Then I stumbled across the room. Before I reached her, the mirrors echoed her long shudder, her eyelids dragged open, and I saw her stare at my reflection wavering toward her. Then her hands relaxed, moved quickly toward the crystal jars along the heavy glass of the table and, without a word, she leaned softly forward, to draw a scarlet line along her white lips.

"How cold it is in here," I said, stupidly, glancing toward the windows, where the heavy silk damask, drawn across, lay in motionless folds. "Fletcher said—" I was awkward, an intruder.

"He startled me." Her voice came huskily. She rouged her hollow cheeks. It was as if she drew another face for herself. "I didn't have time to lock the door." Then turning, she sought him out, huddled at the doorway, like a moth on a pin of fear. "It wasn't nice of you, Son. It's all right now. You see?" She rose, drawing her lovely scarf over her shoulders. "You should never open closed doors." She blew him a kiss from her finger tips. "Now run along and forget you were so careless."

The icy stir of air against my skin had ceased. I stared at her, my mind racing back over what I knew of various drugs and the stigmata of their victims. But her eyes were clear and undilated, a little piteous. "This," she said, "is the last time. I can't endure it." And then, with that amazing flood of vitality, as if a sudden connection had been made and current flowed again, "Come, Mary. It is time we were down stairs."

I thought Fletcher peered over the railing as we went down. But a swift upward glance failed to detect him.

The dinner itself I don't remember definitely except that it glittered and sparkled, moving with slightly alcoholic wit through elaborate courses, while I sat like an abashed poor relation at a feast, unable to stop watching Thalia, wondering whether my week of fever had given me a tendency to hallucinations. At the end a toast was proposed, to Winchester Corson and his extraordinary success. "It's done, then?" Thalia's gaiety had sudden malice—as she looked across at Winchester, seating himself after a slightly pompous speech. "Sealed and cemented forever?"

"Thanks to his charming wife, too," cried a plump, bald man, waving his glass. "A toast to Mrs. Corson!"

Thalia rose, her rouge like flecked scarlet on white paper. One hand drew her floating scarf about her throat, and her painted lips moved without a sound. There was an instant of agitated discomfort, as the guests felt their mood broken so abruptly, into which her voice pierced, thin, high. "I . . . deserve . . . such a toast—"

I pushed back my chair and reached her side.

"I'll take her—" I saw Winchester's face, wine-flushed, angry rather than concerned. "Come, Thalia."

"Don't bother. I'll be all right—now." But she moved ahead of me so swiftly that I couldn't touch her. I thought she tried to close her door against me, but I was too quick for that. The silver candelabra still burned above the mirrors. "Mary!" Her voice was low again as she spoke a telephone number. "Tell him *at once*." She stood away from me, her face a white mask with spots of scarlet, her peacock dress ashimmer. I did as I was bid and when I had said, "Mrs. Corson wishes you at once," there was an emptiness where a man's voice had come which suggested a sudden leap out of a room somewhere.

"I can never get in again!" Her fingers curled under the chiffon scarf. "Never! The black agony of fighting back— If he—" She bent her head, listening. "Go down to the door and let him in," she said.

I crept down the stairs. Voices from the drawing-room. Winchester was seeing the party through. Almost as I reached the door and opened it I found him there: the little doctor with the pointed beard. He brushed past me up the stairs. He knew the way, then! I was scarcely surprised to find Thalia's door fast shut when I reached it. Behind it came not a sound. Fletcher, like an unhappy sleepwalker, his eyes heavy, slipped down beside me, clinging to my hand. I heard farewells, churring of taxis and cars. Then Winchester came up the stairs.

"She's shut you out?" He raised his fist and pounded on the door. "I'm going to stop this nonsense!"

"I sent for a doctor," I said. "He's in there."

"Is it—" his face was puffy and gray— "that same fool?" Then the door opened, and the man confronted us.

"It is over," he said.

"What have you done to her?" Winchester lunged toward the door, but the little man's lifted hand had dignity enough somehow to stop him.

"She won't come back again." He spoke slowly. "You may look if you care to."

"She's dead?"

"She died—months ago. There on the bridge. But you called to her, and she thought you wanted—*her*."

Winchester thrust him aside and strode into the room. I dared one glance and saw only pale hair shining on the pillow. Then Fletcher flung himself against me, sobbing, and I knelt to hold him close against the fear we both felt.

What Winchester saw I never knew. He hurled himself past us, down the stairs. And Thalia was buried with the coffin lid fast closed under the flowers.

MISS HINCH

By Henry Sydnor Harrison

[Henry Sydnor Harrison (1880–1930) reached sudden fame with the publication of two popular novels, *Queed* (1911); and *V. V.'s Eyes* (1913). He was born in Sewanee, Tennessee, and educated in Brooklyn and New York (Columbia University). Mystery stories usually require the length of a volume, but occasionally a good one is cast in the compressed form of a short story. This is an excellent example. Is there any point in the story before the end where you are positive that you know which of the two characters is Miss Hinch? How does the author manage to keep you in doubt? Can you go back through the story after the first reading and satisfy yourself that each step was logical and the conclusion properly prepared for?

Miss Hinch was first published in *McClure's Magazine* (September, 1911), and is here reprinted by permission of Miss Norvell Harrison, holder of the copyright.]

IN going from a given point on 126th Street to a subway station at 125th, it is not usual to begin by circling the block to 127th Street, especially in sleet, darkness, and deadly cold. When two people pursue such a course at the same time, moving unobtrusively on opposite sides of the street, in the nature of things the coincidence is likely to attract the attention of one or the other of them.

In the bright light of the entrance to the tube they came almost face to face, and the clergyman took a good look at her. Certainly she was a decent-looking old body, if any woman was: white-haired, wrinkled, spectacled, and stooped. A poor but thoroughly respectable domestic servant of the better class she looked, in her black hat, neat veil, and nondescript gray cloak; and her brief glance at the reverend gentleman was precisely what it should have been from her to him—deference itself. Nevertheless, he, going more slowly down the draughty steps, continued to study her from behind with a singular intentness.

An express was just thundering in, which the clergyman, handicapped as he was by his clubfoot and stout cane, was barely in time to catch. He entered the same car with the woman, and took a seat directly across from her. It must have been then well past midnight, and the wildness of the weather was discouraging to travel. The car was almost deserted. Even here under the earth the bitter breath of the night blew and bit, and the old woman shivered under her cloak. At last, her teeth chattering, she got up in an apologetic sort of way, and moved toward the rear of the car, feeling the empty seats as she went, in a palpable search for hot pipes. The clergyman's eyes followed her; he watched her sink down, presently, into a seat on his own side of the car. A young couple sat between them now; he could no longer see the woman, beyond glimpses of her black knees and her faded bonnet, fastened on with a long steel hatpin.

Nothing could have seemed more natural or more trivial than this change of seats on the part of a thin-blooded and half-frozen passenger. But it happened to be a time of mutual doubts and general suspiciousness, when men looked askance into every strange face, and the smallest incidents might take on an hysterical importance. Through days of intense searching for a fugitive outlaw of extraordinary gifts, the nerves of the city had been visibly strained. All jumped now when anybody cried "Boo!" and the hue and cry went up falsely twenty times a day.

The clergyman pondered; mechanically he turned up his coat collar and fell to stamping his feet. He was an Episcopal clergyman, by his garb—rather short, very full-bodied, not to say fat, bearded and somewhat puffy-faced, with heavy cheeks cut by deep creases. Well lined against the cold though he was, however, he, too, began to show signs of suffering, and presently rose and moved in his turn, seeking out a new place where the chilled heating apparatus might give a better account of itself. He found a seat just beyond the old serving-woman, limped into it, and relapsed into his own thoughts.

The young couple, half a dozen seats away, appeared thoroughly absorbed in each other's society. The fifth traveler, a withered old gentleman sitting across and down the aisle, napped fitfully upon his cane. The woman in the shapeless cloak sat in a sad kind of silence; and the train hurled itself roaringly through the tube. After a time, she glanced through her spectacles at the meditating clergyman, and her look fell swiftly from his face to the "ten-o'clock extra" in his hand. She removed her gaze and let it travel casually about the car; but before long it returned again, as if magnetized, to the newspaper. Then, with some obvious hesitation, she bent forward and said, above the noises of the train:

"Excuse me, Father, but would you please let me look at your paper a minute, sir?"

The clergyman came out of his reverie instantly, and looked at her with a quick smile.

"Certainly. Keep it, if you like: I am quite through with it. But," he said, in a pleasant deep voice, "I am an Episcopal minister, not a priest."

"Oh, sir—I beg your pardon! I thought—"

He dismissed the apology with a nod and a good-natured hand.

The woman opened the paper with decent cotton-gloved fingers. The garish head-lines told all the story: "Earth Opened and Swallowed

Miss Hinch, Says Inspector—Police Confess 'Practically No Clue'—
Even Jessie Dark"—so the bold capitals ran on— "Seems 'Stumped.'"
Below the spread was a luridly written but flimsy narrative, "By
Jessie Dark," which at once confirmed the odd implications of the cap-
tion. "Jessie Dark," it appeared, was one of those most extraordinary
of the products of yellow journalism, a woman "crime expert," now in
action. More than this, she was a "crime expert" to be taken seriously,
it seemed—no mere office-desk sleuth, but an actual performer with,
unexpectedly enough, a somewhat formidable list of notches on her gun.
So much, at least, was to be gathered from her paper's boxed display
of "Jessie Dark's Triumphs":

> March 2, 1901. Caught Julia Victorian, alias Gregory, the brains of
> the "Healy Ring" kidnappers.
> October 7–29, 1903. Found Mrs. Trotwood and secured the letter
> that convicted her of the murder of her lover, Ellis E. Swan.
> December 17, 1903. Ran down Charles Bartsch in a Newark laundry
> and trapped a confession from him.
> July 4, 1904. Caught Helene Gray, "Blackmail Queen," and recovered
> the Stratford jewels.

And so on—nine "triumphs" in all; and nearly every one of them, as
the least observant reader could hardly fail to notice, involved the capture of a woman.

Nevertheless, it could not be pretended that the "snappy" paragraphs
in this evening's extra seemed to foreshadow a new or tenth triumph for
Jessie Dark at an early date; and the old serving-woman in the car
presently laid down the sheet with a look of marked depression.

The clergyman glanced at her again. Her expression was so speaking
that it seemed almost an invitation; moreover, public interest in the
curious case had created a freemasonry which made conversation between total strangers the rule wherever two or three were gathered.

"You were reading about this strange mystery, I suppose?"

The woman with a sharp intake of breath, answered: "Yes, sir. Oh,
sir, it seems as if I couldn't think of anything else."

"Ah!" he said, calmly. "It certainly appears to be a remarkable
affair."

Remarkable indeed the affair seemed. In a tiny little room within
ten steps of Broadway, at half past nine o'clock on a fine evening, Miss
Hinch had killed John Catherwood with the light sword she used in her
famous representation of the Father of his Country. Catherwood, it
was known, had come to tell her of his approaching marriage; and ten
thousand amateur detectives, stimulated by the unprecedented "rewards," had required no further motive of a creature already notorious
for fierce jealousy. So far the tragedy was commonplace enough, and
even vulgar. What had redeemed it to romance from this point on was

the extraordinary faculty of the woman, which had made her celebrated while she was still in her 'teens. Violent, unmoral, criminal she might be, but she happened also to be the most astonishing impersonator of her time. Her brilliant act consisted of a series of character changes, many of them done "in full view of the audience" with the assistance only of a small table of properties half concealed under a net. Some of these transformations were so amazing as to be beyond belief, even after one had sat and watched them. Not the woman's appearance only, but voice, speech, manner, carriage, all shifted incredibly to fit the new part; so that she appeared to have no permanent form or fashion of her own, but to be only so much plastic human material out of which her cunning could mould at will man, woman, or child, great lady of the Louisan court, or Tammany chieftain with the modernest of East Side modernisms upon his lips.

With this strange gift, hitherto used only to enthrall audiences and wring extortionate contracts from managers, the woman known as Miss Hinch—she appeared to be without a first name—was now fighting for her life somewhere against the police of the whole world. She was an unassuming, tall, thin-chested young woman with strongly marked features and considerable beauty of a bold sort. What she would look like at the present moment nobody could venture a guess. Having stabbed John Catherwood in her dressing-room at the Coliseum, she had donned hat and coat, dropped two wigs and her make-up kit into a hand-bag, and walked out into Broadway. Within ten minutes the dead body of Catherwood was found and the chase begun. At the stage door, as she passed out, Miss Hinch had met an acquaintance, a young comedian named Dargis, and exchanged a word of greeting with him. That had been ten days ago. After Dargis, no one had seen her. The earth, indeed, seemed to have opened and swallowed her. Yet her natural features were almost as well known as a President's, and the newspapers of a continent were daily reprinting them in a hundred variations.

"A very remarkable case," repeated the clergyman, rather absently; and his neighbor, the old woman, agreed mournfully that it was. Then, as the train slowed and quieted for the stop at 86th Street, she spoke again, with sudden bitterness:

"Oh, they'll never catch her, sir—never! She's too smart for 'em all, Miss Hinch is."

Attracted by her tone, the stout divine inquired if she was particularly interested in the case.

"Yes, sir—I got reason to be. Jack Catherwood's mother and me was at school together, and great friends all our life long. Oh, sir," she went on, as if in answer to his look of faint surprise, "Jack was a fine gentleman, with manners and looks and all beyond his people. But he never grew away from his old mother—no, sir, never! And I don't believe ever a Sunday passed that he didn't go up and set the afternoon away with her, talking and laughing just like he was a little boy again. Maybe he done things he hadn't ought, as high-spirited lads will, but oh, sir, he was a good boy in his heart—a good boy. And it does seem too hard for him to die like that—and that hussy free to go her way, ruinin' and killin'—"

"My good woman," said the clergyman presently, after glancing about, "compose yourself. No matter how diabolical this woman's skill is, her sin will assuredly find her out."

The woman dutifully lowered her handkerchief and tried to compose herself, as bidden.

"But oh, she's that clever—diabolical, just as ye say, sir. Through poor Jack we of course heard much gossip about her, and they do say that her best tricks was not done on the stage at all. They say, sir, that, sittin' around a table with her friends, she could begin and twist her face so strange and terrible that they would beg her to stop, and jump up and run from the table—frightened out of their lives, sir, grown-up people, by the terrible faces she could make. And let her only step behind her screen for a minute—for she kept her secrets well, Miss Hinch did—and she'd come walking out to you, and you could go right up to her in the full light and take her hand, and still you couldn't make yourself believe that it was her."

"Yes," said the clergyman, "I have heard that she is remarkably clever—though, as a stranger in this part of the world, I, of course, never saw her. I must say, it is all very interesting and strange."

The express had started again with a jolt, and the rumbling and roaring all but drowned out his voice. He turned his head and stared through the window at the dark flying walls. At the same moment the woman turned her head and stared full at him. When he turned back, her gaze had gone off toward the door.

The clergyman picked up the paper thoughtfully and read for a while. But when, just outside of Grand Central station, the train came to a nameless halt, he at once resumed the conversation.

"I'm a visitor in the city, from Denver, Colorado," he explained in an easy way, "and knew little or nothing about the case until an evening or two ago, when I attended a meeting of gentlemen here. The Men's Club at St. Matthias' Church—perhaps you know the place? Upon my word, they talked of nothing else. I confess they got me quite interested in their gossip. So tonight I bought this paper to see what this extraordinary woman detective it employs had to say about it. We don't have such things in the West, you know. But I must say I was disappointed, after all the talk about her."

"Yes, sir, indeed, and no wonder, for she's told Mrs. Catherwood herself that she's never made such a failure as this, so far. It seemed like she could always catch women, up to this. It seemed like she knew in her own mind just what a woman would do, where she'd try to hide, and all, and so she could find them time and time when the men detectives didn't know where to look. But oh, sir, she's never had to hunt for such a woman as Miss Hinch before!"

"No? I suppose not," said the clergyman. "Her theorizing here certainly seems very sketchy."

"*Theorizing*, sir! Bless my soul!" suddenly exploded the old gentleman across the aisle, to the surprise of both. "You don't suppose the clever little woman is going to show her hand in those newspaper stories, with Miss Hinch in the city and reading every line of them! In the city, sir—such is my positive conviction!"

He had roused from his nap, it seemed, just in time to overhear the episcopate criticism. Now he answered the looks of the old woman and the clergyman with an elderly cackle.

"Excuse my intrusion, I'm sure! But I can't sit silent and hear anybody run down Jessie Dark—Miss Matthewson in private life, as perhaps you don't know. No, sir! Why, there's a man at my boarding-place—remarkable fellow named Hardy, Tom Hardy—who's known her for *years*! As to those *theorizings*, sir, I can assure you she puts in there *exactly the opposite of what she really thinks!*"

"You don't tell me!" said the clergyman.

"Yes, sir! Oh, she plays the game! She has her private ideas, her clues, her schemes. The woman doesn't live who is clever enough to hoodwink Jessie Dark. I look for developments any day, sir!"

A new voice joined in. The pair down the car, their attention caught by the old man's pervasive tones, had been frankly listening: and it was illustrative of the public mind at the moment that, as they now rose for the station, the young fellow felt perfectly free to offer his contribution.

"Dramatic situation, isn't it, when you stop to think? Those two clever women pitted against each other in a life-and-death struggle—fighting it out in the underground somewhere—keen professional pride on one side and fear of the electric chair on the other—"

"Oh, yes! Oh, yes!" exclaimed the old gentleman, rather testily. "But, my dear sir, it's not professional pride that makes Jessie Dark so resolute to win. It's *sex jealousy*—if you follow me—no offense, madam! Yes, sir! Women never have the slightest respect for each other's abilities—not the slightest. No mercy for each other, either! I tell you Jessie Dark'd be ashamed to be beaten by another woman. Read her stories between the lines, sir—invincible determination—no mercy! You catch my point?"

"It sounds reasonable," answered the Colorado clergyman, with his quick smile. "Women, we are told—"

"Oh, I'm for Jessie Dark, all right!" the young fellow broke in—"especially since the police have practically laid down. But—"

"Why, she's told my friend Hardy," the old gentleman rode him down, "that she'll find Hinch if it takes her lifetime! Knows a thing or two about actresses, she says. Says the world isn't big enough for the creature to hide from her. Well! What do you think of that?"

"Tell what we were just talking about, George," prompted the young wife, with an admiring gaze.

"But oh, sir," began the old woman timidly, "Jack Catherwood's been dead ten days now, and—"

"Woman got on my car at nine o'clock tonight," suddenly shouted the guard, who, having flung open the doors, was listening to the symposium eagerly—"wore a brown veil and goggles. I'd 'a' bet every dollar I had—"

"Ten days, madam! And what is that, pray?" barked the old gentleman, rising abruptly but triumphantly. "A lifetime, if necessary!—never fear! Mrs. Victorian was considered pretty clever, eh? Wasn't she? Remember what Jessie Dark did for her? Nan Parmalee, too—though the police did their best to steal her credit. She'll do just as much for Miss Hinch—you may take it from me!"

"But how's she going to make the capture, gentlemen?" cried the young fellow, getting his chance at last. "That's the point my wife and I've been discussing. Suppose she succeeds in spotting this woman-devil, what'll she do? Now—"

"Do, sir! Yell for the police! I say—"

"And have Miss Hinch kill her—and then herself, too? Wouldn't she have to—"

"Grand Central!" cried the guard for the second time; and the young fellow broke off reluctantly as his bride towed him strongly toward the door.

"Hope she nabs her soon," he called back to the clergyman over his shoulder—"getting on my nerves! One of these kindergarten reward-chasers followed my wife five blocks, just because she's got a pointed chin. Don't know what might have happened if I hadn't come along and—"

Doors rolled shut behind him, and the train flung itself on its way. Within the car, a silence ensued. The clergyman stared at the floor, and the old woman fell back upon the borrowed "extra." She appeared to be re-reading the observations of Jessie Dark with considerable care. Presently she lowered the paper and began a quiet search for something under the folds of her cloak; and at length, her hands emerging empty, she broke the silence, in a lifted voice:

"Oh, sir—have you a pencil you could lend me, please? I'd like to mark something in the piece to send to Mrs. Catherwood. It's what she says here about their hide-outs, as she terms them."

The obliging divine felt in his pockets, and, after a good deal of hunting, produced a pencil—a white one, with thick blue lead. She thanked him gratefully.

"How is Mrs. Catherwood bearing all this strain and anxiety?" he asked suddenly, in the loud, empty car. "Have you seen her today?"

"Oh, yes, sir. I've been spending the evening with her since nine o'clock, and am just back from there now. Oh, she's dreadful broke up, sir."

She glanced at him with an uncertain air. He stared straight in front of him, saying nothing, though conceivably he had learned in common with the rest of the world, that Jack Catherwood's mother lived, not on 126th Street, but on West 8th Street. Possibly his silence had been an error of judgment? Perhaps that mis-statement of hers had not been a slip, but something cleverer?

The woman went on, rather easily: "Oh, sir, I only hope and pray those gentlemen may be right, but it does look to Mrs. Catherwood, and me too, that if Jessie Dark was going to catch her at all, she'd have done it before now. Look at those big, bold, blue eyes she had, sir, with lashes an inch long, they say, and that terrible long chin of hers. They do say she can change the color of her eyes, not forever of course, but put a few of her drops into them and make them look entirely different for a time. But that chin, ye'd say—"

She broke off; for the clergyman, without preliminaries of any sort, had picked up his heavy stick and suddenly risen.

"Why!—here we are at Fourteenth Street!" he said, quite astonished. "I must change here—well, well! You go farther, perhaps? Good night! Success to Jessie Dark, I say."

He was watching the woman's sad, faded face, and he saw break into it a look of quick surprise which, it may be, was just what he had expected.

"Fourteenth Street, sir! I'd no notion at all—for I've paid no notice to the stops. It's where I change too, sir, the expresses not stopping at my station."

"Ah!" said the clergyman, smiling a little.

He led the way, limping and leaning on his stick. They emerged upon the chill and cheerless platform, not exactly together, yet still with some reference to their acquaintanceship on the car. But the clergyman, after stumping along a few steps, all at once realized that he was walking alone, and turned. The woman had halted. Over the intervening space their eyes met.

"Come," said the man gently. "Come, let us walk about a little to keep warm."

"Oh, sir—it's too kind of you," said the woman, slowly coming forward.

From other cars two or three chilled travelers had got off to make the change; one or two more came straggling in from the street; but, scattered over the bleak narrow expanse, they detracted little from the isolation that seemed to surround the woman and the clergyman. Step for step, the odd pair made their way to the extreme northern end of the platform.

"By the way," said the clergyman, halting abruptly, "may I see that paper again for a moment?"

"Oh, yes, sir—of course," said the woman, producing it from under her cloak. "I thought you had finished with it, and I—"

He said that he wanted only to glance at it for a moment; but he fell to looking through it page by page, with rather a searching scrutiny. The woman glanced at him several times. At last she said hesitatingly:

"I thought, sir, I'd ask the ticket-chopper could he say how long before the next train. I'm very late as it is, sir, and I still must stop to get something to eat before I go to bed."

"An excellent idea," said the clergyman, putting the newspaper in his pocket. Side by side, they retraced their steps down the platform, questioned the chopper with scant results, and then, as by tacit consent, started slowly back again. However, before they had gone very far, the woman all at once stopped short, and with a drawn face, leaned against a pillar.

"Oh, sir, I'm afraid I'll just have to stop and get a bite somewhere before I go on. You'll think me foolish, sir, but I missed my supper entirely, and there is quite a faint feeling coming over me."

The clergyman eyed her with apparent concern. He said: "Do you know, your mentioning something to eat a moment ago reminded me that I myself am all but famishing." He glanced at his watch, appearing to deliberate. "Yes—it will not take long. Come, we will find some modest eating place together."

"Oh, sir," she stammered, "but—you wouldn't want to eat with a poor old woman like me, sir."

"Why not? Are we not all equal in the sight of God?"

They ascended the stairs together, like any prosperous parson and his poor parishioner, and coming out into Fourteenth Street, started west. On the first block they came to a little restaurant, a brilliantly lighted, tiled and polished place of the quick-lunch sort, well filled with late patrons. But the woman timidly preferred not to stop here, saying that the glare of such places was very bad for her old eyes. The divine accepted the objection, without comment. A block farther on they found on a corner a quieter resort, an old-fashioned establishment which boasted a "Ladies' Entrance" down the side street.

They entered, and sat down at a table, facing each other. The woman read the menu through, and finally, after some embarrassed uncertainty, ordered poached eggs on toast. The clergyman ordered the same. The simple meal was soon served. Just as they were finishing it, the woman said apologetically:

"If you'll excuse me, sir—could I see the bill of fare a minute? I think I'd best take a little pot of tea to warm me up, if they do not charge too high."

"I haven't the bill of fare," said the clergyman.

They looked diligently for the cardboard strip, but it was nowhere to be seen. The waiter drew near.

"Yes, sir! I left it right there when I took the order."

"I'm sure I can't imagine what's become of it," repeated the clergyman.

He looked rather hard at the woman, and found that she was looking hard at him. Both pairs of eyes turned instantly.

The waiter brought another bill of fare; the woman ordered tea; the waiter came back with it. The clergyman paid for both orders with a bill that looked hard-earned.

The tea was very hot; it could not be drunk down at a gulp. The clergyman, watching the woman sidewise as she sipped, seemed to grow more and more restless. His agile fingers drummed the tablecloth; he could hardly sit still. All at once he said: "What is that calling in the street? It sounds like newsboys."

The woman put her old head on one side and listened. "Yes, sir. There seems to be an 'extra' out."

"Upon my word," he said, after a pause. "I believe I'll go get one. Good gracious! Crime is a very interesting thing, to be sure!"

He rose slowly, took down his shovel-hat from the rack near him, and grasping his heavy stick, limped to the door. Leaving it open behind him, much to the annoyance of the proprietor in the cashier's cage, he stood a moment, looking up and down the street. Then he took a few slow steps eastward, beckoning with his hand as he went, and so passed out of sight of the woman at the table.

The eating-place was on the corner, and, outside, the clergyman paused for half a breath. North, east, south, and west he looked, and nowhere he found what his flying glance sought. He turned the corner into the cross-street, and began to walk, at first slowly, continually looking about him. Presently his pace quickened, quickened so that he no longer even stayed to use his stout cane. In another moment he was all but running, his clubfoot pounding the sidewalk heavily as he went. A newsboy thrust a paper under his nose, and he did not see it.

Far down the street, nearly two blocks away, a tall figure in a blue coat stood and stamped in the freezing sleet; and the divine was speeding straight toward him. But he did not get very near. For, as he passed the side entrance at the extreme rear of the restaurant, a departing guest dashed out so recklessly as to run full into him, stopping him dead.

Without looking at her, he knew who it was. In fact, he did not look at her at all, but turned his head hurriedly up and down, sweeping the dark street with a swift eye. But the old woman, having drawn back with a sharp exclamation as they collided, rushed breathlessly into apologies:

"Oh, sir—excuse me! A newsboy popped his head into the side door just after you went out, and I ran to him to get you the paper. But he got away too quick for me, sir. I—"

"Exactly," said the clergyman in his quiet, deep voice. "That must have been the very boy I myself was after."

On the other side, two men had just turned into the street, well muffled against the night, talking cheerfully as they trudged along. Now the clergyman looked full at the woman, and she saw that there was a smile on his face.

"Well! As he seems to have eluded us both, suppose we now return to the subway?"

"Yes, sir; it's full time I—"

"The sidewalk is so slippery," he went on gently. "Perhaps you had better take my arm."

Behind the pair in the dingy restaurant, the waiter came forward to shut the door, and lingered to discuss with the proprietor the sudden departure of his two patrons. After listening to some unfavorable comments on the ways of the clergy, the waiter returned to his table to set it in order.

On the floor in the carpeted aisle between tables lay a white piece of cardboard, which his familiar eye recognized as a torn scrap of one of his own bills of fare, face downward. He stooped and picked it up. On the back of it was some scribbling, made with a blue lead-pencil.

The handwriting was very loose and irregular, as if the writer had had his eyes elsewhere while he wrote, and it was with some difficulty that the waiter deciphered this message:

Miss Hinch 14th St. subway Get police quick

The waiter carried this curious document to the proprietor, who read it over a number of times. He was a dull man, and had a dull man's suspiciousness of a practical joke. However, after a good deal of irresolute discussion, he put on his overcoat and went out for a policeman. He turned west, and half way up the block spied an elderly bluecoat standing in a vestibule. The policeman looked at the scribbling, and dismissed it profanely as a wag's foolishness of the sort that was bothering the life out of him a dozen times a day. He walked along with the proprietor, and as they drew near to the latter's establishment, both became aware of footsteps thudding nearer up the cross-street from the south. As they looked, two young policemen, accompanied by a man in a uniform like a street-car conductor's raced around the corner and dashed into the restaurant.

The first policeman and the proprietor ran in after them, and found them staring about rather vacantly. One of the arms of the law demanded if any suspicious characters had been seen about the place, and the dull proprietor said no. The officers, looking rather flat, explained their errand. It seemed that a few moments before, the third man, who was a ticket-chopper at the subway station, had found a mysterious message lying on the floor by his box. Whence it had come, how long it had lain there, he had not the slightest idea. However, there it was. The policeman exhibited a crumpled strip torn from a newspaper, on which was scrawled in blue pencil:

Miss Hinch Miller's Restaurant police quick

The first policeman, who was both the oldest and the fattest of the three, produced the message on the bill of fare, so utterly at odds with this. The dull proprietor, now bethinking himself, mentioned the clergyman and the old woman who had taken poached eggs and tea together, called for a second bill of fare, and departed so unexpectedly by different doors. The ticket-chopper gasped out that he had seen the same pair at his station: they had come up, he said, and questioned him about trains. The three policemen were momentarily puzzled by this testimony. However, it was soon plain to them that if either the woman or the clergyman really had any information about Miss Hinch—a highly improbable supposition in itself—they would never have stopped with peppering the neighborhood with silly, contradictory messages.

"They're a pair of old fools tryin' to have sport with the police, and if I catch 'em, I'll run 'em in for it," growled the fattest of the officers; and this was the general verdict.

The conference broke up. The dull proprietor returned to his cage, the waiter to his table; the chopper, crestfallen, departed on the run for his chopping box; the three policemen passed out into the bitter night. They walked together, grumbling, and their feet, perhaps by some subconscious impulse, turned eastward toward the subway. And in the middle of the next block a man came running up to them.

"Mister! Look what I picked off'n the sidewalk!"

He held up a white slab which proved to be half of a bill of fare from Miller's Restaurant. On the back of it the three peering officers saw, almost illegibly scrawled in blue pencil:

Police! Miss Hinch 14th subw

The hand trailed off on the *w* as though the writer had been suddenly interrupted. The fat policeman blasphemed and threatened arrests. But the second policeman, who was young and wiry, raised his head from the bill of fare and said suddenly: "Tim, I believe there's something in this."

"There'd ought to be thirty days on the Island in it for thim," growled Tim.

"Suppose, now," said the other policeman, staring intently at him, "the old woman was Miss Hinch herself, f'r instance and the parson was shadowing her while pretendin' he never suspicioned her, and Miss

Hinch not darin' to cut and run for it till she was sure she had a clean getaway. Well now, lissen, what better could he do—"

"That's right!" exclaimed the third policeman. " 'Specially when ye think that Hinch carries a gun, an'll use it, too! Why not have a look in at the subway station, anyway, the three of us?"

The proposal carried the day. The three officers started for the subway, the citizen following. They walked at a good pace and without more talk; and both their speed and their silence had a subtle psychological reaction. As the minds of the men turned inward upon the odd behavior of the pair in Miller's Restaurant, the conviction that, after all, something important might be afoot grew and strengthened within each one of them. Unconsciously their pace quickened. It was the young, wiry policeman who first broke into an open run, but the two others had been for twenty paces on the very edge of it, and followed at a rapid pace.

However, these consultations and vacillations had taken time. The stout clergyman and the poor old woman had five minutes' start of the officers of the law, and that, as it fell out, was all that the occasion required. On the street, as they made their way arm in arm to the station, they were seen, and remembered, by several belated pedestrians. It was observed by more than one that the woman lagged as if she were tired, while the club-footed cleric, supporting her on his arm, steadily kept her up to his own brisk gait.

So walking, the pair descended the subway steps, came out upon the bleak platform again, and presently stood once more at the extreme uptown end of it, just where they had waited three-quarters of an hour before. Nearby, a porter had at some time overturned a bucket of water, and a splotch of thin ice ran out and over the edge of the concrete. The young men, taking turns up and down, distinctly heard the clergyman warn the woman to look out for this ice. Far away to the north was to be heard the faint roar of an approaching train.

The woman stood nearest the track, and the clergyman stood in front of her. In the vague light their looks met, and each must have been struck by the pallor of the other's face. In addition, the woman was breathing hard, and her hands and feet betrayed some nervousness. It was, of course, difficult now to ignore the fact that for an hour they had been clinging rather desperately to each other, at all costs; but the clergyman made a creditable effort to do so. He talked without ceasing, in a voice sounding only a little unnatural, for the most part of the deplorable weather, with a good deal about a train to Jersey, which he had not previously mentioned. And all the time both of them kept turning their heads toward the station entrances, as if expecting some arrival.

As he talked, the clergyman kept his hands quietly busy. From the bottom edge of his black sack-coat he drew a pin, and stuck it deep into the ball of his middle finger. He took out his handkerchief to dust the hard sleet from his hat; and under his overcoat he pressed the handkerchief against his bleeding finger. While making these small arrangements, he held the woman's eyes with his own, talking on; and, still holding them, he suddenly broke off his random talk and peered at her cheek with concern.

"My good woman, you've scratched your cheek somehow! Why, bless me, it's bleeding quite badly."

"Never mind,—never mind," said the woman, hurriedly, and swept her eyes toward the steps.

"But, good gracious— Just allow me—Ah!"

Too quick for her, he leaned forward and, through the thin veil, brushed her cheek hard with the handkerchief; removing it, he held it up so that she might see the blood for herself. But she did not glance at the handkerchief, and neither did he. His gaze was riveted upon her cheek, which looked so smooth and clear where he had smudged the clever wrinkles away.

Down the steps and upon the platform pounded the feet of the three hurrying policemen. But it was evident now that the oncoming train would thunder in just ahead of them. The clergyman, standing close in front of the woman, took a firmer grip on his heavy stick and a look of stern triumph came into his face.

"You're not so terribly clever, after all!"

The woman had sprung back from him with an irrepressible exclamation; and in that instant she was aware of the police.

However, her foot slipped on the treacherous ice—or it may have tripped on the stout cane, when the clergyman suddenly shifted its position. In the next breath the train roared past.

By a curious chance, the body of the woman was not mangled or mutilated at all. There was a deep blue bruise on the left temple, but apparently that was all; even the old black hat remained on her head, skewered fast by the long pin. It was the clergyman who first made out the body, huddled at the side of the dark track where the train had flung it—he who covered the still face and superintended the removal to the platform. Two eye-witnesses pointed out the ice on which the unfortunate woman had slipped, and described their horror as they saw her companion spring forward just too late to save her.

Not wishing to bring on a delirium of excitement among the clustered bystanders, the oldest policeman drew the clergyman aside and showed him the three mysterious messages. Much affected by the shocking end of his sleuthery as he was, he readily admitted having written them. He briefly recounted how the woman's strange movements on 126th Street had arrested his attention, and how, watching her closely on the car, while encouraging every opportunity for conversation, he had finally detected that she wore a wig. Unfortunately, however, her suspicions had been aroused by his interest in her, and thereafter a long battle of wits had ensued between them—he trying to summon the police without her knowledge, she dogging him close to prevent that, and at the same time watching her chance to give him the slip. He re-hearsed how, in the restaurant, when he had invented an excuse to leave her for a minute, she had made a bolt and narrowly missed getting away; and finally how, having brought her back to the subway, and seeing the police at last near, he had decided to risk exposing her make-up, with this unexpectedly shocking result.

"And now," he concluded in a shaken voice, "I am naturally most anxious to know whether I am right—or have made some terrible mistake. Will you look at her, officer, and tell me if it is indeed—she?"

But the old policeman shook his head over the well-known ability of Miss Hinch to look like everybody else in the world but herself.

"It'll take God Almighty to tell us that, sir—saving your presence. I'll leave it f'r headquarters," he continued, as if that were the same thing. "But, if it is her, she's gone to her reward!"

"God pity her!" said the clergyman.

"Amen! Give me your name, sir. They'll likely want you in the morning."

The clergyman gave it: Rev. Theodore Shaler, of Denver; city address, a street and number near Washington Square. Having thus discharged his duty in the affair, he started sadly to go away; but, passing by the silent figure stretched on a bench under the ticket-seller's overcoat, he bared his head and stopped for one last look at it.

The parson's gentleness and efficiency had already won favorable comments from the bystanders, and of the first quality he now gave a final proof. The dead woman's little handbag, which somebody had recovered from the track and laid at her side, had slipped to the floor; and the clergyman, observing it, stooped silently to restore it. This last small service chanced to bring his head close to the drooped head of the dead woman; and, as he straightened up, her projecting hatpin struck his cheek and ripped a straight line down it. This in itself would have been a trifle, since scratches soon heal. But it happened that the point of the hatpin caught under the lining of the clergyman's perfect beard and stripped it clean from him; so that, as he rose, with a suddenly shrilled cry, he turned upon the astonished onlookers the bare, smooth chin of a woman, curiously long and pointed.

There were not many such chins in the world, and the urchins in the street would have recognized this one. Amid a sudden uproar which ill became the presence of the dead, the police closed in on Miss Hinch and handcuffed her with violence, fearing suicide, if not some new witchery; and at the station-house an unemotional matron divested her of the last and best of all her many disguises.

This much the police did. But it was everywhere understood that it was Jessie Dark who had really made the capture, and all the papers next morning printed pictures of the unconquerable little woman, and of the hatpin with which she had reached back from another world to bring her greatest—and her last—adversary to justice.

THE MAN OF THE FAMILY

By Ruth Suckow

[The Middle West is represented in this volume by the realistic story, *The Man of the Family*. Ruth Suckow was born in a small Iowa town, Hawarden, in 1892. Her formal education was acquired in three colleges: Grinnell, Boston School of Expression, and Denver University. She was graduated from the latter in 1917. She is married (Mrs. Ferner Nuhn) and makes her permanent home at Cedar Falls, but travels a good deal and writes wherever she is temporarily sojourning. A generation ago Hamlin Garland wrote very realistic short stories of the Middle West, Iowa, Dakota, Illinois, and Wisconsin. Those were the years when such grim stories as *Up the Coolly* and *Sim Burns' Wife* represented pioneer farm life as it was. Miss Suckow as truly represents the common experiences of the people of this area in the nineteen-twenties and -thirties as Mr. Garland represented the same class of people in his villages and on his farms in the eighteen-nineties.

The Man of the Family first appeared in the *American Mercury* for December, 1926. It is reprinted here from *Children and Older People* by arrangement with Alfred A. Knopf, Inc., publishers.

FLOYD OBERHOLZER was just opening up the drug-store when Gerald came.

"Hello, Gerald. Want something?"

"I come to start in working."

"This morning!" Floyd was startled. "Why, school can't be over yet, is it? What is this—Wednesday?"

"Yes, but we got done with out tests yesterday, all but arithmetic, and I didn't have to take that."

"Oh, you didn't have to take that?" Floyd repeated vaguely. "Well, you come into the store and we'll see what there is for you to do."

Gerald followed him into the drug-store.

Floyd looked around somewhat helplessly. It was only a few months since he and Lois had bought this little business in Independenceville. They knew what to do themselves, but it was a different matter setting some one else to work. They hadn't expected Gerald so soon, or wanted him. Two or three months ago, he had come into the store to ask if he couldn't have a job, and because they hated to turn the kid away—it wasn't very long after the accident in which his father had been killed—

952

Floyd had told him: "Well, you come around when school's out. Maybe we can find something then." And now he was here.

"Well, you're starting in early," Floyd said to him. "You've beat my wife—she isn't in the store yet. Well, I don't know, Gerald—I guess you might as well sweep out, the first thing." He remembered then that Lois had swept the store before they closed last night; the boys had left so many cigarette stubs around. But he guessed it could stand it again. It would keep Gerald busy while Floyd decided what to have him do.

"All right," Gerald answered soberly. "Where do you keep your broom?"

"Right out there in the back, Gerald. See—I'll show you. Then you'll know where it is."

Gerald started in to sweep the wooden floor with awkward, scowling concentration. His back was stooped and intent. He took long hard strokes, trying to do a good job of it. Floyd looked at him, and then turned and went scuttling up the stairs.

"Hey—Lois!" he called softly.

"'Smatter, pop?"

Lois, still in her bungalow apron, came to the door of the kitchen. The Oberholzers were living over the drug-store.

"Say, that kid's here."

"What kid?"

"Gerald Rayburn. He's come to start in working. Seems awful anxious to begin. What in the dickens shall I have him do?"

"You're a fine boss!" Lois began to laugh. "What's he doing now—standing in the middle of the floor and sucking his thumb?"

"I've got him sweeping."

"Why I swept last night, you idiot!"

"Well, I know you did, but I forgot it. I didn't want to tell him to stand around. He goes at it like a little beaver. You ought to watch him. Oh, I suppose the kid *is* anxious to start in earning."

Lois didn't know what to say.

"You come down," said Floyd, "and tell him about the soda-fountain. That's your end of the business."

"Oh, it is, is it? All right, I'll come down and give the boss's orders since he doesn't know what they are himself," she replied with mock commiseration, and pinched Floyd's ear.

"Well, gosh, I didn't expect that kid the minute school let out! Most kids aren't that anxious to go to work. Isn't this the day they have the school picnic? Why, sure—that's why we got that pop."

He started down the stairs and then went back to the next-to-the-top step and stood frowning uncertainly.

"Think we can really use him, Lois?"

"Well, I guess we've got him, anyway!"

"I know we'll have to have somebody, but he's such a kid. I don't know—"

Lois said hastily: "Oh, well, let's try him. You told him he could come. I feel so sorry for that family."

"Well, so do I. But then . . . Well, all right . . ."

Floyd left it at that, and scuttled down the stairs again. Lois went back to the kitchen which she herself had painted blue and white, with figured curtains, changing it from the gloomy old hole that the Twekesburys had left it, to a gay new room. She hated to leave this beloved little place to go and help Floyd in the store. Now that they had hired just a little boy to help them for the Summer, she supposed she would have to be downstairs most of the time. She almost wished she hadn't told Floyd to keep Gerald. Well, if Gerald couldn't do the work, he'd have to go, that was all.

"All right, Gerald," Floyd went into the store saying loudly and cheerfully. "Finished that? Well, then, I guess you'd better—" His eyes, quickly roving, caught sight of the magazine rack. "I guess you'd better straighten up those magazines. Folks take 'em out and read 'em all through and then put 'em back."

"All right."

Floyd whistled as he took the long gray cambric covers off the tables in the middle of the room, where boxes of gilt-edged correspondence cards and leather-bound copies of the works of Edgar Guest had to be displayed until the graduating exercises were over. Gerald went at his work with such silent concentration that it almost embarrassed Floyd.

"What do you want I should do next?"

"Oh, well . . . Guess maybe I better show you about these cigarettes and tobacco. That's probably what they'll be after first. I'll show you how we've got things marked."

"All right."

Lois came down. Floyd gave her an expressive look and nodded toward Gerald. "He's right at it!" Certainly the boy seemed to be trying hard. His freckled face with the crop of red hair was surly with concentration. Floyd couldn't help remembering that he was just a kid and too young to be starting in to work in earnest. He was quite willing to give up his charge and let Lois initiate him into the mysteries of the new white soda-fountain which they had installed in place of the cracked, lugubrious onyx splendor of an earlier day. Gerald stood silently beside Lois, bashfully aware of her bobbed hair and her plump white arms, answering dutifully: "Yes, ma'am."

"You can watch me this morning, Gerald, and run some errands, maybe. Wash up the glasses. Do the dirty work—how's that?"

"Yes, ma'am."

He was a little clumsy, partly out of bashfulness, but so serious and determined that Lois thought: "Goodness, I wonder if it'll last!" She wanted to give him all the help he needed, but she didn't quite know what to make of his surly little face. He hated to ask her questions, and several times she had to say, "Oh, not like that, Gerald!"

II

"Gee, that was an awful thing to happen to that family!" Floyd said to Lois in the back room of the store, where he had gone to look for a special package of hog medicine ordered by old Gus Reinbeck. "I think this kid kind of realizes, don't you?"

"Have they got anything, do you suppose?"

"A little insurance, they say, and that house, but not much more than to keep them until this boy can start earning."

"The mother can earn something herself, I should think," Lois said rather defiantly. *She* worked.

"Yes, but with three kids to look after . . . And anyway, what is there for a woman to do in a burg like this except take in washing?"

"Well, maybe."

Back door and front of the store were open, and through the shimmery blackness of the back screen the garden was green and fresh. A tin cup hung on an old-fashioned pump under the vines. Gerald looked longingly at the boards of the platform, wet with spilled water. There was city water in the soda-fountain, but the pump looked so much cooler out there. "Run out and get a drink if you want to, Gerald," Lois told him. "I always go out there for my water. It's fun to work the pump." Boys never could see a pump or a drinking fountain or even a hydrant without being consumed with thirst, she knew. Lois liked boys. Gerald made her think of her kid brother. It was a shame he had to go to work. She wanted to reassure him somehow, to rumple his red hair or pat his shoulder. But she must remember that they were hiring him. They couldn't afford to keep him out of pity. Beside, he seemed determined to evade all personal advances and stuck doggedly to work. Maybe the kid was miserable at missing that picnic.

It was getting hot in town. Cars began to rattle and whir down the street, and in a few moments Louie Grossman's big red truck drove up to the side door of the drug-store.

"Hey, Floyd! Got the pop?"

"Got the pop? You bet I've got the pop. You want it now?"

"Sure do, if it's goin' on this picnic."

"All right, sir! Want to come and help me take it out, Gerald?"

"All right."

Gerald went with Floyd into the back room of the store, bright and cool and scattered with light from the green leaves outside. He tugged at one end of the big pop case, and helped Floyd carry it outside and shove it into the truck.

"Now, another one, Gerald."

"All right."

"Well, the kids oughtn't to get thirsty today," Floyd said.

"No, they sure got plenty. What are you doing, Gerald?" Louie asked. "Ain't you going to the picnic?"

"I got to work," Gerald answered.

He went back into the store. The two men looked after him.

"He workin' for you now, Floyd?"

"Guess so. It looks like it. He came this morning."

"Goes at it pretty good, don't he?"

"Yes, he seems to be willing. He's pretty young, but then . . . Where they going for the picnic today, Louie?"

"Out to Bailey's Creek. You ever been there?"

"Not yet. Mighty pretty place, I guess," he added.

"Yes, but it ain't much of a road."

"Well, don't tip 'em out, Louie."

"No, I'll try and keep the old bus in her tracks."

Louie started the noisy engine of the big truck. It went roaring up the street between green lawns and white houses and pink peonies, to where the school children, boys in freshly ironed blouses and girls in summery dresses, waited in a flock under the elms of the school-yard . . . then out, spinning down the graveled highway between freshly planted fields, turning into the little woods road, narrow and rutted, where the children had to bend their heads under the switch of honey locusts that left small white petals in their sun-warmed hair . . . on into the depths of green woods through the heart of which the shining creek was flowing. . . .

Lois had come to the doorway to watch the truck leave. "I wouldn't mind going to a picnic myself on a day like this," she murmured.

When she went back into the store, she looked curiously at Gerald. It gave her a guilty feeling, wholly unreasonable, to have him at work in their store today when it was a holiday for all the other children. But he had come of his own accord. They hadn't told him to do it.

"Did your sisters go on the picnic, Gerald?" she asked.

"Yes, *they* went," he answered, rather slightingly.

"How many have you, Gerald? Just Juanita and Betty?"

"Yes, ma'am."

"And you're the only boy?"

"Yes, ma'am."

"You could have started in tomorrow just as well, Gerald."

He did not answer.

III

The bright morning grew hotter and hotter, until to enter the drug-store from the glaring cement outside was like going into a cool, clean-scented cavern. The regular set of loafers drifted in, asked for tobacco, and stayed, sitting on the white-topped stools at the soda fountain and trying to be facetious with Gerald. "Well, you got a new clerk?" every one who came in demanded. It was a new joke every time. In an interval of no customers, Lois stooped down and drew out a pale green bottle frosted over with cold moisture from the case under the counter. It was still a treat to her to think she owned a store.

"I'm going to try some of this new lime stuff," she said. "See how it tastes. Don't you want the other straw, Gerald?"

"No, I guess not," he answered bashfully.

There was a glint of longing and reluctance in his eyes. But Lois thought: Maybe I oughtn't to start offering him things and being too easy with him. After all, Floyd was paying him to help them, and it wasn't her fault that his father had been killed. They were doing the best they could for him by letting him have a job. When, later, she decided to try one of those chocolates Floyd had ordered from a new traveling man, she turned her back while she nibbled it and wiped her fingers on the scrap of oiled paper in which it had been wrapped. Running the business all by themselves was still an adventure to the young Oberholzers; but even now they had run up against the fact more than once that it wasn't just a game. They had halfway discovered the meaning of that term—"If you want to do business—" Lois couldn't pick out from the traveling man's stock the delicately scented toilet waters that she herself liked, but had to choose the red and green brands with big gaudy flowers on the labels that the girls here in town would buy—the kind that "went." She had had to freeze out old Bart Bailey who came in every morning to read the paper and the detective magazines he had no money to buy, and left dirty thumb marks on all the pages.

Noon came with the shriek of the whistle from the powerhouse, with the noise of cars being started and of the men driving home to dinner.

"When does your mamma expect you home for dinner, Gerald?" Lois asked.

"Oh, I guess it don't matter," Gerald mumbled bashfully.

"Didn't you tell her when you'd come?"

"No, ma'am."

They let him go; but if they kept him in the store, he would have to go later and let them have their dinner at noon. That was one reason why they wanted help. He was back in good time. "Well, didn't take *you* long to eat your dinner!" Floyd said. But maybe it wasn't a good thing to act surprised at his promptness. It would wear off soon enough, if they could infer anything from their experiences with Marcelle Johnston, who had pretended to work for them for three weeks in the Winter.

At intervals during the afternoon, Floyd and Lois reported to each other. "We're going to have an awful time teaching him to make a decent sundae. He doesn't catch on any too fast, but he seems to be willing to do whatever you tell him." Whether they wanted to keep him or no, it was evident that he meant to stay. He wanted the job. His surly little freckled face scarcely relaxed into a smile even when there was a dog fight outside and Miss Angie Robinson's little poodle sent that big hound of Ole Swanson's off yelping. He went at whatever he was told to do with dogged earnestness, although he didn't see things for himself. He said "Yes, ma'am" with sober respect; but he would ask: "What's the price of this here kind of tobacco, Lois?" and say to customers: "No, Floyd ain't in just now, he went over to the depot." As the afternoon wore along, his freckled face grew flushed. "Does it seem like a long day, Gerald?" Lois asked him once. He admitted: "Kind of. Not so very."

Late in the afternoon, the picnic trucks came rattling into town with all the children disheveled and shouting. A few moments afterwards, a group of girls came bursting into the store. Their bright-colored Summer dresses were wrinkled, their bobs were wildly rumpled, their tired eyes were shining.

"Oh, gee, but we're thirsty! We're just dying! Oh, look at Gerald Rayburn! Are you working in here, Gerald?"

"Yes, didn't you know he was?" his young sister Juanita asked. "We want six bottles of pop, Gerald," she ordered airily.

"Have you got any money?"

"Yes, I have!"

"Where'd you get it, then?" he demanded suspiciously.

"None of your business, Mr. Smarty! I guess it's not yours, is it?"

A bright pink flared up in Juanita's cheeks. Her eyes sparkled angrily. She was a pretty child, with red hair, like Gerald's, blazing out in a fuzzy aureole around her freckled face. She flounced down into one of the white chairs. "We want a table, don't we kids? We don't want to sit at the fountain, like the boys." When Gerald brought the six cold red bottles carefully toppling on the tray, she lifted her little chin and disdained to look at him.

"You needn't think because I'm working here, you can come in and order what you want," he told her.

"Shut up!" she whispered furiously.

Her eyes were brighter still with tears. Mamma had given her the nickel for helping with the ironing yesterday afternoon instead of going off with the girls. She had given it to her for ironing Julie Bronson's pink chemise, with all the lace, so beautifully. It was none of Gerald's business what she did with it! She said to the other girls, with flashing eyes and quivering lips:

"He thinks he's so smart now just because he's starting in to work and Betty and I aren't. You'd just think he *owned* us to hear the way he talks. I don't care. I guess he isn't the only one who does anything. I guess I do lots of things. I'd like to see Gerald Rayburn ever wash the dishes!"

She stuck two straws into her bottle of strawberry pop and sucked it all up defiantly. Maybe she ought to have saved her nickel, but Gerald had no right trying to boss her in front of all the girls.

He told her, when she was leaving the store:

"You needn't go running around now, you can go home and help mamma."

"You keep still!" She threw her nickel down with a ring on the white counter of the soda fountain. "I guess you aren't my boss *yet!*

"That's all right, I know what I'm talking about."

"That's right, Gerald," old Hod Brunskill shouted, with humorous approval. "You make the womenfolks mind you. Ain't that so, boys?"

"You tell 'em it's so!"

They laughed loudly; and then, clustered together with their arms on the glass counter, that had a sign in red letters "Do not lean!", they tore open their packages of bitter-scented tobacco and began to talk in lowered voices about the Rayburn family: how it had been "left," how it got along, about the tragic death of Frank Rayburn, still disputing over the minutiae of that event which they had never yet been able to settle, although nearly a year had passed since the thing happened. "Well, I never could understand how a fella like that, that was used to climbin' all over everywhere, come to fall off that ladder like that—." "Why, he just kinda stepped backward-like—I s'pose he forgot maybe where he was at—." "Some says the ladder broke and let him down." "Naw, the ladder didn't *break*." "Well, was it true he'd been out drinkin' the night before? That's how I heard it." "Naw, he hadn't been out drinkin' the night *before*." "Well, I can't figger out—." "Why, he just kinda stepped backwards—." It was terrible, they all agreed with solemn faces, to think that poor little woman should have been left with those three children, although there was dispute again about how much they had been left *with*. Some said they "had something," some said they "had nothing." She was a nice woman. Yes, and she was a good-looking woman, too . . . And then they drew closer together, and one of them said something about "Art Fox," and their voices broke into a laugh and a snicker.

Gerald was washing glasses at the soda-fountain. His freckled face flushed a dull red, and when they snickered he looked over at them furiously. He had a notion of what they were saying. When they passed him, leaving the store, they praised him loudly and self-consciously.

"Well, Gerald, you're all right, ain't you? Takin' right a-hold!"

"You bet he's all right."

"Well, Gerald's the man now, ain't that so, Gerald! He's the one."

"That's right."

The six o'clock whistle blew.

Gerald looked about hesitatingly for Floyd. Finally he went out to the back room of the store to find him.

"Shall I go now? The whistle blew."

"Yes, sure, you go along now, Gerald. I wasn't paying any attention."

Floyd was busy over some boxes on the floor. Gerald hesitated. His face was red. He wanted to ask if he had "done all right." But he was ashamed. Finally he blurted:

"Do you want I should come back tomorrow morning?"

Floyd was still busy over the boxes. Gerald waited.

"Yes, you come back in the morning, Gerald," Floyd answered cheerfully.

IV

Gerald got out of the store as fast as he could. How bright the street seemed outside, and how fresh the air was! He felt as if he had been smelling camphor and perfumes all his life. He had a job! It seemed to him that every one must know. He wanted people to ask him what he had been doing, it made him feel proud and important; although when Mr. Baird, the minister, who had been in the store earlier in the day, greeted him with: "Well, is the day's work over, young man?" he was suddenly too bashful to do more than grunt an answer. He walked soberly down the main street, and broke into a run as he cut across the corner.

His feet burned. It was hard to stand all day like that, although he had told Lois he didn't mind it. He grew hot all over when he thought of the mistakes he had made. But the ache that had seemed lodged in his chest somewhere, ever since the day when his father was buried and all the relatives had told him: "Well, you'll have to look after your mamma now, Gerald, won't you?"—when his mother cried and clung to him that night—that ache was strangely eased. He was earning money. He could take care of his mother. It humiliated him that his mother should have to be doing the washing for other people, although it was only some of their neighbors; but she wouldn't have to do it always. He had not heard more than a few words of what those men in the drug-store were saying. But at the thought—the very suspicion of it—his mind felt hot and sore. If they'd been saying anything about his mother, they'd be sorry for it. He'd—he didn't know just what—but anyway, they'd better look out!

The new little semi-bungalow house looked bleak and desolate. It had been that way ever since his father died. No new flowers had been planted this Spring, the clothes-line hadn't been fixed, the garage for the car they had been going to get this Summer stood unpainted just as his father had left it last Fall. But they would have things again. The relatives needn't say anything; he guessed he could take care of his own mother without their telling him. He loved her, but it was none of their business to know it.

She was standing in the doorway. Gerald evaded her kiss, ducked away from her and went tramping out to the kitchen. He was afraid she was going to make a fuss.

"I gotta wash my hands," he told her importantly.

She followed him and stood looking at him, pitiful and proud.

"Why don't you go up to the bathroom, sweetheart?"

"I druther wash down here."

It was what his father had done when he came home from work.

"Are you ready for supper?" she pleaded.

"You bet."

She touched his face, he couldn't avoid that. But he got into the dining-room as fast as he could and sat down with satisfaction. There were all the things that he liked—hot biscuits, and jelly, and strawberries. He demanded coffee, and his mother gave it to him. Betty's little mouth puckered up and her eyes were round with amazement.

"You don't let *us* have coffee," she said.

"Well, brother's been working. He has to have it."

The two little girls chattered eagerly about the school picnic. Gerald stuck to the business of eating. He had never been so hungry; hot biscuits had never tasted so good. He replied briefly to his mother's fond questions about what he had been doing all day.

"Were Floyd and his wife good to you? Did they show you what to do?"

"Yeah, they were all right."

"Did you know how to wait on people?"

"Sure."

"Didn't it seem terribly long to you?"

"Naw."

"Well, you want to eat a good supper."

It was over now, and he didn't want to talk about it. He wished she'd let him alone.

The one cooky left on the plate was given to Gerald. Betty followed her mother into the kitchen, weeping and complaining. She was the baby, and the extra pieces of everything were for her.

"I don't see why you gave it to Gerald, mamma. You didn't even make him give me half."

"Well, darling, listen—when men have been working they get hungrier than women and little girls do, and then we have to let them have what they want to eat. We don't get so hungry."

"*I* was hungry!"

"Were you, pet?" Her mother laughed, half commiseratingly. "Then you eat this strawberry mamma puts into your little mouth."

"I don't want a strawberry. I had enough strawberries. And I was working," Betty insisted. "I put on all the knives and forks, I *was* working, mamma."

"Were you? Well, you were helping. You're a nice little helper."

"Before I'd make a fuss about an old cooky!" Juanita said scornfully.

She flashed a quick indignant glace at Gerald, remembering how he had talked to her in the drug-store. Let him have everything in the house to eat if he wanted it, and if mamma wanted to give it to him. But there was an obscure justice that silenced her even while it made her resentful. Well, she wouldn't be here all her life. She'd get married some day—and then she'd do as she pleased.

Gerald went out and sat on the steps of the porch. This was the time of day when his father always used to come out here and look at the paper. Gerald was ashamed of having eaten the cooky. He thought it belonged to him, but let that baby Betty have it! He would after this. He didn't know when he had had such a good supper. He watched Bobby Parker's yard across the street so that he could shout across at Bobby the instant he came outdoors. Maybe they could go over and see those turtles Bobby's uncle had in his back yard. It would be fun to see if they really could be taught tricks. He could hear the girls complaining about the dishes. "It's your turn tonight." "It isn't!" Gee whizz, if they couldn't even do a little thing like washing dishes!

V

The evening came on cool and bright. Gerald stayed on the porch steps, although Bobby didn't appear in the yard. What he really meant to do was to ask Bobby about the picnic, and try to find out, without saying it in so many words, whether any other boy had hung around Arlene Fedderson. He didn't care, anyway. He had thought about it in the store all the time, but it didn't matter so much now. His mother was the one he had to look after. Again he felt a fine, tired glow of satisfaction. He had put in a good day's work, all right.

Then he blushed. He remembered those men at the drug-store. Here was that old Art Fox coming up the walk with a pailful of strawberries! Well, if he thought he was coming here with those berries, he could just go away again.

"H'lo, Gerald," Art Fox called out cheerfully. He was a good-natured man, a widower, with a red, sunburned face and grayish hair and mustache. He lived about a block away from the Rayburns, in a good-sized house. Gerald had always thought he was a nice man, because he never said any more than "'Lo, boys!" when the boys ran across his lawn playing run-sheep-run.

"H'lo," Gerald answered briefly.

"Your ma around anywhere?"

"I don't know."

Art Fox halted. "Oh, well . . . She ain't gone out anywhere, has she?"

"I guess she has."

What did it matter whether that was true or not? Art Fox had no business coming here. He felt a sense of pain and outrage.

"That's too bad. I thought I'd drop around and see if you folks couldn't use a few strawberries. I got a bunch of 'em ripe—too many for an old fellow to eat by himself," he added with a mild attempt at jocularity. "Didn't know as you folks had any."

"We got some."

"That so? Well, I guess you can use a few more, can't you?"

"No, we got all we want."

"That so? Well, if you got all you need . . ." Art Fox stood there awkwardly for a moment. "Well, I guess I'll have to try to dump these on somebody else."

Gerald was silent.

"Your ma be home pretty soon, will she?"

"No, she ain't here."

"That so? Well . . . good-by, then."

Gerald said nothing. He could feel his heart thumping. He looked away. Art Fox was going down the walk with the strawberries newly washed and freshly red in the bright tin pail. Just as he turned the corner, Mrs. Rayburn came to the door.

"I thought I heard somebody. Have they gone? Was anybody here, Gerald?"

"Art Fox." Gerald did not turn around.

"Oh!" His mother seemed a little flustered. "What did he want? Has he gone away?" she asked.

"He brought some of his strawberries."

"Why Gerald, why didn't you call me?"

"'Cause I told him we didn't want 'em. We got some of our own."

"Why, *Gerald*—"

"Well, we don't want him around here," Gerald said roughly.

He stared straight ahead at a little bird hopping about on the lawn, fighting down the childish tears that made his throat ache and his eyes burn. That sense of pain and outrage swelled in his heart. He thought of the unfinished garage standing bare and desolate in the back yard—his father's old coat still hanging in the kitchen entry. If his mother couldn't take care of herself, he'd do it for her. He was the man of the house now. Art Fox could stay at home where he belonged. This was *their* home. She was *his* mother. Above that ache of unmanly tears he felt a hard exultance. They wouldn't laugh any more in the drug-store. They wouldn't talk about her.

She looked flushed and disconcerted. She stood in the doorway looking at Gerald. The back of his red head was like his father's. So was the set of his sturdy shoulders. She looked at them with an unwilling respect that turned slowly to resentment. All these last few weeks, a secret girlish pleasure had been growing up in her heart most surprisingly out of the blackness of her grief and loneliness. She knew that she was admired. She had thought it hidden from every one. At times she had laughed and called herself a fool; and at times her eyes were dreamy and a warmth settled softly about her. Now it was shamed and trampled . . .

She started to say something to Gerald. But she stopped, as she had always stopped with Frank. She felt her anger melting helplessly away from her. He was so proud of working for her. He was so proud of his strength. He was only a little boy, after all—her little boy, sitting small and pitiful and unapproachable in the twilight.

She turned, her face suddenly quivering, went back into the hot darkness of the empty house, and sat down there alone.

NEITHER JEW NOR GREEK

By *William M. John*

[William M. John (1888–   ) is a native of the section of Colorado, east of the Rocky Mountains, that he has used as the setting for this story. For a number of years he followed ranch life not far from Trinidad. Recently, since he has been following the vocation of authorship, he has made his home in Golden and Denver. The story, *Neither Jew Nor Greek*, is included in this volume because of the convincing picture of ranch life in the West as it was only a decade or two ago. It strikes the note of veracity which the romantic stories of the moving pictures and of the "Western" magazines published in the East almost invariably miss.

Neither Jew Nor Greek was published in the *Century Magazine* (August, 1929), and is reprinted here by permission of the author.]

UNCLE ASY MULBERRY threw back his head and expressed his skepticism with a laugh that was a cross between a chuckle and a whinny.

No, no—he said—you don't believe what you're sayin'. You may think you do, but you don't know your own mind. I ain't doubtin' the truth of your statement; it's as true as gospel. But when a man, and more particularly a woman, says to me, "We're all alike. Everybody's one under the skin," I know right off they haven't stopped to consider what they are talkin' about.

I've heard folks make that remark, in one form or another, off and on, for over seventy years; ever since I was old enough to be interested in what the other fellow was sayin'. Long before the institution you're leanin' against graduated out of the Feed and Livery class into a first-rate Automobile and Accessory business, neighbors and customers would drift in for a snack of small talk, and many's the time I've had 'em say to me, "Asy, you can't get away from it, we're all human, and bein' all human, we're all heir to the same faults and the same virtues."

Well, them are sentiments that would do credit to anybody, but here's the hitch: when you come to find out who the man or woman's referrin' to in such a brotherly or sisterly fashion, it's pretty sure to be somebody they don't know much about, or that they think is a mite better than they are.

Don't I recollect the stirrin' sermon Brother Millsap preached the one and only time Big Annie attended divine services here in the Hopeville Baptist Church? Don't I recollect the amount of brotherly and sisterly feelin' displayed at the close of that service? If I'd never seen it worked out before or since, that was enough to prove to me how much store most folks put in the "We're all alike" idea. About all the education you ever need in this life is to learn to watch the average man and woman when they're just bein' themselves.

At the time Ike Bowan married Big Annie and brought her down here in Tumbleweed Valley to live, she was one of Miss May's steady girls. Miss May run the biggest and best house on Santa Fe Avenue, up in Dawson. A house of ill-repute it would be called now, I reckon, since the general wave| of reform has swept over the country. But in them days our leadin' bankers and lawyers and cattlemen used to rub shoulders in Miss May's parlor, and nobody seemed to think much about it. I don't suppose there was a farmer or ranchman in the valley, that amounted to anything, who Big Annie couldn't call by his first name and not feel she was bein' overly intimate in doin' it.

There was some that said they couldn't understand why Ike married Big Annie, but that was never a mystery to me. Ike had run away from home, down in Texas, when he was nine years old and followed a trail herd north as far as Colorado. He'd been battered and knocked 'round, never knowin' a woman's lovin' care, for more than forty years, so when he found one that would have him, he was smart enough not to let the opportunity slip. He was short and weazened, had a cast in one eye, and if he ever got all the tobacco juice out of his beard at one time, I never happened to be 'round on that occasion.

What I couldn't understand was, why did Big Annie ever marry Ike? It may have been she had made up her mind to retire from active business and Ike was the first gate that opened on her lane, or it may have been that she was suddenly seized with a desire to become an honest woman in the eyes of the world. I ain't sayin' which, but I do know that no woman ever tried harder than Big Annie did to make her husband comfortable and happy, durin' the two years that Ike lived after they was married.

Annie was big. Six feet tall, I reckon, and broad. Her hair was a light sorrel, and her profession hadn't hardened her blue eyes the way it does some women's. She was different, in one way at least, from most of the women in her trade—she was thrifty, kept most everything she got her hands on. Some said Big Annie owned a half interest in Miss May's house when she married Ike. Anyway, Ike added a hundred good white-faced cows to his herd the month after he brought Annie home. And I recollect, some years before that, hearin' Butch Gooch say, "George Stevens was blowin' himself up at Miss May's last night. Big Annie had her rope on him. I'll bet he comes home without his shirt."

But Big Annie must of made up her mind to bury her past, and thought that other folks would be willin' to help her shovel the dirt in on it, for the second Sunday, after she landed in our midst, she walked into the Baptist Church and set down up front beside Lize Sharp, just as Brother Millsap was windin' up the announcements for the mornin'.

The men twisted their necks most off, tryin' to get a better view from their side of the church, and the women on Big Annie's side developed an epidemic of weak lungs, quicker than I ever seen it done before.

Brother Millsap stared at Big Annie as if he was witnessin' one of them miracles bein' performed he'd preached so much about. Then he coughed a couple of times himself and added a special exhortation to the women.

"Dip your hands deep into your lard pails," he roared. "Spare not your spices, cook liberally and your best, for when you cook for our big sociable to be held next Friday evening, you are preparin' for the Lord. Our organ is in bad shape. We have all prayed earnestly, but prayer without works availeth nothin'. Come early, bring plenty of food, ask all your friends. Let us make it a feast of good-fellowship. The cost of this glorious meal will be twenty-five cents for adults and fifteen cents for children."

Then, with a hitch at his white necktie, he opened the big Bible on the pulpit and begun the cheerin' message he'd prepared.

"Sisters and Brethern," he said, "I've chosen for my text this mornin' the twenty-eighth verse of the third chapter of Galatians."

I ain't up on the Bible, the way Ma is, but I can remember every word of that verse as plain as if Brother Millsap was standin' right here in front of us now, readin' it in that low, sanctimonious voice he used when he was in the pulpit. "There is neither Jew nor Greek, there is neither bond nor free, there is neither male nor female: for ye are all one in Christ Jesus."

I reckon he'd of switched to some other subject if he'd had time, but Big Annie sort of took him by surprise, so to speak. He'd worked hard on that sermon, you could see that as he went along. He didn't stop with the one verse, but quoted more than half the Scriptures in his effort to prove how near we all come to bein' cut off the same pattern, in the eyes of God. He mentioned Mary Magdalene and several other right prominent folks who happened along at the time the Bible was set down. Before he finished, you was about convinced that Jesus was the first Democrat.

Big Annie never took her eyes off of Brother Millsap once while he was speakin'. She leaned forward and grasped the back of the bench in front of her with her big white cotton gloves, as if she was afraid she wouldn't catch every word he said. I 'low Big Annie had never been in any church before. It sort of surprised her, maybe, to find how helpful a sermon can be, if you happen to hit the kind suited to your needs.

Brother Millsap brought his talk to a close, with, "Carry this lesson through the week, next to your hearts, Sisters and Brethern. Treat your fellow-man as Jesus would have treated him. For remember, we are all one in Christ Jesus."

Big Annie stepped out into the aisle, after the benediction, flushed and beamin' like a child. Brother Millsap brushed past her to take his stand at the door for the handshakin'. But not another soul looked her way. Them of the men who had handkerchiefs was payin' strict attention to their noses. The women nearest the aisle turned their backs, plumb preoccupied in pickin' up their belongin's or chattin' with the women nearest them. Big Annie, head high, eyes bright, marched to the door alone. As I said, she could of called 'most any man in the gatherin' by his first name, but she didn't even nod to one of 'em.

She stopped at the door and held her hand out to the parson. "If that's what preachin's like, I'm for it," she boomed.

Brother Millsap turned an apple-red and stuttered, "We're—we're glad to have you with us this mornin', Mrs. Bowan, I hope you'll come again."

"I will," she says. "And I'm comin' to your sociable and bring my share of the grub." Then she stalked on out, untied her horse, and drove away.

The tables was set outside, the night of the sociable. Some of the boys had cleared off a patch of sagebrush in front of the church and leveled up the ground. Most of the women were gathered 'round a small table where the food was bein' heaped as it arrived.

Big Annie was a little late in gettin' there. I seen her drive in, jump out of the buggy, and tie her horse. Then she took what looked like a bread-board covered with a white cloth out of the back of her rig and walked to where the women was gathered.

It was a late May evenin' and the sun was just settin' in the crotch between the Spanish Peaks, yonder. Big Annie looked like a pink giant splotched with gold paint, she was that much bigger than most of the others. She laid the board on the table and uncovered three of the brownest, crispest pies it's ever been my pleasure to clap an eye on to. They may have smelt a bit too strong of the cup that cheers to be exactly suitable for a Baptist sociable, but my mouth waters to this day when I think of 'em.

"They're mince," she says.

The women melted away from Big Annie like sin before the wrath of the righteous; all but old lady Parsons, who was president and actin' manager of the Ladies' Aid at that time. Old Lady Parsons took one good squint at them pies, then, with the back of her left hand, she shoved 'em off the table into a box of trash that was settin' beside it. "They ain't fit for hog food," she says, loud enough to be heard all over the lot.

Big Annie backed away a step or two, and her face got redder than the natural rays of the sun was paintin' it. Brother Millsap dodged into the church, no doubt to get somethin' he'd forgot to bring out, and the rest of us present just held our breath and waited for developments.

Big Annie picked up the board the pies had been on—she was still holdin' the white rag in her hand—and turned toward where her horse was tied. She stopped for a minute on her way to the buggy, looked us all over well and smiled. I've wondered many a time since whether Big Annie had seen enough of life to know that she might have done what old lady Parsons did if she had been in her place, or whether she had a sort of presentiment of what was goin' to happen a couple of years later and was takin' a bit of her pleasure in advance.

I don't have to tell you that that ended the Hopeville Baptist Church as far as Big Annie was concerned. Ike's health started failin' along in the summer and she spent most of her time with him, ridin' out lookin' after the cattle or decidin' what they'd have the Mexican help do. She was a heap of satisfaction to Ike, he told me so himself, a few months before he died.

Big Annie didn't have but one woman friend in the valley, and that woman was Clarence Shy's wife. Mrs. Shy was the helpless kind, that a smile or a friend meant a lot to. Ike Bowan's place laid on the other side of the river, on top of that bluff you see yonder, the south bank of the stream; but Shy's land was on this side, just across the creek from Ike's.

Clarence had inherited better than fifteen hundred acres from his pa, one of the first men to settle in the valley, a hard-drinkin', hard-fightin', money-gettin' old timer. But by the time Big Annie was thrust upon us, as you might say, folks had worked Shy out of all but about a hundred acres. He wasn't any more like his pa than a rabbit's like a coyote. The Bible says the meek shall inherit the earth, but if you've ever noticed, you can't catch the Book up on one of its own statements. It don't say a word about how long the meek will keep the earth after they get it. Clarence was one of the meek, and he and his wife made a perfect matched team. They had four children who were like their parents both in body and spirit.

Big Annie took the Shy family under wing; sewed for the kids, put up preserves for Mrs. Shy, and told Clarence when to plant and when to harvest his crops. His land, what he had left of it, was good, and he had plenty of water. His pa built the first ditch on the river. The old man was far-sighted. He knew the land would never be worth much without the water.

With Big Annie to manage for him, Clarence begun to get ahead; paid off some of his debts and had a little money left over to live on. But prosperity is a right dangerous thing, at times. George Stevens looked over Shy's crops in the fall, and said, "Huh, we could all grow crops like them, if we had the water."

That was the beginnin' of the Tumbleweed Valley irrigation ditch. George persuaded a dozen or so of the other ranchers on this side of the river to throw in with him. They built a dam up above Shy's and took out a big ditch. That left Clarence high and dry, except at flood time. And if you know anything about irrigation, you know flood time ain't when you need the water the most.

If Ike hadn't died that fall, Big Annie would of probably figured out some way for Clarence to stop Stevens and his gang from stealin' the water. But after Ike took to his bed for the last time, Big Annie never left his room only to bring him things to make him easier.

I recollect the day Ike died. I was helpin' the Mexican lay adobes in this very wall you're leanin' against, when Big Annie drove up and motioned for me to come out. Me and Ma was livin' in that one room adobe on the back of the lot, at the time, and I had the rigs and horses I was fixin' to start my livery stable with, housed in a frame shed.

"Asy," Big Annie said, "Ike died this mornin'."

"I'm sorry to hear it, Annie," I says. "Is there anything I can do?"

"Well," she says, "maybe there is and maybe there ain't. Ike never was in a church in his life, but he was as good a man as ever wore boots. I've a hankerin' to give him a church burial. What do you think them buzzards would say if I asked for the loan of their church to bury Ike out of?"

"Annie," I says, "if I'd been born with the power to foretell the future, instead of bein' the ornery, no-account cuss I am, even then I'd hesitate to say; I'd rather bet on the weather than most folks I know. Let's drive over and have a talk with Brother Millsap."

I could tell, right away, Brother Millsap wasn't hopeful. He said, "Mrs. Bowan, I'll be glad to preach the service and do everything I can, but—but as to usin' the church, that's a matter for the elders to decide." He glanced out of the window and I seen his face brighten. "There comes Amos Thompson this way. He's one of the elders. I'll go ask him," he says, jumpin' for the door.

His face had lost its cheerful look when he got back from talkin' to Amos. "Mrs. Bowan," he says, "Mr. Thompson don't like to decide a question of that nature without callin' a meetin' of the elders. Can I let you know later?"

Big Annie's shoulders squared. "I see how it is, parson," she says. "They've got to find out for sure that Ike wasn't neither a Jew nor a Greek. I don't believe we'd better put off havin' the funeral till they get through decidin'. If you'll let Mr. Mulberry drive you over to the ranch, day after tomorrow, we'll do the thing in a quiet way."

If it hadn't been for Mrs. Shy havin' to let her baby nurse every five minutes to keep it quiet, Ike's funeral would of been one of the nicest I ever attended. There was no outsider present, except Brother Millsap and myself and the Shy family. We buried Ike on the bluff overlookin' the river. As we was throwin' on the last of the dirt, Big Annie glanced across the stream and seen George Stevens and the rest of 'em, workin' like prairie-dogs on the new ditch.

"What's that gang doin' over there?" she asked, catchin' hold of Clarence's arm.

"I heard somebody say they was buildin' a ditch," Clarence said, pattin' the earth with his shovel.

"That's a funny idea," Big Annie says, and we all started for the house.

Irrigatin' time was here, before Big Annie realized what the new ditch had done to Clarence. When he went to turn the water into his ditch the stream was dry, but the big ditch above him was runnin' bankfull.

I reckon Big Annie did it, or stood by and told Clarence how to do it, for the next mornin' there was a hole cut in the new ditch and all the water was runnin' back into the river.

Amos Thompson and George Stevens rode up to see Clarence. He was out in the alfalfa, spreadin' the water.

"Shy," Thompson roared, "you cut our ditch last night, and if you ever set foot on the bank again, we'll throw you in jail for life."

Clarence wiped the mud off his shovel handle. "I've always had the water to use," he says.

"We've filed on this water accordin' to the laws of Colorado," Stevens put in. "It ain't our funeral if you've been asleep all these years, and if you can't farm without water, you'd better move off and find you another place."

I 'low that's exactly what Shy would of done, too, if it hadn't been for Big Annie. 'Course, he really owned what water he'd used, accordin' to law. But as I say, he was one of the meek. Big Annie's education had been limited to dealin' direct with mankind, so she wasn't up on legal matters. The only way she knew to fight was to cut the ditch, which she did or had Clarence do, the very next night.

The other side knew they was stealin' Shy's water, so they wasn't over anxious to drag him into court, for fear some smart lawyer would get hold of him and tie a knot in their scheme. Thompson and Stevens threatened some more but they didn't have Clarence arrested. Instead, they hired José Marufo, a burly, pock-marked Mexican, to guard the ditch nights.

Marufo hadn't been on the job more than a week till he turned up missin' one sunshiny mornin', and there was no water in the new ditch. When George Stevens rode up to the headgate to see what was the matter, he found the bank cut again, and Marufo's body, all sieved with buckshot, lyin' in a clump of willows, not fifty feet further on.

Well, I reckon there wasn't a person of thinkin' age in the valley who believed Clarence Shy killed Marufo. Clarence wasn't the kind of a man to kill anything. He even hired somebody to come do the butcherin' for him when he happened to have a hog or a heifer fat enough to slaughter. But every last man interested in the new ditch swore he knew for a fact that Shy done the shootin'.

There's nothin' much more annoyin' than to have somebody standin' in your way when you're tryin' to steal somethin', and that was the fix the Tumbleweed Valley Ditch Company was in. The quicker they got rid of Clarence, the quicker they could go about their thievin' unmolested. They had the sheriff down from Dawson to arrest Shy before the sun set that evenin', and persuaded Judge Beck to lay all other matters aside in order to try the nefarious murderer at once.

The trial was short and to the point, as you might say. The courtroom was packed; 'most all of Tumbleweed Valley had come into Dawson to see justice meted out.

Clarence made as poor a witness in his own behalf as the opposin' side could of asked for. He confessed to cuttin' the ditch twice before, but denied killin' Marufo and breakin' the bank the night the Mexican was shot.

Mrs. Shy got on the stand and said, "It—it couldn't of been Clarence. He—he went to bed at the same time I did the night of—the—the night it happened." And when the prosecutin' attorney asked her how she knew he didn't get up later to go out and shoot Marufo, she turned an alkali-white, and stuttered, "I—I couldn't be sure. But I'm a light sleeper, on account of havin' to be up with the children so much, and I'm—I'm almost positive I'd of felt him get out of bed."

Big Annie set in the court-room every minute the trial was goin' on. She wore the black dress she'd bought when Ike died, and all the curl was combed out of her yellow hair. She'd look at Clarence and shake her head when he'd say somethin' on the stand that was hurtin' his case. He'd glance at her, then turn away quick, as if he was afraid.

The prosecutin' attorney made what come pretty near bein' a fatal mistake; he called Big Annie as his last witness. "Mrs. Bowan," he says, "you've been a close neighbor of the defendant for some time. Have you ever heard him say anything which would lead you to believe he was not on friendly terms with the deceased, José Marufo?"

Big Annie slapped her hands down on the arms of the witness-chair, and her eyes blazed. "If you mean," she shouted, "do I think Clarence Shy shot that worthless Mexican? No! And what's more, there ain't a man in this room who knows Shy, that believes it either, if they'd tell the truth."

"That'll do," says the attorney, and Big Annie stomped down off the stand.

Judge Beck made quite a speech on the evils of lettin' greed force you into acts you would afterwards repent of, when he sentenced Clarence. He finished by sayin', "Clarence Shy, you have been found guilty of murder in the first degree by a jury of twelve men. The court has the power to sentence you to life imprisonment at hard labor. But because this is your first offence, and when you enter the prison gates you are leavin' a wife and four children, the court is goin' to show the maximum leniency. I sentence you to hard labor in the penitentiary for twenty years."

When Judge Beck said, "twenty years," Big Annie rose up from the bench where she was settin', her mouth opened and closed, then she sank back without makin' a sound.

Her face was drawn and haggard when she shook Shy's hand, before they led him back into jail. "I'll look after the Missus and kids the best I can, Clarence, while you're away," I heard her say.

And I says to myself, "Well, Annie, you've got a family on your hands for the rest of your life, for they'd better hang a man like Clarence Shy and be done with it, than to send him up for twenty years. He won't last five."

The trial was about the middle of May, and I reckon Big Annie put in one of the busiest summers of her life from then on until fall, runnin' her own place and lookin' after the Shys. She come over to Billy Debusk's store on an average of twice a week to buy provisions, shoes for the kids, and cloth to make 'em clothes.

I was busy roofin' this buildin', buildin' stalls for the horses and one thing and another. Sometimes when Big Annie would be passin', I'd yell and ask how things was movin' along; that is, if Ma wasn't anywheres 'round.

"We're makin' it," she'd call back, happy as a hen that's found herself a brood of chicks.

By September, I'd almost quit wonderin' about Clarence's family. Other folks' troubles have a way of slippin' out of your mind, easy-like. But one mornin' Big Annie pulled her horse to a stop right in front of the barn.

"Asy," she says, "we're havin' a hell of a time at Shy's. Three of the children are down with scarlet fever, and Mrs. Shy's in bed, expectin' another baby any day."

"That's tough, Annie," I says. "What do you suggest?"

"Money and somebody to help nurse," she snapped. "Somethin's got to be done."

"Well," I says, "they're havin' a harvest sociable at the church tonight. Crops have been good under the new ditch. I'll try takin' up a collection and you can count on me for twenty-five dollars."

"That's a grand idea, Asy. I'll count on your help," she says, chuckin' her horse into a trot.

That afternoon I told Ma I was ridin' out to look for a matched team, bein' about ready to open the livery-stable full force. But instead, I rode up the river to Shy's place. If I was goin' to make a plea for aid that evenin', I figured as how I ought to be an eyewitness to the misery.

The fences on the Shy place was down and Amos Thompson's cattle was trompin' the fields into dust. The adobes was showin' through the plasterin' on the house, as if it had just come through a hard case of smallpox.

Big Annie answered the door when I knocked. She was carryin' the youngest child in her arms, a baby less than two years old. The tears was streamin' down Big Annie's face like April rain. She stood there, shakin' her head without sayin' a word. Then she leaned over and kissed the baby. "It's dead!" she sobbed. "That gang killed it."

After a minute or two she straightened up and said, "You've got to go in and tell her, Asy, I can't."

Well, sir, by the time I landed at the sociable that night, I was so het up over the way the Shys had been treated, I was ready to go through the crowd with a gun and take their money away from them.

Brother Millsap suggested that we'd all go into the church and open the festivities with a prayer of thanks.

"When he gets through prayin'," I says to myself, "will be a good time for me to begin on 'em about the Shys."

He prayed at length, as most preachers do. He asked divine guidance for all the known races, singly and united. As I recollect, the Eskimo was the only one he overlooked. He advised the Lord as to their needs and how best to handle them. He mentioned the weather and suggested the kind most acceptable at that time. He thanked the Lord for bein' so generous with the farmers in the valley; told the Lord how we all appreciated the smile of His approval, and how hard we'd struggled to make ourselves worthy of His kindness and mercy and bountiful blessin's. He went on till I reckon there wasn't a person in the church, except myself, who didn't feel like their harp and halo was hangin' on the bench right in front of 'em.

As he breathed a fervent "Amen," I got to my feet and was in the act of clearin' my throat, when I heard somebody stridin' down the aisle. I glanced out the corner of my eye and seen Big Annie. Big Annie in a flamin' red dress, wearin' a whole garden of red poppies on her head, and carryin' a white sack under her arm. She couldn't of been redder, if she'd been the original pillar of fire.

She marched straight on to the platform, elbowed Brother Millsap to one side, and slapped down her sack, square on the big Bible.

"Christians," she says, without takin' time to catch her breath, "I've come here this evenin' to raise some money for the Shy family.

They're in desperate need, and it'll take about five hundred dollars to see 'em through."

I'll swan, you could almost see the walls of the church sway out and in, the folks settin' there was breathin' that hard.

"I've always made my own way," Big Annie went on, "ever since I can remember, and I ain't never asked anybody for a cent I didn't earn. So I ain't come here to beg off of you this evenin'. As most of the men in the audience know, I've been a savin' woman, and it's part of my savin's I've brought along with me." She touched the bag layin' on the Bible and stopped long enough to look us all over good.

"I've got what I call my keepsakes in that bag," she said. "Hat bands, silk shirts, a scatterin' of playin' cards, a letter or two, odds and ends too numerous to mention. But some place on every one of 'em is the name of the party who donated the gift, and in many instances there's a brief sentiment scratched above the name. These keepsakes are dear to me, for they remind me of the days when I had so many friends who were anxious to help me get along in the world. But I'm goin' to offer every one of 'em for sale tonight, auction 'em off to the highest bidders, in order to raise money for Mrs. Shy and her children."

George Stevens shuffled to his feet in the back of the church and took a step toward the door, lookin' as straight down his nose, as a man with a broken nose can.

"Set down, George," Big Annie yelled, and George set down. "I wouldn't like to have you miss this sale. It'll be interestin'. But before we begin the auction, I think it's only fair to call on, say twelve of the most influential men here this evenin'. Some, or all of 'em, might be hankerin' to give as much as fifty dollars apiece, and me not know it. If that was the case, I might not have to part with all my keepsakes. Understand, though, I ain't askin' for the money to be donated. I'm here and ready to sell the last thing in that bag, if it's necessary."

She unfolded a piece of paper she had in her hand and held it off from her, as if she was tryin' to make out what was on it.

"Amos Thompson," Big Annie read.

"I give fifty dollars for the good of the cause," Amos shouted.

"Well done, brother," she said, imitatin' Brother Millsap to a T. "The next name appears to be George Stevens."

"Fifty for me, too," George groaned.

Big Annie went on down the list; Butch Gooch, Lipe Standard, Bruce East, Eli Jefferson, twelve of 'em, and every one of 'em donated the same amount. The walls of that church actually sprung three inches from the sigh of relief that was exhaled when she got through with her list.

The men started shufflin' their feet, gettin' ready to make a break for air, but Big Annie held up her hand and said, "Just a minute. I've got a couple of other little matters I want to call to your attention, before the meetin' adjourns. I know there's not a person in this church who believes that Clarence Shy shot José Marufo. That bein' the case, it won't strain your sense of justice or hurt your standin' as good Christians to do what I'm goin' to ask you."

She reached down into her bosom and pulled out a couple of papers. Her dress was cut low in front, and she brought 'em forth with a flourish.

"I got a lawyer in Dawson to write these papers for me," she said, holdin' 'em out in front of her, careful-like, "when I seen how bad off Mrs. Shy and her babies was gettin', so they're legal. One of 'em is a request for a pardon for Clarence Shy, and the lawyer says he'll have Clarence out of the pen inside of thirty days, if everybody who testified against him will sign it. The other paper is a deed to Shy for a fifth interest in that fine new ditch you've built. The deed's legal too. Step up, gentlemen. I know you'll all want to sign. The drinks are on the house."

A silence louder than a whole army of brass bands hung over that huddled bunch of church members for a minute. Then Big Annie reached out and touched the sack which was layin' on the Bible. If a bolt of lightnin' had struck the buildin', them men couldn't of been on their feet quicker, or struggled harder to reach the pulpit.

After everybody had signed up in full, and Big Annie was makin' her way out, she motioned to me to come too. I followed her 'round to the side of the church.

"Asy," she says, "there's somethin' on my mind that's troublin' me a lot. I want your advice."

"I don't own nothin' that I give as cheerful, Annie," I says.

"Well," she says, "I know who killed José Marufo. It was a Mexican girl by the name of Rafelita Montoya. She's livin' in an adobe shack on my place, now, and José's the father of her baby. She confessed to me because I've been helpin' her to get enough to eat. Do you think it's my duty to turn her over to the law?"

"Annie," I says, "it's always been my plan to let sleepin' dogs take their rest; if they didn't need it, they wouldn't be sleepin'."

"Thanks a lot, Asy, for them comfortin' words. That's the way I feel about it, too," she says, and started for her rig. Then she stopped, come back and chuckled in my ear, "And, Asy, I want to tell you that that there Bible book has got things down pretty pat. We're all alike, neither Jew nor Greek, free or tied up, when we get in a tight place. I ain't got a thing in this bag but some old rags and a strap or two." And she patted the sack under her arm.

WHO KILLED RUTHERFORD?

By *Walter D. Edmonds*

[This story shows a sharp breaking away from the old technique of the short story as established by Maupassant and O. Henry. If you analyze the story, you will discover that skeleton that we call *the plot*, but it is not so clearly visible as in the older stories. It does not protrude. Observe how the story is told in natural, unedited talk of the characters around the stove—nearly all conversation. When the story is finished the *reader* knows who killed Rutherford. He arrives at the truth by merely listening to the talk. But the gossiping group around the stove do not know. That is very clever writing.

Walter D. Edmonds (1903–) has written many stories of life along the Erie Canal in New York, the country which he knows as a native.

Who Killed Rutherford? first appeared in *Scribner's Magazine* (March, 1927). It is included in the volume of Mr. Edmond's collected stories, *Mostly Canallers* (1934), from which it is reprinted by permission of Little, Brown and Company, publishers.]

"WHAT I would like to know," remarked Denslow, when discussion of the early frost had palled—"what I would like to know is who killed old Rutherford—if anybody."

The fat woman, who was Solomon Tinkle's cook on the *Maud Merrick*, raised her folded chin over her glass and nodded her head until the ribbons of her bonnet quivered and the leaden yellow cherries rattled like dice.

"Ah," she said, "that's it—who did?"

The three others lifted their lips from the rims of their glasses and stared at the two. All five of them drew slightly closer to the stove, as if to get their backs as far as possible from the black window-panes on which the frost was already marking gray lines. For the sake of economy, and because of the smallness of the company, only one lamp had been left upon the bar, and it sent its light horizontally over the wood, just touching the long rows of glasses with orange half-moons, and falling squarely on the face of the fat woman who sat with her back to the wall. Bolt upright on her chair, she seemed to be enjoying her conspicuousness, for she smoothed her plaid woollen skirt over her knees and opened the red-centred paisley shawl about her shoulders to let the light fall on the gold locket she wore at her breast. Her immense weight diminished the breadth of her shoulders and her height, and had it not been for the bow-legged diminutiveness of Solomon Tinkle beside her, one might have thought her squat. She arched her bosom and patted her dyed red hair.

"Who did it?" she repeated.

Solomon Tinkle wound his legs intricately through the rungs of his chair. He leaned forward impressively, his right hand on the door of the stove, which he held open.

"If Rutherford was murdered,"—he turned from the Judd brothers and spat neatly into the coals,—"somebody must have done it."

And he closed the door of the stove with a clank.

"Eanh," said the younger Judd; "that's right."

His brother let his sombre eyes wander over the faces of the others and return to the spots of light in the bottles behind the bar. He pulled at the stem of his pipe with pursed lips.

"Eanh," he said slowly; "that's right."

The fat woman held out her glass, her little finger curled pudgily.

"Will I make it another of gin, Mrs. Gurget?" asked Denslow.

"Eanh. On the luke side of hot with a squirt of lemon to cultivate the air with."

Denslow returned with the glass, and the fat woman spread her nostrils over the tingling odor of lemon.

"Well," said Denslow, as he resumed his seat and crossed his legs, "here we be, real sociable, and the last time afore winter, probably. I didn't even expect your boats comin' down so late . . ."—he sipped his gin leisurely—"it comes hard to think of old Rutherford lyin' by and cold, and him with such a taste in whiskeys. He was a good man, too, by his lights; easy on a loan, and friendly when in liquor, but not when drunk. He'd made a load of money with his line of bars 'tween Utica and Syracuse. Made more out of his post-houses. I wonder who got it."

"We was in Boonville the night it happened," said Mrs. Gurget. "But the will wasn't read yet when Solomon let on as how he'd got to get through with them potatoes before the frost got too heavy."

"I said we'd wait a while," interposed the little man. . . .

"Eanh," said the fat woman, looking fixedly at him in a manner unobserved by the rest, "but you was so anxious about 'em, I thought we'd better come."

"You was very sweet, my dear," said Solomon, returning his nose to the rim of his tumbler.

"We stayed there," said the younger Judd. "Joe, here, was barkeep at Bentley's oyster booth and bar in Uticy, when Rutherford had it on his line; and Joe'd done a lot of work for him, so we thought we'd ought to wait, maybe."

"What was into it, in the will?" asked Denslow.

"Nothin'."

"Nothin'?"

"There wasn't any— Not as you could call a will, anyways."

"No?"

"Eanh. There was a paper by his bed, though, in the up-stairs front bedroom."

"What of it?" asked Solomon Tinkle.

Sam Judd wriggled his shoulders and glanced at the fat woman.

"I let on we was cousins of Rutherford, and Williams (he was the old man's lawyer), he took us along that mornin' to cast last eyes at the corp'e. It was a very unpleasant thing to see."

He paused, but seeing Mrs. Gurget's snapping gray eyes fixed on his own watery ones, and being encouraged by Denslow with a tumbler on the house, he took up his narrative.

"Well," he said, after a close reference to the replenished glass; "well, Mr. Williams he took us along with him up to the front bedroom on the second floor, where the old man was layed out in his city clothes and a waistcoat red enough to keep any livin' man warm and his top hat set down orderly on the chair, which was nice enough as far as it went. 'Well,' says Mr. Williams, a-rubbin' his hands and lookin' round the room, which was swept out partic'lar—it bein' Sunday, and a death in the house— 'Well,' he says, 'what a pleasant sight Mr. Bilberry has made of the remains. They look very handsome.' 'Uncommon,' says Joe, 'not to mention this here.' He puts his hand on a knife-handle, which was stickin' so close to the old man it might have been druv' in back'ards from the other side of him. It was that dark in the room— bein' only one candle, and that on the dresser, and the mirror with a crape bow onto it—that I hadn't seen it."

Here Sam paused to refresh his depressed feelings with the tumbler on the house, and to glance at Joe for corroboration, which was given with a lugubrious nod.

"Eanh," he went on. "It was uncommon dark there, and cold, too, so early in the mornin'. 'Very curious, that knife, Mr. Judd,' says Williams; 'we couldn't pull it out at all, though Mr. Bilberry used his feet tryin'. It took a very strong man to put that knife where it is, Mr. Judd.'"

"Man?" cried Denslow. "Then it was a man—and he *was* murdered!"

"No doubt of it, and a strong man at that. 'It took weight skilful applied, Mr. Judd, power, I might say,' the lawyer says to me. 'He was lyin' like that when we found him. He hadn't stirred, sir.' 'Well, Mr. Williams,' says I, 'though the sheriff don't know who done it—nor never will, most likely—you and me and Sam can see he's dead. That bein' so, there's property to be got rid of; and such bein' the case, there must be a will.' 'There wasn't,' says the lawyer, without a blink. 'What's more, there's no more money left than what's needed to bury him and pay my bill for clearin' the estate.' 'No!' says I. 'I am afraid so,' says the lawyer. 'The old man was takin' a long time to die—if somebody hadn't've touched him off, he might still be dyin'—but he went willin', I might say, he went meek.' 'No doubt of it,' says Joe, lookin' at the old feller's legs which was very stiff under the blankets. 'Yes,' said the lawyer, 'he invested his money in charity and told me he hoped the interest, which he'd heard was uncommon big in that line, would help him into heaven. "And anyways," he'd say, "there's somebody I don't want to get it." So he invested it in charity, which is a mighty tight investment so far as gettin' your money back is concerned —whatever the interest.'"

"Jeepers!" exclaimed Denslow. "Who'd have thunk it? He was such a snortin' old boar-hog for hell and high-livin' when he was on the canal."

They all looked at the stove, the walls of which were gradually growing red.

"I've heard tell," said the fat woman, drawing a harsh breath, "he could be meaner than a Baptist."

"So he could," said Sam. "He was a mean man with a horse. . . . But he's dead, and givin' the worms what he took out of the horses."

"So he was stabbed, was he?" mused Denslow.

"Uncommon," said Joe Judd.

"Heart, liver, or lungs?" asked Solomon Tinkle, fogging his glass with a long breath.

"They'd shifted the third button on his waistcoat to let out the handle," said Sam.

The fat woman appeared to be growing nervous over the general interest in Judd's story. She bridled forward in her chair and leaned toward Sam, her hands folded loosely about the empty glass which lay in her lap. The mellow lamplight lent the movement a reminiscence of grace which Solomon Tinkle drank in with staring eyes. She smiled and arched her brows.

"You said there wasn't any will, Mr. Judd. But you did say there was a paper beside the bed, didn't you?"

"So I did, ma'm, and a queer paper it was, at that. Eh, Joe?"

Joe lifted his eyes to the fat woman's.

"Uncommon queer," he said, and looked away.

"It must have been," said Mrs. Gurget. "What was in it?"

"Why," said Sam, rubbing his hands a little diffidently, "I ain't much in the readin' line; but Lawyer Williams give us a copy, seein' as how we was relations like I told him—*he, he, he!* And here it is. Perhaps you'd like to read it, Mrs. Gurget."

"Eanh, Lucy," said Solomon, reclining himself against the back of his chair and looking on her proudly, "take a shot at it, do. You read real nice."

Mrs. Gurget fluttered the paper carelessly about in her lap, and her mouth made inaudible words in a hesitating manner. She laughed nervously and looked up.

"The light's so bad here, and the writin' ain't very good. Mr. Denslow, would you be so kind? You've a better light where you set."

Denslow leaned forward for the paper and leaned back with an air of importance. After a moment's close scrutiny, he cleared his throat and read slowly:

"This is to say, not that I care particular, that Rutherford ain't my real name. I ain't tellin my real name. There's only One person knows it anyhow and I've telled her she wont get none of my money which is bound hard in charities for soul's rest (X) if it can help him which I don't think it will seein as how he was such a mortal mean man for which and other things I done this to him so he could not collect interest, on his damned charities."

"It is queer," said Denslow, looking up and clearing his throat again.

"It doesn't make sense," said Solomon Tinkle. "It's all mixed up with 'I' and 'him.'"

"If it was any other man," said Mrs. Gurget, caressing her bosom with her left hand, "I would call it tragical."

She straightened up with a small sidewise shake of her back that set the cherries clicking on her bonnet.

"If you'd seen the paper it was copied from," said Sam Judd, taking the note back from Denslow, "you'd 've seen it was clear by the writin'. It changed after the word 'rest,' where I've marked a cross. It was quite different from there, wasn't it, Joe?"

"Changed radical," his brother agreed, sombrely.

"The writin' of both parts was uncommon bad, but the second was worse. Lawyer Williams said it would have looked like a woman's hand, only he didn't see as how a woman could have got there after the old feller was killed, him bein' still warm when the cook found him. She must 've been spry and delicate footed for the cook not to have heard her at that, for the stairs creaked real dismal and loud."

"Well," said Denslow, "it don't figger anyhow. You said it must 've took a strong man to put the knife there."

"Eanh," said Sam, "that's right."

They sat silent for a time. The cupola top of the stove had been pushed aside on its pivot to make room for a kettle from which the company might add hot water to their chosen liquor; and, in the stillness, it began suddenly to spout a wisp of steam and to murmur with the boiling water. Now and then the lid lifted and fell back into position with a light clink. The red spots on the wall of the stove had spread and merged until they formed a glowing band; and, as the light of the lamp grew fainter, this glow began to touch the knees of the fat woman and reflect in the rings on her fingers.

Quite suddenly, she took up her opinion of the dead man.

"A mean man," she said.

"Well, I've seen worse," said Denslow.

"He was all right with men, perhaps, but you said he was mean with horses—he probably was with all animals."

"Dogs didn't like him," Solomon Tinkle broke in, "nor any animal I ever see on his place. Once he owned a horse or a dog, they didn't have a show."

"There's lots of men like that," said Sam.

"I wonder who killed him," mused Denslow. "He'd been off the canal so long, and he kept so quiet, you'd think nobody'd have thought of him up there. That old brick house of his'n stood outside of town and off the canal, quite a ways."

"Eanh," said Solomon, "about half a mile, but it wasn't so far from the Watertown branch. You could walk up to it from the first lock in ten minutes."

"Did the sheriff find anything round the house?" asked Denslow.

"Nothin' to point to murder," said Sam. "There was pictures of pretty nigh all his post-houses set into frames in his parlor. But they don't count. And there was calendar pictures which he got for his tradin'."

"Lots of 'em," said Joe. "There was one in his bedroom on the second floor."

"That's right," said Sam, "there was at that. Picture of a woman, taken off a lithograph, and real pretty. Queer thing for him to have."

"He'd an eye for a gal," said Denslow.

"What was it like?" asked Mrs. Gurget, over her glass.

"Real pretty girl, with a yellow skirt, kind of full, and a red shawl, drawed down tight in front of her, with a geranium into her hair. She looked like she was dancing. It was a perfumery calendar, with something about odors made individual to suit the taste, with a special bottle of *Nancy Haskins Perfume* for postage-received, as a tryer."

"Nancy Haskins!" exclaimed Denslow. "There was a girl! I wonder what happened to her."

"She was a good-looker by the picture," said Sam. "I wish I'd 've seen her."

"She was afore your time, young man," said Mrs. Gurget, folding her hands and smiling at him in a patronizing way.

"I've heard tell of her," said Sam. "She used to be at Bentley's oyster-booth in Uticy, didn't she?"

"Yes, she was Bentley's niece afore Rutherford forced him to sell and took over the place. All the boaters knew her. She used to do a dance with red-heeled shoes on, which took 'em all in their Sunday throats and left 'em thirsty. She was good trade for Bentley."

"Dance!" cried Solomon Tinkle, rubbing his palms over the calves of his legs. "She could dance! She'd put a geranium into her mouth, and then she'd stomp her heels on the floor and swing round to every man partic'lar till they was nigh crazy, and they'd stomp to keep her time, and she'd laugh with her head way back and her neck naked in the light, and smile to a man, and whirl till her skirts came up and brushed his legs!"

The fat woman stroked her throat.

"That must 've been when you was workin' the roads, Sol, and afore you settled down respectable."

"So it was," exclaimed Solomon, stiffening up on his chair and planting his feet on the floor. "People knowed me then! Me and Gentleman Jo worked the beat from Syracuse to Utica, and there was good pickin's from the stage and boats for our trade."

He brushed the thin hair from his forehead.

"But you ought to've seen Nancy dancin'," he said, turning to the Judd brothers. "I wonder what ever become of her."

"She wasn't ever seen no more after Bentley sold out," said Denslow.

"That was a thing to see, that last night, I've heard tell. They made a clock round of it, the strong drinkers; and they saw the second mornin' in."

"That they did," said the fat woman.

"Was you there?"

"Eanh. Old Bentley put his head under the spigot of his number one-eight-seven Jamaicy rum, which he kept partic'lar, at the second three o'clock, and the swamper found him there at nine."

"I've heard there was a row about Nancy," said Solomon. "They says she was real riled at Rutherford. And when old Bentley went out broke, she didn't have nobody to keep her."

"It wasn't that," said the fat woman, settling her bonnet a little more over her eyes. "There wasn't a man who wouldn't have turned out his cook with a month's pay ahead and taken on Nancy Haskins. They was all cryin' for her."

"Then what did she take on so for?" asked Sam Judd.

"Well," said the fat woman, "she was kind of young, I reckon, and gals has notions in their heads. She'd always set up above the boat cooks, and she must've thought she was about to make a come-down in society. Gals is notional, that's why men like 'em and lick 'em. She was ashamed, I guess, and she wanted to be ashamed right up to the notch. That's how I figure it."

"She auctioned herself," said Denslow.

"That's right," exclaimed Solomon, "and they says as how she was right smart about it; played the filly and the auctioneer to oncet. And she showed her paces with a dance she done (keepin' up her patter all the while), till the room was bellerin' and the smoke was shook clear to the ceilin'. Knocked herself down for three hundred dollars, owned and broke, to Jotham Klore, who said he was biddin' for somebody else."

"Eanh," said the fat woman, "and then he took her out—cold as a razor—with the money in her fist."

"Cold and straight," said Solomon. "Her skirt was hangin' quiet over her legs, she walked that stiff."

"And they said she didn't look back oncet," added Denslow.

"I wonder who it was bought her," said Sam.

"Klore never telled who."

"He said he never seen her after. She walked with him along in the rain, he says, and never pulled the shawl over her head at all; and the rain wetted her hair so the drops looked red and yeller when they passed a window; and the rain run down her chin and neck, but she didn't take no notice. She was such an uncommon good-looker he said he'd take her for himself, if she'd come, any wages and a free bill of ladin' for anything she wanted to take aboard. But she looked at him kind of queer—and she says she's made a bargain and been bought square, and she'd stick to the man as bought her. So Klore left her in a room at Bagg's Hotel after tellin' her the man that bought her'd come for her there, and he left the number of the room at the desk; and nobody saw her again."

The pause that followed drew out to the ticking of a clock out of sight behind the bar until the sound of measured seconds fell upon their ears with the sharpness of axe-strokes. Solomon Tinkle wiped his eyes with a blue handkerchief and blew his nose loudly.

"I suppose," said Sam Judd, "that Rutherford took hold of Bentley's then."

"Not personal," said Denslow. "But he put in Klore for a barkeep, and quite a come-down it was after seein' Nancy there. But they left the old sign. Bentley wasn't seen afterwards, and Rutherford didn't come down from Boonville for a year or two, only for a trip he made once every six months to see how things was going on. He was real jokin' them days, a good man to take a drink with. But not long after he commenced to sour some, and he got nasty, they say, with men as well as animals."

"I guess," said the fat woman, "he was rich enough then to own some. He was a mean man to the animals he owned.—Mr. Denslow, would you make kind with another glass? With a squirt from the other half of that lemon?"

"Surely," said Denslow, getting up and going to the bar. He turned up the lamp and rummaged about.

"Jeepers!" said Solomon Tinkle, all at once. "Jeepers! Nancy was a pretty gal! Outside of you, Lucy, she was the only gal I ever wanted to live with."

Mrs. Gurget patted out her skirt and made eyes at him so brightly that he caught his breath. She tilted her chin to a laugh.

"Go along," she said.

"I wonder who it was bought Nancy Haskins," said Sam Judd. "Now why did she never come back?"

Denslow called to them from behind the bar.

"Say," he cried excitedly, "I got one of them perfumery calendars right here."

He held up a thin cardboard and a glint of yellow flashed under the lamp.

"Let's see it," said Mrs. Gurget, rising from her chair and going over to the lamp. The others crowded behind her.

"She must have been right pretty," exclaimed Sam, looking over the heavy shoulder.

"No wonder they bid high for her," said Denslow.

"Three hundred dollars is a lot of cash," said Sam. "It seems strange that anybody'd've had it there. He must have been rich."

"Nobody, only me," said Solomon Tinkle, "could have showed that all to once; and me, I was up the Rome road gettin' it. Nancy'd said the day before she was goin' to auction herself. But the mail-guard winged me as I was gettin' away"— he pressed his trouser-leg tight over his knotted right knee—"and I got back too slow. There couldn't have been no one else. . . . Only Rutherford."

"Jeepers!" said Denslow, half under his breath.

"He's dead now," said Sam Judd.

"Uncommon," said Joe.

"You ought to have seen her," said Solomon Tinkle, with a whine in his voice. "You ought to've seen her dance. She was the prettiest gal I ever see. . . ."

The fat woman whirled round on her heels, and her skirt fluttered slightly, flirting with her ankles. She held the picture of the girl in red and yellow in front of her for him to see, and looked down over the top at him.

"She was real pretty," she said, glancing at the dancer's face. "Look at her hair, kind of soft and yeller. And the smile to her mouth."

The little man leaned forward, one hand resting on the bar to steady his bowed legs, his thin nose drooping in reminiscence, and gazed for several seconds. The others watched him silently.

"She was a real pretty gal," said Mrs. Gurget, and her broad mouth curved miraculously between her fat cheeks. Solomon looked up at her.

"Prettiest gal I ever see," he said, the whine in his voice pronounced. "There won't none of us see the like of her again."

The fat woman laid the perfumery calendar face down upon the bar. Denslow handed her her glass of gin with a touch of water from the kettle, and she spread her nostrils over the sharp odor of lemon.

"What I would like to know," he said, "is who killed old Rutherford, anyhow?"

"That's it," said Mrs. Gurget, as they all sat down again, "who did?"

FIFTY GRAND

By Ernest Hemingway

[Ernest Hemingway (1898–) was born in Oak Park, Ill. His first volume of stories and poems was published in 1923. In the twelve years since he has produced a half dozen volumes of stories. Mr. Hemingway's most notable stories have appeared in *Scribner's Magazine* and the *Atlantic Monthly*. His most widely read volumes are *The Sun Also Rises* (1926), *Men Without Women* (1927), and *A Farewell to Arms* (1929).

Fifty Grand appeared first in the *Atlantic Monthly* (July, 1927). It is reprinted here by permission of Charles Scribner's Sons, publishers of Mr. Hemingway's collected volumes.]

I

'HOW are you going yourself, Jack?' I asked him.

'You seen this Walcott?' he says.

'Just in the gym.'

'Well,' Jack says, 'I'm going to need a lot of luck with that boy.'

'He can't hit you, Jack,' Soldier said.

'I wish to hell he couldn't.'

'He couldn't hit you with a handful of birdshot.'

'Birdshot'd be all right,' Jack says. 'I wouldn't mind birdshot any.'

'He looks easy to hit,' I said.

'Sure,' Jack says, 'he ain't going to last long. He ain't going to last like you and me, Jerry. But right now he's got everything.'

'You'll left-hand him to death.'

'Maybe,' Jack says. 'Sure. I got a chance to.'

'Handle him like you handled Kid Lewis.'

'Kid Lewis,' Jack said. 'That kike!'

The three of us, Jack Brennan, Soldier Bartlett, and I, were in Handley's. There were a couple of broads sitting at the next table to us. They had been drinking.

'What do you mean, kike?' one of the broads says. 'What do you mean, kike, you big Irish bum!'

'Sure,' Jack says. 'That's it.'

'Kikes,' this broad goes on. 'They're always talking about kikes, these big Irishmen. What do you mean, kikes?'

'Come on. Let's get out of here.'

'Kikes,' this broad goes on. 'Whoever saw you ever buy a drink?

Your wife sews your pockets up every morning. These Irishmen and their kikes. Ted Lewis could lick you, too.'

'Sure,' Jack says. 'And you give away a lot of things free, too, don't you?'

We went out. That was Jack. He could say what he wanted to when he wanted to say it.

Jack started training out at Danny Hogan's health farm over in Jersey. It was nice out there, but Jack didn't like it much. He didn't like being away from his wife and the kids, and he was sore and grouchy most of the time. He liked me and we got along fine together; and he liked Hogan, but after a while Soldier Bartlett commenced to get on his nerves. A kidder gets to be an awful thing around a camp if his stuff goes sort of sour. Soldier was always kidding Jack, just sort of kidding him all the time. It wasn't very funny and it wasn't very good, and it began to get to Jack.

It was sort of stuff like this. Jack would finish up with the weights and the bag and pull on the gloves. 'You want to work?' he'd say to Soldier.

'Sure. How you want me to work?' Soldier would ask. 'Want me to treat you rough like Walcott? Want me to knock you down a few times?'

'That's it,' Jack would say. He didn't like it any, though.

One morning we were all out on the road. We'd been out quite a way and now we were coming back. We'd go along fast for three minutes and then walk a minute, and then go fast for three minutes again. Jack wasn't ever what you would call a sprinter. He'd move around fast enough in the ring if he had to, but he wasn't any too fast on the road. All the time we were walking, Soldier Bartlett was kidding him. We came up the hill to the farmhouse.

'Well,' says Jack, 'you better go back to town, Soldier.'

'What do you mean?'

'You better go back to town and stay there.'

'What's the matter?'

'I'm sick of hearing you talk.'

'Yes?' says Soldier.

'Yes,' says Jack.

'You'll be a damn sight sicker when Walcott gets through with you.'

'Sure,' says Jack, 'maybe I will. But I know I'm sick of you.'

So Soldier went off on the train to town that same morning. I went down with him to the train. He was good and sore.

'I was just kidding him,' he said. We were waiting on the platform. 'He can't pull that stuff with me, Jerry.'

'He's nervous and crabby,' I said. 'He's a good fellow, Soldier.'

'The hell he is. The hell he's ever been a good fellow.'

'Well,' I said, 'so long, Soldier.'

The train had come in. He climbed up with his bag.

'So long, Jerry,' he says. 'You be in town before the fight?'

'I don't think so.'

'See you then.'

He went in and the conductor swung up and the train went out. I rode back to the farm in the cart. Jack was on the porch writing a letter to his wife. The mail had come and I got the papers and went over on the other side of the porch and sat down to read. Hogan came out the door and came over to me.

'Did he have a jam with Soldier?'

'Not a jam,' I said. 'He just told him to go back to town.'

'I could see it coming,' Hogan said. 'He never liked Soldier much.'

'No. He don't like many people.'

'He's a pretty cold one,' Hogan said.

'Well, he's always been fine to me.'

'Me too,' Hogan said. 'I got no kick on him. He's a cold one, though.'

Hogan went in through the screen door and I sat there on the porch and read the papers. It was just starting to get fall weather and it's nice country there in Jersey up in the hills, and after I read the paper through I sat there and looked out at the country and the road down below against the woods, with a car going along it, lifting the dust up. It was fine weather and pretty nice-looking country. Hogan came to the door and I said, 'Say, Hogan, haven't you got anything to shoot out here?'

'No,' Hogan said. 'Only sparrows.'

'Seen the paper?' I said to Hogan.

'What's in it?'

'Sande booted three of them in yesterday.'

'I got that on the telephone last night.'

'You follow them pretty close, Hogan?' I asked.

'Oh, I keep in touch with them.'

'How about Jack?' I says. 'Does he still play them?'

'Him?' said Hogan. 'Can you see him doing it?'

Just then Jack came around the corner with the letter in his hand. He's wearing a sweater and an old pair of pants and boxing shoes.

'Got a stamp, Hogan?' he asks.

'Give me the letter,' Hogan said. 'I'll mail it for you.'

'Say, Jack,' I said. 'Didn't you used to play the ponies?'

'Sure.'

'I knew you did. I knew I used to see you out at Sheepshead.'

'What did you lay off them for?' Hogan asked.

'Lost money.'

Jack sat down on the porch by me. He leaned back against a post. He shut his eyes in the sun.

'Want a chair?' Hogan asked.

'No,' said Jack. 'This is fine.'

'It's a nice day,' I said. 'It's pretty nice out in the country.'

'I'd a damn sight rather be in town with the wife.'

'Well, you only got another week.'

'Yes,' Jack says. 'That's so.'

We sat there on the porch. Hogan was inside at the office.

'What do you think about the shape I'm in?' Jack asked me.

'Well, you can't tell,' I said. 'You got a week to get around into form.'

'Don't stall me.'

'Well,' I said, 'you're not right.'

'I'm not sleeping,' Jack said.

'You'll be all right in a couple of days.'

'No,' says Jack, 'I got the insomnia.'

'What's on your mind?'

'I miss the wife.'

'Have her come out.'

'No. I'm too old for that.'

'We'll take a long walk before you turn in, and get you good and tired.'

'Tired!' Jack says. 'I'm tired all the time.'

He was that way all week. He wouldn't sleep at night and he'd get up in the morning feeling that way—you know, when you can't shut your hands.

'He's stale as poorhouse cake,' Hogan said. 'He's nothing.'

'I never seen Walcott,' I said.

'He'll kill him,' said Hogan. 'He'll tear him in two.'

'Well,' I said, 'everybody's got to get it sometime.'

'Not like this, though,' Hogan said. 'They'll think he never trained. It gives the farm a black eye.'

'You hear what the reporters said about him?'

'Didn't I! They said he was awful. They said they oughtn't to let him fight.'

'Well,' I said, 'they're always wrong, ain't they?'

'Yes,' said Hogan. 'But this time they're right.'

'What the hell do they know about whether a man's right or not?'

'Well,' said Hogan, 'they're not such fools.'

'All they did was pick Willard at Toledo. This Lardner, he's so wise now, ask him about when he picked Willard at Toledo.'

'Aw, he wasn't out,' Hogan said. 'He only writes the big fights.'

'I don't care who they are,' I said. 'What the hell do they know? They can write, maybe, but what the hell do they know?'

'You don't think Jack's in any shape, do you?' Hogan asked.

'No. He's through. All he needs is to have Corbett pick him to win for it to be all over.'

'Well, Corbett'll pick him,' Hogan says.

'Sure. He'll pick him.'

That night Jack didn't sleep any either. The next morning was the last day before the fight. After breakfast we were out on the porch again.

'What do you think about, Jack, when you can't sleep?' I said.

'Oh, I worry,' Jack says. 'I worry about property I got up in the Bronx. I worry about property I got in Florida. I worry about the kids. I worry about the wife. Sometimes I think about fights. I think about that kike Ted Lewis and I get sore. I got some stocks and I worry about them. What the hell don't I think about?'

'Well,' I said, 'tomorrow night it'll all be over.'

'Sure,' said Jack. 'That always helps a lot, don't it? That just fixes everything all up, I suppose. Sure.'

He was sore all day. We didn't do any work. Jack just moved around a little to loosen up. He shadow-boxed a few rounds. He didn't even look good doing that. He skipped the rope a little while. He couldn't sweat.

'He'd be better not to do any work at all,' Hogan said. We were standing watching him skip rope. 'Don't he ever sweat at all any more?'

'He can't sweat.'

'Do you suppose he's got the con? He never had any trouble making weight, did he?'

'No, he hasn't got any con. He just hasn't got anything inside any more.'

'He ought to sweat,' said Hogan.

Jack came over skipping the rope. He was skipping up and down in front of us, forward and back, crossing his arms every third time.

'Well,' he says, 'what are you buzzards talking about?'

'I don't think you ought to work any more,' Hogan says. 'You'll be stale.'

'Wouldn't that be awful?' Jack says and skips away down the floor, slapping the rope hard.

II

That afternoon John Collins showed up out at the farm. Jack was up in his room. John came out in a car from town. He had a couple of friends with him. The car stopped and they all got out.

'Where's Jack?' John asked me.

'Up in his room, lying down.'

'Lying down?'

'Yes,' I said.

'How is he?'

I looked at the two fellows that were with John.

'They're friends of his,' John said.

'He's pretty bad,' I said.

'What's the matter with him?'

'He don't sleep.'

'Hell,' said John. 'That Irishman could never sleep.'

'He isn't right,' I said.

'Hell,' John said. 'He's never right. I've had him for ten years and he's never been right yet.'

The fellows with him laughed.

'I want you to shake hands with Mr. Morgan and Mr. Steinfelt,' John said. 'This is Mr. Doyle. He's been training Jack.'

'Glad to meet you,' I said.

'Let's go up and see the boy,' the fellow called Morgan said.

'Let's have a look at him,' Steinfelt said.

We all went upstairs.

'Where's Hogan?' John asked.

'He's out in the barn with a couple of his customers,' I said.

'He got many people out here now?'

'Just two.'

'Pretty quiet, ain't it?' Morgan said.

'Yes,' I said. 'It's pretty quiet.'

We were outside Jack's room. John knocked on the door. There wasn't any answer.

'Maybe he's asleep,' I said.

'What the hell's he sleeping in the daytime for?'

John turned the handle and we all went in. Jack was lying asleep on the bed. He was face down and his face was in the pillow. Both his arms were around the pillow.

'Hey, Jack!' John said to him.

Jack's head moved a little on the pillow. 'Jack!' John says, leaning over him. Jack just dug a little deeper in the pillow. John touched him on the shoulder. Jack sat up and looked at us. He hadn't shaved and he was wearing an old sweater.

'Hell! Why can't you let me sleep?' he says to John.

'Don't be sore,' John says. 'I didn't mean to wake you up.'

'Oh no,' Jack says. 'Of course not.'

'You know Morgan and Steinfelt,' John said.

'Glad to see you,' Jack says.

'How do you feel, Jack?' Morgan asks him.

'Fine,' Jack says. 'How the hell would I feel?'

'You look fine,' Steinfelt says.

'Yes, don't I?' says Jack. 'Say,' he says to John. 'You're my manager. You get a big enough cut. Why the hell didn't you come out here when the reporters was out? You want Jerry and me to talk to them?'

'I had Lew fighting in Philadelphia.'

'What the hell's that to me?' Jack says. 'You're my manager. You get a big enough cut, don't you? You aren't making me any money in Philadelphia, are you? Why the hell aren't you out here when I ought to have you?'

'Hogan was here.'

'Hogan,' Jack says. 'Hogan's as dumb as I am.'

'Soldier Bahtlett was out here wukking with you for a while, wasn't he?' Steinfelt says, to change the subject.

'Yes, he was out here,' Jack says. 'He was out here, all right.'

'Say, Jerry,' John said to me. 'Would you go and find Hogan and tell him we want to see him in about half an hour?'

'Sure,' I said.

'Why the hell can't he stick around?' Jack says. 'Stick around, Jerry.'

Morgan and Steinfelt looked at each other.

'Quiet down, Jack,' John said to him.

'I better go find Hogan,' I said.

'All right, if you want to go,' Jack says. 'None of these guys are going to send you away, though.'

'I'll go find Hogan,' I said.

Hogan was out in the gym in the barn. He had a couple of his health-farm patients with the gloves on. They neither one wanted to hit the other for fear the other would come back and hit him.

'That'll do,' Hogan said when he saw me come in. 'You can stop the slaughter. You gentlemen take a shower and Bruce will rub you down.'

They climbed out through the ropes and Hogan came over to me.

'John Collins is out with a couple of friends to see Jack,' I said.

'I saw them come up in the car.'

'Who are the two fellows with John?'

'They're what you call wise boys,' Hogan said. 'Don't you know them two?'

'No,' I said.

'That's Happy Steinfelt and Lew Morgan. They got a pool room.'

'I been away a long time,' I said.

'Sure,' said Hogan. 'That Happy Steinfelt's a big operator.'

'I've heard his name,' I said.

'He's a pretty smooth boy,' Hogan said. 'They're a couple of sharp-shooters.'

'Well,' I said, 'they want to see us in half an hour.'

'You mean they don't want to see us until a half an hour?'

'That's it.'

'Come on in the office,' Hogan said. 'To hell with those sharpshooters.'

After about thirty minutes or so Hogan and I went upstairs. We knocked on Jack's door. They were talking inside the room.

'Wait a minute,' somebody said.

'To hell with that stuff,' Hogan said. 'When you want to see me I'm down in the office.'

We heard the door unlock. Steinfelt opened it.

'Come on in, Hogan,' he says. 'We're all going to have a drink.'

'Well,' says Hogan, 'that's something.'

We went in. Jack was sitting on the bed. John and Morgan were sitting on a couple of chairs. Steinfelt was standing up.

'You're a pretty mysterious lot of boys,' Hogan said.

'Hello, Danny,' John says.

'Hello, Danny,' Morgan says and shakes hands.

Jack doesn't say anything. He just sits there on the bed. He ain't with the others. He's all by himself. He was wearing an old blue jersey and an old pair of pants and had on boxing shoes. He needed a shave. Steinfelt and Morgan were dressers. John was quite a dresser, too. Jack sat there looking Irish and tough.

Steinfelt brought out a bottle and Hogan brought in some glasses and everybody had a drink. Jack and I took one and the rest of them went on and had two or three each.

'Better save some for your ride back,' Hogan said.

'Don't you worry. We got plenty,' Morgan said.

Jack hadn't drunk anything since the one drink. He was standing up and looking at them. Morgan was sitting on the bed where Jack had sat.

'Have a drink, Jack,' John said and handed him the glass and the bottle.

'No,' Jack said, 'I never liked to go to these wakes.'

They all laughed. Jack didn't laugh.

They were all feeling pretty good when they left. Jack stood on the porch when they got into the car. They waved to him.

'So long,' Jack said.

We had supper. Jack didn't say anything all during the meal except 'Will you pass me this?' or 'Will you pass me that?' The two health-farm patients ate at the same table with us. They were pretty nice fellas. After we finished eating we went out on the porch. It was dark early.

'Like to take a walk, Jerry?' Jack asked.

'Sure,' I said.

We put on our coats and started out. It was quite a way down to the main road, and then we walked along the main road about a mile and a half. Cars kept going by and we would pull out to the side until they were past. Jack didn't say anything. After we had stepped out into the bushes to let a big car go by, Jack said, 'To hell with this walking. Come on back to Hogan's.'

We went along a side road that cut up over the hill and cut across the fields back to Hogan's. We could see the lights of the house up on the hill. We came around to the front of the house and there, standing in the doorway, was Hogan.

'Have a good walk?' Hogan asked.

'Oh, fine,' Jack said. 'Listen, Hogan. Have you got any liquor?'

'Sure,' says Hogan. 'What's the idea?'

'Send it up to the room,' Jack says. 'I'm going to sleep tonight.'

'You're the doctor,' Hogan says.

'Come on up to the room, Jerry,' Jack says.

Upstairs Jack sat on the bed with his head in his hands.

'Ain't it a life?' Jack says.

Hogan brought in a quart of liquor and two glasses.

'Want some ginger ale?'

'What do you think I want to do—get sick?'

'I just asked you,' said Hogan.

'Have a drink?' said Jack.

'No, thanks,' said Hogan. He went out.

'How about you, Jerry?'

'I'll have one with you,' I said.

Jack poured out a couple of drinks. 'Now,' he said, 'I want to take it slow and easy.'

'Put some water in it,' I said.

'Yes,' Jack said. 'I guess that's better.'

We had a couple of drinks without saying anything. Jack started to pour me another.

'No,' I said, 'that's all I want.'

'All right,' Jack said. He poured himself out another big shot and put water in it. He was lighting up a little.

'That was a fine bunch out here this afternoon,' he said. 'They don't take any chances, those two.'

Then a little later. 'Well,' he says, 'they're right. What the hell's the good in taking chances?'

'Don't you want another, Jerry?' he said. 'Come on, drink along with me.'

'I don't need it, Jack,' I said. 'I feel all right.'

'Just have one more,' Jack said. It was softening him up.

'All right,' I said.

Jack poured one for me and another big one for himself.

'You know,' he said, 'I like liquor pretty well. If I hadn't been boxing I would have drunk quite a lot.'

'Sure,' I said.

'You know,' he said, 'I missed a lot, boxing.'

'You made plenty of money.'

'Sure, that's what I'm after. You know I miss a lot, Jerry.'

'How do you mean?'

'Well,' he says, 'like about the wife. And being away from home so much. It don't do my girls any good. "Who's your old man?" some of those society kids'll say of them. "My old man's Jack Brennan." That don't do them any good.'

'Hell,' I said. 'All that makes a difference is if they got dough.'

'Well,' says Jack, 'I got the dough for them all right.'

He poured out another drink. The bottle was about empty.

'Put some water in it,' I said. Jack poured in some water.

'You know,' he says, 'you ain't got any idea how I miss the wife.'

'Sure.'

'You ain't got any idea. You can't have an idea what it's like.'

'It ought to be better out in the country than in town.'

'With me now,' Jack said, 'it don't make any difference where I am. You can't have an idea what it's like.'

'Have another drink.'

'Am I getting soused? Do I talk funny?'

'You're coming on all right.'

'You can't have an idea what it's like. They ain't anybody can have an idea what it's like.'

'Except the wife,' I said.

'She knows,' Jack said. 'She knows, all right. She knows. You bet she knows.'

'Put some water in that,' I said.

'Jerry,' says Jack, 'you can't have an idea what it gets to be like.'

He was good and drunk. He was looking at me steady. His eyes were sort of too steady.

'You'll sleep, all right,' I said.

'Listen, Jerry,' Jack says. 'You want to make some money? Get some dough down on Walcott.'

'Yes?'

'Listen, Jerry.' Jack put down the glass. 'I'm not drunk now, see? You know what I'm betting on him? Fifty grand.'

'That's a lot of dough.'

'Fifty grand,' Jack says, 'at two to one. I'll get twenty-five thousand bucks. Get some money on him, Jerry.'

'It sounds good,' I said.

'How can I beat him?' Jack says. 'It ain't crooked. How can I beat him? Why not make money on it?'

'Put some water in that,' I said.

'I'm through after this fight,' Jack says. 'I'm through with it. I got to take a beating. Why shouldn't I make money on it?'

'Sure.'

'I ain't slept for a week,' Jack says. 'All night I lay awake and worry my can off. I can't sleep, Jerry. You ain't got an idea what it's like when you can't sleep.'

'Sure.'

'I can't sleep. That's all. I just can't sleep. What's the use of taking care of yourself all these years when you can't sleep?'

'It's bad.'

'You ain't got an idea what it's like, Jerry, when you can't sleep.'

'Put some water in that,' I said.

Well, about eleven o'clock Jack passes out and I put him to bed. Finally he's so he can't keep from sleeping. I helped him get his clothes off and got him into bed.

'You'll sleep, all right, Jack,' I said.

'Sure,' Jack says, 'I'll sleep now.'

'Good night, Jack,' I said.

'Good night, Jerry,' Jack says. 'You're the only friend I got.'

'Oh, hell,' I said.

'You're the only friend I got,' Jack says. 'The only friend I got.'

'Go to sleep,' I said.

'I'll sleep,' Jack says.

Downstairs Hogan was sitting at the desk in the office reading the papers. He looked up.

'Well, you get your boy friend to sleep?' he asks.

'He's off.'

'It's better for him than not sleeping,' Hogan said.

'Sure.'

'You'd have a hell of a time explaining that to these sport writers, though,' Hogan said.

'Well, I'm going to bed myself,' I said.

'Good night,' said Hogan.

III

In the morning I came downstairs about eight o'clock and got some breakfast. Hogan had his two customers out in the barn doing exercises. I went out and watched them.

'One! Two! Three! Four!' Hogan was counting for them. 'Hello, Jerry,' he said. 'Is Jack up yet?'

'No. He's still sleeping.'

I went back to my room and packed up to go in to town. About nine-thirty I heard Jack getting up in the next room. When I heard him go downstairs I went down after him. Jack was sitting at the breakfast table. Hogan had come in and was standing beside the table.

'How do you feel, Jack?' I asked him.

'Not so bad.'

'Sleep well?' Hogan asked.

'I slept, all right,' Jack said. 'I got a thick tongue, but I ain't got a head.'

'Good,' said Hogan. 'That was good liquor.'

'Put it on the bill,' Jack says.

'What time you want to go in to town?' Hogan asked.

'Before lunch,' Jack says. 'The eleven o'clock train.'

Hogan went out.

'Sit down, Jerry,' Jack said.

I sat down at the table. Jack was eating a grapefruit. When he'd find a seed he'd spit it out in the spoon and dump it on the plate.

'I guess I was pretty stewed last night,' he started.

'You drank some liquor.'

'I guess I said a lot of fool things.'

'You weren't bad.'

'Where's Hogan?' he asked. He was through with the grapefruit.

'He's out in front in the office.'

'What did I say about betting on the fight?' Jack asked. He was holding the spoon and sort of poking at the grapefruit with it.

The girl came in with some ham and eggs and took away the grapefruit.

'Bring me another glass of milk,' Jack said to her. She went out.

'You said you had fifty grand on Walcott,' I said.

'That's right,' Jack said.

'That's a lot of money.'

'I don't feel too good about it,' Jack said.

'Something might happen.'

'No,' Jack said. 'He wants the title bad. They'll be shooting with him, all right.'

'You can't ever tell.'

'No. He wants the title. It's worth a lot of money to him.'

'Fifty grand is a lot of money,' I said.

'It's business,' said Jack. 'I can't win. You know I can't win anyway.'

'As long as you're in there you got a chance.'

'No,' Jack says. 'I'm all through. It's just business.'

'How do you feel?'

'Pretty good,' Jack said. 'The sleep was what I needed.'

'You might go good.'

'I'll give them a good show,' Jack said.

After breakfast Jack called up his wife on the long distance. He was inside the booth telephoning.

'That's the first time he's called her up since he's out here,' Hogan said.

'He writes her every day.'

'Sure,' Hogan says. 'A letter only costs two cents.'

Hogan said good-bye to us, and Bruce, the nigger rubber, drove us down to the train in the cart.

'Good-bye, Mr. Brennan,' Bruce said at the train. 'I sure hope you knock his can off.'

'So long,' Jack said. He gave Bruce two dollars. Bruce had worked on him a lot. He looked kind of disappointed. Jack saw me looking at Bruce holding the two dollars.

'It's all in the bill,' he said. 'Hogan charged me for the rubbing.'

On the train going into town Jack didn't talk. He sat in the corner of the seat with his ticket in his hatband and looked out of the window. Once he turned and spoke to me.

'I told the wife I'd take a room at the Shelby tonight,' he said. 'It's just around the corner from the Garden. I can go up to the house tomorrow morning.'

'That's a good idea,' I said. 'Your wife ever see you fight, Jack?'

'No,' Jack says. 'She never seen me fight.'

I thought, he must be figuring on taking an awful beating if he doesn't want to go home afterward. In town we took a taxi up to the Shelby. A boy came out and took our bags and we went in to the desk.

'How much are the rooms?' Jack asked.

'We only have double rooms,' the clerk says. 'I can give you a nice double room for ten dollars.'

'That's too steep.'

'I can give you a double room for seven dollars.'

'With a bath?'

'Certainly.'

'You might as well bunk with me, Jerry,' Jack says.

'Oh,' I said, 'I'll sleep down at my brother-in-law's.'

'I don't mean for you to pay it,' Jack says. 'I just want to get my money's worth.'

'Will you register, please?' the clerk says.

He looked at the names. 'Number 238, Mr. Brennan.'

We went up in the elevator. It was a nice big room with two beds and a door opening into a bathroom.

'This is pretty good,' Jack says.

The boy who brought us up pulled up the curtains and brought in our bags. Jack didn't make any move, so I gave the boy a quarter. We washed up and Jack said we better go out and get something to eat.

We ate a lunch at Jimmy Handley's place. Quite a lot of the boys were there. When we were about half through eating, John came in and sat down with us. Jack didn't talk much.

'How are you on the weight, Jack?' John asked him. Jack was putting away a pretty good lunch.

'I could make it with my clothes on,' Jack said. He never had to worry about taking off weight. He was a natural welterweight and he'd never gotten fat. He'd lost weight out at Hogan's.

'Well, that's one thing you never had to worry about,' John said.

'That's one thing,' Jack says.

We went around to the Garden to weigh in after lunch. The match was made at a hundred forty-seven pounds at three o'clock. Jack stepped on the scales with a towel around him. The bar didn't move. Walcott had just weighed and was standing with a lot of people around him.

'Let's see what you weigh, Jack,' Freedman, Walcott's manager, said.

'All right, weigh *him* then,' Jack jerked his head toward Walcott.

'Drop the towel,' Freedman said.

'What do you make it?' Jack asked the fellows who were weighing.

'Hundred and forty-three pounds,' the fat man who was weighing said.

'You're down fine, Jack,' Freedman says.

'Weigh *him*,' Jack says.

Walcott came over. He was a blonde with wide shoulders and arms like a heavyweight. He didn't have much legs. Jack stood about half a head taller than he did.

'Hello, Jack,' he said. His face was plenty marked up.

'Hello,' said Jack. 'How you feel?'

'Good,' Walcott says. He dropped the towel from around his waist and stood on the scales. He had the widest shoulders and back you ever saw.

'One hundred and forty-six pounds and twelve ounces.'

Walcott stepped off and grinned at Jack.

'Well,' John says to him, 'Jack's spotting you about four pounds.'

'More than that when I come in, Kid,' Walcott says. 'I'm going to go and eat now.'

We went back and Jack got dressed. 'He's a pretty tough-looking boy,' Jack says to me.

'He looks as though he'd been hit plenty of times.'

'Oh yes,' Jack says. 'He ain't hard to hit.'

'Where are you going?' John asked when Jack was dressed.

'Back to the hotel,' Jack says. 'You looked after everything?'

'Yes,' John says. 'It's all looked after.'

'I'm going to lie down a while,' Jack says.

'I'll come around for you about a quarter to seven and we'll go and eat.'

'All right.'

Up at the hotel Jack took off his shoes and his coat and lay down for a while. I wrote a letter. I looked over a couple of times and Jack wasn't sleeping. He was lying perfectly still, but every once in a while his eyes would open. Finally he sits up.

'Want to play some cribbage, Jerry?' he says.

'Sure,' I said.

He went over to his suitcase and got out the cards and the cribbage board. We played cribbage and he won three dollars off me. John knocked at the door and came in.

'Want to play some cribbage, John?' Jack asked him.

John put his kelly down on the table. It was all wet. His coat was wet, too.

'Is it raining?' Jack asks.

'It's pouring,' John says. 'The taxi I had got tied up in the traffic and I got out and walked.'

'Come on, play some cribbage,' Jack says.

'You ought to go and eat.'

'No,' says Jack. 'I don't want to eat yet.'

So they played cribbage for about half an hour and Jack won a dollar and a half off him.

'Well, I suppose we got to go eat,' Jack says. He went to the window and looked out.

'Is it still raining?'

'Yes.'

'Let's eat in the hotel,' John says.

'All right,' Jack says. 'I'll play you once more to see who pays for the meal.'

After a little while Jack gets up and says, 'You buy the meal, John,' and we went downstairs and ate in the big dining room.

After we ate we went upstairs and Jack played cribbage with John again and won two dollars and a half off him. Jack was feeling pretty good. John had a bag with him with all his stuff in it. Jack took off his shirt and collar and put on a jersey and a sweater, so he wouldn't catch cold when he came out, and put his ring clothes and his bathrobe in a bag.

'You all ready?' John asks him. 'I'll call up and have them get a taxi.'

Pretty soon the telephone rang and they said the taxi was waiting.

We rode down in the elevator and went out through the lobby, and got in the taxi and rode around to the Garden. It was raining hard, but there was a lot of people outside on the streets. The Garden was sold out. As we came in on our way to the dressing room I saw how full it was. It looked like half a mile down to the ring. It was all dark. Just the lights over the ring.

'It's a good thing, with this rain, they didn't try and pull this fight in the ball park,' John said.

'They got a good crowd,' Jack says.

'This is a fight that would draw a lot more than the Garden could hold.'

'You can't tell about the weather,' Jack says.

John came to the door of the dressing room and poked his head in. Jack was sitting there with his bathrobe on; he had his arms folded and was looking at the floor. John had a couple of handlers with him. They looked over his shoulder. Jack looked up.

'Is he in?' he asked.

'He's just gone down,' John said.

We started down. Walcott was just getting into the ring. The crowd gave him a big hand. He climbed through between the ropes and put his two fists together and smiled and shook them at the crowd, first at one side of the ring, then at the other, and then sat down. Jack got a good hand coming down through the crowd. Jack is Irish, and the Irish always get a pretty good hand. An Irishman don't draw in New York like a Jew or an Eyetalian, but they always get a good hand. Jack climbed up and bent down to go through the ropes, and Walcott came over from his corner and pushed the rope down for Jack to go through. The crowd thought that was wonderful. Walcott put his hand on Jack's shoulder and they stood there just for a second.

'So you're going to be one of these popular champions,' Jack says to him. 'Take your goddam hand off my shoulder.'

'Be yourself,' Walcott says.

This is all great for the crowd. How gentlemanly the boys are before the fight! How they wish each other luck!

Solly Freedman comes over to our corner while Jack is bandaging his hands and John is over in Walcott's corner. Jack put his thumb through the slit in the bandage and then wrapped his hand nice and smooth. I taped it around the wrist and twice across the knuckles.

'Hey,' Freedman says. 'Where do you get all that tape?'

'Feel of it,' Jack says. 'It's soft, ain't it? Don't be a hick.'

Freedman stands there all the time while Jack bandages the other hand, and one of the boys that's going to handle him brings the gloves and I pull them on and work them around.

'Say, Freedman,' Jack asks. 'What nationality is this Walcott?'

'I don't know,' Solly says. 'He's some sort of a Dane.'

'He's a Bohemian,' the lad who brought the gloves said.

The referee called them out to the centre of the ring and Jack walks out. Walcott comes out smiling. They met and the referee put his arm on each of their shoulders.

'Hello, Popularity,' Jack says to Walcott.

'Be yourself.'

'What do you call yourself Walcott for,' Jack says. 'Didn't you know he was a nigger?'

'Listen—' says the referee, and he gives them the same old line. Once Walcott interrupts him. He grabs Jack's arm and says, 'Can I hit when he's got me like this?'

'Keep your hands off me,' Jack says. 'There ain't no moving picture of this.'

They went back to their corners. I lifted the bathrobe off Jack and he leaned on the ropes and flexed his knees a couple of times and scuffed his shoes in the rosin. The gong rang and Jack turned quick and went out. Walcott came toward him and they touched gloves, and as soon as Walcott dropped his hands Jack jumped his left into his face twice. There wasn't anybody ever boxed better than Jack. Walcott was after him, going forward all the time with his chin on his chest. He's a hooker and he carries his hands pretty low. All he knows is to get in there and sock. But every time he gets in there close, Jack has the left hand in his face. It's just as though it's automatic. Jack just raises the left hand up and it's in Walcott's face. Three or four times Jack brings the right over, but Walcott gets it on the shoulder or high up on the head. He's just like all these hookers. The only thing he's afraid of is another one of the same kind. He's covered everywhere you can hurt him. He don't care about a left hand in his face.

After about four rounds Jack has him bleeding bad and his face all cut up, but every time Walcott's got in close he's socked so hard he's got two big red patches on both sides just below Jack's ribs. Every time he gets in close, Jack ties him up, then gets one hand loose and uppercuts him, but when Walcott gets his hands loose he socks Jack in the body so they can hear it outside in the street. He's a socker.

It goes along like that for three rounds more. They don't talk any. They're working all the time. We worked over Jack plenty, too, in between the rounds. He don't look good at all, but he never does much work in the ring. He don't move around much, and that left hand is just automatic. It's just like it was connected with Walcott's face and Jack just had to wish it in every time. Jack is always calm in close, and he doesn't waste any juice. He knows everything about working in close, too, and he's getting away with a lot of stuff. While they were in our corner I watched him tie Walcott up, get his right hand loose, turn it, and come up with an uppercut that got Walcott's nose with the heel of the glove. Walcott was bleeding bad and leaned his nose on Jack's shoulder so as to give Jack some of it, too, and Jack sort of lifted his shoulder sharp and caught him against the nose, and then brought down the right hand and uppercut him again.

Walcott was sore as hell. By the time they'd gone five rounds he hated Jack's guts. Jack wasn't sore; that is, he wasn't any sorer than he always was. He certainly did used to make the fellows he fought hate boxing. That was why he hated Kid Lewis so. He never got the Kid's goat. Kid Lewis always had about three new dirty things Jack couldn't do. Jack was as safe as a church all the time he was in there as long as he was strong. He certainly was treating Walcott rough. The funny thing was, it looked as though Jack was an open classic boxer. That was because he had all that stuff, too.

After the seventh round Jack says, 'My left's getting heavy.'

From then he started to take a beating. It didn't show at first. But instead of him running the fight it was Walcott was running it. Instead of being safe all the time, now he was in trouble. He couldn't keep Walcott out with the left hand now. It looked as though it was the same as ever, only now, instead of Walcott's punches just missing him, they were just hitting him. He took an awful beating in the body.

'What's the round?' Jack asked.

'The eleventh.'

'I can't stay,' Jack says. 'My legs are going bad.'

Walcott had been just hitting him for a long time. It was like a baseball catcher pulls the ball and takes some of the shock off. From now on Walcott commenced to land solid. He certainly was a socking machine. Jack was just trying to block everything now. It didn't show what an awful beating he was taking. In between the rounds I worked on his legs. The muscles would flutter under my hands all the time I was rubbing them. He was sick as hell.

'How's it go?' he asked John, turning around, his face all swollen.

'It's his fight.'

'I think I can last,' Jack says. 'I don't want this bohunk to stop me.'

It was going just the way he thought it would. He knew he couldn't beat Walcott. He wasn't strong any more. He was all right, though. His money was all right and now he wanted to finish it off right to please himself. He didn't want to be knocked out.

The gong rang and we pushed him out. He went out slow. Walcott came right out after him. Jack put the left in his face and Walcott took it, came in under it, and started working on Jack's body. Jack tried to tie him up and it was just like trying to hold on to a buzz saw. Jack broke away from it and missed with the right. Walcott clipped him with a left hook and Jack went down. He went down on his hands and knees and looked at us. The referee started counting. Jack was watching us and shaking his head. At eight John motioned to him. You couldn't hear on account of the crowd. Jack got up. The referee had been holding Walcott back with one arm while he counted.

When Jack was on his feet Walcott started toward him.

'Watch yourself, Jimmy,' I heard Solly Freedman yell to him.

Walcott came up to Jack looking at him. Jack stuck the left hand at him. Walcott just shook his head. He backed Jack up against the ropes, measured him, and then hooked the left very light to the side of Jack's head and socked the right into the body as hard as he could sock just as low as he could get it. He must have hit him five inches below the belt. I thought the eyes would come out of Jack's head. They stuck way out. His mouth come open.

The referee grabbed Walcott. Jack stepped forward. If he went down, there went fifty thousand bucks. He walked as though all his insides were going to fall out.

'It wasn't low,' he said. 'It was a accident.'

The crowd were yelling so you couldn't hear anything.

'I'm all right,' Jack says. They were right in front of us.

The referee looks at John and then he shakes his head.

'Come on, you dirty Polack,' Jack says to Walcott.

John was hanging on to the ropes. He had a towel ready to chuck in. Jack was standing just a little way out from the ropes. He took a step forward. I saw the sweat come out on his face like somebody had squeezed it, and a big drop went down his nose.

'Come on and fight,' Jack says to Walcott.

The referee looked at John and waved Walcott on.

'Go in there, you slob,' he says.

Walcott went in. He didn't know what to do either. He never thought Jack could have stood it. Jack put the left in his face. There was all this yelling going on. They were right in front of us. Walcott hit him twice.

Jack's face was the worst thing I ever saw—the look on it. He was holding himself and all his body together, and it all showed on his face. All the time he was thinking and holding his body in where it was busted.

Then he started to sock. His face looked awful all the time. He started to sock with his hands low down by his side, swinging at Walcott. Walcott covered up and Jack was swinging wild at Walcott's head. Then he swung the left and it hit Walcott in the groin and the right hit Walcott right bang where he'd hit Jack. Way low. Walcott went down and grabbed himself there and rolled and twisted around.

The referee grabbed Jack and pushed him toward his corner. John jumps into the ring. There was all this yelling going on. The referee was talking with the judges and then the announcer got into the ring with the megaphone and says, 'Walcott on a foul.'

The referee is talking to John and he says, 'What could I do? Jack wouldn't take the foul. Then when he's groggy he fouls him.'

'He'd lost it anyway,' John says.

Jack's sitting on the chair. I've got his gloves off and he's holding himself in down there with both hands.

'Go over and say you're sorry,' John says into his ear. 'It'll look good.'

Jack stands up and the sweat comes out all over his face. I put the bathrobe around him and he holds himself in with one hand under the bathrobe and goes across the ring. They've picked Walcott up and they're working on him. There's a lot of people in Walcott's corner. Nobody speaks to Jack. He leans over Walcott.

'I'm sorry,' Jack says. 'I didn't mean to foul you.'

Walcott doesn't say anything. He looks too damned sick.

'Well, you're the champion now,' Jack says to him. 'I hope you get a hell of a lot of fun out of it.'

'Leave the kid alone,' Solly Freedman says.

'Hello, Solly,' Jack says. 'I'm sorry I fouled your boy.'

Freedman just looks at him.

Jack went over to his corner walking that funny jerky way, and we got him down through the ropes and through the reporters' tables and out down the aisle. A lot of people want to slap Jack on the back. He goes out through all that mob in his bathrobe to the dressing room. It's a popular win for Walcott. That's the way the money was bet in the Garden.

Once we got inside the dressing room Jack lay down and shut his eyes.

'We want to get to the hotel and get a doctor,' John says.

'I'm all busted inside,' Jack says.

'I'm sorry as hell, Jack,' John says.

'It's all right,' Jack says.

He lies there with his eyes shut.

'They certainly tried a nice double cross,' John said.

'Your friends Morgan and Steinfelt,' Jack said. 'You got nice friends.'

He lies there; his eyes are open now. His face has still got that awful drawn look.

'It's funny how fast you can think when it means that much money,' Jack says.

'You're some boy, Jack,' John says.

'No,' Jack says. 'It was nothing.'

CIVILIZATION

By R. Hernekin Baptist

[The idea that makes this story significant is evident and is used with fine restraint but with great emphasis. What is civilization? Is the civilization of Europe so much superior to that of Africa that it should be greatly admired? These questions are implied as the reader follows the record of the experiences of Mundasi. The story is essentially a character study with a dominating theme. The author is a resident of South Africa but prefers to conceal his identity behind the pen name used here.

Civilization was published in *Harper's Magazine* (April, 1932), and is reprinted by arrangement with Brandt and Brandt, literary agents.]

MUNDASI lived in such fair, wide country. It was a country of high yellow grass, but from one point not far from his father's kraal you could see a blue line which he had been told was water.

As a young boy in the kraal how happy he had been, as happy as any young boy should be that has never known the corroding influence of civilization—those strange stealthy changes which spread in a night or two like the blighting fungus under the leaves of a lusty plant. A night or two . . . a decade . . . a century or so. . . . What is time?

How did it begin, this great trouble which tore Mundasi's heart in two as he stumbled away from the dark stairway of a London office into a terrifying fog? It was fog, that dreadful manifestation of the white man's world, which had all but driven Mundasi back to the docks and to the sea which was his one link with [happiness. Now, today, fog wept dolorously around him, chilled his shivering heart, blinded his staring incredulous eyes.

What did they stare at, those suffering eyes? Nothing but the fading of a dream. Only a dream, but it was the same dream which had beckoned Mundasi to cross the sea.

To cross the sea! Why, even that is adventure enough for a man bred in a kraal, a boy to whom the word *sea* means one bright strip of blue in the landscape. Mundasi remembered the day—he was only fifteen at the time—when the news came that the youngest of his uncles, a fine man of twenty-five, had gone down with eight hundred other young warriors while on their way over the water to protect the white king from enemy tribes. Gone down into the deep water as if the watchful monarch of all crocodiles had pulled them under.

They at least had kept their dreams, for they certainly believed they were to be allowed to fight for the king, although not, unfortunately, with assegai and shield in the old proud way of young men defending their chief. Yet some of his father's friends who had been on other ships had safely returned, although always drunk and at the beer-pot: these had told the kraal that honorable fighting was allowed only to white men, and that proud young black warriors had been made, in view of all the world, to work like women at fetching and carrying and digging. Yes, they had been herded defilingly together, not even allowed to go afar into the bush to perform those daily acts which even the animals do in secret.

Oh, yes, yes, his uncle who had gone down in the sea with his companions had at least saved his pride. And these young men had not spent two hundred golden sovereigns collected by the tribe for their great journey. Yes, his uncle the headman had insisted on showing the assembled council the wonderful sight of two hundred gold sovereigns. All had crowded forward with deep cries to see the dazzling sight.

If only the Reverend Mr. Macdonald had not taken those beautiful sovereigns into a bank and exchanged them for paper money, surely then it could not have wasted away so quickly. But who can watch over paper money? The Reverend Mr. Macdonald had given him a few sheets of it, and all the rest, he said, was sent to London to be kept safe there for his use. All he would have to do would be to sign his name whenever he wanted money.

If only they had let him keep the gold in his old monkey-skin bag hanging on his belt, it would not now be nearly gone. Even a stupid person understands gold.

All but gone, they told him at the bank, and his long delayed mission . . .

At the thought of his failure shame hit him a sudden sickening blow in the pit of his stomach.

The fog was getting thicker. At that moment Mundasi stumbled badly against a black and greasy curbstone. For a moment he knelt helplessly there on the London pavement, one arm thrown over his eyes with that child's gesture peculiar to the savage. He wept aloud.

"My heart is so sore!" he cried once in his beautiful tongue. "My heart is so sore!" he crooned softly over and over.

But no one heard Mundasi except two thin little London boys. Having observed this exciting phenomenon they hastened to the corner where the "Red Bull" sent its brave lights out into the fog to tell the policeman on duty there that there was a drunken nigger on the pavement.

Constable Jenkins' bulky form walked leisurely to the scene and he had a good look. His experienced eyes saw something in that forlorn figure which had not been visible to the room full of clever politicians who had assembled in preoccupied haste for half an hour in order to listen to the lifelong grievance of an important tribe like the Xemandas.

"Come, sir, don't take it so hard. We all has our ups and downs. There's a place round the corner here. Go and have a cup o' coffee or a drop of something warm."

"Oh, Cunsbel," wept Mundasi, clutching at the great red hand on his shoulder. "I can't help it—my heart is so sore!"

"To be sure. To be sure," rumbled Constable Jenkins. "We all get like that sometimes. Come, sir, up you get!"

He raised the shivering form of Mundasi. The figure that had looked so beautiful and imposing only a few years back, before he had begun copying the dismal European fashion of other mission natives, now looked like some New York negro-revue artist.

He had spent eight guineas on the suit, thirty shillings for the hat, the same for the shoes. The tie and gloves alone had cost ten shillings.

But how could he help it? Can a chief from one tribe visit the chief of another tribe and not do him the honor of full ceremonial dress? What would these members of the King's parliament have thought of his tribe had he appeared before them in Reverend Mr. Macdonald's old gray suit and the magistrate's hat and old coat, with which they had dowered him—fussing over his appearance like any mother on that important day when he departed for the port of Bombasa.

"Like this, Mundasi. This is the angle you must wear it."

Without a smile Mr. Hilary had instructed him by putting the hat on his own head as white men do. Mr. Hilary never smiled except at something called punch which he read every Monday morning. He was not one of those white men who regard the black man as a joke.

On the boat Mundasi had been proud of his clothes. But a few months in London had made him conscious that even Reverend Mr. Macdonald's suit and Mr. Hilary's gray hat failed to reach the prevailing standard. Subtly and gradually his faith in those two beloved mentors was undermined. They had not told him about these wonderful pale young men with their scornful eyes and sleek clothes, their hats so foolish yet so desirable. Mundasi, son of a headman, grandson of the Chief, was made to feel the vague gnawing bitterness of an inferiority complex.

So when at last the day approached for the reading of his "Petition to ameliorate Present Conditions of Living of the Xemanda peoples, with Special Reference to their Need of Recovering certain of the old Tribal Lands for Agricultural Purposes; with a view to easing the heavy burden of Taxes now suffered by them: together with some notes on the enforced labor of their women in certain parts of the Territory," Mundasi had visited an outfitter's establishment. With beating heart and shining eyes he had let them array him for the great *indaba*.

"You see," he prattled to the shop assistant, "I have to meet some gentlemen of the Parliament for important discussion."

"Have you indeed, sir?" said the sprightly automatic voice of the salesman.

How wonderful that had sounded at first—to be called "sir," as if he had been a magistrate or a clergyman. As if he had been a white . . . No wonder it lured money from the pocket.

The assistant had brought his tired stock-size mind to bear upon the question, while Mundasi watched his face trustfully, like an earnest child scrutinizing its helpful mother.

"Something dark is what I recommend. No, sir, not that plum color. All right for a touch of it in the tie and the socks. These Parliamentary gentlemen are all for dark effects. But a little self-expression in the tie is allowable on most occasions."

Yes, that gentleman in the shop knew exactly what he was feeling. So did this policeman. How was it that Those Others had so utterly? . . .

Mundasi looked drearily down at his mud-stained knees. *Eight guineas*.

"You've got a good deal of mud on those good clothes of yours, sir. What I advise, if you'll allow me, is to come with me to the wife. Only five minutes away, and she'll sponge those trousers and brush you down in no time. I'm just going off duty, so I'll take you round with me."

Half an hour later Mundasi was sitting at table with his hosts, eating a good solid British tea, featuring toast and butter and jam and shrimps and cake. The shrimps he had not touched as his was not a fish-eating tribe. But all else . . .

And there was such a fine big fire at his back, a good solid coal fire that felt like hot sun.

Repressions poured out of his mouth in a swelling stream only interrupted by the influx of jam and cake. It was the first time in England he had felt the melting warmth of intimate kindness. It was true he had gone to lunch with the kindly and bluff clergy. Bluffness, however, is a British quality not always understood by foreigners. He had been to lunch again with various good people of the social-worker type. He had also been taken to the theater by others not quite so good although more social. Kindly young men . . . But here, round Constable Jenkins' table, was the atmosphere which, for the first time in England, released the festering sores of a wounded heart, transforming that cruel sickness for the African sun into something he could talk about eagerly, endlessly.

Constable Jenkins, his wife Mabel, and their little boy of four, Leslie, listened like three Desdemonas to this chance Othello at their humble board. Beautiful it was to Mundasi to be spoken to as a human being who for months had been treated as a Social Problem. The Native Question in the flesh.

Yes, they spoke to him as a simple human being; but yet, with the wise recognition of the peasant class of one born to a higher estate, they called him "sir." Mabel had been a gamekeeper's daughter in Lancashire. Her husband too was a village man. Leslie, their son, was not yet at school: so he was still a fragment of unspoilt childhood as natural, as smiling, or as solemn as any naked kraal baby. Long before tea was over the little boy abandoned his shrimp débris and came to stand with unconscious admiration at the black man's knee.

"Now, Leslie, don't pester the gentleman. Go back to your place at once."

But Leslie had solemnly uttered one word. Gazing up with his blue eyes of innocence into the sensitive, lively, dark face he said firmly, "Knee."

"He means 'e wants you to hold him on your knee, sir. You must excuse his bad manners."

Mundasi stopped his torrent of speech for the minute to meet the calm blue eyes of the being who offered this balm to this spirit. Uttering a deep and tender word in his own tongue, he gathered up the heavy little figure against his breast, as if it were a shield against all such icy beings as Parliamentary gentlemen. The little boy's ear was pressed close to the black gentleman's chest. The clock inside it, he thought, beat far quicker than Daddy's. Sometimes very quick and then slower again.

"You understand, Cunsbel, you understand, Missis, that for many months I prepare to be deputation for my people to great white Queen's country, now unhappily demised. It was supreme honor reposed in my integrity. Reverend Macdonald, Mr. Hilary, they help me write it out in Queen's English. Everyday I go to their houses to be closeted there with important matters of state. Every day I take messages from my grandfather the Chief to Mr. Hilary and Reverend Macdonald. Mr. Hilary and Reverend Macdonald they send diplomatic messages to my grandfather the Chief. I deliver those messages. My father and the other headmen confer very often with the Chief concerning something called a policy. (Your good husband, Missis, will explain these matters to you. In my country the women know not the meanings of such words.)"

Constable Jenkins cleared his throat appreciatively, authoritatively, while Mabel, his wife, said:

"Well, that's nature, as you may say," and cosily poured out a third cup for her overlord.

"You understand, council meeting held very often in the Chief's kraal. I am in attendance with my notes of reference. Sometimes Mr. Hilary and Reverend Macdonald also in attendance. They write in notebooks what the Chief, my grandfather, say. They write what my father and the other headmen say. They even listen to my father's chief wife as spokesman for the women of the tribe. Mr. Hilary most impressed by representation of all sections. All is cheerful. My people decide to evoke destiny by removing a deputation to English Parliament. Every day Mr. Hilary's clerk writes out all the notes we have made on the big typewriter. Twelve pages only it made, the grievances and hardships of my people from memorial times to present day. The day comes for my departure. In my new clothes, presented by esteem of Mr. Hilary and Reverend Macdonald, I pay solemn farewell to the Chief and the headmen. I show them the manuscript tied up with official tape, very pink and pretty. There is beer. An ox is killed to honor the occasion. The young men dance. The young girls also dance. The Chief gives me wise words concerning deportment of deputation to friendly tribe. The Chief and headmen then make official presentation of bag of solid gold. Two hundred sovereigns collected in four years for important undertaking. Diplomatic importance . . ."

Mundasi's voice thinned off shakily into silence. Mabel said, "Tt! Tt!" Constable Jenkins said, "My word, that's a tidy sum!"

"All crowd round to see it," proceeded Mundasi, recovering himself and giving Leslie a pat. "They want feel weight, etc., etc. Many young children and women have never seen coin of gold. There is considerable astonishment at the power of our Chief. We drink beer. We laugh, we leap and shout. We think our troubles at a timely end—"

At the picture he had again conjured up Mundasi hid his sad, London face in the curly hair of Leslie while he felt for his expensive London handkerchief of purple silk—one of those aids to self-expression which the salesman had thought allowable in Parliamentary circles.

"There, sir, don't you take on so about it. Another cup for the gentleman, Mabel. Cut that seed-cake."

Constable Jenkins' heavy voice was rich with the kindness of generations of English village folk, blended with the soothing quality of the London policeman.

"What 'ave these Parliamentary gents been doing to you, sir? Better tell us all about it and you'll feel better. Won't he, Mabel?"

After wiping his eyes in the unconscious open way of savages who have not yet learned to be ashamed of tears, Mundasi was able to take up the tale.

"Naturally, Cunsbel, I think to myself I come to London, see Parliament very rapidly and return to report successful issues to the Chief and anxious European friends. I am not ignorant; I have seen pictures of Parliament. Very grand house. Gentlemen sitting in large chairs like the late white Queen. Some with long white hair like witch-doctor—"

"Long white hair? Don't you mean the Speaker's wig, sir?"

"Yes, yes! Speaker's wig! That is correct nomination. To resume subject, naturally I think I enter Parliament where *indabas* are held. Have I not on several occasions seen my grandfather visit the aged Chief of the Sheganas? No ceremony is spared to conduct proceedings to successful issue. For three days important matters of the country are discussed. Or it may be a week. The Chiefs and their headmen sit in serious conclave. The young men sit in outer circles, learning precept upon precept but uttering no opinion. A sheep is killed, even an ox. At night much merriment . . . "

Mundasi finds it hard to tear himself away from those pictures of home.

"To return with the subject. I arrive in London with letters. A gentleman meets me. He says he will convey letters to proper destination. I go to lodgings recommend by him. I expect reply to my letters very quickly. On advice of a Zulu gentleman staying in the same house I do much shopping. I buy umbrella, notebooks, pencils, etc. Every day I study my address for redress of the disabilities suffered by my tribe. I read it aloud many times that the words do not seem strange to me. Then I wait one, two, three, four weeks at two pounds ten shillings per week with bath sixpence extra. Then, one letter appears. It informs me—"

Mundasi felt in his pockets and produced a handsome leather notebook.

"It informs me:

"Dear Sir,

I am in receipt of the letters of introduction from the Governor of B and from Mr. Robert Hilary. I am sorry to say, however, that this is a most unfortunate time in which to gain a hearing for your petition. Had you arrived a fortnight earlier it would have been comparatively easy to manage meetings with the various members of the group that will be most useful to you. I will, however, do my best to get you a hearing even if it should have to be after the election.

Have you met Mr. Gordon-Hillsworthy? I think he is likely to be sympathetic with the grievances of an important people like the Fingoes.

With all good wishes,

I am, dear Sir, cordially yours,

Richard Sheldrake."

"Nicely put, sir, if I may say so," said Constable Jenkins. "Seems kindly meant."

"Ah, Cunsbel, so I too think until I reach the end. He is so insulting as to forget the name of my tribe. Forget the Xemandas whose Chief is paramount in a very large area? And for those bastards the Fingoes—"

"I beg pardon, sir?"

His kind host's voice gave him the impression of an approaching turkey-cock. Mundasi stared at him anxiously.

"I was just saying, sir, excuse me, I can't allow Language in front of Mrs. Jenkins and the boy."

"Language? What have I—"

"Well, sir, that there word beginning with a b. Can't allow it, sir, excuse me."

"B? B? Oh! You mean *bastard?* Well, but the Fingoes *are* bastards as all the world knows. When the Xosas defeated them they . . . But pardon me if I offend. I had no idea . . ."

He looked anxiously into the scarlet laughter-suppressing face of Mabel, into the shocked masculine stronghold that was Constable Jenkins' face. He must not offend these kind people. He felt such a piteous need to talk himself out.

"Bassard," murmured Leslie drowsily against his new friend's chest. It was the one word he had uttered since he had established himself on the black gentleman's knee.

"There!" said Mabel triumphantly. "Didn't I always say he was a clever one? Don't go repeating that, dear. That isn't a pretty word for little boys, is it, dad?"

Order and confidence once more established, Mundasi felt again for the beautiful pocketbook and produced another letter.

"To proceed. I then wait another fortnight before I am delivered with this letter of Mr. Gordon-Hillsworthy. I will read it to you:

"S. Mundasi, Esq.
Dear Sir,

I have been most interested to hear from my friend Mr. Richard Sheldrake of your important mission in England at the present moment. I have been extremely interested in your people ever since I paid a visit some years ago to Uganda. I sincerely hope I may be able to meet you. Unfortunately, as you may have heard, I am very busy with electioneering matters, and I fear my many engagements may prevent me from naming a day and hour for some weeks. Possibly not until the Election is over. If you will kindly keep me in touch with your movements I shall be grateful.

Believe me,

Very truly yours,
G. Gordon-Hillsworthy."

"Well, that's a bit of allright, I should say, sir," said Constable Jenkins lighting his pipe with a spill.

"A most charitable letter indeed. But I again fear that this gentleman speaks in ignorance of my people. We are nine hundred miles from Uganda. Howbeit I felt that it was a friend if I only could wait to see him. In meantime I had letters from friends of Mr. Hilary and Reverend Macdonald. They also wrote to other gentlemen as they were too busy themselves to lend an ear, as Shakespeare says, at the moment."

As the mention of Shakespeare indicated, Mundasi was getting into his stride.

"So, I wait till after the Election when all should be nice and quiet again. Nobody to hurry. All calm. But instead of going honorably with petition into the House of Parliament I get short angry letters from the gentlemen saying there is great stress of work immediately following an election but they could give me half an hour 3:30 P.M. to

4 P.M. at an office where those interested could meet and hear my petition. They urge upon me to be punctual as time is short.

"I am disappointed. All seems different from my anticipation of many
months, even years. But at last I go. The alleged rendezvous was in a
dull and dirty street. That office was up some dark and steep stairs
which smelt of the toilet."

"Toilet?" said Mabel, interested and puzzled.

"Pardon me, Missis. The English language has many choices, perhaps I should—"

"Go on, sir," said Constable Jenkins hastily. "Did they treat you
kindly when you got there?"

"Ah!" said Mundasi dramatically. "At first I am kept waiting for
half an hour by my new watch. A young lady tells me there is a committee meeting. She say my petition come next. I wait. I pull myself
together. All is not lost, I say to myself, even if I am not in the House of
Parliament, yet some of these gentlemen are headmen—how do you say
it? Members. Yes, members of Parliament.

"I support myself by thoughts of my people. I think of Mr. Hilary
and the Reverend Macdonald, those good men and true. I think of the
Chief, of my father, and the other headmen. I think of the young men
like me. I think they are safe in the bright sun. Perhaps they are hunting or perhaps they are in the Mission School learning to be carpenters.
At night the bright fire for all . . ."

"Is the gentleman going to cry again, Mummy?" piped Leslie.

"Be *quiet*, Leslie. Can't you let the gentleman speak?"

With a sigh registering a slight sense of injustice, the little boy snug-
gled closer to that interesting chest.

"At last the door opens. One of the gentlemen say, 'Ready? There's
not much time. That other business before you took a wretched long
time. You've got a quarter of an hour if you can be quick.'

"Quick! We know not the word! What is this quick? Is the sun
quick which keeps the time for us? Does the moon hasten through the
sky? Assuredly not. All goes with propriety in my country. Very nice,
no quickness. Time for everything when no clocks. Yes. . . .

"I follow the gentleman very hastily with my gorge in my throat.
There are several other gentlemen in the room, but that room is how
small! Not so big as Mr. Hilary's office. All is crowded. I cannot see
their faces; all have their backs to the light. I am told to sit down.
Two gentlemen look at their watch and say they hope it won't be long.
I begin . . .

"I begin to read the petition of my people, the Xemandas, to the
Parliament of England. To King George's Parliament. I tremble. . . .
They are only *men!* Should I have trembled in the Great House before
the Chief with the white hair? No, I should have deported myself as
the grandson of a Chief, the son of a headman. My voice would have

been strong and clear. Standing there in the big Parliament . . . But those very little men . . .

"I begin to read. My voice shakes; it sounds so very quiet, I cannot see very well. When—when I have read only two pages one of the gentlemen snatches my petition from me and counts the pages quickly with angry looks, wetting his fingers. He say he had no idea there would be such a lot of it. He says to compress it to save time.

"My hand shakes. I do not know what to do, I forget what *compress* is. And just as I am going to ask what *compress* is, another gentleman swiftly takes my petition away and says that he will get at the jiss of it. To save time, he said. What is jiss, I say to myself. Then they all say thank-you to that gentleman, but not to me. They look at their watches and listen again. Two go out very quick. I do not see them again. The gentleman turns my pages very quick, crumpling the paper. He says very quick words I cannot understand. He make my petition to sound of no matter . . . of no importance . . .

"Of no importance that our women are made to work on the roads when they are far gone in pregnancy? . . . Our land and cattle? . . .

"In five minutes that gentleman fold it up and return it to me. I begin again to read. They stop me, saying they know all that is in it. I am bewildered with agitation, knowing not what to do to save the importance of my petition. My money nearly gone . . . I return a disgraceful failure. Two hundred sovereigns in gold . . ."

"That's a bloody shame, sir, if you'll excuse me using the word when off duty. Didn't they say they would help you or anything?"

"Oh, indeed yes. They talk quickly together, not looking at me. I feel forgotten. Then one of them offers remark, 'Well, Mr. Mundasi, we are very much interest in your petition and we can assure you it will receive most serious attention at early opportunity.' That's what they said. But they did not *stand* to speak, not like the Parliament! I feel deepest insult to my Chief.

"Then they speak to the telephone. 'Miss Smith, please show Mr. Mundasi out.' . . . Miss Smith! I, a grandson of the Chief, to be said farewell after important mission by a woman! The gentlemen are all talking about some new election matters. I feel forgotten. Only one little gentleman comes and hold me tight by the hand. He say, in my own tongue, 'They mean no insult, Mundasi; they know no better, poor fellows. I'll do the best I can for you over here. I love your country! I wish I was there again out of this damn chicken-coop!'

"It—it was that little gentleman made me cry. His voice . . . *He* love my country! He know it! How could I see the steps for my weeping . . . Lead stairs, very dark, and most unpleasant perfume."

Today Mundasi is a headman as his father, now Chief, had been before him. Today Mundasi finds sartorial self-expression in the clay-dyed blanket and the leopard's skin. His notebook is a wallet of monkeys' tails. Mundasi sits round the fire, he smokes in the sun, he hunts. He drinks beer, he speaks in the Council, gravely and at great length.

Mr. Hilary's successor says of Mundasi, "I can't understand why an unprogressive heathen like Mundasi should call his eldest picannins Mabel and Jenkins. That fellow always gives me the impression of being completely anti-white. I can't get at him, somehow or other. And you say he doesn't go to your church either?"

And Reverend Mr. Macdonald says sadly, "I can tell you. He was one of my best boys. And now . . ."

The tale is told.

In the meantime, Mabel, in one bead bracelet, plays in the sunny kraal in her father's hut. And Jenkins, with not even a bracelet towards self-expression, struts about with other fat young bloods of three, playing at hunting, with sticks for assegais.

NIGHT CLUB

By Katharine Brush

[Every youthful writer wishes he might be able to live in Java, the Yukon, or Wyoming, where things are happening that stories could be made of. In *Night Club* Miss Brush has made an ironic picture of a little area, a spot, in which romance and tragedy may break out at any moment. The life-stuff that gets itself into fiction lies all around us and within touching distance, but we do not see it.

Katharine Ingham Brush was born in Middletown, Connecticut, in 1902. Her present home is in New York.

Night Club was first published in *Harper's Magazine* (September, 1927). It is here reprinted by arrangement with Ann Watkins, Inc., literary agent.]

PROMPTLY at quarter of ten P.M. Mrs. Brady descended the steps of the Elevated. She purchased from the newsdealer in the cubbyhole beneath them a next month's magazine and a tomorrow morning's paper and, with these tucked under one plump arm, she walked. She walked two blocks north on Sixth Avenue, turned and went west. But not far west. Westward half a block only, to the place where the gay green awning marked Club Français painted a stripe of shade across the glimmering sidewalk. Under this awning Mrs. Brady halted briefly, to remark to the six-foot doorman that it looked like rain and to await his performance of his professional duty. When the small green door yawned open she sighed deeply and plodded in.

The foyer was a blackness, an airless velvet blackness like the inside of a jeweler's box. Four drum-shaped lamps of golden silk suspended from the ceiling gave it light (a very little) and formed the jewels: gold signets, those, or cuff-links for a giant. At the far end of the foyer there were black stairs, faintly dusty, rippling upward toward an amber radiance. Mrs. Brady approached and ponderously mounted the stairs, clinging with one fist to the mangy velvet rope that railed their edge.

From the top, Miss Lena Levin observed the ascent. Miss Levin was the checkroom girl. She had dark-at-the-roots blonde hair and slender hips upon which, in moments of leisure she wore her hands, like buckles of ivory loosely attached. This was a moment of leisure. Miss Levin waited behind her counter. Row upon row of hooks, empty as yet, and seeming to beckon—wee curved fingers of iron—waited behind her.

"Late," said Miss Levin, "again."

"Go wan!" said Mrs. Brady. "It's only ten to ten. *Whew!* Them *stairs!*"

She leaned heavily, sideways, against Miss Levin's counter and, applying one palm to the region of her heart, appeared at once to listen and to count. "Feel!" she cried then in a pleased voice.

Miss Levin obediently felt.

"Them stairs," continued Mrs. Brady darkly, "with my bad heart, will be the death of me. Whew! Well, dearie! What's the news?"

"You got a paper," Miss Levin languidly reminded her.

"Yeah!" agreed Mrs. Brady with sudden vehemence. "I got a paper!" She slapped it upon the counter. "An' a lot of time I'll get to *read* my paper, won't I now? On a Saturday night!" She moaned. "Other nights is bad enough, dear knows—but *Saturday* nights! How I dread 'em! Every Saturday night I say to my daughter, I say, 'Geraldine, I can't,' I say, 'I can't go through it again, an' that's all there is to it,' I say. 'I'll *quit*,' I say. An' I *will* too!" added Mrs. Brady firmly, if indefinitely.

Miss Levin, in defense of Saturday nights, mumbled some vague something about tips.

"Tips!" Mrs. Brady hissed it. She almost spat it. Plainly money was nothing, nothing at all, to this lady. "I just wish *you* had to spend one Saturday night, just one, in that dressing room! Bein' pushed an' stepped on an' near knocked down by that gang of hussies, an' them orderin' an' bossin' you 'round like you was *black*, an' usin' your things an' then sayin' they're sorry, they got no change, they'll be back. Yah! They *never* come back!"

"There's Mr. Costello," whispered Miss Levin through lips that, like a ventriloquist's, scarcely stirred.

"An' as I was sayin','" Mrs. Brady said at once brightly, "I got to leave you. Ten to ten, time I was on the job."

She smirked at Miss Levin, nodded, and right-about-faced. There, indeed, Mr. Costello was. Mr. Billy Costello, manager, proprietor, monarch of all he surveyed. From the doorway of the big room, where the little tables herded in a ring around the waxen floor, he surveyed Mrs. Brady, and in such a way that Mrs. Brady, momentarily forgetting her bad heart, walked fast, scurried faster, almost ran.

The door of her domain was set politely in an alcove, beyond silken curtains looped up at the sides. Mrs. Brady reached it breathless, shouldered it open, and groped for the electric switch. Lights sprang up, a bright white blaze, intolerable for an instant to the eyes, like sun on snow. Blinking, Mrs. Brady shut the door.

The room was a spotless, white-tiled place, half beauty shop, half dressing room. Along one wall stood washstands, sturdy triplets in a row, with pale-green liquid soap in glass balloons afloat above them. Against the opposite wall there was a couch. A third wall backed an elongated glass-topped dressing table; and over the dressing table and over the washstands long rectangular sheets of mirror reflected lights, doors, glossy tiles, lights multiplied. . . .

Mrs. Brady moved across this glitter like a thick, dark cloud in a hurry. At the dressing table she came to a halt, and upon it she laid her newspaper, her magazine, and her purse—a black purse worn gray with much clutching. She divested herself of a rusty black coat and a hat of the mushroom persuasion, and hung both up in a corner cupboard which she opened by means of one of a quite preposterous bunch of keys. From a nook in the cupboard she took down a lace-edged handkerchief with long streamers. She untied the streamers and tied them again around her chunky black alpaca waist. The handkerchief became an apron's baby cousin.

Mrs. Brady relocked the cupboard door, fumbled her key-ring over, and unlocked a capacious drawer of the dressing table. She spread a fresh towel on the plate-glass top, in the geometrical center, and upon the towel she arranged with care a procession of things fished from the drawer. Things for the hair. Things for the complexion. Things for the eyes, the lashes, the brows, the lips, and the finger nails. Things in boxes and things in jars and things in tubes and tins. Also, an ash tray, matches, pins, a tiny sewing kit, a pair of scissors. Last of all, a handprinted sign, a nudging sort of sign:

NOTICE!

These articles, placed here for your convenience, are the property of the *maid*.

And directly beneath the sign, propping it up against the looking-glass, a china saucer, in which Mrs. Brady now slyly laid decoy money: two quarters and two dimes, in four-leaf-clover formation.

Another drawer of the dressing table yielded a bottle of bromo seltzer, a bottle of aromatic spirits of ammonia, a tin of sodium bicarbonate, and a teaspoon. These were lined up on a shelf above the couch.

Mrs. Brady was now ready for anything. And (from the grim, thin pucker of her mouth) expecting it.

Music came to her ears. Rather, the beat of music, muffled, rhythmic, remote. Umpa-um, umpa-um, umpa-um-mm—Mr. "Fiddle" Baer and his band, hard at work on the first foxtrot of the night. It was teasing, foot-tapping music; but the large solemn feet of Mrs. Brady were still. She sat on the couch and opened her newspaper; and for some moments she read uninterruptedly, with special attention to the murders, the divorces, the breaches of promise, the funnies.

Then the door swung inward, admitting a blast of Mr. "Fiddle" Baer's best, a whiff of perfume, and a girl.

Mrs. Brady put her paper away.

The girl was *petite* and darkly beautiful; wrapped in fur and mounted on tall jeweled heels. She entered humming the ragtime song the orchestra was playing, and while she stood near the dressing table, stripping off her gloves, she continued to hum it softly to herself:

> "Oh, I know my baby loves me,
> I can tell my baby loves me."

Here the dark little girl got the left glove off, and Mrs. Brady glimpsed a platinum wedding ring.

> " 'Cause there ain't no maybe
> In my baby's
> Eyes."

The right glove came off. The dark little girl sat down in one of the chairs that faced the dressing table. She doffed her wrap, casting it carelessly over the chair-back. It had a cloth-of-gold lining, and "Paris" was embroidered in curlicues on the label. Mrs. Brady hovered solicitously near.

The dark little girl, still humming, looked over the articles "placed here for your convenience," and picked up the scissors. Having cut off a very small hangnail with the air of one performing a perilous major operation, she seized and used the manicure buffer, and after that the eyebrow pencil. Mrs. Brady's mind, hopefully calculating the tip, jumped and jumped again like a taximeter.

> "Oh, I know my baby loves me—"

The dark little girl applied powder and lipstick belonging to herself. She examined the result searchingly in the mirror and sat back, satisfied. She cast some silver Klink! Klink! into Mrs. Brady's saucer, and half rose. Then, remembering something, she settled down again.

The ensuing thirty seconds were spent by her in pulling off her platinum wedding ring, tying it in a corner of a lace handkerchief, and tucking the handkerchief down the bodice of her tight white-velvet gown.

"There!" she said.

She swooped up her wrap and trotted toward the door, jeweled heels merrily twinkling.

> " 'Cause there ain't no maybe—"

The door fell shut.

Almost instantly it opened again, and another girl came in. A blonde, this. She was pretty in a round-eyed babyish way; but Mrs. Brady, regarding her, mentally grabbed the spirits of ammonia bottle. For she looked terribly ill. The round eyes were dull, the pretty, silly little face was drawn. The thin hands, picking at the fastenings of a spacious bag, trembled and twitched.

Mrs. Brady cleared her throat. "Can I do something for you, Miss?"

Evidently the blonde girl had believed herself alone in the dressing room. She started violently, and glanced up, panic in her eyes. Panic, and something else. Something very like murderous hate—but for an instant only, so that Mrs. Brady, whose perceptions were never quick, missed it altogether.

"A glass of water?" suggested Mrs. Brady.

"No," said the girl, "no." She had one hand in the beaded bag now. Mrs. Brady could see it moving, causing the bag to squirm like a live thing, and the fringe to shiver. "Yes!" she cried abruptly. "A glass of water—please—you get it for me."

She dropped onto the couch. Mrs. Brady scurried to the water cooler in the corner, pressed the spigot with a determined thumb. Water trickled out thinly. Mrs. Brady pressed harder, and scowled, and thought, "Something's wrong with this thing. I mustn't forget, next time I see Mr. Costello—"

When again she faced her patient, the patient was sitting erect. She was thrusting her clenched hand back into the beaded bag again.

She took only a sip of the water, but it seemed to help her quite miraculously. Almost at once color came to her cheeks, life to her eyes. She grew young again—as young as she was. She smiled up at Mrs. Brady.

"Well!" she exclaimed. "What do you know about that!" She shook her honey-colored head. "I can't imagine what came over me."

"Are you better now?" inquired Mrs. Brady.

"Yes. Oh, yes. I'm better now. You see," said the blonde girl confidentially, "we were at the theater, my boy friend and I, and it was hot and stuffy—I guess that must have been the trouble." She paused, and the ghost of her recent distress crossed her face. "God! I thought that last act *never* would end!" she said.

While she attended to her hair and complexion she chattered gayly to Mrs. Brady, chattered on with scarcely a stop for breath, and laughed much. She said, among other things, that she and her "boy friend" had not known one another very long, but that she was "ga-ga" about him. "He is about me, too," she confessed. "He thinks I'm grand."

She fell silent then, and in the looking-glass her eyes were shadowed, haunted. But Mrs. Brady, from where she stood, could not see the looking-glass; and half a minute later the blonde girl laughed and began again. When she went out she seemed to dance out on little winged feet; and Mrs. Brady, sighing, thought it must be nice to be young . . . and happy like that.

The next arrivals were two. A tall, extremely smart young woman in black chiffon entered first, and held the door open for her companion; and the instant the door was shut, she said, as though it had been on the tip of her tongue for hours, "Amy, what under the sun *happened?*"

Amy, who was brown-eyed, brown-bobbed-haired, and patently annoyed with something, crossed to the dressing table and flopped into a chair before she made reply.

"Nothing," she said wearily then.

"That's nonsense!" snorted the other. "Tell me. Was it something she said? She's a tactless ass, of course. Always was."

"No, not anything she said. It was—" Amy bit her lip. "All right! I'll tell you. Before we left your apartment I just happened to notice that Tom had disappeared. So I went to look for him—I wanted to ask him if he'd remembered to tell the maid where we were going— Skippy's subject to croup, you know, and we always leave word. Well, so I went into the kitchen, thinking Tom might be there mixing cocktails—and there he was—and there *she* was!"

The full red mouth of the other young woman pursed itself slightly. Her arched brows lifted. "Well?"

Her matter-of-factness appeared to infuriate Amy. "He was *kissing* her!" she flung out.

"Well?" said the other again. She chuckled softly and patted Amy's shoulder, as if it were the shoulder of a child. "You're surely not going to let *that* spoil your whole evening? Amy *dear!* Kissing may once have been serious and significant—but it isn't nowadays. Nowadays, it's like shaking hands. It means nothing."

But Amy was not consoled. "I hate her!" she cried desperately. "Red-headed *thing!* Calling me 'darling' and 'honey,' and s-sending me handkerchiefs for C-Christmas—and then sneaking off behind closed doors and k-kissing my h-h-husband. . . ."

At this point Amy quite broke down, but she recovered herself sufficiently to add with venom, "I'd like to slap her!"

"Oh, oh, oh," smiled the tall young woman, "I wouldn't do that!"

Amy wiped her eyes with what might well have been one of the Christmas handkerchiefs, and confronted her friend. "Well, what *would* you do, Claire? If you were I?"

"I'd forget it," said Claire, "and have a good time. I'd kiss somebody myself. You've no idea how much better you'd feel!"

"I don't do—" Amy began indignantly; but as the door behind her opened and a third young woman—red-headed, earringed, exquisite— lilted in, she changed her tone. "Oh, hello!" she called sweetly, beaming at the newcomer via the mirror. "We were wondering what had become of you!"

The red-headed girl, smiling easily back, dropped her cigarette on the floor and crushed it out with a silver-shod toe. "Tom and I were talking to 'Fiddle' Baer," she explained. "He's going to play 'Clap Yo' Hands' next, because it's my favorite. Lend me a comb, will you, somebody?"

"There's a comb there," said Claire, indicating Mrs. Brady's business comb.

"But imagine using it!" murmured the red-headed girl. "Amy darling, haven't you one?"

Amy produced a tiny comb from her rhinestone purse. "Don't forget to bring it when you come," she said, and stood up. "I'm going on out; I want to tell Tom something."

She went.

The red-headed young woman and the tall black-chiffon one were alone, except for Mrs. Brady. The red-headed one beaded her incredible lashes. The tall one, the one called Claire, sat watching her. Presently she said, "Sylvia, look here." And Sylvia looked. Anybody, addressed in that tone, would have.

"There is one thing," Claire went on quietly, holding the other's eyes, "that I want understood. And that is, '*Hands off!*' Do you hear me?"

"I don't know what you mean."

"You do know what I mean!"

The red-headed girl shrugged her shoulders. "Amy told you she saw us, I suppose."

"Precisely. And," went on Claire, gathering up her possessions and rising, "as I said before, you're to keep away." Her eyes blazed sudden white-hot rage. "Because, as you very well know, he belongs to *me*," she said and departed, slamming the door.

Between eleven o'clock and one Mrs. Brady was very busy indeed. Never for more than a moment during those two hours was the dressing room empty. Often it was jammed, full to overflowing with curled cropped heads, with ivory arms and shoulders, with silk and lace and chiffon, with legs. The door flapped in and back, in and back. The mirrors caught and held—and lost—a hundred different faces. Powder veiled the dressing table with a thin white dust; cigarette stubs, scarlet at the tips, choked the ash-receiver. Dimes and quarters clattered into Mrs. Brady's saucer—and were transferred to Mrs. Brady's purse. The original seventy cents remained. That much, and no more, would Mrs. Brady gamble on the integrity of womankind.

She earned her money. She threaded needles and took stitches. She powdered the backs of necks. She supplied towels for soapy, dripping hands. She removed a speck from a teary blue eye and pounded the heel on a slipper. She curled the straggling ends of a black bob and a gray bob, pinned a velvet flower on a lithe round waist, mixed three doses of bicarbonate of soda, took charge of a shed pink-satin girdle, collected, on hands and knees, several dozen fake pearls that had wept from a broken string.

She served chorus girls and school girls, gay young matrons and gayer young mistresses, a lady who had divorced four husbands, and a lady who had poisoned one, the secret (more or less) sweetheart of a Most Distinguished Name, and the Brains of a bootleg gang. . . . She saw things. She saw a yellow check, with the ink hardly dry. She saw four tiny bruises, such as fingers might make, on an arm. She saw a girl strike another girl, not playfully. She saw a bundle of letters some man wished he had not written, safe and deep in a brocaded handbag.

About midnight the door flew open and at once was pushed shut, and a gray-eyed, lovely child stood backed against it, her palms flattened on the panels at her sides, the draperies of her white chiffon gown settling lightly to rest around her.

There were already five damsels of varying ages in the dressing room. The latest arrival marked their presence with a flick of her eyes and standing just where she was, she called peremptorily, "Maid!"

Mrs. Brady, standing just where she was, said, "Yes, Miss?"

"Please come here," said the girl.

Mrs. Brady, as slowly as she dared, did so.

The girl lowered her voice to a tense half-whisper. "Listen! Is there any way I can get out of here except through this door I came in?"

Mrs. Brady stared at her stupidly.

"Any window?" persisted the girl. "Or anything?"

Here they were interrupted by the exodus of two of the damsels-of-varying ages. Mrs. Brady opened the door for them—and in so doing caught a glimpse of a man who waited in the hall outside, a debonair, old-young man with a girl's furry wrap hung over his arm, and his hat in his hand.

The door clicked. The gray-eyed girl moved out from the wall, against which she had flattened herself—for all the world like one eluding pursuit in a cinema.

"What about that window?" she demanded, pointing.

"That's all the farther it opens," said Mrs. Brady.

"Oh! And it's the only one—isn't it?"

"It is."

"Damn," said the girl. "Then there's *no* way out?"

"No way but the door," said Mrs. Brady testily.

The girl looked at the door. She seemed to look *through* the door, and to despise and to fear what she saw. Then she looked at Mrs. Brady. "Well," she said, "then I s'pose the only thing to do is to stay in here."

She stayed. Minutes ticked by. Jazz crooned distantly, stopped, struck up again. Other girls came and went. Still the gray-eyed girl sat on the couch, with her back to the wall and her shapely legs crossed, smoking cigarettes, one from the stub of another.

After a long while she said, "Maid!"

"Yes, Miss?"

"Peek out that door, will you, and see if there's anyone standing there."

Mrs. Brady peeked, and reported that there was. There was a gentleman with a little bit of a black mustache standing there. The same gentleman, in fact, who was standing there "just after you came in."

"Oh, Lord," sighed the gray-eyed girl. "Well . . . I can't stay here all *night*, that's one sure thing."

She slid off the couch, and went listlessly to the dressing table. There she occupied herself for a minute or two. Suddenly, without a word, she darted out.

Thirty seconds later Mrs. Brady was elated to find two crumpled one-dollar bills lying in her saucer. Her joy, however, died a premature death. For she made an almost simultaneous second discovery. A saddening one. Above all, a puzzling one.

"Now what for," marveled Mrs. Brady, "did she want to walk off with them *scissors?*"

This at twelve twenty-five.

At twelve-thirty a quartette of excited young things burst in, babbling madly. All of them had their evening wraps with them; all talked at once. One of them, a Dresden-china girl with a heart-shaped face, was the center of attention. Around her the rest fluttered like monstrous butterflies; to her they addressed their shrill exclamatory cries. "Babe," they called her.

Mrs. Brady heard snatches: "Not in this state unless . . ." "Well, you can in Maryland, Jimmy says." "Oh, there must be some place nearer than . . ." "Isn't this *marvelous?*" "When did it happen, Babe? When did you decide?"

"Just now," the girl with the heart-shaped face sang softly, "when we were dancing."

The babble resumed. "But listen, Babe, what'll your mother and father? . . ." "Oh, never mind, let's hurry." "Shall we be warm enough with just these thin wraps, do you think? Babe, will you be warm enough? Sure?"

Powder flew and little pocket combs marched through bright marcels. Flushed cheeks were painted pinker still.

"My pearls," said Babe, "are *old*. And my dress and my slippers are *new*. Now let's see—what can I *borrow?*"

A lace handkerchief, a diamond bar-pin, a pair of earrings were proffered. She chose the bar-pin, and its owner unpinned it proudly, gladly.

"I've got blue garters!" exclaimed another girl.

"Give me one, then" directed Babe. "I'll trade with you. . . . There! That fixes that."

More babbling, "Hurry! Hurry up!" . . . "Listen, are you *sure* we'll be warm enough? Because we can stop at my house; there's nobody home." "Give me that puff, Babe; I'll powder your back." "And just to think a week ago you'd never even met each other!" "Oh, hurry *up*, let's get *started!*" "I'm ready." "So'm I." "Ready, Babe? You look adorable." "Come on, everybody."

They were gone again, and the dressing room seemed twice as still and vacant as before.

A minute of grace, during which Mrs. Brady wiped the spilled powder away with a damp gray rag. Then the door jumped open again. Two evening gowns appeared and made for the dressing table in a bee line. Slim tubular gowns they were, one silver, one palest yellow. Yellow hair went with the silver gown, brown hair with the yellow. The silver-gowned, yellow-haired girl wore orchids on her shoulder, three of them, and a flashing bracelet on each fragile wrist. The other girl looked less prosperous; still, you would rather have looked at her.

Both ignored Mrs. Brady's cosmetic display as utterly as they ignored Mrs. Brady, producing full field equipment of their own.

"Well," said the girl with the orchids, rouging energetically, "how do you like him?"

"Oh-h—all right."

"Meaning, 'not any,' hmm? I suspected as much!" The girl with the orchids turned in her chair and scanned her companion's profile with disapproval. "See here, Marilee," she drawled, "are you going to be a damn fool *all* your life?"

"He's fat," said Marilee dreamily. "Fat, and—greasy, sort of. I mean, greasy in his mind. Don't you know what I mean?"

"I know *one* thing," declared the girl with orchids. "I know Who He Is! And if I were you, that's all I'd need to know. *Under the circumstances.*"

The last three words, stressed meaningly, affected the girl called Marilee curiously. She grew grave. Her lips and lashes drooped. For some seconds she sat frowning a little, breaking a black-sheathed lipstick in two and fitting it together again.

"She's worse," she said finally, low.

"Worse?"

Marilee nodded.

"Well," said the girl with orchids, "there you are. It's the climate. She'll never be anything *but* worse, if she doesn't get away. Out West, or somewhere."

"I know," murmured Marilee.

The other girl opened a tin of eye shadow. "Of course," she said dryly, "suit yourself. She's not *my* sister."

Marilee said nothing. Quiet she sat, breaking the lipstick, mending it, breaking it.

"Oh, well," she breathed finally, wearily, and straightened up. She propped her elbows on the plate-glass dressing-table top and leaned toward the mirror, and with the lipstick she began to make her coral-pink mouth very red and gay and reckless and alluring.

Nightly at one o'clock Vane and Moreno dance for the Club Français. They dance a tango, they dance a waltz; then, by way of encore, they do a Black Bottom, and a trick of their own called the Wheel. They dance for twenty, thirty minutes. And while they dance you do not leave your table—for this is what you came to see. Vane and Moreno. The New York thrill. The sole justification for the five-dollar *couvert* extorted by Billy Costello.

From one until half past, then, was Mrs. Brady's recess. She had been looking forward to it all the evening long. When it began—when the opening chords of the tango music sounded stirringly from the room outside—Mrs. Brady brightened. With a right good will she sped the parting guests.

Alone, she unlocked her cupboard and took out her magazine—the magazine she had bought three hours before. Heaving a great breath of relief and satisfaction, she plumped herself on the couch and fingered the pages. Immediately she was absorbed, her eyes drinking up printed lines, her lips moving soundlessly.

The magazine was Mrs. Brady's favorite. Its stories were true stories, taken from life (so the Editor said); and to Mrs. Brady they were live, vivid threads in the dull, drab pattern of her night.

GUESTS OF THE NATION

By Frank O'Connor

[Frank O'Connor (1903–   ) is one of the younger of the new Irish writers. He was born in Cork. His literary work first came to public notice as it appeared in the *Irish Statesman*, edited by the poet Æ (George W. Russell).

Guests of the Nation is reprinted from the collection of which it forms the title-story, by permission of the Macmillan Company, publishers.]

AT dusk the big Englishman Belcher would shift his long legs out of the ashes and ask, 'Well, chums, what about it?' and Noble or me would say, 'As you please, chum' (for we had picked up some of their curious expressions), and the little Englishman 'Awkins would light the lamp and produce the cards. Sometimes Jeremiah Donovan would come up of an evening and supervise the play, and grow excited over 'Awkins's cards (which he always played badly), and shout at him as if he was one of our own, 'Ach, you divil you, why didn't you play the tray?' But, ordinarily, Jeremiah was a sober and contented poor devil like the big Englishman Belcher, and was looked up to at all only because he was a fair hand at documents, though slow enough at these, I vow. He wore a small cloth hat and big gaiters over his long pants, and seldom did I perceive his hands outside the pockets of that pants. He reddened when you talked to him, tilting from toe to heel and back and looking down all the while at his big farmer's feet. His uncommon broad accent was a great source of jest to me, I being from the town as you may recognize.

I couldn't at the time see the point of me and Noble being with Belcher and 'Awkins at all, for it was and is my fixed belief you could have planted that pair in any untended spot from this to Claregalway and they'd have stayed put and flourished like a native weed. I never seen in my short experience two men that took to the country as they did.

They were handed on to us by the Second Battalion to keep when the search for them became too hot, and Noble and myself, being young, took charge with a natural feeling of responsibility. But little 'Awkins made us look right fools when he displayed he knew the countryside as well as we did and something more. 'You're the bloke they calls Bonaparte?' he said to me. 'Well, Bonaparte, Mary Brigid Ho'Connell was arskin abaout you and said 'ow you'd a pair of socks belonging to 'er young brother.' For it seemed, as they explained it, that the Second used to have little evenings of their own, and some of the girls of the neigh-

1028

borhood would turn in, and, seeing they were such decent fellows, our lads couldn't well ignore the two Englishmen, but invited them in and were hail-fellow-well-met with them. 'Awkins told me he learned to dance 'The Walls of Limerick' and 'The Siege of Ennis' and 'The Waves of Tory' in a night or two, though naturally he could not return the compliment, because our lads at that time did not dance foreign dances on principle.

So whatever privileges and favors Belcher and 'Awkins had with the Second they duly took with us, and after the first evening we gave up all pretence of keeping a close eye on their behavior. Not that they could have got far, for they had a notable accent and wore khaki tunics and overcoats with civilian pants and boots. But it's my belief they never had an idea of escaping and were quite contented with their lot.

Now, it was a treat to see how Belcher got off with the old woman of the house we were staying in. She was a great warrant to scold, and crotchety even with us, but before ever she had a chance of giving our guests, as I may call them, a lick of her tongue, Belcher had made her his friend for life. She was breaking sticks at the time, and Belcher, who hadn't been in the house for more than ten minutes, jumped up out of his seat and went across to her.

'Allow me, madam,' he says, smiling his queer little smile; 'please allow me,' and takes the hatchet from her hand. She was struck too parlatic to speak, and ever after Belcher would be at her heels carrying a bucket, or basket, or load of turf, as the case might be. As Noble wittily remarked, he got into looking before she lept, and hot water or any little thing she wanted Belcher would have it ready for her. For such a huge man (and though I am five foot ten myself I had to look up to him) he had an uncommon shortness—or should I say lack—of speech. It took us some time to get used to him walking in and out like a ghost, without a syllable out of him. Especially because 'Awkins talked enough for a platoon, it was strange to hear big Belcher with his toes in the ashes come out with a solitary 'Excuse me, chum,' or 'That's right, chum.' His one and only abiding passion was cards, and I will say for him he was a good card-player. He could have fleeced me and Noble many a time; only if we lost to him, 'Awkins lost to us, and 'Awkins played with the money Belcher gave him.

'Awkins lost to us because he talked too much, and I think now we lost to Belcher for the same reason. 'Awkins and Noble would spit at one another about religion into the early hours of the morning; the little Englishman as you could see worrying the soul out of young Noble (whose brother was a priest) with a string of questions that would puzzle a cardinal. And to make it worse, even in treating of these holy subjects, 'Awkins had a deplorable tongue; I never in all my career struck across a man who could mix such a variety of cursing and bad language into the simplest topic. Oh, a terrible man was little 'Awkins, and a fright to argue! He never did a stroke of work, and when he had no one else to talk to he fixed his claws into the old woman.

I am glad to say that in her he met his match, for one day when he tried to get her to complain profanely of the drought she gave him a great comedown by blaming the drought upon Jupiter Pluvius (a deity neither 'Awkins nor I had ever even heard of, though Noble said among the pagans he was held to have something to do with rain). And another day the same 'Awkins was swearing at the capitalists for starting the German war, when the old dame laid down her iron, puckered up her little crab's mouth and said, 'Mr. 'Awkins, you can say what you please about the war, thinking to deceive me because I'm an ignorant old woman, but I know well what started the war. It was that Italian count that stole the heathen divinity out of the temple in Japan, for believe me, Mr. 'Awkins, nothing but sorrow and want follows them that disturbs the hidden powers!' Oh, a queer old dame, as you remark!

II

So one evening we had our tea together, and 'Awkins lit the lamp and we all sat in to cards. Jeremiah Donovan came in too, and sat down and watched us for a while. Though he was a shy man and didn't speak much, it was easy to see he had no great love for the two Englishmen, and I was surprised it hadn't struck me so clearly before. Well, like that in the story, a terrible dispute blew up late in the evening between 'Awkins and Noble, about capitalists and priests and love for your own country.

'The capitalists,' says 'Awkins, with an angry gulp, 'the capitalists pays the priests to tell you all abaout the next world, so's you waon't notice what they do in this!'

'Nonsense, man,' says Noble, losing his temper, 'before ever a capitalist was thought of people believed in the next world.'

'Awkins stood up as if he was preaching a sermon. 'Oh, they did, did they?' he says with a sneer. 'They believed all the things you believe, that's what you mean? And you believe that God created Hadam and Hadam created Shem and Shem created Jehosphophat? You believe all the silly hold fairy-tale abaout Heve and Heden and the happle? Well, listen to me, chum. If you're entitled to 'old to a silly belief like that, I'm entitled to 'old to my own silly belief—which is, that the fust thing your God created was a bleedin' capitalist with mirality and Rolls Royce complete. Am I right, chum?' he says then to Belcher.

'You're right, chum,' says Belcher, with his queer smile, and gets up from the table to stretch his long legs into the fire and stroke his moustache. So, seeing that Jeremiah Donovan was going, and there was no knowing when the conversation about religion would be over, I took my hat and went out with him. We strolled down towards the village together, and then he suddenly stopped, and blushing and mumbling, and shifting, as his way was, from toe to heel, he said I ought to be behind keeping guard on the prisoners. And I, having it put to me so suddenly, asked him what the hell he wanted a guard on the prisoners at all for, and said that so far as Noble and me were concerned we had talked it over and would rather be out with a column. 'What use is that pair to us?' I asked him.

He looked at me for a spell and said, 'I thought you knew we were keeping them as hostages.' 'Hostages—?' says I, not quite understanding. 'The enemy,' he says in his heavy way, 'have prisoners belong to us, and now they talk of shooting them. If they shoot our prisoners we'll shoot theirs, and serve them right.' 'Shoot them?' said I, the possibility just beginning to dawn on me. 'Shoot them, exactly,' said he. 'Now,' said I, 'wasn't it very unforeseen of you not to tell me and Noble that?' 'How so?' he asks. 'Seeing that we were acting as guards upon them of course.' 'And hadn't you reason enough to guess that much?' 'We had not, Jeremiah Donovan, we had not. How were we to know when the men were on our hands so long?' 'And what difference does it make? The enemy have our prisoners as long or longer, haven't they?' 'It makes a great difference,' said I. 'How so?' said he sharply; but I couldn't tell him the difference it made, for I was struck too silly to speak. 'And when may we expect to be released from this anyway?' said I. 'You may expect it tonight,' says he 'Or tomorrow or the next day at latest. So if it's hanging round here that worries you, you'll be free soon enough.'

I cannot explain it even now, how sad I felt, but I went back to the cottage, a miserable man. When I arrived the discussion was still on, 'Awkins holding forth to all and sundry that there was no next world at all and Noble answering in his best canonical style that there was. But I saw 'Awkins was after having the best of it. 'Do you know what, chum?' he was saying, with his saucy smile, 'I think you're jest as big a bleedin' hunbeliever as I am. You say you believe in the next world and you know jest as much abaout the next world as I do, which is sweet damn-all. What's 'Eaven? You dunno. Where's 'Eaven? You dunno. Who's in 'Eaven? You dunno. You know sweet damn-all! I arsk you again, do they wear wings?'

'Very well then,' says Noble, 'they do; is that enough for you? They do wear wings.' 'Where do they get them, then? Who makes them? 'Ave they a fact'ry for wings? 'Ave they a sort of store where you 'ands in your chit and tikes your bleedin' wings? Answer me that.'

'Oh, you're an impossible man to argue with,' says Noble. 'Now listen to me—.' And off the pair of them went again.

It was long after midnight when we locked up the Englishmen and went to bed ourselves. As I blew out the candle I told Noble what Jeremiah Donovan had told me. Noble took it very quietly. After we had been in bed about an hour he asked me did I think we ought to tell the Englishmen. I having thought of the same thing myself (among many others) said no, because it was more than likely the English wouldn't shoot our men, and anyhow it wasn't to be supposed the Brigade who were always up and down with the second battalion and knew the Englishmen well would be likely to want them bumped off. 'I think so,' says Noble. 'It would be sort of cruelty to put the wind up them now.' 'It was very unforeseen of Jeremiah Donovan anyhow,' says I, and by Noble's silence I realised he took my meaning.

So I lay there half the night, and thought and thought, and picturing myself and young Noble trying to prevent the Brigade from shooting 'Awkins and Belcher sent a cold sweat out through me. Because there were men on the Brigade you daren't let nor hinder without a gun in your hand, and at any rate, in those days disunion between brothers seemed to me an awful crime. I knew better after.

It was next morning we found it so hard to face Belcher and 'Awkins with a smile. We went about the house all day scarcely saying a word. Belcher didn't mind us much; he was stretched into the ashes as usual with his usual look of waiting in quietness for something unforeseen to happen, but little 'Awkins gave us a bad time with his audacious gibing and questioning. He was disgusted at Noble's not answering him back. 'Why can't you tike your beating like a man, chum?' he says. 'You with your Hadam and Heve! I'm a Communist—or an Anarchist. An Anarchist, that's what I am.' And for hours after he went round the house, mumbling when the fit took him 'Hadam and Heve! Hadam and Heve!'

III

I don't know clearly how we got over that day, but get over it we did, and a great relief it was when the tea-things were cleared away and Belcher said in his peaceable manner, 'Well, chums, what about it?' So we all sat round the table and 'Awkins produced the cards, and at that moment I heard Jeremiah Donovan's footsteps on the path, and a dark presentiment crossed my mind. I rose quietly from the table and laid my hand on him before he reached the door. 'What do you want?' I asked him. 'I want those two soldier friends of yours,' he says reddening. 'Is that the way it is, Jeremiah Donovan?' I ask. 'That's the way. There were four of our lads went west this morning, one of them a boy of sixteen.' 'That's bad, Jeremiah,' says I.

At that moment Noble came out, and we walked down the path together talking in whispers. Feeney, the local intelligence officer, was standing by the gate. 'What are you going to do about it?' I asked Jeremiah Donovan. 'I want you and Noble to bring them out; you can tell them they're being shifted again; that'll be the quietest way.' 'Leave me out of that,' says Noble suddenly. Jeremiah Donovan looked at him hard for a minute or two. 'All right so,' he said peaceably. 'You and Feeney collect a few tools from the shed and dig a hole by the far end of the bog. Bonaparte and I'll be after you in about twenty minutes. But whatever else you do, don't let anyone see you with the tools. No one must know but the four of ourselves.'

We saw Feeney and Noble go round to the houseen where the tools were kept, and sidled in. Everything, if I can so express myself, was tottering before my eyes, and I left Jeremiah Donovan to do the explaining as best he could, while I took a seat and said nothing. He told them they were to go back to the Second. 'Awkins let a mouthful of curses out of him at that, and it was plain that Belcher, though he said nothing, was duly perturbed. The old woman was for having them stay in spite of us, and she did not shut her mouth until Jeremiah Donovan lost his temper and said some nasty things to her. Within the house by this time it was pitch dark, but no one thought of lighting the lamp, and in the darkness the two Englishmen fetched their khaki topcoats and said good-bye to the woman of the house. 'Just as a man mikes a 'ome of a bleedin' place,' mumbles 'Awkins shaking her by the hand, 'some bastard at headquarters thinks you're too cushy and shunts you off.' Belcher shakes her hand very hearty. 'A thousand thanks, madam,' he says, 'a thousand thanks for everything . . .' as though he'd made it all up.

We go round to the back of the house and down towards the fatal bog. Then Jeremiah Donovan comes out with what is in his mind. 'There were four of our lads shot by your fellows this morning so now you're to be bumped off.' 'Cut that stuff out,' says 'Awkins flaring up. 'It's bad enough to be mucked about such as we are without you plying at soldiers.' 'It's true,' says Jeremiah Donovan, 'I'm sorry, 'Awkins, but it is true,' and comes out with the usual rigmarole about doing our duty and obeying our superiors. 'Cut it out,' says 'Awkins irritably, 'Cut it out!'

Then, when Donovan sees he is not being believed he turns to me. 'Ask Bonaparte here,' he says. 'I don't need to arsk Bonaparte. Me and Bonaparte are chums.' 'Isn't it true, Bonaparte?' says Jeremiah Donovan solemnly to me. 'It is,' I say sadly, 'it is.' 'Awkins stops. 'Now, for Christ's sike . . .' 'I mean it, chum,' I say. 'You don't saound as if you mean it. You knaow well you don't mean it.' 'Well, if he don't I do,' says Jeremiah Donovan. 'Why the 'ell sh'd you want to shoot me, Jeremiah Donovan?' 'Why the hell should your people take out four prisoners and shoot them in cold blood upon a barrack square?' I perceive Jeremiah Donovan is trying to encourage himself with hot words.

Anyway, he took little 'Awkins by the arm and dragged him on, but it was impossible to make him understand that we were in earnest. From which you will perceive how difficult it was for me, as I kept feeling my Smith and Wesson and thinking what I would do if they happened to put up a fight or ran for it, and wishing in my heart they would. I knew if only they ran I would never fire on them. 'Was Noble in this?' 'Awkins wanted to know and we said yes. He laughed. But why should Noble want to shoot him? Why should we want to shoot him? What had he done to us? Weren't we chums (the word lingers painfully in my memory)? Weren't we? Didn't we understand him and didn't he understand us? Did either of us imagine for an instant that he'd shoot us for all the so-and-so brigadiers in the so-and-so British Army? By this time I began to perceive in the dusk the desolate edges of the bog that was to be their last earthly bed, and, so great a sadness overtook my mind, I could not answer him. We walked along the edge of it in the darkness, and every now and then 'Awkins would call a halt and begin again, just as if he was wound up, about us being chums, and I was in despair that nothing but the cold and open grave made ready for his presence would convince him that we meant it all. But all the same, if you can understand, I didn't want him to be bumped off.

IV

At last we saw the unsteady glint of a lantern in the distance and made towards it. Noble was carrying it, and Feeney stood somewhere in the darkness behind, and somehow the picture of the two of them so silent in the boglands was like the pain of death in my heart. Belcher, on recognising Noble, said ''Allo, chum' in his usual peaceable way, but 'Awkins flew at the poor boy immediately, and the dispute began all over again, only that Noble hadn't a word to say for himself, and stood there with the swaying lantern between his gaitered legs.

It was Jeremiah Donovan who did the answering. 'Awkins asked for the twentieth time (for it seemed to haunt his mind) if anybody thought he'd shoot Noble. 'You would,' says Jeremiah Donovan shortly. 'I wouldn't, damn you!' 'You would if you knew you'd be shot for not doing it.' 'I wouldn't, not if I was to be shot twenty times over; he's my chum. And Belcher wouldn't—isn't that right, Belcher?' 'That's right, chum,' says Belcher peaceably. 'Damned if I would. Anyway, who says Noble'd be shot if I wasn't bumped off? What d' you think I'd do if I was in Noble's place and we were out in the middle of a blasted bog?' 'What would you do?' 'I'd go with him wherever he was going. I'd share my last bob with him and stick by 'im through thick and thin.'

'We've had enough of this,' says Jeremiah Donovan, cocking his revolver. 'Is there any message you want to send before I fire?' 'No, there isn't, but . . . ' 'Do you want to say your prayers?' 'Awkins came out with a cold-blooded remark that shocked even me and turned to Noble again. 'Listen to me, Noble,' he said. 'You and me are chums. You won't come over to my side, so I'll come over to your side. Is that fair? Just you give me a rifle and I'll go with you wherever you want.'

Nobody answered him.

'Do you understand?' he said. 'I'm through with it all, I'm a deserter or anything else you like, but from this on I'm one of you. Does that prove to you that I mean what I say?' Noble raised his head, but as Donovan began to speak he lowered it again without answering. 'For the last time have you any messages to send?' says Donovan in a cold and excited voice.

'Ah, shut up, you, Donovan; you don't understand me, but these fellows do. They're my chums; they stand by me and I stand by them. We're not the capitalist tools you seem to think us.'

I alone of the crowd saw Donovan raise his Webley to the back of 'Awkins's neck, and as he did so I shut my eyes and tried to say a prayer. 'Awkins had begun to say something else when Donovan let fly, and, as I opened my eyes at the bang, I saw him stagger at the knees and lie out flat at Noble's feet, slowly, and as quiet as a child, with the lantern-light falling sadly upon his lean legs and bright farmer's boots. We all stood very still for a while watching him settle out in the last agony.

Then Belcher quietly takes out a handkerchief, and begins to tie it about his own eyes (for in our excitement we had forgotten to offer the same to 'Awkins), and, seeing it is not big enough, turns and asks for a loan of mine. I give it to him and as he knots the two together he points with his foot at 'Awkins. ''E's not quite dead,' he says, 'better give 'im another.' Sure enough 'Awkins's left knee as we see it under the lantern is rising again. I bend down and put my gun to his ear; then, recollecting myself and the company of Belcher, I stand up again with a few hasty words. Belcher understands what is in my mind. 'Give 'im 'is first,' he says. 'I don't mind. Poor bastard, we dunno what's 'appening to 'im now.' As by this time I am beyond all feeling I kneel down again and skilfully give 'Awkins the last shot so as to put him for ever out of pain.

Belcher who is fumbling a bit awkwardly with the handkerchiefs comes out with a laugh when he hears the shot. It is the first time I have heard him laugh, and it sends a shiver down my spine, coming as it does so inappropriately upon the tragic death of his old friend. 'Poor blighter,' he says quietly, 'and last night he was so curious abaout it all. It's very queer, chums, I always think. Naow, 'e knows as much abaout it as they'll ever let 'im know, and last night 'e was all in the dark.'

Donovan helps him to tie the handkerchiefs about his eyes. 'Thanks, chum,' he says. Donovan asks him if there are any messages he would like to send. 'Naow, chum,' he says, 'none for me. If any of you likes to write to 'Awkins's mother you'll find a letter from 'er in 'is pocket. But my missus left me eight years ago. Went away with another fellow and took the kid with her. I likes the feelin' of a 'ome (as you may 'ave noticed) but I couldn't start again after that.'

We stand around like fools now that he can no longer see us. Donovan looks at Noble and Noble shakes his head. Then Donovan raises his Webley again and just at that moment Belcher laughs his queer nervous laugh again. He must think we are talking of him; anyway, Donovan lowers his gun. ''Scuse me, chums,' says Belcher, 'I feel I'm talking the 'ell of a lot . . . and so silly . . . abaout me being so 'andy abaout a 'ouse. But this thing come on me so sudden. You'll forgive me, I'm sure.' 'You don't want to say a prayer?' asks Jeremiah Donovan. 'No, chum,' he replies, 'I don't think that'd 'elp. I'm ready if you want to get it over.' 'You understand,' says Jeremiah Donovan, ''tis not so much our doing. It's our duty, so to speak.' Belcher's head is raised like a real blind man's, so that you can only see his nose and chin in the lamplight. 'I never could make out what duty was myself,' he said, 'but I think you're all good lads, if that's what you mean. I'm not complaining.' Noble, with a look of desperation, signals to Donovan, and in a flash Donovan raises his gun and fires. The big man goes over like a sack of meal, and this time there is no need of a second shot.

I don't remember much about the burying, but that it was worse than all the rest, because we had to carry the warm corpses a few yards before we sunk them in the windy bog. It was all mad lonely, with only a bit of lantern between ourselves and the pitch-blackness, and birds hooting and screeching all round disturbed by the guns. Noble had to search 'Awkins first to get the letter from his mother. Then having smoothed all signs of the grave away, Noble and I collected our tools, said good-bye to the others, and went back along the desolate edge of the treacherous bog without a word. We put the tools in the houseen and went into the house. The kitchen was pitch-black and cold, just as we left it, and the old woman was sitting over the hearth telling her beads. We walked past her into the room, and Noble struck a match to light the lamp. Just then she rose quietly and came to the doorway, being not at all so bold or crabbed as usual.

'What did ye do with them?' she says in a sort of whisper, and Noble took such a mortal start the match quenched in his trembling hand. 'What's that?' he asks without turning round. 'I heard ye,' she said. 'What did you hear?' asks Noble, but sure he wouldn't deceive a child the way he said it. 'I heard ye. Do you think I wasn't listening to ye putting the things back in the houseen?' Noble struck another match and this time the lamp lit for him. 'Was that what ye did with them?' she said, and Noble said nothing—after all what could he say?

So then, by God, she fell on her two knees by the door, and began telling her beads, and after a minute or two Noble went on his knees by the fireplace, so I pushed my way out past her, and stood at the door, watching the stars and listening to the damned shrieking of the birds. It is so strange what you feel at such moments, and not to be written afterwards. Noble says he felt he seen everything ten times as big, perceiving nothing around him but the little patch of black bog with the two Englishmen stiffening into it; but with me it was the other way, as though the patch of bog where the two Englishmen were was a thousand miles away from me, and even Noble mumbling just behind me and the old woman and the birds and bloody stars were all far away, and I was somehow very small and very lonely. And anything that ever happened me after I never felt the same about again.

SELECTED BIBLIOGRAPHIES

I. General Reference Books and Bibliographies

Authoritative brief biographies and bibliographies of most recent writers of the short story in English may be found in the British *Who's Who* (published annually) and the American *Who's Who in America* (published biennially since 1899–1900). Two standard books containing an abundance of rich material on many short story writers are *Contemporary American Literature* and *Contemporary British Literature*, both by John Matthews Manly and Edith Rickert. Two books of interesting studies of fiction writers are Blanche Colton Williams's *Our Short Story Writers* and Frederick T. Cooper's *Some American Story-Tellers*. Three large reference books of special value to all students of recent literature are *Living Authors*, *Authors Today and Yesterday*, and *Junior Book of Authors*, all edited by Stanley J. Kunitz. Entertaining biographies and autobiographies of writers of the modern short story, together with valuable bibliographies, may be found in these volumes. The most complete bibliography of short stories is Ina Firkins's *Index to Short Stories*, which with its Supplement brings the record down to 1929. For locating short stories which have appeared in the leading magazines in more recent years, the student will find much help by consulting the *Index to Periodical Literature*, which quite literally keeps the record up to date.

II. Studies of the Short Story and Books on Short Story Writing

Albright, Evelyn M., *The Short Story—Its Principles and Structure*
Baker, H. T., *The Contemporary Short Story*
Barrett, C. R., *Short Story Writing*
Beach, Stewart, *Short-Story Technique*
Canby, H. S., *A Study of the Short Story*
Canby, H. S., *The Short Story in English*
Campbell, O. J., and Rice, R. A., *A Book of Narratives*
Clark, Glenn, *A Manual of the Short Story Art*
Conrad, L. H., *Descriptive and Narrative Writing*
Esenwein, J. B., *Writing the Short Story*
Frederick, John T., *A Handbook of Short Story Writing*
Gallishaw, John, *Only Two Ways to Write a Story*

Gallishaw, John, *Twenty Problems of the Fiction Writer*
Goodman, Henry, *Creating the Short Story*
Grabo, Carl, *The Art of the Short Story*
Hamilton, Clayton, *Materials and Methods of Fiction*
Hamilton, Clayton, *A Manual of the Art of Fiction*
Hoffman, A. S., *Fundamentals of Fiction Writing*
Jessup, Alexander, *The American Short Story*
Johnson, R. I., *Study and Appreciation of the Short Story*
Mirrielees, Edith R., *Writing the Short Story*
Neal, R. W., *Short Stories in the Making*
O'Brien, Edward J., *The Advance of the American Short Story*
Pattee, F. L., *The Development of the American Short Story*
Perry, Bliss, *The Study of Prose Fiction*
Pitkin, W. B., *The Art and the Business of Story Writing*
Smith, L. W., *The Writing of the Short Story*
Wells, Carolyn, *The Technique of the Mystery Story*
Williams, Blanche C., *A Handbook on Story Writing*
Williams, Blanche C., *How to Study "The Best Short Stories"*

III. Anthologies of Short Stories

Atkinson, W. P., *The Short Story*
Bates, Sylvia C., *Twentieth Century Short Stories*
Benecke, Else, and Busch, Marie, *Selected Polish Tales*
Benecke, Else, and Busch, Marie, *More Tales by Polish Authors*
Bercovici, Konrad, *Best Short Stories of the World*
Boas, R. P., and Hahn, B. M., *Short Stories for Class Reading*
Brewster, Dorothy, *A Book of Modern Short Stories*
Brown, Demetra, and Phoutrides, A. E., *Modern Greek Stories*
Brown, Leonard, *Modern American and British Short Stories*
Chirikov, E., *Short Stories from Russian Authors*
Clark, B. H., and Lieber, Maxim, *Great Short Stories of the World*
Dawson, W. J. and C. W., *The Great English Short-Story Writers*
Eaton, Richard, *The Best Continental Short Stories*. (Several volumes beginning with 1923–24.)
Frank, Helena, *Yiddish Tales*
Fuess, Claude, *Selected Short Stories*
Fulcher, P. M., *Short Narratives*
Gerould, G. H., and Bayly, C., *Contemporary Types of the Short Story*
Grove, John, *Omnibus of Adventure*
Hastings, W. T., *Short Stories*

Howells, W. D., *Great Modern American Stories*

Hrbkova, S. B., *Czechoslovak Stories*

Jessup, Alexander, *Best American Humorous Short Stories*

Jessup, Alexander, *Little French Masterpieces*

Jessup, Alexander, *Representative American Short Stories*

Jessup, Alexander, *Representative Modern Short Stories*

Larsen, Hanna A., *Denmark's Best Stories*

Larsen, Hanna A., *Sweden's Best Stories*

Larsen, Hanna A., *Norway's Best Stories*

Law, F. H., *Modern Short Stories*

Long, Ray, *20 Best Stories in Ray Long's 20 Years as an Editor*

Lynch, Bohun, *Best Ghost Stories*

MacMinn, G. R., and Eagleson, H., *College Readings in the Modern Short Story*

McMichael, C. B., *Short Stories from the Spanish*

Matthews, Brander, *The Short-Story; Specimens Illustrating Its Development*

Maude, A., *Russian Tales*

Maxcy, C. L., *Representative Narratives*

Melville, Lewis, *Great English Short Stories*

Meyer, R. M., *Twelve Best Short Stories in the German*

Mikels, Rosa, *Short Stories for English Courses*

Nethercot, A. H., *A Book of Long Stories*

O'Brien, Edward J., *The Twenty-five Finest Short Stories*

O'Brien, Edward J., *The Best Short Stories.* (A series of annual volumes from 1915, with extended bibliographies, constituting invaluable yearbooks of the American short story.)

O'Brien, Edward J., *The Best British Short Stories.* (Beginning with 1922. Similar in plan to the American series.)

Overton, Grant, *World's One Hundred Best Short Stories*

Overton, Grant, *Great Modern Short Stories*

Pattee, F. L., *Century Readings in the American Short Story*

Pence, Raymond W., *Short Stories of Today*

Pettoello, Decio, *Italian Short Stories*

Popović, Pavle, *Jugo-Slav Stories*

Pritchard, F. H., *Short Stories of Yesterday*

Ramsay, R. L., *Short Stories of America*

Robinson, K. A., *Contemporary Short Stories*

Ryttenberg, Lillie, and Lang, Beatrice, *Samples; A Collection of Short Stories*

Schweikert, H. C., *Short Stories*

Schweikert, H. C., *Russian Short Stories*
Seltzer, Thomas, *Best Russian Short Stories*
Sherman, S. P., *A Book of Short Stories*
Stork, C. W., *Modern Swedish Masterpieces*
Taylor, Warner, *Varied Narratives*
Townsend, R. S., *Short Stories by Russian Authors*
Underwood, E. W., *Short Stories from the Balkans*
Waite, Alice V., *Modern Masterpieces of Short Prose Fiction*
Walker, Hugh, *Selected English Short Stories*
Ward, Bertha C., *Short Stories of Today*
Williams, Blanche C., *Thrice Told Tales*
Williams, Blanche C., *A Book of Short Stories*
Williams, Blanche C., *New Narratives*
Williams, Blanche C., *O'Henry Memorial Award Prize Stories*. (Annual
    volumes since 1919.)
Wright, W. H., *Great Modern French Stories*

IV. LISTS OF SHORT STORIES

Authors are arranged alphabetically under groupings according to nationality

AMERICAN

Achmed ABDULLAH (1881–   )
A Simple Act of Piety
Cobbler's Wax
The Honorable Gentleman

Samuel Hopkins ADAMS (1871–   )
Such as Walk in Darkness
The Flying Death
Orpheus

George ADE (1866–   )
Effie Whittlesy
To Make a Hoosier Holiday

Conrad AIKEN (1889–   )
The Dark City
Spider, Spider

Raymond Macdonald ALDEN (1873–1924)
In the Promised Land

Thomas Bailey ALDRICH (1836–1907)
Père Antoine's Date-Palm
Quite So
Marjorie Daw
Miss Mehetabel's Son
Mademoiselle Olympe Zabriski

Two Bites at a Cherry
A Sea Turn
The White Feather
Goliath
A Struggle for Life

James Lane ALLEN (1849–1925)
Two Gentlemen of Kentucky
The White Cowl
King Solomon of Kentucky
Flute and Violin
A Kentucky Cardinal

Sherwood ANDERSON (1876–   )
A Man of Ideas
An Awakening
The Door of the Trap
I'm a Fool
I Want to Know Why
Death in the Woods

Mary Raymond Shipman ANDREWS
A Good Samaritan
The Perfect Tribute
The Courage of the Commonplace
The Captains

Mary ANTIN (1881–   )
 The Amulet

Elizabeth ASHE (pseud. of Georgiana Pent-
 large)
 The Glory-Box
 Appraisement

Margaret Eliza ASHMUN
 The Birthplace

Gertrude Franklin ATHERTON
 (1857–   )
 The Bell in the Fog
 The Sacrificial Altar

Mary Hunter AUSTIN (1868–1934)
 The House of Offence

William AUSTIN (1778–1841)
 Peter Rugg, the Missing Man

Edwina Stanton BABCOCK
 Willum's Vanilla
 Gargoyle

Irving BACHELLER (1859–   )
 Keeping Up with Lizzie

Josephine Dodge Daskam BACON
 (1876–   )
 The Madness of Philip
 In the Valley of the Shadow
 The Miracle

Rex BEACH (1877–   )
 North of Fifty-Three
 The Test

Thomas BEER (1889–   )
 The Brothers
 The House of Atreus

Henry Augustin BEERS (1847–1926)
 A Comedy of Errors
 Split Zephyr

Barry BENEFIELD (1883–   )
 Miss Willett
 Carrie Snyder

Konrad BERCOVICI (1882–   )
 Ghitza
 Lena
 The Bear Tamer's Daughter

Ambrose BIERCE (1842–1914?)
 A Horseman in the Sky
 An Occurrence at Owl Creek Bridge
 The Damned Thing
 The Middle Toe of the Right Foot

Hjalmar Hjorth BOYESEN (1848–1895)
 The Story of an Outcast
 The Man Who Lost His Name

Virginia Frazer BOYLE (1863–   )
 De Hant er Buzzard's Nest
 Black Silas

Roark BRADFORD (1896–   )
 Child of Glory

Alice BROWN (1857–   )
 Told in the Poorhouse
 A Second Marriage
 The Miracle
 Praying Sally

Katharine Holland BROWN (d. 1931)
 Buster
 The Talisman

Katharine BRUSH (1902–   )
 Good Wednesday
 Night Club

Henry Cuyler BUNNER (1855–1896)
 The Documents in the Case (with
  Brander Matthews)
 Love in Old Cloathes
 The Love-Letters of Smith
 The Two Churches of Quawket
 A Sisterly Scheme
 Our Aromatic Uncle
 Father Anastatius

Dana BURNET (1888–   )
 Fog
 Butterfly

Maxwell Struthers BURT (1882–   )
 The Water-Hole
 A Cup of Tea
 John o' May
 Beauty and the Blantons

Ellis Parker BUTLER (1869–   )
 Pigs is Pigs
 Mr. Perkins of Portland

Katharine BUTLER (1890–   )
 The Black Pearl

Francis BUZZELL (1882–   )
 Ma's Pretties
 Lonely Places

James Branch CABELL (1879–   )
 In the Second April
 The Wedding Jest

George Washington CABLE (1844–1925)
  Jean-ah Poquelin
  "Posson Jone'"
  Madame Delphine
  Père Raphaël

Henry Seidel CANBY (1878–   )
  Business is Business
  The Best Bait for Mosquitoes

Dorothy CANFIELD (1879–   )
  An Academic Question
  A Sleep and a Forgetting
  Flint and Fire
  The Bedquilt
  Remembrance
  The Heyday of the Blood

Willa CATHER (1875–   )
  The Profile
  Coming, Aphrodite!
  The Sculptor's Funeral
  Paul's Case
  A Wagner Matinée

Mary Hartwell CATHERWOOD
  (1847–1902)
  Serena
  A Vacant House
  The Little Renault
  The Kidnapped Bride
  The Chase of Saint-Castin

Robert William CHAMBERS (1865–1933)
  A Young Man in a Hurry
  The Tree of Heaven
  The Case of Mr. Helmer

George Randolph CHESTER (1869–1924)
  A Fortune in Smoke
  The Triple Cross
  Straight Business

Richard Washburn CHILD (1881–   )
  The Man in the Shadow
  The Avenger

Kate CHOPIN (1851–1904)
  Désirée's Baby
  Beyond the Bayou
  Madame Célestin's Divorce

Irvin Shrewsbury COBB (1876–   )
  Local Color
  The Great Auk

  Boys Will Be Boys
  A Colonel of Kentucky
  Faith, Hope, and Charity
  The Belled Buzzard

Octavus Roy COHEN (1891–   )
  Without Benefit of Virgie
  Not Wisely But Too Well

Lincoln COLCORD (1883–   )
  The Measure of a Man
  An Instrument of the Gods

Cornelia Atwood Pratt COMER
  The Preliminaries
  The Long Inheritance

Will Levington COMFORT (1878–1932)
  Fear

Marc CONNELLY (1890–   )
  Coroner's Inquest

James Brendan CONNOLLY (1868–   )
  The Truth of the "Oliver Cromwell"
  The Trawler
  The Undersea Man

Charles Egbert CRADDOCK (pseud. of
  Mary N. Murfree) (1850–1922)
  The Dancin' Party at Harrison's Cove
  Taking the Blue Ribbon at the County
    Fair
  'Way Down in Lonesome Cove
  The Mystery of Witchface Mountain
  His Unquiet Ghost
  The Star in the Valley

Stephen CRANE (1871–1900)
  The Little Regiment
  The Open Boat
  The Angel Child

F. Marion CRAWFORD (1854–1909)
  Love in Idleness
  For the Blood Is the Life

Mary Stewart CUTTING (1851–1924)
  Fairy Gold
  The House of Life
  The Measure

Rebecca Harding DAVIS (1831–1910)
  The Wife's Story
  The Luck of Abel Steadman
  Across the Gulf

Richard Harding DAVIS (1864–1916)
Gallegher
The Hungry Man Was Fed
The Derelict
The Bar Sinister

John William DE FOREST (1826–1906)
An Inspired Lobbyist
The Brigade Commander

Margaret Wade DELAND (1857–   )
Good for the Soul
The Face on the Wall
"Many Waters"
An Old Chester Secret
The Unexpectedness of Mr. Horace
  Shields

Beulah Marie DIX (1876–   )
Into Action
Across the Border

Charles Caldwell DOBIE (1881–   )
The Failure
The Open Window
The Arrested Moment

Theodore DREISER (1871–   )
The Lost Phoebe
Married
The Second Choice
Free

Norman DUNCAN (1871–1916)
The Strength of Men
The Ordination of John Fairmeadow

Harry Griswold DWIGHT (1875–   )
The Leopard of the Sea
In the Pasha's Garden
The Emperor of Elam

James Francis DWYER (1874–   )
The Citizen

Mary Tracy EARLE (1864–   )
The Tinkling Simlins
King James of the Strawberry Patch

Walter D. EDMONDS (1903–   )
Who Killed Rutherford?

Harry Stillwell EDWARDS (1855–   )
Two Runaways
"De Valley an' de Shadder"
An Idyl of "Sinkin' Mount'in"
Eneas Africanus

William Chester ESTABROOK
The Magic of Sourness

William FALKNER (1897–   )
Dry September
Dr. Martino

Edna FERBER (1887–   )
Roast Beef, Medium
April 25th, As Usual
Mother Knows Best
The Gay Old Dog
They Brought Their Women

George Helgeson FITCH (1877–1915)
Ole Skjarsen's First Touchdown
Saving a Brother

Mary Hallock FOOTE (1847–   )
Friend Barton's "Concern"
The Cup of Trembling

Paul Leicester FORD (1865–1902)
His Version of It
Wanted—A Matchmaker

John FOX (1863–1919)
A Cumberland Vendetta
Christmas Eve on Lonesome

Mary E. Wilkins FREEMAN (1862–1930)
A Humble Romance
The Revolt of "Mother"
A New England Nun
A Village Lear
The Copy-Cat
Silence

Zona GALE (1874–   )
The Ancient Dawn
White Bread
The Party
Bill's Little Girl

Hamlin GARLAND (1860–   )
Mrs. Ripley's Trip
Among the Corn Rows
Up the Coolly
Sim Burns's Wife
Martha's Fireplace

Katharine Fullerton GEROULD
  (1879–   )
Vain Oblations
The Wine of Violence
The Knight's Move
Habakkuk

Charlotte Perkins Stetson GILMAN
(1860–   )
The Yellow Wall-Paper

Susan GLASPELL (1882–   )
A Jury of Her Peers
"Beloved Husband"

Abbie Carter GOODLOE (1867–   )
Claustrophobia

Armistead Churchill GORDON (1855–1931)
Maje
The Silent Infare

Anna Katharine GREEN (1846–   )
A Mysterious Case

Frederick Stuart GREENE (1870–   )
The Cat of the Cane-Brake
The Bunker Mouse
The Black Pool

Edward Everett HALE (1822–1909)
My Double, and How He Undid Me
The Man Without a Country
Susan's Escort

Richard Matthews HALLETT (1887–   )
Making Port
Rainbow Pete

Joel Chandler HARRIS (1848–1908)
The Wonderful Tar-Baby Story
A Ghost Story
Ananias
Brother Rabbit's Cradle

Henry Sydnor HARRISON (1880–1930)
Miss Hinch
The White Mole

Bret HARTE (1836–1902)
The Luck of Roaring Camp
The Outcasts of Poker Flat
Tennessee's Partner
An Ingénue of the Sierras

Nathaniel HAWTHORNE (1804–1864)
David Swan: a Fantasy
Dr. Heidegger's Experiment
Rappaccini's Daughter
The Great Stone Face
Ethan Brand

Ernest HEMINGWAY (1898–   )
My Old Man
The Killers
Fifty Grand

O. HENRY (pseud. of William Sydney
Porter) (1862–1910)
A Retrieved Reformation
An Unfinished Story
The Last Leaf
The Gift of the Magi
A Municipal Report
Whistling Dick's Christmas Stocking
The Hiding of Black Bill
The Whirligig of Life
The Furnished Room

Joseph HERGESHEIMER (1880–   )
Tol'able David
The Token
The Meeker Ritual

Robert HERRICK (1868–   )
The Avalanche
In the Doctor's Office
The Master of the Inn
The Miracle

Helen R. HULL
Clay Shuttered Doors

Fannie HURST (1889–   )
T. B.
Bitter-Sweet
"Ice-Water, Pl——"
Humoresque

Washington IRVING (1783–1859)
Rip Van Winkle
The Specter Bridegroom
The Legend of Sleepy Hollow
The Devil and Tom Walker

Henry JAMES (1843–1916)
The Real Thing
The Lesson of the Master
The Turn of the Screw
Julia Bride
The Madonna of the Future

Sarah Orne JEWETT (1849–1909)
Miss Tempy's Watchers
Fame's Little Day

William M. JOHN (1888–   )
Neither Jew nor Greek

Owen JOHNSON (1878–   )
One Hundred in the Dark
Murder in Any Degree

Myra KELLY (1876–1910)
A Christmas Present for a Lady

Manuel KOMROFF (1890–)
The Grace of Lambs

Ring LARDNER (1885–1933)
Champion
Haircut
The Golden Honeymoon
The Love Nest

Alfred Henry LEWIS (1858–1914)
The Man from Red Dog
Wolfville Thanksgiving

Sinclair LEWIS (1885–)
Young Man Axelbrod
The Willow Walk
The Enchanted Hour
Travel is so Broadening

Jack LONDON (1876–1916)
The God of His Fathers
The Seed of McCoy
Samuel
War
South of the Slot
The Sheriff of Kona

John Luther LONG (1861–1927)
Madame Butterfly

Helen R. MARTIN (1868–)
The Wooing of Addie Swisher

Brander MATTHEWS (1852–1929)
The Documents in the Case (with H. C.
Bunner)
In the Vestibule Limited
In Search of Local Color

Margaret Prescott MONTAGUE
(1878–)
Of Water and the Spirit
England to America
The Last Tenth

Frank NORRIS (1870–1902)
The Passing of Cockeye Blacklock

Fitz-James O'BRIEN (1828–1862)
The Diamond Lens
What Was It?

Lloyd OSBOURNE (1868–)
The Happiest Day of His Life

Thomas Nelson PAGE (1853–1922)
Marse Chan

Meh Lady
Ole 'Stracted

Edgar Allan POE (1809–1849)
Ligeia
The Fall of the House of Usher
The Murders in the Rue Morgue
The Masque of the Red Death
The Pit and the Pendulum
The Cask of Amontillado

Melville Davisson POST (1871–1930)
The Great Legend
The Nameless Thing
The Doomdorf Mystery
After He Was Dead
Five Thousand Dollars' Reward

Mary Brecht PULVER (1883–)
A Love Story
The Path of Glory

Leonard H. ROBBINS (1877–)
Mr. Downey Sits Down
Professor Todd's Used Car

John RUSSELL (1885–)
The Fourth Man
The Price of the Head
Jetsam
The Red Mark

Ruth SAWYER (1880–)
The Princess and the Vagabone

Robert E. SHERWOOD (1896–)
Extra! Extra!

Gordon Arthur SMITH (1886–)
Feet of Gold
The End of the Road
The Return
No Flowers

Wilbur Daniel STEELE (1886–)
"For They Know Not What They Do"
The Yellow Cat
Down on Their Knees
The Man Who Saw Through Heaven
The Woman at Seven Brothers
Blue Murder
Bubbles
Can't Cross Jordan By Myself
Footfalls
Ching, Ching, Chinaman
Fouled Anchor
The Shame Dance

Frank Richard STOCKTON (1834–1902)
The Transferred Ghost
The Lady, or the Tiger?
The Widow's Cruise

Ruth McEnery STUART (1856–1917)
Aunt Amity's Silver Wedding
Sonny's Schoolin'
The Gentleman of the Plush Rocker
Milady

Ruth SUCKOW (1892–   )
The Man of the Family
Uprooted
The Golden Wedding
Susan and the Doctor

Booth TARKINGTON (1869–   )
Penrod's Busy Day
Monsieur Beaucaire
Girl—Girl—Girl!
Cherry
Cider of Normandy
"Clothes Make the Man"

Arthur Russell TAYLOR (d. 1918)
Mr. Squem
The Retnrn of Mr. Squem

Chauncey THOMAS (1872–   )
The Snow Story

Mark TWAIN (Samuel Clemens)
(1835–1910)
The £1,000,000 Bank Note
Traveling with a Reformer
A Double-Barreled Detective Story

Henry VAN DYKE (1852–1933)
The Other Wise Man
The Sad Shepherd
The Broken Soldier and the Maid of
France
The Keeper of the Light

Edith WHARTON (1862–   )
Ethan Frome
The Triumph of Night
Afterward
Xingu
The Eyes

William Allen WHITE (1868–   )
The King of Boyville

Ben Ames WILLIAMS (1889–   )
Sheener
One Crowded Hour
They Grind Exceeding Small

Jesse Lynch WILLIAMS (1871–1929)
The Stolen Story
Not Wanted

Owen WISTER (1860–   )
How Lin McLean Went East
Specimen Jones
The Drake Who Had Means of His Own

Anzia YEZIERSKA (1885–   )
The Fat of the Land
Hunger

ENGLISH

F. ANSTEY (1856–   )
The Black Poodle

Martin Donisthorpe ARMSTRONG
(1882–   )
Little Miss Millett
The Bazaar

Stacy AUMONIER (1887–1928)
Where Was Wych Street?
"A Source of Irritation"
The Golden Windmill

R. Hernekin BAPTIST
Civilization

James Matthew BARRIE (1860–   )
My Husband's Book
How Gavin Birse Put It to Mag Lownie
The Inconsiderate Waiter
The Courting of T'nowhead's Bell

Arnold BENNETT (1867–1931)
The Idiot
A Letter Home
The Matador of the Five Towns
Mary With the High Hand

Phyllis BOTTOME (1884–   )
Brother Leo

John BROWN (1810–1882)
Rab and His Friends

Thomas BURKE (1887–   )
Gina of the Chinatown
The Chink and the Child

Gilbert K. CHESTERTON (1874–   )
The Blue Cross
The Worst Crime in the World

Joseph CONRAD (1857–1924)
The Lagoon
Heart of Darkness
The Secret Sharer
The Inn of the Two Witches

Alfred E. COPPARD (1878–   )
The Black Dog
The Field of Mustard
Fifty Pounds
Arabesque: The Mouse
The Higgler

• *Daniel DEFOE* (1661–1731)
True Relation of the Apparition of One
  Mrs. Veale

Walter DE LA MARE (1873–   )
The Almond Tree

Charles DICKENS (1812–1870)
The Signal-Man
A Christmas Carol
A Child's Dream of a Star
Dr. Marigold's Prescriptions

Arthur Conan DOYLE (1859–1930)
The Hound of the Baskervilles
The Red-Headed League
The Adventure of the Speckled Band

John GALSWORTHY (1867–1933)
Quality
The Apple Tree
The Man Who Kept His Form
"Cafard"
The First and the Last

Thomas HARDY (1840–1928)
The Three Strangers
The Son's Veto
The Withered Arm

Maurice HEWLETT (1861–1923)
The Madonna of the Peach-Tree
Brazenhead the Great
The Ruinous Face

James HOGG (1770–1835)
The Mysterious Bride

Anthony HOPE (Hawkins) (1863–1933)
The Philosopher in the Apple Orchard
The House Opposite

Ernest W. HORNUNG (1866–1921)
The Last Laugh

William Wymark JACOBS (1863–   )
A Change of Treatment
The Monkey's Paw
Easy Money
The Toll-House

Rudyard KIPLING (1865–   )
The Man Who Would Be King
Without Benefit of Clergy
Moti-Guj, Mutineer
The Brushwood Boy
They
In the Matter of a Private
An Habitation Enforced

David Herbert LAWRENCE (1885–1930)
The Horse Dealer's Daughter
Glad Ghosts

Ian MACLAREN (pseud. of John Watson)
  (1850–1907)
A Doctor of the Old School

Katherine MANSFIELD (1888–1923)
A Dill Pickle
The Garden Party
The Fly
A Cup of Tea
The Doll's House
Marriage à la Mode
Miss Brill
Life of Ma Parker

John MASEFIELD (1874–   )
The Tarry Buccaneer
A Wanderer's Story

W. Somerset MAUGHAM (1874–   )
The Right Thing is the Kind Thing
The Taipan

Arthur MORRISON (1863–   )
That Brute Simmons
On the Stairs
Lizerunt

Edward Henry PEPLE (1869–1924)
A Night Out

Marjorie PICKTHALL (1883–1922)
The Stove
Luck
White Magic

Arthur T. QUILLER-COUCH (1863-   )
  The Drawn Blind
  The Roll-Call of the Reef

"SAKI" (Hector Hugh Munro)
  (1870–1916)
  The Background
  Gabriel-Ernest

Sir Walter SCOTT (1771–1832)
  The Tapestried Chamber
  Wandering Willie's Tale

Robert Louis STEVENSON (1850–1894)
  A Lodging for the Night
  The Sire de Malétroit's Door
  Markheim
  The Bottle Imp
  Will o' the Mill
  Thrawn Janet
  The Beach of Falesá
  The Ebb Tide

Hugh WALPOLE (1884–   )
  Major Wilbraham
  Old Elizabeth
  The Thirteen Travellers

Herbert George WELLS (1866–   )
  The Country of the Blind
  The Door in the Wall
  Under the Knife
  The Man Who Could Work Miracles

Oscar WILDE (1856–1900)
  The Happy Prince
  The Selfish Giant

Israel ZANGWILL (1864–1926)
  A Rose of the Ghetto
  Transitional
  They That Walk in Darkness

BELGIAN

Charles de KOSTER (1827–1879)
  The Mysterious Picture

Camille LEMONNIER (1844–1913)
  The Soul of Veere

Maurice MAETERLINCK (1862–   )
  The Massacre of the Innocents

Emile VERHAEREN (1855–1916)
  One Night

CENTRAL EUROPE

HUNGARIAN
Karoly KISFALUDI (1788–1830)
  The Invisible Wound

Maurus JÓKAI (1825–1904)
  A Ball

Kálmán MIKSZÁTH (1849–1922)
  The Green Fly

Ferenc MOLNÁR (1878–   )
  The Silver Hilt

POLISH
Henryk SIENKIEWICZ (1846–1916)
  The Lighthouse Keeper of Aspinwall

Boleslav PRUS (1847–1912)
  The Human Telegraph

Stefan ZEROMSKI (1864–1925)
  Forebodings

CROATIAN
Antun Gustav MATOS (1873–1914)
  The Neighbor

SLOVENIAN
Ivan CANKAR (1876–1918)
  Children and Old Folk

SERBIAN
Laza K. LAZAREVICH (1851–1890)
  At the Well

CZECHO-SLOVAKIAN
Karel CAPEK (1890–   )
  The Imprint

Svatopluk CECH (1846–1908)
  Foltyn's Drum

Jan NERUDA (1834–1891)
  The Vampire

ROUMANIAN
I. L. CARAGIALE (1853–1912)
  The Easter Torch

MARIE, Queen of Roumania
  (1875–   )
  What Vasile Saw

BULGARIAN
Dimitr IVANOV (1878–   )
  The Commissioner's Christmas

Anguel KARALYITCHEV
  (1903?–   )
  The Stone Bridge on the Rossitza

DANISH

Hans Christian ANDERSEN (1805–1875)
The Shepherdess and the Chimney-
Sweeper

Herman BANG (1857–1912)
Irene Holm
In Rosenborg Park

Steen Steensen BLICHER (1782–1848)
The Parson at Vejlby

Holger DRACHMANN (1846–1908)
A Ship in Church

Meïr Aron GOLDSCHMIDT (1819–1887)
The Nightingale
Henrik and Rosalie

Gunnar GUNNARSSON (1889–   )
The Dark Mountains

Jens Peter JACOBSEN (1847–1885)
Fru Fönss

Johannes V. JENSEN (1873–   )
Lost Forests

Karl LARSEN (1860–   )
Peasants

Henrik PONTOPPIDAN (1857–   )
The Royal Guest

Sophus SCHANDORPH (1836–1901)
Stina Becomes a Farmer's Wife

Johan SKJOLDBORG (1861–   )
Per Hywer's Summer Day

Harry SÖIBERG (1880–   )
The Old Boat

Gustav WIED (1858–1914)
Children of Men

DUTCH

Jacob CATS (1577–1660)
The Higher the Flight, the Lower the Fall

Eduard D. DEKKER (1820–1887)
The Story of Saïdjah

Herman HEIJERMANS (1864–1924)
Grandfather's Birthday Present

FRENCH

Honoré de BALZAC (1799–1850)
Jesus Christ in Flanders
A Passion in the Desert

La Grenadière
The Mysterious Mansion
An Episode under the Terror

Maurice BARRÈS (1862–1923)
Love in Thule

François COPPÉE (1842–1908)
The Substitute
A Piece of Bread
The Captain's Vices

Alphonse DAUDET (1840–1897)
The Death of the Dauphin
The Elixir of the Reverend Father
Gaucher
The Last Class
The Pope's Mule
The Siege of Berlin

Alexandre DUMAS (*père*) (1802–1870)
A Bal Masqué
Zodomirsky's Duel

Alexandre DUMAS (*fils*) (1824–1895)
The Silver Snuff-Box

Gustave FLAUBERT (1821–1885)
A Simple Heart

Anatole FRANCE (1844–1924)
The Procurator of Judea
Our Lady's Juggler

Théophile GAUTIER (1811–1872)
Arria Marcella
The Nest of Nightingales
The Mummy's Foot

Guy de MAUPASSANT (1850–1893)
The Piece of String
The Necklace
A Coward
Happiness
Miss Fifi
The Horla
On the Journey
A Ghost
The Wreck
Tallow Ball

Prosper MÉRIMÉE (1803–1870)
The Venus of Ille
The Taking of the Redoubt
The Vision of Charles XI
Mateo Falcone

Alfred de MUSSET (1810–1857)
Mlle. Mimi Pinson

Victorien SARDOU (1831–1908)
The Black Pearl

Auguste de VILLIERS DE L'ISLE-ADAM (1838–1889)
The Torture of Hope

Émile ZOLA (1840–1902)
The Fairy Amoureuse
The Attack on the Mill

GERMAN

Rudolf BAUMBACH (1840–1905)
The Egyptian Fire-Eater

Adelbert von CHAMISSO (1781–1838)
Peter Schlemihl

Christian GELLERT (1715–1769)
The Sick Wife

Wilhelm HAUFF (1802–1827)
The Severed Hand

Heinrich HEINE (1797–1856)
When Paganini Played

Paul HEYSE (1830–1914)
Blind
L'Arrabiata [The Fury]

E. T. W. HOFFMAN (1776–1822)
The Cremona Violin
The Story of Serapion

Gottfried KELLER (1819–1890)
A Legend of the Dance

Leopold KOMPERT (1822–1886)
A Ghetto Violet
Silent Woman

Rudolf LINDAU (1829–1910)
The Philosopher's Pendulum
All In Vain

Leopold von SACHER-MASOCH (1835–1895)
The Bookbinder of Hort

Arthur SCHNITZLER (1862–1931)
The Triple Warning
The Fate of the Baron von Leisenborg

Hermann SUDERMANN (1857–1928)
A New-Year's Eve Confession

Heinrich ZSCHOKKE (1771–1848)
Adventures of a New-Year's Eve
The Broken Pitcher

GREEK

Avedis AHARONIAN (1866–   )
(Armenian)
In the Shadow of Death

Demetrios BIKELAS (1835–1908)
The Priest's Tale

Georgios T. BIZYENOS (1848–   )
The Sin of My Mother

Georgios DROSINES (1859–   )
The God-Father

Argyres EFTALIOTES
Angelica

A. KARKAVISTAS
The Sea

Thrasyvoulos KOSTANAKES
The Frightened Soul

Kostes PALAMAS (1859–   )
A Man's Death

A. PAPADIAMANTY
She That Was Homesick

Iakovas POLYAS
Forgiveness

Gregorios XENOPOULOS (1867–   )
Mangalos

IRISH

Lord Edward DUNSANY (1878–   )
The Dreamer of Dreams
The Sword and the Idol

James JOYCE (1882–   )
Araby
Ivy Day in the Committee Room
Eveline

George MOORE (1853–1933)
Julia Cahill's Curse

Frank O'CONNOR (1903–   )
Guests of the Nation

Seán O'FAOLÁIN (1900–   )
Midsummer Night's Madness
The Small Lady
The Bomb-Shop
The Death of Stevey Long
The Patriot

Liam O'FLAHERTY (1896–)
Spring Sowing
The Doctor's Visit

Seumas O'KELLY (1881–1918)
The Golden Barque
The Weaver's Grave

James STEPHENS (1882–)
Hunger
Darling

William Butler YEATS (1865–)
The Secret Rose

ITALIAN

Edmondo de AMICIS (1846–1908)
A Great Day
College Friends
Mendicant Melody

Gabriele D'ANNUNZIO (1863–)
San Pantaleone
The Hero

Giovanni BOCCACCIO (1313–1375)
The Falcon
Patient Griselda

Enrico CASTELNUOVO (1839–)
It Snows

Grazia DELEDDA (1875–)
Two Miracles
Two Men and a Woman

Antonio FOGAZZARO (1842–1911)
The Peasant's Will

Carlo GOZZI (1720–1806)
The Venetian Silk-Mercer

Luigi PIRANDELLO (1867–)
A Mere Formality
The Tight Frock Coat
The Reserved Coffin

Rafael SABATINI (1875–)
His Insolence of Buckingham
His Last Chance
The Night of Gems

Franco SACCHETTI (c. 1335–c. 1400)
The Two Ambassadors

Matilde SERAO (1856–)
Lulu's Triumph

Giovanni VERGA (1840–1922)
Cavalleria Rusticana

LATIN–AMERICAN

COSTA RICA
Ricardo FERNÁNDEZ-GARCÍA
(1867–)
Chivalry

BRAZIL
J. M. MACHADO DE ASSIS
(1839–1908)
The Attendant's Confession

PERU
Ventura GARCÍA-CALDERÓN
(1890–)
The Legend of Pygmalion

VENEZUELA
Rufino BLANCO-FOMBONA
(1874–)
Creole Democracy

NICARAGUA
Rubén DARÍO (1867–1916)
The Deaf Satyr

NORWEGIAN

Hans AANRUD (1863–)
When the Frost Comes

Björstjerne BJÖRNSON (1832–1910)
How The Mountain Was Clad
The Brothers
The Fisher Maiden
The Father
The Bridal March

Johan BOJER (1872–)
The Home-Coming

Jacob Breda BULL (1853–)
Coffee-Kari

Olav DUUN (1876–)
At Christmas

Peter EGGE (1869–)
When Peder Solberg Came Home

Johan FALKBERGET (1879–)
Old Heggeli's Last Polka

Mikkjel FÖNHUS (1894–)
The Moose-Hunter

Arne GARBORG (1851–1924)
Death

Knut HAMSUN (1859–)
The Call of Life
The Ring

Jacob HILDITCH (1864–   )
Guinea-Jack or Skipper Gerhardtsen's
Cock

Alexander KIELLAND (1849–1906)
Siesta
The Spirit of the Ball

Hans E. KINCK (1865–1926)
Nocturne

Thomas KRAG (1868–1913)
Jörgen Dam, Philologist

Jonas LIE (1833–1908)
Elias and the Draug

Amalie SKRAM (1847–1905)
A Rose

Gabriel SCOTT (1874–   )
Nils Punctual and His Clocks

Sigrid UNDSET (1882–   )
Simonsen

RUSSIAN

Leonid Nikolaievich ANDREYEV
(1871–1919)
The Little Angel
The Seven That Were Hanged
Silence
The Grand Slam

Ivan BUNIN (1870–   )
The Gentleman from San Francisco
Sunstroke

Anton Pavlovich CHEKHOV (1860–1904)
The Darling
The Bet
Easter Eve
The Black Monk
A Work of Art
The Kiss

Fedor DOSTOYEVSKY (1821–1881)
The Christmas Tree and the Wedding
A Gentle Soul
The Thief

Vsevolod GARSHIN (1855–1888)
The Red Flower
The Signal

Nikolai Vassilievitch GOGOL (1809–1852)
St. John's Eve
The Cloak
The Overcoat

Maxim GORKY (1868–   )
Comrades
My Fellow Traveller
One Autumn Night
The Song of the Falcon

Vladimir KOROLENKO (1853–1921)
The Old Bell-Ringer

Alexander KUPRIN (1870–   )
The Outrage
The Idiot
Captain Rybnikov

Alexander PUSHKIN (1799–1837)
The Pistol Shot
The Snow Storm
The Queen of Spades

S. T. SEMYONOV
The Servant

Fedor SOLOGUB (1863–1927)
The White Mother

Leo N. TOLSTOY (1828–1910)
What Men Live By
Three Arshins of Land
The Long Exile
Where Love Is, There God Is Also
A Prisoner in the Caucasus

Ivan TURGENEV (1818–1883)
A Lear of the Steppes
The Story of Father Alexis
Klara Milich
The District Doctor
Biryuk [The Wolf]

SPANISH

Pedro de ALARCÓN (1833–1891)
The Tall Woman
Moors and Christians

Leopoldo ALAS (1852–1901)
Adios, Cordera!

Mateo ALEMAN (1547–c. 1614)
Guzmán and My Lord Cardinal

Gustavo Adolfo BÉCQUER (1836–1870)
Maese Pérez, the Organist
Nurse Perette
The Devil's Cross

Fernán CABALLERO (pseud. of Cecilia Böhl de Faber) (1796–1877)
Bread Cast Upon the Waters

Miguel CERVANTES (1547–1616)
Rinconete and Cortadillo

Juan MANUEL (c. 1280–1347)
The Son and His Friends

Diego MENDOZA (1503–1574)
How Lazaro Served a Bulero

José SELGAS (1824–1882)
The White Butterfly

SWEDISH

Ernst AHLGREN (1850–1888)
Mother Malena's Hen

Bo BERGMAN (1869–   )
The Sign

Anna Lenah ELGSTRÖM (1882–   )
Out of Chaos

Albert ENGSTRÖM (1869–   )
Charles XII, Hercules, and Gustav Mattson

Gustaf af GEIJERSTAM (1858–1909)
Karin

Per HALLSTRÖM (1866–   )
The Falcon
Out of the Dark
A Florentine Fantasy

Verner von HEIDENSTAM (1859–   )
When the Bells Rang
The Fortified House
The Queen of the Marauders
Captured
The Shield-Maiden
A Clean White Shirt

Selma LAGERLÖF (1858–   )
The Silver Mine
The Legend of the Christmas Rose
Hatto the Hermit
Christmas Night
The Eclipse
The Outlaws

Oscar LEVERTIN (1862–1906)
Middle-Class Rococo

Pelle MOLIN (1864–1896)
Men's Men

Ludwig NORDSTRÖM (1882–   )
The Awakening

Märta af SILLÉN (1899–   )
The Golden Circle

Sigfrid SIWERTZ (1882–   )
The Lady in White
The Café of Transfiguration
Leonard and the Fisherman
In Spite of Everything

Hjalmar SÖDERBERG (1869–   )
The Chimney-Sweeper's Wife
Bloom
The Fur Coat
The Wages of Sin
Margot
The Burning City
Archimedes' Point

August STRINDBERG (1849–1912)
Autumn
The Stone Man
Half a Sheet of Paper
Love and Bread

Zakarias TOPELIUS (1818–1898)
The Pitch Burner Who Always Got to the Top

STUDY NOTES

It is not the editor's purpose to supply notes here for a complete technical study of each story nor to save the student from an occasional appeal to the dictionary. Some suggestions are made for the study of each story. Other items will occur to teachers and students. Where words and phrases are so unusual as not to appear in an English dictionary, the editor has supplied the meanings. This is infrequent, however. Questions are asked to bring out peculiarities of construction or some special point in connection with the central idea of a story. While the notes and questions on any one story are not sufficient for a complete study of the form and meaning of that story, the student will have gone through a complete analysis three or four times while following the suggestions for the study of the sixty-odd stories in the volume.

THE PRODIGAL SON

A parable is a narrative of an actual or imagined occurrence used to illustrate some truth about life or to point out a lesson or moral. The story of *The Prodigal Son* is offered here, not as an example of an early perfect *short story*, but as one of those ancient forms of prose fiction that were used before the short story became a recognized form of literary art with a recognized technique. Even so it conforms in many ways to the technique of the modern short story.

Try to state the theme (author's purpose, central thought, thesis, or main idea) of *The Prodigal Son*, using the formula suggested on p. 19: The author's purpose in telling or writing this story was to show that. . . .

Do you think *The Forgiving Father* would have been a better title than *The Prodigal Son?* Give reasons on both sides of the question.

The story naturally divides into two distinct parts. At what point? Would it have been well to stop there, omitting the second part entirely? What purpose does the second part serve?

Would the story have gained anything by giving names to the three characters, and naming the place where the father lived and the "far country" to which the younger son went?

Here are some devices which a modern storyteller might use in telling this same tale: 1. He could give names to the three characters. 2. He could describe each of them. 3. He could name and describe the places. 4. He could make an initial incident out of the son's leaving home by the use of conversation, or perhaps even a quarrel. 5. He could enlarge upon the son's experiences in "riotous living" and his life as a swineherd by giving several incidents in each and developing them by means of conversation. 6. He could explain the theme of the story. 7. He could thus extend the story from its present length of about four hundred and fifty words to four thousand five hundred. Would it be a finer or a poorer story told thus? Take the seven suggestions one at a time.

THE MYSTERIOUS BRIDE

From what point of view is the story told? What device does the author use in the first two paragraphs to convince the reader that this ghost story is true? Why did the author not have McMurdie see the ghost (p. 79)? She was seen by others later (p. 86). Why did he have the ghost appear in broad daylight?

Does the author anywhere in the story insert his own opinions independent of the story or the characters? If so, cite examples. Do these mar the telling of the story? Why was the Rev. Joseph Taylor brought by name into the story (p. 87)? Would it seem probable that Sandison would not have known of the mysterious deaths of his father and grandfather, twenty and forty years earlier, on St. Lawrence's Eve on the Birky Brow? How does the author conceal this improbability or minimize it?

Do you regard this as a good, convincing ghost story? Did you find your interest and nervous tension increasing as the story neared the end? Did you foresee the outcome before you reached the middle of page 86?

Is the story realistic, or romantic? Is it mainly a story of setting, incident, or character?

Has the story a theme that can be stated in the form of a moral lesson? Does it teach anything?

Does the author "practice the greatest economy of means consistent with the necessary emphasis to be obtained"? Would the story have lost anything by omitting the visit to Ireland? What purpose in advancing the narrative does that visit serve?

Is there any significance in having the ghost of Jane Ogilvie dressed in white with the green veil? Why does the author want the ring to be real (visible and tangible to other people as well as to the Laird)? Since nothing else about Jane is substance, wouldn't it have been better to have the ring imaginary, too? Why was the setting of the ring an emerald?

This story was written some twenty years before Poe and Hawthorne began to write. Do you find that it falls short of being a short story in the modern sense in any way? If so, in what way or ways?

Would you accept the following statement as the *theme* of *The Mysterious Bride:* "The purpose of the author was to entertain the readers with a good romantic ghost story."

The meanings of many of the Scottish words in this story will be clear to all, but a few may need to be explained.

The Laird of Birkendelly is Allan Sandison, master or owner of the estate or farms named Birkendelly. He is usually called Birkendelly, rather than Sandison.

> *muckle*, large
> *burn*, brook
> *knowe*, knoll
> *joe*, sweetheart
> *callant*, a chap, lad
> *daft*, insane
> *ycleped*, called, named
> *Windy-wa's*, windy walls
> *nae*, not
> *fa's*, falls
> *baith*, both
> *shoon*, shoes.

RIP VAN WINKLE

Rip Van Winkle and *The Mysterious Bride* were written and published near the same time, about 1820. The prevailing tone of Irving's story is one of mock seriousness; that is, a species of humor. Was there any hint of humor in *The Mysterious Bride*? Could you say that the prevailing tone of that story is humorous? Is Irving's story realism or romance?

In what Irving says about Rip, Dame Van Winkle, and other characters, is he true to human nature, or does he exaggerate human traits? Cite examples to support your view. Do you find Irving too leisurely in getting through his story, too slow for the twentieth century? What devices does the author use to make you like Rip rather than despise him as he points out Rip's indolence and other faults?

Ancient tales were usually stories of strange events, with a frequent resort to the supernatural. These were told to entertain with the strangeness of the circumstances without much reference to character or setting. In what way is *Rip Van Winkle* like those old tales and in what way like modern stories?

Does Irving make an effort to convince you of the reality of the twenty-year sleep? If you accept the one improbability of the long sleep, is the rest of the story consistent, true to life, without any slips or improbabilities?

Is the style pleasing? Do you like the author's use of language? Is it easy to read aloud and pleasant-sounding when so read?

Do you think Irving was trying to teach a moral lesson with this story? If so, what? If not, try to state the author's intention, or theme, in your own words.

Is the plot a complex one? In a single narrative paragraph try to tell the story of Rip Van Winkle. If you succeed, you will have a simple statement of the plot of the story.

Admitting that the events in this story never happened to Rip Van Winkle or anybody else, do you think the author was justified in telling such a made-up story?

If you think lying is wrong, what distinction do you make between a lie that you disapprove, and a piece of literary fiction that you approve?

Are you as well acquainted with Washington Irving, the author who lived seventy-five years, as you are with Rip, who never lived at all? Explain.

This story has approximately six thousand words. Only about five or six hundred words of it are in direct discourse—conversation. Do you miss the vividness of conversation? Point out sections of the story that you think would have been improved by reporting the direct speech instead of the substance of what was said in narrative.

Does the story induce a strong emotional response in you?

WANDERING WILLIE'S TALE

Again we have a story of strange, supernatural things, told only for the entertainment of the reader. Sir Walter Scott was a diligent collector of old ballads, old bits of furniture and pieces of odd gear, and of old folk tales. This story is related by an old blind fiddler and is about an experience of his grandfather, long since dead. Scott hints that the visit of Steenie Steenson to Hell to get his receipt from Robert Redgauntlet had a good deal of brandy and dreaming in it, and that the legend of the fire-defying, satanic receipt grew up in the mind of a senile old man long years after the money was found in the Cat's Cradle. He refuses, however, to explain it all away and thus spoil a good story.

The author's purpose is only to entertain us with a good story of uncanny incidents told by a very interesting narrator. The story has a setting that is interesting in itself, and Scott must have been as much interested in the characters in the piece as he was in the incidents the tale is made of. Another of his interests doubtless was in the language of Wandering Willie—the colorful and expressive lowland Scots speech so freely and skillfully used.

The editor began to make a list of the difficult Scottish words and their English equivalents, but soon discovered that their number was too great to be included in these brief study notes. Much of the reader's pleasure in reading this tale comes from the very language in which it is cast. To be obliged to make a word for word translation as one goes along would take the life out of it. The reader should, however, underscore with pencil as he reads the words that are so obscure as to make it impossible to get the meaning at a number of points through the piece. These may then be looked up after the first rapid reading of the whole story. To hear this story read aloud by one who has a thorough knowledge of the dialect is a rare literary experience.

THE PISTOL SHOT

Observe these dates: *The Mysterious Bride*, 1820; *Rip Van Winkle*, 1819; *Wandering Willie's Tale*, 1824; and now *The Pistol Shot*, about 1829. We are still in the 1820's. The modern short story is not yet past the experimental stage, but we are approaching Hawthorne and Poe and a greater certainty about the materials and the form of the short story. The next two stories in the sequence of this volume are Poe's *Ligeia*, 1838; and Hawthorne's *Dr. Heidegger's Experiment*, 1837.

One of the customs of the earlier writers was to leave the names of places and characters blank or to use an initial and a dash. Pushkin uses both devices. See pages 117 and 121. Do you think of anything gained by so doing? Why is the custom no longer followed?

What advantages are gained by telling the story in the first person? What disadvantages? Observe that the narrator in *The Pistol Shot* is a character in the story, but not the principal. Why not let Silvio tell his own story?

The three preceding stories are all romantic. With this Russian story we are on the threshold of realism. Are there any items in the story that do not convince you as probable or possible? Does the author avoid unpleasant things in order to make his story pleasing? Does he choose ideal and pleasingly beautiful places for his two scenes or settings? Or are the places, rooms, and houses just the kind that would be natural for the events that take place? Are the characters idealized in any way, or are they convincingly real? Do you find anything in the story that is idealized, thus marring the effect of realism?

Is this story mainly one of character, incidents, or setting? Is it a study of cowardice? Do you understand that Silvio did not shoot his opponent because at neither time did he have the physical or mental courage to do so? Why do you think he did not shoot the Count the first time? Why not the second? Do you admire Silvio? Why? Do you admire the Count, his opponent? Why? Does the story show character development or does it stop with character portrayal?

How many distinct incidents, or scenes, are there? Was the ending a surprise? As you look back through the story, does it seem improbable that it should end thus? The ending should be just what *those* characters would have done under the circumstances the author has pictured. As the end approached, were you anxious about the outcome or merely curious? Or did you, perhaps, not care at all?

If you had to choose one of the following words to indicate the tone of the story, which one would it be—amusing, hilarious, sarcastic, serious, tragic, pensive, happy?

Here are four statements offered as the theme of the story. Which one do you think most nearly describes the author's purpose?

1. *The Pistol Shot* was written to show the breaking down of a noble character on account of innate cowardice.
2. *The Pistol Shot* is a psychological study of an individual when confronted with a series of situations each demanding some positive action.
3. *The Pistol Shot* is an account of the development of the character of a natural coward from cowardice to courage and nobility.
4. *The Pistol Shot* was written to give the reader an accurate and convincing picture of the life of Russian army officers in Pushkin's times.

Compared with good modern short stories, do you think this one of Pushkin's superior or inferior to the best of the stories you have read since 1930? Why?

LIGEIA

Starting with the assumption that human beings die only because the will is too weak to resist death, Poe has told the story of one will strong enough to overcome death itself. The story is in five parts.

First, the author uses sixteen hundred words to portray a character with great intellectual ability and a will perhaps ten times as strong as any you have ever known—Ligeia. He gives her a motive for an overpowering desire to live—her love for her husband.

Second, he permits Ligeia to die although strongly resisting death. We must be convinced that she is actually dead, not merely fainting or in a trance lasting a few days. The author allows several months to elapse, before the second marriage of the narrator.

Third, to provide an appropriate setting for the resurrection of Ligeia and a human body for her soul to occupy, Poe shifts the scene from that "decaying city near the Rhine" to an unnamed abbey "in one of the wildest and least frequented portions of fair England" and permits the narrator to marry "the fair-haired and blue-eyed Lady Rowena Trevanion, of Tremaine." There he ardently wishes for his dark lost love, Ligeia, and actually calls aloud for her.

Fourth, Rowena, afflicted with some mysterious malady, is allowed to die about two months after her marriage.

Fifth, after four nights, sufficient time to convince the reader that Rowena is dead, the soul of Ligeia returns, and with supernatural power enters into the body of the fair Rowena and transforms it into the black-haired, black-eyed Ligeia.

For fear you might miss his theme, "man dies only because of the feebleness of his will," Poe uses the statement of Glanvill as a preface to the story, and repeats it three times in the body of the narrative.

The vagueness of characters and setting are necessary. Otherwise the reader would want to go to some real place to see this woman who had conquered death. Trace for yourself the devices Poe has used to picture convincing people and places and yet to leave them extremely vague as to time and place.

How many characters are there? Their names? How much time elapses from the beginning to the end of the story?

It is very improbable that the husband never knew Ligeia's family name. Are there other improbabilities, apparent or hidden, in the story?

The full effect of this story can be experienced only by hearing it read aloud. The language is poetic and often loosely rhythmic. Observe: "Her singular yet placid cast of beauty, and the thrilling and enthralling eloquence of her low musical language" and "by the almost magical melody, modulation, distinctness, and placidity of her very low voice." Find other passages that seem especially musical.

Find situations and passages that sound artificial, bordering upon the absurd and claptrap.

Can you think of a reason or two for inserting the poem in this prose story?

Was the close of the story too abrupt? Would it have been better to have shown that Ligeia's victory over death was permanent? For all you know she may have collapsed two minutes after Poe's final word— "of the LADY LIGEIA."

Observe that the story is told in the first person and in narrative form. There is no dialogue or conversation.

DR. HEIDEGGER'S EXPERIMENT

If you can say what Hawthorne thought would happen if old people had a chance to live their lives over again, you will have a good statement of the theme of this story.

You will observe from now on a growing skill in using direct discourse. The writers will fall into the way of using the conventional paragraph for conversation; that is, making a paragraph out of each speech and the authors' guide words (*he said*, *she exclaimed*, etc.) and comments that go with the speech. In early fiction there was very little variety in the guide words. *He said*, *she said*, *said he*, and *said she* were nearly always used. The next development will be in the use of more than a hundred different substitutes for *said*. And finally the writers will come to present many speeches without guide words at all. They will manage the talk so skillfully that it will be clear, from the speech itself, who is speaking and the manner in which it is spoken. Guide words will be used only when more than two are speaking, to help the reader to understand who out of three, four, or five persons in a group is talking. The aim of the modern writer is to make the speeches sound as natural as possible. The writer comes between the character speaking and the reader as little as possible. This requires skill. It is better to use the necessary guide words and comments than to be obscure.

In *Dr. Heidegger's Experiment* Hawthorne inserted twenty-nine paragraphs containing direct speaking. He used *said* nine times, *cried* seven times, *answered* three, *replied* and *exclaimed* twice each, and *repeated*, *asked*, *quoth*, *shouted*, *ejaculated*, and *observed* once each. In all there are eleven of these words of *saying*.

Does this story intentionally *teach* anything? If you think Hawthorne intended that it should, state what you imagine it was designed to teach.

THE OUTCASTS OF POKER FLAT

Choose from the following words one or more that will apply to the emotional tone of this story: grim, pathetic, tragic, humorous, light, sarcastic, sweet, sentimental.

Passing from Poe and Hawthorne we have left a gap of thirty-one years between Poe's *Ligeia* and Harte's *The Outcasts of Poker Flat*. In those three decades much has happened to the short story. Bret Harte has learned economy of words. This story uses about four thousand. Harte has acquired skill in delineating character. Each of the six— Oakhurst, Uncle Billy, The Duchess, Mother Shipton, The Innocent, and Piney—is convincingly real, and each different from the others. How does Bret Harte accomplish this? Does he describe them, or let them reveal themselves by what they say, or by what they do, or by combining all those devices? How much is accomplished by subtle, indirect suggestion?

This is unquestionably a character story. It has a theme. It says something very definite about human nature. That is its theme. Can you state it? Note that the story is told in the third person.

The first paragraph on p. 150 contains one or two remarks of mildly ironic humor. What are they? What makes the statement, "Piney ... emerged from behind the pine-tree, where she had been blushing unseen," (p. 152, line 10) seem funny? Does this line (p. 154) make you smile: "Piney Woods managed to pluck several reluctant melodies from its [the accordion's] keys"? What is amusing about that? Does it seem good taste on the author's part to mingle pathos, irony, sentiment, and humor in a story that is essentially pathetically tragic? If you think so, justify your position.

Do not fail, in connection with this story, to read two others by the same author: *Tennessee's Partner* and *The Luck of Roaring Camp*.

DR. MARIGOLD'S PRESCRIPTIONS

The length of *Dr. Marigold's Prescriptions* is about 10,000 words, more than twice as long as the average short story. Its construction is not like that of a short story, but more nearly like that of a novel. It is a narrative covering about thirty years of the life of a traveling auction peddler, a "cheap Jack." There are more incidents and more characters in it than are in the typical short story. The plot structure is different.

It has no theme in the usual meaning of that word. The author's purpose is to tell the story of the life of a cheap Jack through a period of thirty years. By increasing the number of incidents the story could have been extended to four or five hundred pages, making a full-length novel.

The story is a good example of that type of prose fiction halfway between the short story and the novel; that is, the novelette. Examine its structure and point out its resemblances to the short story and to the novel.

Does it seem to you that Dickens was well acquainted with the life, manners, and speech of the cheap Jack? Is the talk convincingly real?

Dickens has been accused of deliberately playing upon the emotions and of being sentimental. Is this story so over-sentimentalized that you dislike it? If you shed tears over it, did you resent the author's way of stirring up your emotions?

If you are unacquainted with Dickens's novels, has the reading of this novelette prompted you to read other pieces of his or to avoid them?

TAKING THE REDOUBT

This story takes us once more back to the eighteen-twenties. It shows characteristics thus early that mark the French short story through a hundred years. They are usually short, terse. They aim at making a single impression, and do it quickly and clearly.

Notice again the conventional initial and dash instead of a name. Observe the narrative paragraphs (not dialogue) made of a single line or a single sentence.

The author's purpose seems to be to set forth clearly a single impression about life. Is he trying to make a realistic picture of military life, or trying to say that physical courage is overrated and is mostly unconscious action without the deliberate driving force of mind? Or is he saying that there is really something in the proverb "Never twice in the same place"? Or is he giving an impression of the thoughts and feelings of a young officer the first time under gunfire?

Would you call this a real short story or only a sketch? Is the impression one of realism or of romance? Does Mérimée's manner of storytelling remind you of Poe or of Pushkin?

MARJORIE DAW

This is obviously a story intended only to interest and amuse the readers with an account, cleverly written, of an imaginary love affair. Your interest in it will not be in any philosophy of Mr. Aldrich, but in his characters and in the way he manages to get the story told.

The chief objection usually raised to telling a story by means of letters or documents is that too much time and space are consumed. In the exchange of letters a single incident is likely to be referred to twice or three times. In *Marjorie Daw* Mr. Aldrich has used approximately

7000 words. The story could be told in narrative and conversation very effectively in four or five thousand. Or a less skillful writer might have required ten thousand.

There are fourteen letters, five short telegrams, and a hundred and ninety-two words of simple narrative in the story. Examine this material to see if you can detect the devices used to keep the story moving and to avoid repetition and consequent length. Does the author reproduce *all* the letters supposedly written by Dillon, Delaney, and Flemming? If not, how does he maintain the continuity of the narrative? How many letters are written by each of the three? Was the narrative paragraph (p. 207) necessary?

How is the setting pictured for the reader? How does the author make you acquainted with the characters? What is the tone of the story? Is there any pathos in it? Do you find yourself really concerned over Flemming's disappointment when he discovers that there is no Marjorie Daw? Up to what point in the story did you believe in the reality of Marjorie? Did the ending come as a surprise to you, as it was to John Flemming?

THE LOVE LETTERS OF SMITH

Point of View: Third person. Does this observer who tells the story know everything about the characters, what they are thinking, etc? Or does he know only what the seamstress does and thinks?

Author's Purpose: State the theme (author's purpose) of the story.

Tone: Find a word or phrase that will represent the tone of the story.

Plot: Select the Initial Incident that sets this love story going. Now divide the story into steps or scenes that lead up to the culmination.

Questions: This story was first published in 1890 in *Puck*, a magazine of humor. Does it strike you as suited to that kind of magazine? In actual life are humor and pathos (smiles and tears) as closely associated as they are in this story? Do you smile, or laugh aloud as you read it? What is funny about the story? What is pathetic? Anything sad about it? Did you think the ending too abrupt? Should you have liked it better if the author had shown the two together in a scene or two before the seamstress said "Yes"? Why do you suppose he didn't? Do you find the combination of narrative and the letters an effective way of getting the story told? There is very little description of the characters. Do you have a fairly clear picture in your mind of their appearance? Do you feel that you would know them if you should see them in a crowd? How does the author manage to make you know them?

You should not neglect to read that other very clever story by H. C. Bunner and Brander Matthews entitled *The Documents in the Case.* It is made by carefully piecing together bits of letters, telegrams, scraps of newspapers, and miscellaneous odds and ends.

THE LAST CLASS

Again we have the French compactness in story writing. The length of *The Last Class* is about 1600 words. Examine the story to discover how Daudet managed the preliminary matters—setting, introduction of characters, establishing the tone, time of the action, etc.

How do you know that the time is at the close of the Franco-Prussian War (1871)? How much time elapses from the beginning of the story to the end? Does the story close on the high point of emotional tension? Do you regard the ending as a good one?

Make your own statement of the theme.

The story is told in the first person and from the point of view of the schoolboy. Is this effective? Could it have been told from the point of view of the schoolmaster, of old Hauser, of a Prussian officer sitting on that bench in the rear of the schoolroom? Would such a point of view change the tone of the story? Is the principal character the schoolboy, the schoolmaster, or old Hauser?

How many distinct scenes in the story?

Does it have a sharp initial incident?

THE LESSON OF THE MASTER

The Lesson of the Master is a novelette in six chapters of about 4000 words each. It is as long as five or six short stories of average length. Here is an outline of the story by chapters.

Time—Modern, Henry James's own time.

Time Scheme of the story—Parts I, II, and III, Sunday noon till Monday morning. Then a lapse of three days or so. Then three meetings scattered through two or three weeks. Next a lapse of two years between Parts V and VI, followed by a single afternoon and evening in London.

Settings for the scenes—Summersoft, a country house of Lady Watermouth, a short driving distance from London, for Parts I, II, and III. Other scenes at the houses of the Fancourts and St. Georges in London.

Theme—The author's purpose in writing the story was to put a question to the reader for consideration. What is the question? (Instead of answering the question Henry James causes the reader to think it through himself. He seems to be sure of himself till he nears the end. There he leaves the reader in doubt as to the author's own view of the situation.)

Point of View—The third person until near the end of the story. There the author occasionally shifts to the first person and uses the capital I.

Characters—(Principal) Paul Overt, young novelist; Henry St. George, an older novelist, the "Master"; and Marian Fancourt, a young girl. (Minor) Mrs. St. George, General Fancourt, and house guests.

Part I. Paul Overt, a successful young novelist, arrives as a guest at the summer house of Lady Watermouth at noon on a Sunday. Other week-end guests are General Fancourt and his daughter Marian, Mr. and Mrs. Henry St. George, and others who do not appear later in the story.

The time, place, tone, and relationship of the characters to each other are taken care of in this chapter. Theme is not mentioned, but Mrs. St. George tells of inducing her husband to burn the manuscript of a novel.

Part II. This chapter gives Overt an opportunity to become acquainted with Mrs. St. George, and to have a friendly chat with Marian Fancourt alone. There is a hint of the beginning of love.

Part III. After the group had broken up for the night Overt at last found his opportunity for a talk with St. George, the man whom he had hoped to meet at Lady Watermouth's. The *theme* of the story is now placed squarely before the reader. The lesson the Master places before Overt is presented on page 230. "Look at me well, take my lesson to heart. . . . Don't become in your old age what I have in mine—the depressing, the deplorable illustration of the worship of false gods!" What are these false gods? James has St. George answer: "The idols of the market; money and luxury and 'the world'; placing one's children and dressing one's wife; everything that drives one to the short and easy way."

Part IV. In her London house Paul Overt discusses the doctrine of artistic perfection with Marian. The love affair of these two young people makes some progress.

Part V. In St. George's study the two novelists have a long and intimate talk. St. George admonishes Overt not to let money or marriage stand between himself and perfection. He shows the younger man how the obligations of a family, wife, and children have made it impossible for him to keep up to the artistic standard he had attained in his first great success. He also lets Overt see how Mrs. St. George manages him and dictates what he does and even what he publishes. The manuscript she had compelled him to burn was one about himself and his falling short of his own ideal of literary perfection. "An artist," says St. George, "marries at his peril." He advises Overt against marrying Marian Fancourt.

Part VI. Paul Overt gives Marian up temporarily, at least, spends two years in Switzerland and Italy, and writes a very fine novel. Before returning to London he hears of the death of Mrs. St. George. Upon his return he calls at once upon Marian, and learns that she is soon to marry St. George.

Questions: This story could have been told in true short story form in five or six thousand words. What is gained by writing it in twenty-four thousand? Is anything lost by so doing? Why not close the narration with General Fancourt's remark, "To Mr. St. George—it has just been settled"?

Henry James has been praised for his ability to analyze the character of people of the upper classes. Do you think that skill is shown in this novelette?

The author expects you to think through the case he has presented here and to answer for yourself the question implied in "the lesson." What answer do you offer?

Comparing this novelette with some typical short story, like *The Piece of String*, point out some of the similarities between the two types of prose story. Some of the differences.

Do you notice any disregard for the generally accepted rules of punctuation in this story? (The editor has, to a certain extent, followed the punctuation Henry James approved in the final revision of it.) Point out several specific examples of such disregard.

Foreign Phrases. Henry James wrote in a period when it was customary to use an occasional foreign word or phrase. His are usually French. Some that may need translation for the student are given below:

P. 218, *Il s'attache à ses pas*, he follows her everywhere.

P. 224, *à fleur de peau*, skin deep.

P. 227, *mot*, remark.

P. 233, *Cela s'est passé comme ça*, that is what happened (lit., it happened like that).

P. 234, *jamais de la vie*, never in the world.

P. 236, *père de famille*, father of a family.

P. 236, *mornes*, dull, gloomy.

P. 237, *mœurs*, customs, habits.

P. 239, *C'est d'un trouvé*, it is a gift.

P. 241, *Comment donc?* how, then? Indeed!

P. 245, *il ne manquerait plus que ça*, that would be the last straw.

P. 247, *carton-pierre*, imitation stone, papier-mâché.

P. 247, *brummagem* (English), shoddy stuff.

P. 247, *Lincrusta-Walton* (English), a trade name for a kind of patterned linoleum or oilcloth, hence, any cheap, shoddy decorative material.

P. 249, *n'en parlons plus*, let us say no more about it.

THE LADY, OR THE TIGER?

Theme—This story was written to ask the question, What would a girl do if she had to allow her lover to be either devoured by a tiger or married to her rival?

Is the tone of the story established in the first paragraph? If so, point out the words or phrases that give you an insight into the nature of the story.

Is the second paragraph ironic? Show why you think so. If the theme is as serious as stated, why does the author begin in so light a manner?

How many characters are there in the story?

How much do you know about the young man? How much do you know about the princess? What difference does it make how much or how little you know?

How much conversation is there in the story?

Is there a distinct initial incident? If so, what is it?

How many scenes in the plot? Describe each.

Let each girl in the class hand to the teacher a bit of paper with only the word *Lady*, or the word *Tiger* upon it, to indicate whether she would have sent the young man to the lady or the tiger. Have the boys do the same, thus showing which they would have expected to meet if they had stood in the young man's place and had just got the signal from the princess to open the door at the right. No mark of identification should be on the slips. Count the girls' votes and the boys' votes and announce the answers. This ought to determine whether the lady or the tiger came out, if civilized and semi-barbaric human nature are the same.

THE THREE STRANGERS

Try making a diagram of this story similar to that on page 38 or that on page 39. Indicate what each step or number stands for in this particular story.

What do you think the theme (author's purpose) is?

Do you regard it as primarily a story of incident, or of character? Did you find the setting interesting in itself?

What have you to say about the tone?

The story was written in 1883. Is the time represented in the narrative about 1883, or much earlier? How do you know? How much time elapses between the initial incident and the culmination?

Who are the principal characters?

Who are the characters of secondary importance?

Who are those who merely make up the crowd, the supernumeraries?

Does Hardy succeed in making the principal characters stand out as individuals different from each other? If so, how does he do it—by action and speech, or by direct description, or both? Does he make any effort to individualize his secondary characters? The supernumeraries?

Hardy has been praised for his understanding of working people. Does he show that in this story?

Hardy has been compared to Shakespeare for his skill in making humorous figures out of common people. Does he do that in *The Three*

Strangers? If so, what devices does he employ to make them seem funny?

When did you first suspect that "the man in the chimney-corner" was the one intended to be the hangman's customer the next morning? Was your sympathy with the escaped prisoner or with the law, as represented by the hangman? How does Hardy manage to throw your sympathy on the side of the escaped prisoner?

Was your nervous tension ever so high that you were intensely fearful that the man would be caught and hanged? If not, do you still regard it as a good story well told? Explain your attitude toward that question.

Have you any comment to make about Hardy's style?

P. 280, *circulus, cujus centrum diabolus*, a circle whose center is the devil.

WILL O' THE MILL

This beautifully quiet story is only one phase of Stevenson's art. In contrast, think of *Dr. Jekyll and Mr. Hyde, Markheim, Treasure Island, Kidnapped, The Master of Ballantrae, The Ebb Tide, The Beach at Falesá,* and *Thrawn Janet.* The student should now begin to think of *style.* It would be a good thing to read Stevenson's own essay *On Some Technical Elements of Style in Literature,* or Poe's essay, *The Philosophy of Composition,* or Clayton Hamilton's chapter on style in his *Materials and Methods of Fiction.* If you are interested in style, there are several other excellent essays on the subject by eminent practitioners of the literary art.

Some items that most writers agree upon are: a pleasing variety and combination of sounds, choosing the right word, finding appropriate similes and metaphors but avoiding the trite, finding satisfying prose rhythms, avoiding the appearance of artificiality. Examine the final paragraph (p. 290) to see if it satisfies all these requirements. Almost any other paragraph of descriptive or narrative matter in the story would do as well. Read also the first paragraph for style.

This story was written when Stevenson was twenty-eight and a bachelor. It has been said that until late in his life and after he had married Mrs. Osbourne and come to know her and her daughter, Mrs. Isobel Strong, Stevenson was slow to introduce girls and women into his fiction, and that he was vague and general in describing and characterizing them. What do you think of his Parson's Marjory?

Stevenson said that in writing *Will o' the Mill* the place he had in mind was vaguely and generally the Brenner Pass over the Alps from Switzerland into Italy. The great war he refers to as taking place in Will's youth was probably the Napoleonic campaign about 1809 or 1810. The story covers the whole life of Will from about his twelfth to his seventy-second year—sixty years in all.

Theme. Stevenson, an invalid waging a twenty-year losing fight against tuberculosis and compelled to live a very quiet life, often in bed for weeks at a time, ardently wished for a life of vigorous action. He had no patience with the man who lacked resolution, who hesitated to undertake a hard task, who could not take the plunge. But of *Will o' the Mill* he said he undertook to make out the best case he could for "the hanger-back." That is the thesis, theme, or author's purpose in this story.

Does he convince you in the case of the Parson's Marjory that it was better not to take the plunge?

Do you like Will's proposal to Marjory? Did you smile over it or were you scornful of the man's lack of directness and show of affection? Do you find any fault with his reasoning on p. 297?

Do you approve of the author's inserting bits of his own philosophy into the story? For example, the five lines in the middle of p. 295 beginning, "It is the property," etc. Find other examples. Some critics say a story writer should never interpose his own thoughts into a story except as they are the thoughts of one of the characters. What do you think?

As to point of view, do you think the story is told from that of the first person, the limited third person, or the omniscient third person?

Punctuation. Does Stevenson's punctuation conform more nearly to the customs you find in the writers' handbooks and college composition books than Hardy's or Henry James's?

Try a diagram of this story, following one of the forms on pages 38–39.

THE MAN WHO WOULD BE KING

Why did Kipling not call the story *The Men Who Would Be Kings?* Do you think this six-word title is a good one for this story? Does it arouse the reader's curiosity and accurately advertise the contents without telling too much? Does it have a pleasing sound? Can you make up a better title? Would you like any one of these better: *The Crucified Carnehan, The King Who Lost His Head, The Fallen Idols, Carnehan and Dravot, Kings, Inc., The Master's Secret,* or *The Third Degree.* If so, why?

Does it strike you as at all remarkable that this story of 13,500 words should have been written by a young man of twenty-one or twenty-two? How could he have come into knowledge of so wide a group of people and such vast territories as he uses here? Does he make the people and the places seem real? Does he make Carnehan and Dravot seem like individual men, and does he have a thorough insight into their characters? How could he have come to know such men as intimately as he knows them?

Why did he choose to have the story told by an outsider—a young newspaper man? Why not have the whole story told in the first person by Carnehan—as he does have Carnehan relate what happened in Kafiristan? Or why not tell it in the omniscient third person?

Does the story seem too long? Could what happened have been narrated as effectively in fewer words? If you had read this one story in 1890 would you have regarded the writer as a first-rate, second-rate, or third-rate story writer?

Do you find any fault with the language of the story—unconvincing speeches, poor choice of words, grammar, limited vocabulary, lack of style, etc.?

Make an effort to divide the story into steps or scenes. What do you regard as the initial incident? The culmination? Does the conclusion seem a good one to you? What was gained by having Carnehan bring Dravot's head *and* the crown back with him? What became of that five-pound gold crown? Wouldn't it have been a good closing touch to have Carnehan give it to the newspaper man as his reward in the end? Why so, or why not? Would you have preferred to see the two men escape after untold hardships, like Ulysses, and return from their Odyssey with the two crowns as convincing souvenirs? Why, or why not?

Is the main emphasis on character, incident, or setting, or is it pretty evenly divided among the three? How many primary characters are in the story? Would you call the newspaper man and Billy Fish primary or secondary?

Has the story a lesson in it? If so, what is it? Or would you say that its primary purpose (theme) is to interest the readers with the *events* (incidents) in the careers of these two colossal rogues, or to picture their characters?

Is there any marked character development, or are the two practically the same in the end as at the beginning?

Did you like the story? If you disliked it, was your dislike from an aversion to that kind of story, that kind of people, and that kind of ending, or from faulty construction, lack of skill, etc., in the writer?

Young men readers of this story who are members of the Masonic order will be surprised to observe how much of the ritual and customs of that fraternity are woven into the tale. Carnehan and Dravot are quite obviously renegade Masons who take advantage of their partial recollection of the ritual to use it in gaining a standing with a barbaric tribe whose priests have once known it. And young Rudyard Kipling had an insight into Masonic customs that only a member could have had.

THE NECKLACE

The Necklace is one of the world's famous short stories. Can you see why it is so regarded? The language is very simple; the setting is commonplace; it deals with ordinary people; outside of the minister's ball and the loss of the necklace, the events are not unusual; it is so brief (25 or 26 hundred words) that it required no sustained effort of creation. Is it possible that it is quite an ordinary story and that the critics have echoed each other and given a great reputation to a story of only average worth?

De Maupassant has divided the story, by leaving space between the sections, into an Introduction and six scenes or steps. Make a diagram for the plot.

The story opens with a study of Mathilde Loisel and the situation in which she lives. Is it a "character story"?

The theme is stated at the close of the fifth scene just before the culmination. What is it?

What is the initial incident?

What is the culmination?

Would you have invented a different ending if you had been writing the story? Write out the scene with Madame Forestier as you would have written it if it had been your story.

This is called a realistic story. What makes it that? Could it have been written as a romantic story? What would you have done to it to make it romantic?

Do you think Maupassant's observation about women in the last sentence of the second paragraph is true? Defend your position.

Does the author make the losing of the necklace and the following results seem probable? How does he guard against the appearance of improbability? There are several little touches and manipulations put in for that purpose. See if you can detect some of them.

Who are the principal characters?

Who are the secondary characters?

Who are the supernumeraries, if there are any?

In the fourth line from the bottom of page 338 the word *noctambulant* occurs. See if the word is in the dictionary. It is a very unusual word used by the translator. Do you like unusual words in stories? Is this one justified in this place?

Would the story have been improved if the author had told us what happened to Mathilde after the last sentence in the story as it now stands?

Someone has said that the story was written to show that seeming calamity is often a blessing in disguise. This person says that Mathilde was a dissatisfied, complaining, worthless wife until faced with calamity, and then her hidden native worth came to the surface and made a woman of her. Do you think this was Maupassant's view?

The theme is what the author intended to show, not what you can read into (or out of) the piece. Give arguments for your statement of the theme of *The Necklace*.

THREE ARSHINS OF LAND

The theme of *Three Arshins of Land* is quite obvious. It was written by a Russian nobleman who chose to live among peasants as one of them.

He wrote several stories for common people to teach them some of the common lessons of life. He needed to make his purpose obvious to his unlearned readers. He saw many of them becoming land-greedy and "land-poor"; and so he wrote this story and put his theme in the title: *Three Arshins of Land, or How Much Land Does a Man Need?* Pakhom's neighbors were contented when they had the few acres needed for their simple wants. By acquiring more and more land he becomes less and less contented with what he has and at last finds that "six feet of ground" is what a man in the end really can make use of.

Make the usual diagram of the plot.

From what point of view is the story told?

Do you approve of a title that reveals the theme?

Is Pakhom drawn so that you feel that you know him? Is he anywhere described? If not, how do you get an impression of how he looks, the kind of man he is, etc.? How many principal characters in the story? What other characters do you know by name?

Does the ending strike you as pathetic, humorous, or tragic?

Is the tone of the story light, serious, pathetic, humorous, tragic, grim, gay, pensive, somber? Choose one of these words, or offer one of your own.

WHERE LOVE IS, THERE GOD IS ALSO

What is the theme of this story?

As you read the story, see if you can find places where Tolstoy seems to have intentionally tucked in some bit of instruction for his readers among the common people. For example, see lines 12 to 16, page 352.

In the opening paragraphs the point of view seems to be that of a third person inside Martin's shop. That is, it is the "limited third person," who can see and know only what an observer inside the room could see and know—only what Martin could see and know. Is that point of view adhered to throughout the story? Or does it change to the all-seeing, all-knowing third person?

Look up the older meaning of *gossip* (p. 357) in a good dictionary.

Did you like the total effect of the story? Were there parts in it that you did not like? Did it seem to be a sincere piece of Christian teaching, like a parable, or did it seem sentimental?

THE FATHER

The problem Björnson is trying to present in this short short story is not so easy to discover as in some other stories we have read—the two by Tolstoy, for example. The structure is simple. The story is told in the third person, and very simply told in five very short scenes. Four of these are the four times when Thord came to the village priest on account of his son. The other is the scene of the accidental drowning of the son. The whole length of the story is under a thousand words.

Examine the setting, the characters, the tone, the initial incident, the steps in the plot-ladder, the culmination.

Three times when Thord came to the priest his coming was on his own account, his pride in his son, and to have the priest do something for him. The last time was when he wished in his son's name to devote half of all he had to some good cause outside his own selfish interests. It was only then that the priest thought the son had brought a blessing to his father.

Now, can you make a statement that will express the author's purpose in telling the story—its theme?

See if you can discover the devices used to tell this story effectively in such a few words. How much direct quotation is used? How much description, etc.?

THE DARLING

Would you call this a love story?

Is it realistic or romantic?

The several names a Russian has—his formal name, and two or three affectionate diminutives, and shortened forms, first names, middle names, and family names—are a bit confusing.

Chekhov is obviously dealing with character. Is he merely drawing a picture of a "darling" who has no mind of her own, merely made to love something; or is he trying to say something in general about women of her kind?

THE REVOLT OF "MOTHER"

We have here a typical modern short story, one that might well be studied for its construction as well as for what it says. It was written as a study of the character of a seemingly meek and submissive woman who under her appearance of meekness had the strength to demand and take what was justly due her. Let us say that that is the theme.

Now construct a diagram of its plot.

Who are the primary characters? The secondary? The supernumeraries? How does the author delineate her characters? By direct description, or by what they say and do?

What is the initial incident, and where does it come in the story? What is the culmination?

Now see how she manages direct discourse.

How many speeches directly quoted are there?

What words of *saying*—guide words—are used, and how many times is each used?

How many speeches are quoted with no guide words?

Sometimes adverbs or adverbial phrases are used to indicate *how* a thing is said.

How many times in the story are such words and phrases used?

List all such words and phrases.

Some questions about probability: A writer must be careful not to use an improbability in a story unless there is a pressing need for it, and even then must carefully conceal it.

Is it probable that such a man as Adoniram is represented to be would give in without a struggle?

Is it probable that the Penns, married forty years, would have a son of fourteen or fifteen and a daughter of eighteen or twenty? It would have been just as easy, and more probable, if the author had said that they had lived in the old house twenty-five years. She must have had some strong reason for saying forty. Can you think of one? If the forty-year period is improbable, how does the author keep you from becoming conscious of the improbability?

The length of the story is approximately six thousand words.

What is the point of view?

THE SNOW STORY

In this story do the incidents seem to have come out of the personal experience of the author? Does the setting seem convincing? A good story does not need to be true; the whole thing—background, incidents, and characters—may be invention, the product of the writer's imagination; but it is essential that it should *seem* true. Sometimes writers draw from their own actual experiences or the actual experiences of their acquaintances, but in putting those experiences into fiction fail to give them the convincing appearance of truth, or verisimilitude, to use a long technical word.

Does this story anywhere lack verisimilitude? If so, point out the place or places. Make your study of this particular story a search for spots where it falls short of the appearance of truth.

First, examine the setting. Berthoud Pass from Empire to Hot Sulphur Springs is a very real place, those are the real names, and Mr. Thomas has been over the Pass in all weathers and at all times of the year. Does he convince you that he is picturing it as it actually is? Does he fall short of reality, or go beyond to exaggerate reality?

Second, as to what happens, does that convince you? Does it seem possible that those two men could ride an avalanche a mile without injury and then *both* of them have their feet caught in a trap made by two parallel logs four or five feet below the surface of the snow? Or does that seem to strain probability and overwork coincidence? Would it seem more real if only one of the men had been caught rather than the two ten feet apart? Did the author so much need to have both the men trapped (for the purpose of his story) that he could risk the appearance of improbability to bring that situation about?

Third, consider the two characters. Are their acts consistent with what they are in real life, or are they made to say and do what is expected in fiction? In other words, are they allowed to act as these two particular men would have acted in this situation in real life, or are they made to act as readers wish them to act in romantic fiction? If you take the latter position, point out the spots where their speeches, attitudes, and actions are inconsistent with their natures as the author has created and represented them.

Fourth, observe the language carefully. A characteristic of newspaper feature stories is the use of the strong word, seeking out the unusual word, overemphasis, exaggeration. The writers of the artistic short story practice *restraint* in the language and avoid the unusual in the choice of words. If you find *The Snow Story* leaning toward the faults of the popular newspaper feature, point out the specific instances.

Fifth, as your final comment, do you regard this as an unusually good Western story? Indicate its excellent qualities, and cite also the shortcomings, if there are any.

THE YELLOW WALLPAPER

The situation is this: A literary woman, the wife of a physician, is confined in a private sanitarium for treatment of a mental disorder. Her sister-in-law is with her in the day, and her husband at night. From her own point of view we see her going into violent insanity.

Mrs. Gilman has divided the narrative into sections to show us the steps of the woman's growing insanity.

Why is the story written in those sentence-paragraphs?

Does the author wish us to believe that the wallpaper drove the woman into insanity, and that her physician-husband, through ignorance, put her into a situation where she could not escape madness?

Does the speed and intensity of the story increase as the story progresses? Should it do so?

Why did Mrs. Gilman choose to tell the story from the point of view of the deranged woman? Would it have been just as well to tell it from the point of view of a limited third person—one who could know only what he could see and surmise by actually watching the woman? How would the omniscient third person do, as a point of view?

Do you sense the horror of this situation in your own *feelings* as you read the story, or do you only have an intellectual curiosity about it, and understanding of it, as you go through it?

If it is effectively written, and you have read it with a full understanding of its meaning, you should *feel* the horror of it.

Do you think Mrs. Gilman as a social worker has become convinced that yellow is the color of insanity and that she is warning her readers to avoid yellow wallpaper in rooms if they wish to remain sane?

What indications are there in the story that other insane people have been confined in that room, have had an obsession about the wallpaper, and have crept on all fours round and round the room?

KING SOLOMON OF KENTUCKY

State the theme.

The author has divided the story into five numbered sections. Has he thus recognized that there are five scenes used to build up the narrative from beginning to end? Do his five sections correspond to the steps of the story as you would arrange them on a diagram of the plot?

In the first section has he definitely presented *time, place, characters,* and *tone?* Is the *initial incident* in this section? If so, what is it?

Do you regard this story as romantic or realistic? If you think it is romantic, point out some features or qualities in it that stamp it as romantic. Do the same if you think it is realistic.

Is it a touch of romance or realism to have the first approach of cholera contrasted with the gayety of the ballroom (p. 421, second paragraph from the bottom)? Is the way the approach is worded realistic or romantic?

Is it realistic or romantic to represent nature in sympathy with the sorrows of mankind, or as reflecting those sorrows, as in p. 428, middle paragraph, "In the trees of poplar and locust," etc.?

The happy ending (p. 430) has been criticized as sentimental. Do you find it so? Do you object to the sentimental note in fiction?

Page 429, first two lines: "Nature soon smiles upon her own ravages and strews our graves with flowers, not as memories, but for other flowers when the spring returns."

This is an observation or a bit of philosophy spoken by the author apart from the story. Do you object to such "asides" in story telling? If so, why?

The supreme test of fiction is its adherence to truth. Realism and romance are only names for two ways of telling stories. Each can represent a truth about life. Does *King Solomon of Kentucky* tell the truth? Are things like that in life?

There is no objection to true sentiment in fiction, for there is much sentiment in life, and it often makes life worth while. It is *sentimentality* that is objected to. Some critics find this story objectionably sentimental and think its place is in the waste basket, not in a book to be studied by college students. Do you take that view of it? If not, defend the story. If so, point out your objections to it.

HEART OF DARKNESS

An editor a few years ago asked some professional story writers to name for him the story that had made the deepest impression upon them of any story they had ever read. *Heart of Darkness* got more votes than any other. Does it make a profound emotional impression upon you? Is it the language that does it? or the unusual place? or the disintegration of the moral nature of Mr. Kurtz? or what?

Conrad says in this story that a man of noble character and high moral purpose will go to pieces when isolated and entirely surrounded by savagery—that civilization is only a thin veneer. That is the theme of the story. Are you convinced that it is true?

This story of 35,000 words was written by a sea-captain with a limited early education, who spoke Polish as his mother tongue, learned French before he was sixteen, but English only in his twenties. What do you think of his ability to use the English language, as shown in this story? Some critics have called him one of the greatest masters of English literary prose of our time. Does this estimate seem exaggerated?

Notice that Conrad introduces a fictitious narrator, Charlie Marlow, and then has him tell the story to three listeners. The narrative is all in the first person and relates only what Marlow could have seen or learned.

What did Kurtz do that indicated that he had reverted to savagery? Conrad only hints at several acts and attitudes. Would it have made a better story if he had been more direct, giving a whole catalog of his moral lapses? Was the savage woman a priestess of savage religious rites? Had Kurtz entered into relations of love, possibly marriage, with her?

To what does Kurtz refer in his last words, "The horror! The horror!"?

Conrad has been called "a man's writer." This implies that men like his stories, and women do not. Do you find this the case?

Does Conrad convince you that he has seen that place he describes as the Heart of Darkness, or does it seem that he is drawing it all from imagination?

Do you detect any ironical reference to the efforts of missionaries in Africa?

Conrad uses the word *nigger*, not *negro*. This is the regular word used in England. No disrespect is implied in it.

If you like this story, you should read three other stories (each shorter than this one), *Youth*, *The Lagoon*, and *The Secret-Sharer*. All are stories of experiences in the South Seas. Four novels are also fascinating studies of sea life and sea characters. These are: *Lord Jim*, *Nostromo*, *The Nigger of the Narcissus*, and *Victory*.

ON THE STAIRS

The point of view is most interesting here. The story is told in the third person, but the third person is limited in his view of what goes on. He never takes the reader inside the room or out into the street. Examine the story and find out where this imaginary observer is placed. Then see if the author violates his assumption. Does he tell the reader anything that this observer could not have known or inferred from what he saw and heard?

Here are some statements of a possible theme for the story:

1. Mr. Morrison wrote *On the Stairs* to show that the poor are superstitious.
2. The story was written to show that when death is approaching three spirit raps give warning, and that medical aid is useless after that moment.
3. *On the Stairs* was written to give the reader an insight into the life of the city poor.
4. *On the Stairs* was written to show the inborn or inbred superstition of simple, poor people.

Choose one of the four, or make a more satisfactory statement of your own.

Assemble the bits of description, speech, and action that the author uses in making you see and understand Mrs. Curtis. The same for Mrs. Manders.

How does the author keep you from taking an attitude of strong sympathy for the dying young man, or from a feeling of horror at his being allowed, through his mother's neglect, to die?

Is this a story of amusing entertainment, of pathos, or of tragedy? If none of these, suggest a word of your own.

On the Stairs has about 1450 words. Is there enough of it to be effective? Do you regard it as skillfully written?

MARTHA'S FIREPLACE

What difference do you recognize between pathos and tragedy? Is this story essentially pathetic or tragic? Is *pensive* a good word to apply to the tone of this story?

Does Mr. Garland make Stephen talk and act like a Middle Western retired farmer, whose ancestors had lived in New England? Select some words or phrases that are characteristic.

Theme. The theme is obvious. State it. Ruth Suckow has a more recent story on the same theme. It is *Uprooted*. Mr. Garland's setting is Wisconsin. Miss Suckow's is Iowa.

In the early stories of the *Main-Travelled Roads* volume Mr. Garland was an uncompromising realist. Do you detect a tendency to become romantic in this story, written when he was forty-five?

Do you agree with the author's bit of philosophy at the bottom of page 512?

Do you like the ending? In realistic fiction death would come from some known cause, and not quite so "appropriately" in time and place. But in romance we accept things that are necessary in a fully satisfying ending, even though there might be a doubt as to their probability.

THE ADVENTURE OF THE SPECKLED BAND

The problem before the author of a mystery or detective story is in the beginning to create a situation that demands a solution and then to proceed to work out that solution so cleverly that the interest of the reader is brought up to a high pitch as the end is approached. The reader should be stimulated to try to "guess the answer," but this should hardly be possible until the author gives it. Once the answer is given, the reader should be willing to accept it, and able to go back through the story step by step and find that everything logically and inevitably leads up to the solution given by the author. Judged by these standards, is *The Adventure of the Speckled Band* a *good* detective story?

Even in the detective story skillful choice of words, style, variety, and all the other items that go to make up literary composition are expected. Do you find these in this story?

The initial incident is that incident that places the mystery before the reader and demands a solution. What is it in *The Speckled Band?*

The *culmination* is the solution. How many lines, or words, does Sir Arthur use to let the story down from this culmination to the conclusion? What does he do in these lines? Is it necessary?

Do you regard the detective story as a legitimate form of literary art? Or do you think reading detective stories, even the best of them, an unjustified waste of time? Would you be embarrassed if your mother, or your Aunt Margaret, or the minister caught you reading *The Adventure of the Speckled Band*, *The Hound of the Baskervilles*, or *The Red-Headed League?*

In a story of this kind it is a common practice to introduce suggestions or circumstances that will for a time mislead the reader, but later will be found to be real clues in the right direction. Are there any such clues in this story?

Many detective stories have a character in them who is fairly clever, but not so keen as the hero detective. This character tells the story in the first person. He is mystified and unable to solve the problem, just as the reader is. Dr. Watson is that narrator in most of the Sherlock Holmes stories. Why not let Holmes tell the stories himself?

Conan Doyle says he learned the art of writing the detective story by reading Poe's mystery stories. It might be worth your while to read *The Gold Bug*, *The Murders in the Rue Morgue*, and *The Mystery of Marie Roget*, to see whether Conan Doyle surpassed Poe in skill or fell short.

THE DOOR IN THE WALL

The chief interest in this story is not in the construction of the piece but in what Mr. Wells was trying to say—the idea or theme. In the last ten lines he is offering us a hint of what the wall, the door, and the enchanted garden symbolize. "I am more than half convinced that he [Wallace] had . . . an abnormal gift, and a sense, something . . . that in the guise of wall and door offered him an outlet, a secret and peculiar passage of escape into another and altogether more beautiful world."

Perhaps you can get at Mr. Wells's meaning by going through the story and examining the circumstances that surrounded each occasion when he saw the door and wished to enter it. Inquire, too, why he didn't enter the garden each time. What was it in each situation that kept him from going in—when by an exercise of his will he could enter or pass it by?

And what was the garden? Was it Heaven? Was it an earthly paradise, his own dream of an ideal and beautiful life? Was it a realm of fancy in contrast to the world of reality in which most of us have to live?

On page 542 there is an artistic bit of characterization as the author makes us acquainted with Lionel Wallace. Look it through to see how he does it. On the same page see how Mr. Wells gives the story an air of reality and makes Wallace's vision of the wall, the door, and the garden, seem actual, substantial.

Did you wish the author would permit the youth or the mature man one more glimpse into the dream world before the story closed? The answer to this question will measure your emotional reaction to the story.

THE RESERVED COFFIN

Does *The Reserved Coffin* seem to conform to the technique of the short story as followed by American and French writers? Point out differences.

Does this story seem to have any purpose beyond entertaining the reader by combining two anecdotes—a man orders his coffin long before he expects to need it, and a lawyer's dog steals a tavern keeper's sausages?

Are the character sketches well done? Is the principal character Mèndola, the City Councillor, Sacramento, the keeper of the cemetery, Dolcemascolo, the tavern keeper, or Piccarone, the lawyer?

If the real story is the effort made by Dolcemascolo to collect forty or fifty cents for the sausages, does it seem that the author takes too much space in getting to it?

If the real story is the reserved coffin, are all the items tied together in good proportion?

Try making a plot diagram of the story. Does it fit into that well-ordered arrangement as easily as a story of O. Henry's or De Maupassant's?

Did the author expect the reader to regard this as a grim story of sudden death, or as an amusing story of a close-fisted, queer old lawyer who bought a coffin in anticipation of a future need, and an inkeeper who tried to collect money for sausages stolen by the lawyer's dog?

Were you amused or indignant when the lawyer offered to pay eighty cents for the sausages, but charged five dollars for his legal opinion?

Were you shocked and grieved when the old lawyer fell dead? Do you think the author expected you to be?

P. 557, *cari miei*, my friends (literally, my dears).

P. 557, *caro mio*, my friend (masculine).

P. 557, *perdio*, by God.

P. 558, *malva di tre cotte*, "mallow thrice brewed," hence, strong.

P. 560, *figliuolo*, little son.

P. 560, *ecco*, see, behold.

P. 560, a *lira* at the time was about twenty cents.

THE SEVEN THAT WERE HANGED

Again we have a novelette, this time a terribly grim story, doubtless written as propaganda against capital punishment. Russian stories have a tendency to be gloomy, tragic. In this one Andreyev selects seven people who are to be hanged. Some of them deserve to be taken out of society, some are victims of misfortune or accident, good people whose loss society can ill afford.

Section I. The Plot.

Why did Andreyev give a whole section to the experiences and emotions of the official who was to have been assassinated—but was not? Why (p. 570) did the judges *pity* Golovin and *hate* Musya?

Section II. The characters in the assassination plot.

1. Sergey Golovin, a former officer, about twenty-five or six, the son of a retired colonel.
2. Musya, a girl younger than Golovin.
3. Werner, probably twenty-eight, upper class, and seemingly the leader of the five.
4. Vasily Kashirin, aged twenty-three.
5. Tanya Kovalchuk, a young girl, with a motherly nature. The bombs were made at her house.

Section III. The criminal imbecile.

6. The character and crime of the sixth person, Ivan Yanson, a farm laborer from Esthonia. Low mentality. "I must not be hanged."

Section IV. The Man of Orel. The boastful brigand.

7. Michael Goloubetz (Michka the Tzigane), a peasant of Orel, a robber who had murdered three persons.

Section V. Sergey and Vasily take leave of their families.

Section VI. Tanya Kovalchuk prepares for her execution.

Section VII. Musya, the night before the execution.

Section VIII. Sergey Golovin prepares to be hanged.

Section IX. The psychological and physical effects of the last day on Vasily Kashirin.

Section X. Werner's last days.

Section XI. How the seven acted on the way to the gallows.

Section XII. The arrival at the place of execution, and the hanging.

Do you think the girls would have shown the steadiness and courage that Andreyev represents here in the final scene?

What is the point of view?

As you read the story did it seem to you that you were reading something that a writer had "just made up," or did it seem to be a detailed account of seven persons that were hanged—an account written by a man who had actually been present in every scene, had heard everything that was said, and understood the emotions of each of the seven? Do you think Andreyev had actually seen and known such a case? Or did he imagine the whole thing?

Has Andreyev succeeded in his propaganda so far as you are concerned? Even though you may intellectually approve of putting out of the way those who are a menace to society, do you find that emotionally you revolt against the idea of hanging or killing a human being as a punishment?

Do you call this story realistic or romantic?

The story is outlined here so that the student may see just how the material that makes the brief steps in a short story may be expanded into the chapters or sections of a novelette.

Do you see any good reason why Andreyev did not confine his analysis to the five revolutionary plotters—why he brought in the imbecile laborer and the boasting brigand? And why did he think it necessary to bring in the two girls?

If you wish to try an exercise in writing, take this same material, condense the first ten sections, and make a short story of it, using the material of the last two sections more freely as the substance of your short story.

Do you feel that a story like this ought not to be printed?

THE TRUTH OF THE OLIVER CROMWELL

The construction of this story is somewhat different from any we have had. The main story, the loss of the *Oliver Cromwell*, is enclosed in the story of Martin Carr's mishap and rescue. The enveloping story suggests other sea adventures, and Martin is prompted to tell about the *Oliver Cromwell*. That being done, the thread of the first story is picked up to tie the two together.

Theme. This story was written to show the lengths to which jealousy may drive a man.

Point of View. The enveloping story of the accident to Martin and Johnnie is told from the point of view of the third person. But the main story of the wreck of the *Oliver Cromwell* is related in the first person by Martin Carr.

Characters. In counting the characters consider only those on the *Cromwell*, not those in the group around Martin as he told the story. Examine the story with care to see if you can determine how Mr. Connolly makes his imaginary people "come alive."

Reality. Do you think this would have been a better story if the whole enveloping story had been omitted? What would have been gained by starting the narrative at the bottom of page 620 and closing it with the words, "I said, and let slip the line"? What would have been lost? Are you convinced that the events in this narrative could have happened?

Tone. What word would describe the tone of the story?

Read Mr. Connolly's $2500 Collier prize story, *The Trawler*, and compare it with *The Truth of the Oliver Cromwell*, as to quality.

SAMUEL

Jack London is best known for his stories of the so-called "red-blooded he-man" type. There was another side to him—his tendency to inquire into the philosophy, the springs of conduct, of his people. This story of *Samuel* is one of the latter kind. The word that comes up over and over as he describes Margaret Henan is *certitude*. Here is a woman sure of herself. She goes on her way from misfortune to misfortune with never a doubt about her own rightness. Observe that London leads you to understand her character partly through direct description, but in larger part by the things she does and says and by her manner of doing and saying.

As a writer he had several interests in the story. He wanted, for one thing, to make his readers acquainted with this woman of immense certitude, as he makes us acquainted with that fine descendant of the Pitcairn Island *Bounty* mutineer in *The Seed of McCoy*. But in *Samuel* his main theme was a philosophic one—the "why of like." He asks his readers why it is that we human beings sometimes have likes so strong and seemingly so unreasonable that we endure hardships and invite calamity to attain and serve the thing we like. He offers no answer. He only raises the question.

The Manner of Telling the Story. Mrs. Ross outlines all the early events of the story in one page (pp. 644–645). The rest of the space is taken up with filling out the items she has mentioned in outline and adding the final section. And the filling out is managed in the story as it often actually is in life—by piecing together bit by bit what one picks up first from one source and then from another.

Dialect. Is the story marred for you by the spelling of the Island McGill dialect?

Other London stories recommended: *The Call of the Wild* (novelette), *The God of His Fathers*, *The Sheriff of Kona*, *The Seed of McCoy*, *The Strength of the Strong*, and *South of the Slot*.

THE PRINCESS AND THE VAGABONE

Realistic or romantic? Prove your answer.

Notice the first paragraph, the setting (descriptive) for the main story. Which play of "Willie" Shakespeare resembles this story?

Is the dialect used by Michael Hegarty convincing, or do you detect in it a resemblance to the conventional "stage" Irish, the language of the "funny" Irishman in cheap plays?

Tone. Find a word or phrase that describes the tone of the story. Is the tone suggested early? Where? By what means?

Initial Incident. What incident sets the story going by bringing in a conflict of ideas, that make it necessary for something to happen that will solve the difficulty?

The Plot. Outline the plan of the story scene by scene.

Setting. The place is Donegal. Look it up on a map. The time of the telling is modern, but the events of the story go back perhaps to the fifteenth century or farther.

Theme. Does Ruth Sawyer seriously propose that the way to get along with a high-tempered wife is to break her spirit? A bride once said to the bishop who was to officiate at her wedding that the word *obey* in the ritual was obsolete and she hoped he would omit it. He answered, "My dear, I've noticed that when two ride the same horse, one has to ride behind." Is that what the author means? Maybe the story is told merely to entertain the reader by recounting an old tale. What do *you* think the author's purpose was?

Are your sympathies with the princess, or with the vagabone? If with the vagabone, how does the author manage to make them so.

Time Scheme. Work out the time that passed between the king's determination to have the princess married and the close of the story.

A MUNICIPAL REPORT

Tone. *A Municipal Report* turns out to be a serious treatment of an important theme, serious, if not to say tragic. Do you sense that seriousness on the first page, or is the opening apparently a bit light, or cynical, or supercilious? Do you approve the telling of this pathetic tragedy in this whimsical, half humorous manner?

Theme. Do you think O. Henry is seriously interested in proving that Nashville, Tennessee, is a city in which the materials for fiction may be found, and that such materials may be discovered in any town—not alone in New York, New Orleans, and San Francisco? Or is it his principal purpose to show you the devotion of a former slave to a member of the family that he had served?

Initial Incident. Remember that the initial incident is that incident that sets into motion the action that leads up to the culmination or solution of the particular problem the author is dealing with. The narrator could have arrived in Nashville without anything significant happening. But when his experiences have reached a certain point a situation arises or a character is encountered that starts something that can't be dropped until something has been done about it. Now, where is that point in this story about Nashville?

Point of View?

Plot. Construct the usual plot diagram.

Appearance of Truth. Does the story sound as if the events in it really happened? Do you discover any inconsistencies or improbabilities in it? If so, what?

Approval. Do you approve the action of the narrator in disposing of the evidence against old Cæsar? Should not the law be allowed to take its course? Do you like the story? What are its good points? What are its faults?

THE PROCURATOR OF JUDEA

The author's purpose has already been suggested in connection with the sketch of the life and writings of Anatole France (p. 678).

What did you learn about Roman customs from the two meetings of Lælius Lamia and Pontius Pilate?

Do you think they were fair in their analysis of Jewish nature and character (pp. 687 and 688)?

Does this story have a plot arranged in a manner similar to the plots of other stories you have examined?

Does Anatole France succeed in recreating the atmosphere of Rome of about 50 A.D. so that it seems real?

The fifth paragraph on page 680 allows Pilate to recite a series of facts to Lamia known to both Lamia and himself. Do you think it is good writing to get information to the reader in that way? Does it happen that way in real life?

THE DRAKE WHO HAD MEANS OF HIS OWN

Tone. Is the tone of the story apparent on the first page? Can you suggest a word or phrase that will describe it?

Beginning. Observe that the story after five lines, starts with conversation. The story is related by a narrator speaking in the first person. Is this narrator or Scipio a principal character in the piece?

Characters. Who are the principal characters—those three ducks or Mr. and Mrs. Culloden?

Theme. In *The Princess and the Vagabone* the author was saying half seriously, as Shakespeare said in *The Taming of the Shrew*, that the way to get along with a sharp-tongued wife is to subdue her—by force, if necessary. How does Owen Wister say the trick should be turned? Does he say it seriously, or is his proposal to be taken only in fun? Would you yourself propose beating, or at least mentally conquering, the shrewish wife, or would you follow Wister's prescription of competition and "keeping her guessing"? Perhaps you would reject both and offer a formula of your own. If so, what is it?

Effect. Were you ever really concerned, anxious about the outcome of this story? Did you laugh over it at all? Or weep? Or grow indignant? Or hold your breath in suspense?

Time scheme. Make it out.

Ending. Does the ending (p. 707) seem too brief and too indefinite? Are you left in doubt about the outcome? Are you left in doubt about the connection between the method of Sir Francis and that of Jimsy Culloden? Is the tone of the story maintained to the end?

THE OUTLAWS

Have you noticed a decided difference in the kind of themes chosen by foreign authors and American? You have read thus far American, English, French, Russian, Italian, Norwegian, and Swedish stories. if the themes and treatment are different, point out some of the differences.

The Outlaws is essentially the story of the awakening of conscience in a boy associated with an outlaw in hiding, the development of that conscience, and finally the betrayal of the outlaw when the bidding of the boy's conscience becomes so strong that he cannot resist. The story is not told in strict chronological order. It is divided into sections by the author. In a sentence or two for each section write out what the sections develop in the progress of the story. Do you find the author's order logical if you assume that her purpose was to trace the development of conscience in this child of nature?

Would you be willing to take the last clause of the story as its theme, the author's purpose in writing it—to demonstrate "that justice is the cornerstone of the world?"

Do you approve or disapprove of the act of Tord in betraying Berg to the people, and in slaying him with his own hands?

THE BEAR TAMER'S DAUGHTER

Why does Konrad Bercovici use up one sixth of his space in describing Costa, and how he practiced his trade of catching and taming bears? The story is to be about Margarita, if the title correctly labels it.

At last we have a love story in this volume, but it is on both sides a strange love-making, in strong contrast to the love stories that fill the popular magazines.

Is it a fast-moving story?

Does it hold your attention and interest at a high pitch?

Does the author seem to know his places and his people, or do you detect slips that would indicate that he had built the whole thing up out of his imagination?

Is it true to nature?

Caution. If you were intensely interested in the story—emotionally keyed up—and if you think it is true to nature, you are in effect tacitly admitting that it is natural for women to want to be ruled by men. Here is a primitive girl who despises all weak, tame men. She can love only the man who can conquer her—beat her up and drag her away to his cave if necessary. That is something to consider and to call forth an hour's rather fiery discussion.

Do you detect any inconsistencies in the descriptions, speech of characters, or the actions of characters? If so, what?

tziganes, gypsies
brumal, winterlike

AFTER HE WAS DEAD

Is the title one that would arouse curiosity about the story? Do you like the sound of the title? Styles in titles change much as styles in clothes do. Looking over a hundred titles of stories written in the past five or six years, what would you say some of the present tendencies are?

Are they long or short?

Are stories often named after the principal character?

Do the titles often hint at the nature or theme of the story?

Is there commonly a strained effort to get an unusual or striking combination of words in a title?

Are double titles such as *The Bear Tamer's Daughter, or How Petrackio Won His Wife* much used?

Is the smart or clever or "catchy" title popular?

Are authors apparently careful to avoid bad rhythms in titles, like *Hard Clambering up Steep Elevations?*

List a few of the positive qualities that you find in modern titles.

Theme. The theme of *After He Was Dead* is apparent. State it.

Construction. The construction of this story is conventional and easy to follow. First, the author gives you a background, and places in that picture the figure of the man who is to commit a murder. Firing the shot is the initial incident. After that the steps in the story must be those that will lead up to the apprehension and conviction of the murderer through testimony supplied by the murdered man "after he was dead." Trace this process, step by step, to the culmination. As you do this, observe the emotional state of the murderer advancing from mere curiosity to panic.

Is the story romantic or realistic? Is there any symbolism in it? Any idealism?

Is the speech of the characters convincingly real? Point out examples.

Are you convinced in this case that the murderer could not conceal his crime?

In general, do you believe that there is some superhuman law that prevents the permanent concealment of the crime of murder? Do you imagine Mr. Post thought so?

THE WATER-HOLE

As in *The Truth of the Oliver Cromwell* you have here two settings and two groups of characters. One is the place where the story was told and the other the scene of the action of the story itself. One set of characters listen to the story and the other act in it.

Make up the two lists of characters.

Mention the two settings.

There is a love thread running through the story. Do you think Mr. Burt regarded that as the main story or was he most interested in the question of instinctive courage?

When are you first conscious that it is Hardy, himself, who is in love with Mrs. Whitney? Look back through the story and observe how the author keeps that fact concealed. But when it does come out, is it a complete surprise? That is, does it come without any preparation? How is it prepared for?

Again, do you like a story with a setting made for its telling? What is gained by that device? What, if anything, is lost?

Is the story convincing? the scene? the characters?

Work out the time scheme.

Do you now coolly believe that Hardy would have risked his life to save the man whom he wanted to see dead?

If the story is well done, you should be convinced, when you finish reading it, that Hardy would have acted as he did.

THE GREAT AUK

If you know why Mr. Cobb called this story *The Great Auk*, you can easily state the theme of it. Can you do so?

Were you amused at the descriptions of scene and characters on the first two pages?

How much time is represented from beginning to the end of the story?

Do you get a clear picture of "Old Bird Bateman"? How is the picture made?

There is no particular dramatic conflict of persons or ideas in the story. Then in what does its interest lie?

Do not neglect to read some of Mr. Cobb's *Old Judge Priest* stories; for example, *Boys Will Be Boys*. And by all means read, as an example of a terribly grim short story, his *Faith, Hope, and Charity*.

THE SILENT INFARE

The purpose of this story is to allow you to see the town Negro a generation after the Civil War, and to see him (and her) with the eyes of an old before-the-war slave woman who remained devoted to her white family. Like *The Great Auk* it has no dramatic conflict, and does not rise to an emotional high pitch in a culmination. Nor does it have a sharp initial incident and distinct steps in its development.

The author's purpose was to entertain you with this picture of Negro life in the South after the war. The recital of the progress of Imogen's preparation for her wedding is the thread that holds the narrative together.

JETSAM

Find a word to describe the tone of the story as it is struck in the first three paragraphs. Do you suspect at the end of the second page that the story is going to be humorous?

Notice that the very first paragraph is a reference to character. Is the story throughout a story of character, setting, or incident?

Observe how the author pictures the setting—by means of the sobering-up attempt of Junius Peabody to account for his being on the island of Fufuti and "broke."

If you do not already know what jetsam is, use the dictionary. Is it a good title for this story? Does it suggest the theme?

State the theme if you can.

Does the story in any way resemble *King Solomon of Kentucky?*

Is the picture of this South Sea Island attractive to you?

Would you say that the story is romantic or realistic?

The author has divided the story into sections by leaving a one-line space between the sections. Make notes on what each section does toward forwarding the narrative, and then construct the plot diagram of the story.

3000 MILES AWAY

We have here another love story, and more than that an excellent story done in a combination of straightforward narrative and letters and telegrams—a very difficult way to write an effective short story.

Was the ending a surprise? Too sudden?

If you guessed that there was no John Scarborough, at what point in the story did you first suspect it?

Comparing it with other forms of storytelling, how do you like the letter form? Would you like it if half the stories you read were written in that form?

Did the story strike you as light and silly, or were you genuinely emotionally stirred by it?

THE WEAVER'S GRAVE

Regard this not as a story that grows and develops to a culmination after having worked out some idea of the author, some philosophic theme. It is not that. To us it makes no difference at all where the traditional grave of the weavers was—where generation after generation they had been buried. Nor did it make any great difference to the two gravediggers. Even to the widow it was not a matter of supreme importance, even though she feared that the weaver's soul in heaven might not be at peace unless his body was laid to rest in the grave of his clan.

The story is merely the clotheshorse upon which Seumas O'Kelly hangs the portraits of four old men, Mortimer Hehir, the dead weaver, Meehaul Lynskey, the nail-maker, Cahir Bowes, the stone-breaker, and Malachi Roohan, the cooper. And what portraits! It seems hardly decent that any young man should know as intimately as this how those old men, each different from the other, should think, speak, act, and feel.

Read the story and observe how O'Kelly makes his pictures of the old men. Does he leave a sharp image of each of them in your mind's eye? Do you feel that you know them?

There is very little happening in the thirty-eight pages of the story. Does it seem slow to you? Do you feel repaid for the time consumed in reading by the knowledge about these old men that comes to you thereby?

Is the writer's attitude toward the whole business serious, or does he see it as humorous?

ENGLAND TO AMERICA

In the first paragraph of *England to America* Miss Montague has made clear what the steps of the story will be. They will be the steps necessary to clear up the mystery of what it is that the Sherwoods are keeping from young Cary. Trace the progress of the story (i.e., make a diagram of the plot) with that in mind.

Find a word that will describe the tone of the story. Is the tone apparent in the first page? Second page? Third?

Do you detect any indications in the story that the author did not know at first hand the technical details about war, flying, etc., but had to depend upon oral and written accounts of others? Cite instances.

The culmination of the story is, of course, the revelation of what was the matter with the Sherwood family. That comes on p. 868, line 30. If you guessed it before that, at what point did you first suspect it?

State the theme of the story. Be sure it is not: What was the matter with the Sherwoods?

The note of sentiment is strong. Does it ever break over into what seems to you to be sentimentality? If so, cite the place or places.

Make a list of all the *he said*'s and equivalents of *said*, marking the number of times each is used as a "guide word." Does Miss Montague use adverbs to indicate *how* a thing was said? If so, list those adverbs or adverbial phrases that go with the *he said*'s or the equivalents.

Make a time scheme.

FOR THEY KNOW NOT WHAT THEY DO

Would it have been better, do you think, if Agnes Kain had told her son early that he was of the fourth generation, and that the preceding three generations of Kains had been insane? Give reasons for your position.

This story was written to show what? Write a sentence that will state the author's purpose or theme.

In drawing his characters is Mr. Steele convincing? Do people such as he pictures here really live, and do they talk and act as he has them talk and act here?

The author has the boy two or three times imagine he hears drums, waves, and the sound of marching men. Why does he put that into the story?

Does it seem necessary to show the boy in a fit of actual insanity? Hasn't it been indicated clearly enough without that terrifying scene?

Often in fiction, writers show insane fits coming upon their characters in some connection with the full moon. Does the moon have anything to do with insanity, or is that just an old belief? Insanity, you will recall used always to go by the name *lunacy*. Luna is the moon. Lunacy is moon-sickness, and we say sometimes that an insane man is moon-struck.

Do you think it is possible for a woman to blush voluntarily?

Point of view?

Time scheme?

Take the last long paragraph (p. 884) and read it aloud. Listen to it for the music of its language—music appropriate to the situation. Try to find some of the devices by which the author arrives at *style*, artistic expression in prose.

Does this story seem true to life? Does Mr. Steele seem to have accurate technical knowledge of insanity?

From your knowledge of people are you convinced that a mother would lead her son to believe he was the illegitimate child of a sane man, rather than the legitimate descendant of three generations of insane men? Does Mr. Steele convince you that this particular woman, Agnes Kain, would have done so?

A SOURCE OF IRRITATION

Tone?

Time scheme?

Theme?

Construct a plot diagram for the story.

If you found the story at all funny, pick out a few spots that seem humorous and try to determine what makes each one laughable. For example, look at the five-line paragraph at the bottom of p. 895, or the last long paragraph, on p. 896.

THE FAT OF THE LAND

What is the author saying about immigrants? Whatever it is, that is the theme of the story.

Does the author seem to have learned about her people, the language they speak, the way they act, their outlook on life from personal experience, from hearsay, or from books?

Tone?

Characters?

Discuss some of the characteristics of realism and romanticism with this story as a starting point.

THE FLY

Does the grief of the boss seem real, or only a kind of luxury he indulges in from time to time?

Is the story convincingly real?

Is there a note of sarcasm or irony running through the story?

What use does the introduction of old Woodifield serve in the story? Did the author give you a clear picture of the old man?

What is the author saying? Is it merely a picture, or is she saying something about human beings?

Is the story a nice bit of romance?

CLAY SHUTTERED DOORS

The title is important here. Is there some hint of the meaning of the story in it?

The theme of this story is the most important thing about it. Perhaps you may find some difficulty in finding it and stating it. Try.

Several suggestions and questions appear in the editor's introductory paragraph preceding the story (p. 920).

Does the author consistently stick to the point of view of the first person, allowing nothing to come into the story except what this first person saw, heard, or could come into possession of?

What do you think of the author's philosophy in the second paragraph, p. 921, beginning, "There are, I have decided—"?

Examine the middle paragraph, p. 923, and give your opinion of it as effective description.

You may possibly find something in the second paragraph, p. 924, that will later help you in solving some of the problems in this story.

Time scheme? Reckon the time from the automobile accident to the end.

Did Mary, the narrator, ever touch Thalia after the accident at the bridge? What did the boy see when he went into his mother's room (p. 933)?

P. 927, *savoir faire*, social adaptability, or tact.

MISS HINCH

Look at the questions and suggestions in the editor's preliminary statement (p. 936).

Point of view?

Make a diagram of the plot of the story.

Did you find this an excellent, medium, or poor detective story?

At what point in the story do you think Jessie Dark recognized Miss Hinch? And where did Miss Hinch first recognize Jessie Dark?

THE MAN OF THE FAMILY

In *The Man of the Family* we have the story of an adolescent boy's day. Nothing much happens in it. Nothing of any great consequence happens in anybody's ordinary day to make a story of. Life day by day is not very dramatic. It is only on the exceptional days that tense and dramatic things occur. But does that necessarily mean that there is nothing in a boy's *workday* in a Midwestern village that a story can be made of?

This story is realistic without being grim, or drab, or revolting— words that are too often associated with realism. Follow the conversations. Does Miss Suckow make Floyd and Lois talk like young business people in a small town? Does she know how a boy and his younger sisters in a small town act toward each other, and how they talk?

Look through the whole story to see if you can discover any situation, bit of talk, or bit of action that is not convincingly real.

Are you disappointed when the story closes without leading up to a sharp dramatic culmination?

Do you regard this as primarily a story of setting, of character, or of incident?

Would you look for a story of this kind in the *Pictorial Review, The Ladies' Home Journal,* or *Good Housekeeping?*

Why would it seem more appropriate to find it in the *American Mercury?*

If you look upon the story as a study of character, is it a success? As a story of incident, is it much of a success?

Who is the principal character in the piece?

What are some of the characteristics of realism that you find in *The Man of the Family?*

NEITHER JEW NOR GREEK

Neither Jew Nor Greek was selected as the prize story for the 1930 *O. Henry Memorial Award* volume. Do you think it a fine story? Observe that the story is told in the first person—an imaginary narrator, Uncle Asy Mulberry. When we say a story is narrated in the first person, we mean usually that the author is that first person. There is no reason, however, why he may not delegate his storytelling duty to another person, allowing that narrator to use the pronouns *I* and *we*, *me* and *us*. Is the talk of Uncle Asy consistent with his character throughout, or do you detect lapses, exaggerations, burlesque, etc?

The theme is a question: Is it true that we are all alike under the skin? Or, There is neither Jew nor Greek, there is neither bond nor free; there is neither male nor female: for ye are all one.

The passage quoted from Paul's letter to the Galatians meant to say that in the Christian church all are on the same level, no one higher than another, no one better than another. Uncle Asy rather strains the point when he assumes that it means, by nature we are all alike. Putting the theme in the form of a question makes it almost necessary for the author to give an answer either directly or by suggestion and implication. What answer, *yes* or *no*, does Mr. John suggest to his own question?

Is this story funny or serious to you?

Do you question the propriety of using in a magazine story such a character as Big Annie and such incidents as we have here? If you think the characters and incidents are improper, why? If you accept both as justified, give reasons for your position.

Make a plot diagram of this story. You will observe that Mr. John has divided it into sections for you.

WHO KILLED RUTHERFORD?

Who Killed Rutherford? and the story that follows it, *Fifty Grand*, are representative of a new turn in the short story in the past few years. There is a tendency to deal with characters belonging to the lower levels of society, to use conversation almost exclusively in developing the plot, to dispense with guide words whenever it can otherwise be made clear who is speaking, and to be faithful to characters and situations in representing people in speech and action.

The editor of this volume has read this story aloud to groups of students a number of times. Nearly all the listeners get the idea that Mrs. Gurget in her girlhood was the famous Nancy Haskins, that it was Rutherford who bought her, and that it was she who killed him. But the four men around the saloon stove do not sense that situation.

See if you can discover how the reader reaches that conclusion, and the listeners in the story miss it.

This is the kind of story some readers will like very much; but many others will strongly dislike it. To which group do you belong? Give your reasons for approving or disapproving it.

Does the young author (he was twenty-four when he wrote *Who Killed Rutherford?*) seem to know at first hand the setting and the people of the story?

Is there any theme to the story beyond that which is expressed in the following statement: *"Who Killed Rutherford?* was written to entertain the readers with a picture of a certain situation and allow them to see a certain group of characters in action?" If you see more in the story than that, make your own statement of the author's purpose.

FIFTY GRAND

Listening to the conversation of these pugilists and fight-promoters, are you impressed with their mentality? Do you think Hemingway represents them as they are, or underestimates them?

If you had been looking through *Liberty, Collier's, The Saturday Evening Post, Atlantic Monthly, Scribner's, Harper's,* or *Red Book* in July, 1927, where would you have expected to find *Fifty Grand?* Where would have been the last place you would have looked for it?

What qualities in the story, do you suppose, prompted the editor of the *Atlantic* to buy it?

Look through page 995 again. How do you like that passage as an example of intelligent conversation?

It appears that the author's purpose is to give the reader a picture of prize fighting as it really is. Do you come out of the reading with a highly elevated opinion of the "manly art"? Or has Mr. Hemingway helped to fix in your mind the often reiterated statement that prize fighting is the dirtiest (most dishonest) sport there is?

Make a diagram of the plot.

CIVILIZATION

Do you see Mundasi and his tribe from the English or the African (barbarian) point of view? Is your sympathy with Mundasi or the "Parliamentary gentlemen"? What purpose had the author in writing the story? Does he succeed in his purpose? Does he convince you that Mundasi would have been treated as here represented on his visit to London?

Was the device of having Mundasi tell his story to Constable Jenkins and his wife Mabel an effective one?

Is there a note of pathos running through the story? Does the author permit a humorous note to break through the pathos? Does that seem natural and satisfying? Point out some of the humorous passages.

In real life are humor, pathos, and even tragedy all mixed up together? Does a humorous note in a pathetic setting seem funnier than when standing alone?

What is your feeling when you finish the story? Are you laughing over the simplicity of this Negro who went to London with his petition about the wrongs of an unheard-of and insignificant tribe, or are you mildly indignant over the treatment the presumably civilized conquering and governing world metes out to the so-called savage or barbarous tribes?

Does this story cause you to question whether we really do more good than harm in our efforts to civilize and Christianize those people?

Make a guess as to the personality of the author. Man or woman? Missionary or professional writer? A chance visitor to Africa, a long resident of Africa, or one who has never seen Africa?

NIGHT CLUB

State the theme of *Night Club*.

Do you regard this as a satire upon modern social life?

Does Miss Brush convince you that she knows the life she writes about through direct contact and observation?

Make a list of the "what's-wrong" with each of the individuals or groups who visit the dressing room. For example, the first girl was a married woman probably out alone or with a man not her husband; the second one was a drug addict in dire need of her narcotic.

Are people really like that? women and girls you know? Or do you feel that it's only that way with people in night clubs in some city a thousand or two thousand miles away?

"The original seventy cents remained. That much, and no more, would Mrs. Brady gamble on the integrity of womankind." (P. 1023.) Is that just Mrs. Brady's opinion, or do you suspect it is Katharine Brush's?

Do you laugh over the last two paragraphs of the story, or do you leave it with a puzzled, cynical smile that says, "Well, that's life, I suppose"?

GUESTS OF THE NATION

Narrative in the first person.

A number of the new Irish plays came out of the recent struggle for separation from England. The same is true of recent Irish short stories. This one is typical.

You will get the same feeling of tragic futility out of other stories in O'Connor's *Guests of the Nation* volume. You may find the same note in Seán O'-Faoláin's *Midsummer Night's Madness* and the stories in his volume bearing that title.

GENERAL INDEX

Titles of short stories included in this volume are in italics; the names of the authors are in small capitals. The chief subject entries are in ordinary roman type. Page entries in parentheses indicate where the Study Notes may be found.

ADAMS, FRANK R., 804
Adventure of the Speckled Band, The, (1081) 520
After He Was Dead, (1090) 736
ALDRICH, THOMAS BAILEY, 184
ALLEN, JAMES LANE, 414
American short stories, list of, 1042
ANDREYEV, LEONID NIKOLAIEVICH, 564
atmosphere, 13
AUMONIER, STACY, 886

BAPTIST, R. HERNEKIN, 1006
Bear Tamer's Daughter, The, (1089) 722
Belgian short stories, list of, 1050
BERCOVICI, KONRAD, 722
bibliographies, selected, 1039
   anthologies of short stories, 1040
   general reference books and bibliographies, 1039
   lists of short stories, 1042
   studies of the short story and books on short story writing, 1039
BJÖRNSON, BJÖRNSTJERNE, 362
BRUSH, KATHARINE, 1017
BUNNER, HENRY CUYLER, 200
BURT, MAXWELL STRUTHERS, 746

Central European short stories, list of, 1050
characters, 41
   how many, 41
   kind, 42
   methods of delineating, 44
   portrayal and development, 44
CHEKHOV, ANTON PAVLOVICH, 365
Civilization, (1098) 1006
Clay Shuttered Doors, (1095) 920
COBB, IRVIN S., 760
CONNOLLY, JAMES B., 615
CONRAD, JOSEPH, 431

Danish short stories, list of, 1051
Darling, The, (1076) 365
DAUDET, ALPHONSE, 209
DICKENS, CHARLES, 158
Doctor Marigold's Prescriptions, (1064) 158
Door in the Wall, The, (1082) 541
DOYLE, SIR ARTHUR CONAN, 520
Drake Who Had Means of His Own, The, (1088) 690
Dr. Heidegger's Experiment, (1063) 141
Dutch short stories, list of, 1051

EDMONDS, WALTER D., 977
emotion, 47
England to America, (1093) 858
English short stories, list of, 1048

Father, The, (1075) 362
Fat of the Land, The, (1095) 897
Fifty Grand, (1098) 986
Fly, The, (1095) 915
For They Know Not What They Do, (1094) 871
FRANCE, ANATOLE, 678
FREEMAN, MARY E. WILKINS, 375
French short stories, list of, 1051

GARLAND, HAMLIN, 506
German short stories, list of, 1052
GILMAN, CHARLOTTE PERKINS, 400
GORDON, ARMISTEAD C., 781
Great Auk, The, (1091) 760
Greek short stories, list of, 1052
Guests of the Nation, (1099) 1028

HARDY, THOMAS, 269
HARRISON, HENRY SYDNOR, 936
HARTE, BRET, 149
HAWTHORNE, NATHANIEL, 141

Heart of Darkness, (1079) 431
HEMINGWAY, ERNEST, 986
HENRY, O., 64, 665
history of the short story, 3
  antiquity of story telling, 3
  beast fables and picaresque tales, 7
  Egyptian tales, 4
  episodes in longer stories, 8
  essayists, influence of the, 9
  Greek and Roman tales, 6
  Hawthorne and Poe, 9
  Hindu stories, 6
  modern short story, 10
  oriental tales, 5
HOGG, JAMES, 77
HULL, HELEN, 920

idealism, 52
Irish short stories, list of, 1052
IRVING, WASHINGTON, 89
Italian short stories, list of, 1053

JAMES, HENRY, 213
Jetsam, (1092) 789
JOHN, WILLIAM M., 965

King Solomon of Kentucky, (1079) 414
KIPLING, RUDYARD, 307

Lady, or the Tiger? The, (1069) 263
LAGERLÖF, SELMA, 708
Last Class, The, (1067) 209
Latin-American short stories, list of, 1053
Lesson of the Master, The, (1067) 213
Ligeia, (1062) 128
LONDON, JACK, 639
Love Letters of Smith, The, (1066) 200

Man of the Family, The, (1096) 952
Man Who Would Be King, The, (1072) 307
MANSFIELD, KATHERINE, 915
Marjorie Daw, (1065) 184
Martha's Fireplace, (1081) 506
MAUPASSANT, GUY DE, 31, 335
MÉRIMÉE, PROSPER, 179
Miss Hinch, (1096) 936
MONTAGUE, MARGARET PRESCOTT, 858

MORRISON, ARTHUR, 502
Municipal Report, A, (1087) 665
Mysterious Bride, The, (1058) 77

Necklace, The, (1073) 335
Neither Jew Nor Greek, (1097) 965
Night Club, (1099) 1017
Norwegian short stories, list of, 1053

O'CONNOR, FRANK, 1028
O'KELLY, SEUMAS, 819
On the Stairs, (1080) 502
Outcasts of Poker Flat, The, (1064) 149
Outlaws, The, (1089) 708

Piece of String, The, (38) 31
PIRANDELLO, LUIGI, 555
Pistol Shot, The, (1061) 117
plot, 26
  construction in a drama, 27
  construction in a short story, 31
  definition, 26
  diagrams, 30, 37, 39
  in a detective story, 40
POE, EDGAR ALLAN, 128
POST, MELVILLE DAVISSON, 736
Princess and the Vagabone, The, (1087) 665
Procurator of Judea, The, (1088) 678
Prodigal Son, The, (1057) 75
PUSHKIN, ALEXANDER, 117

realism, 51
Reserved Coffin, The, (1083) 555
Revolt of "Mother," The, (1076) 375
Rip Van Winkle, (1059) 89
romance, 51
RUSSELL, JOHN, 789
Russian short stories, list of, 1054

Samuel, (1086) 639
SAWYER, RUTH, 655
SCOTT, SIR WALTER, 102
setting, 13, 47
Seven That Were Hanged, The, (1084) 564
short story
  beginnings, 57
  characters, 12, 41
  classification, 14

short story—*Continued*
  conversation in, 58
  distinguished from novelette and novel, 53
  endings, 61
  history of, 3
  impression from life, 17
  incidents, 12
  management of materials, 55
  materials from which made, 12
  means used in developing a theme, 18, 47
  plot, 26
  point of view, 55
  setting, 13, 47
  study notes, 1057
  study plan, 62
  suggestion and restraint, 59
  suspense, 59
  titles, 56
  two methods of beginning, 57
  two methods of ending, 61
Silent Infare, The, (1092) 781
Snow Story, The, (1077) 388
Source of Irritation, A, (1094) 886
Spanish short stories, list of, 1054
STEELE, WILBUR DANIEL, 871
STEVENSON, ROBERT LOUIS, 287
STOCKTON, FRANK R., 263
SUCKOW, RUTH, 952
Swedish short stories, list of, 1055

Taking the Redoubt, (1065) 179
theme, 17
  greatest themes, 25
  groups of themes, 20
  impression from life, 17
  meaning of, 18
  means in developing, 18, 47
  moral, 18
THOMAS, CHAUNCEY, 388
Three Arshins of Land, (1074) 343
Three Strangers, The, (1070) 269
3000 Miles Away, (1092) 804
TOLSTOY, LEO N., 343, 352
tone, 13, 48
truth, appearance of, 50
Truth of the Oliver Cromwell, The, (1085) 615

Wandering Willie's Tale, (1060) 102
Water Hole, The, (1091) 746
Weaver's Grave, The, (1093) 819
WELLS, HERBERT GEORGE, 541
Where Love Is, There God Is Also, (1075) 352
Whirligig of Life, The, (69) 64
Who Killed Rutherford? (1097) 977
Will o' the Mill, (1071) 287
WISTER, OWEN, 690

Yellow Wallpaper, The, (1078) 400
YEZIERSKA, ANZIA, 897